PLUNKETT'S ENGINEERING & RESEARCH INDUSTRY ALMANAC 2009

The Only Comprehensive Guide to the Engineering & Research Industry

Jack W. Plunkett

Published by:
Plunkett Research, Ltd., Houston, Texas
www.plunkettresearch.com

Customer Support Information

Plunkett's Engineering & Research Industry Almanac 2009

Please register your book immediately...

if you did not purchase it directly from Plunkett Research, Ltd. This will enable us to fulfill your replacement request if you have a damaged product, or your requests for assistance. Also it will enable us to notify you of future editions, so that you may purchase them from the source of your choice.

If you are an actual, original purchaser but did not receive a FREE CD-ROM version with your book...*

you may request it by returning this form.

____ YES, please register me as a purchaser of the book.
I did not buy it directly from Plunkett Research, Ltd.

____ YES, please send me a free CD-ROM version of the book.
I am an actual purchaser, but I did not receive one with my book. (Proof of purchase may be required.)

Customer Name ______________________________

Title ______________________________

Organization ______________________________

Address ______________________________

City ____________________ State ________ Zip ____________

Country (if other than USA) ______________________________

Phone ____________________ Fax ____________________

E-mail ______________________________

Mail or Fax to: **Plunkett Research, Ltd.**
Attn: FREE CD-ROM and/or Registration
P.O. Drawer 541737, Houston, TX 77254-1737 USA
713.932.0000 · Fax 713.932.7080 · www.plunkettresearch.com

* Purchasers of used books are not eligible to register. Use of CD-ROMs is subject to the terms of their end user license agreements.

PLUNKETT'S ENGINEERING & RESEARCH INDUSTRY ALMANAC 2009

Editor and Publisher:
Jack W. Plunkett

Executive Editor and Database Manager:
Martha Burgher Plunkett

Senior Editors and Researchers:
Brandon Brison
Addie K. FryeWeaver
Christie Manck
John Peterson

Editors, Researchers and Assistants:
Kalonji Bobb
Elizabeth Braddock
Michelle Dotter
Michael Esterheld
Austin Hansell
Kathi Mestousis
Lindsey Meyn
Jana Sharooni
Jill Steinberg
Kyle Wark
Suzanne Zarosky

E-Commerce Managers:
Mark Cassells
Emily Hurley
Lynne Zarosky

Information Technology Manager:
Wenping Guo

Cover Design:
Kim Paxson, Just Graphics
Junction, TX

Special Thanks to:
Pharmaceutical Research and Manufacturers of America (PhRMA)
U.S. Bureau of the Census
U.S. Bureau of Labor Statistics
U.S. Department of Energy, Office of Science
U.S. National Aeronautics & Space Administration (NASA)
U.S. National Nanotechnology Initiative
U.S. National Science Foundation
U.S. Patent and Trademark Office

Plunkett Research, Ltd.
P. O. Drawer 541737, Houston, Texas 77254, USA
Phone: 713.932.0000 Fax: 713.932.7080 www.plunkettresearch.com

Published by:
Plunkett Research, Ltd.
P. O. Drawer 541737
Houston, Texas 77254-1737

Phone: 713.932.0000
Fax: 713.932.7080
Internet: www.plunkettresearch.com

ISBN10 # 1-59392-129-2
ISBN13 # 978-1-59392-129-3

Disclaimer of liability
for use and results of use:

The editors and publishers assume no responsibility for your own success in making an investment or business decision, in seeking or keeping any job, in succeeding at any firm or in obtaining any amount or type of benefits or wages. Your own results and the job stability or financial stability of any company depend on influences outside of our control. All risks are assumed by the reader. Investigate any potential employer or business relationship carefully and carefully verify past and present finances, present business conditions and the level of compensation and benefits currently paid. Each company's details are taken from sources deemed reliable; however, their accuracy is not guaranteed. The editors and publishers assume no liability, beyond the actual payment received from a reader, for any direct, indirect, incidental or consequential, special or exemplary damages, and they do not guarantee, warrant nor make any representation regarding the use of this material. Trademarks or tradenames are used without symbols and only in a descriptive sense, and this use is not authorized by, associated with or sponsored by the trademarks' owners. Ranks and ratings are presented as an introductory and general glance at corporations, based on our research and our knowledge of businesses and the industries in which they operate. The reader should use caution.

PLUNKETT'S
ENGINEERING & RESEARCH INDUSTRY
ALMANAC 2009

CONTENTS

Continued on the next page

Continued from the previous page

A Short Engineering & Research Industry Glossary

10-K: An annual report filed by publicly held companies. It provides a comprehensive overview of the company's business and its finances. By law, it must contain specific information and follow a given form, the "Annual Report on Form 10-K." The U.S. Securities and Exchange Commission requires that it be filed within 90 days after fiscal year end. However, these reports are often filed late due to extenuating circumstances. Variations of a 10-K are often filed to indicate amendments and changes. Most publicly held companies also publish an "annual report" that is not on Form 10-K. These annual reports are more informal and are frequently used by a company to enhance its image with customers, investors and industry peers.

3-D Printing: Refers to systems that use an inkjet-like technology to rapidly apply layers of plastics, ceramics or metal powders to create design prototypes or finished manufactured objects.

510 K: An application filed with the FDA for a new medical device to show that the apparatus is "substantially equivalent" to one that is already marketed.

802.11a (Wi-Fi5): A faster wireless network standard than 802.11b ("Wi-Fi"). 802.11a operates in the 5-GHz band at speeds of 50 Mbps or more. This standard may be affected by weather and is not as suitable for outdoor use. 802.11 standards are set by the IEEE (Institute of Electrical and Electronics Engineers).

802.11b (Wi-Fi): An extremely popular, Wi-Fi short-range wireless connection standard created by the IEEE (Institute of Electrical and Electronics Engineers). It operates at 11 Mbps and can be used to connect computer devices to each other. 802.11b competes with the Bluetooth standard. Its range is up to 380 feet, but 150 feet or so may be more practical in some installations.

802.11g: A recent addition to the series of 802.11 specifications for Wi-Fi wireless networks, 802.11g provides data transfer at speeds of up to 54 Mbps in the 2.4-GHz band. It can easily exchange data with 802.11b-enabled devices, but at much higher speed. 802.11g equipment, such as wireless access points, will be able to provide simultaneous WLAN connectivity for both 802.11g and 802.11b equipment. The 802.11 standards are set by the IEEE (Institute of Electrical and Electronics Engineers).

802.11n (MIMO): Multiple Input Multiple Output antenna technology. MIMO is a new standard in the series of 802.11 Wi-Fi specifications for wireless networks. It has the potential of providing data transfer speeds of 100 to perhaps as much as 500 Mbps. 802.11n also boasts better operating distances than current networks. MIMO uses spectrum more efficiently without any loss of reliability. The technology is based on several different antennas all tuned to the same channel, each transmitting a different signal. MIMO will be widely used as an enhancement to WiMAX networks.

802.15: See "Ultrawideband (UWB)." For 802.15.1, see "Bluetooth."

802.15.1: See "Bluetooth."

802.16 (WiMAX): An advanced wireless standard with significant speed and distance capabilities, WiMax is officially known as the 802.16 standard. Using microwave technologies, it has the potential to broadcast at distances up to 30 miles and speeds of up to 70 Mbps. The 802.XX standards are set by the IEEE (Institute of Electrical and Electronics Engineers).

Abbreviated New Drug Application (ANDA): An application filed with the FDA showing that a substance is the same as an existing, previously approved drug (i.e., a generic version).

Absorption, Distribution, Metabolism and Excretion (ADME): In clinical trials, the bodily processes studied to determine the extent and duration of systemic exposure to a drug.

Access Network: The network that connects a user's telephone equipment to the telephone exchange.

Active Server Page (ASP): A web page that includes one or more embedded programs, usually written in Java or Visual Basic code. See "Java."

Active X: A set of technologies developed by Microsoft Corporation for sharing information across different applications.

ADME: See "Absorption, Distribution, Metabolism and Excretion (ADME)."

ADN: See "Advanced Digital Network (ADN)."

ADSL: See "Asymmetrical Digital Subscriber Line (ADSL)."

Advanced Digital Network (ADN): See "Integrated Digital Network (IDN)."

Adverse Event (AE): In clinical trials, a condition not observed at baseline or worsened if present at baseline. Sometimes called Treatment Emergent Signs and Symptoms (TESS).

AE: See "Adverse Event (AE)."

AI (Artificial Intelligence): The use of computer technology to perform functions normally associated with human intelligence, such as reasoning, learning and self-improvement.

Ambient: Refers to any unconfined portion of the air. Also refers to open air.

Analog: A form of transmitting information characterized by continuously variable quantities. Digital transmission, in contrast, is characterized by discrete bits of information in numerical steps. An analog signal responds to changes in light, sound, heat and pressure.

Analog IC (Integrated Circuit): A semiconductor that processes a continuous wave of electrical signals based on real-world analog quantities such as speed, pressure, temperature, light, sound and voltage.

ANDA: See "Abbreviated New Drug Application (ANDA)."

ANSI: American National Standards Institute. Founded in 1918, ANSI is a private, non-profit organization that administers and coordinates the U.S. voluntary standardization and conformity assessment system. Its mission is to enhance both the global competitiveness of U.S. business and the quality of U.S. life by promoting and facilitating voluntary consensus standards and conformity assessment systems, and safeguarding their integrity. See www.ansi.org.

Application Program Interface (API): An application program interface (commonly referred to as an API) is a set of protocols, routines and tools. It is used by computer programmers as a way of setting common definitions regarding how one piece of software communicates with another.

Application Service Provider (ASP): A web site that enables utilization of software and databases that reside permanently on a service company's remote web server, rather than having to be downloaded to the user's computer. Advantages include the ability for multiple remote users to access the same tools over the Internet and the fact that the ASP provider is responsible for developing and maintaining the software. (ASP is also an acronym for "active server page," which is not related.) For the latest developments in ASP, see "Software as a Service (SaaS)."

Applied Research: The application of compounds, processes, materials or other items discovered during basic research to practical uses. The goal is to move discoveries along to the final development phase.

ARPANet: Advanced Research Projects Agency Network. The forefather of the Internet, ARPANet was developed during the latter part of the 1960s by the United States Department of Defense.

ASCII: American Standard Code for Information Exchange. There are 128 standard ASCII codes that represent all Latin letters, numbers and punctuation. Each ASCII code is represented by a seven-digit binary number, such as 0000000 or 0000111. This code is accepted as a standard throughout the world.

ASEAN: Association of Southeast Asian Nations. A regional economic development association established in 1967 by five original member countries: Indonesia, Malaysia, Philippines, Singapore, and Thailand. Brunei joined on 8 January 1984, Vietnam on 28 July 1995, Laos and Myanmar on 23 July 1997, and Cambodia on 30 April 1999.

ASP: See "Application Service Provider (ASP)."

Assay: A laboratory test to identify and/or measure the amount of a particular substance in a sample. Types of assays include endpoint assays, in which a single measurement is made at a fixed time; kinetic assays, in which increasing amounts of a product are formed with time and are monitored at multiple points; microbiological assays, which measure the concentration of antimicrobials in biological material; and immunological assays, in which analysis or measurement is based on antigen-antibody reactions.

Asymmetrical Digital Subscriber Line (ADSL): High-speed technology that enables the transfer of data over existing copper phone lines, allowing more bandwidth downstream than upstream.

Asynchronous Communications: A stream of data routed through a network as generated instead of in organized message blocks. Most personal computers use this format to send data.

Asynchronous Transfer Mode (ATM): A digital switching and transmission technology based on high speed. ATM allows voice, video and data signals to be sent over a single telephone line at speeds from 25 million to 1 billion bits per second (bps). This digital ATM speed is much faster than traditional analog phone lines, which allow no more than 2 million bps. See "Broadband."

Backbone: Traditionally, the part of a communications network that carries the heaviest traffic; the high-speed line or series of connections that forms a large pathway within a network or within a region. The combined networks of AT&T, MCI and other large telecommunications companies make up the backbone of the Internet.

Baseline: A set of data used in clinical studies, or other types of research, for control or comparison.

Basic Research: Attempts to discover compounds, materials, processes or other items that may be largely or entirely new and/or unique. Basic research may start with a theoretical concept that has yet to be proven. The goal is to create discoveries that can be moved along to applied research. Basic research is sometimes referred to as "blue sky" research.

Baud: Refers to how many times the carrier signal in a modem switches value per second or how many bits a modem can send and receive in a second.

Beam: The coverage and geographic service area offered by a satellite transponder. A global beam effectively covers one-third of the earth's surface. A spot beam provides a very specific high-powered downlink pattern that is limited to a particular geographical area to which it may be steered or pointed.

Binhex: A means of changing non-ASCII (or non-text) files into text/ASCII files so that they can be used, for example, as e-mail.

Bioavailability: In pharmaceuticals, the rate and extent to which a drug is absorbed or is otherwise available to the treatment site in the body.

Biochemical Engineering: A sector of chemical engineering that deals with biological structures and processes. Biochemical engineers may be found in the pharmaceutical, biotechnology and environmental fields, among others.

Bioengineering: Engineering principles applied when working in biology and pharmaceuticals.

Bioequivalence: In pharmaceuticals, the demonstration that a drug's rate and extent of absorption are not significantly different from those of an existing drug that is already approved by the FDA. This is the basis upon which generic and brand name drugs are compared.

Bioinformatics: Research, development or application of computational tools and approaches for expanding the use of biological, medical, behavioral or health data, including those to acquire, store, organize, archive, analyze or visualize such data. Bioinformatics is often applied to the study of genetic data. It applies principles of information sciences and technologies to make vast, diverse and complex life sciences data more understandable and useful.

Biologics: Drugs that are synthesized from living organisms. That is, drugs created using biotechnology, sometimes referred to as biopharmaceuticals. Specifically, biologics may be any virus, therapeutic serum, toxin, antitoxin, vaccine, blood, blood component or derivative, allergenic or analogous product, or arsphenamine or one of its derivatives used for the prevention, treatment or cure of disease. Also, see "Biologics License Application (BLA)," "Follow-on Biologics," and "Biopharmaceuticals."

Biologics License Application (BLA): An application to be submitted to the FDA when a firm wants to obtain permission to market a novel, new biological drug product. Specifically, these are drugs created through the use of biotechnology. It was formerly known as Product License Application (PLA). Also see "Biologics."

Biopharmaceuticals: That portion of the pharmaceutical industry focused on the use of biotechnology to create new drugs. A biopharmaceutical can be any biological compound that is intended to be used as a therapeutic drug, including recombinant proteins, monoclonal and polyclonal antibodies, antisense oligonucleotides, therapeutic genes, and recombinant and DNA vaccines. Also, see "Biologics."

Biotechnology: A set of powerful tools that employ living organisms (or parts of organisms) to make or modify products, improve plants or animals (including humans) or develop microorganisms for specific uses. Biotechnology is most commonly thought of to include the development of human medical therapies and processes using recombinant DNA, cell fusion, other genetic techniques and bioremediation.

Bit: A single digit number, either a one or a zero, which is the smallest unit of computerized data.

Bits Per Second (Bps): An indicator of the speed of data movement.

BLA: See "Biologics License Application (BLA)."

Bluetooth: An industry standard for a technology that enables wireless, short-distance infrared connections between devices such as cell phone headsets, Palm Pilots or PDAs, laptops, printers and Internet appliances.

BPO: See "Business Process Outsourcing (BPO)."

Bps: See "Bits Per Second (Bps)."

Branding: A marketing strategy that places a focus on the brand name of a product, service or firm in order to increase the brand's market share, increase sales, establish credibility, improve satisfaction, raise the profile of the firm and increase profits.

BRIC: An acronym representing Brazil, Russia, India and China. The economies of these four countries are seen as some of the fastest growing in the world. A 2003 report by investment bank Goldman Sachs is often credited for popularizing the term; the report suggested that by 2050, BRIC economies will likely outshine those countries which are currently the richest in the world.

Broadband: The high-speed transmission range for telecommunications and computer data. Broadband refers to any transmission at 2 million bps (bits per second) or higher (much higher than analog speed). A broadband network can carry voice, video and data all at the same time. Internet users enjoying broadband access typically connect to the Internet via DSL line, cable modem or T1 line. Several wireless methods now offer broadband as well.

B-to-B, or B2B: See "Business-to-Business."

B-to-C, or B2C: See "Business-to-Consumer."

B-to-G, or B2G: See "Business-to-Government."

Buffer: A location for temporarily storing data being sent or received. It is usually located between two devices that have different data transmission rates.

Business Process Outsourcing (BPO): The process of hiring another company to handle business activities. BPO is one of the fastest-growing segments in the offshoring sector. Services include human resources management, billing and purchasing and call centers, as well as many types of customer service or marketing activities, depending on the industry involved. Also, see "Knowledge Process Outsourcing (KPO)."

Business-to-Business: An organization focused on selling products, services or data to commercial customers rather than individual consumers. Also known as B2B.

Business-to-Consumer: An organization focused on selling products, services or data to individual consumers rather than commercial customers. Also known as B2C.

Business-to-Government: An organization focused on selling products, services or data to government units rather than commercial businesses or consumers. Also known as B2G.

Byte: A set of eight bits that represent a single character.

Cable Modem: An interface between a cable television system and a computer or router. Most cable modems are external devices that connect to the PC through a standard 10Base-T Ethernet card and twisted-pair wiring. External Universal Serial Bus (USB) modems and internal PCI modem cards are also available.

Caching: A method of storing data in a temporary location closer to the user so that it can be retrieved quickly when requested.

CAD: See "Computer-Aided Design (CAD)."

CAE: See "Computer-Aided Engineering (CAE)."

CAFTA-DR: See "Central American-Dominican Republic Free Trade Agreement (CAFTA-DR)."

CAM: See "Computer-Aided Manufacturing (CAM)."

CANDA: See "Computer-Assisted New Drug Application (CANDA)."

Capability Maturity Model (CMM): A global process management standard for software development established by the Software Engineering Institute at Carnegie Mellon University.

Capacitor: An electronic circuit device for temporary storage of electrical energy.

Captive Offshoring: Used to describe a company-owned offshore operation. For example, Microsoft owns and operates significant captive offshore research and development centers in China and elsewhere that are offshore from Microsoft's U.S. home base. Also see "Offshoring."

Cardiac Catheterization Laboratory: Facilities offering special diagnostic procedures for cardiac patients, including the introduction of a catheter into the interior of the heart by way of a vein or artery or by direct needle puncture. Procedures must be performed in a laboratory or a special procedure room.

Carrier: In communications, the basic radio, television or telephony center of transmit signal. The carrier in an analog signal is modulated by varying volume or shifting frequency up or down in relation to the incoming signal. Satellite carriers operating in the analog mode are usually frequency-modulated.

CASE: See "Computer-Aided Software Engineering (CASE)."

CAT Scan: See "Computed Tomography (CT)."

Catheter: A tubular instrument used to add or withdraw fluids. Heart or cardiac catheterization involves the passage of flexible catheters into the great vessels and chambers of the heart. IV catheters add intravenous fluids to the veins. Foley catheters withdraw fluid from the bladder. Significant recent advances in technology allow administration of powerful drug and diagnostic therapies via catheters.

CATV: Cable television.

CBER: See "Center for Biologics Evaluation and Research (CBER)."

CDER: See "Center for Drug Evaluation and Research (CDER)."

CDMA: See "Code Division Multiple Access (CDMA)."

CDRH: See "Center for Devices and Radiological Health (CDRH)."

Center for Biologics Evaluation and Research (CBER): The branch of the FDA responsible for the regulation of biological products, including blood, vaccines, therapeutics and related drugs and devices, to ensure purity, potency, safety, availability and effectiveness. www.fda.gov/cber

Center for Devices and Radiological Health (CDRH): The branch of the FDA responsible for the regulation of medical devices. www.fda.gov/cdrh

Center for Drug Evaluation and Research (CDER): The branch of the FDA responsible for the regulation of drug products. www.fda.gov/cder

Central Processing Unit (CPU): The part of a computer that interprets and executes instructions. It is composed of an arithmetic logic unit, a control unit and a small amount of memory.

Ceramic: Ceramics are nonmetallic materials that have been created under intense heat. Ceramics tend to be extremely hard, heat-resistant and corrosion-resistant. They are generally poor conductors of temperature changes or electricity. Ceramics are used in low-tech and high-tech applications, ranging from the insulators in spark plugs to the heat shield on the Space Shuttle.

CGI: See "Common Gateway Interface (CGI)."

Common Gateway Interface (CGI): A set of guidelines that determines the manner in which a web server receives and sends information to and from software on the same machine.

CGI-BIN: The frequently used name of a directory on a web server where CGI programs exist.

Channel Definition Format (CDF): Used in Internet-based broadcasting. With this format, a channel serves as a web site that also sends an information file about that specific site. Users subscribe to a channel by downloading the file.

Chemical Engineering: The sector that deals with technologies, safety issues, refining, production and delivery of chemicals and products that are manufactured partly or largely through the use of chemicals. Chemical engineers are also involved in the design and construction of major industrial plants, as well as the application of chemicals to scientific and industrial needs.

CIS: See "Commonwealth of Independent States (CIS)."

Class I Device: An FDA classification of medical devices for which general controls are sufficient to ensure safety and efficacy.

Class II Device: An FDA classification of medical devices for which performance standards and special controls are sufficient to ensure safety and efficacy.

Class III Device: An FDA classification of medical devices for which pre-market approval is required to ensure safety and efficacy, unless the device is substantially equivalent to a currently marketed device. See "510 K."

CLEC: See "Competitive Local Exchange Carrier (CLEC)."

Client/Server: In networking, a way of running a large computer setup. The server is the host computer that acts as the central holding ground for files, databases and application software. The clients are all of the PCs connected to the network that share data with the server. This represents a vast change from past networks, which were connected to expensive, complicated "mainframe" computers.

Climate Change (Greenhouse Effect): A theory that assumes an increasing mean global surface temperature of the Earth caused by gases in the atmosphere (including carbon dioxide, methane, nitrous oxide, ozone and chlorofluorocarbons). The greenhouse effect allows solar radiation to penetrate the Earth's atmosphere but absorbs the infrared radiation returning to space.

Cloning (Reproductive): A method of reproducing an exact copy of an animal or, potentially, an exact copy of a human being. A scientist removes the nucleus from a donor's unfertilized egg, inserts a nucleus from the animal to be copied and then stimulates the nucleus to begin dividing to form an embryo. In the case of a mammal, such as a human, the embryo would then be implanted in the uterus of a host female. Also see "Cloning (Therapeutic)."

Cloning (Therapeutic): A method of reproducing exact copies of cells needed for research or for the development of replacement tissue or organs. A scientist removes the nucleus from a donor's unfertilized egg, inserts a nucleus from the animal whose cells are to be copied and then stimulates the nucleus to begin dividing to form an embryo. However, the embryo is never allowed to grow to any significant stage of development. Instead, it is allowed to grow for a few hours or days, and stem cells are then removed from it for use in regenerating tissue. Also see "Cloning (Reproductive)."

CMM: See "Capability Maturity Model (CMM)."

CMOS: Complementary Metal Oxide Semiconductor; the technology used in making modern silicon-based microchips.

Coaxial Cable: A type of cable widely used to transmit telephone and broadcast traffic. The distinguishing feature is an inner strand of wires surrounded by an insulator that is in turn surrounded by another conductor, which serves as the ground. Cable TV wiring is typically coaxial.

Code Division Multiple Access (CDMA): A cellular telephone multiple-access scheme whereby stations use spread-spectrum modulations and orthogonal codes to avoid interfering with one another. IS-95 (also known as CDMAOne) is the 2G CDMA standard. CDMA2000 is the 3G standard. CDMA in the 1xEV-DO standard offers data transfer speeds up to 2.4 Mbps. CDMA 1xRTT is a slower standard offering speeds of 144 kbps.

Code of Federal Regulations (CFR): A codification of the general and permanent rules published in the Federal Register by the executive departments and agencies of the Federal Government. The code is divided into 50 titles that represent broad areas subject to federal regulation. Title 21 of the CFR covers FDA regulations.

Codec: Hardware or software that converts analog to digital and digital to analog (in both audio and video formats). Codecs can be found in digital telephones, set-top boxes, computers and videoconferencing equipment. The term is also used to refer to the compression of digital information into a smaller format.

Co-Location: Refers to the hosting of computer servers at locations operated by service organizations. Co-location is offered by firms that operate specially designed co-location centers with high levels of security, extremely high-speed telecommunication lines for Internet connectivity and reliable backup electrical power systems in case of power failure, as well as a temperature-controlled environment for optimum operation of computer systems.

Commerce Chain Management (CCM): Refers to Internet-based tools to facilitate sales, distribution, inventory management and content personalization in the e-commerce industry. Also see "Supply Chain."

Committee for Veterinary Medicinal Products (CVMP): A committee that is a veterinary equivalent of the CPMP (see "Committee on Proprietary Medicinal Products (CPMP)") in the EU. See "European Union (EU)."

Committee on Proprietary Medicinal Products (CPMP): A committee, composed of two people from each EU Member State (see "European Union (EU)"), that is responsible for the scientific evaluation and assessment of marketing applications for medicinal products in the EU. The CPMP is the major body involved in the harmonization of pharmaceutical regulations within the EU and receives administrative support from the European Medicines Evaluation Agency. See "European Medicines Evaluation Agency (EMEA)."

Commonwealth of Independent States (CIS): An organization consisting of 11 former members of the Soviet Union: Russia, Ukraine, Armenia, Moldova, Georgia, Belarus, Kazakhstan, Uzbekistan, Azerbaijan, Kyrgyzstan and Tajikistan. It was created in 1991. Turkmenistan recently left the Commonwealth as a permanent member, but remained as an associate member. The Commonwealth seeks to coordinate a variety of economic and social policies, including taxation, pricing, customs and economic regulation, as well as to promote the free movement of capital, goods, services and labor.

Communications Satellite Corporation (COMSAT): Serves as the U.S. Signatory to INTELSAT and INMARSAT.

Competitive Local Exchange Carrier (CLEC): A newer company providing local telephone service that competes against larger, traditional firms known as ILECs (incumbent local exchange carriers).

Compression: A technology in which a communications signal is squeezed so that it uses less bandwidth (or capacity) than it normally would. This saves storage space and shortens transfer time. The original data is decompressed when read back into memory.

Computed Tomography (CT): An imaging method that uses x-rays to create cross-sectional pictures of the body. The technique is frequently referred to as a "CAT Scan." A patient lies on a narrow platform while the machine's x-ray beam rotates around him or her. Small detectors inside the scanner measure the amount of x-rays that make it through the part of the body being studied. A computer takes this information and uses it to create several individual images, called slices. These images can be stored, viewed on a monitor, or printed on film. Three-dimensional models of organs can be created by stacking the individual slices together. The newest machines are capable of operating at 64 slice levels, creating very high resolution images in a short period of time. Eventually, 256 slice technology will be introduced.

Computer-Aided Design (CAD): A tool used to provide three-dimensional, on-screen design for everything from buildings to automobiles to clothing. It generally runs on workstations.

Computer-Aided Engineering (CAE): The use of computers to assist with a broad spectrum of engineering design work, including conceptual and analytical design.

Computer-Aided Manufacturing (CAM): The use of computers to assist with manufacturing processes, thereby increasing efficiency and productivity.

Computer-Assisted New Drug Application (CANDA): An electronic submission of a new drug application (NDA) to the FDA.

Computer-Assisted Software Engineering (CASE): The application of computer technology to systems development activities, techniques and methodologies. Sometimes referred to as "computer-aided systems engineering."

COMSAT: See "Communications Satellite Corporation (COMSAT)."

Consumer Price Index (CPI): A measure of the average change in consumer prices over time in a fixed market basket of goods and services, such as food, clothing and housing. The CPI is calculated by the U.S. Federal Government and is considered to be one measure of inflation.

Contract Manufacturer: A company that manufactures products that will be sold under the brand names of its client companies. For example, a large number of consumer electronics, such as laptop computers, are manufactured by contract manufacturers for leading brand-name computer companies such as Dell. Many other types of products are made under contract manufacturing, from apparel to pharmaceuticals. Also see "Original Equipment Manufacturer (OEM)" and "Original Design Manufacturer (ODM)."

Contract Research Organization (CRO): An independent organization that contracts with a client to conduct part of the work on a study or research project. For example, drug and medical device makers frequently outsource clinical trials and other research work to CROs.

Coordinator: In clinical trials, the person at an investigative site who handles the administrative responsibilities of the trial, acts as a liaison between the investigative site and the sponsor, and reviews data and records during a monitoring visit.

Cost Plus Contract: A contract that sets the contractor's compensation as a percentage of the total cost of labor and materials.

COSTART: In medical and drug product development, a dictionary of adverse events and body systems used for coding and classifying adverse events.

CPMP: See "Committee on Proprietary Medicinal Products (CPMP)."

CPU: See "Central Processing Unit (CPU)."

CRO: See "Contract Research Organization (CRO)."

CT: See "Computed Tomography (CT)."

CVMP: See "Committee for Veterinary Medicinal Products (CVMP)."

Data Over Cable Service Interface Specification (DOCSIS): A set of standards for transferring data over cable television. DOCSIS 3.0 will enable very high-speed Internet access that may eventually reach 160 Mbps.

Decompression: See "Compression."

Defibrillator: In medicine, an instrument used externally (as electrodes on the chest) or implanted (as a small device similar in size to a pacemaker) that delivers an electric shock to return the heart to its normal rhythm.

Demand Chain: A similar concept to a supply chain, but with an emphasis on the end user.

Dendrimer: A type of molecule that can be used with small molecules to give them certain desirable characteristics. Dendrimers are utilized in technologies for electronic displays. See "Organic LED (OLED)."

Design Patent: A patent that may be granted by the U.S. Patent and Trademark Office to anyone who invents a new, original, and ornamental design for an article of manufacture.

Development: The phase of research and development (R&D) in which researchers attempt to create new products from the results of discoveries and applications created during basic and applied research.

Device: In medical products, an instrument, apparatus, implement, machine, contrivance, implant, in vitro reagent or other similar or related article, including any component, part or accessory, that 1) is recognized in the official National Formulary or United States Pharmacopoeia or any supplement to them, 2) is intended for use in the diagnosis of disease or other conditions, or in the cure, mitigation, treatment or prevention of disease, in man or animals or 3) is intended to affect the structure of the body of man or animals and does not achieve any of its principal intended purposes through chemical action within or on the body of man or animals and is not dependent upon being metabolized for the achievement of any of its principal intended purposes.

Diagnostic Radioisotope Facility: A medical facility in which radioactive isotopes (radiopharmaceuticals) are used as tracers or indicators to detect an abnormal condition or disease in the body.

Digital Local Telephone Switch: A computer that interprets signals (dialed numbers) from a telephone caller and routes calls to their proper destinations. A digital switch also provides a variety of calling features not available in older analog switches, such as call waiting.

Digital Rights Management (DRM): Restrictions placed on the use of digital content by copyright holders and hardware manufacturers. DRM for Apple, Inc.'s iTunes, for example, allows downloaded music to be played only on Apple's iPod player and iPhones, per agreement with music production companies Universal Music Group, SonyBMG, Warner Music and EMI.

Digital Signal Processor: A chip that converts analog signals such as sound and light into digital signals.

Digital Subscriber Line (DSL): A broadband (high-speed) Internet connection provided via telecommunications systems. These lines are a cost-effective means of providing homes and small businesses with relatively fast Internet access. Common variations include ADSL and SDSL. DSL competes with cable modem access and wireless access.

Disaster Recovery: A set of rules and procedures that allow a computer site to be put back in operation after a disaster has occurred. Moving backups off-site constitutes the minimum basic precaution for disaster recovery. The remote copy is used to recover data if the local storage is inaccessible after a disaster.

Discrete Semiconductor: A chip with one diode or transistor.

Disk Mirroring: A data redundancy technique in which data is recorded identically on multiple separate disk drives at the same time. When the primary disk is off-line, the alternate takes over, providing continuous access to data. Disk mirroring is sometimes referred to as RAID.

Distributed Power Generation: A method of generating electricity at or near the site where it will be consumed, such as the use of small, local generators or fuel cells to power individual buildings, homes or neighborhoods. Distributed power is thought by many analysts to offer distinct advantages. For example, electricity generated in this manner is not reliant upon the grid for distribution to the end user.

Distributor: An individual or business involved in marketing, warehousing and/or shipping of products manufactured by others to a specific group of end users. Distributors do not sell to the general public. In order to develop a competitive advantage, distributors often focus on serving one industry or one set of niche clients. For example, within the medical industry, there are major distributors that focus on providing pharmaceuticals, surgical supplies or dental supplies to clinics and hospitals.

DNA Chip: A revolutionary tool used to identify mutations in genes like BRCA1 and BRCA2. The chip, which consists of a small glass plate encased in plastic, is manufactured using a process similar to the one used to make computer microchips. On the surface, each chip contains synthetic single-stranded DNA sequences identical to a normal gene.

Drug Utilization Review: A quantitative assessment of patient drug use and physicians' patterns of prescribing drugs in an effort to determine the usefulness of drug therapy.

DS-1: A digital transmission format that transmits and receives information at a rate of 1,544,000 bits per second.

DSL: See "Digital Subscriber Line (DSL)."

Duplicate Host: A single host name that maps to duplicate IP addresses.

Dynamic HTML: Web content that changes with each individual viewing. For example, the same site could appear differently depending on geographic location of the reader, time of day, previous pages viewed or the user's profile.

Ecology: The study of relationships among all living organisms and the environment, especially the totality or pattern of interactions; a view that includes all plant and animal species and their unique contributions to a particular habitat.

ELA: See "Establishment License Application (ELA)."

Electronic Data Interchange (EDI): An accepted standard format for the exchange of data between various companies' networks. EDI allows for the transfer of e-mail as well as orders, invoices and other files from one company to another.

Emission: The release or discharge of a substance into the environment. Generally refers to the release of gases or particulates into the air.

Endpoint: A clinical or laboratory measurement used to assess safety, efficacy or other trial objectives of a test article in a clinical trial.

Enterprise Resource Planning (ERP): An integrated information system that helps manage all aspects of a business, including accounting, ordering and human resources, typically across all locations of a major corporation or organization. ERP is considered to be a critical tool for management of large organizations. Suppliers of ERP tools include SAP and Oracle.

Environmental Audit: An independent assessment of a facility's compliance procedures, policies and controls. Many pollution prevention initiatives require an audit to determine where wastes may be reduced or eliminated or energy conserved.

Establishment License Application (ELA): Required for the approval of a biologic (see "Biologic"). It permits a specific facility to manufacture a biological product for commercial purposes. Compare to "Product License Agreement (PLA)."

ESWL: See "Extracorporeal Shock Wave Lithotripter (ESWL)."

Ethernet: The standard format on which local area network equipment works. Abiding by Ethernet standards allows equipment from various manufacturers to work together.

EU: See "European Union (EU)."

EU Competence: The jurisdiction in which the EU can take legal action.

European Community (EC): See "European Union (EU)."

European Medicines Evaluation Agency (EMEA): The European agency responsible for supervising and coordinating applications for marketing medicinal products in the European Union (see "European Union (EU)" and "Committee on Proprietary Medicinal Products (CPMP)"). The EMEA is headquartered in the U.K. www.eudraportal.eudra.org

European Union (EU): A consolidation of European countries (member states) functioning as one body to facilitate trade. Previously known as the European Community (EC), the EU expanded to include much of Eastern Europe in 2004, raising the total number of member states to 25. In 2002, the EU launched a unified currency, the Euro. See europa.eu.int.

Expert Systems: A practical development of AI that requires creation of a knowledge base of facts and rules furnished by human experts and uses a defined set of rules to access this information in order to suggest solutions to problems. See "AI (Artificial Intelligence)."

Extensible Markup Language (XML): A programming language that enables designers to add extra functionality to documents that could not otherwise be utilized with standard HTML coding. XML was developed by the World Wide Web Consortium. It can communicate to various software programs the actual meanings contained in HTML documents. For example, it can enable the gathering and use of information from a large number of databases at once and place that information into one web site window. XML is an important protocol to web services. See "Web Services."

Extranet: A computer network that is accessible in part to authorized outside persons, as opposed to an intranet, which uses a firewall to limit accessibility.

Fab Lab: See "3-D Printing."

Fabless: A method of operation used by a product supplier that does not have its own fabrication or manufacturing facilities. This phrase is often used to describe certain semiconductor firms that design chips but rely on outside, contract manufacturers for their actual fabrication.

FDA: See "Food and Drug Administration (FDA)."

FDDI: See "Fiber Distributed Data Interface (FDDI)."

Federal Communications Commission (FCC): The U.S. Government agency that regulates broadcast television and radio, as well as satellite transmission, telephony and all uses of radio spectrum.

Femtosecond: One a billionth of one millionth of a second.

Fiber Distributed Data Interface (FDDI): A token ring passing scheme that operates at 100 Mbps over fiber-optic lines with a built-in geographic limitation of 100 kilometers. This type of connection is faster than both Ethernet and T-3 connections. See "Token Ring."

Fiber Optics (Fibre Optics): A type of telephone and data transmission cable that can handle vast amounts of voice, data and video at once by carrying them along on beams of light via glass or plastic threads embedded in a cable. Fiber optics are rapidly replacing older copper wire technologies. Fiber optics offer much higher speeds and the ability to handle extremely large quantities of voice or data transmissions at once.

Field Emission Display (FED): A self-luminescent display that can be extremely thin, draw very low power, and be very bright from all angles and in all types of light.

The latest FEDs are based on carbon nanotubes. Samsung is a leader in this field. Early applications include high-end television and computer monitors.

File Server: A computer that is modified to store and transfer large amounts of data to other computers. File servers often receive data from mainframes and store it for transfer to other, smaller computers, or from small computers to mainframes.

File Transfer Protocol (FTP): A widely used method of transferring data and files between two Internet sites.

Finite Element Analysis (FEA): Finite Element Analysis (FEA) is a tool in computerized design that can detect flaws in a computer-generated model. It analyzes how the model would react to extremes in heat, vibration and pressure by breaking it down into small pieces or cells in a three-dimensional grid. The computer applies simulated stimuli to one cell in the model and then tracks the response of that cell and those that surround it.

Firewall: Hardware or software that keeps unauthorized users from accessing a server or network. Firewalls are designed to prevent data theft and unauthorized web site manipulation by "hackers."

Fissure: A long narrow crack or opening.

Food and Drug Administration (FDA): The U.S. government agency responsible for the enforcement of the Federal Food, Drug and Cosmetic Act, ensuring industry compliance with laws regulating products in commerce. The FDA's mission is to protect the public from harm and encourage technological advances that hold the promise of benefiting society. www.fda.gov

Fracture: A break or rupture in the surface of a laminate due to external or internal forces.

Frame Relay: An accepted standard for sending large amounts of data over phone lines and private datanets. The term refers to the way data is broken down into standard-size "frames" prior to transmission.

Frequency: The number of times that an alternating current goes through its complete cycle in one second. One cycle per second is referred to as one hertz; 1,000 cycles per second, one kilohertz; 1 million cycles per second, one megahertz; and 1 billion cycles per second, one gigahertz.

Frequency Band: A term for designating a range of frequencies in the electromagnetic spectrum.

FTP: See "File Transfer Protocol (FTP)."

Fuel Cell: An environmentally friendly electrochemical engine that generates electricity using hydrogen and oxygen as fuel, emitting only heat and water as byproducts.

Fusion: See "Nuclear Fusion."

Fuzzy Logic: Recognizes that some statements are not just "true" or "false," but also "more or less certain" or "very unlikely." Fuzzy logic is used in artificial intelligence. See "Artificial Intelligence (AI)."

Gateway: A device connecting two or more networks that may use different protocols and media. Gateways translate between the different networks and can connect locally or over wide area networks.

GCP: See "Good Clinical Practices (GCP)."

GDP: See "Gross Domestic Product (GDP)."

Gene Chip: See "DNA Chip."

Genetically Modified (GM) Foods: Food crops that are bioengineered to resist herbicides, diseases or insects; have higher nutritional value than non-engineered plants; produce a higher yield per acre; and/or last longer on the shelf. Additional traits may include resistance to temperature and moisture extremes. Agricultural animals also may be genetically modified organisms.

Genomics: The study of genes, their role in diseases and our ability to manipulate them.

Geological Information System (GIS): A computer software system which captures, stores, updates, manipulates, analyzes, and displays all forms of geographically referenced information.

Geostationary: A geosynchronous satellite angle with zero inclination, making a satellite appear to hover over one spot on the earth's equator.

Gigabyte: A gigabytye is 1,024 megabytes.

Gigahertz (GHz): One billion cycles per second. See "Frequency."

Global System for Mobile Communications (GSM): The standard cellular format used throughout Europe, making one type of cellular phone usable in every nation on the continent and in the U.K. In the U.S., Cingular and T-Mobile also run GSM networks. The original GSM, introduced in 1991, has transfer speeds of only 9.6 kbps. GSM EDGE offers 2.75G data transfer speeds of up to 384 kbps. GSM GPRS offers slower 2.5G speeds of 170 kbps.

Global Warming: An increase in the near-surface temperature of the Earth. Global warming has occurred in the distant past as the result of natural influences, but the term is most often used to refer to a theory that warming occurs as a result of increased use of hydrocarbon fuels by man. See "Climate Change (Greenhouse Effect)."

Globalization: The increased mobility of goods, services, labor, technology and capital throughout the world. Although globalization is not a new development, its pace has increased with the advent of new technologies, especially in the areas of telecommunications, finance and shipping.

GLP: See "Good Laboratory Practices (GLP)."

GLP (Good Laboratory Practices): A collection of regulations and guidelines to be used in laboratories where research is conducted on drugs, biologics or devices that are intended for submission to the FDA.

GMP: See "Good Manufacturing Practices (GMP)."

Good Clinical Practices (GCP): FDA regulations and guidelines that define the responsibilities of the key figures involved in a clinical trial, including the sponsor, the investigator, the monitor and the Institutional Review Board. See "Institutional Review Board (IRB)."

Good Manufacturing Practices (GMP): A collection of regulations and guidelines to be used in manufacturing drugs, biologics and medical devices.

Graphic Interchange Format (GIF): A widely used format for image files.

Gross Domestic Product (GDP): The total value of a nation's output, income and expenditures produced with a nation's physical borders.

Gross National Product (GNP): A country's total output of goods and services from all forms of economic activity measured at market prices for one calendar year. It differs from Gross Domestic Product (GDP) in that GNP includes income from investments made in foreign nations.

GSM: See "Global System for Mobile Communications (GSM)."

Handheld Devices Markup Language (HDML): A text-based markup language designed for display on a smaller screen (e.g., a cellular phone, PDA or pager). Enables the mobile user to send, receive and redirect e-mail as well as access the Internet (HDML-enabled web sites only).

HD Radio (High Definition Radio): A technology that enables station operators to slice existing radio spectrum into multiple, thin bands. Each band is capable of transmitting additional programming. One existing radio station's spectrum may be sliced into as many as eight channels.

HDML: See "Handheld Devices Markup Language (HDML)."

HDSL: See "High-Data-Rate Digital Subscriber Line (HDSL)."

Hertz: A measure of frequency equal to one cycle per second. Most radio signals operate in ranges of megahertz or gigahertz.

High-Data-Rate Digital Subscriber Line (HDSL): High-data-rate DSL, delivering up to T1 or E1 speeds.

High-Throughput Screening (HTP): Makes use of techniques that allow for a fast and simple test on the presence or absence of a desirable structure, such as a specific DNA sequence. HTP screening often uses DNA chips or microarrays and automated data processing for large-scale screening, for instance, to identify new targets for drug development.

HTML: See "Hypertext Markup Language (HTML)."

HTTP: See "Hypertext Transfer Protocol (HTTP)."

Hypertext Markup Language (HTML): A language for coding text for viewing on the World Wide Web. HTML is unique because it enables the use of hyperlinks from one site to another, creating a web.

Hypertext Transfer Protocol (HTTP): The protocol used most frequently on the World Wide Web to move hypertext files between clients and servers on the Internet.

ICANN: The Internet Corporation for Assigned Names and Numbers. ICANN acts as the central coordinator for the Internet's technical operations.

ICD9: International Classification of Diseases - Version 9. A government coding system used for classifying diseases and diagnoses.

IDE: See "Investigational New Device Exemption (IDE)."

IDN: See "Integrated Digital Network (IDN)."

IEEE: The Institute of Electrical and Electronic Engineers. The IEEE sets global technical standards and acts as an authority in technical areas including computer engineering, biomedical technology, telecommunications, electric power, aerospace and consumer electronics, among others. www.ieee.org.

ILEC: See "Incumbent Local Exchange Carrier (ILEC)."

Imaging: In medicine, the viewing of the body's organs through external, high-tech means. This reduces the need for broad exploratory surgery. These advances, along with new types of surgical instruments, have made minimally invasive surgery possible. Imaging includes MRI (magnetic resonance imaging), CT (computed tomography or CAT scan), MEG (magnetoencephalography), improved x-ray technology, mammography, ultrasound and angiography.

Immunoassay: An immunological assay. Types include agglutination, complement-fixation, precipitation, immunodiffusion and electrophoretic assays. Each type of assay utilizes either a particular type of antibody or a specific support medium (such as a gel) to determine the amount of antigen present.

In Vitro: Laboratory experiments conducted in the test tube, or otherwise, without using live animals and/or humans.

In Vivo: Laboratory experiments conducted with live animals and/or humans.

Incumbent Local Exchange Carrier (ILEC): A traditional telephone company that was providing local service prior to the establishment of the Telecommunications Act of 1996, when upstart companies (CLECs, or competitive local exchange carriers) were enabled to compete against the ILECS and were granted access to their system wiring.

IND: See "Investigational New Drug Application (IND)."

Inert Ingredients: Substances that are not active, such as water, petroleum distillates, talc, corn meal or soaps.

Information Technology (IT): The systems, including hardware and software, that move and store voice, video and data via computers and telecommunications.

Infrastructure: 1) The equipment that comprises a system. 2) Public-use assets such as roads, bridges, sewers and other assets necessary for public accommodation and utilities. 3) The underlying base of a system or network.

Infrastructure (Telecommunications): The entity made up of all the cable and equipment installed in the worldwide telecommunications market. Most of today's telecommunications infrastructure is connected by copper and fiber-optic cable, which represents a huge capital investment that telephone companies would like to continue to utilize in as many ways as possible.

Initial Public Offering (IPO): A company's first effort to sell its stock to investors (the public). Investors in an up-trending market eagerly seek stocks offered in many IPOs because the stocks of newly public companies that seem to have great promise may appreciate very rapidly in price, reaping great profits for those who were able to get the stock at the first offering. In the United States, IPOs are regulated by the SEC (U.S. Securities Exchange Commission) and by the state-level regulatory agencies of the states in which the IPO shares are offered.

INMARSAT: The International Maritime Satellite Organization. INMARSAT operates a network of satellites used in transmissions for all types of international mobile services, including maritime, aeronautical and land mobile.

Institutional Review Board (IRB): A group of individuals usually found in medical institutions that is responsible for reviewing protocols for ethical consideration (to ensure the rights of the patients). An IRB also evaluates the benefit-to-risk ratio of a new drug to see that the risk is acceptable for patient exposure. Responsibilities of an IRB are defined in FDA regulations.

Integrated Circuit (IC): Another name for a semiconductor, an IC is a piece of silicon on which thousands (or millions) of transistors have been combined.

Integrated Digital Network (IDN): A network that uses both digital transmission and digital switching.

Integrated Services Digital Networks (ISDN): Internet connection services offered at higher speeds than standard "dial-up" service. While ISDN was considered to be an advanced service at one time, it has been eclipsed by much faster DSL, cable modem and T1 line service.

INTELSAT: The International Telecommunications Satellite Organization. INTELSAT operates a network of 20 satellites, primarily for international transmissions, and provides domestic services to some 40 countries.

Interactive TV (ITV): Allows two-way data flow between a viewer and the cable TV system. A user can exchange information with the cable system—for example, by ordering a product related to a show he/she is watching or by voting in an interactive survey.

Interexchange Carrier (IXC or IEC): Any company providing long-distance phone service between LECs and LATAs. See "LEC (Local Exchange Carrier)" and "LATA (Local Access and Transport Area)."

Interface: Refers to (1) a common boundary between two or more items of equipment or between a terminal and a communication channel, (2) the electronic device that interconnects two or more devices or items of equipment having similar or dissimilar characteristics or (3) the electronic device placed between a terminal and a communication channel to protect the network from the hazard of excess voltage levels.

International Telecommunications Union (ITU): The international body responsible for telephone and computer communications standards describing interface techniques and practices. These standards include those that define how a nation's telephone and data systems connect to the worldwide communications network.

Internet: A global computer network that provides an easily accessible way for hundreds of millions of users to send and receive data electronically when appropriately connected via computers or wireless devices. Access is generally through HTML-enabled sites on the World Wide Web. Also known as the Net.

Internet Appliance: A non-PC device that connects users to the Internet for specific or general purposes. A good example is an electronic game machine with a screen and Internet capabilities. It is anticipated that many types of Internet appliances will be of common use in homes in the near future.

Internet Protocol (IP): A set of tools and/or systems used to communicate across the World Wide Web.

Internet Service Provider (ISP): A company that sells access to the Internet to individual subscribers. Leading examples are MSN and AOL.

Internet Telephony: See "VOIP (Voice Over Internet Protocol)."

Intranet: A network protected by a firewall for sharing data and e-mail within an organization or company. Usually, intranets are used by organizations for internal communication.

Investigational New Device Exemption (IDE): A document that must be filed with the FDA prior to initiating clinical trials of medical devices considered to pose a significant risk to human subjects.

Investigational New Drug Application (IND): A document that must be filed with the FDA prior to initiating clinical trials of drugs or biologics.

Investigator: In clinical trials, a clinician who agrees to supervise the use of an investigational drug, device or biologic in humans. Responsibilities of the investigator, as defined in FDA regulations, include administering the drug, observing and testing the patient, collecting data and monitoring the care and welfare of the patient.

IP Number/IP Address: A number or address with four parts that are separated by dots. Each machine on the Internet has its own IP (Internet protocol) number, which serves as an identifier.

IRB: See "Institutional Review Board (IRB)."

ISDN: See "Integrated Services Digital Networks (ISDN)."

ISO 9000, 9001, 9002, 9003: Standards set by the International Organization for Standardization. ISO 9000, 9001, 9002 and 9003 are the highest quality certifications awarded to organizations that meet exacting standards in their operating practices and procedures.

IT: See "Information Technology (IT)."

IT-Enabled Services (ITES): The portion of the Information Technology industry focused on providing business services, such as call centers, insurance claims processing and medical records transcription, by utilizing the power of IT, especially the Internet. Most ITES functions are considered to be back-office procedures. Also, see "Business Process Outsourcing (BPO)."

ITES: See "IT-Enabled Services (ITES)."

ITU: See "International Telecommunications Union (ITU)."

ITV: See "Interactive TV (ITV)."

Java: A programming language developed by Sun Microsystems that allows web pages to display interactive graphics. Any type of computer or operating systems can read Java.

Joint Photographic Experts Group (JPEG): A widely used format for digital image files.

Just-in-Time (JIT) Delivery: Refers to a supply chain practice whereby manufacturers receive components on or just before the time that they are needed on the assembly line, rather than bearing the cost of maintaining several days' or weeks' supply in a warehouse. This adds greatly to the cost-effectiveness of a manufacturing plant and puts the burden of warehousing and timely delivery on the supplier of the components.

Ka-Band: The frequency range from 18 to 31 GHz. The spectrum allocated for satellite communications is 30 GHz for the up-link and 20 GHz for the downlink.

Kbps: One thousand bits per second.

Kilobyte: 1,000 (or 1,024) bytes.

Kilohertz (kHz): A measure of frequency equal to 1,000 Hertz.

Knowledge Process Outsourcing (KPO): The use of outsourced and/or offshore workers to perform business tasks that require judgment and analysis. Examples include such professional tasks as patent research, legal research, architecture, design, engineering, market research, scientific research, accounting and tax return preparation. Also, see "Business Process Outsourcing (BPO)."

LAC: An acronym for Latin America and the Caribbean.

Large-Scale Integration (LSI): The placement of thousands of electronic gates on a single chip. This makes the manufacture of powerful computers possible.

LATA: See "Local Access and Transport Area (LATA)."

LDCs: See "Least Developed Countries (LDCs)."

Leased Line: A phone line that is rented for use in continuous, long-term data connections.

Least Developed Countries (LDCs): Nations determined by the U.N. Economic and Social Council to be the poorest and weakest members of the international community. There are currently 50 LDCs, of which 34 are in Africa, 15 are in Asia Pacific and the remaining one (Haiti) is in Latin America. The top 10 on the LDC list, in descending order from top to 10th, are Afghanistan, Angola, Bangladesh, Benin, Bhutan, Burkina Faso, Burundi, Cambodia, Cape Verde and the Central African Republic. Sixteen of the LDCs are also Landlocked Least Developed Countries (LLDCs) which present them with additional difficulties often due to the high cost of transporting trade goods. Eleven of the LDCs are Small Island Developing States (SIDS), which are often at risk of extreme weather phenomenon (hurricanes, typhoons, Tsunami); have fragile ecosystems; are often dependent on foreign energy sources; can have high disease rates for HIV/AIDS and malaria; and can have poor market access and trade terms.

LEC: See "Local Exchange Carrier (LEC)."

Light Emitting Diode (LED): A small tube containing material that emits light when exposed to electricity. The color of the light depends upon the type of material. The LED was first developed in 1962 at the University of Illinois at Urbana-Champaign. LEDs are important to a wide variety of industries, from wireless telephone handsets to signage to displays for medical equipment, because they provide a very high quality of light with very low power requirements. They also have a very long useful life and produce very low heat output when. All of these characteristics are great improvements over a conventional incandescent bulb. Several advancements have been made in LED technology. See "Organic LED (OLED)," "Polymer Light Emitting Diode (PLED)," "Small Molecule Organic Light Emitting Diode (SMOLED)" and "Dendrimer."

LINUX: An open, free operating system that is shared readily with millions of users worldwide. These users continuously improve and add to the software's code. It can be used to operate computer networks and Internet appliances as well as servers and PCs.

Lithography: In the manufacture of semiconductors and MEMS (microelectromechanical systems), lithography refers to the transfer of a pattern of photosensitive material by exposing it to light or radiation. The photosensitive material changes physical properties when exposed to a source of radiation. Typically, a mask is employed that creates a desired pattern by blocking out light to some areas. Using this process to deposit materials on a substrate, integrated circuits can be manufactured.

Local Access and Transport Area (LATA): An operational service area established after the breakup of AT&T to distinguish local telephone service from long-distance service. The U.S. is divided into over 160 LATAs.

Local Area Network (LAN): A computer network that is generally within one office or one building. A LAN can be very inexpensive and efficient to set up when small numbers of computers are involved. It may require a network administrator and a serious investment if hundreds of computers are hooked up to the LAN. A LAN enables all computers within the office to share files and printers, to access common databases and to send e-mail to others on the network.

Local Exchange Carrier (LEC): Any local telephone company, i.e., a carrier, that provides ordinary phone service under regulation within a service area. Also see "Incumbent Local Exchange Carrier (ILEC)" and "Competitive Local Exchange Carrier (CLEC)."

LSI: See "Large-Scale Integration (LSI)."

M3 (Measurement): Cubic meters.

Machine-to-Machine (M2M): Refers to the transmission of data from one device to another, typically through wireless means such as Wi-Fi. For example, a Wi-Fi network might be employed to control several machines in a household from a central computer. Such machines might include air conditioning and entertainment systems. In logistics and retailing, M2M can refer to the use of RFID tags to transmit information. See "Radio Frequency Identification (RFID)."

Managed Service Provider (MSP): An outsourcer that deploys, manages and maintains the back-end software and hardware infrastructure for Internet businesses.

Manufacturing Resource Planning (MRP II): A methodology that supports effective planning with regard to all resources of a manufacturing company, linking MRP with sales and operations planning, production planning and master production scheduling.

Marketing: Includes all planning and management activities and expenses associated with the promotion of a product or service. Marketing can encompass advertising, customer surveys, public relations and many other disciplines. Marketing is distinct from selling, which is the process of sell-through to the end user.

Material Safety Data Sheet (MSDS): A document, required by OSHA (U.S. Occupational Safety and Health Administration) regulations, that provides a thorough profile of a potentially hazardous substance or product. The MSDS profile includes recommendations of how to handle the product, as well as how to treat a person who swallows the product, gets the product in the eyes or is otherwise overexposed. Manufacturers of such products, such as cleansers, solvents and coatings, provide these MSDS sheets at no cost to customers and end users. Employers using these substances in the workplace are required to have MSDS sheets on hand.

Materials Science: The study of the structure, properties and performance of such materials as metals, ceramics, polymers and composites.

Mbps (Megabits per second): 1 million bits transmitted per second.

M-Commerce: Mobile e-commerce over wireless devices.

Medical Device: See "Device."

Megabytes: 1 million bytes, or 1,024 kilobytes.

Megahertz (MHz): A measure of frequency equal to 1 million Hertz.

Metrology: The science of measurement.

Metropolitan Area Network (MAN): A data and communications network that operates over metropolitan areas and recently has been expanded to nationwide and even worldwide connectivity of high-speed data networks. A MAN can carry video and data.

Microprocessor: A computer on a digital semiconductor chip. It performs math and logic operations and executes instructions from memory. (Also known as a central processing unit or CPU.)

Microwave: Line-of sight, point-to-point transmission of signals at high frequency. Microwaves are used in data, voice and all other types of information transmission. The growth of fiber-optic networks has tended to curtail the growth and use of microwave relays.

MIME: See "Multipurpose Internet Mail Extensions (MIME)."

MMS: See "Multimedia Messaging System (MMS)."

Modem: A device that allows a computer to be connected to a phone line, which in turn enables the computer to receive and exchange data with other machines via the Internet.

Modulator: A device that modulates a carrier. Modulators are found in broadcasting transmitters and satellite transponders. The devices are also used by cable TV companies to place a baseband video television signal onto a desired VHF or UHF channel. Home video tape recorders also have built-in modulators that enable the recorded video information to be played back using a television receiver tuned to VHF channel 3 or 4.

MPEG, MPEG-1, MPEG-2, MPEG-3, MPEG-4: Moving Picture Experts Group. It is a digital standard for the compression of motion or still video for transmission or storage. MPEGs are used in digital cameras and for Internet-based viewing.

MSDS: See "Material Safety Data Sheet (MSDS)."

MSP: See "Managed Service Provider (MSP)."

Multimedia Messaging System (MMS): See "Text Messaging."

Multipoint Distribution System (MDS): A common carrier licensed by the FCC to operate a broadcast-like omni-directional microwave transmission facility within a given city. MDS carriers often pick up satellite pay-TV programming and distribute it, via their local MDS transmitter, to specially installed antennas and receivers.

Multipurpose Internet Mail Extensions (MIME): A widely used method for attaching non-text files to e-mails.

NAFTA: See "North American Free Trade Agreement (NAFTA)."

NAND: An advanced type of flash memory chip. It is popular for use in consumer electronics such as MP3 players and digital cameras.

Nanoparticle: A nanoscale spherical or capsule-shaped structure. Most, though not all, nanoparticles are hollow, which provides a central reservoir that can be filled with anticancer drugs, detection agents, or chemicals, known as reporters, that can signal if a drug is having a therapeutic effect. The surface of a nanoparticle can also be adorned with various targeting agents, such as antibodies, drugs, imaging agents, and reporters. Most nanoparticles are constructed to be small enough to pass through blood capillaries and enter cells.

Nanosecond (NS): A billionth of a second. A common unit of measure of computer operating speed.

Nanotechnology: The science of designing, building or utilizing unique structures that are smaller than 100 nanometers (a nanometer is one billionth of a meter). This involves microscopic structures that are no larger than the width of some cell membranes.

Nanowires: A nanometer-scale wire made of metal atoms, silicon, or other materials that conduct electricity. Nanowires are built atom by atom on a solid surface, often as part of a microfluidic device. They can be coated with molecules such as antibodies that will bind to proteins and other substances of interest to researchers and clinicians. By the very nature of their nanoscale size, nanowires are incredibly sensitive to such binding events and respond by altering the electrical current flowing through them, and thus can form the basis of ultra sensitive molecular detectors.

National Institutes of Health (NIH): A branch of the U.S. Public Health Service that conducts biomedical research. www.nih.gov

NDA: See "New Drug Application (NDA)."

Network: In computing, a network is created when two or more computers are connected. Computers may be connected by wireless methods, using such technologies as 802.11b, or by a system of cables, switches and routers.

Network Numbers: The first portion of an IP address, which identifies the network to which hosts in the rest of the address are connected.

New Drug Application (NDA): An application requesting FDA approval, after completion of the all-important Phase III Clinical Trials, to market a new drug for human use in the U.S. The drug may contain chemical compounds that were previously approved by the FDA as distinct molecular entities suitable for use in drug trials. See "New Molecular Entity (NME)."

New Molecular Entity (NME): Defined by the FDA as a medication containing chemical compound that has never before been approved for marketing in any form in the U.S. An NME is sometimes referred to as a New Chemical Entity (NCE). Also, see "New Drug Application (NDA)."

New Urbanism: A relatively new term that refers to neighborhood developments that feature shorter blocks, more sidewalks and pedestrian ways, access to convenient mass transit, bicycle paths and conveniently placed open spaces. The intent is to promote walking and social interaction while decreasing automobile traffic. The concept may also include close proximity to stores and offices that may be reached by walking rather than driving.

NIH: See "National Institutes of Health (NIH)."

NME: See "New Molecular Entity (NME)."

Node: Any single computer connected to a network or a junction of communications paths in a network.

Nonclinical Studies: In vitro (laboratory) or in vivo (animal) pharmacology, toxicology and pharmacokinetic studies that support the testing of a product in humans. Usually at least two species are evaluated prior to Phase I clinical trials. Nonclinical studies continue throughout all phases of research to evaluate long-term safety issues.

North American Free Trade Agreement (NAFTA): A trade agreement signed in December 1992 by U.S. President George H. W. Bush, Canadian Prime Minister Brian Mulroney and Mexican President Carlos Salinas de Gortari. The agreement eliminates tariffs on most goods originating in and traveling between the three member countries. It was approved by the legislatures of the three countries and had entered into force by January 1994. When it was created, NAFTA formed one of the largest free-trade areas of its kind in the world.

NS: See "Nanosecond (NS)."

NTIA: National Telecommunications and Information Administration. A unit of the Department of Commerce that addresses U.S. government telecommunications policy, standards setting and radio spectrum allocation. www.ntia.doc.gov

Nuclear Fusion: An atomic energy-releasing process in which light weight atomic nuclei, which might be hydrogen or deuterium, combine to form heavier nuclei, such as helium. The result is the release of a tremendous amount of energy in the form of heat. As of 2007, nuclear fusion had yet to be made practical as a commercial energy source, but several well-funded efforts are attempting to do so.

Object Technology: By merging data and software into "objects," a programming system becomes object-oriented. For example, an object called "weekly inventory sold" would have the data and programming needed to construct a flow chart. Some new programming systems–including Java–contain this feature. Object technology is also featured in many Microsoft products. See "Java."

OC3, up to OC192: Very high-speed data lines that run at speeds from 155 to 9,600 Mbps.

ODM: See "Original Design Manufacturer (ODM)."

OECD: See "Organisation for Economic Co-operation and Development (OECD)."

OEM: See "Original Equipment Manufacturer (OEM)."

Offshoring: The rapidly growing tendency among U.S., Japanese and Western European firms to send knowledge-based and manufacturing work overseas. The intent is to take advantage of lower wages and operating costs in such nations as China, India, Hungary and Russia. The choice of a nation for offshore work may be influenced by such factors as language and education of the local workforce, transportation systems or natural resources. For example, China and India are graduating high numbers of skilled engineers and scientists from their universities. Also, some nations are noted for large numbers of workers skilled in the English language, such as the Philippines and India. Also see “Captive Offshoring” and “Outsourcing.”

OLED: See “Organic LED (OLED).”

Open Source (Open Standards): A software program for which the source code is openly available for modification and enhancement as various users and developers see fit. Open software is typically developed as a public collaboration and grows in usefulness over time. See “LINUX.”

Operating System (OS): The software that allows applications like word processors or web browsers to run on a computer. For example, Windows 2000 is an operating system.

Optical Character Recognition (OCR): An industry-wide classification system for coding information onto merchandise. It enables retailers to record information on each SKU when it is sold and to transmit that information to a computer. This is accomplished through computerized cash registers that include bar-code scanners (called point-of-sale terminals).

Optical Fiber (Fibre): See “Fiber Optics (Fibre Optics).”

Organic LED (OLED): A type of electronic display based on the use of organic materials that produce light when stimulated by electricity. Also see “Polymer,” “Polymer Light Emitting Diode (PLED),” “Small Molecule Organic Light Emitting Diode (SMOLED)” and “Dendrimer.”

Organic Polymer: See “Polymer.”

Organisation for Economic Co-operation and Development (OECD): A group of 30 countries that are strongly committed to the market economy and democracy. Some of the OECD members include Japan, the U.S., Spain, Germany, Australia, Korea, the U.K., Canada and Mexico. Although not members, Chile, Estonia, Israel, Russia and Slovenia are invited to member talks; and Brazil, China, India, Indonesia and South Africa have enhanced engagement policies with the OECD. The Organisation provides statistics, as well as social and economic data; and researches social changes, including patterns in evolving fiscal policy, agriculture, technology, trade, the environment and other areas. It publishes over 250 titles annually; publishes a corporate magazine, the OECD Observer; has radio and TV studios; and has centers in Tokyo, Washington, D.C., Berlin and Mexico City that distributed the Organisation’s work and organizes events.

Original Design Manufacturer (ODM): A contract manufacturer that offers complete, end-to-end design, engineering and manufacturing services. ODMs design and build products, such as consumer electronics, that client companies can then brand and sell as their own. For example, a large percentage of laptop computers, cell phones and PDAs are made by ODMs. Also see “Original Equipment Manufacturer (OEM)” and “Contract Manufacturer.”

Original Equipment Manufacturer (OEM): A company that manufactures a product or component for sale to a customer that will integrate the component into a final product or assembly. The OEM’s customer will distribute the end product or resell it to an end user. For example, a personal computer made under a brand name by a given company may contain various components, such as hard drives, graphics cards or speakers, manufactured by several different OEM “vendors,” but the firm doing the final assembly/manufacturing process is the final manufacturer. Also see “Original Design Manufacturer (ODM)” and “Contract Manufacturer.”

Orphan Drug: A drug or biologic designated by the FDA as providing therapeutic benefit for a rare disease affecting less than 200,000 people in the U.S. Companies that market orphan drugs are granted a period of market exclusivity in return for the limited commercial potential of the drug.

OS: See “Operating System (OS).”

OTC: See “Over-the-Counter Drugs (OTC).”

Outsourcing: The hiring of an outside company to perform a task otherwise performed internally by the company, generally with the goal of lowering costs and/or streamlining work flow. Outsourcing contracts are generally several years in length. Companies that hire outsourced services providers often prefer to focus on their core strengths while sending more routine tasks outside for others to perform. Typical outsourced services include the running of human resources departments, telephone call centers and computer departments. When outsourcing is performed overseas, it may be referred to as offshoring. Also see “Offshoring.”

Over-the-Counter Drugs (OTC): FDA-regulated products that do not require a physician’s prescription.

Some examples are aspirin, sunscreen, nasal spray and sunglasses.

Packet Switching: A higher-speed way to move data through a network, in which files are broken down into smaller "packets" that are reassembled electronically after transmission.

Patent: A property right granted by the U.S. government to an inventor to exclude others from making, using, offering for sale, or selling the invention throughout the U.S. or importing the invention into the U.S. for a limited time in exchange for public disclosure of the invention when the patent is granted.

PCMCIA: Personal Computer Memory Card International Association.

PDE Pulse Detonation Engine: Pulse detonation (PDE) is an advanced technology for jet engines. It does away with the intricate high-pressure compressor and the turbine found in today's jet engines, relying instead on the PDE Combustor. As a result, much higher output per engine may be possible, which may push aircraft to new levels of speed. Commercial models may be between 2015 and 2020.

Peer Review: The process used by the scientific community, whereby review of a paper, project or report is obtained through comments of independent colleagues in the same field.

Petabyte: 1,024 terabytes, or about one million gigabytes.

Pharmacodynamics (PD): The study of reactions between drugs and living systems. It can be thought of as the study of what a drug does to the body.

Pharmacoeconomics: The study of the costs and benefits associated with various drug treatments.

Pharmacogenetics: The investigation of the different reactions of human beings to drugs and the underlying genetic predispositions. The differences in reaction are mainly caused by mutations in certain enzymes responsible for drug metabolization. As a result, the degradation of the active substance can lead to harmful by-products, or the drug might have no effect at all.

Pharmacokinetics (PK):): The study of the processes of bodily absorption, distribution, metabolism and excretion of compounds and medicines. It can be thought of as the study of what the body does to a drug. See "Absorption, Distribution, Metabolism and Excretion (ADME)."

Phase I Clinical Trials: Studies in this phase include initial introduction of an investigational drug into humans. These studies are closely monitored and are usually conducted in healthy volunteers. Phase I trials are conducted after the completion of extensive nonclinical or pre-clinical trials not involving humans. Phase I studies include the determination of clinical pharmacology, bioavailability, drug interactions and side effects associated with increasing doses of the drug.

Phase II Clinical Trials: Include randomized, masked, controlled clinical studies conducted to evaluate the effectiveness of a drug for a particular indication(s). During Phase II trials, the minimum effective dose and dosing intervals should be determined.

Phase III Clinical Trials: Consist of controlled and uncontrolled trials that are performed after preliminary evidence of effectiveness of a drug has been established. They are conducted to document the safety and efficacy of the drug, as well as to determine adequate directions (labeling) for use by the physician. A specific patient population needs to be clearly identified from the results of these studies. Trials during Phase III are conducted using a large number of patients to determine the frequency of adverse events and to obtain data regarding intolerance.

Phase IV Clinical Trials: Conducted after approval of a drug has been obtained to gather data supporting new or revised labeling, marketing or advertising claims.

Pivotal Studies: In clinical trials, a Phase III trial that is designed specifically to support approval of a product. These studies are well-controlled (usually by placebo) and are generally designed with input from the FDA so that they will provide data that is adequate to support approval of the product. Two pivotal studies are required for drug product approval, but usually only one study is required for biologics.

PLA: See "Product License Agreement (PLA)."

Plant Patent: A plant patent may be granted by the U.S. Patent and Trademark Office to anyone who invents or discovers and asexually reproduces any distinct and new variety of plant.

PLED: See Polymer Light Emitting Diode (PLED)."

PLM: See "Product Lifecyle Management (PLM)."

Plug-In: Any small piece of software that adds extra functions to a larger piece of software.

PMA: See "Pre-Market Approval (PMA)."

Polymer: An organic or inorganic substance of many parts. Most common polymers, such as polyethylene and polypropylene, are organic. Organic polymers consist of molecules from organic sources (carbon compounds). Polymer means many parts. Generally, a polymer is constructed of many structural units (smaller, simpler molecules) that are joined together by a chemical bond. Some polymers are natural. For example, rubber is a natural polymer. Scientists have developed ways to manufacture synthetic polymers from organic materials. Plastic is a synthetic polymer.

Polymer Light Emitting Diode (PLED): An advanced technology that utilizes plastics (polymers) for the creation of electronic displays (screens). It is based on the use of organic polymers which emit light when stimulated with electricity. They are solution processable, which means they can be applied to substrates via ink jet printing. Also referred to as P-OLEDs.

POP: An acronym for both "Point of Presence" and "Post Office Protocol." Point of presence refers to a location that a network can be connected to (generally used to count the potential subscriber base of a cellular phone system). Post office protocol refers to the way in which e-mail software obtains mail from a mail server.

Port: An interface (or connector) between the computer and the outside world. The number of ports on a communications controller or front-end processor determines the number of communications channels that can be connected to it. The number of ports on a computer determines the number of peripheral devices that can be attached to it.

Portal: A comprehensive web site that is designed to be the first site seen when a computer logs on to the web. Portal sites are aimed at broad audiences with common interests and often have links to e-mail usage, a search engine and other features. Yahoo! and msn.com are portals.

Positron Emission Tomography (PET): Positron Emission Tomography (often referred to as a PET scan) is a nuclear medicine imaging technology that uses computers and radioactive (positron emitting) isotopes, which are created in a cyclotron or generator, to produce composite pictures of the brain and heart at work. PET scanning produces sectional images depicting metabolic activity or blood flow rather than anatomy.

Post-Marketing Surveillance: The FDA's ongoing safety monitoring of marketed drugs.

Powerline: A method of networking computers, peripherals and appliances together via the electrical wiring that is built in to a home or office. Powerline competes with 802.11b and other wireless networking methods.

PPP: See "Purchasing Power Parity (PPP)."

Preclinical Studies: See "Nonclinical Studies."

Pre-Market Approval (PMA): Required for the approval of a new medical device or a device that is to be used for life-sustaining or life-supporting purposes, is implanted in the human body or presents potential risk of illness or injury.

Product License Agreement (PLA): See "Biologics License Application (BLA)."

Product Lifecycle: The prediction of the life of a product or brand. Stages are described as Introduction, Growth, Maturity and finally Sales Decline.

Product Lifecycle Management (PLM): See "Product Lifecycle."

Proteomics: The study of gene expression at the protein level, by the identification and characterization of proteins present in a biological sample.

Protocol: A set of rules for communicating between computers. The use of standard protocols allows products from different vendors to communicate on a common network.

PSTN: See "Public Switched Telephone Network (PSTN)."

Public Switched Telephone Network (PSTN): A term that refers to the traditional telephone system.

Purchasing Power Parity (PPP): Currency conversion rates that attempt to reflect the actual purchasing power of a currency in its home market, as opposed to examining price levels and comparing an exchange rate. PPPs are always given in the national currency units per U.S. dollar.

Qdots: See "Quantum Dots (Qdots)."

QOL: See "Quality of Life (QOL)."

Quality of Life (QOL): In medicine, an endpoint of therapeutic assessment used to adjust measures of effectiveness for clinical decision-making. Typically, QOL endpoints measure the improvement of a patient's day-to-day living as a result of specific therapy.

Quantum Computing: A technology that uses the unique abilities of quantum systems, to be in multiple states at once. Such superpositions would allow the computer to perform many different computations simultaneously. This is a merger of physics (and its laws of quantum mechanics) with computer science. Quantum computing works quantum bits, also known as qubits. The laws of quantum mechanics differ radically from the laws of traditional physics. Eventually, quantum computers incredible processing speeds may become feasible.

Quantum Dots (Qdots): Nanometer sized semiconductor particles, made of cadmium selenide (CdSe), cadmium sulfide (CdS) or cadmium telluride (CdTe) with an inert polymer coating. The semiconductor material used for the core is chosen based upon the emission wavelength range being targeted: CdS for UV-blue, CdSe for the bulk of the visible spectrum, CdTe for the far red and near-infrared, with the particle's size determining the exact color of a given quantum dot. The polymer coating safeguards cells from cadmium toxicity but also affords the opportunity to attach any variety targeting molecules, including monoclonal antibodies directed to tumor-specific biomarkers. Because of their small size, quantum dots can function as cell- and even molecule-specific markers that will not interfere with the normal workings of a cell. In addition, the availability of quantum dots of different colors provides a powerful tool for following the actions of multiple cells and molecules simultaneously.

Qubit: The basic unit of information in a quantum computer. A qubit can exist not only in a state corresponding to 0 or 1 as in a binary bit, but also in states corresponding to a blend or superposition of these states. See "Quantum Computing."

R&D: Research and development. Also see "Applied Research" and "Basic Research."

R&D-Flex Building: Industrial-type buildings that are designed to satisfy tenants that require an above-average amount of office space as well as an above-average level of finish that presents a more office-like environment, such as more windows and better landscape. From 30% to 100% of the space in such buildings may be devoted to office or laboratory space, with the balance devoted to light assembly or warehouse space.

Radiation Therapy: Radiation therapy is frequently used to destroy cancerous cells. This branch of medicine is concerned with radioactive substances and the usage of various techniques of imaging, for the diagnosis and treatment of disease. Services can include megavoltage radiation therapy, radioactive implants, stereotactic radiosurgery, therapeutic radioisotope services, or the use of x-rays, gamma rays and other radiation sources.

Radio Frequency Identification (RFID): A technology that applies a special microchip-enabled tag to an individual item or piece of merchandise or inventory. RFID technology enables wireless, computerized tracking of that inventory item as it moves through the supply chain from factory to transport to warehouse to retail store or end user. Also known as radio tags.

Radioisotope: An object that has varying properties that allows it to penetrate other objects at different rates. For example, a sheet of paper can stop an alpha particle, a beta particle can penetrate tissues in the body and a gamma ray can penetrate concrete. The varying penetration capabilities allow radioisotopes to be used in different ways. (Also called radioactive isotope or radionuclide.)

RAM: See "Random Access Memory (RAM)."

Random Access Memory (RAM): Computer memory used to hold programs and data temporarily.

Rapid Prototyping: See "3-D Printing."

RBOC: See "Regional Bell Operating Company (RBOC)."

Real Time: A system or software product specially designed to acquire, process, store and display large amounts of rapidly changing information almost instantaneously, with microsecond responses as changes occur.

Regional Bell Operating Company (RBOC): Former Bell system telephone companies (or their successors), created as a result of the breakup of AT&T by a Federal Court decree on December 31, 1983 (e.g., Bell Atlantic, now part of Verizon).

Request for Bids (RFB): A bid, sent by a firm that requires products or outsourced services, outlining all requirements to various bidding companies. Proposing companies are asked to place a bid based on the requested goods or services.

Request for Qualifications (RFQ): A proposal that asks companies to submit qualifications to provide goods or perform a described level of service. It is used to screen who is qualified to respond to an RFB. See "Request for Bids (RFB)."

Return on Investment (ROI): A measure of a company's profitability, expressed in percentage as net profit (after taxes) divided by total dollar investment.

RFID: See "Radio Frequency Identification (RFID)."

Router: An electronic device that enables networks to communicate with each other. For example, the local area network (LAN) in an office connects to a router to give the LAN access to an Internet connection such as a T1 or DSL. Routers can be bundled with several added features, such as firewalls.

S&R: Science and research.

Saas: See Software as a Service (Saas)."

SACD: See Super Audio Compact Disc (SACD)."

Safe Medical Devices Act (SMDA): An act that amends the Food, Drug and Cosmetic Act to impose additional regulations on medical devices. The act became law in 1990.

SAN: See "Storage Area Network (SAN)."

SBIR: See "Small Business Innovative Research (SBIR)."

Scalable: Refers to a network that can grow and adapt as customer needs increase and change. Scalable networks can easily manage increasing numbers of workstations, servers, user workloads and added functionality.

SCSI: See "Small Computer System Interface (SCSI)."

Semiconductor: A generic term for a device that controls electrical signals. It specifically refers to a material (such as silicon, germanium or gallium arsenide) that can be altered either to conduct electrical current or to block its passage. Carbon nanotubes may eventually be used as semiconductors. Semiconductors are partly responsible for the miniaturization of modern electronic devices, as they are vital components in computer memory and processor chips. The manufacture of semiconductors is carried out by small firms, and by industry giants such as Intel and Advanced Micro Devices.

Serial Line Internet Protocol (SLIP): The connection of a traditional telephone line, or serial line, and modem to connect a computer to an Internet site.

Server: A computer that performs and manages specific duties for a central network such as a LAN. It may include storage devices and other peripherals. Competition within the server manufacturing industry is intense among leaders Dell, IBM, HP and others.

Short Messaging System (SMS): See "Text Messaging."

Simple Mail Transfer Protocol (SMTP): The primary form of protocol used in the transference of e-mail.

Simple Network Management Protocol (SNMP): A set of communication standards for use between computers connected to TCP/IP networks.

Six Sigma: A quality enhancement strategy designed to reduce the number of products coming from a manufacturing plant that do not conform to specifications. Six Sigma states that no more than 3.4 defects per million parts is the goal of high-quality output. Motorola invented the system in the 1980s in order to enhance its competitive position against Japanese electronics manufacturers.

SLIP: See "Serial Line Internet Protocol (SLIP)."

Small Business Innovative Research (SBIR): A three-phase program developed by the U.S. Department of Defense that allocates early-stage research and development funding to small technology companies.

Small Computer System Interface (SCSI): A dominant, international standard interface used by UNIX servers and many desktop computers to connect to storage devices; a physical connection between devices.

Small Molecule Organic Light Emitting Diode (SMOLED): A type of organic LED that relies on expensive manufacturing methods. Newer technologies are more promising. See "Polymer" and "Polymer Light Emitting Diode (PLED)."

Smart Buildings: Buildings or homes that have been designed with interconnected electronic and electrical systems which can be controlled by computers. Advantages include the ability to turn appliances and systems on or off remotely or on a set schedule, leading to greatly enhanced energy efficiency.

SMDA: See "Safe Medical Devices Act (SMDA)."

SMDS: See "Switched Multimegabit Data Service (SMDS)."

SMOLED: See "Small Molecule Organic Light Emitting Diode (SMOLED)."

SMS: See "Short Messaging System (SMS)."

SMTP: See "Simple Mail Transfer Protocol (SMTP)."

SNMP: See "Simple Network Management Protocol (SNMP)."

Software as a Service (SaaS): Refers to the practice of providing users with software applications that are hosted on remote servers and accessed via the Internet. Excellent examples include the CRM (Customer Relationship Management) software provided in SaaS format by Salesforce. An earlier technology that operated in a similar, but less sophisticated, manner was called ASP or Application Service Provider.

SONET: See "Synchronous Optical Network Technology (SONET)."

SPECT: Single Photon Emission Computerized Tomography. A nuclear medicine imaging technology that combines existing technology of gamma camera imaging with computed tomographic (CT) imaging technology to provide a more precise and clear image.

Sponsor: The individual or company that assumes responsibility for the investigation of a new drug, including compliance with the FD&C Act and regulations. The sponsor may be an individual, partnership, corporation or governmental agency and may be a manufacturer, scientific institution or investigator regularly and lawfully engaged in the investigation of new drugs. The sponsor assumes most of the legal and financial responsibility of the clinical trial.

SRDF: See “Symmetrix Remote Data Facility (SRDF).”

Stem Cells: Cells found in human bone marrow, the blood stream and the umbilical cord that can be replicated indefinitely and can turn into any type of mature blood cell, including platelets, white blood cells or red blood cells. Also referred to as pluripotent cells.

Storage Area Network (SAN): Links host computers to advanced data storage systems.

Study Coordinator: See “Coordinator.”

Subsidiary, Wholly-Owned: A company that is wholly controlled by another company through stock ownership.

Super Audio Compact Disc (SACD): A technology that offers high-resolution digital audio.

Superconductivity: The ability of a material to act as a conductor for electricity without the gradual loss of electricity over distance (due to resistance) that is normally associated with electric transmission. There are two types of superconductivity. “Low-temperature” superconductivity (LTS) requires that transmission cable be cooled to -418 degrees Fahrenheit. Even newer technologies are creating a so-called “high-temperature” superconductivity (HTS) that requires cooling to a much warmer -351 degrees Fahrenheit.

Supply Chain: The complete set of suppliers of goods and services required for a company to operate its business. For example, a manufacturer's supply chain may include providers of raw materials, components, custom-made parts and packaging materials.

Sustainable Development: Development that ensures that the use of resources and the environment today does not impair their availability to be used by future generations.

Switch: A network device that directs packets of data between multiple ports, often filtering the data so that it travels more quickly.

Switched Multimegabit Data Service (SMDS): A method of extremely high-speed transference of data.

Symmetrix Remote Data Facility (SRDF): A high-performance, host-independent business solution that enables users to maintain a duplicate copy of all or some of their data at a remote site.

Synchronous Optical Network Technology (SONET): A mode of high-speed transmission meant to take full advantage of the wide bandwidth in fiber-optic cables.

T1: A standard for broadband digital transmission over phone lines. Generally, it can transmit at least 24 voice channels at once over copper wires, at a high speed of 1.5 Mbps. Higher speed versions include T3 and OC3 lines.

T3: Transmission over phone lines that supports data rates of 45 Mbps. T3 lines consist of 672 channels, and such lines are generally used by Internet service providers. They are also referred to as DS3 lines.

Taste Masking: The creation of a barrier between a drug molecule and taste receptors so the drug is easier to take. It masks bitter or unpleasant tastes.

TCP/IP: Transmission Control Protocol/Internet Protocol. The combination of a network and transport protocol developed by ARPANet for internetworking IP-based networks.

TDMA: See “Time Division Multiple Access (TDMA).”

Technical Barriers to Trade (TBT): Instances when technical regulations and industrial standards differ from country to country, making free trade of goods difficult if not impossible.

Telecommunications: Systems of hardware and software used to carry voice, video and/or data between locations. This includes telephone wires, satellite signals, cellular links, coaxial cable and related devices.

Telnet: A terminal emulation program for TCP/IP networks like the Internet, which runs on a computer and connects to a particular network. Directions entered on a computer that is connected using Telnet will be read and followed just as if they had been entered on the server itself. Through Telnet, users are able to control a server and communicate with other servers on the same network at the same time. Telnet is commonly used to control web servers remotely.

Terabyte: A measure of data equal to 1,024 gigabytes, or about 1 trillion bytes of data.

TESS: See “Adverse Event (AE).”

Text Messaging: The transmission of very short, text messages in a format similar to e-mail. Generally, text messaging is used as an additional service on cell phones. The format has typically been SMS (Short Messaging System), but a newer standard is evolving: MMS

(Multimedia Messaging System). MMS can transmit pictures, sound and video as well as text.

Time Division Multiple Access (TDMA): A 2G digital service for relatively large users of international public-switched telephony, data, facsimile and telex. TDMA also refers to a method of multiplexing digital signals that combines a number of signals passing through a common point by transmitting them sequentially, with each signal sent in bursts at different times. TDMA is sometimes referred to as IS-136 or D-AMPS.

Tokamak: A reactor used in nuclear fusion in which a spiral magnetic field inside doughnut-shaped tube is used to confine high temperature plasma produced during fusion. See "Nuclear Fusion."

Token Ring: A local area network architecture in which a token, or continuously repeating frame, is passed sequentially from station to station. Only the station possessing the token can communicate on the network.

Transistor: A device used for amplification or switching of electrical current.

Trial Coordinator: See "Coordinator."

UDDI: Universal Description, Discovery and Integration. A vital protocol used in web services. UDDI enables businesses to create a standard description of their activities so that they can be searched for appropriately by automatic software tools.

Ultrashort Pulse Laser (USP): A technology that utilizes ultrafast lasers that pulse on and off at almost immeasurable speed. Scientists estimate that USP flashes once every femtosecond, which is a billionth of a millionth of a second. USP destroys atoms by knocking out electrons, which causes no rise in temperature in surrounding atoms as is associated with traditional lasers. Potential applications include vastly improved laser surgery, scanning for explosives, gemstone verification and processing donated human tissue for transplantation.

Ultrasound: The use of acoustic waves above the range of 20,000 cycles per second to visualize internal body structures. Frequently used to observe a fetus.

Ultrawideband (UWB): A means of low-power, limited-range wireless data transmission that takes advantage of bandwidth set aside by the FCC in 2002. UWB encodes signals in a dramatically different way, sending digital pulses in a relatively secure manner that will not interfere with other wireless systems that may be operating nearby. It has the potential to deliver very large amounts of data to a distance of about 230 feet, even through doors and other obstacles, and requires very little power. Speeds are scalable from approximately 100 Mbps to 2Gbps. UWB works on the 802.15.3 IEEE specification.

Universal Design: An approach to residential as well as commercial building design that attempts to accommodate as many people as possible, regardless of physical or mental limitations. For example, design elements may include wider doorways and stepless entries that are easy for the physically challenged to navigate.

Universal Memory: Future-generation digital memory storage systems that would be ultradense and run on extremely low power needs. Potentially, universal memory could replace today's flash memory, RAM and many other types of memory. The technology may be based on the use of vast numbers of tiny carbon nanotubes resulting in the storage of trillions of bits of data per square centimeter.

UNIX: A multi-user, multitasking operating system that runs on a wide variety of computer systems, from PCs to mainframes.

URL (Uniform Resource Locator): The address that allows an Internet browser to locate a homepage or web site.

Utility Patent: A utility patent may be granted by the U.S. Patent and Trademark Office to anyone who invents or discovers any new, useful, and non-obvious process, machine, article of manufacture, or composition of matter, or any new and useful improvement thereof.

UWB: See "Ultrawideband (UWB)."

Validation of Data: The procedure carried out to ensure that the data contained in a final clinical trial report match the original observations.

Value Added Tax (VAT): A tax that imposes a levy on businesses at every stage of manufacturing based on the value it adds to a product. Each business in the supply chain pays its own VAT and is subsequently repaid by the next link down the chain; hence, a VAT is ultimately paid by the consumer, being the last link in the supply chain, making it comparable to a sales tax. Generally, VAT only applies to goods bought for consumption within a given country; export goods are exempt from VAT, and purchasers from other countries taking goods back home may apply for a VAT refund.

VDSL: Very high-data-rate digital subscriber line, operating at data rates from 12.9 to 52.8 Mbps.

Vertical Integration: A business model in which one company owns many (or all) of the means of production of the many goods that comprise its product line. For example, founder Henry Ford designed Ford Motor Company's early River Rogue plant so that coal, iron ore and other needed raw materials arrived at one end of the plant and were processed into steel, which was then converted on-site into finished components. At the final stage of the plant, completed automobiles were assembled.

Very Small Aperture Terminal (VSAT): A small Earth station terminal, generally 0.6 to 2.4 meters in size, that is often portable and primarily designed to handle data transmission and private-line voice and video communications.

Voice Over Internet Protocol (VOIP): The ability to make telephone calls and send faxes over IP-based data networks, i.e., real-time voice between computers via the Internet. Leading providers of VOIP service include independent firms Skype and Vonage. However, all major telecom companies, such as SBC are planning or offering VOIP service. VOIP can offer greatly reduced telephone bills to users, since toll charges, certain taxes and other fees can be bypassed. Long-distance calls can pass to anywhere in the world using VOIP. Over the mid-term, many telephone handsets, including cellular phones, will have the ability to detect wireless networks offering VOIP connections and will switch seamlessly between landline and VOIP or cellular and VOIP as needed.

VOIP: See "Voice Over Internet Protocol (VOIP)."

WAN: See "Wide Area Network (WAN)."

WAP: See "Wireless Access Protocol (WAP)."

Web Services: Self-contained modular applications that can be described, published, located and invoked over the World Wide Web or another network. Web services architecture evolved from object-oriented design and is geared toward e-business solutions. Microsoft Corporation is focusing on web services with its .NET initiative. Also see "XML (Extensible Markup Language)."

Web Services Description Language (WSDL): An important protocol to web services that describes the web service being offered.

Wide Area Network (WAN): A regional or global network that provides links between all local area networks within a company. For example, Ford Motor Company might use a WAN to enable its factory in Detroit to talk to its sales offices in New York and Chicago, its plants in England and its buying offices in Taiwan. Also see "Local Area Network (LAN)."

Wi-Fi: A popular phrase that refers to 802.11b and other 802.11 specifications. See "802.11b (Wi-Fi)."

Wi-Fi5: A popular phrase that refers to 802.11a. See "802.11a (Wi-Fi5)."

WiMAX (802.16): A wireless standard with exceptional speed and distance capabilities, officially known as the 802.16 standard. See "802.16 (WiMAX)." Wi-Fi stands for "World Interoperability for Microwave Access."

Wireless Access Protocol (WAP): A technology that enables the delivery of World Wide Web pages in a smaller format readable by screens on cellular phones.

WLAN (Wireless LAN): A wireless local area network. WLANs frequently operate on 802.11-enabled equipment (Wi-Fi).

Workstation: A high-powered desktop computer, usually used by engineers.

World Health Organization (WHO): A United Nations agency that assists governments in strengthening health services, furnishing technical assistance and aid in emergencies, working on the prevention and control of epidemics and promoting cooperation among different countries to improve nutrition, housing, sanitation, recreation and other aspects of environmental hygiene. Any country that is a member of the United Nations may become a member of the WHO by accepting its constitution. The WHO currently has 191 member states.

World Trade Organization (WTO): One of the only globally active international organizations dealing with the trade rules between nations. Its goal is to assist the free flow of trade goods, ensuring a smooth, predictable supply of goods to help raise the quality of life of member citizens. Members form consensus decisions that are then ratified by their respective parliaments. The WTO's conflict resolution process generally emphasizes interpreting existing commitments and agreements, and discovers how to ensure trade policies to conform to those agreements, with the ultimate aim of avoiding military or political conflict.

World Wide Web: A computer system that provides enhanced access to various sites on the Internet through the use of hyperlinks. Clicking on a link displayed in one document takes you to a related document. The World Wide Web is governed by the World Wide Web Consortium, located at www.w3.org. Also known as the web.

WSDL: See "Web Services Description Language (WSDL)."

WTO: See "World Trade Organization (WTO)."

ZigBee: May become the ultimate wireless control system for home and office lighting and entertainment systems. The ZigBee Alliance is an association of companies working together to enable reliable, cost-effective, low-power, wirelessly networked monitoring and control

products based on an open global standard, 802.15.4
entertainment systems.

INTRODUCTION

PLUNKETT'S ENGINEERING & RESEARCH INDUSTRY ALMANAC, the seventh edition of our guide to the engineering and research field, is designed as a general source for researchers of all types.

The data and areas of interest covered are intentionally broad, ranging from the various aspects of the engineering and research industry, to emerging technology, to an in-depth look at the major firms (which we call "THE ENGINEERING & RESEARCH 500") within the many segments that make up the engineering and research industry.

This reference book is designed to be a general source for researchers. It is especially intended to assist with market research, strategic planning, employment searches, contact or prospect list creation (be sure to see the export capabilities of the accompanying CD-ROM that is available to book and eBook buyers) and financial research, and as a data resource for executives and students of all types.

PLUNKETT'S ENGINEERING & RESEARCH INDUSTRY ALMANAC takes a rounded approach for the general reader. This book presents a complete overview of the engineering and research field (see "How To Use This Book"). For example, advances in design automation are discussed, as well as changes in research and development spending and patents.

THE ENGINEERING & RESEARCH 500 is our unique grouping of the biggest, most successful corporations in all segments of the engineering and research industry. Tens of thousands of pieces of information, gathered from a wide variety of sources, have been researched and are presented in a unique form that can be easily understood. This section includes thorough indexes to THE ENGINEERING & RESEARCH 500, by geography, industry, sales, brand names, subsidiary names and many other topics. (See Chapter 4.)

Especially helpful is the way in which PLUNKETT'S ENGINEERING & RESEARCH INDUSTRY ALMANAC enables readers who have no business background to readily compare the financial records and growth plans of engineering and research companies and major industry groups. You'll see the mid-term financial record of each firm, along with the impact of earnings, sales and strategic plans on each company's potential to fuel growth, to serve new markets and to provide investment and employment opportunities.

No other source provides this book's easy-to-understand comparisons of growth, expenditures, technologies, corporations and many other items of great importance to people of all types who may be studying this, one of the most important industries in the world today.

By scanning the data groups and the unique indexes, you can find the best information to fit your personal research needs. The major companies in engineering and research are profiled and then ranked using several different groups of specific criteria. Which firms are the biggest employers? Which companies earn the most profits? These things and much more are easy to find.

In addition to individual company profiles, an overview of engineering and research technology and its trends is provided. This book's job is to help you sort through easy-to-understand summaries of today's trends in a quick and effective manner.

Whatever your purpose for researching the engineering and research field, you'll find this book to be a valuable guide. Nonetheless, as is true with all resources, this volume has limitations that the reader should be aware of:

- Financial data and other corporate information can change quickly. A book of this type can be no more current than the data that was available as of the time of editing. Consequently, the financial picture, management and ownership of the firm(s) you are studying may have changed since the date of this book. For example, this almanac includes the most up-to-date sales figures and profits available to the editors as of early 2009. That means that we have typically used corporate financial data as of late-2008.

- Corporate mergers, acquisitions and downsizing are occurring at a very rapid rate. Such events may have created significant change, subsequent to the publishing of this book, within a company you are studying.

- Some of the companies in THE ENGINEERING & RESEARCH 500 are so large in scope and in variety of business endeavors conducted within a parent organization, that we have been unable to completely list all subsidiaries, affiliations, divisions and activities within a firm's corporate structure.

- This volume is intended to be a general guide to a vast industry. That means that researchers should look to this book for an overview and, when conducting in-depth research, should contact the specific corporations or industry associations in question for the very latest changes and data. Where possible, we have listed contact names, toll-free telephone numbers and web site addresses for the companies, government agencies and industry associations involved so that the reader may get further details without unnecessary delay.

- Tables of industry data and statistics used in this book include the latest numbers available at the time of printing, generally through mid-2008. In a few cases, the only complete data available was for earlier years.

- We have used exhaustive efforts to locate and fairly present accurate and complete data. However, when using this book or any other source for business and industry information, the reader should use caution and diligence by conducting further research where it seems appropriate. We wish you success in your endeavors, and we trust that your experience with this book will be both satisfactory and productive.

Jack W. Plunkett
Houston, Texas
April 2009

HOW TO USE THIS BOOK

The two primary sections of this book are devoted first to the engineering and research industry as a whole and then to the "Individual Data Listings" for THE ENGINEERING & RESEARCH 500. If time permits, you should begin your research in the front chapters of this book. Also, you will find lengthy indexes in Chapter 4 and in the back of the book.

THE ENGINEERING & RESEARCH INDUSTRY

Glossary: A short list of engineering and research industry terms.

Chapter 1: Major Trends Affecting the Engineering & Research Industry. This chapter presents an encapsulated view of the major trends that are creating rapid changes in the engineering and research industry today.

Chapter 2: Engineering & Research Industry Statistics. This chapter presents in-depth statistics ranging from an industry overview to national research expenditures, patents and much more.

Chapter 3: Important Engineering & Research Industry Contacts – Addresses, Telephone Numbers and Internet Sites. This chapter covers contacts for important government agencies and trade groups. Included are numerous important Internet sites.

THE ENGINEERING & RESEARCH 500

Chapter 4: THE ENGINEERING & RESEARCII 500: Who They Are and IIow They Were Chosen. The companies compared in this book (the actual count is 503) were carefully selected from the engineering and research industry, largely in the United States. 250 of the firms are based outside the U.S. For a complete description, see THE ENGINEERING & RESEARCH 500 indexes in this chapter.

Individual Data Listings:

Look at one of the companies in THE ENGINEERING & RESEARCH 500's Individual Data Listings. You'll find the following information fields:

Company Name:

The company profiles are in alphabetical order by company name. If you don't find the company you are seeking, it may be a subsidiary or division of one of the firms covered in this book. Try looking it up in the Index by Subsidiaries, Brand Names and Selected Affiliations in the back of the book.

Ranks:

Industry Group Code: An NAIC code used to group companies within like segments. (See Chapter 4 for a list of codes.)

Ranks Within This Company's Industry Group: Ranks, within this firm's segment only, for annual sales and annual profits, with 1 being the highest rank.

Business Activities:

A grid arranged into six major industry categories and several sub-categories. A "Y" indicates that the firm operates within the sub-category. A complete Index by Industry is included in the beginning of Chapter 4.

Types of Business:

A listing of the primary types of business specialties conducted by the firm.

Brands/Divisions/Affiliations:

Major brand names, operating divisions or subsidiaries of the firm, as well as major corporate affiliations—such as another firm that owns a significant portion of the company's stock. A complete Index by Subsidiaries, Brand Names and Selected Affiliations is in the back of the book.

Contacts:

The names and titles up to 27 top officers of the company are listed, including human resources contacts.

Address:

The firm's full headquarters address, the headquarters telephone, plus toll-free and fax numbers where available. Also provided is the World Wide Web site address.

Financials:

Annual Sales (2008 or the latest fiscal year available to the editors, plus up to four previous years): These are stated in thousands of dollars (add three zeros if you want the full number). This figure represents consolidated worldwide sales from all operations. 2008 figures may be estimates or may be for only part of the year—partial year figures are appropriately footnoted.

Annual Profits (2008 or the latest fiscal year available to the editors, plus up to four previous years): These are stated in thousands of dollars (add three zeros if you want the full number). This figure represents consolidated, after-tax net profit from all operations. 2008 figures may be estimates or may be for only part of the year—partial year figures are appropriately footnoted.

Stock Ticker, International Exchange, Parent Company: When available, the unique stock market symbol used to identify this firm's common stock for trading and tracking purposes is indicated. Where appropriate, this field may contain "private" or "subsidiary" rather than a ticker symbol. If the firm is a publicly-held company headquartered outside of the U.S., its international ticker and exchange are given. If the firm is a subsidiary, its parent company is listed.

Total Number of Employees: The approximate total number of employees, worldwide, as of the end of 2008 (or the latest data available to the editors).

Apparent Salaries/Benefits:

(The following descriptions generally apply to U.S. employers only.) A "Y" in appropriate fields indicates "Yes."

Due to wide variations in the manner in which corporations report benefits to the U.S. Government's regulatory bodies, not all plans will have been uncovered or correctly evaluated during our effort to research this data. Also, the availability to employees of such plans will vary according to the qualifications that employees must meet to become eligible. For example, some benefit plans may be available only to salaried workers—others only to employees who work more than 1,000 hours yearly. Benefits that are available to employees of the main or parent company may not be available to employees of the subsidiaries. In addition, employers frequently alter the nature and terms of plans offered.

NOTE: Generally, employees covered by wealth-building benefit plans do not *fully* own ("vest in") funds contributed on their behalf by the employer until as many as five years of service with that employer have passed. All pension plans are voluntary—that is, employers are not obligated to offer pensions.

Pension Plan: The firm offers a pension plan to qualified employees. In this case, in order for a "Y" to appear, the editors believe that the employer offers a defined benefit or cash balance pension plan (see discussions below).The type and generosity of these plans vary widely from firm to firm. Caution: Some employers refer to plans as "pension" or "retirement" plans when they are actually 401(k) savings plans that require a contribution by the employee.

- Defined Benefit Pension Plans: Pension plans that do not require a contribution from the employee are infrequently offered. However, a few companies, particularly larger employers in high-profit-margin industries, offer defined benefit pension plans where the employee is guaranteed to receive a set pension benefit upon retirement. The amount of the benefit is determined by the years of service with the company and the employee's salary during the later years of employment. The longer a person works for the employer, the higher the retirement benefit. These defined benefit plans are funded entirely by the employer. The benefits, up to a reasonable limit, are guaranteed by the Federal Government's Pension Benefit Guaranty Corporation. These plans are not portable—if you leave the company, you cannot transfer your benefits into a different plan. Instead, upon retirement you will receive the benefits that vested during your service with the company. If your employer offers a pension plan, it must give you a summary plan description within 90 days of the date you join the plan. You can also request a summary annual report of the plan, and once every 12 months you may request an individual benefit statement accounting of your interest in the plan.

- Defined Contribution Plans: These are quite different. They do not guarantee a certain amount of pension benefit. Instead, they set out circumstances under which the employer will make a contribution to a plan on your behalf. The most common example is the 401(k) savings plan. Pension benefits are not guaranteed under these plans.
- Cash Balance Pension Plans: These plans were recently invented. These are hybrid plans—part defined benefit and part defined contribution. Many employers have converted their older defined benefit plans into cash balance plans. The employer makes deposits (or credits a given amount of money) on the employee's behalf, usually based on a percentage of pay. Employee accounts grow based on a predetermined interest benchmark, such as the interest rate on Treasury Bonds. There are some advantages to these plans, particularly for younger workers: a) The benefits, up to a reasonable limit, are guaranteed by the Pension Benefit Guaranty Corporation. b) Benefits are portable—they can be moved to another plan when the employee changes companies. c) Younger workers and those who spend a shorter number of years with an employer may receive higher benefits than they would under a traditional defined benefit plan.

ESOP Stock Plan (Employees' Stock Ownership Plan): This type of plan is in wide use. Typically, the plan borrows money from a bank and uses those funds to purchase a large block of the corporation's stock. The corporation makes contributions to the plan over a period of time, and the stock purchase loan is eventually paid off. The value of the plan grows significantly as long as the market price of the stock holds up. Qualified employees are allocated a share of the plan based on their length of service and their level of salary. Under federal regulations, participants in ESOPs are allowed to diversify their account holdings in set percentages that rise as the employee ages and gains years of service with the company. In this manner, not all of the employee's assets are tied up in the employer's stock.

Savings Plan, 401(k): Under this type of plan, employees make a tax-deferred deposit into an account. In the best plans, the company makes annual matching donations to the employees' accounts, typically in some proportion to deposits made by the employees themselves. A good plan will match one-half of employee deposits of up to 6% of wages. For example, an employee earning $30,000 yearly might deposit $1,800 (6%) into the plan. The company will match one-half of the employee's deposit, or $900. The plan grows on a tax-deferred basis, similar to an IRA. A very generous plan will match 100% of employee deposits. However, some plans do not call for the employer to make a matching deposit at all. Other plans call for a matching contribution to be made at the discretion of the firm's board of directors. Actual terms of these plans vary widely from firm to firm. Generally, these savings plans allow employees to deposit as much as 15% of salary into the plan on a tax-deferred basis. However, the portion that the company uses to calculate its matching deposit is generally limited to a maximum of 6%. Employees should take care to diversify the holdings in their 401(k) accounts, and most people should seek professional guidance or investment management for their accounts.

Stock Purchase Plan: Qualified employees may purchase the company's common stock at a price below its market value under a specific plan. Typically, the employee is limited to investing a small percentage of wages in this plan. The discount may range from 5 to 15%. Some of these plans allow for deposits to be made through regular monthly payroll deductions. However, new accounting rules for corporations, along with other factors, are leading many companies to curtail these plans—dropping the discount allowed, cutting the maximum yearly stock purchase or otherwise making the plans less generous or appealing.

Profit Sharing: Qualified employees are awarded an annual amount equal to some portion of a company's profits. In a very generous plan, the pool of money awarded to employees would be 15% of profits. Typically, this money is deposited into a long-term retirement account. Caution: Some employers refer to plans as "profit sharing" when they are actually 401(k) savings plans. True profit sharing plans are rarely offered.

Highest Executive Salary: The highest executive salary paid, typically a 2008 amount (or the latest year available to the editors) and typically paid to the Chief Executive Officer.

Highest Executive Bonus: The apparent bonus, if any, paid to the above person.

Second Highest Executive Salary: The next-highest executive salary paid, typically a 2008 amount (or the latest year available to the editors) and typically paid to the President or Chief Operating Officer.

Second Highest Executive Bonus: The apparent bonus, if any, paid to the above person.

Other Thoughts:

Apparent Women Officers or Directors: It is difficult to obtain this information on an exact basis, and employers generally do not disclose the data in a public way. However, we have indicated what our best efforts reveal to be the apparent number of women who either are in the posts of corporate officers or sit on the board of directors. There is a wide variance from company to company.

Hot Spot for Advancement for Women/Minorities: A "Y" in appropriate fields indicates "Yes." These are firms that appear either to have posted a substantial number of women and/or minorities to high posts or that appear to have a good record of going out of their way to recruit, train, promote and retain women or minorities. (See the Index of Hot Spots For Women and Minorities in the back of the book.) This information may change frequently and can be difficult to obtain and verify. Consequently, the reader should use caution and conduct further investigation where appropriate.

Growth Plans/ Special Features:

Listed here are observations regarding the firm's strategy, hiring plans, plans for growth and product development, along with general information regarding a company's business and prospects.

Locations:

A "Y" in the appropriate field indicates "Yes." Primary locations outside of the headquarters, categorized by regions of the United States and by international locations. A complete index by locations is also in the front of this chapter.

Chapter 1

Major Trends Affecting the Engineering & Research Industry

Major Trends Affecting the Engineering & Research Industry:

1) **Introduction to the Engineering & Research Industry**
2) **A Short History of U.S. Industrial Research & Development**
3) **R&D in China Becomes a Major Factor**
4) **Offshore Research, Development & Engineering Grows in India, Singapore, Taiwan and Korea**
5) **Original Design Manufacturing (ODM) Booms**
6) **The State of the Biotechnology Industry Today**
7) **From India to Singapore to Australia, Nations Compete Fiercely in Biotech Development**
8) **U.S. Government Reverses Ban on Funding for New Stem Cell Research**
9) **Emphasis on R&D in Nanotechnology**
10) **Government Nanotechnology Funding is Strong**
11) **Nanotechnology Converges with Biotech**
12) **Globalization and Worldwide Collaboration Fuel the Research Efforts of Major Corporations**
13) **Growth Continues in Research Partnerships Between Corporations and Universities**
14) **Number of Patent Applications Remains High**
15) **The Automation of Research and Design Steams Ahead**
16) **Governments Encourage Renewable Energy, Energy Conservation, Research and Investment**
17) **Fuel Cell and Hydrogen Power Research Continues**
18) **Electric Cars and Plug-in Hybrids (PHEVs) Will Quickly Gain Popularity/Major Research in Advanced Lithium Batteries**
19) **The Future: Pervasive Computing and Complete Mobility Will Be Standard**
20) **Supercomputing Hits 1.105 Petaflops**
21) **Superconductivity Comes of Age**
22) **Massive Funding for Nuclear Fusion Projects**

1) Introduction to the Engineering & Research Industry

On a global basis, spending on R&D has increased rapidly in recent years. In industrialized nations, R&D investment has risen from an average of about 1.5% of Gross Domestic Product (GDP) in 1980 to more than 2.2% today. Large numbers of university students around the globe are enrolled in engineering and scientific disciplines—many of them dreaming about potential rewards if their future research efforts become commercialized. Global research collaboration (between companies, and between companies and universities) is booming, as is patenting; in fact, it is difficult for patent authorities in the U.S. and elsewhere to keep up with demand. Globalization and cross-national collaboration have such a dramatic effect on research and design that nearly one-half of all patents granted in America list at least one non-U.S. citizen as a coinventor. Major U.S. universities, like the University of Texas and the University of Wisconsin, as well as universities in such nations as China, Korea and Singapore, are eager to patent their inventions and to reap the benefits of commercialized research. Top research universities earn millions of dollars each in yearly royalties on their patents.

The "2009 Global R&D Funding Forecast," published by Battelle and R&D Magazine, estimates global spending on research and development at $1.143 trillion for 2009, up from $1.108 trillion in 2008, on a PPP or purchasing power parity basis. This means that the amounts are adjusted to account for the difference in the cost of living from nation to nation, relative to the United States. For example, PPP analysis finds that the cost of buying a given standard of living is considerably lower in China or India than it is in the U.S. Thus, $1 spent in China or India has more purchasing power than $1 spent in America.

The U.S. continues to lead the world in terms of total investment in research and development, at about $375 billion during 2008. However, it ranks behind many other industrialized nations in terms of R&D as a percent of GDP at 2.6%. For example, Japan's annual spending on R&D is 3.2% of GDP. Massive research outlays by the U.S. federal government are a big boost. The proposed federal research budget for 2009 was $142.6 billion (up from $138.3 billion the previous year) including $84.5 billion for medical care research. These figures do not include any extra research dollars passed by Congress in stimulus packages. Substantial new federal research dollars are expected to flow in 2009 and beyond into such areas as advanced automobile batteries, electronic patient health records and renewable energy. Government research dollars feed projects at universities throughout the U.S. and at many types of private corporations.

California launched an interesting initiative in research funding at the state level when voters there approved, in November 2004, $3 billion in stem cell research funding. By 2007, California's stem cell research program was slowly getting underway after combating lawsuits questioning the authority of the state government to create such a program. Other states across the U.S. quickly began discussing the potential of launching such initiatives of their own. In 2007, voters in the State of Texas approved a $3 billion cancer research initiative spearheaded by former cancer patient and globally recognized athlete Lance Armstrong. The end result may be heightened competition between tech-savvy states for leading-edge research efforts, at both corporate and university facilities.

Meanwhile, U.S. corporations continue to fund massive engineering projects and research budgets of their own. Top research investors among U.S. companies include IBM, Johnson & Johnson, Microsoft and Intel. Unfortunately, the continuing financial strife and declining market share of U.S. car makers will likely lead to a significant decline in funding available for R&D at General Motors, Ford and Chrysler unless the federal government picks up future costs.

Engineering, science, research and development provide large numbers of well-paying jobs in America and around the world. Officially, the U.S. Bureau of Labor Statistics estimates 1.4 million people working in architectural and engineering services. This is up from 1.2 million in 2003. In addition, as of its mid-2007 survey (the latest data available), the same source counts 1.25 million in life, physical and social sciences, and, as of November 2008, 1.4 million people in computer systems design, programming and related services.

Rapidly growing sectors in U.S., Japanese, Indian and Chinese research include virtually all sectors within the energy field; from renewable energy such as solar power, to oil exploration technologies, to superconductivity, to nuclear generation. Renewable energy will continue to be a focus of global R&D, as will nuclear electric power generation.

The convergence of information technology, biotechnology and nanotechnology is fueling the imaginations and the research budgets of scientists and engineers. Likewise, the convergence of information technology, entertainment and telephony is booming. Great research emphasis is also placed on chemicals, health care, defense, transportation, aerospace, telecommunications, chips, computer hardware and computer software.

For several years, due to the long-term global boom in residential and commercial construction, building and infrastructure design and engineering firms were enjoying a steady stream of large, lucrative contracts. For now, however, the global financial crisis has put a damper on construction from the U.S. to Spain to Dubai.

Meanwhile, corporations know that they must invest in R&D in order to stay competitive, but in many cases their R&D strategies are evolving. One change is the way in which this funding is allocated. Strategies are shifting to include more alliances and joint ventures with other companies; more subsidiary spin-offs based on established technologies; more contracts and cooperative efforts with federal labs and agencies; and higher grants and projects of greater scope at the university level. Companies are also looking for ways to leverage their R&D investments in order to get more bang for their bucks.

Historically, corporate America's R&D dollars were spent at labs within the bounds of the U.S., but today, more and more projects are going to company-owned or outsourced labs overseas. Due to relatively low costs and large talent pools (including large numbers of new graduates with engineering and scientific degrees), the nations of Eastern Europe, China and India in particular have been attracting more and more of the total research dollars invested by major companies.

China has one of the fastest-growing research budgets in the world, and by 2020 the government's goal is to invest 2.5% of GDP annually in research, which will cause China to rank third in the world in terms of total annual investment. It remains to be seen whether they came come close to that goal. In 2007, China's government invested $52.4 billion in R&D (about 1.49% of GDP, up from $29.4 billion in 2005). This does not include R&D expenses at labs owned by foreign companies. If China continues a ratio of R&D spending of about 1.5% of GDP for 2009, its research will total about $72 billion.

India's government, according to its Ministry of Science and Technology, invested about 0.77% of GDP in R&D during the fiscal year ending in March 2005. If India continues a ratio of R&D spending of about 0.8% of GDP for 2009, its research spending will total about $12 billion.

Technical education is emphasized in India. The 2008 education budget included funds for two new schools of planning and architecture, along with three new institutes of technology.

Certain countries have the lion's share of R&D activity. Corporations with the largest R&D budgets are nearly all headquartered in the U.S. and Canada in North America; in the U.K., France, Germany, Switzerland, The Netherlands, Sweden and Italy in the European region; and in the Asia-Pacific nations of Taiwan, Japan, South Korea and Singapore.

South Korea's R&D spending was about 3.5% of GDP in 2007, and the nation has a goal of increasing that figure to 5% in 2012. However, the nation was hit hard by the global financial crisis, particularly in terms of currency values. Korean government leaders are focused on increasing basic research capabilities and basic sciences, particularly at research-oriented universities.

Technology-oriented Israel invests as much as 4.53% of GDP in research and development. Finland and Sweden also spend very high ratios of their domestic economies on R&D.

Many American employers are frustrated in their efforts to hire either U.S. citizens or eligible immigrants who have specific degrees and experience suitable to fill niche jobs that are vital for corporate R&D. These employers feel that the current H1-B immigration program is much too restrictive. Temporary, job-related immigration status under the H1-B program has, in recent years, been limited to 65,000 people per annum, plus a special additional allotment of 20,000 expressly for immigrants who hold advanced degrees from U.S. universities.

2) A Short History of U.S. Industrial Research & Development

Organized corporate research efforts began in the chemical dyes industry in Europe in the mid-1800s and soon were launched at a fairly rapid rate in America. In 1876, at the age of 29, Thomas Alva Edison opened a private laboratory in Menlo Park, New Jersey. Edison's efforts led to his record-setting 1,093 U.S. patents, including those for the phonograph and the incandescent light bulb. Edison's creativity and drive eventually enabled the birth of what would become the General Electric Company, still one of the world's premier research and manufacturing organizations. By 1900, about 40 various corporate research facilities were operating in the U.S. Rapid acceleration was fostered by a growing middle class that created demand for new products, and was later further fueled by the intense demands for leading-edge armaments, transport and other products created by World War II.

During the war, a man named Vannevar Bush was posted as the director of the Office of Scientific Research and Development within the U.S. Government. Bush's mandate was to spur intense innovation that would give America a technological edge in warfare. The results, over an astonishingly short period of time, ranged from advanced radar to the atomic bomb. Vannevar Bush argued persuasively for a long-term federal commitment to supporting industrial research. By 1962, the federal government was subsidizing nearly 60% of America's corporate research budget, for everything from medical breakthroughs to electronics to defense systems.

Thereafter, corporations rapidly increased their own investments in research and development efforts, resulting in a nationwide research base of unprecedented scope and cost. By 1992, however, corporate restructuring and cost cutting led to a brief period of retrenching and research budget slashing.

In the mid-1990s, companies creating or embracing new technologies were among the most exciting and successful firms in America. As corporations were striving to compete, the floodgates of research dollars were once again cranked open. Corporate America's investments in R&D have climbed at an impressive rate nearly every year since 1996, and federal government investments in research have also risen at a steady rate.

As a result, a disproportionate share of America's economic growth has been created by the technology sector, and the R&D population has blossomed. Despite the massive scope and highly competitive nature of corporate research, many major companies succeed without significant research efforts. Instead, they rely on components or processes developed by others. A good example is the personal computer manufacturing industry, where some companies prosper by building and marketing computers constructed from components, like hard drives and semiconductors, that were created through the research and development efforts of their suppliers. Industry leader Dell initially did little R&D of its own. Today, however, Dell has grown to the point that it has thousands of engineers on its staff, both in the U.S. and in offshore nations such as India.

A final important thought about the development of industrial R&D: Depending on the nature of their industries, various firms enter into research with widely varying expectations. For example, while aircraft maker Boeing invested $3.9 billion in R&D in 2007, that effort may yield a completely new aircraft model only once every eight or 10 years. In contrast, semiconductor maker Intel, which invested $5.8 billion in 2007 in R&D, introduces breakthrough chip designs on a continual basis and invests only a tiny amount of its total budget in truly long-term research. Pharmaceutical makers are accustomed to a research-to-market cycle of as long as 10 years in order to discover, develop and commercially launch a new drug.

In short, some companies are driven to vast R&D efforts in order to compete in their own rapidly evolving industries, while others patiently invest in long-term R&D hoping it will pay off handsomely through the introduction of entirely new types of products several years hence. Thanks to the beginning of the Biotech Era, a continuing focus on investment in information technology, growing interest in nanotechnology and a very intense focus on potential advancement in renewable energy and energy conservation, investment in research and development remains strong—much of it fueled by investments from venture capital firms.

3) R&D in China Becomes a Major Factor

There are three trends at work in the growth of R&D in China. The first is that the government of China has an aggressive goal for the nation's R&D investment, with plans to foster growth to 2.5% of GDP by 2020, up from about 1.5% in 2008. In comparison, U.S. spending in 2008 accounted for 2.6% of GDP.

Second, many Chinese companies are enjoying escalating success in the global marketplace. Telecommunications equipment makers such as Huawei Technologies, computer hardware makers such as Lenovo Group (now the owner of the IBM laptop brand) and a host of growing companies like them are finding increased investments in research to be key to their continued growth. At the same time, Chinese firms are increasing their investments in quality research, design and production in order to create products suitable for the rapidly growing number of middle-class Chinese consumers. Local markets are becoming much more important for Chinese-based companies when they formulate strategies for product development.

Next, hundreds of non-Chinese companies of many types have set up serious research labs in China. This includes companies such as Microsoft, Nokia, Nortel and Roche. GE alone has more than two dozen labs in China. Major computer research labs include IBM China Research Laboratory, Intel China Research Center, Bell Labs Research China and Motorola China Research Center. This trend is driven by multiple factors, including relatively low operating costs and salaries, the large base of well-trained engineers and scientists coming out of Chinese universities and the desire to have labs in close proximity to Chinese manufacturing centers and business markets.

There is no let-up in sight for this trend. Today, the U.S. has more researchers at work than any other nation, at about 1.3 to 1.4 million. As of 2007 (the latest data available), China had about 1 million researchers, nearly double that of 1995; it will soon catch up to and surpass the U.S., which will earn China the right to claim the number-one rank among the world's research centers in terms of people involved. This trend is fed by the fact that China is cranking out engineers and PhD-level researchers from its universities at a rapid clip, while those degrees are often unpopular among American students. China produces hundreds of thousands of electrical engineering graduates on the bachelor's level yearly. Also, China is going out of its way to lure home thousands of Chinese-born scientists and engineers who have been working in the U.S. and elsewhere abroad. As of late 2008, there were an estimated 2,500 life sciences faculty at U.S. research universities who were born in China, and between 10% and 20% of the scientists working in U.S. drug and biotech firms were Chinese.

However, there remains a vast difference in total research budgets among nations. While China has hordes of people at work in research, the government's research investment, at an estimated $72 billion for 2009, falls far behind that of more developed nations.

Meanwhile, patenting is rising in China. According to the Chinese State Intellectual Property Office (SIPO), 828,328 patent applications were received from Chinese applicants in 2008. This is a 19.4% increase over 2007. SIPO granted a total of 411,982 patents in 2008, an increase of 17.1% over 2007.

Chinese research facilities tend to be located in the same districts as the manufacturing centers that cater to foreign markets: the southern and eastern coastal regions. For example, on the eastern coast near Beijing, you'll find the Zhongguancun Science Park and the Tianjin High-Tech Industrial Park. Further down the coast, near Shanghai, you'll find the Caohejing and Zhangjiang High-Tech Parks.

Chinese technology sectors are quickly expanding well beyond consumer electronics and computer and telecom hardware where China has long had strength. For example, the automotive, biotechnology and nanotechnology industries are developing rapidly there.

SPOTLIGHT: Microsoft's China Labs

In Beijing, Microsoft Research Asia was established in 1998 as a major software R&D center. Microsoft is taking advantage of the Chinese talent pool and work ethic, creating not a mere token presence but a highly productive software lab. In November 2003, the firm launched its Advanced Technology Center at Beijing to focus on groundbreaking products (www.microsoft.com/china/CTC/english.mspx). This was followed in late 2007 by the opening of the Shenzhen Park research facility, which houses the Microsoft Asia Hardware Center and the Microsoft Mobile Internet Technology R&D Center. In Microsoft's facilities, hundreds of full-time researchers work with hundreds of top college interns each year. The labs' operating cultures encourage innovation and unique approaches. New ideas proliferate on a regular basis, and hundreds of patent filings have already resulted. Management stresses that this is not an outsourcing strategy. Instead, it is an effort to hire some of the best minds in Asia and put them to work on complex problems. Dozens of technologies developed at Microsoft Research Asia are already in use in Microsoft products ranging from operating systems to Xbox games. Areas of focus at the labs include unified communication, digital entertainment, Internet technologies and mobile technologies.

4) Offshore Research, Development & Engineering Grows in India, Singapore, Taiwan and Korea

China certainly isn't the only nation to watch for trends in research and innovation. Growing global demand for technology products and for many types of engineering, coupled with the communications capabilities of the Internet, have launched an R&D boom in many other nations as well. As in China, some of this research is for locally owned manufacturers, but a great deal of it is conducted as offshoring for companies based in other nations. These nations with growing research and development bases include Ireland, Russia, Israel, Singapore, Taiwan, Korea and certain Eastern European nations.

For example, consider Taiwan, where total R&D spending has grown more than fivefold since 1990 to over $10 billion by government and industry combined in 2007. Taiwan's government plans to invest $3.28 billion in 2009, up 8.06% from 2008. This is a significant amount for a relatively small nation. Taiwan is on the leading edge of technology-based manufacturing, and many of the world's top-ranked corporations by R&D budget are headquartered there. The country has great expertise, both in the laboratory and on the manufacturing floor, in such sectors as networking gear, semiconductors, computer memory and PC components. Taiwan's researchers are so prolific that they account for more than 5,000 U.S. patent filings yearly. The country invests 2.9% of annual GDP into research and development (a bit more than the U.S.) and graduates 49,000 scientists and engineers from its universities each year—an amazing number for a nation with a total population of a little more than 22 million. Taiwan operates three major science parks containing nearly 800 total manufacturers.

In India, Western drug discovery and manufacturing companies are forging partnerships with Indian firms at a great rate. For example, Eli Lilly, Amgen and Forest Laboratories have all entered into agreement with Bangalore-based Jubilant Biosys to develop potential candidates for the next blockbuster drugs. In a surprising shift from the Indian focus on developing low-cost generic versions of Western drugs, Indian firms are now working on developing new drugs with Western partners. This is partly due to the Indian government's decision in 2003 to begin protecting the rights of foreign patent holders. At the same time, Western pharma firms are offering to share intellectual property rights on new drugs as well as a portion of the profits. GlaxoSmithKline was the first to begin this practice in its partnership with Ranbaxy Laboratories Limited. Lucrative partnerships is spurring booming growth in Indian drug companies, especially when it comes to employing experienced chemists and drug discovery experts. Where Jubilant Biosys once had a team of 50 in its development labs, it boasted 700 staff members in 2008.

South Korea's R&D spending was about 3.5% of GDP in 2007, and the nation has a goal of increasing that figure to 5% in 2012. However, the nation was hit hard by the global financial crisis, particularly in terms of currency values. Korean government leaders are focused on increasing basic research capabilities and basic sciences, particularly at research-oriented universities.

5) Original Design Manufacturing (ODM) Booms

For many years, the world of manufacturing has been acquainted with the concept of original equipment manufacturers (OEMs). An OEM is a company that manufactures a product or component for sale to a customer that will integrate that component into a final product or assembly. The OEM's customer will distribute the end products or resell them to end users. For example, a personal computer made under a brand name by a given company may contain various components, such as hard drives, graphics cards or speakers, manufactured by several different OEM "vendors," but the firm doing the final assembly/manufacturing process is the final manufacturer and the owner of the brand name.

Today, however, engineering and R&D enter the picture, as many OEMs are evolving into "original design manufacturers" (ODMs): contract manufacturers that offer complete, end-to-end design, engineering and manufacturing services. ODMs design and build components or products, such as consumer electronics, that client companies can then brand and sell as their own. For example, a large percentage of notebook computers, cell phones and PDAs are made by ODMs. ODMs are the ultimate result of the convergence of several trends at once, including offshoring, globalization, value-added services, contract manufacturing, outsourcing and design collaboration via the Internet.

Savvy managers at OEMs and contract manufacturers (companies that manufacture partial or complete products to be sold under a client company's brand) began to see that they could differentiate themselves by becoming more than mere manufacturers. After all, manufacturing services alone can be commoditized—that is, they can become common services offered by a large number of firms at increasingly competitive prices. However, when manufacturers combine the ability to offer complete engineering, design and manufacturing in one turnkey deal, it's a new story. Thus, ODM was born.

ODM services can be particularly effective in nations that are noted for having an experienced talent pool in particular sectors. An example is Taiwan's expertise in personal computers, where such firms as Quanta Computer, Inc., Compal Electronics, Inc. and Inventec Corporation are known to be world-leading laptop designers and manufacturers for clients that sell under name brands. Other examples include India's expertise in chips and Israel's expertise in optical communications equipment.

ODM has also been particularly effective in the automobile and passenger aircraft manufacturing industries. To a rapidly growing extent, carmakers are relying on their suppliers to perform the design, engineering and manufacturing of everything from transmissions to dashboard assemblies. The same holds true in the aircraft business. To a large degree, Boeing and Airbus are conducting final assembly of components manufactured (and in many cases designed and engineered) by their suppliers. The fact that components used in transportation equipment can be heavy and bulky doesn't mean that ODMs in these sectors have to be close to home. In fact, components for Boeing's new 787 are being made as far away as Japan, and automobile components are often manufactured in China for use in U.S. automotive plants.

6) The State of the Biotechnology Industry Today

Prescription drug purchases in the U.S. totaled about $247 billion during 2008, according to U.S. government estimates, representing about $813 per capita. The total is up from a mere $40 billion in 1990. In 2016, government estimates show that American drug purchases may reach $497 billion, thanks to a rapidly aging U.S. population, inflation and the continued introduction of expensive new drugs.

The IMS Retail Drug Monitor shows retail pharmacy drug sales in the U.S. at $206.5 billion for the twelve months ended May 2008, up about 2%. This figure does not include drugs delivered through institutions such as hospitals. Generic drugs account for about 67% of all drug expenditures in the U.S., up from only 51% in 2000 and 33% in 1990. Veterinary drugs are about a $2.5 billion market in the U.S., and about $5 billion globally. IMS Health estimates Canadian retail drug sales for the twelve months ended May 2008 at $16.7 billion, Japan at $63.2 billion (including sales at hospitals), Brazil at $11.6 billion and Mexico at $8.7 billion. In Europe's top five markets, IMS ranked Germany first, during the same twelve-month period, at $34.4 billion, followed by France at $30.8 billion, the UK at $17.1 billion, Italy at $16.9 billion and Spain at $14.8 billion. (See www.imshealth.com.)

Biotech-related drugs accounted for about $44 billion of the U.S. market in 2007, or a bit more than 20%. IMS Health places the global biotech market at $75 billion for 2007, up 12.5% over the previous year. Ernst & Young reports that revenues of publicly-held biotech companies in the U.S. rose more than 11% from $58.6 billion in 2006 to $65.2 billion in 2007. On a global scale, 2007 public biotech company revenues exceeded $80 billion for the first time, rising by 8% over 2006. Plunkett Research estimates that in 2008, public biotech company revenues reached $86.4 billion.

For 2008, the Pharmaceutical Research and Manufacturers of America (PhRMA, www.phrma.org) estimated that $50.3 billion was invested in R&D by its members in the U.S. (PhRMA estimates that the total pharmaceuticals industry, including non-PhRMA members, invested $63.2 billion in research in 2008.) At the end of 2006 (the latest data available), PhRMA estimated that there were 686,422 direct jobs relating to the biopharmaceutical sector. As of early 2009, there were more than 2,900 medicines in development in the U.S.

Advanced generations of drugs developed through biotechnology continue to enter the marketplace. The results promise to be spectacular for patients, as a technology tipping point of medical care is nearing, where drugs that target specific genes and proteins will become widespread. However, it continues to become more difficult and more expensive to introduce a new drug in the U.S. For example, during 2008, the FDA (Food and Drug Administration) approved only three new biologics (new biotechnology-based drugs, based on living organisms, that have never been marketed in the U.S. in any form) along with 21 new molecular entities or "NMEs" (medications containing chemical compounds that have never before been approved for marketing in the U.S.). This is up from the 18 approved in 2007, but down from the 22 in 2006 (there were 20 approved during 2005 and 36 in 2004).

These NMEs and biologics are novel new active substances that are categorized differently from "NDAs" or New Drug Applications. NDAs may seek approval for drugs based on combinations of substances that have been approved in the past. During 2008, 98 NDAs were approved by the FDA, 2007 (compared to 94 NDAs in 2007, 93 in 2006 and 79 in 2005).

New Drug Application Categories

Applications for drug approval by the FDA fall under the following categories:

BLA (Biologics License Application): An application for approval of a drug synthesized from living organisms. That is, drugs created using biotechnology. Such drugs are sometimes referred to as biopharmaceuticals.

NME (New Molecular Entity): A new chemical compound that has never before been approved for marketing in any form in the U.S.

NDA (New Drug Application): An application requesting FDA approval, after completion of the all-important Phase III Clinical Trials, to market a new drug for human use in the U.S. The drug may contain active ingredients that were previously approved by the FDA.

Follow-On Biologics: A term used to describe generic versions of drugs that have been created using biotechnology. Because biotech drugs ("biologics") are made from living cells, a generic version of a drug probably won't be biochemically identical to the original branded version of the drug. Consequently, they are described as "follow-on" drugs to set them apart. Since these drugs won't be exactly the same as the originals, there are concerns that they may not be as safe or effective unless they go through clinical trials for proof of quality. In Europe, these drugs are referred to as "biosimilars."

Priority Reviews: The FDA places some drug applications that appear to promise "significant improvements" over existing drugs for priority approval, with a goal of returning approval within six months.

Accelerated Approval: A process at the FDA for reducing the clinical trial length for drugs designed for certain serious or life-threatening diseases.

Fast Track Development: An enhanced process for rapid approval of drugs that treat certain life-threatening or extremely serious conditions. Fast Track is independent of Priority Review and Accelerated Approval.

Developing a new drug is an excruciatingly slow and expensive endeavor. According to PhRMA, the average time required for the drug discovery, development and clinical trials process is 16 years. The good news is that the median FDA approval time for a "priority" NME is down to about six months since 2003, compared to 16.3 months in 2002, and for "standard" NMEs to 12.9 months in 2007 from 23.0 in 2005.

The promising era of personalized medicine is slowly, slowly moving closer to fruition. Dozens of exciting new drugs for the treatment of dire diseases such as cancer, AIDS, Parkinson's and Alzheimer's are either on the market or are very close to regulatory approval.

Stem cell research is moving ahead briskly on a global basis, despite the previously negative effect of restrictive research funding rules of the U.S. Federal Government. This should change over the near term due to President Obama's relaxing of the limits on federal funding of stem cell research that were established by his predecessor, President Bush. In 2009, the National Institutes of Health will set new guidelines for funding that will dramatically expand the number of stem cell lines that qualify for research funds from a previous 21 to as many as 700. However, research into certain extremely controversial stem cells, such as those developed via cloning, will not be funded with federal dollars.

Stem cell breakthroughs are occurring rapidly. There is truly exciting evidence of the potential for stem cells to treat many problems, from cardiovascular disease to neurological disorders. Menlo Park, California-based Geron Corporation, for example, has published the results of its experiments that show that when certain cells (OPCs) derived from stem cells were injected in rats that had spinal cord injuries, the rats quickly recovered. According to the company, "Rats transplanted seven days after injury showed improved walking ability compared to animals receiving a control transplant. The OPC-treated animals showed improved hind limb-forelimb coordination and weight bearing capacity, increased stride length, and better paw placement compared to control-treated animals."

Despite exponential advances in biopharmaceutical knowledge and technology, biotech companies enduring the task of getting new drugs to market continue to face long timeframes, daunting costs and immense risks. Although the number of NDAs submitted to the FDA has grown dramatically since 1996, the number of new drugs receiving final approval remains relatively small. On average, of every 1,000 experimental drug compounds in some form of pre-clinical testing, only one actually makes it to clinical trials. Then, only one in five of those drugs makes it to market. Of the drugs that get to market, only one in three recover their costs. Meanwhile, the patent expiration clock is ticking—soon enough, manufacturers of generic alternatives steal market share from the firms that invested all that time and money in the development of the original drug.

Global Factors Boosting Biotech Today:

1) A rapid aging of the population base of industrialized nations such as Japan and the U.S., including the 78 million Baby Boomers in America who are entering senior years and needing a growing level of health care
2) A renewed, global focus on developing effective vaccines
3) Aggressive, global investment firms that are willing to risk their funds on biotech research and development
4) Vast research investments by major pharmaceuticals firms
5) A growing global dependence on genetically-engineered agricultural seeds

6) Aggressive investment in biotechnology research in Singapore, China and India, often with government sponsorship
7) A government-subsidized emphasis on bioethanol as a substitute for petroleum

Source: Plunkett Research, Ltd.

Internet Research Tip:
You can review current and historical drug approval reports at the following page at the Center for Drug Evaluation and Research (CDER).
www.fda.gov/cder/rdmt

The Center for Biologics Evaluation and Research (CBER) regulates biologic products for use in humans. It is a source of a broad variety of data on drugs, including blood products, counterfeit drugs, exports, drug shortages, recalls and drug safety.
www.fda.gov/cber

According to a study released in 2001 by the Tufts Center for the Study of Drug Development, the cost of developing a new drug and getting it to market averaged $802 million, up from about $500 million in 1996. (Averaged into these figures are the costs of developing and testing drugs that never reach the market.) Expanding on the study to include post-approval research (Phase IV clinical studies), Tufts increased the number to $897 million. Tufts estimated the average cost to develop a new biologic at $1.2 billion in 2006. Even more pessimistic is research released in 2003 by Bain & Co., a consulting firm, which states that the cost is more on the order of $1.7 billion, including such factors as marketing and advertising expenses.

The typical time elapsed from the synthesis of a new chemical compound to its introduction to the market remains 12 to 20 years. Considering that the patent for a new compound only lasts about 20 years, a limited amount of time is available to reclaim the considerable investments in research, development, trials and marketing. As a result of these costs and the lengthy time-to-market, young biotech companies encounter a harsh financial reality: commercial profits take years and years to emerge from promising beginnings in the laboratory.

However, advances in systems biology (the use of a combination of state-of-the-art technologies, such as molecular diagnostics, advanced computers and extremely deep, efficient genetic databases) may eventually lead to more efficient, faster drug development at reduced costs. Much of this advance will stem from the use of technology to efficiently target the genetic causes of, and develop novel cures for, niche diseases.

The FDA is attempting to help the drug industry bring the most vital drugs to market in shorter time with three programs: Fast Track, Priority Review and Accelerated Approval. The benefits of Fast Track include scheduled meetings to seek FDA input into development as well as the option of submitting a New Drug Application in sections rather than all components at once. The Fast Track designation is intended for drugs that address an unmet medical need, but is independent of Priority Review and Accelerated Approval. Priority drugs are those considered by the FDA to offer improvements over existing drugs or to offer high therapeutic value. The priority program, along with increased budget and staffing at the FDA, are having a positive effect on total approval times for new drugs.

For example, the FDA quickly approved Novartis' new drug Gleevec (a revolutionary and highly effective treatment for patients suffering from chronic myeloid leukemia). After priority review and Fast Track status, it required only two and one-half months in the approval process (compared to a more typical six months). This rapid approval, which enabled the drug to promptly begin saving lives, was possible because of two factors aside from the FDA's cooperation. One, Novartis mounted a targeted approach to this niche disease. Its research determined that a specific genetic malfunction causes the disease, and its drug specifically blocks the protein that causes the genetic malfunction. Two, thanks to its use of advanced genetic research techniques, Novartis was so convinced of the effectiveness of this drug that it invested heavily and quickly in its development.

Key Food & Drug Administration (FDA) terms relating to human clinical trials:

Phase I—Small-scale human trials to determine safety. Typically include 20 to 60 patients and are six months to one year in length.
Phase II—Preliminary trials on a drug's safety/efficacy. Typically include 100 to 500 patients and are one and a half to two years in length.
Phase III—Large-scale controlled trials for efficacy/safety; also the last stage before a request for approval for commercial distribution is made to the FDA. Typically include 1,000 to 7,500 patients and are three to five years in length.
Phase IV—Follow-up trials after a drug is released to the public.

Generally, Fast Track approval is reserved for life-threatening diseases such as rare forms of cancer, but new policies are setting the stage for accelerated approval for less deadly but more pervasive conditions such as diabetes and obesity. Approval is also being made easier by the use of genetic testing to determine a drug's efficacy, as well as the practice of drug companies working closely with federal organizations. Examples of these new policies are exemplified in the approval of Iressa, which helps fight cancer in only 10% of patients but is associated with a genetic marker that can help predict a patient's receptivity; and VELCADE, a cancer drug that received initial approval in only four months because the company that makes it, Millennium Pharmaceuticals, worked closely with the National Cancer Institute to review trials.

Small- to mid-size biotech firms continue to look to mature, global pharmaceutical companies for cash, marketing muscle, distribution channels and regulatory expertise. Good examples are the agreement between Millennium Pharmaceuticals and Johnson & Johnson for the development of VELCADE, and Isis Pharmaceuticals' multiple deals with Novartis, Pfizer and other partners for research into new antisense drugs for inflammatory and metabolic diseases.

Meanwhile, major projects are underway, backed by diverse sponsors, to add to or build from scratch massive databases of genetic data on a scale not before imagined. In Iceland, for example, a group called DeCode Genetics has amassed a database of essentially all of the DNA in Iceland's unique, isolated population.

Internet Research Tip:
For extensive commentary and analysis on the development and approval of new drugs see:

Tufts Center for the Study of Drug Development
csdd.tufts.edu
Note: This web site gives you the opportunity to download the latest annual edition of the "Outlook", an excellent summary review of trends in drug development.

With progress come setbacks, including a massive award for damages (more than $250 million) that occurred in a small-town Texas court in August 2005. The award was made to the widow of a patient who allegedly had a fatal reaction to Merck & Co.'s Vioxx pain medication (which had previously been removed from the market due to safety concerns). Texas laws capping medical case awards reduced the damages significantly. Nonetheless, recent drug safety issues and a proliferation of lawsuits such as this may accelerate changes in the business models of drug development firms, discouraging them from risking funds on long-shot drugs intended to benefit the mass market. Meanwhile, drug makers will continue to alter marketing methods and greatly reduce consumer advertising. Virtually all drugs have significant side effect risks for certain types of patients. While drug makers have long practiced a high level of disclosure, those risks will be more clearly communicated in the future.

Global trends are affecting the biotech industry in a big way. Post 9/11, an emphasis was placed by government agencies on the prevention of bioterror risks, such as attacks by the spread of anthrax. This factor, combined with global concern about the possible spread of avian flu, has been a significant boost to vaccine research and production. At the same time, the rapid rise of offshoring and globalization is contributing to the movement of research, development and clinical trials away from the U.S., U.K. and France into lower cost technology centers in India and elsewhere. In fact, biotech firms are rising rapidly in India, China, Singapore and South Korea that will provide serious future competition to older companies in the West.

Likewise, retail drug markets have tremendous potential in emerging nations over the mid term. For example, consultants at McKinsey estimated that the drug market in India will grow from $6.3 billion in 2005 to $20 billion in 2015. China offers similar opportunities. This means that major international drug makers will be expanding their presence in these nations. However, it also means that local drug manufacturers have tremendous incentive to expand their research, product lines and marketing within their own nations.

Global panic over quickly rising food prices in 2007 and part of 2008 finally gave the genetically modified seed industry the boost it needs. Agribio (agricultural biotechnology) will become a top agenda item in government and corporate research budgets, and consumer acceptance of genetically modified food products will grow quickly.

7) From India to Singapore to Australia, Nations Compete Fiercely in Biotech Development

While pharmaceutical companies based in the nations with the largest economies, such as the U.S., U.K. and Japan, struggle to discover the next important drug, companies and government agencies in many other countries are enhancing their positions on the biotech playing field, building their own educational and technological infrastructures. Not surprisingly, countries such as India, Singapore and China, which have already made deep inroads into other technology-based industries, are making major efforts in biotechnology, which is very much an information-based science. Firms that manufacture generics and provide contract research, development and clinical trials services are already common in such nations (in India alone, clinical trials spending may reach as much as $1 billion annually by 2010). In most cases, this is just a beginning, with original drug and technology development the ultimate goal.

The government of Singapore, for example, has made biotechnology one of its top priorities for development, vowing to make it one of the staples of its economy. Its $286-million "Biopolis," a research and development center opened in 2004 that encompasses 2 million square feet of laboratories and offices, is only a small part of its $2.3-billion initiative to foster biotech in Singapore. An additional 400,000 square feet of space in the lab complex opened in late 2006. Eventually, Biopolis may house more than 2,000 scientists.

Outsourcing of biotech tasks to India is growing at a very high annual rate. (India has dozens of drug manufacturing plants that meet FDA specifications.) Plunkett Research estimates that India's total pharmaceuticals industry revenues, largely from the manufacturing of generics, approached $11.8 billion in 2008.

India already has over 300 firms involved in biotechnology and related support services. In 2005, the nation tightened its intellectual property laws in order to provide strong patent protection to the drug industry. As a result, drug development activity by pharma firms from around the world has increased in Indian locations. Drug sector firms to watch that are based in India include Piramal Healthcare Limited (formerly Nicholas Piramal, India Ltd.), Ranbaxy Laboratories Ltd. and Dr. Reddy's Laboratories Ltd. Services firms and research labs in India will continue to have a growing business in outsourced services for the biotech sector. The costs of developing a new drug in India can be a small fraction of those in the U.S., although drugs developed in India still are required to go through the lengthy and expensive U.S. FDA approval process before they can be sold to American patients. By 2008, India's biopharma market had reached $1 billion and ranked 11th in the world, according to BioPlan Associates, Inc.

Stem cell (and cloning) research activity was brisk in a number of nations outside the U.S. as well. To begin with, certain institutions around the world have stem cell lines in place, and some make them available for purchase. Groups that own existing lines include the National University of Singapore, Monash University in Australia and Hadassah Medical Centre in Israel. Sweden has also stepped onto the stage as a major player in stem cell research, with 40 companies focused on the field, including rising stars such as Cellartis AB, which has one of the largest lines of stem cells in the world, and NeuroNova AB, which is focusing on regenerating nerve tissue. It is estimated that Sweden is home to 32% of all harvested stem cells worldwide.

More importantly, several Asian nations, including Singapore, South Korea, Japan and China, are investing intensely in biotech research centered on cloning and the development of stem cell therapies. The global lead in the development of stem cell therapies may eventually pass to China, where the Chinese Ministry of Science and Technology readily sees the commercial potential and is enthusiastically funding research. On top of funding from the Chinese government, investments in labs and research are being backed by Chinese universities, private companies, venture capitalists and Hong Kong-based investors.

In late 2007, the FDA approved a Chinese drug used to fight AIDS, the first time a Chinese firm (specifically, Zhejiang Huahai Pharmaceutical Co.) has won the right to export a drug to the U.S. China is the world's largest producer of raw materials for drugs, although it falls far behind India in the export of finished generic drugs.

In addition, China and India both are booming offshore business centers for clinical trials. The savings can be up to 50% to 80% over conducting trials in the U.S. This is a very large global industry sector involving tens of billions of dollars in annual expenses.

Meanwhile, leading biotech firms, including Roche, Pfizer and Eli Lilly, are taking advantage of China's very high quality education systems and low operating costs to establish R&D centers there. This is a model that has already been used successfully by leading IT firms operating large research labs in China, such as IBM and Microsoft. Clinical trials are underway in China for what could become one of the first vaccines against SARS, and at least four AIDS vaccines are under development or trials there.

Taiwan has opened the second of four planned biotech research parks. Vietnam has plans to open six biotech research labs. Australia also has a rapidly developing biotechnology industry.

South Korea is a world leader in research and development in a wide variety of technical sectors, and it is pushing ahead boldly into biotechnology. Initiatives include the Korea Research Institute of Bioscience and Biotechnology. The combination of government backing and extensive private capital in Korea could make this nation a biotech powerhouse. One area of emphasis there is stem cell research.

In addition to fewer restrictions, many countries outside of the U.S. have lower labor costs, even for highly educated professionals such as doctors and scientists.

8) U.S. Government Reverses Ban on Funding for New Stem Cell Research

Shortly after taking office, U.S. President Barack Obama reversed an eight-year ban on the use of federal funding for embryonic stem cell research. Specifically, Obama issued Executive Order 13505, entitled "Removing Barriers to Responsible Scientific Research Involving Human Stem Cells." This executive order, dated March 9, 2009, charged the National Institutes of Health (NIH) with issuing new guidelines for stem cell research within 120 days. The order further authorized the NIH to "support and conduct responsible, scientifically worthy human stem cell research, including human embryonic stem cell research, to the extent permitted by law." The important words here are "human embryonic," since the harvesting of stem cells from discarded human embryos is what started the stem cell funding controversy in the first place. Further, this wording clearly eliminates the possibility of funding research projects involving stem cells that result from cloning. Under previous U.S. regulations, federal research funds were granted only for work with 21 specific lines of stem cells that existed in 2001. Harvesting and developing new embryonic lines did not qualify.

By mid-April 2009, the NIH had issued a new policy statement and posted it for a 30-day public comment period. The issue of funding remains politically charged. The NIH is taking a middle road. Its proposed guidelines state that embryos donated for such research must be given voluntarily and without financial inducement. (Such embryos typically are donated by couples who have completed fertility treatments and have no need for remaining, redundant embryos. This is a common practice in seeking laboratory-aided pregnancies.)

Also of note: the NIH received $10 billion in new funds from recent economic stimulus legislation. It is possible, but not required, that NIH could use a part of that funding to boost stem cell efforts.

Once a stem cell starts to replicate, a large colony, or line, of self-replenishing cells can theoretically continue to reproduce forever. Unfortunately, only about a dozen of the stem cell lines existing at the time were considered to be useful, and some scientists believe that these lines were getting tired.

The use of non-federal funding, however, was not restricted during the eight-year ban, although many groups did want to see further state or federal level restrictions on stem cell research or usage. A major confrontation continues between American groups that advocate the potential health benefits of stem cell therapies and groups that decry the use of stem cells on ethical or religious terms. Meanwhile, stem cell development forged ahead in other technologically advanced nations.

In November 2004, voters in California approved a unique measure that provides $3 billion in state funding for stem cell research. Connecticut, Massachusetts and New Jersey also passed legislation that permits embryonic-stem cell research. California already has a massive biotech industry, spread about San Diego and San Francisco in particular. As approved, California's Proposition 71 created an oversight committee that determines how and where grants will be made, and an organization, the California Institute for Regenerative Medicine (www.cirm.ca.gov), to issue bonds for funding and to manage the entire program. The money is being invested in research at a rate of about $295 million yearly over 10 years.

In June 2007, the California Institute for Regenerative Medicine (CIRM) approved grants totaling more than $50 million to finance construction of shared research laboratories at 17 academic and non-profit institutions. These facilities are scheduled to be complete and available to researchers within six months to two years of the grant awards. By April 2009, CIRM had approved 279 grants totaling more than $693 million. The grants are funding dedicated laboratory space for the culture of human embryonic stem cells (HESCs), particularly those that fall outside federal guidelines. In early 2008, the first clinical trial began using CIRM funds at the University of California, San Diego for a therapy to treat a blood disorder.

In the private sector, funding for stem cell research was generous up until the global economic crisis beginning in 2008. For example, the Juvenile Diabetes Research Foundation has an $8 million stem cell research program underway and Stanford

University has used a $12 million donation to create a research initiative. Likewise, major, privately funded efforts have been launched at Harvard and at the University of California at San Francisco.

Corporate investment in stem cells was also strong. AstraZeneca Pharmaceuticals invested $77 million in a startup firm in San Diego called BrainCells, Inc. to study how antidepressants might be used to spur brain cell growth. GlaxoSmithkline agreed to pay OncoMed Pharmaceuticals up to $1.4 billion in late 2007 for four radical new drugs that target cancer stem cells. In 2009, Geron Corporation began an FDA-approved trial of embryonic stem cells in recent spinal cord injuries in eight to ten patients.

President Obama's reversal of the stem cell funding ban comes at a time when funding from private and state sources is drying up. This is good news for further research, but it may be a bit late due to recent breakthroughs in stem cell research. In 2007, Shinya Yamanaka, a research scientist in Japan, discovered that adult cells can be reprogrammed to an embryonic state using a relatively easy process. This discovery opens to door to an almost unlimited supply of stem cells in the future and lifts most ethical arguments against using the cells for research.

9) Emphasis on R&D in Nanotechnology

Nanotechnology is the science of designing, building or utilizing unique structures that are smaller than 100 nanometers. (A nanometer is one-billionth of a meter.) The science involves microscopic structures that might be no larger than the width of some cell membranes. In practical terms, nanotechnology will ultimately allow scientists and engineers to piece tiny structures together to build all manner of objects, from miniscule semiconductors to medical treatments that work on the molecular level, to the clothes we wear and the structures in which we live. All associated U.S. departments and agencies plan to focus on nanotech manufacturing processes, uses of nanotechnology for chemical-biological-radioactive-explosive detection and protection and also on instrumentation and metrology (the science of measurement).

In the private sector, companies both large and small are investing in the tiny technology in a big way. For example, Motorola Labs, a research subsidiary of telecom company Motorola, Inc., is making strides in carbon nanotechnology for use in flat-panel displays. Concurrently, tiny Sirna Therapeutics (a subsidiary of Merck & Co.) is focused on breakthroughs in RNA interference (RNAi) technology to fight diseases such as asthma, diabetes, macular degeneration and Huntington 's disease.

Nanotechnology continues to attract a reasonable flow of new money from the venture capital community. Professional investors see great potential in firms that may become early leaders and patent-holders in this field. Much of the future of technology in general will be based on miniaturization, and nanotechnology, the smallest possible level of product development, will play a key role in this miniaturization trend.

In 2006, sales of nano-enabled products reaped $50 billion worldwide, according to Lux Research. The U.S. National Science Foundation projects nano-enabled product sales to reach $1 trillion by 2015. Products include nano-formulated drugs, in addition to a wide variety of products from stain resistant clothing to power tool batteries. After 20 years of R&D funding, investors and manufacturers are beginning to see healthy progress as a result of their investments.

10) Government Nanotechnology Funding is Strong

Nanotechnology research and development in the U.S. now exceeds $2 billion yearly from both government and private funds. The U.S. government established the National Nanotechnology Initiative (NNI) in 2001, setting up an agency to oversee billions of dollars in mid-term funding of nanotech research. For fiscal 2009, federal dollars proposed for this research totaled $1.53 billion. Most of this money is filtered through the National Science Foundation, the Department of Defense and the Department of Energy, while programs are coordinated by the National Nanotechnology Initiative, for applications in aerospace, defense, intelligence, energy production and distribution and computing. This funding is in stark contrast to the mere $116 million provided in 1997.

Nanotech is not only reaching the point where it is a valuable technology (the U.S. Government considers it a matter of national importance), but it is now able to absorb a greater amount of money and apply it usefully to research and development. Japan is essentially on par with the U.S. at about $1 billion in yearly funding for nanotech research. The EU also invests about on par with the U.S., and Asian nations are investing heavily, particularly on nanotech research for corporate use.

Of course, tech giants such as IBM and Intel have significant investments, internal research efforts and research partnerships in nanotech, pushing for the next generation in computer and communications technology.

11) Nanotechnology Converges with Biotech

Because of their small size, nanoscale devices can readily interact with biomolecules on both the surface and the inside of cells. By gaining access to so many areas of the body, they have the potential to detect disease and deliver treatment in unique ways. Nanotechnology will create "smart drugs" that are more targeted and have fewer side effects than traditional drugs.

Current applications of nanotechnology in health care include immunosuppressants, hormone therapies, drugs for cholesterol control, and drugs for appetite enhancement, as well as advances in imaging, diagnostics and bone replacement. For example, the NanoCrystal technology developed by Elan, a major biotechnology company, enhances drug delivery in the form of tiny particles, typically less than 2,000 nanometers in diameter. The technology can be used to provide more effective delivery of drugs in tablet form, capsules, powders and liquid dispersions. Abbot Laboratories uses Elan's technology to improve results in its cholesterol drug Tricor. Par Pharmaceutical Companies uses NanoCrystal in its Megace ES drug for the improvement of appetite in people with anorexia.

Since biological processes, including events that lead to cancer, occur at the nanoscale at and inside cells, nanotechnology offers a wealth of tools that are providing cancer researchers with new and innovative ways to diagnose and treat cancer. In America, the National Cancer Institute has established the Alliance for Nanotechnology in Cancer (http://nano.cancer.gov) in order to foster breakthrough research.

Nanoscale devices have the potential to radically change cancer therapy for the better and to dramatically increase the number of effective therapeutic agents. These devices can serve as customizable, targeted drug delivery vehicles capable of ferrying large doses of chemotherapeutic agents or therapeutic genes into malignant cells while sparing healthy cells, greatly reducing or eliminating the often unpalatable side effects that accompany many current cancer therapies.

At the University of Michigan at Ann Arbor, Dr. James Baker is working with molecules known as dendrimers to create new cancer diagnostics and therapies, thanks to grants from the National Institutes of Health and other funds. This is part of a major effort named the Michigan Nanotechnology Institute for Medicine and Biological Sciences.

A dendrimer is a spherical molecule of uniform size (five to 100 nanometers) and well-defined chemical structure. Dr. Baker's lab is able to build a nanodevice with four or five attached dendrimers. To deliver cancer-fighting drugs directly to cancer cells, Dr. Baker loads some dendrimers on the device with folic acid, while loading others with drugs that fight cancer. Since folic acid is a vitamin, many proteins in the body will bind with it, including proteins on cancer cells. When a cancer cell binds to and absorbs the folic acid on the nanodevice, it also absorbs the anticancer drug. For use in diagnostics, Dr. Baker is able to load a dendrimer with molecules that are visible to an MRI. When the dendrimer, due to its folic acid, binds with a cancer cell, the location of that cancer cell is shown on the MRI. Each of these nanodevices may be developed to the point that they are able to perform several advanced functions at once, including cancer cell recognition, drug delivery, diagnosis of the cause of a cancer cell, cancer cell location information and reporting of cancer cell death. Universities that are working on the leading edge of cancer drug delivery and diagnostics using nanotechnology include MIT and Harvard, as well as Rice University and the University of Michigan.

Meanwhile, at the University of Washington, a research group led by Babak A. Parviz is investigating manufacturing methods that resemble plants and other natural organisms by "self-assembly." If man-made machines could be designed to assemble themselves, it could revolutionize manufacturing, especially on the nanoscale level. Researchers are studying ways to program the assembly process by sparking chemical synthesis of nanoscale parts such as quantum dots or molecules which then bind to other parts through DNA hybridization or protein interactions. The group led by Professor Parviz is attempting to produce self-assembled high performance silicon circuits on plastic. It is conceivable that integrated circuits, biomedical sensors or displays could be "grown" at rates exponentially faster than current processes.

12) Globalization and Worldwide Collaboration Fuel the Research Efforts of Major Corporations

Globalization is deeply affecting the corporate world at all levels. This can be seen in everything from the inexpensive consumer goods flooding into the U.S. from manufacturers in China to the growing business that American software makers have found overseas. The advent of extremely fast communication systems, such as the Internet, global fiber-optic lines, e-mail and instant messaging, as well as overnight international courier services and well-established jet airliner service to nearly anywhere in the world, helps to spur on globalization.

Meanwhile, there are legions of extremely well-educated scientists and engineers in areas such as India, China and Eastern Europe who can be hired for salaries that are significantly below those of their U.S.-based peers. These factors all combine to make globalized research efforts attractive for many reasons. For example, a major automotive, pharmaceutical, software or hardware company in the U.S. can create a cost-effective, 24/7 research department by handing off research or design work from America to Ireland to Russia to India to Japan—it will always be daylight in some part of the world, and collaboration software makes it possible for employees to work together on the same project from anywhere on the planet.

One of the hottest spots for U.S. firms to open foreign research centers is the city of Bangalore in India. Initially a center for writing software code, Bangalore's supply of highly educated, English-speaking residents has enabled the city to evolve into a truly world-class research and development center. The labor pool is not only high-quality but also low-cost.

SPOTLIGHT: InnoCentive

At www.innocentive.com, drug maker Eli Lilly has created a collaborative research portal. Companies needing answers to research problems can post details regarding their projects, along with a stated fee they are willing to pay for completion of research needs. Scientists and engineers from anywhere in the world can log in to select projects to work on. Fees offered run from a few thousand dollars to $1 million.

Participants who log in may choose to view the site in English, Chinese, Japanese, Korean, German, Russian or Spanish. The site was launched in June 2001. By early 2008, InnoCentive boasted more then 140,000 scientists and scientific organizations in over 175 countries to work on research problems. Client companies include Avery, Eli Lilly and Company, Janssen, Proctor & Gamble and Solvay.

13) Growth Continues in Research Partnerships Between Corporations and Universities

Corporations have long seen the benefit of tapping the intellectual powers of labs, graduate students and professors at universities that focus on technology-intensive disciplines. At the same time, such universities have been anxious to receive corporate funding for their research projects. This has always been a win-win situation. Lately, however, universities have enhanced their position in such partnerships by negotiating research collaboration contracts that are potentially more lucrative than was the norm in years past. Cash-strapped universities are anxious to capitalize on commercial successes that stem from their research. At the same time, cash-strapped corporations are happy to utilize top grad students who work in university labs at nominal pay.

Pharmaceutical giant Pfizer is an excellent example of a major corporation conducting research and development with the assistance of universities. Its Research Technology Center, located in Cambridge, Massachusetts, regularly offers fellowships to students from nearby campuses such as Harvard, MIT and the Whitehead Institute. In addition to academic institutions, Pfizer also has close ties with other companies.

Intel is another example of a company with major in-house R&D efforts as well as external alliances. The technology giant has delivered approximately 500 active research grants to universities, which create small labs or "lablets" that combine the efforts of students and Intel staff. Associated institutions include the University of California at Berkeley, Carnegie Mellon and the University of Washington. Meanwhile, universities continue to aggressively seek patents on their discoveries. For example, during 2008, the U.S. university receiving the most patents was the University of California System, with 237 granted. Other universities high on the list of U.S. patents granted in 2008 were The University of Texas, (79 patents); MIT (134); Stanford (120); and the California Institute of Technology (96).

14) Number of Patent Applications Remains High

In 2007, the U.S. Patent & Trademark Office (PTO) received 484,955 patent applications (the latest available data), up from 452,633 in 2006. There were 315,015 applications in 2000 and only 109,359 in 1970. To some extent, patents tend to reflect the health of R&D budgets. The greater the funding, the more patents are filed. At the same time, however, the rapid growth in the number of patent applications reflects today's increased focus on protection of intellectual property by corporations and universities along with the extremely high traffic from biotech firms attempting to patent gene expressions and other biological discoveries.

A patent application leads either to a patent grant or to a denial. The PTO granted 185,224 total patents during calendar-year 2008, up from 182,901 in 2007, and up from only 67,964 in 1970. A patent typically takes 18 to 24 months after application to receive a grant. The term of patent protection is currently defined as beginning on the date the patent is granted and ending 20 years from the earliest filing date of the application.

Internet Research Tip:
For the latest official statistics from the U.S. Patent & Trademark Office, visit the web site of TAF, the patent office's Technology Assessment and Forecast branch.
www.uspto.gov/web/offices/ac/ido/oeip/taf

Globally, there are 120 different national patent systems, and recent proposals to create a unified global patent system are creating buzz. "Harmonization" is the word used to describe the effort, and it will be difficult to bring about. According to the World Intellectual Property Organization (www.wipo.int), 90% of the 7 million applications filed annually worldwide are filed in more than one country, which exponentially multiplies application fees, legal fees and hours spent (fees for multinational applications can surpass $75,000, and legal fess often reach $200,000 or more). IBM, which holds more patents than any other company in the world, spends more than $200 million annually on the protection of its intellectual property both at home and abroad. According to WIPO, approximately 727,000 patents were granted worldwide in 2006 (the latest data available), while 1.76 million applications were filed. Globally, about 6.1 million patents were in force during that year.

An aborted 1989 attempt to establish an international system was bogged down when the U.S. could not agree with most other participating countries on a simple first-to-file regulation when awarding patents to filers with similar claims. In the U.S., the practice has traditionally been to award a patent to the filer who is proven to be the first to conceive an idea and develop it. Although fair, the system can prove costly as applicants spend time and money in the court systems to establish who was first with an idea.

Since patent applications have grown exponentially in recent years, examiners have less and less time to spend studying each application and researching past inventions. Some detractors claim that patents awarded in recent years may not have been for original ideas. One solution may be to use a wiki approach, in which scientists and inventors around the world could publish their opinions regarding a patent application in a central, online forum. New York Law School professor Beth Noveck, in concert with IBM and the U.S. Patent and Trademark Office, developed a system which scores wiki input so that patent examiners are given only the 10 highest-rating opinions, thereby safeguarding (to some extent) the veracity of the opinions entered. The system is undergoing testing and is supported by IBM, Microsoft and HP.

Critics of the current patent system also cite unscrupulous patent-licensing companies called "trolls" that seek licensing fees by sending demand letters to presumed patent infringers, in many cases without basis of proof. Trolls also seek injunctions against large numbers of defendants, hoping to become enough of a nuisance that the supposed infringers will pay license fees just to make the problem go away. The U.S. Supreme Court made rulings in late 2006 and 2007 that limit injunctions, enable alleged infringers to file their own suits and/or make it easier for frivolous patents to be declared invalid. All three rulings are expected to curtail troll activity.

Another critical difference between the U.S. patent system and those elsewhere around the globe is the one-year waiting period, during which American filers may publish or speak at public forums about their ideas without jeopardizing their patent rights. Abroad, filers are required to keep their ideas top secret until a patent is awarded.

Yet another point of argument centers on patent subject matter. Traditionally, in the U.S., just about anything or any idea can be patented. Business practices, for example, are commonly patented, such as Amazon.com's "one-click" technology, as well as genetic discoveries and treatments. The latter is a particularly sticky point for developing nations such as those in Latin America and Africa.

However, a landmark case heard by the U.S. Court of Appeals for the Federal Circuit in 2008 may vastly change the nature of items that can be patented. The case, known as *In re Bilski*, created a new legal environment in which patents granted in the past for advances that would otherwise occur in the ordinary course of events without real innovation may be deemed invalid. This means, for example, that advances in business practices and software may have to be shown to be truly innovative in order to receive patent protection. This also may have a broad effect on organizations attempting to patent discoveries in the areas of biotechnology and genetics, such as proteins and genomes.

Meanwhile, the European Commission established a plan in 2007 for making it easier to apply for, obtain and defend patents across the nation members of the EU. Previously, patents were granted individually by each member nation, which created immense costs and delays. A similar effort failed in 2003 when members were unable to come to terms. As of 2009, a uniform application procedure applies for individual investors and companies in up to 38 European countries. The process is overseen by the intergovernmental European Patent Organisation (www.epo.org). The EPO reports that about 140,000 patent applications were filed in Europe during 2007, of which 57% were international filings, mostly from the U.S. and Japan.

Among competing tech companies, patents are something like badges of honor. Patents protect ideas and technologies as well as exclude competitors from making strides in particular areas of research. IBM leads the pack in the total number of patents awarded in the U.S. yearly, with 4,169 new patents granted during calendar-year 2008. Patents are an immense asset to IBM, and it garners more than $1.5 billion in yearly licensing revenue from the patents it holds. To finish up the top private sector firms in U.S. patents, IBM is followed by Samsung (3,502), Canon (1,983), Microsoft (2,026), Intel (1,772), Toshiba (1,575), Fujitsu (1,461), Matsushita (1,469), Sony (1,461) and Hewlett-Packard (1,422). IBM has long been the leader by far in top patenting organizations. As you can see by the above list, Japanese firms loom large among top companies receiving U.S. patents. India is also reaping early rewards on its decade-long patent campaign. Its 38 publicly-funded laboratories have seen U.S. patent counts grow from 37 in 1995 to 672 in 2008.

The firms on this list are consistently among the leaders, along with Fuji and GE. Not only do these extraordinary numbers of patents give these companies substantial bragging rights, the revenues generated can often make the difference between profits or losses in a difficult economy. As a result, watch for continued growth in the number of patent applications.

Patent Categories in the United States:

Utility Patent: may be granted to anyone who invents or discovers any new, useful and non-obvious process, machine, article of manufacture, or composition of matter, or any new and useful improvement thereof.

Design Patent: may be granted to anyone who invents a new, original, and ornamental design for an article of manufacture.

Plant Patent: may be granted to anyone who invents or discovers and asexually reproduces any distinct and new variety of plant.

15) The Automation of Research and Design Steams Ahead

The news for automated research tools is excellent, and many firms that manufacture such tools are enjoying booming business. Advances in CAD (computer-aided design) and CAE (computer-aided engineering) hybrids are revolutionizing the way in which new designs are tested and enhanced. The combination of disciplines creates virtual prototypes on computers that make R&D faster and more efficient than ever before.

One of these automation tools, Finite Element Analysis (FEA), checks a computer-generated model for flaws. It analyzes how the model would react to extremes in heat, vibration and pressure by breaking it down into small pieces or cells in a three-dimensional grid. The computer applies simulated stimuli to one cell in the model and then tracks the response of that cell and those that surround it. The results often keep a flawed design from progressing to production and distribution.

The next big thing to define automated R&D was Design of Experiments (DOE). This statistical technology helps researchers program FEA to concentrate on particularly vulnerable areas, rather than running thousands of scans on all parts of a model, which may not be necessary.

Another stride in automation is behavioral modeling, a software application that forms the results found by the combination of FEA and DOE into family trees of cause-and-effect scenarios. Major variables such as model size and power are represented by large limbs, which branch out into scenarios showing how those variables react to different situations. The process allows researchers to isolate deal-breaking problems early on and pinpoint exact circumstances in which problems will likely occur. Industries adopting this new technology include automotive manufacturing, aerospace and shipyards.

Rapid prototyping, sometimes referred to as 3-D printing since the technology is somewhat like inkjet printing, is helping to boost the results of design engineers. A U.S. firm, Stratasys (www.stratasys.com) is working in conjunction with IBM to build an exciting new machine that creates 3-D design prototypes. Design tools from Stratasys use proprietary Fused Deposition Modeling technology for rapid prototyping in materials such as polycarbonate. The machines use digitized designs, created with CAD software, as blueprints. The technology is marketed under the Fortus brand.

The use of 3-D printing technology is evolving. Today, it is being adapted into the creation of mini-manufacturing plants (sometimes called "fab labs") that create complicated parts or machinery one piece at a time, using this inkjet-like technology to fabricate on the fly. Eventually, it will be possible to manufacture effectively with these systems using materials as ceramic powders or metal powders as well as plastics. Sales of 3-D printing systems were already in the $1 billion range by 2006 (unit prices run between $15,000 and $50,000). Leading firms in this sector include Z Corporation and Germany's EOS, in addition to Stratasys. Potential uses are nearly endless. For example, Therics, Inc. (www.therics.com) uses 3-D printing to manufacture ceramic bone substitutes for use by orthopedic surgeons. In fact, medical applications are among the fastest growing use of this technology. (Therics was acquired by Integra LifeSciences Holdings Corporation in 2008.)

The next step for 3-D printing will be for these printers to appear in the home. Desktop Factory (www.desktopfactory.com), founded by technology incubator IdeaLab, offers a 3-D printer priced at $4,995 and small enough to sit on a desktop. The machine can make small plastic toys, but may also be used to fabricate design models and custom prototypes. Even smaller and simpler units are entering the marketplace, such as 3D Outlook Corp.'s $100 model that produces models of terrains such as mountains, ski slopes and golf courses (www.landprint.com).

Product lifecycle management (PLM) has become a useful science in a range of sectors from automotive to consumer goods. The goal of PLM is to decrease design and development time, enhance manufacturing and speed distribution to the extent that sales and return on investment are maximized. Many companies are now using state-of-the-art PLM software systems to enhance the process.

Dassault Systemes (www.3ds.com), a firm based in France, has developed a software package that not only provides computer-aided design and modeling, but simulates the production, operation and maintenance phases of a product as well. For example, Boeing is using this software in the design of its highly advanced new 787. Since the 787 is based on global design and engineering collaboration, Boeing hopes that the Dassault system will enable its engineers to see exactly how a change in the design of a part will affect all of the other engineered parts of the aircraft, regardless of whether they are being designed in Japan or in Seattle.

Meanwhile, combinatorial chemistry, DNA chips and many other technology-intensive tools have automated research in biotechnology. The collaborative automation is helping the field to accelerate dramatically.

16) Governments Encourage Renewable Energy, Energy Conservation, Research and Investment

The U.S. government has earmarked $38.7 billion in economic stimulus funds in 2009 for the Department of Energy (DOE), up from $24.2 billion budget in 2008. The 2009 budget is further augmented by $27 billion in appropriations. Within that overall budget, the U.S. Congress approved $7.8 billion for energy-related research and development, up 18% from 2008. More than anytime in history, the U.S. government, as well as governments around the world, are committed to energy independence, conservation and climate change prevention. U.S. President Obama recently announced a new goal to cut emissions by 80% by 2050.

New York State already produces 19% of its electricity through renewable sources. It wants to increase that number to 25% by 2013. Likewise, the city of Austin, Texas has passed a resolution to get 20% of its electricity from renewables by 2020. In fact, the State of Texas passed legislation in 2005 that set a goal for the entire state to get 5% of its electricity from renewable by 2015 and 10% by 2025. While governments are continually setting high goals for energy conservation, reduction in carbon emissions and use of zero-emission vehicles (such as all-electric cars), it remains to be seen whether technologies and available funding can come close to meeting these goals.

California is the leading U.S. state in terms of solar power generation. The capitol city, Sacramento, has solar generation totaling about 10 megawatts, including one of the world's largest solar facilities, located at the Sacramento Municipal Utility District. San Francisco has also passed legislation seeking to build a similar amount over the short-term. Long-term, San Francisco planners hope to develop 40 megawatts of solar power, enough to meet about 5% of the city's peak electricity needs. City residents have authorized the issuance of revenue bonds of up to $100 million to back the development of renewable power sources. For example, the roof of the city's huge convention center has been layered with solar panels—enough to generate 675 kilowatts. (San Francisco's long-range plans also call for the use of smaller, cleaner gas-fired conventional generating stations, and perhaps the use of tidal energy.) California's legislature has set a statewide goal of requiring retail sellers of electricity to obtain at least 20% of their electricity from renewable sources by 2010, and 33% by 2020.

The U.S. federal government is also pushing green initiatives. The Energy Policy Act of 2005 stipulates that oil refiners vastly increase the amount of biofuels added to gasoline and diesel fuel by 2012. Refiners are responding by blending ethanol with gasoline. Specifically, refiners were required to add 4.0 billion gallons of biofuels (ethanol and biodiesel) to gasoline and diesel in 2006, (up from 0.7 billion in 2005) increasing to 7.5 billion by 2012. By 2022, Congress has mandated that America will be using 22 billion gallons of advanced biofuels yearly, including ethanol made from cellulosic materials like switch grass. Considering the rate at which ethanol producers were going bankrupt in 2008 and 2009, dwindling gasoline demand and the massive federal subsidies necessary to keep the biofuel industry afloat, meeting the long-term goals seems extremely unlikely.

Off the road, an energy-saving lighting standard proposed by the U.S. Congress would phase out common incandescent light bulbs by 2016 and replace them with compact fluorescent lights (CFL). GE is the biggest seller of these bulbs, which use 75% less energy than incandescent bulbs and last six times longer. GE has developed a new, more efficient incandescent bulb that is comparable to CFLs. At the same time, manufacturers are also working to reduce prohibitive costs of light-emitting diodes, which have the potential to save billions of dollars in electricity costs while greatly reducing pollution. PolyBrite International, www.polybrite.com, is one such company.

Outside of the U.S., major initiatives in Germany, the United Kingdom, Japan, Spain and handful of other countries spur on technology research and implementation of renewable power.

The European Union in March 2007 set a goal for its member countries to increase the amount of total energy needs met by renewable sources to 20% by 2020. (As of the end of 2006, the EU was at 6.92% renewable, still a long way from the 2020 goal.) On January 23, 2008, the EU further refined its goals by setting differentiated targets for each EU nation, based on a nation's GDP per capita.

Furthermore, in April 2009, the EU enacted additional climate change regulations hoped to assist meeting its renewable energy goals. It also enacted new regulations aimed at furthering its goal of reducing greenhouse gas emissions, by 2020, to a level amounting to 20% less than emissions of the year 1990. Major changes in the emissions trading program for electric generation firms will go into effect in 2013. Additional changes for emissions traders of all types will be staged in through 2027.

Japanese firms, notably Sharp, Sanyo (now part of Panasonic) and Kyocera, have massive solar power research and development projects underway, and are significant competitors to American manufacturers of solar equipment. Consumers in Japan are encouraged to invest in solar power by government incentives, and the Japanese Government's strategy is to get 38% of the nation's total power needs from renewable sources by the year 2020—a logical goal for a country with high energy demands and major dependence on foreign supplies of fossil fuels. Citizens are encouraged to take energy conserving steps by the imposition of stiff gasoline taxes and generous subsidies to homes that use home fuel cells.

Based in China, Suntech is one of the largest producers of solar cells in the world, and its China-based design, development and manufacturing facilities provide it with several competitive advantages, including access to low-cost technical expertise, labor and facilities. The company leverages its cost advantages by optimizing the balance between automation and manual operations in manufacturing. Its strategic use of manual labor has helped keep the wafer breakage rate in the company's facilities at an enviable level of less than 1%.

Germany has been investing in both wind and solar power. The country is the world's largest producer of wind power, and second in solar only to Japan. Through powerful incentives that include rebates and payment for excess power, German consumers and companies alike have been building nonstop.

In Spain, government incentives are promoting the use of concentrating solar power (CSP). The Spanish government has set a goal of building 500 megawatts of solar-thermal generation capacity over the near term. To do so, it has instituted "feed-in" tariffs that require utility companies to buy CSP plant generated power at premium rates.

17) Fuel Cell and Hydrogen Power Research Continues

The fuel cell is nothing new, despite the excitement it is now generating. It has been around since 1839, when Welsh physics professor William Grove created an operating model based on platinum and zinc components. Much later, the U.S. Apollo space program used fuel cells for certain power needs in the Apollo space vehicles that traveled from the Earth to the Moon.

In basic terms, a fuel cell consists of quantities of hydrogen and oxygen separated by a catalyst. Inside the cell, a chemical reaction within the catalyst generates electricity. Byproducts of this reaction include heat and water. Several enhancements to basic fuel cell technology are under research and development at various firms worldwide. These include fuel cell membranes manufactured with advanced nanotechnologies and "solid oxide" technologies that could prove efficient enough to use on aircraft. Another option for fuel cell membranes are those made of hydrocarbon, which cost about one-half a much as membranes using fluorine compounds. California-based PolyFuel (www.polyfuel.com) is a leader in engineered hydrocarbon membranes.

Fuel cells require a steady supply of hydrogen. Therein lies the biggest problem in promoting the widespread use of fuel cells: how to create, transport and store the hydrogen. At present, no one has been able to put a viable plan in place that would create a network of hydrogen fueling stations substantial enough to meet the needs of everyday motorists in the U.S. or anywhere else.

Many currently operating fuel cells burn hydrogen extracted from such sources as gasoline, natural gas or methanol. Each source has its advantages and disadvantages. Unfortunately, burning a hydrocarbon such as oil, natural gas or coal to produce the energy necessary to create hydrogen results in unwanted emissions. Ideally, hydrogen would be created using renewable, non-polluting means, such as solar power or wind power. Also, nuclear or renewable sources could be used to generate electricity that would be used to extract hydrogen molecules from water.

The potential market for fuel cells encompasses diverse uses in fixed applications (such as providing an electric generating plant for a home or a neighborhood), portable systems (such as portable generators for construction sites) or completely mobile uses (powering anything from small hand-held devices to automobiles). The potential advantages of fuel cells as clean, efficient energy sources are enormous. The fuel cell itself is a proven technology—fuel cells are already in use, powering a U.S. Post Office in Alaska, for example. (This project, in Chugach, Alaska, is the result of a joint venture between the local electric association and the U.S. Postal Service to install a one megawatt fuel cell facility.) Tiny fuel cells are also on the market for use in powering cellular phones and laptop computers.

Shipments of fuel cell-equipped mobile devices could grow very rapidly if they can eliminate the need for frequent recharging of current battery-powered models. The "Medis 24/7 Power Pack" is a portable, disposable power source for small electronic devices such as cell phones and MP3 players. Manufactured by Medis Technologies, it is based on Direct Liquid Fuel cell technology, and may be of particular utility in military applications. Elsewhere, MTI MicroFuel Cells manufactures a power pack for portable electronics that is based on direct methanol fuel cell technology that it calls Mobion.

Internet Research Tip: Micro Fuel Cells

For more information on research involving fuel cells for small applications, visit:

Medis Technologies	www.medistechnologies.com
MTI MicroFuel Cells	www.mtimicrofuelcells.com
PolyFuel	www.polyfuel.com
Tekion Solutions, Inc.	www.tekion.com

Electric Vehicles vs. Fuel Cells

Nearly all of the major automobile makers had significant fuel cell research initiatives at one time. While the potential for fuel-cell powered vehicles seemed extremely promising at one time, the automobile industry has made a profound and long-lasting shift toward plug-in electric hybrids and all-electric vehicles as the new technology base of choice. This is due to several reasons, including:

1) The tremendous success and wide consumer acceptance of Toyota's Prius hybrid car. This success gave Toyota early dominance in the electric car field while other makers were still dreaming about fuel cells. An important feature of the Prius is its very affordable price—something that might never be accomplished in a fuel cell vehicle.

2) The technical hurdles of distributing, storing and transporting hydrogen as a fuel have proven extremely difficult to overcome.

3) The costs of building a fuel cell platform for automobiles remains vastly more expensive than building an electric or hybrid vehicle.

4) Consumers, bureaucrats, investors and legislators already understand and trust the safety and ease of use of electricity, whether fixed or portable. This cannot be said for hydrogen.

Now, GM, Toyota and other leading automobile firms have ambitious plans for launching electric-drive vehicles in the near future (as opposed to today's hybrid electric cars which run on electricity only part of the time, relying on a gasoline engine the rest of the time). Given the financial constraints that automakers are working under today, these car manufacturers have downgraded or abandoned their focus on fuel cells. In particular, technical breakthroughs in advanced batteries for electric vehicles are occurring quickly. This will spur a huge rush into the electric car market while lessening the near-term interest in fuel cells.

GM has invested $1 billion in fuel cell vehicle research. The company leased 100 fuel cell-equipped Equinox crossover vehicles to customers as a test, starting in early 2008. The Equinox will go about 200 miles on a hydrogen fill up. Initially, the vehicles were provided to government officials, celebrities, journalists and business leaders in New York City, Washington D.C. and Los Angeles. GM has long had aggressive goals for commercializing and producing fuel cell vehicles. However, the financial and technical hurdles would be high, and GM assigned itself a daunting task. It may never happen, unless GM can see its way to real profits from fuel cells. Nonetheless, in January 2008, the firm unveiled a fuel cell concept car, the Cadillac Provoq, at the Consumer Electronics Show, which is held in Las Vegas each year. However, the firm's deep financial problems of 2008-2009 and its intense focus on the Chevy Volt electric car have combined to move GM's fuel cell project to the back burner, perhaps forever.

One of GM's thoughts for eventual commercial development is a wide variety of car and truck bodies that would mount onto a single, radical "skateboard" chassis design, which integrates the engine directly into the chassis. The skateboard stores fuel cell stacks and hydrogen supplies as well as circuitry that manages the flow of electric power through the various systems necessary to stop, start and maneuver the vehicle. The chassis would include a docking port that links the body above to the electronic control systems.

GM is not the only manufacturer with significant investments in fuel cells. Honda has started leasing test models of its "FCX" fuel cell-powered car to small numbers of customers in the U.S. and Japan. Honda's goal is to be able to offer fuel cell cars at a cost comparable to gasoline-powered cars by 2020. Toyota began making a small number of fuel cell powered cars available on 30 month leases in July 2006. In late 2007, a prototype Highlander hydrogen-hybrid fuel cell vehicle traveled 2,300 miles from Alaska to Vancouver, Canada, getting more than 300 miles per tank of hydrogen. As at GM, economic and technical realities will defer (or eventually cancel) major fuel cell or hydrogen power programs at Toyota and Honda. Nonetheless, the technology remains intriguing, if difficult to commercialize.

The former DaimlerChrysler invested about $1 billion in its own fuel cell initiative. In 2008 Chrysler featured its ecoVoyager concept car at the Detroit Auto Show. As of 2007, Ford had 30 fuel cell powered Focus compact cars in customer trials, but decided in 2009 to divert hydrogen fuel-cell research funds to focus on electric vehicles.

Meanwhile, BMW unveiled a hybrid of sorts in 2006 that allows drivers to use either hydrogen or gasoline at the flick of a switch. (The hydrogen is not used in a fuel cell. Instead, it is burned as a fuel in an internal-combustion engine that ordinarily would burn gasoline.) The car uses a V-12 engine that can be powered by either fuel. BMW put 100 of its Hydrogen 7 cars on loan to celebrities in California and Germany in 2007. Since more hydrogen than gasoline is required to run an engine the same number of miles, the prototype has a hydrogen tank that utilizes space usually reserved for luggage or passengers. The use of hydrogen offers multiple technical challenges.

Marketability of fuel-cell-powered vehicles would depend both on their initial cost and the ready availability of hydrogen in convenient filling stations. Prototype cars are on the road in a few cities, and large-scale production might have the potential to eventually make such vehicles affordable and competitive, but the obstacles are significant.

After the initial enthusiasm over fuel cells, during which many governments planned to introduce large numbers of fuel cell power plants and vehicles, energy agencies have scaled back their goals. The difficulties surrounding the technology are proving much more stubborn than they initially appeared to be. For example, Japan, one of the largest proponents of fuel cell technology, initially wanted 50,000 fuel cell vehicles on the road by 2010, a goal that couldn't be met.

Unfortunately, fuel cells remain grossly expensive due to their limited production and the industry's current low-technology base. For example, the cost of one 200-horsepower fuel cell system runs around $75,000. Moreover, hydrogen is not readily available to drivers. GM's head of strategic planning projects that 12,000 stations in the largest cities across the U.S. would put 70% of the population within two miles of a hydrogen filling station. The cost would be about $1 million per station. Honda is promoting a Home Energy Station in Southern California that it hopes will convert natural gas into enough hydrogen to power fuel cells that could run a family's vehicle, as well as supply electricity and hot water for the family home.

Another problem is that many people still have concerns about the safety of hydrogen. Naturally gaseous at room temperature, storing hydrogen involves using pressurized tanks that can leak and, if punctured, could cause explosions. It is also difficult to store enough hydrogen in a vehicle to take it the 300+ miles that drivers are used to getting on a tank of gasoline. To do so, hydrogen must be compressed to 10,000 pounds per square inch and stored on board in bulky pressure tanks.

One idea for storage is cooling the hydrogen to a liquid state and storing it in a cooled tank, but this requires constant refrigeration. A mid-term solution to the problem of creation and storage of hydrogen is to use existing fuels, such as methane, gasoline and diesel. These fuels can be broken down in the car, on-demand, to produce hydrogen, and then power the fuel cell. Although this would relieve the hydrogen storage problems, it would not remove the need for fossil fuels and it would still produce emissions such as carbon dioxide, though in reduced quantities. The next step would be to create hydrogen on-demand from ethanol, thereby creating less pollution.

Meanwhile, UPS tested a fuel-cell-powered vehicle in Ann Arbor, Michigan, and another in Ontario, California. Honda and Toyota are both testing fuel-cell-powered cars in California and Japan. Ford built a hydrogen internal combustion engine as an interim step to fuel cells, as a V10 intended for trucks or vans.

The Bush administration launched a "Hydrogen Fuel Initiative" in 2003, and Congress has provided over $1 billion for research. In May 2008, the EU's government funded 470 million Euros for fuel cell and hydrogen research, and Germany has promised as much as 500 million Euros. Will this be enough to bring fuel cells to the mass market? Probably not. There is still a massive problem in the manufacture and distribution of hydrogen on a scale suitable to serve the needs of vehicles. A U.S. Department of Energy study determined that it would take public funding of $45 billion to get 10 million fuel cells cars on the road by 2025, assuming that mass production would create a dramatic reduction in the cost of manufacturing fuel cells, and that public funding would encourage the development of a network of fueling stations. Meanwhile, electric cars are clearly the next wave.

18) Electric Cars and Plug-in Hybrids (PHEVs) Will Quickly Gain Popularity/Major Research in Advanced Lithium Batteries

For the near term, electric cars may range from 100% electric power vehicles that have relatively short ranges and are plugged-in at home overnight to recharge—to cars like the proposed Chevrolet Volt that will run on electric motors only, but will include a small gasoline-powered generator engine that will recharge the batteries when needed. The Volt will be designed to go up to 40 miles without recharging, and it will have the capability to be recharged by plug-in at home. Meanwhile, other challenges face 100% electric cars. In addition to adequate battery life, engineers are wrestling with the fact that conveniences such as air conditioning, heating and stereos drain a lot of electricity. Technical advances in these accessories may be necessary, since consumers will not buy such cars in volume without them.

Plug-in hybrids (PHEVs) will be on the market soon. These will be similar to today's hybrids, but will feature a larger battery with longer range. More importantly, they will enable the owner to plug-in at home overnight to recharge that battery. Today's hybrids recharge by running the gasoline-powered side of the car, and by drawing on the drag produced by using the brakes.

Such cars are about to make a massive push into the market. This is due to several factors, including:

1) Technical breakthroughs in lithium-ion. batteries making them safer and longer-lasting are leading to true breakthroughs in electric cars.

2) An electric car research, development and investment focus at major car manufacturers.

3) Toyota quickly proved global consumer acceptance (and technological superiority) by selling more than 1 million Prius hybrid vehicles worldwide from its 1997 debut in Japan through the one million milestone in April 2008. Soon, Toyota hopes to be selling one million hybrid vehicles each year.

4) Electricity is user-friendly, easy to understand, and easy to obtain. Electric utility companies are generally in favor of the electric car trend. Governments are wildly enthusiastic and supportive (including incentives to manufacturers and consumers alike). Tremendously innovative entrepreneurs are on the bandwagon. Last, but not at all least, in the proper package and at an affordable price, consumers see electric cars as green (low- to no-emissions), highly desirable modes of transportation.

First, a little history: An all-electric car has long sounded logical to many people. GM launched the EV1, an all-electric vehicle, in 1996. Unfortunately, the car was a complete flop, and the $1-billion project was abandoned in 1999. In 2002, Ford announced that it would give up on the Think, an electric car model in which it had invested $123 million. These efforts were an attempt to satisfy government demands, not an attempt to fill early consumer needs.

Times have changed, however, and many manufacturers are rethinking electric-powered cars. There are several low-production electric models currently on the market that run strictly on electricity. In the U.S., they include souped-up sports cars such as the $100,000 Tesla Roadster, which can go up to 125 miles per hour and run 244 miles per charge; and the $100,000 Wrightspeed X1, which can make 120 mph and run up to 200 miles per charge. With regard to acceleration, both of these models are comparable to top gasoline-powered sports cars such as the Ferrari Enzo and the Ford GT. The Tesla Roadster can accelerate from zero to 60 mph in about 4 seconds! Another notable high-end electric vehicle is the Tango T600, made by Commuter Cars Corporation. For $108,000, drivers can take the two-seater (one seat behind the other) from zero to 60 miles per hour in about four seconds, and reach a top speed of more than 130 mph.

Tesla is a serious business startup, with more than $100 million raised in capital as of mid-2007. By April 2009, regular production of the Tesla Roadster was underway and 300 vehicles had been delivered. Another model, the Model S family sedan capable of carrying seven people was unveiled in 2009, with commercial production to start in late 2011. The Model S is to have a base price of $57,400. Tesla has taken a simple route to solve the problem of storage batteries: the Tesla Roadster has 6,831 lithium ion, laptop computer batteries linked together in the trunk! Tesla Motors builds the Roadster at a Lotus Cars manufacturing plant in the U.K.

Companies to Watch in Advanced Battery Technology:
Johnson-Saft joint venture
EnerDel division of Ener1
A123
Quantum Technologies
Altair Nanotechnologies
ActaCell
NEC
Sharp
Panasonic
Better Place

Source: Plunkett Research, Ltd.

On the lowest end of the electric-powered spectrum are small vehicles that began several years ago as glorified golf carts. Recent technological advances, such as the use of lightweight, long-lasting lithium-ion batteries (the type used in cellular phones and laptop computers) have helped the vehicles evolve into marketable alternatives for short-trip driving. The ZAP Xebra, a three-wheel, four-door vehicle with a sticker price of $11,700, can reach speeds of up to 40 mph and have a range of 40 miles per charge. ZAP stands for "zero air pollution." Chrysler's Global Electric Motorcars LLC subsidiary offers several models, including vehicles with options such as heated seats, steel bumpers and cup holders. Prices start at about $7,395.

While the cars listed above are low production models, the era of high volume electric vehicle manufacturing is nearing rapidly. GM is backing a new electric vehicle with release hoped for by late 2010, the Chevy Volt. Although it will have a gasoline-powered generator which runs if the charge in the batteries is depleted, the Volt is designed to run fully on electricity using lithium-ion batteries. GM calls this system "E-Flex." The $40,000 sedan will be able to run at cruising speed for about 40 miles (a range long enough to allow for typical city driving, with plug-ins at home or work between trips). This vehicle's entry into the marketplace is so timely that it may turn out to be the car that saves GM. (The Detroit firm hopes that at least 1 million E-Flex vehicles will be produced yearly by 2020.) On the other hand, the price is nearly double that of a Toyota Prius hybrid, and the limited range on batteries will be a huge barrier in the minds of many consumers. At the same time, the beleaguered GM faces possible bankruptcy along with U.S. government interference in its business plans because of bail-out funding awarded in 2008. The Volt may turn out to be brilliant, or it may be remembered as simply another car that never came to market.

GM is collaborating with utility companies in nearly 40 states to work out issues relating to power grids and the added demand that electric vehicles pose. GM and other manufacturers are working on computer chips and software to imbed in electric vehicles that will communicate with utility systems regarding the best times to recharge for the best prices. Recharging on a summer afternoon, for example, would put a strain on grids already powering air conditioners while off-peak charging would not only be cheaper but more efficient since power plants typically have excess electrical capacity at night. Some utilities are promoting electric vehicles. Austin Energy of Austin, Texas is offering $100 to $500 incentives to plug-in car drivers.

There are many obstacles to all-electric vehicles. The biggest potential problems are battery capacity and battery cost. Lithium-ion batteries are becoming more powerful and efficient thanks to technological breakthroughs like those of startup manufacturer A123Systems. Lithium ion batteries continued to face multiple technical problems as of early 2009. The batteries have shown a tendency to overheat, catch fire or explode. However, A123Systems is building batteries made of nanoparticles of lithium iron phosphate modified with trace metals instead of cobalt oxide. The result is a more stable power source with twice and much energy as nickel-metal hydride batteries. A123Systems submitted an application to the DOE's Advanced Technology Vehicles Manufacturing Incentive Program in early 2009, hoping to qualify for $1.84 billion in direct loans for the construction of a new manufacturing facilities, the first to be in southeast Michigan. As of early 2009, A123 manufactured most of its batteries in China and Korea.

U.S.-based companies actively trying to become leaders in advanced batteries for electric vehicles also include Quantum Technologies, Altair Nanotechnologies and ActaCell. However, A123's largest American competitor may be Ener1, which owns an advanced lithium-ion electric vehicle battery unit called EnerDel. EnerDel has two cutting-edge manufacturing plants in Indiana and, as of early 2009, was seeking a $480 million loan with which to build a third.

A joint venture comprised of U.S.-based Johnson Controls (a leader in automotive systems and a major manufacturer of traditional car batteries) and France-based Saft (a leader in battery technology) plans to convert a former Johnson Controls automobile parts factory in Michigan into an advanced lithium-ion battery plant. The factory will make batteries for Ford's planned plug-in hybrid as early as 2012.

The Obama administration has stated a goal of 1 million plug-in hybrids on U.S. roads by 2015, and the federal government will likely be the early buyer of many of them for its fleets. However, the most successful market for electric cars will more likely be Europe than the U.S. European drivers are generally accepting of small vehicles. More importantly, gasoline prices in Europe are extremely expensive, often $5 per gallon or more due to high taxes, providing much greater incentive for plug-in cars. Moreover, European drivers are generally accustomed to taking shorter trips that consumers who drive the wide open spaces of the U.S. and Canada.

Elsewhere, Renault-Nissan is heavily committed to all-electric vehicles. The company plans to launch an electric car in the U.S. market as early as 2010 or 2011. The car will be designed to have a range of up to 100 miles and hoped-for performance comparable to that of a V-6 gasoline-powered car. A quick plug in of about one hour will deliver a recharge of about 80% of the batteries' capacity. In 2009, the company announced plans to sell its electric vehicles in China by early 2011.

In France, electric cars are popular enough to inspire plans for models from manufacturers including Renault SA. and Societe de Vehicules Electriques (SVE, a part of Dassault Group), which ran a successful 2005 trial of eight experimental electric mail delivery vans for La Poste, the French postal service that now plans an all-electric fleet by 2013. Nissan has entered into a $1 billion joint investment partnership with Japan's NEC for the development of advanced electric car batteries.

Despite all of the battery technology investment in the U.S. and Europe, the early leaders in advanced batteries are in Asia, particularly Japan, Korea and China. This is logical when you consider the fact that Asian firms have long been world leaders in advanced batteries for mobile consumer electronics such as cellphones. Without their advances in smaller, longer-lasting batteries, today's tiny mobile phones and iPods would not have been possible.

China is miles ahead in the battery and electric car race. The most exciting developments there are at BYD Company Limited. With $3.9 billion in 2008 revenues, BYD is already a global leader in contract manufacturing of batteries and handsets for mobile phones, even though the firm was founded only a few years ago in 1995. For example, BYD manufactures RAZR cell phone handsets for Motorola, as well as batteries for iPhones and iPods. This background gave it the technical edge that boosted it to a high level in electric automobile technology. The firm is so exciting that Warren' Buffet's Berkshire Hathaway has agreed to invest $230 million in exchange for 10% of the company's stock, subject to Chinese government approval.

BYD entered the car manufacturing business in 2003 by acquiring a small, floundering firm that was owned by the Chinese government. Under BYD, its inexpensive F3 sedan became the best-selling car in China in late 2008. More importantly, BYD has begun selling a plug-in hybrid in China, the F3DM. This launch was well in advance of the competing plug-in hybrid Toyota Prius expected in 2010. At about $22,000, the F3DM can go about 63 miles in electric-only mode, and can recharge quickly from its backup gasoline engine or from a plug-in feature. Watch for a continuing stream of breakthroughs from this extremely innovative company. It could easily grow to be one of the world's leading makers of inexpensive electric cars, and its new E6 plug-in electric car will get a head start on competitors.

The Chinese government's plans will give a huge boost to BYD. To begin with, the government provides some subsidies for electric vehicle research. In a very important development, the Chinese government is also providing major subsidies to purchasers of electric cars. For example, in 2009, fleet purchasers, such as taxi companies, could receive subsidies of 60,000 yuan (about $8,800) per car. At the same time, as part of its economic stimulus package, the government is providing subsidies to consumers who purchase automobiles while ensuring that low-cost financing is available.

A China-built Miles XS500 may go on sale at dealerships in the U.S. in late 2009 or beyond. The $30,000 to $40,000 sedan would have a 120-mile range and its American importer, Miles Electric Vehicles hopes to sell 30,000 of them in 2010. Currently, Miles sells small, low-speed electric vehicles designed for fleet use (see www.milesev.com).

Among the biggest problems facing consumer adoption of electric cars is the cost of the battery, which is estimated to be $10,000 to $30,000 in 2009, depending on the type and the place of manufacture. Factoring this into the initial purchase price of the car makes electric vehicles expensive. Thus, among the big ideas in electric cars is a radical concept spearheaded by Shai Agassi, formerly of enterprise software giant SAP. Agassi's startup, called Better Place, is promoting an electric grid that dispenses power in a business model similar to cellular telephone service. Drivers would swap depleted batteries for charged batteries, or plug into convenient power stations, paying for their choice of plans: unlimited miles, a monthly maximum or pay as they go. Under one potential business model, electric cars would be purchased by consumers without the battery costs built-in. Instead, the batteries would be paid for and owned by Better Place. Better Place would provide swappable, charged batteries as a service at a cost-per-mile driven, or cost-per-battery swapped. The initial price of the car would then be comparable to that of a gasoline-powered vehicle, and the consumer would pay for the battery as used, rather than up-front.

Making consumers comfortable that they can have charged batteries when needed is key to this plan. Better Place will provide convenient, closely-spaced charging stations in places like parking garages and shopping centers. Hundreds of charging stations are already planned or underway for Better Place's initial markets in Denmark, Israel and Hawaii. The San Francisco area is scheduled to receive charging stations around 2012.

Those charging stations will be useful for drivers who have time to wait for a charge between trips to and from work or the grocery store. But what about drivers whose batteries are nearly depleted, or who are on longer non-stop trips? This is where the swappable batteries and swapping stations come in. In early 2009, Better Place demonstrated the first such swapping station, in Tel Aviv, Israel. There, robot arms can remove a car's battery, clean it of road dirt and install a fully-charged battery. In about the same amount of time it takes to pump a small tank full of gasoline, the driver is back on the road. Such swapping stations are estimated to cost about $500,000 each.

Better Place calls its grid the Electric Recharge Grid Operator (ERGO). Its job is to not only supply the electricity, it would also monitor the electricity needs of the cars on the road and their locations, supply directions to drivers for the nearest power supply (using special software and in-car GPS) and negotiate with the local electricity utility with regard to the power supply and bulk electricity pricing. Hopefully, much of the power will come from solar and wind generation. That may be particularly true in initial markets like Denmark.

Agassi and his staff have made major strides in reaching their goal of independence from oil. Better Place has negotiated with the Israeli government to alter its tax code to make electric vehicles attractive to consumers. The tax proposal calls for a 10% tax on zero-emission vehicles and a 72% tax on traditional vehicles that run on gasoline. Better Place hopes to have recharge points throughout Israel, and has similar plans for Denmark and Portugal. Meanwhile, Agassi signed an agreement with Carlos Ghosn, CEO of Nissan and Renault, to develop the cars. In addition, Better Place raised $200 million in capital from Israeli investor Idan Ofer, U.S. investment bank Morgan Stanley and venture firms VantagePoint Venture Partners and Maniv Energy Capital. A prototype vehicle has been built using a Renault Megane sedan as a base, and the country of Denmark signed on in March 2008 when its largest utility, DONG energy, pledged to supply electricity largely produced by wind farms.

The cost savings to drivers promise to be substantial. Better Place figures a driver getting 20 mpg in a traditional car and clocking 15,000 miles per year at $4 per gallon would spend about $3,000 for fuel. Better Place's fuel costs for the same 15,000 miles is projected to be approximately $1,050. Stay tuned for more developments on Better Place's grid operator and vehicles.

Internet Research Tip: Electric Cars

For the latest on electric car manufacturers see:
Better Place, www.betterplace.com
Commuter Cars Corporation, www.commutercars.com
Electric Drive Transportation Association, www.electricdrive.org
Global Electric Motorcars, www.gemcar.com
Tesla Motors, www.teslamotors.com
Wrightspeed, www.wrightspeed.com
ZAP, www.zapworld.com

Over the long-term, watch for further advances in battery technology that may fuel vehicles for up to 300 miles per charge. That will make a tremendous difference in consumer interest. The expensive Tesla roadster already claims a relatively long range of more than 240 miles.

19) The Future: Pervasive Computing and Complete Mobility Will Be Standard

To get an astonishing look at one nation's vision of technology's future, visit the web site of Korea's Electronics and Telecommunications Research Institute (ETRI, www.etri.re.kr). The site has a link to access its English language version.

ETRI has established very aggressive research goals in initiatives that may transform the future. The program includes the enhancement of services to Korea's already amazing cell phone system. For example, ETRI's WiBro technology enables cell phones and mobile computers to receive signals, such as Internet pages or streaming video, when traveling at speeds of up to 40 miles per hour. DMB (digital multimedia broadcasting) enables cell phone users to receive unlimited live television programming while on the go. Commuters on a train on the way to work can watch live news or a live sports event.

Elsewhere at ETRI, the BCN, or broadband convergence network, hopes to integrate virtually all types of receiving and transmitting via one standard cell phone network. Other projects include advanced RFID (which will be used in cell phones for personal ID and payment systems, as well as in industrial devices), systems on a chip (SoC) and advanced telematics.

In the U.S., MIT Project Oxygen (www.oxygen.lcs.mit.edu) is attempting to define the nature of the personal computer of the future. It began in the Massachusetts Institute of Technology's Laboratory for Computer Science. The goal of this initiative is to design new user interfaces that will create natural, constant utilization of information technology. The project states its goal as designing a new system that will be pervasive—it must be everywhere; embedded—it must live in our world, sensing and affecting it; nomadic—users must be free to move around according to their needs; and external—it must never shut down or reboot.

The initiative is centered on developing speech recognition technology and video recognition to the point that computer data receptors can be embedded in the walls surrounding us, responding to our spoken commands and actions. In another Project Oxygen tool, a portable device will provide an ultimate array of personal functions. The project's prototypes include the H21, a handheld device; the E21, a workstation-like device; and N21, a network architecture. In keeping with the web services trend of Internet-based applications, most of this system's functions will operate by downloading software from the Internet on an as-needed basis. This is very similar to Microsoft's .NET initiative in terms of delivery of applications and data.

Another major project, a joint effort of several institutions, is PlanetLab (www.planet-lab.org). Its purpose is to give the Internet an upgrade, making it smarter, faster and safer. The project involves setting up numerous networked "nodes" that are connected to the existing Internet, over 1,006 of which PlanetLab has already installed at 487 sites worldwide. These nodes will perform several duties in overseeing the Internet, including scanning and squashing viruses and worms before they have a chance to infect PCs; routing and rerouting bandwidth as necessary to get the maximum efficiency out of existing networks; and recognizing different users so anyone can set up their own preferences and software at any computer terminal instantly; as well as many other functions.

20) Supercomputing Hits 1.105 Petaflops

The claim to the title of the world's fastest computer is a moving target. The title was briefly held by the Japanese, when in March 2002, NEC unveiled the Earth Simulator. The Earth Simulator is the size of four tennis courts, took four years to build and cost almost $350 million.

How was NEC able to produce such a massively expensive computer? It convinced the Japanese Government to subsidize the project. NEC's goal was to advance scientists' understanding of the world's climates by producing a computer that performs better weather simulations and modeling than traditional weather-related systems. The Earth Simulator was built from the bottom up using a technique called vector computing, a concept in which a computer executes one instruction at a time, but does so on multiple data simultaneously. This technique was used by computer pioneer Seymour Cray, who built the first supercomputer in the early '70s.

Internet Search Tip: The Top Supercomputers in the World

For a complete list of the world's fastest supercomputers and details about recent developments, see: Top 500 Supercomputer Sites, www.top500.org. This site is presented by experts at the University of Mannheim, Germany; the University of Tennessee; and the National Energy Research Scientific Computing Center (U.S.).

For the past several years in the U.S., the focus of supercomputing has been on the linking of clusters of commodity processors designed for everyday applications. These are known as parallel configurations. In contrast, the Japanese focus has been on specialized, massive single architectures developed for the high-performance market.

The commodity approach utilized in the U.S. has enjoyed many measures of success. Americans have understood the need to work on new, advanced systems in order to avoid falling behind in areas where strong computing matters most, such as simulating complex systems like weather on the macroscopic end, and biotechnology projects like protein folding on the microscopic end. Simulation capability is vital for national security (for example, where simulations take the place of underground testing for weapons of mass destruction) and the advancement of basic science.

In late 2004, IBM launched the BlueGene/L, a machine that surpassed rivals made by Japanese firms. When IBM first conceived the BlueGene line, it was seen as a tremendous tool for genetic research. IBM also realized that BlueGene would have myriad additional uses. BlueGene/L sits at the Lawrence Livermore National Laboratory (operated in Livermore, California by the University of California for the U.S. Department of Energy's National Nuclear Security Administration). In late 2004, the machine set a world record by scoring a speed of 92 teraflops. That's equal to 92 trillion floating-point calculations each second (more than twice the speed of Earth Simulator's 41 teraflops—the world record of only two and a half years earlier). Better still, by late 2005, the BlueGene at Lawrence Livermore Labs hit 280.6 teraflops, tripling its initial speed. In late 2007, BlueGene still held the top spot among supercomputers, having been expanded so that it achieved a benchmark performance of 478.2 teraflops per second.

As of early 2009, the leader in supercomputing is a $133 million IBM system at Los Alamos national Laboratory that's nicknamed Roadrunner. It clocked 1.105 petaflops (a petaflop represents 1 quadrillion floating-point operations per second) in 2008, followed by the Cray XT5 supercomputer at oak Ridge National Laboratory called Jaguar which clocked 1.059 petaflops. Of the top 10 supercomputers in the world as of 2008, seven are located at U.S. Department of Energy facilities and nine are located in the U.S. The fastest non-U.S. system is the Dawning 5000A at the Shanghai Supercomputer Center, and is the largest system that operates using the Windows HPC 2008 operating system.

Government and corporate customers alike will benefit from this race. While aerospace and biotech researchers want enhanced computing power for breakthrough research, government agencies may be able to benefit from supercomputers for such areas as studying weather and climate change as well as for defense needs. Additionally, major manufacturers in such areas as automobiles and health imaging equipment see supercomputers as a tool for improved product engineering and faster time-to-market.

Meanwhile, the results of the IBM/Toshiba joint venture that created the "Cell" chip are exciting for several reasons. Built on technology from IBM's Power processor, the Cell contains multiple processing cores and can act like more than one chip at any given time. Because of its potential power, Cell is being touted as the equivalent of supercomputer on a single chip. It was initially launched as the processor in Sony's PlayStation 3 game machine, which was introduced in the U.S. in November 2006. The Roadrunner system uses an advanced version of Cell technology. IBM is also using Cell technology to power server computers. The units are priced between $25,000 and $35,000 U.S. and will run typically on Linux operating systems.

21) Superconductivity Comes of Age

Superconductivity is based on the concept of using super-cooled cable to distribute electricity over distance with little of the significant loss of electric power incurred during traditional transmission over copper wires. It is one of the most promising technologies for upgrading the ailing electricity grid.

Superconductivity dates back to 1911, when a Dutch physicist determined that the element mercury, when cooled to minus 452 degrees Fahrenheit, has virtually no electrical resistance. That is, it lost zero electric power when used as a means to distribute electricity from one spot to another. Two decades later, in 1933, a German physicist named Walther Meissner discovered that superconductors have no interior magnetic field. This property enabled superconductivity to be put to commercial use by 1984, when magnetic resonance imaging machines (MRIs) were commercialized for medical imaging.

In 1986, IBM researchers K. Alex Muller and Georg Bednorz paved the path to superconductivity at slightly higher temperatures using a ceramic alloy as a medium. Shortly thereafter, a team led by University of Houston physicist Paul Chu created a ceramic capable of superconductivity at temperatures high enough to encourage true commercialization.

In May 2001, the Danish city of Copenhagen established a first when it implemented a 30-meter-long "high temperature" superconductivity (HTS) cable in its own energy grids. Other small but successful implementations have occurred in the U.S.

Internet Research Tip:
For an easy-to-understand overview of superconductivity and its many current and future applications, visit the Superconductivity Technology Center of the Los Alamos National Labs:
www.lanl.gov/orgs/mpa/mpastc.shtml

Today, the Holy Grail for researchers is a quest for materials that will permit superconductivity at temperatures above the freezing point, even at room temperature. There are two types of super-conductivity: "low-temperature" superconductivity (LTS), which requires temperatures lower than minus 328 degrees Fahrenheit; and "high-temperature" superconductivity (HTS), which operates at any temperature higher than that. The former type requires the use of liquid helium to retain these excessively cold temperatures, while the latter type can reach the required temperatures with much cheaper liquid nitrogen. Liquid nitrogen is pumped through HTS cable assemblies, chilling thin strands of ceramic material that can carry electricity with no loss of power as it travels through the super-cooled cable. HTS wires are capable of carrying more than 130 times the electrical current of conventional copper wire of the same dimension. Consequently, the weight of such cable assemblies can be one-tenth the weight of old-fashioned copper wire.

While cable for superconductivity is both exotic and expensive, the cost is plummeting as production ramps up, and the advantages can be exceptional. Increasing production to commercial levels at an economic cost, as well as producing lengths suitable for transmission purposes remain among the largest hurdles for the superconductor industry. Applications that are currently being implemented include use in electric transmission bottlenecks and in expensive engine systems such as those found in submarines.

In 2008, SuperPower, Inc., an electric power component manufacturer in Schenectady, New York, produced a 1,311 meter (.814 mile) length of HTS wire, a new record for the industry. SuperPower recently completed the Albany Cable Project in which a 350 meter (1,148 feet) HTS underground cable was installed in the National Grid power system connecting two substations in Albany, New York.

Another major player in HTS components is Sumitomo Electric Industries, the largest cable and wire manufacturer in Japan. The firm has begun commercial production of HTS wire at a facility in Osaka. Sumitomo is focusing its initial marketing efforts on U.S. utility companies, and has already made a bargain with Niagara Mohawk Power Corp., a utility company in upstate New York. In addition, Sumitomo has developed electric motors based on HTS coil. The superconducting motors are much smaller and lighter than conventional electric motors, at about 90% less volume and 80% less weight.

Another leading firm, American Superconductor (www.amsuper.com), won a $90 million contract with the U.S. Navy for the design and optimization of the world's first 36.5 megawatt HTS motor. The firm is also working closely with the Department of Energy's Tennessee Valley Authority to utilize the same technology to deliver electricity grid stabilization products. The SuperVAR dynamic synchronous condensers are the result of the collaboration, and they serve as reactive power "shock absorbers" than can generate or absorb power from the electric grid as needed. As of 2008, American Superconductor was scaling manufacturing capacity for its second generation HTS wire, branded 344 superconductors, and projecting manufacturing costs for the new wire of up to five times less than first generation wire. In 2009, the company announced a collaboration with the U.S. Department of Energy's National Renewable Energy Laboratory and its National Wind Technology Center to study the costs and feasibility of a full 10 megawatt class superconductor wind turbine. American Semiconductor is separately developing component and system designs for the turbine.

Second-generation (2G) HTS cable has been developed, utilizing multiple coatings on top of a substrate. The goal is to achieve the highest level of alignment of the atoms in the superconductor material resulting in higher electrical current transmission capacity. This is a convergence of nanotechnology with superconductivity, since it deals with materials at the atomic level.

Leading Firms in Superconductivity Technology:
Sumitomo Electric Industries, Ltd., www.sei.co.jp
American Superconductor, www.amsc.com
Nexans, www.nexans.com
SuperPower, Inc., www.superpower-inc.com

22) Massive Funding for Nuclear Fusion Projects

Nuclear fusion is an atomic energy-releasing process in which light weight atomic nuclei, which might be hydrogen or deuterium, combine to form heavier nuclei, such as helium. The result is the release of a tremendous amount of energy in the form of heat. This is essentially the same process that produces energy in the Sun and other stars. As of early 2009, nuclear fusion had yet to be made practical as a commercial energy source, but several well-funded efforts are attempting to do so. The hope is that fusion could eventually be used as a high output, low pollution energy source for the production of electric power.

In 2009, the Lawrence Livermore National Laboratory in California completed the National Ignition Facility (www.llnl.gov/nif). Laser technology is one of today's bright hopes for making fusion popular, and this facility will utilize one of the largest lasers in the world. It is capable of delivering 500 million megawatts of power in a pulse that lasts 20 billionths of a second. The facility took 12 years to build and cost $3.5 billion.

Meanwhile, the Thermonuclear Experimental Reactor (ITER, www.iter.org) is under construction at Cadarache, France. A prominent technology for nuclear fusion is called magnetic-confinement fusion. This method relies on a magnetic field to hold hydrogen isotopes together in a vessel called a tokamak. The ITER project is based on a tokamak. The $15 billion dollar project budget is funded by a consortium that includes the United States, the EU, Russia, China, Japan, India and Korea. Completion is scheduled for 2016. Japan also has a smaller, laser technology fusion project that is underway.

SPOTLIGHT: Ultrashort Pulse Laser Technology

Ultrashort Pulse (USP) technology utilizes ultrafast lasers that pulse on and off at almost immeasurable speed, about once every femtosecond, which is a billionth of a millionth of a second. These lasers can destroy atoms by knocking out electrons. Unlike typical lasers, matter around the destroyed atom(s) is not subjected to heat. Therefore, USP lasers could more effectively treat malignant tumors, perform LASIK surgery, scan aircraft for explosives or even remove tattoos. Startup laser company Raydiance, Inc. (www.raydiance-inc.com) has raised $25 million in venture funding, and has developed a software-controlled, desktop-sized USP laser. The firm is working in partnership with Rutgers University and the Musculoskeletal Transplant Foundation to test the Raydiance laser platform as a method to maximize transplants processed from donated dermal tissue. In early 2008, researchers at New Mexico State University began using the Raydiance USP platform to differentiate fake gemstones from genuine gemstones. Other potential applications for the technology include a scalable method for machining thin film photovoltaic cells; better systems for building semiconductors; and combining USP with nanoparticle technology for improved medical imaging and treatment.

Chapter 2

ENGINEERING & RESEARCH INDUSTRY STATISTICS

Contents:

Engineering & Research Industry Overview

	Quantity	Unit	Year	Source
Total R&D Spending, Worldwide	1,100	Bil. US$	2008	PRE
Total U.S. R&D Spending	375	Bil. US$	2008	PRE
Spending on R&D as a Percent of GDP:				
All Industrialized Nations	2.2	%	2008	PRE
U.S.	2.6	%	2008	PRE
Japan	3.2	%	2008	PRE
EU	2.0	%	2008	PRE
China	1.5	%	2008	PRE
India	0.8	%	2008	PRE
Total Proposed U.S. Federal R&D Budget	142.6	Bil. US$	2009	NSF
Proposed R&D, National Defense	84.5	Bil. US$	2009	NSF
Proposed R&D, National Institutes of Health	28.7	Bil. US$	2009	NSF
Proposed R&D, Space Research & Technology	12.3	Bil. US$	2009	NSF
Proposed R&D, General Science & Basic Research	10.2	Bil. US$	2009	NSF
Proposed R&D, Energy	2.5	Bil. US$	2009	NSF
Proposed R&D, Natural Resources & Environment	2.1	Bil. US$	2009	NSF
Proposed R&D, Agriculture	1.6	Bil. US$	2009	NSF
Proposed R&D, Transportation	1.4	Bil. US$	2009	NSF
Department of Energy Funding for Scientific Research	9.4	Bil. US$	2009	NSF
U.S. Employment in Architecture & Engineering Occupations	1.4	Billion	2008	BLS
U.S. Employment in Life, Physical & Social Science Occupations	1.3	Billion	May-07	BLS
U.S. Employment in Scientific R&D Occupations	621.7	Million	2008	BLS
Requested Budget for Nanotechnology R&D, U.S. Government	1.53	Bil. US$	2009	NNI
Private & Public Investment in Nanotechnology, Worldwide	10.0	Bil. US$	2009	PRE
Biopharmaceutical R&D Spending, PhRMA Member Companies, U.S.	38.4	Bil. US$	2008	PhRMA
Biopharmaceutical R&D Spending, PhRMA Member Companies, World	50.3	Bil. US$	2008	PhRMA

U.S. Patents

Patents Granted by Recipient, 2008:	Number	%	Source
Total Patents Granted	157,063	100.0	USPTO
U.S. Corporation	69,962	44.5	USPTO
U.S. Individual	9,021	5.7	USPTO
Foreign Corporation	74,465	47.4	USPTO
Foreign Individual	3,615	2.3	USPTO
Top Patenting University, 2008	Univ. of California: 237 Patents		USPTO
Top Private Sector Patent Recipient, 2008	IBM: 4,169 Patents		USPTO
Top Country Receiving Patents, 2008	Japan: 36,679 Patents		USPTO

PRE = Plunkett Research estimate.

PhRMA = Pharmaceutical Research and Manufacturers of America

NNI = U.S. National Nanotechnology Initiative

NSF = National Science Foundation

BLS = U.S. Bureau of Labor Statistics

USPTO = U.S. Patent and Trademark Office

Plunkett's Engineering & Research Industry Almanac 2009

www.plunkettresearch.com

Engineering & Research Industry Revenues, U.S.: 2008

(In Millions of US$)

Kind of Business Class of Customer	Revenue				Prelim. Total
	4Q[P]	3Q	2Q	1Q	
Engineering Svcs. (NAICS 54133)	50,865	49,266	47,265	44,463	191,859
Government	23,325	21,458	20,279	18,868	83,930
Business	27,113	27,353	26,805	25,114	106,385
Household consumers & individual users	427*	455	541	481	1,904
Scientific R&D Svcs. (NAICS 5417)	28,416	27,998	27,419	25,503	109,336
Government	8,709	9,390	9,528	8,518	36,145
Business	18,742	17,922	17,390	16,290	70,344
Household consumers & individual users	695	686	501	695	2,577
Kind of Business Class of Customer	**Percent of Revenue**				**Prelim. Total**
	4Q[P]	**3Q**	**2Q**	**1Q**	
Engineering Svcs. (NAICS 54133)	100.0	100.0	100.0	100.0	100.0
Government	45.9	43.6	42.6	42.4	43.6
Business	53.3	55.5	56.3	56.5	55.4
Household consumers & individual users	0.8*	0.9	1.1	1.1	1.0
Scientific R&D Svcs. (NAICS 5417)	100.0	100.0	100.0	100.0	100.0
Government	30.9	33.5	34.7	33.4	33.1
Business	66.6	64.0	63.4	63.9	64.5
Household consumers & individual users	2.5	2.5	1.8	2.7	2.4

Note: Estimates have not been adjusted for seasonal variation, holiday or trading-day differences, or price changes. Estimates are based on data from the Quarterly Services Survey and have been adjusted using results of the 2007 Service Annual Survey. All estimates are based on the 2002 North American Industry Classification System (NAICS). For additional information see www.census.gov/qss. Sector totals and subsector totals may include data for kinds of business not shown. Detail percents may not add to 100 percent due to rounding. Data users who create their own estimates using data from this report should cite the U.S. Census Bureau as the source of the original data only. Additional information on confidentiality protection, sampling error, nonsampling error, sample design, and definitions may be found at www.census.gov/svsd/www/qssreliability.html.

P = Preliminary. Plunkett Research estimate.

Source: U.S. Census Bureau
Plunkett Research, Ltd.
www.plunkettresearch.com

Revenues, U.S. Engineering & Scientific Research Industries: 2001-2007

(In Millions of US$; Latest Year Available)

NAICS	Kind of business	2007/06	2006/05	2005/04	2004/03	2003/02	2002/01
Change in Revenue for Taxable Firms							
54133	Engineering services	7.2	8.6	11.7	13.0	0.5	0.9
54138	Testing laboratories	26.0	7.8	4.8	12.0	0.9	11.5
5417	Scientific R&D services	9.6	14.0	10.9	12.7	4.7	10.6
54171	R&D in the physical, engineering & life sciences	9.4	14.7	10.9	12.8	4.6	10.6
Change in Revenue for Tax-Exempt Firms							
5417	Scientific R&D services	7.0	8.9	9.5	9.1	1.7	7.8
54171	R&D in the physical, engineering & life sciences	5.6	8.1	10.0	8.6	1.3	8.4
Sources of Revenue				**2007**	**2006**	**2005**	**07/06 %**
Total Operating Revenue: Engineering Services (NAICS 54133)				**172,744**	**161,099**	**148,352**	**7.2**
Engineering Services				101,998	95,324	86,198	7.0
Residential engineering projects				5,660	6,211	5,241	-8.9
Commercial, public & institutional engineering projects				13,551	11,554	11,068	17.3
Industrial & manufacturing engineering projects				16,529	13,211	12,101	25.1
Transportation infrastructure engineering projects				10,843	9,789	8,530	10.8
Municipal utility engineering projects				6,739	5,855	5,882	15.1
Power generation & distribution engineering projects				10,186	8,831	S	15.3
Telecommunications & broadcasting engineering projects				1,822	S	S	S
Hazardous & industrial waste engineering projects				4,910	3,857	4,027	27.3
Other engineering projects				31,757	32,219	26,624	-1.4
Other Services (performed independent of the eng. projects above)				19,084	16,223	13,448	17.6
Engineering advisory services				S	S	S	S
Construction services				12,821	10,105	6,916	26.9
Drafting services				S	962	S	S
Surveying & mapping services				1,991	2,033	2,172	-2.1
All other operating revenue				S	S	48,706	S
Total Operating Revenue: Scientific R&D Svcs. (NAICS 5417), Taxable Employer Firms				**75,171**	**68,607**	**60,169**	**9.6**
Basic & applied research in natural & exact sciences, except biological sciences				21,220	19,375	16,340	9.5
Basic & applied research in biotechnology				20,756	18,924	15,924	9.7
Basic & applied research in engineering & technology				10,768	9,820	8,977	9.7
Basic & applied research in the biological & biomedical sciences				14,883	13,082	11,102	13.8
Basic & applied research in medical & health sciences				14,223	12,472	10,529	14.0
Basic & applied research in other biological sciences				660	610	573	8.2
Production services for development				S	2,513	2,404	S
Other operating revenue				24,241	S	20,043	S
Licensing of right to use intellectual property				3,603	3,191	2,722	12.9
All other operating revenue				20,539	S	17,320	S

(Continued on next page)

Revenues, U.S. Engineering & Scientific Research Industries: 2001-2007 (cont.)

(In Millions of US$; Latest Year Available)

Sources of Revenue	2007	2006	2005	07/06 %
Total Oper. Revenue: Scientific R&D Svcs. (NAICS 5417), Tax-Exempt Employer Firms	**26,187**	**24,469**	**22,460**	**7.0**
Basic & applied research in natural & exact sciences, except biological sciences	1,405	1,143	1,148	22.9
Basic & applied research in biotechnology	359	313	245	14.7
Basic & applied research in other natural & exact sciences, except biological sciences	1,047	830	903	26.1
Basic & applied research in engineering & technology	3,970	3,904	3,603	1.7
Basic & applied research in the biological & biomedical sciences	3,098	2,909	2,701	6.5
Basic & applied research in medical & health sciences	2,336	2,226	2,118	4.9
Basic & applied research in other biological sciences	762	683	584	11.6
Basic & applied research in the social sciences & humanities	1,047	964	958	8.6
Production services for development	S	212	208	S
Other operating revenue	3,730	3,460	3,138	7.8
Licensing of right to use intellectual property	S	S	S	S
Original works of intellectual property	S	33	S	S
All other operating revenue	3,503	3,207	2,930	9.2
Contributions, gifts & grants received	8,773	8,153	7,627	7.6
Investment & property income	1,920	1,856	1,298	3.4
All other non-operating revenue	2,053	1,868	1,777	9.9

Notes: Estimates are based on data from the 2007 Service Annual Survey and administrative data. Estimates for 2006 and prior years have been revised to reflect historical corrections to individual responses. Dollar volume estimates are published in millions of dollars; consequently, results may not be additive. Estimates have been adjusted using results of the 2002 Economic Census. Estimates cover taxable and tax-exempt firms and are not adjusted for price changes. The introduction and appendixes give information on confidentiality protection, sampling error, nonsampling error, sample design, and definitions. Links to this information on the Internet may be found at <www.census.gov/svsd/www/cv.html>. Appendix A, Tables A-6.6, 6,10, and 6.11 provide estimated measures of sampling variability.

S = Estimate does not meet publication standards because of high sampling variability (coefficient of variation is greater than 30%) or poor response quality (total quantity response rate is less than 50%). Unpublished estimates derived from this table by subtraction are subject to these same limitations and should not be attributed to the U.S. Census Bureau. For a description of publication standards and the total quantity response rate, see http://www.census.gov/quality/S20-0_v1.0_Data_Release.pdf.

Source: U.S. Census Bureau

Plunkett Research, Ltd.

www.plunkettresearch.com

National R&D Expenditures & R&D as a Percentage of GDP, by Country: 1985-2006

(In Billions of Constant 2000 US$[1]; Latest Year Available)

Year	U.S.	Japan[2]	Germany[3]	France	U.K.	Italy	Canada	Russian Federation	Total OECD
1985	164.5	58.3	34.8	23.7	22.6	11.8	8.1	NA	356.3
1990	186.3	80.4	41.0	30.0	25.5	15.8	9.9	33.0	431.2
1995	199.9	83.8	41.6	31.3	25.1	13.1	12.1	8.0	478.8
1996	210.8	89.2	42.2	31.4	24.8	13.3	12.0	8.8	500.1
1997	222.9	92.7	43.8	31.0	24.6	14.2	12.5	9.7	523.0
1998	236.4	95.0	45.3	31.4	25.3	14.6	13.8	8.4	544.4
1999	250.8	95.3	48.8	32.7	27.1	14.5	14.9	9.3	572.2
2000	267.8	98.8	51.6	33.8	28.0	15.4	16.7	10.8	606.9
2001	271.7	101.6	52.4	35.2	28.3	16.3	18.6	12.7	625.7
2002	265.9	103.2	53.7	35.1	28.7	16.8	18.7	14.1	627.3
2003	272.2	105.8	54.2	34.6	28.8	16.5	18.9	15.5	640.5
2004	275.0	107.6	54.1	35.1	28.5	16.6	19.7	14.9	652.7
2005	287.1	115.1	54.4	35.3	29.9	16.6	19.9	14.7	682.7
2006	294.9	120.4	57.1	35.8	31.1	NA	19.7	16.0	707.2

Expenditure as Percentage of GDP

Year	U.S.	Japan[2]	Germany[3]	France	U.K.	Italy	Canada	Russian Federation	Total OECD
1985	2.72	2.58	2.60	2.15	2.24	1.10	1.42	NA	2.22
1990	2.62	2.81	2.61	2.33	2.15	1.25	1.51	2.03	2.26
1995	2.51	2.71	2.19	2.29	1.95	0.97	1.70	0.85	2.07
1996	2.55	2.81	2.19	2.27	1.87	0.99	1.65	0.97	2.10
1997	2.58	2.87	2.24	2.19	1.81	1.03	1.66	1.04	2.12
1998	2.62	3.00	2.27	2.14	1.80	1.05	1.76	0.95	2.15
1999	2.66	3.02	2.40	2.16	1.87	1.02	1.80	1.00	2.18
2000	2.74	3.04	2.45	2.15	1.86	1.05	1.92	1.05	2.22
2001	2.76	3.12	2.46	2.20	1.83	1.09	2.09	1.18	2.27
2002	2.66	3.17	2.49	2.23	1.82	1.13	2.04	1.25	2.24
2003	2.66	3.20	2.52	2.17	1.78	1.11	2.03	1.28	2.24
2004	2.59	3.17	2.49	2.15	1.71	1.10	2.05	1.15	2.21
2005	2.62	3.32	2.48	2.13	1.76	1.09	2.01	1.07	2.25
2006	2.62	3.39	2.53	2.11	1.78	NA	1.94	1.08	2.26

NA = Not available. GDP = Gross Domestic Product. OECD = Organization for Economic Co-operation and Development.

[1] Conversions of foreign currencies to U.S. dollars are calculated with each country's GDP implicit price deflator and OECD purchasing power parity exchange rates.

[2] Data on Japanese research and development in 1996 and later years may not be consistent with data in earlier years because of changes in methodology.

[3] Data for 1985 and 1990 are for West Germany.

Source: U.S. National Science Foundation

Plunkett Research, Ltd.

www.plunkettresearch.com

Federal R&D Funding & Distribution by Budget Function, U.S.: Fiscal Years 2007-2009

(In Millions of US$)

Funding Category	2007 Actual	2008 Prelim.	% Change (07-08)	2009 Proposed	% Change (08-09)	% of Total R&D (09)
All functions conducting R&D	138,087	137,972	-0.1	142,605	3.4	100.0
National defense	82,272	81,050	-1.5	84,091	3.8	59.0
Health	29,461	29,634	0.6	29,783	0.5	20.9
Space research & technology	9,024	9,233	2.3	9,728	5.4	6.8
General science & basic research	7,809	7,915	1.4	9,012	13.9	6.3
Natural resources & environment	1,893	2,374	25.4	2,463	3.7	1.7
Agriculture	1,936	2,008	3.7	1,987	-1.0	1.4
Energy	1,857	1,852	-0.3	1,616	-12.7	1.1
Transportation	1,361	1,340	-1.5	1,345	0.4	0.9
Administration of justice	820	891	8.7	884	-0.8	0.6
Veterans benefits & services	536	567	5.8	546	-3.7	0.4
Education, training, employment & social services	428	420	-2.0	448	6.8	0.3
Commerce & housing credit	369	355	-4.0	356	0.3	0.2
International affairs	246	255	3.7	255	0.0	0.2
Community & regional development	49	51	4.1	55	7.8	*
Income security	27	27	0.0	35	29.6	*

Notes: Detail may not add to total because of rounding. Percent change derived from unrounded data. Data for 2007 reflect appropriations enacted in Public Laws 110-5 and 110-28. Data derived from agencies' submissions to Office of Management and Budget per MAX Schedule C, agencies' budget justification documents, and supplemental data obtained from agencies' budget offices.

* Less than 0.05%.

Source: U.S. National Science Foundation

Plunkett Research, Ltd.

www.plunkettresearch.com

Federal Funding for R&D by Character of Work, U.S.: Fiscal Years 1975-2008

(In Millions of Current US$)

Fiscal Year	Total R&D and R&D Plant	Total R&D	Basic Research	Applied Research	Development	R&D Plant
1975	19,860	19,039	2,588	4,141	12,309	821
1976	21,616	20,780	2,767	4,852	13,160	837
1977	24,818	23,450	3,259	5,255	14,936	1,367
1978	27,141	25,845	3,699	5,908	16,238	1,296
1979	29,621	28,145	4,193	6,342	17,610	1,475
1980	31,386	29,830	4,674	6,923	18,233	1,556
1981	34,590	33,104	5,041	7,171	20,891	1,486
1982	37,822	36,433	5,482	7,541	23,410	1,390
1983	40,009	38,712	6,260	7,993	24,458	1,297
1984	44,012	42,225	7,067	7,911	27,246	1,787
1985	50,180	48,360	7,819	8,315	32,226	1,821
1986	52,951	51,412	8,153	8,349	34,910	1,539
1987	57,100	55,254	8,942	8,998	37,313	1,846
1988	58,827	56,769	9,474	9,177	38,119	2,057
1989	63,572	61,406	10,602	10,164	40,641	2,165
1990	65,831	63,559	11,286	10,337	41,937	2,272
1991	64,148	61,295	12,171	11,798	37,327	2,853
1992	68,577	65,593	12,490	12,001	41,102	2,985
1993	70,415	67,314	13,399	13,491	40,424	3,101
1994	69,451	67,235	13,523	13,888	39,824	2,215
1995	70,443	68,187	13,877	14,557	39,752	2,256
1996	69,399	67,653	14,464	13,796	39,393	1,746
1997	71,753	69,827	14,942	14,423	40,461	1,927
1998	73,914	72,101	15,613	15,309	41,178	1,813
1999	77,386	75,341	17,444	16,084	41,813	2,046
2000	77,356	72,863	19,570	18,901	34,393	4,493
2001	84,003	79,933	21,958	22,756	35,219	4,070
2002	90,158	85,853	23,668	24,338	37,846	4,305
2003	97,928	93,661	24,751	26,320	42,589	4,267
2004	105,371	54,450	26,121	27,237	48,019	3,994
2005	112,995	53,738	27,140	26,598	55,485	3,771
2006	112,271	53,536	26,585	26,951	56,610	2,125
2007[P]	116,700	55,075	27,477	27,598	59,427	2,198
2008[R]	113,213	54,709	27,721	26,988	56,637	1,867

Note: In FY 2000 the National Institutes of Health (NIH) reclassified as research the activities that it had previously classified as development. Also in FY 2000, the National Aeronautics and Space Administration (NASA) reclassified Space Station as a physical asset, reclassified Space Station Research as equipment, and transferred funding for the program from R&D to R&D plant. NIH and NASA data for FY 2000 forward reflect these changes. In FY 2006 NASA began reporting funding for Space Operations, the Hubble Space Telescope, Stratospheric Observatory for Infrared Astronomy, and the James Webb Space Telescope as operational costs; previously these had been reported as R&D plant.

P = Preliminary. R = Projected.

Source: U.S. National Science Foundation
Plunkett Research, Ltd.
www.plunkettresearch.com

Federal Funding for Research, by Agency & Field of Science & Engineering, U.S.: Fiscal Year 2008

(In Millions of Current US$)

Field	All	HHS	DOD	DOE	NASA	NSF	USDA	Other
Total research, all fields	54,709	28,781	6,487	6,083	4,358	3,195	1,807	3,999
Environmental sciences	3,408	435	326	326	734	730	16	841
Life sciences	27,533	23,359	320	712	649	184	1,469	840
Mathematics & computer sciences	3,129	184	920	958	849	56	19	144
Physical sciences	5,607	392	2,450	728	829	854	91	262
Psychology	1,758	1,612	0	55	5	12	0	74
Social sciences	1,146	312	0	15	198	1	143	478
Other sciences, nec	2,869	1,550	10	282	304	157	4	562
Engineering	9,258	937	2,461	3,007	789	1,202	64	799

Notes: Agencies reported projected obligations for FY 2007 during FY 2006. Detail may not sum to total due to rounding.

DOD = Department of Defense; DOE = Department of Energy; HHS = Department of Health and Human Services; NASA = National Aeronautics and Space Administration; NSF = National Science Foundation; USDA = Department of Agriculture.

nec = Not Elsewhere Classified.

Source: U.S. National Science Foundation

Plunkett Research, Ltd.

www.plunkettresearch.com

Federal R&D & R&D Plant Funding for National Defense, U.S.: Fiscal Years 2007-2009

(In Millions of US$)

Funding Category and Agency	2007 Actual	2008 Prelim.	2009 Proposed	% Chg. (08-09)
Total	82,658	81,500	84,513	3.7
Department of Defense (DOD)	79,009	77,782	80,688	3.7
Research, development, test & evaluation (RDT&E)	77,549	76,387	79,616	4.2
Defense agencies	21,862	20,499	21,499	4.9
Defense Advanced Research Projects Agency	2,908	2,959	3,286	11.0
Missile Defense Agency	9,381	8,552	8,891	4.0
Other defense agencies	9,573	8,988	9,323	3.7
Department of the Air Force	24,566	25,902	28,067	8.4
Department of the Army	11,303	12,032	10,524	-12.5
Department of the Navy	19,638	17,776	19,337	8.8
Operational test & evaluation	180	178	189	6.2
Other military funding[1]	1,460	1,395	1,072	-23.2
Department of Energy, atomic energy defense activities (DOE)	3,649	3,718	3,825	2.9
Environmental restoration & waste management	21	22	33	50.0
Naval reactors development	752	743	794	6.9
Nonproliferation	209	208	208	0.0
Weapons activities	2,664	2,742	2,787	1.6
Other defense activities	3	3	3	0.0

Notes: Detail may not add to total because of rounding. Percent change derived from unrounded data. Data for 2008 reflect requested supplemental appropriations; data for 2007 reflect appropriations enacted in Public Laws 110-5 and 110-28. Data derived from DOD, DOE, and DHS submissions to Office of Management and Budget per MAX Schedule C; DOD, RDT&E Programs (R-1).

[1] This item includes appropriate personnel costs in direct support of conduct of R&D, other appropriations funding certain DOD programs, and medical research funded outside RDT&E accounts.

Source: U.S. National Science Foundation

Plunkett Research, Ltd.

www.plunkettresearch.com

Federal R&D & R&D Plant Funding for National Institutes of Health, U.S.: Fiscal Years 2007-2009

(In Millions of US$)

Agency, by 2009 Funding Level	2007 Actual	2008 Prelim.	2009 Proposed	% Chg. (08-09)
Total	28,350	28,676	28,666	0.0
National Cancer Institute	4,725	4,734	4,738	0.1
National Institute of Allergy and Infectious Diseases	4,306	4,503	4,510	0.2
National Heart, Lung, and Blood Institute	2,823	2,826	2,828	0.1
National Institute of General Medical Sciences	1,742	1,739	1,738	-0.1
National Institute of Diabetes and Digestive and Kidney Diseases	1,800	1,801	1,801	0.0
National Institute of Neurological Disorders and Stroke	1,501	1,510	1,512	0.1
National Institute of Mental Health	1,350	1,352	1,353	0.1
National Institute of Child Health and Human Development	1,214	1,215	1,216	0.1
National Center for Research Resources	1,138	1,144	1,155	1.0
Office of the Director	1048	1,109	1,057	-4.7
National Institute on Aging	1022	1023	1023	0.1
National Institute on Drug Abuse	976	977	978	0.1
National Institute of Environmental Health Sciences[1]	701	700	701	0.1
National Eye Institute	656	657	657	0.1
National Institute of Arthritis and Musculoskeletal and Skin Diseases	492	492	493	0.1
National Human Genome Research Institute	480	480	481	0.2
National Institute on Alcohol Abuse and Alcoholism	424	424	425	0.1
National Institute on Deafness and Other Communication Disorders	380	380	381	0.2
National Institute of Dental and Craniofacial Research	375	373	374	0.1
National Library of Medicine	320	321	323	0.8
National Institute of Biomedical Imaging and Bioengineering	288	289	288	-0.2
National Center for Minority Health and Health Disparities	199	200	200	0.1
National Institute of Nursing Research	127	127	127	0.1
Buildings and Facilities	81	119	126	5.6
National Center for Complementary and Alternative Medicine	117	118	118	0.1
John E. Fogarty International Center	66	67	67	0.1

Notes: Detail may not add to total because of rounding. Percent change derived from unrounded data. Institute totals exclude non-R&D components of institute budgets. Data for 2007 reflect appropriations enacted in Public Laws 110-5 and 110-28. Data derived from departmental submission to Office of Management and Budget per MAX Schedule C and supplemental data obtained from National Institutes of Health budget office.

[1] Includes funding from Superfund-related transfers and appropriations.

Source: U.S. National Science Foundation
Plunkett Research, Ltd.
www.plunkettresearch.com

Federal R&D & R&D Plant Funding for Space Research & Technology, U.S.: Fiscal Years 2007-2009

(In Millions of US$)

Funding Agency	2007 Actual	2008 Prelim.	2009 Proposed	% Chg. (08-09)
Total	10,988	11,677	12,334	5.6
National Aeronautics and Space Administration (NASA)				
Advanced capabilities	755	671	452	-33
Astrophysics	1,365	1,338	1,162	-13.1
Constellation systems	2,115	2,472	3,048	23.3
Earth science	1,872	2,083	2,176	4.5
Education	1,190	1,269	1,360	7.1
Heliophysics	831	841	577	-31.4
Innovative partnerships	189	147	176	19.7
Planetary science	1,203	1,235	1,322	7.0
Shared capabilities	1,469	1,813	2,060	13.6
Space station	0	-193	0	-100.0

Notes: Includes funds for research and research program management but excludes fixed capital equipment costs. Detail may not add to total because of rounding. Percent change derived from unrounded data. Data for 2007 reflect appropriations enacted in Public Laws 110-5 and 110-28. Data derived from NASA submissions to Office of Management and Budget per MAX Schedule C, NASA budget justification documents, and supplemental data obtained from NASA budget and NASA budget office.

Source: U.S. National Science Foundation

Plunkett Research, Ltd.

www.plunkettresearch.com

NASA Budget Appropriations & Projections: 2007-2013

(In Millions of US$)

By Mission Directorate & Theme	2007	2008	2009	2010	2011	2012	2013
Total Appropriations[1]	**16,285.0**	**17,309.4**	**17,614.2**	**18,026.3**	**18,460.4**	**18,905.0**	**19,358.8**
Science	4,609.9	4,706.2	4,441.5	4,482.0	4,534.9	4,643.4	4,761.6
Earth Science	1,198.5	1,280.3	1,367.5	1,350.7	1,250.9	1,264.4	1,290.3
Planetary Science	1,215.6	1,247.5	1,334.2	1,410.1	1,537.5	1,570.0	1,608.7
Astrophysics	1,365.0	1,337.5	1,162.5	1,122.4	1,057.1	1,067.7	1,116.0
Heliophysics	830.8	840.9	577.3[2]	598.9	689.4	741.2	746.6
Aeronautics	593.8	511.7	446.5	447.5	452.4	456.7	467.7
Exploration systems	2,869.8	3,143.1	3,500.5	3,737.7	7,048.2	7,116.8	7,666.8
Constellation Systems	2,114.7	2,471.9	3,048.2	3,252.8	6,479.5	6,521.4	7,080.5
Advanced Capabilities	755.1	671.1	452.3	484.9	568.7	595.5	586.3
Space Operations	5,113.5	5,526.2	5,774.7	5,872.8	2,900.1	3,089.9	2,788.5
Space Shuttle	3,315.3	3,266.7	2,981.7	2,983.7	95.7	-	-
International Space Station	1,469.0	1,813.2	2,060.2	2,277.0	2,176.4	2,448.2	2,143.1
Space & Flight Support	329.2	446.3	732.8[3]	612.1	628.0	641.7	645.4
Education	115.9	146.8	115.6	126.1	123.8	123.8	123.8
Cross-Agency Support	2,949.9	3,242.9	3,299.9	3,323.9	3,363.7	3,436.1	3,511.3
Center Management & Operations	1,754.9	2,013.0	2,045.6	2,046.7	2,088.0	2,155.3	2,211.6
Agency Management & Operations	971.2	830.2	945.6	945.5	939.8	950.5	961.3
Institutional Investments	223.8	319.7	308.7	331.7	335.9	330.4	338.3
Congressionally Directed Items	-	80.0	-	-	-	-	-
Inspector General	32.2	32.6	35.5	36.4	37.3	38.3	39.2
*FY 2008 Rescission***		*-192.5*					
Year to Year Percent Change		**6.3**	**1.8**	**2.3**	**2.4**	**2.4**	**2.4**

Notes: Budgets include all direct costs required to execute the programs. Indirect costs are now budgeted within Cross-Agency Support. FY 2008 budgets are the enacted levels per the FY 2008 Appropriation as shown in the Agency's FY 2009 Budget Estimates. Totals may not add due to rounding.

[1] According to the most recent report of the U.S. Office of Management and Budget (OMB), actual expenditures were $16.7 billion in 2006, $16.3 billion in 2007 and $17.2 billion in 2008. Projections for 2009 and 2010 have been revised upward to $17.8 and $18.7 billion, respectively. The 2008 figure does not include $1 billion from the American Recovery and Reinvestment Act of 2009.
[2] Deep Space and Near Earth Networks Transfer $256M to Space & Flight Support (SFS) in FY 2009.
[3] FY 2008 Appropriation rescinded $192.475M in prior-year unobligated balances, effectively reducing FY 2008 authority. Not included in totals.

Source: U.S. National Aeronautics & Space Administration (NASA)

Plunkett Research, Ltd.

www.plunkettresearch.com

Federal R&D & R&D Plant Funding for General Science & Basic Research, U.S.: Fiscal Years 2007-2009

(In Millions of US$)

Funding Category and Agency	2007 Actual	2008 Prelim.	2009 Proposed	% Chg. (08-09)
Total	8,712	8,744	10,225	16.9
Department of Energy (DOE)	3,560	3,574	4,314	20.7
Advanced scientific computing research	276	351	369	5.0
Basic energy sciences	1,221	1,270	1,568	23.5
Biological & environmental research	480	544	569	4.4
Human genome	70	73	70	-3.8
All other research	410	472	499	5.7
Fusion energy sciences	312	287	493	72.1
High energy physics	732	689	805	16.8
Nuclear physics	412	433	510	17.9
Small business innovation research[1]	126	0	0	NA
National Science Foundation (NSF)	4,440	4,479	5,175	15.5
Biological sciences	609	612	675	10.3
Computer & information science & engineering	527	535	639	19.5
Education & human resources	56	59	66	11.9
Engineering	630	637	759	19.2
Geosciences	746	753	849	12.8
Integrative activities	220	232	276	18.8
Major research equipment	191	206	148	-28.2
Mathematical & physical sciences	1,151	1,167	1,403	20.2
Office of cyberinfrastructure	182	185	220	18.8
Social, behavioral & economic sciences	215	215	233	8.5
U.S. polar research programs	438	443	491	10.9
Budget authority adjustment[2]	-524	-564	-584	NA
Department of Homeland Security (DHS)	712	692	737	6.5

Notes: Detail may not add to total because of rounding. Percent change derived from unrounded data. Not all federally sponsored basic research is categorized in subfunction 251. Data for 2007 reflect appropriations enacted in Public Laws 110-5 and 110-28. Data derived from agencies' submissions to Office of Management and Budget per MAX Schedule C, agencies' budget justification documents, and supplemental data obtained from agencies' budget offices.

[1] DOE treats this activity as a budget execution program (i.e., funds are collected from existing appropriations and are not allocated until three-quarters into the fiscal year).
[2] Budget authority adjustment subtracts costs for research facilities, major equipment support, and other non-R&D from total NSF budget authority.
[3] In FY 2007 DHS changed its R&D portfolio to reclassify funding in defense and most administration of justice as general science and basic research.

NA = Not applicable.

Source: U.S. National Science Foundation
Plunkett Research, Ltd.
www.plunkettresearch.com

Federal R&D & R&D Plant Funding for Natural Resources & Environment, U.S.: Fiscal Years 2007-2009

(In Millions of US$)

Funding Agency	2007 Actual	2008 Prelim.	2009 Proposed	% Chg. (08-09)
Total	2,096	2,153	2,060	-4.3
Conservation and land management	363	374	356	-4.8
Department of the Interior[1]	38	37	41	10.8
Forest Service (USDA)	325	337	315	-6.5
Pollution control and abatement	557	548	541	-1.3
Environmental Protection Agency	557	548	541	-1.3
Leaking underground storage tanks	1	1	0	-42.9
Oil spill response research	1	1	1	-22.2
Science and technology	525	520	513	-1.4
Superfund	30	26	26	2.7
Recreational resources	200	199	200	0.7
National Park Service (DOI)	19	19	20	5.3
U.S. Geological Survey (DOI)	181	180	180	0.3
Water resources	27	45	22	-51.1
Army Corps of Engineers (DOD)	11	11	11	0.0
Bureau of Reclamation (DOI)	16	34	11	-67.6
Other natural resources	950	988	941	-4.7
National Oceanic and Atmospheric Administration (DOC)	557	581	576	-0.9
National environmental satellite, data & information service	28	29	29	-0.9
National marine fisheries service	50	52	52	-0.9
National ocean service	56	58	58	-0.9
National weather service	22	23	23	-0.9
Oceanic & atmospheric research	279	291	288	-0.9
Climate research	176	193	196	1.5
All other research	102	98	93	-5.5
All other NOAA	123	128	127	-0.9
U.S. Geological Survey	393	407	365	-10.1
Enterprise information	5	5	5	3.9
Geographic research	44	48	42	-11.8
Geologic hazards and resources	218	219	185	-15.3
Global change[2]	0	7	27	260.1
Water resources investigations	126	128	107	-16.7

Notes: Detail may not add to total because of rounding. Percent change derived from unrounded data. Data for 2007 reflect appropriations enacted in Public Laws 110-5 and 110-28. Data derived from agencies' submissions to Office of Management and Budget per MAX Schedule C, agencies' budget justification documents, and supplemental data obtained from agencies' budget offices.

DOC = Department of Commerce; DOD = Department of Defense; DOI = Department of the Interior; NOAA = National Oceanic and Atmospheric Administration; USDA = U.S. Department of Agriculture.

[1] Includes Bureau of Land Management, Office of Surface Mining and Reclamation, and Minerals Management Service.
[2] New account within U.S. Geological Survey.

Source: U.S. National Science Foundation
Plunkett Research, Ltd.
www.plunkettresearch.com

Federal R&D & R&D Plant Funding for Agriculture, U.S.: Fiscal Years 2007-2009

(In Millions of US$)

Funding Category and Agency	2007 Actual	2008 Prelim.	2009 Proposed	% Chg. (08-09)
Total	1,950	1,987	1,640	-17.5
Department of Agriculture (USDA)				
Agricultural Marketing Service	4	4	4	0.0
Agricultural Research Service	1,151	1,188	1,003	-15.6
Animal & Plant Health Inspection Service	27	27	27	0.0
Cooperative State Research, Education & Extension Service	666	662	508	-23.3
McEntire-Stennis Cooperative Forestry	30	25	20	-21.5
National Research Initiative	190	191	257	34.4
Payments to 1890 Colleges & Tuskegee Institute	41	41	38	-6.6
Payments under the Hatch Act	323	196	139	-28.9
Special research grants	0	92	3	-96.5
Other research programs	83	118	51	-56.5
Economic Research Service	75	77	82	6.5
Federal Grain Inspection Service	7	7	8	14.3
Foreign Agricultural Service	1	1	1	0.0
National Agricultural Statistics Service	5	7	7	0.0
Natural Resources Conservation Service	14	14	0	-100.0

Notes: Detail may not add to total because of rounding. Percent change derived from unrounded data. Source data from USDA submission to Office of Management and Budget, Circulat No. A-11, MAX Schedule C; USDA budget justification documents; and supplemental data obtained from USDA budget office.

Source: U.S. National Science Foundation
Plunkett Research, Ltd.
www.plunkettresearch.com

Federal R&D & R&D Plant Funding for Transportation, U.S.: Fiscal Years 2007-2009

(In Millions of US$)

Funding Category & Agency	2007 Actual	2008 Prelim.	2009 Proposed	% Chg. (08-09)
Total	1,380	1,359	1,366	0.5
Air transportation	827	783	782	-0.1
Federal Aviation Administration (DOT)	234	271	335	23.7
National Aeronautics & Space Administration, aeronautics[1]	594	512	447	-12.7
Ground transportation (DOT)	504	515	538	4.4
Federal Highway Administration	371	373	393	5.4
Federal Motor Carrier Safety Administration	9	8	7	-16.7
Federal Railroad Administration	37	39	37	-4.8
Federal Transit Administration	8	13	18	42.1
National Highway Traffic Safety Administration	79	83	83	0.2
Water transportation	19	27	18	-33.3
U.S. Coast Guard (DHS)	19	27	18	-33.3
Other transportation[2] (DOT)	29	35	29	-16.0

Notes: Detail may not add to total because of rounding. Percent change derived from unrounded data. Data derived from agencies' submissions to Office of Management and Budget, Circular No. A-11, MAX Schedule C; and supplemental data obtained from agencies' budget offices.

DOT = U.S. Department of Transportation; DHS = U.S. Department of Homeland Security.

[1] Excludes funds for research program management.
[2] Includes Office of the Secretary, Pipeline and Hazardous Materials Safety Administration and the Research and Innovative Technology Administration.

Source: U.S. National Science Foundation

Plunkett Research, Ltd.

www.plunkettresearch.com

Federal R&D & R&D Plant Funding for Energy, U.S.: Fiscal Years 2007-2009

(In Millions of US$)

Funding Category and Agency	2007 Actual	2008 Prelim.	2009 Proposed	% Chg. (08-09)
Total	1,922	2,460	2,474	0.6
Department of Energy	1,826	2,369	2,380	0.5
Energy programs	1,335	1,790	1,755	-2.0
Energy efficiency & renewable energy	938	1,238	1,025	-17.2
Electricity delivery & energy reliability	97	111	100	-9.9
Nuclear energy	300	441	630	42.9
Fossil energy	481	576	625	8.5
Cooperative R&D	0	5	0	-100.0
Petroleum, coal & gas program[1]	481	571	625	9.4
Radioactive waste management	10	3	0	-100.0
Nuclear Regulatory Commission	76	71	77	8.5
Tennessee Valley Authority	20	20	17	-15.0

Source: U.S. National Science Foundation

Plunkett Research, Ltd.

www.plunkettresearch.com

U.S. Department of Energy
Funding for Scientific Research: 2007-2009

(In Thousands of US$)

Area of Scientific Research	2007 Current Operating Plan	2008 Current Appropriation	2009 Congressional Request
Energy Programs	**8,042,345**	**9,019,929**	**9,350,399**
Energy Efficiency & Renewable Energy	**2,145,149**	**1,722,407**	**1,255,393**
Hydrogen Technology	189,511	211,062	146,213
Biomass & Biorefinery Systems R&D	196,277	198,180	225,000
Solar Energy	157,028	168,453	156,120
Wind Energy	48,659	49,545	52,500
Geothermal Technology	5,000	19,818	30,000
Water Power		9,909	3,000
Vehicle Technologies	183,580	213,043	221,086
Building Technologies	102,983	108,999	123,765
Industrial Technologies	55,763	64,408	62,119
Federal Energy Management Program	19,480	19,818	22,000
Electricity Delivery & Energy Reliability	134,363	138,556	134,000
Nuclear Energy	628,516	961,665	853,644
R&D	300,452	258,597	629,700
Fuel Cycle Research & Facilities		458,142	
Infrastructure	236,417	239,315	143,400
Fossil Energy Programs	**774,669**	**904,202**	**1,126,929**
Clean Coal Technology		-58,000	
Fossil Energy Research & Development	580,946	742,838	754,030
Coal	414,438	493,382	623,732
Fuels & Power Systems	303,176	349,702	382,732
Clean Coal Power Initiative	58,758	69,363	85,000
FutureGen	52,504	74,317	156,000
Naval Petroleum & Oil Shale Reserves	21,316	20,272	19,099
Strategic Petroleum Reserve	172,407	199,092	353,800
Northeast Home Heating Oil Reserve	7,966	12,335	9,800
Science	**3,836,613**	**3,973,142**	**4,721,969**
High Energy Physics	732,434	689,331	804,960
Proton accelerator-based physics	343,633	368,825	419,577
Electron accelerator-based physics	101,284	65,594	48,772
Non-accelerator physics	60,655	74,199	86,482
Theoretical physics	59,955	60,234	63,036
Advanced technology R&D	166,907	120,479	187,093
Nuclear Physics	400,210	415,187	479,019
Biological & Environmental Research	480,104	544,397	568,540
Basic Energy Sciences	1,221,380	1,269,902	1,568,160
Other			
Uranium Enrichment D&D Fund	556,606	622,162	480,333
Energy Information Administration	90,653	95,460	110,595
Non-Defense Environmental Cleanup	349,687	182,263	213,411

Source: U.S. Department of Energy, Office of Science

Plunkett Research, Ltd.

www.plunkettresearch.com

Research Funding for Biological Sciences, U.S. National Science Foundation: Fiscal Year 2007-2009

(In Millions of US$)

	FY 2007 Actual	FY 2008 Estimated	FY 2009 Requested	Change over 2008 Request	
				Amount	Percent
Molecular and Cellular Biosciences (MCB)	$111.50	$112.51	$126.10	$13.59	12.1%
Integrative Organismal Systems (IOS)	202.31	199.86	216.27	16.41	8.2%
Environmental Biology (EB)	109.60	110.86	125.64	14.78	13.3%
Biological Infrastructure (BI)	80.23	86.94	86.99	0.05	0.1%
Emerging Frontiers (EF)	104.90	101.85	120.06	18.21	17.9%
Total Biological Sciences Activity	**$608.54**	**$612.02**	**$675.06**	$63.04	10.3%

Totals may not add due to rounding. The Plant Genome Research program has been assigned as a program element within the IOS Subactivity.

Source: U.S. National Science Foundation
Plunkett Research, Ltd.
www.plunkettresearch.com

Domestic U.S. Biopharmaceutical R&D Breakdown, PhRMA Member Companies: 2007

(In Millions of US$; Latest Year Available)

	Dollars	Share (%)
R&D Expenditures for Human-Use Pharmaceuticals		
Domestic	36,178.3	75.5
Abroad*	11,006.4	23
Total Human-Use R&D	47,184.7	98.5
R&D Expenditures for Veterinary-Use Pharmaceuticals		
Domestic	430.0	0.9
Abroad*	288.4	0.6
Total Vet-Use R&D	718.4	1.5
Total R&D	**47,903.1**	**100.0**

Domestic R&D by Type of Project

	Dollars	Share (%)
Licensed-In	6,294.2	17.2
Self-Originated	27,126.9	74.1
Uncategorized	3,187.3	8.7
Total R&D	**36,608.4**	**100.0**

R&D By Function

	Dollars	Share (%)
Prehuman/Preclinical	13,087.4	27.3
Phase I	3,547.7	7.4
Phase II	6,251.0	13.0
Phase III	13,664.7	28.5
Approval	2,413.8	5.0
Phase IV	6,439.9	13.4
Uncategorized	2,498.6	5.2
Total R&D	**47,903.1**	**100.0**

Note: All figures include company-financed R&D only. Total values may be affected by rounding.

* R&D Abroad includes expenditures outside the United States by U.S.-owned PhRMA member companies and R&D conducted abroad by the U.S. divisions of foreign-owned PhRMA member companies. R&D performed abroad by the foreign divisions of foreign-owned PhRMA member companies is excluded. Domestic R&D, however, includes R&D expenditures within the United States by all PhRMA member companies.

Source: Pharmaceutical Research and Manufacturers Association (PhRMA), *PhRMA Annual Membership Survey*, 2009

Plunkett Research, Ltd.

www.plunkettresearch.com

Domestic U.S. Biopharmaceutical R&D & R&D Abroad, PhRMA Member Companies: 1970-2008

(In Millions of US$)

Year	Domestic R&D	Annual Chg.	R&D Abroad**	Annual % Chg.	Total R&D	Annual Chg.
2008*	38,427.8	5	11,825.7	4.7	50,253.6	4.9
2007	36,608.4	7.8	11,294.8	25.4	47,903.1	11.5
2006	33,967.9	9.7	9,005.6	1.3	42,973.5	7.8
2005	30,969.0	4.8	8,888.9	19.1	39,857.9	7.7
2004	29,555.5	9.2	7,462.6	1.0	37,018.1	7.4
2003	27,064.9	5.5	7,388.4	37.9	34,453.3	11.1
2002	25,655.1	9.2	5,357.2	-13.9	31,012.2	4.2
2001	23,502.0	10.0	6,220.6	33.3	29,772.7	14.4
2000	21,363.7	15.7	4,667.1	10.6	26,030.8	14.7
1999	18,471.1	7.4	4,219.6	9.9	22,690.7	8.2
1998	17,127.9	11.0	3,839.0	9.9	20,966.9	10.8
1997	15,466.0	13.9	3,492.1	6.5	18,958.1	12.4
1996	13,627.1	14.8	3,278.5	-1.6	16,905.6	11.2
1995	11,874.0	7.0	3,333.5	***	15,207.4	***
1994	11,101.6	6.0	2,347.8	3.8	13,449.4	5.6
1993	10,477.1	12.5	2,262.9	5.0	12,740.0	11.1
1992	9,312.1	17.4	2,155.8	21.3	11,467.9	18.2
1991	7,928.6	16.5	1,776.8	9.9	9,705.4	15.3
1990	6,802.9	13.0	1,617.4	23.6	8,420.3	14.9
1989	6,021.4	15.0	1,308.6	0.4	7,330.0	12.1
1988	5,233.9	16.2	1,303.6	30.6	6,537.5	18.8
1987	4,504.1	16.2	998.1	15.4	5,502.2	16.1
1986	3,875.0	14.7	865.1	23.8	4,740.1	16.2
1985	3,378.7	13.3	698.9	17.2	4,077.6	13.9
1984	2,982.4	11.6	596.4	9.2	3,578.8	11.2
1983	2,671.3	17.7	546.3	8.2	3,217.6	16.0
1982	2,268.7	21.3	505.0	7.7	2,773.7	18.6
1981	1,870.4	20.7	469.1	9.7	2,339.5	18.4
1980	1,549.2	16.7	427.5	42.8	1,976.7	21.5
1979	1,327.4	13.8	299.4	25.9	1,626.8	15.9
1978	1,166.1	9.7	237.9	11.6	1,404.0	10.0
1977	1,063.0	8.1	213.1	18.2	1,276.1	9.7
1976	983.4	8.8	180.3	14.1	1,163.7	9.6
1975	903.5	13.9	158.0	7.0	1,061.5	12.8
1974	793.1	12.0	147.7	26.3	940.8	14.0
1973	708.1	8.1	116.9	64.0	825.0	13.6
1972	654.8	4.5	71.3	24.9	726.1	6.2
1971	626.7	10.7	57.1	9.2	683.8	10.6
1970	566.2	-----	52.3	-----	618.5	-----
Average		11.8%		15.5%		12.3%

Note: All figures include company-financed R&D only. Total values may be affected by rounding.

* Estimated. ** R&D Abroad includes expenditures outside the United States by U.S.-owned PhRMA member companies and R&D conducted abroad by the U.S. divisions of foreign-owned PhRMA member companies. R&D performed abroad by the foreign divisions of foreign-owned PhRMA member companies is excluded. Domestic R&D, however, includes R&D expenditures within the United States by all PhRMA member companies. *** R&D Abroad affected by merger and acquisition activity.

Source: Pharmaceutical Research and Manufacturers of America (PhRMA), *PhRMA Annual Membership Survey*, 2009

Plunkett Research, Ltd.

www.plunkettresearch.com

R&D as a Percentage of U.S. Biopharmaceutical Sales, PhRMA Member Companies: 1970-2008

Year	Domestic R&D as a % of Domestic Sales	Total R&D as a % of Total Sales
2008*	20.3	17.4
2007	19.8	17.5
2006	19.4	17.1
2005	18.6	16.9
2004	18.4	16.1
2003	18.3	16.5
2002	18.4	16.1
2001	18.0	16.7
2000	18.4	16.2
1999	18.2	15.5
1998	21.1	16.8
1997	21.6	17.1
1996	21.0	16.6
1995	20.8	16.7
1994	21.9	17.3
1993	21.6	17.0
1992	19.4	15.5
1991	17.9	14.6
1990	17.7	14.4
1989	18.4	14.8
1988	18.3	14.1
1987	17.4	13.4
1986	16.4	12.9
1985	16.3	12.9
1984	15.7	12.1
1983	15.9	11.8
1982	15.4	10.9
1981	14.8	10.0
1980	13.1	8.9
1979	12.5	8.6
1978	12.2	8.5
1977	12.4	9.0
1976	12.4	8.9
1975	12.7	9.0
1974	11.8	9.1
1973	12.5	9.3
1972	12.6	9.2
1971	12.2	9.0
1970	12.4	9.3

*Estimated

Source: Pharmaceutical Research and Manufacturers of America (PhRMA), *PhRMA Annual Membership Survey*, 2009

Plunkett Research, Ltd.

www.plunkettresearch.com

R&D by Global Geographic Area, PhRMA Member Companies: 2007

(In Millions of US$; Latest Year Available)

Geographic Area*	Dollars	Share
Africa	28.6	0.1
Americas		
United States	36,608.4	76.4
Canada	612.4	1.3
Mexico	63.0	0.1
Brazil	81.2	0.2
Other Latin America[1]	217.9	0.5
Asia-Pacific		
Japan	954.2	2.0
China	62.9	0.1
India	33.3	0.1
Other Asia-Pacific	191.8	0.4
Australia & New Zealand	161.0	0.3
Europe		
France	521.8	1.1
Germany	714.7	1.5
Italy	240.1	0.5
Spain	235.5	0.5
United Kingdom	2,892.9	6.0
Other Western European nations	3,568.6	7.4
Turkey	39.0	0.1
Russia	40.1	0.1
Central & Eastern European nations[2]	481.8	1.0
Middle East[3]	29.7	0.1
Uncategorized	124.2	0.3
Total R&D	47,903.1	100.0

Note: All figures include company-financed R&D only. Total values may be affected by rounding.

* R&D Abroad includes expenditures outside the United States by U.S.-owned PhRMA member companies and R&D conducted abroad by the U.S. divisions of foreign-owned PhRMA member companies. R&D performed abroad by the foreign divisions of foreign-owned PhRMA member companies is excluded. Domestic R&D, however, includes R&D expenditures within the United States by all PhRMA member companies.

[1] Other South American, Central American, and all Caribbean nations.
[2] Cyprus, Czech Republic, Estonia, Hungary, Poland, Slovenia, Bulgaria, Lithuania, Latvia, Romania, Slovakia, Malta and the Newly Independent States.
[3] Saudi Arabia, Yemen, United Arab Emirates, Iraq, Iran, Kuwait, Israel, Jordan, Syria, Afghanistan and Qatar.

Source: Pharmaceutical Research and Manufacturers of America (PhRMA), *PhRMA Annual Membership Survey*, 2009.

Plunkett Research, Ltd.

www.plunkettresearch.com

Top Foreign Countries by Number of Residents Receiving U.S. Patents: 2007-2008

Rank in 2008	# of Patents in 2008	Share of All Patents in 2008 (%)	Country*	Rank in 2007	# of Patents in 2007	% Change: # of Patents
1	36,679	19.8	Japan	1	35,941	2.1
2	10,086	5.4	Germany	2	10,012	0.7
3	8,731	4.7	South Korea	4	7,264	20.2
4	7,779	4.2	Taiwan	3	7,491	3.8
5	4,125	2.2	Canada	6	3,970	3.9
6	3,843	2.1	United Kingdom	5	4,031	-4.7
7	3,813	2.1	France	7	3,720	2.5
8	1,916	1.0	Italy	8	1,836	4.4
9	1,874	1.0	China	13	1,235	51.7
10	1,724	0.9	Netherlands	9	1,596	8.0
	92,000	49.7	United States		93,690	-1.8
	93,244	50.3	All Countries		89,238	4.5

* Please note that the country of origin is determined by the residence of the first-named inventor.

Source: U.S. Patent and Trademark Office (USPTO)
Plunkett Research, Ltd.
www.plunkettresearch.com

Top 30 Private Sector Patent Recipients, U.S.: 2008

Rank	Patents	Organization
1	4,169	International Business Machines Corporation
2	3,502	Samsung Electronics Co., Ltd.
3	2,107	Canon Kabushiki Kaisha
4	2,026	Microsoft Corporation
5	1,772	Intel Corporation
6	1,575	Toshiba Corporation
7	1,475	Fujitsu Limited
8	1,469	Matsushita Electric Industrial Co., Ltd.
9	1,461	Sony Corporation
10	1,422	Hewlett-Packard Development Company, L.P.
11	1,301	Hitachi, Ltd.
12	1,250	Micron Technology, Inc.
13	1,219	Seiko Epson Corporation
14	911	General Electric Company
15	863	Fujifilm Corporation
16	851	Ricoh Company, Ltd.
17	809	Infineon Technologies AG
18	805	LG Electronics Inc
19	755	Texas Instruments, Incorporated
20	721	Siemens Aktiengesellschaft
21	704	Cisco Technology, Inc.
22	703	Honda Giken Kogyo K.K. (Honda Motor Co., Ltd.)
23	655	Denso Corporation
24	643	Broadcom Corporation
25	619	Honeywell International Inc.
26	608	Nokia Corporation
26	608	Silberbrook Research Pty. Ltd.
28	585	Sharp Kabushiki Kaisha (Sharp Corporation)
29	529	Xerox Corporation
30	527	NEC Corporation

Source: U.S. Patent and Trademark Office (USPTO)
Plunkett Research, Ltd.
www.plunkettresearch.com

Top Patenting U.S. Universities: 2008

Rank	Patents	U.S. University
1	237	University of California
2	134	Massachusetts Institute of Technology
3	120	Stanford University
4	96	California Institute of Technology
5	90	Wisconsin Alumni Research Foundation
6	79	University of Texas
7	66	John Hopkins University
7	66	University of Michigan
9	54	Columbia University
10	50	Cornell Research Foundation Inc.
11	47	University of Illinois
12	46	Michigan State University
13	45	University of Pennsylvania
14	43	Harvard College, President & Fellows
14	43	University of Florida Research Foundation, Inc.
16	42	University of Washington
17	42	Georgia Tech Research Corp.
18	40	University of Central Florida

Note: Only those universities with 40 or more patents are listed.

Source: U.S. Patent and Trademark Office (USPTO)
Plunkett Research, Ltd.
www.plunkettresearch.com

The U.S. Drug Discovery & Approval Process

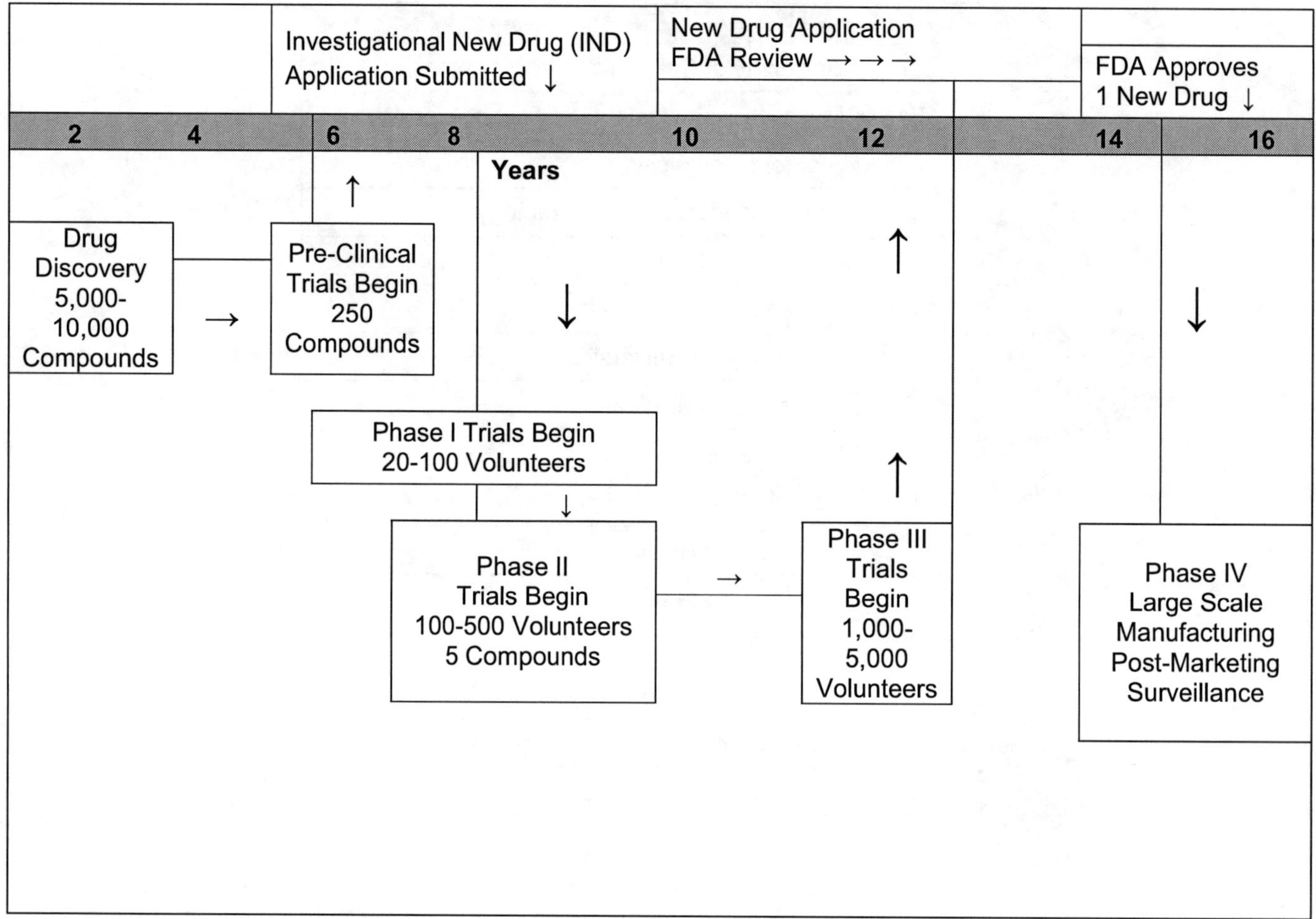

Source: Pharmaceutical Research and Manufacturers Association (PhRMA)
Plunkett Research, Ltd.
www.plunkettresearch.com

Domestic Biopharmaceutical R&D Scientific, Professional & Technical Personnel by Function, PhRMA Member Companies: 2007

(Latest Year Available)

Function	Personnel	Share (%)
Prehuman/Preclinical	30,023	31.1
Phase I	6,117	6.3
Phase II	10,098	10.5
Phase III	18,579	19.3
Approval	4,108	4.3
Phase IV	13,332	13.8
Uncategorized	3,613	3.7
Total R&D Staff	85,870	89.0
Supported R&D Nonstaff	10,616	11.0
TOTAL R&D PERSONNEL	96,486	100.0

Source: Pharmaceutical Research and Manufacturers of America (PhRMA), *PhRMA Annual Membership Survey*, 2009.

Plunkett Research, Ltd.

www.plunkettresearch.com

Employment in Engineering Occupations by Business Type, U.S.: 2003-2008

NAICS[1]	Industry Sector	2003	2004	2005	2006	2007	2008
Number of Employed Workers: 2003-2008 *(Annual Estimates in Thousands of Employed Workers)*							
5413	Architectural & engineering services	1,226.9	1,258.2	1,310.9	1,385.7	1,432.2	1,444.8
54133,4	Engineering & drafting services	775.2	796.9	839.0	886.5	921.3	942.6
54138	Testing laboratories	144.9	143.0	141.1	147.1	150.5	149.3
5417	Scientific research & development services	539.3	549.7	576.8	591.9	602.2	621.7
54171	Physical, engineering & biological research	473.3	485.6	512.9	526.9	537.6	558.0
541711	Biotechnology research	120.5	123.6	130.6	134.1	136.5	139.9
541712	Physical, engineering & life sciences research	352.8	362.0	382.4	392.7	401.2	418.1

Engineering Employment & Wage Estimates: May 2007 *(Wage & Salary in US$; Latest Year Available)*	Employ-ment[2]	Median Hourly Wage	Mean Hourly Wage	Mean Annual Salary[3]	Mean RSE[4] (%)
Aerospace Engineers	85,510	43.71	44.57	92,700	0.9
Agricultural Engineers	2,480	32.55	33.88	70,460	1.1
Biomedical Engineers	15,400	36.27	38.28	79,610	1.4
Chemical Engineers	28,780	39.18	40.50	84,240	0.9
Civil Engineers	247,370	34.48	36.17	75,230	0.4
Computer Hardware Engineers	79,330	44.16	45.32	94,270	0.9
Electrical Engineers	148,800	38.10	39.47	82,090	0.4
Electronics Engineers, Except Computer	133,870	40.07	41.13	85,550	0.5
Environmental Engineers	51,210	34.78	35.97	74,820	0.7
Health & Safety Engineers, Except Mining Safety Engineers & Inspectors	24,770	33.45	34.12	70,970	0.5
Industrial Engineers	204,210	34.34	35.33	73,490	0.3
Marine Engineers & Naval Architects	6,620	36.64	37.60	78,200	1.8
Materials Engineers	21,910	37.10	37.90	78,840	0.8
Mechanical Engineers	222,330	34.76	36.12	75,130	0.4
Mining & Geological Engineers, Including Mining Safety Engineers	7,150	35.74	38.23	79,520	2.6
Nuclear Engineers	14,300	45.40	46.70	97,130	1.6
Petroleum Engineers	16,060	49.98	54.75	113,890	2.4
Engineers, All Other	169,950	40.99	41.07	85,430	0.5
Architectural & Civil Drafters	111,460	20.82	21.77	45,280	0.6
Electrical & Electronics Drafters	32,350	23.68	24.86	51,710	0.6
Mechanical Drafters	74,260	21.51	22.45	46,690	0.6
Drafters, All Other	23,280	21.49	22.76	47,340	1.6
Aerospace Engineering & Operations Technicians	7,870	26.41	27.30	56,780	1.6
Civil Engineering Technicians	88,030	20.47	21.10	43,890	0.7
Electrical & Electronic Engineering Technicians	162,460	25.07	25.23	52,470	0.4
Electro-Mechanical Technicians	15,730	22.41	23.14	48,120	1.1
Environmental Engineering Technicians	21,970	19.56	20.95	43,570	0.9
Industrial Engineering Technicians	74,930	22.83	24.72	51,410	1.3
Mechanical Engineering Technicians	46,230	22.73	23.70	49,290	0.6
Engineering Technicians, Except Drafters, All Other	78,140	26.95	26.80	55,730	0.7
Surveying & Mapping Technicians	72,410	16.17	17.26	35,900	0.6

[1] For a full description of the NAICS codes used in this table, see www.census.gov/epcd/www/naics.html.
[2] Estimates for detailed occupations do not sum to the totals because the totals include occupations not shown separately. Estimates do not include self-employed workers.
[3] Annual wages have been calculated by multiplying the hourly mean wage by a "year-round, full-time" hours figure of 2,080 hours; for those occupations where there is not an hourly mean wage published, the annual wage has been directly calculated from the reported survey data.
[4] The relative standard error (RSE) is a measure of the reliability of a survey statistic. The smaller the relative standard error, the more precise the estimate.

Source: U.S. Bureau of Labor Statistics
Plunkett Research, Ltd.
www.plunkettresearch.com

Employment in Life & Physical Science Occupations by Business Type, U.S.: May 2007

(Latest Year Available; Wage & Salary in US$)

	Employ-ment[1]	Median Hourly Wage	Mean Hourly Wage	Mean Annual Salary[2]	Mean RSE[3] (%)
Life, Physical & Social Science Occupations	**1,255,670**	**26.6**	**29.8**	**62,020**	**0.4**
Animal Scientists	4,210	23.25	26.10	54,290	2.5
Food Scientists & Technologists	9,910	27.82	30.09	62,580	1.6
Soil & Plant Scientists	10,270	27.89	30.28	62,970	2.4
Biochemists & Biophysicists	19,490	38.11	41.01	85,290	1.7
Microbiologists	14,610	29.17	31.94	66,430	1.8
Zoologists & Wildlife Biologists	17,830	26.49	28.11	58,480	1.4
Biological Scientists, All Other	27,070	30.45	31.85	66,240	1.0
Conservation Scientists	16,570	27.00	27.51	57,220	0.8
Foresters	10,510	25.21	25.98	54,030	0.7
Epidemiologists	3,960	28.85	30.58	63,600	1.1
Medical Scientists, Except Epidemiologists	87,440	30.87	35.65	74,160	1.6
Life Scientists, All Other	12,470	28.37	32.18	66,930	1.7
Astronomers	1520	47.61	47.21	98,200	2.7
Physicists	13,980	46.56	48.03	99,900	1.4
Atmospheric & Space Scientists	8,750	37.69	37.96	78,960	3.2
Chemists	79,860	30.52	32.94	68,520	0.6
Materials Scientists	9,740	36.62	37.47	77,930	1.4
Environmental Scientists & Specialists, Including Health	80,070	28.07	30.71	63,870	1.2
Geoscientists, Except Hydrologists & Geographers	31,390	36.44	40.43	84,100	1.4
Hydrologists	7,670	32.76	33.77	70,250	1.2
Physical Scientists, All Other	23,300	42.15	42.41	88,210	1.8
Agricultural & Food Science Technicians	19,280	16.17	17.08	35,520	1.0
Biological Technicians	69,110	18.18	19.35	40,240	0.6
Chemical Technicians	64,450	19.58	20.39	42,420	0.6
Geological & Petroleum Technicians	13,060	24.50	26.60	55,330	4.1
Nuclear Technicians	5,920	31.80	31.66	65,850	1.9
Environmental Science & Protection Technicians, Including Health	33,950	18.93	20.28	42,190	0.9
Forensic Science Technicians	12,030	22.92	24.19	50,310	0.9
Forest & Conservation Technicians	26,900	16.12	17.20	35,770	0.3

[1] Estimates for detailed occupations do not sum to the totals because the totals include occupations not shown separately. Estimates do not include self-employed workers.
[2] Annual wages have been calculated by multiplying the hourly mean wage by a "year-round, full-time" hours figure of 2,080 hours; for those occupations where there is not an hourly mean wage published, the annual wage has been directly calculated from the reported survey data.
[3] The relative standard error (RSE) is a measure of the reliability of a survey statistic. The smaller the relative standard error, the more precise the estimate.

Source: U.S. Bureau of Labor Statistics

Plunkett Research, Ltd.

www.plunkettresearch.com

Chapter 3

IMPORTANT ENGINEERING & RESEARCH INDUSTRY CONTACTS

Addresses, Telephone Numbers and Internet Sites

Contents:

I. Aerospace & Defense Industry Associations

Aerospace Industries Association
1000 Wilson Blvd., Ste. 1700
Arlington, VA 22209-3928 US
Phone: 703-358-1000
E-mail Address: *globalcustomerservice@ihs.com*
Web Address: www.aia-aerospace.org
The Aerospace Industries Association represents the nation's leading manufacturers and suppliers of civil, military, and business aircraft, helicopters, unmanned aerial vehicles, space systems, aircraft engines, missiles, materiel, and related components, equipment, services, and information technology.

Aerospace Industries Association of Canada (AIAC)
60 Queen St., Ste. 1200
Ottawa, ON K1P 5Y7 Canada
Phone: 613-232-4297
Fax: 613-232-1142
E-mail Address: *info@aiac.ca*
Web Address: www.aiac.ca
The Aerospace Industries Association of Canada (AIAC) is the national trade organization of Canada's aerospace manufacturing and service sector.

China National Space Administration
China National Space Administration
Beijing, China
Phone: 86-10-88581377
Fax: 86-10-88581515
E-mail Address: *liuxiaohong@cnsa.gov.cn*
Web Address: www.cnsa.gov.cn
The China National Space Administration is the governmental agency representing China in the space science, technology and the aerospace industry.

Council of Defense & Space Industry Associations (CODSIA)
Contract Services Association
1000 Wilson Blvd., Ste. 1800
Arlington, VA 22209 US
Phone: 703-243-2020
Fax: 703-243-8539
E-mail Address: *info@codsia.org*
Web Address: www.codsia.org
The Council of Defense and Space Industry Associations (CODSIA) provides a central channel of communications for improving industry-wide consideration of the many policies, regulations, implementation problems, procedures and questions involved in federal procurement actions.

Defense MicroElectronics Activity (DMEA)
4234 54th St.
McClellan, CA 95652-2100 US
Phone: 916-231-1568
Fax: 916-231-2868
Web Address: www.dmea.osd.mil
Defense MicroElectronics Activity (DMEA) was established by the Department of Defense to provide a broad spectrum of microelectronics services.

National Defense Industrial Association (NDIA)
2111 Wilson Blvd., Ste. 400
Arlington, VA 22201 US
Phone: 703-522-1820
Fax: 703-522-1885
E-mail Address: *info@ndia.org*
Web Address: www.ndia.org
The National Defense Industrial Association (NDIA), an association with more than 47,000 individuals as well as 1,375 corporate members, is dedicated to discussing defense industry concerns and promoting national security.

Washington Space Business Roundtable (WSBR)
c/o Longbottom Communications, LLC
2343 N. Vernon St.
Arlington, VA 22207-4056 US
Phone: 703-528-5490
Fax: 703-528-5492
E-mail Address: *info@wsbr.org*
Web Address: www.wsbr.org
Washington Space Business Roundtable (WSBR) is a leadership forum for the promotion of commercial space business and education in the national capital region.

II. Aerospace Resources

Defense Science Technology Lab (DSTL)
Porton Down
Salisbury, Wiltshire SP4 0JQ UK
Phone: 44-1980-613121
Fax: 44-1980-613004
E-mail Address: *centralenquiries@dstl.gov.uk*
Web Address: www.dstl.gov.uk
Defense Science Technology Lab (DSTL) supplies scientific research and advice to the Ministry of Defense (MOD) and other government departments.

NASA Learning Technologies Project (LTP)
NASA Headquarters, Ste. 5K39

Washington, DC 20546-0001 US
Phone: 202-358-0001
Fax: 202-358-3469
E-mail Address: *daniel.laughlin@gsfc.nasa.gov*
Web Address: learn.arc.nasa.gov
The NASA Learning Technologies Project (LTP) is the space association's educational technology research and development division.

Space Foundation
310 S. 14th St.
Colorado Springs, CO 80904 US
Phone: 719-576-8000
Fax: 719-576-8801
Web Address: www.spacefoundation.org
Space Foundation represents the global space community. The Space Foundation is a nonprofit organization supporting space activities, professionals and education.

III. Automotive Industry Associations

Alliance of Automobile Manufacturers
1401 Eye St. NW, Ste. 900
Washington, DC 20005 US
Phone: 202-326-5500
Fax: 202-326-5598
Web Address: www.autoalliance.org
The Alliance of Automobile Manufacturers is a trade association composed of 9 car including BMW Group, DaimlerChrysler, Ford Motor Company, General Motors, Mazda, Mitsubishi Motors, Porsche, Toyota and Volkswagen. Alliance members account for more than 90% of vehicles sold in the U.S.

Association of International Automobile Manufacturers, Inc. (AIAM)
2111 Wilson Blvd., Ste. 1150
Arlington, VA 22201 US
Phone: 703-525-7788
Fax: 703-525-8817
E-mail Address: *webmaster2@aiam.org*
Web Address: www.aiam.org
The Association of International Automobile Manufacturers, Inc. (AIAM) is a trade association representing 14 international motor vehicle manufacturers. Members concentrate on improving the safety and efficiency of vehicles, as well as investing in American communities.

Canadian Transportation Equipment Association (CTEA)
16 Barrie Blvd., Unit 3B
St. Thomas, Ontario N5P 4B9 Canada
Phone: 519-631-0414
Fax: 519-631-1333
E-mail Address: *transportation@ctea.on.ca*
Web Address: www.ctea.ca
The Canadian Transportation Equipment Association (CTEA) standardizes the commercial vehicle equipment manufacturing industry in Canada.

Canadian Vehicle Manufacturers' Association (CVMA)
170 Attwell Dr., Ste. 400
Toronto, Ontario M9W 5Z5 Canada
Phone: 416-364-9333
Fax: 416-367-3221
Toll Free: 800-758-7122
E-mail Address: *info@cvma.ca*
Web Address: www.cvma.ca
The Canadian Vehicle Manufacturers' Association (CVMA) is the industry organization representing manufacturers of light and heavy duty motor vehicles in Canada. Association members collaborate to solve industry objectives in the way of consumer protection, the environment and vehicle safety.

Engine Manufacturers Association (EMA)
2 N. LaSalle St., Ste. 2200
Chicago, IL 60602 US
Phone: 312-827-8700
Fax: 312-827-8737
E-mail Address: *ema@enginemanufacturers.org*
Web Address: www.enginemanufacturers.org
The Engine Manufacturers Association (EMA) is the voice of the engine manufacturing industry on domestic and international public policy, as well as regulatory and technical issues that affect manufacturers of engines used in a broad array of mobile and stationary applications.

Motor & Equipment Manufacturers Association (MEMA)
10 Laboratory Dr.
P.O. Box 13966
Research Triangle Park, NC 27709-3966 US
Phone: 919-549-4800
Fax: 919-549-4824
E-mail Address: *info@mema.org*
Web Address: www.mema.org
The Motor & Equipment Manufacturers Association (MEMA) exclusively represents and serves manufacturers of motor vehicle components, tools and equipment, automotive chemicals and related products used in the production, repair and maintenance of all classes of motor vehicles.

IV. Automotive Industry Resources

American Traffic Safety Services Institute (The) (ATSSA)
15 Riverside Pkwy., Ste. 100
Fredericksburg, VA 22406-1022 US
Phone: 540-368-1701
Fax: 540-368-1717
Toll Free: 800-272-8772
E-mail Address: *jimb@atssa.com*

Web Address: www.atssa.com
The American Traffic Safety Services Institute (ATSSA) is an international trade association whose members provide pavement markings, signage, work zone traffic control devices and other safety features on our nation's roadways.

Automotive Learning Center (ALC)
1800 Crooks Rd.
Troy, MI 48084 US
Phone: 248-244-8920
Web Address: www.plastics-car.org
The Automotive Learning Center (ALC), sponsored by the American Chemistry Council's Plastics Division, strives to provide the automobile designer, stylist or engineer with up-to-the-minute research and information on plastics applications in cars.

International Motor Vehicle Program (IMVP)
MIT Center for Technology, Policy, and Industrial Development
MIT E40-207, 1 Amherst St.
Cambridge, MA 02139-4307 US
Phone: 617-253-8973
Fax: 617-253-7140
E-mail Address: *ctpidcom@mit.edu*
Web Address: imvp.mit.edu
The International Motor Vehicle Program (IMVP) is a research project, funded by leading global car makers as well as government agencies, focused on enhancing automotive design and manufacturing methods. Through the program, more than 50 senior scientists, management experts, social scientists and engineers have conducted interdisciplinary automotive research at more than 25 universities on six continents. The IMVP is based at the Center for Technology, Policy, and Industrial Development (CTPID) at the Massachusetts Institute of Technology (MIT).

Sloan Automotive Laboratory
MIT, 77 Massachusetts Ave., Rm. 31-153
Cambridge, MA 02139-4307 US
Phone: 617-253-4529
Fax: 617-253-9433
E-mail Address: *kstryker@mit.edu*
Web Address: web.mit.edu/sloan-auto-lab
The Sloan Automotive Laboratory at MIT was founded in 1929 by Professor C.F. Taylor, with a grant from Alfred P. Sloan, Jr., CEO of General Motors, as a major laboratory for automotive research in the US and the world. The goals of the Laboratory are to provide the fundamental knowledge base for automotive engineering and to educate students to become technological leaders in the automotive industry.

USCAR (United States Council for Automotive Research Inc.)
1000 Town Center Dr., Ste. 300
Southfield, MI 48075 US
Phone: 248-223-9000
Web Address: www.uscar.org
The United States Council for Automotive Research (USCAR) was founded in 1992. Its goal is to further strengthen the technology base of the U.S. auto industry through cooperative research and development. Its main focus is to create, support and direct U.S. cooperative research and development to advance automotive technologies. USCAR is composed of a number of specialized groups that focus on specific research areas. USCAR is governed by the three-member USCAR Council, whose membership includes the R&D vice presidents from each of the U.S. automakers.

V. Automotive Parts & Supplies

Hong Kong Auto Parts Industry Association (HKAPIA)
5/F HKPC Bldg.
78 Tat Chee Ave.
Kowloon, Hong Kong
Phone: 852-278-85457
Fax: 852-2788-5543
E-mail Address: *autopart@hkpc.org*
Web Address: www.hkapia.com
The Hong Kong Auto Parts Industry Association (HKAPIA) represents the automotive components industry in Hong Kong. Its members are engaged in the design, manufacturing and business investment in the auto parts industry.

VI. Biology-Synthetic

Synthetic Biology
Web Address: syntheticbiology.org
Synthetic Biology is a consortium of individuals, labs and groups working together to advance the development of biological engineering. Its members include 19 labs from 11 different universities, including MIT, Princeton and Harvard. The site's FAQ includes discussions of synthetic biology, its applications and the difference between synthetic and systems biology. Synthetic Biology does not maintain a headquarters, instead allowing members to update and edit the web site in order to disseminate knowledge.

VII. Biotechnology & Biological Industry Associations

Biomedical Engineering Society of India
Sree Chitra Tirunal Institute for Medical Sciences and Technology
Satelmond Palace Campus, Poojapura
Thiruvananthapuram, 695 012 India

Phone: 91-471-2520-282
Fax: 91-471-2341-814
E-mail Address: *niranjan@sctimst.ac.in*
Web Address: www.bmesi.org.in
The Biomedical Engineering Society of India is an all India association which seeks to advance interdisciplinary co-operation among scientists, engineers, and medical doctors for the growth of teaching, research and practices of biomedical engineering.

Biotechnology Industry Organization (BIO)
1201 Maryland Ave. SW, Ste. 900
Washington, DC 20024 US
Phone: 202-962-9200
Fax: 202-488-6301
E-mail Address: *info@bio.org*
Web Address: www.bio.org
The Biotechnology Industry Organization (BIO) is involved in the research and development of health care, agricultural, industrial and environmental biotechnology products. BIO has both small and large member organizations.

Centre for Cellular and Molecular Biology (CCMB)
Council of Scientific & Industrial Research
Uppal Road
Hyderabad, 500 007 India
Phone: 91-40-27160222
Fax: 91-040-27160591
Web Address: www.ccmb.res.in
Centre for Cellular and Molecular Biology (CCMB) is one of the constituent Indian national laboratories of the Council of Scientific and Industrial Research (CSIR), the multidisciplinary research and development organization of the Government of India.

Institute of Biological Engineering (IBE)
1020 Monarch St., Ste. 300B
Lexington, KY 40512 US
Phone: 859-977-7450
Fax: 859-977-7441
E-mail Address: *sclements@ibe.org*
Web Address: www.ibeweb.org
The Institute of Biological Engineering (IBE) is a professional organization encouraging inquiry and interest in biological engineering and professional development for its members.

VIII. Biotechnology Resources

Bioengineering Industry Links
Dept. of Bioengineering, School of Eng. & Applied Science
UPenn, 210 S. 33rd St., Rm. 240 Skirkanich Hall
Philadelphia, PA 19104 US
Phone: 215-898-8501
Fax: 215-573-2071
E-mail Address: *beoffice@seas.upenn.edu*
Web Address:
www.seas.upenn.edu/be/misc/bmelink/cell.html
Bioengineering Industry Links is a web site provided by the University of Pennsylvania's Department of Bioengineering. This site features links to companies involved in cell and tissue engineering.

BioTech
The Ellington Lab, University of Texas at Austin
Chem & Biochem Dept., 1 University Station A4800
Austin, TX 78712-0165 US
E-mail Address: *feedback@biotech.icmb.utexas.edu*
Web Address: biotech.icmb.utexas.edu
The BioTech web site offers a comprehensive dictionary of biotech terms, plus extensive research data regarding biotechnology. BioTech is located in The Ellington Lab at the University of Texas at Austin.

Biotech Rumor Mill
E-mail Address: *info@biofind.com*
Web Address: www.biofind.com/rumor-mill
The Biotech Rumor Mill is an online discussion forum that attracts participants from many biotech disciplines. Rumor Mill service is provided by Biofind Limited.

IX. Broadcasting, Cable, Radio & TV Associations

Broadcast Engineering Society (India)
912, Surya Kiran Bldg.
19, K.G. Marg
New Delhi, 110 001 India
Phone: 91-11-23316709
Fax: 91-11-23316709
E-mail Address: *rrprasad13@yahoo.com*
Web Address: www.besindia.com
The Broadcast Engineering Society (India) aims to promote the interests of the broadcast engineering profession at the national and international levels.

X. Canadian Government Agencies-Communications

Canadian Radio-Television and Telecommunications Commission (CRTC)
Les Terrasses de la Chaudière, Central Bldg.
1 Promenade du Portage
Gatineau, QC J8X 4B1 Canada
Phone: 819-997-0313
Fax: 819-994-0218
Toll Free: 877-249-2782
Web Address: www.crtc.gc.ca
The Canadian Radio-Television and Telecommunications Commission (CRTC) is the government agency responsible for the regulation of the Canadian broadcasting and telecommunications industries.

XI. Canadian Government Agencies-Defense

Defense Research & Development Canada (DRDC)
305 Rideau St.
Ottawa, ON K1A 0K2 Canada
Phone: 613-998-2127
Fax: 613-998-2675
E-mail Address: *info@drdc-rddc.gc.ca*
Web Address: www.drdc-rddc.gc.ca
The DRDC is a branch of the Canadian Department of National Defense responsible for the technological and scientific R&D for the Canadian Forces.

XII. Canadian Government Agencies-General

Infrastructure Canada
90 Sparks St., 6th Fl.
Ottawa, ON K1P 5B4 Canada
Phone: 613-948-1148
Toll Free: 800-622-6232
E-mail Address: *info@infc.gc.ca*
Web Address: www.infrastructure.gc.ca
Infrastructure Canada works with Transport Canada and sixteen crown corporations to coordinate federal projects that focus on cities and communities, as well as supports infrastructure improvement nationwide.

Institute for Measurement Standards (IMS)
1200 Montreal Road, Bldg. M-36
Ottawa, ON K1A 0R6 Canada
Phone: 613-998-7018
Fax: 613-954-1473
E-mail Address: *alexandra.shaw@nrc-cnrc.gc.ca*
Web Address: inms-ienm.nrc-cnrc.gc.ca
The Institute for Measurement Standards (IMS) is a member of Canada's National Research Council and focuses on programs designed to develop, maintain and improve standards of mass, length, time, electricity, temperature and luminosity measurement.

XIII. Canadian Government Agencies-Scientific

Canada Institute for Scientific and Technical Information (CISTI)
1200 Montreal Rd., M-55
Ottawa, ON K1A 0R6 Canada
Phone: 613-998-8544
Fax: 613-993-7619
Toll Free: 800-668-1222
E-mail Address: *info.cisti@nrc-cnrc.gc.ca*
Web Address: cisti-icist.nrc-cnrc.gc.ca
The Canada Institute for Scientific and Technical Information (CISTI) is one of the largest information source service organizations in the world, with particular emphasis on the scientific and technical sectors.

Industrial Materials Institute (IRI)
75 de Mortagne Blvd.
Boucherville, QC J4B 6Y4 Canada
Phone: 450-641-5000
Fax: 450-641-5102
E-mail Address: *Imi-Info@cnrc-nrc.gc.ca*
Web Address: imi.cnrc-nrc.gc.ca
The Industrial Materials Institute (IRI) is a branch of Canada's National Research Council focusing its research on advanced materials design used in the manufacture of industrial components.

Institute for Chemical Process and Environmental Technology (ICPET)
1200 Montreal Road
Ottawa, ON K1A 0R6 Canada
Phone: 613-993-3692
Web Address: icpet-itpce.nrc-cnrc.gc.ca
The Institute for Chemical Process and Environmental Technology (ICPET), or, in French, Institut de technologie des procedes chimiques et de l'environnement ((ITCPE), focuses its research and development activities on chemical science and engineering, particularly in the area of multiphase reactive systems. It is a branch of Canada's National Research Council (NRC), or, in French, the Conseil national de recherches Canada (CNRC).

National Research Council of Canada's Herzberg Institute of Astrophysics (NRC-HIA)
5071 W. Saanich Rd.
Victoria, BC V9E 2E7 Canada
Phone: 250-363-0001
Fax: 250-363-0045
E-mail Address: *HIA-WWW@nrc-cnrc.gc.ca*
Web Address: hia-iha.nrc-cnrc.gc.ca
The National Research Council of Canada's Herzberg Institute of Astrophysic (NRC-HIA) manages Canada's involvement in major astronomical observatories.

XIV. Careers-Computers/Technology

Computerjobs.com, Inc.
280 Interstate N. Cir. SE, Ste. 300
Atlanta, GA 30339-2411 US
Toll Free: 800-850-0045
E-mail Address: *michael@marketingmax.com*
Web Address: www.computerjobs.com
Computerjobs.com, Inc. is an employment web site that offers users a link to computer-related job opportunities organized by skill and market.

Dice
4101 NW Urbandale Dr.
Urbandale, IA 50322 US
Phone: 515-280-1144
Fax: 515-280-1452
Toll Free: 877-386-3323
Web Address: www.dice.com

Dice provides free employment services for IT jobs. The site includes advanced job searches by geographic location and category, availability announcements and resume postings, as well as employer profiles, a recruiter's page and career links. Dice is owned by Dice Holdings, Inc., a publicly traded company.

Institute for Electrical and Electronics Engineers (IEEE) Job Site
IEEE
445 Hoes Ln.
Piscataway, NJ 08855-1331 US
Phone: 732-981-0060
Toll Free: 800-678-4333
E-mail Address: *candidatejobsite@ieee.org*
Web Address: www.careers.ieee.org
The Institute for Electrical and Electronics Engineers (IEEE) Job Site provides a host of employment services for technical professionals, employers and recruiters. The site offers job listings by geographic area, a resume bank and links to employment services.

Pencom Systems, Inc.
152 Remsen St.
New York, NY 11201 US
Phone: 718-923-1111
Fax: 718-923-6066
E-mail Address: *tom@pencom.com*
Web Address: www.pencom.com
Pencom Systems, Inc., an open systems recruiting company, offers a web site geared toward high-technology and scientific professionals, featuring an interactive salary survey, career advisor, job listings and technology resources.

SearchTech Solutions
307 Orchard City Dr., Ste. 300
Campbell, CA 95008 US
Phone: 408-540-1800
Fax: 408-540-1815
Toll Free: 888-695-4362
E-mail Address: *resumes@stecs.com*
Web Address: www.stecs.com
SearchTech Solutions is a recruiting, placement and consulting firm focused on engineering, product development and innovation, supply chain and information technology industries. Its web site offers resume writing assistance, including editing, writing and customizing.

XV. Careers-First Time Jobs/New Grads

Black Collegian Online (The)
140 Carondelet St.
New Orleans, LA 70130 US
Phone: 504-523-0154
Web Address: www.black-collegian.com
The Black Collegian Online features listings for job and internship opportunities, as well as other tools for students of color; it is the web site of The Black Collegian Magazine, published by IMDiversity, Inc. The site includes a list of the top 100 minority corporate employers and an assessment of job opportunities.

Collegegrad.com, Inc.
234 E. College Ave., Ste. 200
State College, PA 16801 US
Phone: 262-375-6700
Toll Free: 1-800-991-4642
Web Address: www.collegegrad.com
Collegegrad.com, Inc. offers in-depth resources for college students and recent grads seeking entry-level jobs.

Job Web
Nat'l Association of Colleges & Employers (NACE)
62 Highland Ave.
Bethlehem, PA 18017-9085 US
Phone: 610-868-1421
Fax: 610-868-0208
Toll Free: 800-544-5272
E-mail Address: *editors@jobweb.com*
Web Address: www.jobweb.com
Job Web, owned and sponsored by National Association of Colleges and Employers (NACE), displays job openings and employer descriptions. The site also offers a database of career fairs, searchable by state or keyword, with contact information.

MBAjobs.net
Fax: 413-556-8849
E-mail Address: *contact@mbajobs.net*
Web Address: www.mbajobs.net
MBAjobs.net is a unique international service for MBA students and graduates, employers, recruiters and business schools. The MBAjobs.net service is provided by WebInfoCo.

MonsterTRAK
11845 W. Olympic Blvd., Ste. 500
Los Angeles, CA 90064 US
Toll Free: 800-999-8725
E-mail Address: *trakstudent@monster.com*
Web Address: www.monstertrak.monster.com
MonsterTRAK features links to hundreds of university and college career centers across the U.S. with entry-level job listings categorized by industry. Major companies can also utilize MonsterTRAK.

National Association of Colleges and Employers (NACE)
62 Highland Ave.
Bethlehem, PA 18017-9085 US
Phone: 610-868-1421
Fax: 610-868-0208
Toll Free: 800-544-5272
E-mail Address: *mcollins@naceweb.org*
Web Address: www.naceweb.org

The National Association of Colleges and Employers (NACE) is a premier U.S. organization representing college placement offices and corporate recruiters who focus on hiring new grads.

XVI. Careers-General Job Listings

JobCentral
DirectEmployers Association, Inc.
9002 N. Purdue Rd., Quad III, Ste. 100
Indianapolis, IN 46268 US
Phone: 317-874-9000
Fax: 317-874-9100
Toll Free: 866-268-6206
E-mail Address: *info@jobcentral.com*
Web Address: www.jobcentral.com
JobCentral, operated by the nonprofit DirectEmployers Association, Inc., links users directly to hundreds of thousands of job opportunities posted on the sites of participating employers, thus bypassing the usual job search sites. This saves employers money and allows job seekers to access many more job opportunities.

XVII. Careers-Job Reference Tools

Vault.com, Inc.
75 Varick St., 8th Fl.
New York, NY 10013 US
Phone: 212-366-4212
E-mail Address: *feedback@staff.vault.com*
Web Address: www.vault.com
Vault.com, Inc. is a comprehensive career web site for employers and employees, with job postings and valuable information on a wide variety of industries. Vault gears many of its features toward MBAs. The site has been recognized by Forbes and Fortune Magazines.

XVIII. Chemicals Industry Associations

Chemical Industry and Engineering Society of China (CIESC)
Xiaoguan Jie 53
Anwai, 100029 Beijing
Phone: 010-64441885
Fax: 010-64411194
E-mail Address: *ciesc@ciesc.cn*
Web Address: www.ciesc.cn
The Chemical Industry and Engineering Society of China (CIESC) aims to advance chemical engineering professionals and the chemical industry through academic and educational development. CIESC is affiliated with the China Association for Science and Technology.

China Petroleum & Chemical Industry Association (CPCIA)
Bldg 16 Qu 4 Anhuili
Asian Games Village
Beijing, 100723 China
Phone: 86-10-8488-5056
Fax: 86-10-8488-5087
E-mail Address: *bgs@cpcia.org.cn*
Web Address: www.cpcia.org
The China Petroleum & Chemical Industry Association (CPCIA) is a non-government and non-profit association composed of regional and local associations including the China Polyurethane Industry Association.

XIX. Chinese Government Agencies-General

China Association for Science and Technology (CAST)
3 Fuxing Rd.
Beijing, 100863 China
Phone: 8610-68571898
Fax: 8610-68571897
E-mail Address: *english@cast.org.cn*
Web Address: english.cast.org.cn
The China Association for Science and Technology (CAST) is the largest national non-governmental organization of scientific and technological workers in China. The association has 167 member organizations in the field of engineering, science and technology.

Ministry of Science and Technology of the People´s Republic of China
15B, Fuxing Rd.
Beijing, 100862 China
Web Address: www.most.gov.cn
The Ministry of Science and Technology of the People's Republic of China (MOST) has information and links to its various departments including the Departments of: Personnel; Social Development; Rural Science and Technology; Basic Research; and High and New Technology Development and Industrialization.

XX. Computer & Electronics Industry Associations

AeA
5201 Great America Pkwy., Ste. 400
Santa Clara, CA 95054 US
Phone: 408-987-4200
Fax: 408-987-4298
Toll Free: 800-284-4232
E-mail Address: *csc@aeanet.org*
Web Address: www.aeanet.org
AeA, formerly the American Electronics Association, is a trade association which represents thousands of U.S. electronics firms, including electronic systems and component manufacturers, suppliers and end users. It also publishes the annual AeA Directory with geographic and product indexes.

Business Technology Association (BTA)
12411 Wornall Rd., Ste. 200

Kansas City, MO 64145 US
Phone: 816-303-4082
Fax: 816-941-4838
Toll Free: 800-505-2821
E-mail Address: *info@bta.org*
Web Address: www.bta.org
The Business Technology Association (BTA) is an organization for resellers and dealers of business technology products. Its site offers buying groups, message boards, legal advice, news on industry trends and live chats.

Computer & Communications Industry Association (CCIA)
900 17th St. NW, Ste. 1100
Washington, DC 20006 US
Phone: 202-783-0070
Fax: 202-783-0534
E-mail Address: *ccia@ccianet.org*
Web Address: www.ccianet.org
The Computer & Communications Industry Association (CCIA) is a nonprofit membership organization for companies and senior executives representing the computer, Internet, information technology (IT) and telecommunications industries.

Electronic Industries Alliance (EIA)
2500 Wilson Blvd., Ste. 500
Arlington, VA 22201 US
Phone: 703-907-7500
E-mail Address: *kschweers@eia.org*
Web Address: www.eia.org
The Electronic Industries Alliance (EIA) is a trade organization which represents more than 1,300 electronics firms, including governmental information technology associations and telecommunications, electronic components and consumer electronics manufacturers. The EIA consists of an alliance between the following trade organizations: The Electronic Components, Assemblies & Materials Association (ECA); the Telecommunications Industry Association (TIA); the JEDEC Solid State Technology Association (JEDEC); and the Government Electronics and Information Technology Association (GEIA).

Electronics Technicians Association (ETA)
5 Depot St.
Greencastle, IN 46135 US
Phone: 765-653-8262
Fax: 765-653-4287
Toll Free: 800-288-3824
E-mail Address: *eta@eta-i.org*
Web Address: www.eta-i.org
The Electronics Technicians Association (ETA) is a nonprofit professional association for electronics technicians. The firm provides recognized professional credentials for electronics technicians.

Global Semiconductor Alliance (GSA)
3 Lincoln Ctr.
5430 LBJ Fwy., Ste. 280
Dallas, TX 75240 US
Phone: 972-866-7579
Fax: 972-239-2292
E-mail Address: *jshelton@fsa.org*
Web Address: www.fsa.org
The Global Semiconductor Alliance (GSA), formerly the Fabless Semiconductor Association (FSA), represents semiconductor manufacturers that do not have fabrication plants. GSA's mission is to positively impact the growth and investment return for fabless companies (those without fabrication plants) and their partners.

Hong Kong Electronic Industries Association (HKEIA)
Unit 1201, 12/F. Harbour Crystal Ctr.
100 Granville Rd., TST East
Kowloon, Hong Kong
Phone: 852-2778-8328
Fax: 852-2788-2200
E-mail Address: *hkeia@hkeia.org*
Web Address: www.hkeia.org
The Hong Kong Electronic Industries Association (HKEIA) represents the views of the electronics industry and collects and disseminates statistical information relating to the electronics industry in Hong Kong.

Institute for Interconnecting and Packaging Electronic Circuits (IPC)
3000 Lakeside Dr., Ste. 309 S
Bannockburn, IL 60015 US
Phone: 847-615-7100
Fax: 847-615-7105
E-mail Address: *SharonStarr@ipc.org*
Web Address: www.ipc.org
The Institute for Interconnecting and Packaging Electronic Circuits (IPC) is a trade association for participants in the global electronic interconnect industry.

International Disk Drive Equipment and Materials Association (IDEMA)
1136 Jacklin Rd.
Milpitas, CA 95035 US
Phone: 408-719-0082
Fax: 408-719-0087
E-mail Address: *awhitlock@idema.org*
Web Address: www.idema.org
The International Disk Drive Equipment and Materials Association (IDEMA) is a not-for-profit trade association that represents its members on issues concerning the hard drive industry worldwide.

International Microelectronics and Packaging Society (IMAPS)
611 2nd St. NE
Washington, DC 20002 US
Phone: 202-548-4001

Fax: 202-548-6115
E-mail Address: *imaps@imaps.org*
Web Address: www.imaps.org
The International Microelectronics and Packaging Society (IMAPS) is dedicated to the advancement and growth of the use of microelectronics and electronic packaging through professional and public education and the dissemination of information.

Korea Association of Information and Telecommunications (KAIT)
NO. 1678-2, 2nd Fl. Dong-Ah Villat 2 Town
Seocho-dong, Seocho-gu
Seoul, 137-070 Korea
Phone: 82-2-580-0580
Fax: 82-2-580-0599
E-mail Address: *webmaster@kait.or.kr*
Web Address: www.kait.or.kr/eng
The KAIT was created to develop and promote the InfoTech, computer, consumer electronics, wireless, software and telecommunications sectors in Korea.

Korea Electronics Association (KEA)
1599 Sangam-dong, Mapo-Gu
Seoul, 135-080 Korea
Phone: 82-2-6388-6000
Fax: 82-2-6388-6009
E-mail Address: *webmaster@gokea.org*
Web Address: www.gokea.org
The Korea Electronics Association (KEA) is an organization for professionals in the electronics industry.

Korea Semiconductor Industry Association (KSIA)
5F Dong-IL Bldg.
#107 Yangjae-Dong Seocho-Ku
Seoul, 137-130 Korea
Phone: 82-2-570-5232
Fax: 82-2-577-1719
E-mail Address: *steve@ksia.or.kr*
Web Address: www.ksia.or.kr
The Korean Semiconductor Industry Association (KSIA) represents the interests of Korean semiconductor manufacturers.

North American Chinese Semiconductor Association (NACSA)
P.O. Box 61086
Sunnyvale, CA 94088 US
E-mail Address: *info@nasca.com*
Web Address: www.nacsa.com
The North American Chinese Semiconductor Association (NACSA), founded in Silicon Valley in 1996, is dedicated to the advancement of Chinese professionals in high-tech and related industries, including chip design, chip manufacture, system manufacture, equipment manufacture and software.

SEMATECH
2706 Montopolis Dr.
Austin, TX 78741 US
Phone: 512-356-3500
E-mail Address: *media.relations@sematech.org*
Web Address: www.sematech.org
SEMATECH is an international consortium of semiconductor manufacturing companies. The researches advanced technology and manufacturing effectiveness in the semiconductor industry, working to decrease time between innovation and manufacturing.

Semiconductor Equipment and Materials International (SEMI)
3081 Zanker Rd.
San Jose, CA 95134 US
Phone: 408-943-6900
Fax: 408-428-9600
E-mail Address: *semihq@semi.org*
Web Address: www.wps2a.semi.org
Semiconductor Equipment and Materials International (SEMI) is a trade association serving the global semiconductor equipment, materials and flat-panel display industries.

Semiconductor Industry Association (SIA)
181 Metro Dr., Ste. 450
San Jose, CA 95110 US
Phone: 408-436-6600
Fax: 408-436-6646
E-mail Address: *mailbox@sia-online.org*
Web Address: www.sia-online.org
The Semiconductor Industry Association (SIA) is a trade association representing the semiconductor industry in the U.S. Through its coalition of 95 companies, SIA represents more than 85% of semiconductor production in the U.S. The coalition aims to advance the competitiveness of the chip industry and shape public policy on issues particular to the industry.

Storage Network Industry Association (SNIA)
500 Sansome St., Ste. 504
San Francisco, CA 94111 US
Phone: 415-402-0006
Fax: 415-402-0009
E-mail Address: *lesley.bakker@snia.org*
Web Address: www.snia.org
The Storage Network Industry Association (SNIA) is a trade associated dedicated to viability of storage networks within the IT industry. SNIA sponsors technical work groups, produces the Storage Networking Conference series and maintains a Technology Center in Colorado Springs, Colorado.

Surface Mount Technology Association (SMTA)
5200 Willson Rd., Ste. 215
Edina, MN 55424 US
Phone: 952-920-7682

Fax: 952-926-1819
E-mail Address: *tom_forsythe@kyzen.com*
Web Address: www.smta.org
The Surface Mount Technology Association (SMTA) is an international network of professionals whose careers encompass electronic assembly technologies, microsystems, emerging technologies and associated business operations.

USB Implementers Forum (USB-IF)
E-mail Address: *admin@usb.org*
Web Address: www.usb.org
USB Implementers Forum, Inc. is a nonprofit corporation founded by the group of companies that developed the Universal Serial Bus specification. The USB-IF was formed to provide a support organization and forum for the advancement and adoption of Universal Serial Bus technology. The Forum facilitates the development of high-quality compatible USB peripherals (devices), and promotes the benefits of USB and the quality of products that have passed compliance testing. Some of the many activities that the USB-IF supports include USB compliance workshops and USB compliance test development.

XXI. Computer-Aided Engineering Resources

Center for Design Research (CDR) at Stanford University
Stanford University
424 Panama Mall
Stanford, CA 94305-2232 US
Phone: 650-723-9233
Fax: 650-725-8475
E-mail Address: *judy@cdr.stanford.edu*
Web Address: www-cdr.stanford.edu
The web site of the Center for Design Research (CDR) at Stanford University provides information on the center's staff, laboratories and projects on design process and design tool development for engineering.

Tri-Service CADD/GIS Technology Center
U.S. Army Research and Development Ctr., ATTN: CEERD-ID
3909 Halls Ferry Rd.
Vicksburg, MS 39180-6199 US
Phone: 601-634-4109
Fax: 601-634-4584
E-mail Address: *Kenneth..Cook@us.army.mil*
Web Address: tsc.wes.army.mil
The Tri-Service CADD/GIS Technology Center's computer-aided design and drafting services, as well as geographic information services resources, are available through this site provided by the Army Corp of Engineers.

XXII. Construction Industry Resources & Associations

Precast/Prestressed Concrete Institute
209 W. Jackson Blvd., Ste. 500
Chicago, IL 60606 US
Phone: 312-786-0300
Fax: 312-786-0353
E-mail Address: *info@pci.org*
Web Address: www.pci.org
The Precast/Prestressed Concrete Institute (PCI) is an organization dedicated to the precast and prestressed concrete industry and includes a staff of technical and marketing specialists.

XXIII. Consulting Industry Associations

Association of Consulting Engineers Singapore (ACES)
70 Palmer Rd. 04-06
Palmer House
079427 Singapore
Phone: 65-63242682
Fax: 65-63242581
E-mail Address: *aces@starhub.net.sg*
Web Address: www.aces.org.sg
The Association of Consulting Engineers Singapore (ACES) is a nonprofit association representing the independent consulting engineering profession in Singapore.

Consulting Engineers Association of India (CEAI)
A-8 Green Park
New Delhi, 110 016 India
Phone: 011-26863000
Fax: 011-26855252
E-mail Address: *cmd@ictonline.com*
Web Address: www.ceaindia.org
The Consulting Engineers Association of India (CEAI) is the member association from India representing the Indian engineering consultancy profession within India and abroad. CEAI represents the merger of the Association of Consulting Engineers (India) and the National Association of Consulting Engineers (India).

XXIV. Corporate Information Resources

bizjournals.com
120 W. Morehead St., Ste. 400
Charlotte, NC 28202 US
Web Address: www.bizjournals.com
Bizjournals.com is the online media division of American City Business Journals, the publisher of dozens of leading city business journals nationwide. It provides access to research into the latest news regarding companies small and large.

Business Wire
44 Montgomery St., 39th Fl.
San Francisco, CA 94104 US
Phone: 415-986-4422
Fax: 415-788-5335
Toll Free: 800-227-0845
Web Address: www.businesswire.com
Business Wire offers news releases, industry- and company-specific news, top headlines, conference calls, IPOs on the Internet, media services and access to tradeshownews.com and BW Connect On-line through its informative and continuously updated web site.

Edgar Online, Inc.
50 Washington St., 11th Fl.
Norwalk, CT 06854 US
Phone: 203-852-5666
Fax: 203-852-5667
Toll Free: 800-416-6651
Web Address: www.edgar-online.com
Edgar Online, Inc. is a gateway and search tool for viewing corporate documents, such as annual reports on Form 10-K, filed with the U.S. Securities and Exchange Commission.

PR Newswire Association LLC
810 7th Ave., 32nd Fl.
New York, NY 10019 US
Phone: 201-360-6700
Toll Free: 800-832-5522
E-mail Address: *information@prnewswire.com*
Web Address: www.prnewswire.com
PR Newswire Association LLC provides comprehensive communications services for public relations and investor relations professionals ranging from information distribution and market intelligence to the creation of online multimedia content and investor relations web sites. Users can also view recent corporate press releases. The Association is owned by United Business Media plc.

Silicon Investor
100 W. Main
P.O. Box 29
Freeman, MO 64746 US
E-mail Address: *admin_dave@techstocks.com*
Web Address: www.siliconinvestor.advfn.com
Silicon Investor is focused on providing information about technology companies. The company's web site serves as a financial discussion forum and offers quotes, profiles and charts.

XXV. Design Industry Resources & Associations

Center for Universal Design (The) (CUD)
College of Design, North Carolina State University
Campus Box 8613
Raleigh, NC 27695-8613 US
Phone: 919-515-3082
Fax: 919-515-8951
Toll Free: 800-647-6777
E-mail Address: *cud@ncsu.edu*
Web Address: www.design.ncsu.edu/cud/
The Center for Universal Design (CUD) is a national information, technical assistance and research center that evaluates, develops and promotes products and environments so that they can be used by all people, regardless of physical or mental limitations.

XXVI. Economic Data & Research

Eurostat
Phone: 32-2-299-9696
Toll Free: 80-0-6789-1011
Web Address: www.epp.eurostat.ec.europa.eu
Eurostat is the European Union's service that publishes a wide variety of comprehensive statistics on European industries, populations, trade, agriculture, technology, environment and other matters.

STAT-USA/Internet
STAT-USA, HCHB, Rm. 4885
U.S. Department of Commerce
Washington, DC 20230 US
Phone: 202-482-1986
Fax: 202-482-2164
Toll Free: 800-782-8872
E-mail Address: *statmail@esa.doc.gov*
Web Address: www.stat-usa.gov
STAT-USA/Internet offers daily economic news, statistical releases and databases relating to export and trade, as well as the domestic economy. It is provided by STAT-USA, which is an agency in the Economics & Statistics Administration of the U.S. Department of Commerce. The site mainly consists of two main databases, the State of the Nation (SOTN), which focuses on the current state of the U.S. economy; and the Global Business Opportunities (GLOBUS) & the National Trade Data Bank (NTDB), which deals with U.S. export opportunities, global political/socio-economic conditions and other world economic issues.

XXVII. Electrical Engineering Industry Associations

International Society for Optical Engineering (SPIE)
1000 20th St.
Bellingham, WA 98225-6705 US
Phone: 360-676-3290
Fax: 360-647-1445
Toll Free: 888-504-8171
E-mail Address: *CustomerService@SPIE.org*
Web Address: www.spie.org
The International Society for Optical Engineering (SPIE) is a nonprofit technical society aimed at the advancement and dissemination of knowledge in optics, photonics and imaging.

XXVIII. Energy Associations-Nuclear

China Atomic Energy Authority
China Atomic Energy Authority
Beijing, 100037 China
E-mail Address: *webmaster@caea.gov.cn*
Web Address: www.caea.gov.cn
The China Atomic Energy Authority is involved in developing policies and regulations and the development programming, planning and industrial standards for peaceful uses of nuclear energy.

XXIX. Energy Associations-Petroleum, Exploration, Production, etc.

China Energy Association (CEA)
7th of Nanlishi St.
Xicheng District
Beijing, 100045 China
Phone: 86-010-68051807
Fax: 86-010-68051799
E-mail Address: *znx18303@126.com*
Web Address: www.zhnx.org.cn
The China Energy Association (CEA) is a membership organization that represents the energy sources sector and energy industry. The organization publishes the Energy Resource World magazine.

International Association of Drilling Contractors (IADC)
10370 Richmond Ave., Ste. 760
Houston, TX 77042 US
Phone: 713-292-1945
Fax: 713-292-1946
E-mail Address: *info@iadc.org*
Web Address: www.iadc.org
The International Association of Drilling Contractors (IADC) represents the worldwide oil and gas drilling industry and promotes commitment to safety, preservation of the environment and advances in drilling technology.

Oil and Gas UK
232-242 Vauxhall Bridge Rd., 2nd Fl.
London, SW1V 1AU UK
Phone: 44-020-7802-2400
Fax: 44-020-7802-2401
E-mail Address: *info@oilandgasuk.co.uk*
Web Address: www.oilandgas.org.uk
The United Kingdom Offshore Operators Association (UKOOA) is the representative organization for the U.K. offshore oil and gas industry.

Petroleum Equipment Suppliers Association (PESA)
9225 Katy Fwy., Ste. 310
Houston, TX 77024 US
Phone: 713-932-0168
Fax: 713-932-0497
E-mail Address: *webmaster@pesa.org*
Web Address: www.pesa.org
The Petroleum Equipment Suppliers Association (PESA) is an organization of equipment manufacturers, well site service providers and supply companies serving the drilling and production segments of the petroleum industry.

XXX. Energy Education Resources

Uranium Information Centre (UIC)
Australian Uranium Association Ltd.
GPO Box 1649
Melbourne, Victoria 3001 Australia
Phone: 03-8616-0440
Fax: 03-8616-0441
E-mail Address: *info@aua.org.au*
Web Address: www.uic.com.au
The Uranium Information Centre (UIC) provides information about the development of the Australian uranium industry, uranium mining and nuclear energy. The UIC is part of the Australian Uranium Association Ltd. (AUA).

XXXI. Engineering Indices

Engineering Library
Cornell University
Carpenter Hall
Ithaca, NY 14853 US
Phone: 607-255-5933
Fax: 607-255-0278
E-mail Address: *engranswers@cornell.edu*
Web Address: www.astech.library.cornell.edu/ast/engr
Cornell University's Engineering Library web site has a number of resources concerning engineering research.

XXXII. Engineering, Research & Scientific Associations

Agency For Science, Technology And Research (A*STAR)
1 Fusionopolis Way
20-10 Connexis North Tower
138632 Singapore
Phone: 65-6826-6111
Fax: 65-6777-1711
Web Address: www.a-star.edu.sg
The Agency For Science, Technology And Research (A*STAR) of Singapore comprises the Biomedical Research Council (BMRC), the Science and Engineering Research Council (SERC), Exploit Technologies Pte Ltd (ETPL), the A*STAR Graduate Academy (A*GA) and the Corporate Planning and Administration Division (CPAD). Both Councils fund the A*STAR public research institutes

which conducts research in specific niche areas in science, engineering and biomedical science.

Alfred P. Sloan Foundation
630 5th Ave., Ste. 2550
New York, NY 10111 US
Phone: 212-649-1649
Fax: 212-757-5117
Web Address: www.sloan.org
The Alfred P. Sloan Foundation funds science and technology, economic performance, education, national issues and civics programs through research fellowships and grants.

American Association for the Advancement of Science (AAAS)
1200 New York Ave. NW
Washington, DC 20005 US
Phone: 202-326-6400
E-mail Address: *webmaster@aaas.org*
Web Address: www.aaas.org
The American Association for the Advancement of Science (AAAS) is the world's largest scientific society and the publisher of Science magazine. It is an international non-profit organization dedicating to advancing science.

American Association of Petroleum Geologists (AAPG)
1444 S. Boulder Ave.
Tulsa, OK 74119 US
Phone: 918-584-2555
Fax: 918-560-2665
Toll Free: 800-364-2274
E-mail Address: *lnation@aapg.org*
Web Address: www.aapg.org
The American Association of Petroleum Geologists (AAPG) is an international geological organization that supports educational and scientific programs and projects related to geosciences.

American Chemical Society (ACS)
1155 16th St. NW
Washington, DC 20036 US
Phone: 202-872-4600
Fax: 202-776-8258
Toll Free: 800-227-5558
E-mail Address: *help@acs.org*
Web Address: portal.acs.org/portal/acs/corg/content
The American Chemical Society (ACS) is a nonprofit organization aimed at promoting the understanding of chemistry and chemical sciences. It represents a wide range of disciplines including chemistry, chemical engineering and other technical fields.

American Institute of Aeronautics and Astronautics (AIAA)
1801 Alexander Bell Dr., Ste. 500
Reston, VA 20191-4344 US
Phone: 703-264-7500
Fax: 703-264-7551
Toll Free: 800-639-2422
E-mail Address: *klausd@aiaa.org*
Web Address: www.aiaa.org
The American Institute of Aeronautics and Astronautics (AIAA) is a nonprofit society aimed at advancing the arts, sciences and technology of aeronautics and astronautics. The institute represents the U.S. in the International Astronautical Federation and the International Council on the Aeronautical Sciences.

American Institute of Chemical Engineers (AIChE)
3 Park Ave.
New York, NY 10016-5991 US
Phone: 203-702-7660
Fax: 203-775-5177
Toll Free: 800-242-4363
E-mail Address: *xpress@aiche.org*
Web Address: www.aiche.org
The American Institute of Chemical Engineers (AIChE) provides leadership in advancing the chemical engineering profession. The organization, which is comprised of 40,000 members from 93 countries, provides informational resources to chemical engineers.

American Institute of Mining, Metallurgical and Petroleum Engineers (AIME)
8307 Shaffer Pkwy.
Littleton, CO 80127 US
Phone: 303-948-4255
Fax: 303-948-4260
E-mail Address: *aime@aimehq.org*
Web Address: www.aimehq.org
The American Institute of Mining, Metallurgical and Petroleum Engineers (AIME) is a trade association devoted to the science of the production and use of minerals, metals, energy sources and materials.

American Institute of Physics (AIP)
1 Physics Ellipse
College Park, MD 20740-3843 US
Phone: 301-209-3100
E-mail Address: *atorres@aip.org*
Web Address: www.aip.org
The American Institute of Physics (AIP) is a nonprofit organization aimed at the advancement and diffusion of knowledge of the science of physics and its application to human welfare.

American National Standards Institute (ANSI)
1819 L St. NW, 6th Fl.
Washington, DC 20036 US
Phone: 202-293-8020
Fax: 202-293-9287
E-mail Address: *info@ansi.org*
Web Address: www.ansi.org

The American National Standards Institute (ANSI) is a private, nonprofit organization that administers and coordinates the U.S. voluntary standardization and conformity assessment system. Its mission is to enhance both the global competitiveness of U.S. business and the quality of life by promoting and facilitating voluntary consensus standards and conformity assessment systems and safeguarding their integrity.

American Nuclear Society (ANS)
555 N. Kensington Ave.
La Grange Park, IL 60526 US
Phone: 708-352-6611
Fax: 708-352-0499
Toll Free: 800-323-3044
Web Address: www.ans.org
The American Nuclear Society (ANS) is a nonprofit organization unifying professional activities within the nuclear science and technology fields. ANS seeks to promote the awareness and understanding of the application of nuclear science and technology.

American Physical Society (APS)
1 Physics Ellipse
College Park, MD 20740-3844 US
Phone: 301-209-3100
Fax: 301-209-0865
Web Address: www.aps.org
The American Physical Society (APS) develops and implements effective programs in physics education and outreach.

American Society for Engineering Education (ASEE)
1818 North St. NW
Ste. 600
Washington, DC 20036-2479 US
Phone: 202-331-3500
Fax: 202-265-8504
E-mail Address: *publicaffairs@asee.org*
Web Address: asee.org
The American Society for Engineering Education (ASEE) is dedicated to promoting and improving engineering and technology education.

American Society for Healthcare Engineering (ASHE)
1 N. Franklin, 28th Fl.
Chicago, IL 60606 US
Phone: 312-422-3800
Fax: 312-422-4571
E-mail Address: *ashe@aha.org*
Web Address: www.ashe.org
The American Society for Healthcare Engineering (ASHE) is the advocate and resource for continuous improvement in the health care engineering and facilities management professions.

American Society for Nondestructive Testing (ASNT)
P.O. Box 28518
1711 Arlingate Ln.
Columbus, OH 43228-0518 US
Phone: 614-274-6003
Fax: 614-274-6899
Toll Free: 800-222-2768
Web Address: www.asnt.org
The American Society for Nondestructive Testing (ASNT) is the world's largest technical society for nondestructive testing professionals. It promotes the discipline of nondestructive testing as a profession and facilitates nondestructive testing research and technology applications.

American Society for Testing & Materials (ASTM)
100 Barr Harbor Dr.
P.O. Box C700
West Conshohocken, PA 19428-2959 US
Phone: 610-832-9500
Fax: 610-832-9555
E-mail Address: *service@astm.org*
Web Address: www.astm.org
The American Society for Testing & Materials (ASTM) provides and develops voluntary consensus standards and related technical information, and services that promote public health and safety. It also contributes to the reliability of materials, as well as, providing technical standards for industries worldwide.

American Society of Agricultural and Biological Engineers (ASABE)
2950 Niles Rd.
St. Joseph, MI 49085 US
Phone: 269-429-0300
Fax: 269-429-3852
E-mail Address: *hq@asabe.org*
Web Address: www.asabe.org
The American Society of Agricultural and Biological Engineers (ASABE) is a nonprofit professional and technical organization interested in engineering knowledge and technology for food and agriculture and associated industries.

American Society of Civil Engineers (ASCE)
1801 Alexander Bell Dr.
Reston, VA 20191-4400 US
Phone: 703-295-6300
Fax: 703-295-6222
Toll Free: 800-548-2723
Web Address: www.asce.org
The American Society of Civil Engineers (ASCE) is a leading professional organization serving civil engineers. It ensures safer buildings, water systems and other civil engineering works by developing technical codes and standards.

American Society of Mechanical Engineers (ASME)
3 Park Ave.
New York, NY 10016-5990 US

Phone: 973-882-1170
Fax: 973-882-1717
Toll Free: 800-843-2763
E-mail Address: *infocentral@asme.org*
Web Address: www.asme.org
The American Society of Mechanical Engineers (ASME) offers quality programs and activities in mechanical engineering. It also facilitates the development and application of technology in areas of interest to the mechanical engineering profession.

American Society of Mechanical Engineers (ASME), Textile Engineering Division
3 Park Ave.
New York, NY 10016-5990 US
Phone: 973-882-1170
Fax: 973-882-5155
Toll Free: 800-843-2763
E-mail Address: *infocentral@asme.org*
Web Address: divisions.asme.org/ted
The textile engineering division of the American Society of Mechanical Engineers (ASME) promotes product and process technology improvement in the retail fiber industry.

American Society of Naval Engineers (ASNE)
1452 Duke St.
Alexandria, VA 22314-3458 US
Phone: 703-836-6727
Fax: 703-836-7491
E-mail Address: *asnehq@navalengineers.org*
Web Address: www.navalengineers.org
The American Society of Naval Engineers (ASNE) is a nonprofit professional organization dedicated to advancing the knowledge and practice of naval engineering in public and private operations.

American Society of Safety Engineers (ASSE)
Customer Service
1800 E. Oakton St.
Des Plaines, IL 60018 US
Phone: 847-699-2929
Fax: 847-768-3434
E-mail Address: *customerservice@asse.org*
Web Address: www.asse.org
The American Society of Safety Engineers (ASSE) is the world's oldest and largest professional safety organization. It manages, supervises and consults on safety, health and environmental issues in industry, insurance, government and education.

American Vacuum Society (AVS)
120 Wall St., 32nd Fl.
New York, NY 10005 US
Phone: 212-248-0200
Fax: 212-248-0245
E-mail Address: *ricky@avs.org*
Web Address: www.avs.org
The American Vacuum Society (AVS) is a nonprofit organization that promotes communication, dissemination of knowledge, recommended practices, research and education in the use of vacuum and other controlled environments to develop new materials, process technology and devices. AVS facilitates communication between academia, government laboratories and industry.

Asia Pacific Confederation of Chemical Engineers (APCChE)
APCChE Secretariat, C/- Engineers
Australia 11 National Circuit
Barton, ACT 2600 Australia
Phone: 61-02-6270-6539
Fax: 61-02-6273-2358
E-mail Address: *jarmstrong@engineersaustralia.org.au*
Web Address: www.apcche.org.
The Asia Pacific Confederation of Chemical Engineers (APCChE) was formed to provide a focus for various non-profit societies, associations and institutions working in the field of chemical engineering in the Asian Pacific region. APPChE consists of member societies in 13 countries and regions, People's Republic of China, Korea, Japan, New Zealand, Thailand, India, Philippines, Indonesia, Singapore, Australia, Malaysia, Taiwan, China and Hong Kong. The American Institute of Chemical Engineers and the Institution of Chemical Engineers (UK) are corresponding members.

ASM International
9639 Kinsman Rd.
Materials Park, OH 44073-0002 US
Phone: 440-338-5151 x0
Fax: 440-338-4634
Toll Free: 800-336-5152
E-mail Address: *customerservice@asminternational.org*
Web Address: www.asminternational.org
ASM International is a worldwide network of materials engineers, aimed at advancing industry, technology and applications of metals and materials.

Association for Facilities Engineering (AFE)
12100 Sunset Hills Rd., Ste. 130
Reston, VA 20190 US
Phone: 703-234-4066
E-mail Address: *info@afe.org*
Web Address: www.afe.org
The Association for Facilities Engineering (AFE) provides education, certification, technical information and other relevant resources for plant and facility engineering, operations and maintenance professionals worldwide.

Association of Consulting Chemists and Chemical Engineers (ACC&CE)
P.O. Box 297
Sparta, NJ 07871 US
Phone: 973-729-6671
Fax: 973-729-7088

E-mail Address: *info@chemconsult.org*
Web Address: www.chemconsult.org
The Association of Consulting Chemists and Chemical Engineers (ACC&CE) was founded in 1928 by a group of distinguished chemists. The association exists to advance the practices of consulting chemists and chemical engineers.

Association of Consulting Engineers (ACE)
Alliance House
12 Caxton St.
London, SW1H 0QL UK
Phone: 44-20-7222-6557
Fax: 44-20-7222-0750
E-mail Address: *consult@acenet.co.uk*
Web Address: www.acenet.co.uk
The Association of Consulting Engineers (ACE) represents the business interests of the consultancy and engineering industry in the U.K.

Association of Consulting Engineers of Hong Kong
20/F Tung Wai Commercial Bldg.
109-111 Gloucester Rd.
Wanchai, Hong Kong
Phone: 852-2598-0023
Fax: 852-2877-0181
Web Address: www.acehk.org.hk
The Association of Consulting Engineers of Hong Kong promotes the professional consulting engineers and sets standards of professional conduct and ethics for this consulting engineers.

Association of Federal Communications Consulting Engineers (AFCCE)
P.O. Box 19333
Washington, DC 20036 US
Web Address: www.afcce.org
The Association of Federal Communications Consulting Engineers (AFCCE) is a professional organization of individuals who regularly assist clients on technical issues before the Federal Communications Commission (FCC).

Association of Official Analytical Chemists (AOAC)
481 N. Frederick Ave., Ste. 500
Gaithersburg, MD 20877-2417 US
Phone: 301-924-7077
Fax: 301-924-7089
Toll Free: 800-379-2622
E-mail Address: *aoac@aoac.org*
Web Address: www.aoac.org
The Association of Official Analytical Chemists (AOAC) is a non-profit scientific association committed to worldwide confidence in analytical results.

Association of Professional Engineers of Nova Scotia (APENS)
1355 Barrington St.
Halifax, Nova Scotia B3J 1Y9 Canada
Phone: 902-429-2250
Fax: 902-423-9769
Toll Free: 888-802-7367
E-mail Address: *info@apens.ns.ca*
Web Address: www.apens.ns.ca
The Association of Professional Engineers of Nova Scotia (APENS) is the licensing and regulatory body for the more than 4,500 professional engineers and engineers-in-training practicing in Nova Scotia.

Audio Engineering Society, Inc. (AES)
60 E. 42nd St., Rm. 2520
New York, NY 10165-2520 US
Phone: 212-661-8528
Fax: 212-682-0477
Web Address: www.aes.org
The Audio Engineering Society (AES) provides information on educational and career opportunities in audio technology and engineering.

Biomedical Engineering Society
8401 Corporate Dr., Ste. 140
Landover, MD 20785-2224 US
Phone: (301) 459-1999
Fax: (301) 459-2444
E-mail Address: *info@bmes.org*
Web Address: www.bmes.org
The Biomedical Engineering Society (BMES) members are the in biomedical engineering and bioengineering industry.

Broadcast Technological Society (BTS) of the Institute of Electrical & Electronics Engineers, Inc.
Kathy Colabaugh, BTS Administrator
445 Hoes Ln.
Piscataway, NJ 08854 US
Phone: 732-562-3906
Fax: 732-981-1769
E-mail Address: *bts@ieee.org*
Web Address:
www.ieee.org/organizations/society/bt/index.html
The Broadcast Technological Society (BTS) is the arm of the Institute of Electrical & Electronics Engineers (IEEE) devoted to devices, equipment, techniques and systems related to broadcast technology.

Canadian Council of Professional Engineers (CCPE)
180 Elgin St., Ste. 1100
Ottawa, Ontario K2P 2K3 Canada
Phone: 613-232-2474
Fax: 613-230-5759
E-mail Address: *info@engineerscanada.ca*
Web Address: www.engineerscanada.ca
The CCPE is a national organization in Canada consisting of 12 provincial and territorial associations and organizations that license more than 160,000 professional engineers.

China Engineering Cost Association
No. 9 Sanlihe Rd.
Beijing, 100835 China
Phone: 86-10-58934013
Fax: 86-10-58934648
Web Address: www.ceca.org.cn
The China Engineering Cost Association aims to improve and promote the profession of engineering cost engineers and engineering project managers. The association provides examinations for engineering cost engineers, establishes standards in the industry and collects price information on materials and equipment. The association intercommunicates with many engineering cost organizations and specialists from Great Britain, Hong Kong, Korea, Japan, New Zealand, and Australia.

China National Association of Engineering Consultants (CNAEC)
11th Floor, Sichuan Mansion (East Wing)
No 1 Fuchengmen Wai Street
Beijing, 100037 China
Phone: 86(10) 6833-2683
Fax: 86(10) 6836-4843
E-mail Address: *cnaec@cnaec.org.cn*
Web Address: www.cnaec.org.cn
The China National Association of Engineering Consultants (CNAEC) is a non-governmental organization representing engineering consulting firms as well as experts others in the field of engineering. In addition, CNAEC represents China's engineering consulting profession in international affairs.

Chinese Association of Earthquake Engineering (CAEE)
No 29 Xuefu Rd. Harbin
Heilongjiang, 150080 China
Phone: 86-45186652663
Fax: 86-45186664755
Web Address: www.caee.org.cn
Chinese Association of Earthquake Engineering (CAEE) promotes the field of earthquake engineering and the research in seismic activity and earthquake sciences.

Chinese Ceramic Society (CCS)
11 Sanlihe Rd.
Beijing, 100831 China
Phone: 86-10-68342024
Fax: 86-10-68313364
Web Address: www.ceramsoc.com
The Chinese Ceramic Society (CCS) is an academic, non-profit organization for professionals engaged in the science and technology of inorganic nonmetallic materials.

Chinese Hydraulic Engineering Society (CHES)
2-2 BaiGuang Rd.
Beijing, 100053 China
Phone: 86-1063202163
Fax: 86-1063202154
E-mail Address: *Ches@mwr.gov.cn*
Web Address: www.ches.org.cn
The Chinese Hydraulic Engineering Society (CHES) aims to promote hydraulic engineering professionals and the water resources sciences and technologies. CHES has 31 regional socieites in China.

Chinese Society of Agricultural Machinery (CSAM)
No.1 Beishatan
Deshengmen Wai
Beijing, 100083 China
Phone: 010-64882291
Fax: 010-64882291
Web Address: www.agro-csam.org
The Chinese Society of Agricultural Machinery (CSAM) is a national society under the China Association for Science and Technology (CAST) and its administrative body set up the Chinese Academy of Agricultural Mechanization Sciences (CAAMS). CSAM promotes the growth and improvement of scientific and technological personnel in the field of agricultural mechanization and farm machinery engineering.

CIEMAT
Avda. Complutense, 22
Madrid, 28040 Spain
Phone: 91-346-60-00
Fax: 91-346-60-05
E-mail Address: *contacto@ciemat.es*
Web Address: www.ciemat.es
The CIEMAT, a unit of Spain's Ministry of Education and Science, is a public research agency. Its areas of focus include solar energy, biomass energy, wind energy, environment, basic research, fusion by magnetic confinement, nuclear safety, and technology transfer. Primary operations include PSA, the Solar Platform of Almeria, where concentrating solar power (CSP) is researched; CEDER, the Centre for the Development of Renewable Energy Sources; and CETA-CIEMAT, a center for information technology research.

Civil Engineering Forum for Innovation (CEFI)
American Society of Civil Engineers
1801 Alexander Bell Dr.
Reston, VA 20191-4400 US
Phone: 703-295-6314
Fax: 703-295-6015
E-mail Address: *mdalton@asce.org*
Web Address: content.asce.org/cefi
The Civil Engineering Forum for Innovation (CEFI) is an independent nonprofit organization established by the American Society of Civil Engineers (ASCE) to strengthen the civil engineering profession and industry through technical innovation and public policy.

Community Research and Development Information Service (CORDIS)
Office for Official Publications of the European Union Communities
2 rue Mercier
Luxembourg, L-2985 Luxembourg
Phone: 352-2929-42210
E-mail Address: *helpdesk@cordis.europa.eu*
Web Address: cordis.europa.eu
The Community Research and Development Information Service (CORDIS) provides information about research and development sponsored and supported by the European Union. It is managed by the Office for Official Publications of the European Union Communities (Publications Office).

Council for Chemical Research (CCR)
1730 Rhode Island Ave. NW., Ste. 302
Washington, DC 20036 US
Phone: 202-429-3971
Fax: 202-429-3976
E-mail Address: *wmadison@ccrhq.org*
Web Address: www.ccrhq.org
The Council for Chemical Research (CCR) is an organization based in Washington, D.C., whose membership represents industry, academia, and government. CCR was formed in 1979 to promote cooperation in basic research and encourage high quality education in the chemical sciences and engineering.

Cryogenic Society of America, Inc. (CSA)
218 Lake St.
Oak Park, IL 60302-2609 US
Phone: 708-383-6220
Fax: 708-383-9337
E-mail Address: *laurie@cryogenicsociety.org*
Web Address: www.cryogenicsociety.org
The Cryogenic Society of America, Inc. (CSA) is a nonprofit organization that brings together those in all disciplines concerned with the applications of low-temperature technology. It also increases public awareness of the usefulness of cryogenic technology, and publishes the magazine Cold Facts five times per year.

DECHEMA (Society for Chemical Engineering and Biotechnology)
Theodor-Heuss-Allee 25
Frankfurt am Main, 60486 Germany
Phone: 0049 69 7564-0
Fax: 0049 69 7564-201
Web Address: http://dechema.de/
The DECHEMA (Society for Chemical Engineering and Biotechnology) is a non-profit making scientific and technical society based in Frankfurt on Main. It was founded in 1926. Today it has over 5000 private and institutional members. Its aim is to promote research and technical advances in the areas of chemical engineering, biotechnology and environmental protection. The group's work is interdisciplinary, with scientists, engineers, and technologists working together under one roof. Experts from science, business, and government departments cooperate in working parties and subject divisions.

Earthquake Engineering Research Institute (EERI)
499 14th St., Ste. 320
Oakland, CA 94612-1934 US
Phone: 510-451-0905
Fax: 510-451-5411
E-mail Address: *eeri@eeri.org*
Web Address: www.eeri.org
The Earthquake Engineering Research Institute (EERI) is a national nonprofit technical organization of engineers, geoscientists, architects, planners, public officials and social scientists aimed at reducing earthquake risk by advancing the science and practice of earthquake engineering.

Engineer's Club (The) (TEC)
1737 Silverwood Dr.
San Jose, CA 95124 US
Phone: 408-316-0488
E-mail Address: *tec@engineers.com*
Web Address: www.engineers.com/index.htm
The Engineer's Club (TEC) provides resources and web sites for engineers and technical professionals, including an online forum.

European Association of Geoscientists & Engineers (EAGE)
P.O. Box 59
Db Houten, 3990 The Netherlands
Phone: 31-88-995-5055
Fax: 31-30-6343524
E-mail Address: *eage@eage.org*
Web Address: www.eage.org
EAGE is a professional association for geoscientists and engineers. It is a European-based organisation with a worldwide membership providing a global network of commercial and academic professionals to all members. The association is truly multi-disciplinary and international in form and pursuits.

Hong Kong Institution of Engineers (HKIE)
9/F Island Beverley
No 1 Great George St.
Causeway Bay Hong, Hong Kong
Phone: 852-2895-4446
Fax: 852-2577-7791
E-mail Address: *hkie-sec@hkie.org.hk*
Web Address: www.hkie.org.hk
The Hong Kong Institution of Engineers (HKIE) promotes engineering professionals and maintains the standards of the profession.

IEEE Communications Society (ComSoc)
3 Park Ave., 17th Fl.

New York, NY 10016 US
Phone: 212-705-8900
Fax: 212-705-8999
E-mail Address: *society@comsoc.org*
Web Address: www.comsoc.org
The IEEE Communications Society (ComSoc) is composed of industry professionals with a common interest in advancing communications technologies.

IEEE Oceanic Engineering Society (OES)
15 Rocky Brook Rd.
Cranbury, NJ 08512 US
Phone: 609-865-6797
E-mail Address: *elcreed@ieee.org*
Web Address: www.oceanicengineering.org
The IEEE Oceanic Engineering Society (OES) is the division of the IEEE that deals with electrical engineering at sea, including unmanned submarines and offshore oil platforms.

Illuminating Engineering Society of North America (IESNA)
120 Wall St., 17th Fl.
New York, NY 10005 US
Phone: 212-248-5000
Fax: 212-248-5017
E-mail Address: *iesna@iesna.org*
Web Address: www.iesna.org
A recognized authority on lighting in North America, the Illuminating Engineering Society of North America (IESNA) establishes scientific lighting recommendations. Members include engineers, architects, designers, educators, students, manufacturers and scientists.

Industrial Research Institute (IRI)
2200 Clarendon Blvd., Ste. 1102
Arlington, VA 22201 US
Phone: 703-647-2580
Fax: 703-647-2581
E-mail Address: *information@iriinc.org*
Web Address: www.iriinc.org
The Industrial Research Institute (IRI) is a nonprofit organization of over 200 leading industrial companies, representing industries such as aerospace, automotive, chemical, computers and electronics, which carry out industrial research efforts in the U.S. manufacturing sector. IRI helps members improve research and development capabilities.

Institute for Research in Construction (IRC)
National Research Council of Canada
1200 Montreal Rd., Bldg. M-24
Ottawa, ON K1A 0R6 Canada
Phone: 613-993-2607
Fax: 613-952-7673
E-mail Address: *irc.client-services@nrc-cnrc.gc.ca*
Web Address: irc.nrc-cnrc.gc.ca
The Institute for Research in Construction (IRC) provides research, building code development and materials evaluation services. The IRC is Canada's construction technology center and a division of the National Research Council.

Institute of Electrical and Electronics Engineers (IEEE)
3 Park Ave., 17th Fl.
New York, NY 10016-5997 US
Phone: 212-419-7900
Fax: 212-752-4929
E-mail Address: *ieeeusa@ieee.org*
Web Address: www.ieee.org
The Institute of Electrical and Electronics Engineers (IEEE) is a nonprofit, technical professional association of more than 375,000 individual members in approximately 160 countries. The IEEE sets global technical standards and acts as an authority in technical areas ranging from computer engineering, biomedical technology and telecommunications, to electric power, aerospace and consumer electronics.

Institute of Industrial Engineers (IIE)
3577 Parkway Ln., Ste. 200
Norcross, GA 30092 US
Phone: 770-449-0460
Fax: 770-441-3295
Toll Free: 800-494-0460
E-mail Address: *execoffice@iienet.org*
Web Address: www.iienet.org
The Institute of Industrial Engineers (IIE) is dedicated to the professional needs of industrial engineers.

Institute of Marine Engineering, Science and Technology (IMarEST)
80 Coleman St.
London, EC2R 5BJ UK
Phone: 44-0-20-7382-2600
Fax: 44-0-20-7382-2670
E-mail Address: *info@imarest.org*
Web Address: www.imarest.org
The Institute of Marine Engineering, Science and Technology (IMarEST) works to promote the development of marine engineering, science and technology.

Institute of Structural Engineers (IStructE)
11 Upper Belgrave St.
London, SW1X 8BH UK
Phone: 44-(0)20-7235-4535
Fax: 44-(0)20-7235-4294
Web Address: www.istructe.org.uk
The Institute of Structural Engineers (IStructE) is a professional organization, headquartered in the U.K., that sets and maintains standards for professional structural engineers.

Institution of Engineering and Technology (The) (IET)
Michael Faraday House
Stevenage
Herts, SG1 2AY UK
Phone: 44-1438-313-311
Fax: 44-1438-765-526
E-mail Address: *postmaster@theiet.org*
Web Address: www.theiet.org
The Institution of Engineering and Technology (IET) is an innovative international organization for electronics, electrical, manufacturing and IT professionals.

Institution of Engineers, Singapore
70 Bukit Tinggi Rd.
289758 Singapore
Phone: 6469-5000
Fax: 6467-1108
Web Address: www.ies.org.sg
The Institution of Engineers, Singapore is the national society of engineers and its mission is the advancement of engineering in Singapore, and to advance and to promote the science, art and the profession of engineering.

Institution of Engineers, The (India)
8 Gokhale Rd.
Kolkata, 700 020 India
Phone: 033-4010 6266
E-mail Address: *sdg@ieindia.org*
Web Address: www.ieindia.org
The Institution of Engineers (India) is one of the largest multi-disciplinary engineering professional societies in India and was established to promote and advance the science, practice and business of engineering.

Institution of Mechanical Engineers-UK
1 Birdcage Walk
Westminster
London, SW1H 9JJ UK
Phone: 44(0)20-7222-7899
Fax: 44(0)20-7222-4557
E-mail Address: *membership@imeche.org*
Web Address: www.imeche.org
Institution of Mechanical Engineers represents the mechanical engineering profession in UK. The UK has the sixth largest manufacturing industry in the world and this association recognizes engineering professionals in this field. In addition, its other major themes are the energy, environment and transport industries as well as hosting educational opportunities for engineers.

International Association of Geophysical Contractors (IAGC)
2550 North Loop W., Ste. 104
Houston, TX 77092 US
Phone: 713-957-8080
Fax: 713-957-0008
E-mail Address: *iagc@iagc.org*
Web Address: www.iagc.org
The International Association of Geophysical Contractors (IAGC) is the international trade association representing the industry that provides geophysical services to the oil and gas industry.

International Commission of Agricultural and Biosystems Engineering (CIGR)
Univ. of Tsukuba-Life and Environmental Sciences
1-1-1 Tennodai
Tsukuba, Ibaraki 305-8572 Japan
Phone: 81-29-853-6989
Fax: 81-29-853-7496
E-mail Address: *biopro@sakura.cc.tsukuba.ac.jp*
Web Address: www.cigr.org
International Commission of Agricultural and Biosystems Engineering (CIGR) encourages and facilitates interregional exchange and the development of sciences and technologies in the field of agricultural engineering.

International Electrotechnical Commission (IEC)
3 rue de Varembe
Geneva 20, CH-1211 Switzerland
Phone: 41-22-919-02-11
Fax: 41-22-919-03-00
E-mail Address: *inmail@iec.ch*
Web Address: www.iec.ch
The International Electrotechnical Commission (IEC) is one of the world's leading organizations that prepares and publishes international standards for all electrical, electronic and related technologies, collectively known as electrotechnology.

International Electrotechnical Commission (IEC)
3, rue de Varembe
P.O. Box 131
Geneva 20, CH-1211 Switzerland
Phone: 41-22-919-02-11
Fax: 41-22-919-03-00
E-mail Address: *info@iec.ch*
Web Address: www.iec.ch
The International Electrotechnical Commission (IEC), based in Switzerland, promotes international cooperation on all questions of standardization and related matters in electrical and electronic engineering.

International Federation for Medical and Biological Engineering
Faculty of Electrical Engineering and Computing
Univ. of Zagreb, Unska 3
Zagreb, HR 10000 Croatia
Phone: 385-1-6129-938
Fax: 385-1-6129-652
E-mail Address: *ratko.magjarevic@fer.hr*
Web Address: www.ipem.ac.uk
The International Federation for Medical and Biological Engineering (IFMBE) is a federation of national and transnational organizations that represent national interests in medical and biological engineering. The objectives of

the IFMBE are scientific, technological, literary, and educational.

International Federation of Automotive Engineering Societies (FISITA)
30 Percy St.
London, W1T 2DB UK
Phone: 44-(0)-20-7299-6630
Fax: 44-(0)-20-7299-6633
E-mail Address: *info@fisita.com*
Web Address: www.fisita.com
The Federation Internationale des Societes d'Ingenieurs des Techniques de l'Automobile (FISITA) was founded in Paris in 1948 with the purpose of bringing engineers from around the world together in a spirit of cooperation to share ideas and advance the technological development of the automobile. FISITA is the umbrella organisation for the national automotive societies in 38 countries around the world. Its network of member societies represents more than 147,000 automotive engineers around the globe.

International Federation of Consulting Engineers (FIDIC)
World Trade Center II, Geneva Airport
29 Route de Pre-Bois, Cointrin
Geneva 15, CH-1215 Switzerland
Phone: 41-22-799-49-00
Fax: 41-22-799-49-01
E-mail Address: *fidic@fidic.org*
Web Address: www1.fidic.org
The International Federation of Consulting Engineers (FIDIC) represents globally its national member associations and the consulting engineering industry and profession. Its website also promotes best practices in areas such as international contracts, risk management, and sustainable development.

International Petroleum Technology Institute (IPTI)
11757 Katy Fwy., Ste. 865
Houston, TX 77079 US
Phone: 281-493-3491
Fax: 281-493-3493
E-mail Address: *irelandm@asme.org*
Web Address: www.asme-ipti.org
The International Petroleum Technology Institute (IPTI) is the division of the ASME concerned with the special engineering needs of the petroleum industry.

International Society for Measurement and Control (ISA)
67 Alexander Dr.
Research Triangle Park, NC 27709 US
Phone: 919-549-8411
Fax: 919-549-8288
E-mail Address: *info@isa.org*
Web Address: www.isa.org
The International Society for Measurement and Control (ISA) is a nonprofit organization which serves the professional development and credential needs of control system engineers, instrument technicians and others within the field of measurement and control.

International Standards Organization (ISO)
1, ch. de la Voie-Creuse
Case postale 56
Geneva 20, CH-1211 Switzerland
Phone: 41-22-749-01-11
Fax: 41-22-733-34-30
E-mail Address: *central@iso.org*
Web Address: www.iso.org
The International Standards Organization (ISO) is a global consortium national standards institutes from 157 countries. The established International Standards are designed to make products and services more efficient, safe and clean.

Marine Technology Society (MTS)
5565 Sterrett Pl., Ste. 108
Columbia, MD 21044 US
Phone: 410-884-5330
Fax: 410-884-9060
E-mail Address: *membership@mtsociety.org*
Web Address: www.mtsociety.org
The Marine Technology Society (MTS) is an organization devoted to marine science and technical knowledge.

Materials Research Society (MRS)
506 Keystone Dr.
Warrendale, PA 15086-7573 US
Phone: 724-779-3003
Fax: 724-779-8313
E-mail Address: *info@mrs.org*
Web Address: www.mrs.org
The Materials Research Society (MRS) is dedicated to basic and applied research on materials of technological importance. MRS emphasizes an interdisciplinary approach to materials science and engineering.

Minerals, Metals & Materials Society (TMS)
184 Thorn Hill Rd.
Warrendale, PA 15086-7514 US
Phone: 724-776-9000
Fax: 724-776-3770
Toll Free: 800-759-4867
E-mail Address: *webmaster@tms.org*
Web Address: www.tms.org
The Minerals Metals & Materials Society (TMS) is an organization of professionals and students involved in metallurgy and material engineering, promoting the exchange of information, education and technology transference.

National Academy of Engineering (NAE)
500 5th St., NW
Washington, DC 20001 US
Phone: 202-334-3200

Fax: 202-334-2290
E-mail Address: *atkins@nae.edu*
Web Address: www.nae.edu
The National Academy of Engineering (NAE) is a nonprofit institution that conducts independent studies to examine important topics in engineering and technology. It is the portal for all engineering activities at the National Academies, which include the National Academy of Sciences, the Institute of Medicine and the National Research Council.

National Academy of Science (NAS)
500 5th St. NW
Washington, DC 20001 US
Phone: 202-334-2000
E-mail Address: *worldwidewebfeedback@nas.edu*
Web Address: www.nationalacademies.org
The National Academies are private, nonprofit, self-perpetuating societies of scholars engaged in scientific and engineering research dedicated to the furtherance of science and technology and to their use for the general welfare. Four organizations comprise the Academies: The National Academy of Engineering, the National Research Council, the National Academy of Sciences and the Institute of Medicine.

National Research Council
500 Fifth St. NW
Washington, DC 20001 US
E-mail Address: *worldwidewebfeedback@nas.edu*
Web Address: http://www.nationalacademies.org/nrc/
The National Research Council is part of the National Academies, which also comprise the National Academy of Sciences, National Academy of Engineering and Institute of Medicine. They are private, nonprofit institutions that provide science, technology and health policy advice under a congressional charter. The Research Council was organized by the National Academy of Sciences in 1916 to associate the broad community of science and technology with the Academy's purposes of further knowledge and advising the federal government.

National Society of Professional Engineers (NSPE)
1420 King St.
Alexandria, VA 22314-2794 US
Phone: 703-684-2800
Fax: 703-836-4875
Toll Free: 888-285-6773
E-mail Address: *memserv@nspe.org*
Web Address: www.nspe.org
The National Society of Professional Engineers (NSPE) represents individual engineering professionals and licensed engineers across all disciplines. NSPE serves approximately 45,000 members and has more than 500 chapters.

Netherlands Organization for Applied Scientific Research (TNO)
Schoemakerstraat 97 (Building A)
Delft, NL-2628 VK The Netherlands
Phone: 31-15-269-69-00
Fax: 31-15-261-24-03
E-mail Address: *infodesk@tno.nl*
Web Address: www.tno.nl
The Netherlands Organization for Applied Scientific Research (TNO) is a contract research organization that provides a link between fundamental research and practical application.

Optical Society of America (OSA)
2010 Massachusetts Ave. NW
Washington, DC 20036-1023 US
Phone: 202-223-8130
Fax: 202-223-1096
E-mail Address: *info@osa.org*
Web Address: www.osa.org
The Optical Society of America (OSA) is an interdisciplinary society offering synergy between all components of the optics industry, from basic research to commercial applications such as fiber-optic networks. It has a membership group of over 14,000 individuals from over 81 countries. Members include scientists, engineers, educators, technicians and business leaders.

Professional Engineers Board Singapore (PEB)
1st Story, Tower Block, MND Complex
5 Maxwell Rd.
069110 Singapore
Phone: 65-6222-9293
Fax: 65-6222-9471
E-mail Address: *registrar@peb.gov.sg*
Web Address: www.peb.gov.sg
The Professional Engineers Board Singapore (PEB) is a statutory board in the Ministry of National Development. PEB was established since 1971 under the Professional Engineers Act in order to keep and maintain a register of professional engineers, a register of practitioners and a register of licensed corporations.

Royal Society (The)
6-9 Carlton House Ter.
London, SW1Y 5AG UK
Phone: 44-20-7451-2500
Fax: 44-20-7930-2170
E-mail Address: *info@royalsociety.org*
Web Address: www.royalsoc.ac.uk
The Royal Society is the UK's leading scientific organization. It operates as a national academy of science, supporting scientists, engineers, technologists and research. On its website, you will find a wealth of data about the research and development initiatives of its Fellows and Foreign Members.

Royal Society of Chemistry (RSC)
Burlington House, Piccadilly
London, W1J 0BA UK
Phone: 44-20-7437-8656
Fax: 44-20-7437-8883
Web Address: www.rsc.org
The Royal Society of Chemistry (RSC) is one of Europe's largest organizations for advancing the chemical sciences.

Society of Automotive Engineers (SAE)
755 W. Big Beaver, Ste. 1600
Troy, MA 48084 US
Phone: 248-273-2455
Fax: 248-273-2494
Toll Free: 877-606-7323
E-mail Address: *automotive_hq@sae.org*
Web Address: www.sae.org
The Society of Automotive Engineers (SAE) is a resource for technical information and expertise used in designing, building, maintaining and operating self-propelled vehicles for use on land, sea, air or space.

Society of Broadcast Engineers, Inc. (SBE)
9102 N. Meridian St., Ste. 150
Indianapolis, IN 46260 US
Phone: 317-846-9000
Fax: 317-846-9120
E-mail Address: *mclappe@sbe.org*
Web Address: www.sbe.org
The Society of Broadcast Engineers (SBE) exists to increase knowledge of broadcast engineering and promote its interests, as well as to continue the education of professionals in the industry.

Society of Cable Telecommunications Engineers (SCTE)
140 Philips Rd.
Exton, PA 19341-1318 US
Phone: 610-363-6888
Fax: 610-363-5898
Toll Free: 800-542-5040
E-mail Address: *scte@scte.org*
Web Address: www.scte.org
The Society of Cable Telecommunications Engineers (SCTE) is a nonprofit professional association dedicated to advancing the careers and serving the industry of telecommunications professionals by providing technical training, certification and standards.

Society of Consulting Marine Engineers and Ship Surveyors (SCMS)
202 Lambeth Rd.
London, SE1 7JW UK
Phone: 44-207-261-0869
Fax: 44-207-261-0871
E-mail Address: *sec@scmshq.org*
Web Address: www.scmshq.org
The Society of Consulting Marine Engineers and Ship Surveyors (SCMS) is a professional organization for marine engineers in the U.K.

Society of Exploration Geophysicists (SEG)
8801 S. Yale, Ste. 500
Tulsa, OK 74137-3575 US
Phone: 918-497-5500
Fax: 918-497-5557
E-mail Address: *membership@seg.org*
Web Address: www.seg.org
The Society of Exploration Geophysicists (SEG) promotes the science of geophysics. The website provides access to their foundation, online publications and employment and education services.

Society of Hispanic Professional Engineers (SHPE)
5400 E. Olympic Blvd., Ste. 210
Los Angeles, CA 90022 US
Phone: 323-725-3970
Fax: 323-725-0316
E-mail Address: *shpenational@shpe.org*
Web Address: oneshpe.shpe.org
The Society of Hispanic Professional Engineers (SHPE) is a national nonprofit organization that promotes Hispanics in science, engineering and math.

Society of Manufacturing Engineers (SME)
1 SME Dr.
Dearborn, MI 48121 US
Phone: 313-425-3000
Fax: 313-425-3412
Toll Free: 800-733-4763
E-mail Address: *communications@sme.org*
Web Address: www.sme.org
The Society of Manufacturing Engineers (SME) a leading professional organization serving engineers in the manufacturing industries.

Society of Motion Picture and Television Engineers (SMPTE)
3 Barker Ave., 5th Fl.
White Plains, NY 10601 US
Phone: 914-761-1100
Fax: 914-761-3115
Web Address: www.smpte.org
The Society of Motion Picture and Television Engineers (SMPTE) is the leading technical society for the motion imaging industry. The firm publishes recommended practice and engineering guidelines, as well the SMPTE Journal.

Society of Naval Architects and Marine Engineers (SNAME)
601 Pavonia Ave.
Jersey City, NJ 07306 US
Phone: 201-798-4800
Fax: 201-798-4975

Toll Free: 800-798-2188
E-mail Address: *ldavis@sname.org*
Web Address: www.sname.org
The Society of Naval Architects and Marine Engineers (SNAME) is an internationally recognized nonprofit, professional society of members serving the maritime and offshore industries and their suppliers.

Society of Petroleum Engineers (SPE)
222 Palisades Creek Dr.
Richardson, TX 75080-2040 US
Phone: 972-952-9393
Fax: 972-952-9435
Toll Free: 800-456-6863
E-mail Address: *service@spe.org*
Web Address: www.spe.org
The Society of Petroleum Engineers (SPE) helps connect engineers in the oil and gas industry with ideas, answers, resources and technological information.

Society of Plastics Engineers (SPE)
14 Fairfield Dr.
P.O. Box 403
Brookfield, CT 06804-0403 US
Phone: 203-775-0471
Fax: 203-775-8490
E-mail Address: *info@4spe.org*
Web Address: www.4spe.org
The Society of Plastics Engineers (SPE) is a recognized medium of communication among scientists and engineers engaged in the development, conversion and applications of plastics.

Society of Women Engineers (SWE)
230 E. Ohio St., Ste. 400
Chicago, IL 60611 US
Phone: 312-596-5223
Toll Free: 877-793-4636
E-mail Address: *hq@swe.org*
Web Address: www.swe.org
The Society of Women Engineers (SWE) is a nonprofit educational and service organization of female engineers.

United Engineering Foundation (UEF)
P.O. Box 70
Mt. Vernon, VA 22121-0070 US
Phone: 973-244-2328
Fax: 973-882-5155
E-mail Address: *engfnd@aol.com*
Web Address: www.uefoundation.org
The United Engineering Foundation (UEF) is a nonprofit organization chartered for the advancement of engineering arts and sciences in all branches.

Virginia Center for Innovative Technology
2214 Rock Hill Rd., Ste. 600
Herndon, VA 20170-4228 US
Phone: 703-689-3000
Fax: 703-689-3041
E-mail Address: *hconnors@cit.org*
Web Address: www.cit.org
The Virginia Center for Innovative Technology is a non-profit organization designed to enhance the research and development capability of Virginia's major research universities.

World Federation of Engineering Organizations
Maison de l'UNESCO 1
rue Miollis
Paris, Cedex 15 F-75732 France
Phone: 33-1-45-68-48-46
Fax: 33-1-45-68-48-65
E-mail Address: *tl.fmoi@unesco.org*
Web Address: www.wfeo.org
World Federation of Engineering Organizations (WFEO) is an international non-governmental organization that represents major engineering professional societies in over 90 nations. It has several standing committees including engineering and the environment, technology, communications, capacity building, education, energy and women in engineering.

XXXIII. Environmental & Ecological Organizations

Environment Canada
351 St. Joseph Blvd.
Place Vincent Massey, 8th Fl.
Gatineau, QC K1A 0H3 Canada
Phone: 819-997-2800
Fax: 819-994-1412
Toll Free: 800 668-6767
E-mail Address: *enviroinfo@ec.gc.ca*
Web Address: www.ec.gc.ca
Environment Canada is the Canadian government's natural environment preservation department.

XXXIV. Food Industry Associations, General

Institute of Food Technologies (IFT)
525 W. Van Buren, Ste. 1000
Chicago, IL 60607 US
Phone: 312-782-8424
Fax: 312-782-8348
Toll Free: 800-438-3663
E-mail Address: *info@ift.org*
Web Address: www.ift.org
The Institute of Food Technologies (IFT) is devoted to the advancement of the science and technology of food through the exchange of knowledge. The site also provides information and resources for job seekers in the food industry. Members work in food science, food technology and related professions in industry, academia and government.

XXXV. Government Agencies-Hong Kong

GovHK
16/F-22/F and 25/F Wanchai Tower
12 Harbour Rd.
Wan Chai, Hong Kong
Phone: 852-183-5500
E-mail Address: *enquiry@1835500.gov.hk*
Web Address: www.gov.hk
GovHK is the one-stop portal of the Hong Kong Special Administrative Region (HKSAR) Government. GovHK features links to governmental agencies, information and services. It also organizes them by user groups (transport, business, trade) and subjects (education, youth, etc.).

XXXVI. Government Agencies-Singapore

Singapore Government Online (SINGOV)
140 Hill St., 5th Storey, MICA Bldg.
179369 Singapore
E-mail Address: *singov_webmaster@mica.gov.sg*
Web Address: www.gov.sg
Singapore Government Online (SINGOV), is the default homepage for the Singapore Government and is a portal for governmenal information. The website lists governmental agencies, news, information, policies and inititives.

XXXVII. Industry Research/Market Research

Forrester Research
400 Technology Sq.
Cambridge, MA 02139 US
Phone: 617-613-6000
Fax: 617-613-5200
Toll Free: 866-367-7378
Web Address: www.forrester.com
Forrester Research identifies and analyzes emerging trends in technology and their impact on business. Among the firm's specialties are the financial services, retail, health care, entertainment, automotive and information technology industries.

Marketresearch.com
11200 Rockville Pike, Ste. 504
Rockville, MD 20852 US
Phone: 240-747-3000
Fax: 240-747-3004
Toll Free: 800-298-5699
E-mail Address: *customerservice@marketresearch.com*
Web Address: www.marketresearch.com
Marketresearch.com is a leading broker for professional market research and industry analysis. Users are able to search the company's database of research publications including data on global industries, companies, products and trends.

Plunkett Research, Ltd.
P.O. Drawer 541737
Houston, TX 77254-1737 US
Phone: 713-932-0000
Fax: 713-932-7080
E-mail Address: *customersupport@plunkettresearch.com*
Web Address: www.plunkettresearch.com
Plunkett Research, Ltd. is a leading provider of market research, industry trends analysis and business statistics. Since 1985, it has served clients worldwide, including corporations, universities, libraries, consultants and government agencies. At the firm's web site, visitors can view product information and pricing and access a great deal of basic market information on industries such as financial services, infotech, e-commerce, health care and biotech.

XXXVIII. Internet Industry Associations

Cooperative Association for Internet Data Analysis (CAIDA)
CAIDA, UCSD/SDSC
9500 Gilman Dr., Mail Stop 0505
La Jolla, CA 92093-0505 US
Phone: 858-534-5000
E-mail Address: *info@caida.org*
Web Address: www.caida.org
The Cooperative Association for Internet Data Analysis (CAIDA) works to promote an atmosphere of greater cohesion on the Internet. Member organizations come from the government, commercial and research sectors. CAIDA is located at the San Diego Supercomputer Center (SDSC) on the campus of the University of California, San Diego (UCSD).

Internet Alliance
1111 19th St. NW, Ste. 1100
Washington, DC 20035-5782 US
Phone: 202-861-2476
E-mail Address: *emilyh@internetalliance.org*
Web Address: www.internetalliance.org
The Internet Alliance strives to assist the Internet industry in becoming the most important mass-market medium of the 21st century.

Internet Society (ISOC)
1775 Wiehle Ave., Ste. 102
Reston, VA 20190-5108 US
Phone: 703-439-2120
Fax: 703-326-9881
E-mail Address: *isoc@isoc.org*
Web Address: www.isoc.org
The Internet Society (ISOC) is a nonprofit organization that provides leadership in public policy issues that influence the future of the Internet. The organization is the home of groups that maintain infrastructure standards for the Internet, such as the Internet Engineering Task Force (IETF) and the Internet Architecture Board (IAB).

Internet Systems Consortium, Inc. (ISC)
950 Charter St.
Redwood City, CA 94063 US
Phone: 650-423-1300
Fax: 650-423-1355
E-mail Address: *info@isc.org*
Web Address: www.isc.org
The Internet Systems Consortium, Inc. (ISC) is a nonprofit organization with extensive expertise in the development, management, maintenance and implementation of Internet technologies.

World Wide Web Consortium (W3C)
32 Vassar St., Rm. 32-G515
Cambridge, MA 02139 US
Phone: 617-253-2613
Fax: 617-258-5999
E-mail Address: *ij@w3.org*
Web Address: www.w3.org
The World Wide Web Consortium (W3C) develops technologies and standards to enhance the performance and utility of the World Wide Web. The W3C is hosted by three different organizations: the European Research Consortium for Informatics and Mathematics (ERICM) handles inquiries about the W3C in the EMEA region; Keio University handles W3C's Japanese and Korean correspondence; and the Computer Science & Artificial Intelligence Lab (CSAIL) at MIT handles all other countries, include Australia and the U.S.

XXXIX. Internet Industry Resources

American Registry for Internet Numbers (ARIN)
3635 Concorde Pkwy., Ste. 200
Chantilly, VA 20151-1130 US
Phone: 703-227-0660
Fax: 703-227-0676
E-mail Address: *hostmaster@arin.net*
Web Address: www.arin.net
The American Registry for Internet Numbers (ARIN) is a nonprofit organization that administers and registers Internet protocol (IP) numbers. The organization also develops policies and offers educational outreach services.

Berkman Center for Internet & Society
Harvard Law School
23 Everett St., 2nd Fl.
Cambridge, MA 02138 US
Phone: 617-495-7547
Fax: 617-495-7641
E-mail Address: *cyber@law.harvard.edu*
Web Address: cyber.law.harvard.edu
The Berkman Center for Internet & Society focuses on the exploration of the development and inner-workings of laws pertaining to the Internet. The center offers Internet courses, conferences, advising and advocacy.

Congressional Internet Caucus Advisory Committee (ICAC)
1634 Eye St. NW, Ste. 1107
Washington, DC 20006 US
Phone: 202-638-4370
Fax: 202-637-0968
E-mail Address: *arodway@netcaucus.org*
Web Address: www.netcaucus.org
The Congressional Internet Caucus Advisory Committee (ICAC) works to educate the public and a bipartisan group of over 170 members of the U.S. House and Senate about internet-related policy issues.

Internet Assigned Numbers Authority (IANA)
Internet Corporation for Assigned Names and Numbers
4676 Admiralty Way, Ste. 330
Marina del Rey, CA 90292-6601 US
Phone: 310-823-9358
Fax: 310-823-8649
E-mail Address: *iana@iana.org*
Web Address: www.iana.org
The Internet Assigned Numbers Authority (IANA) serves as the central coordinator for the assignment of parameter values for Internet protocols. IANA is operated by the Internet Corporation for Assigned Names and Numbers (ICANN).

XL. Internet Usage Statistics

comScore, Inc.
11950 Democracy Dr.
Reston, VA 20190 US
Phone: 703-438-2000
Fax: 703-438-2051
Toll Free: 866-638-3835
Web Address: www.comscore.com
comScore, Inc. provides data analytics and solutions that help companies build profitable, sustainable businesses. The firm's consumer behavior insights are a guide for marketing and trading strategies.

XLI. Manufacturing Associations-General

Association for Manufacturing Technology (AMT)
7901 Westpark Dr.
McLean, VA 22102-4206 US
Phone: 703-893-2900
Fax: 703-893-1151
Toll Free: 800-524-0475
E-mail Address: *amt@amtonline.org*
Web Address: www.amtonline.org
The Association for Manufacturing Technology (AMT) actively supports and promotes American manufacturers of machine tools and manufacturing technology.
National Center for Manufacturing Sciences (NCMS)
3025 Boardwalk Dr.
Ann Arbor, MI 48108-3230 US

Fax: 734-995-1150
Toll Free: 800-222-6267
Web Address: www.ncms.org
The National Center for Manufacturing Sciences (NCMS) is a nonprofit membership organization dedicated to advancing the global competitiveness of North American industry through collaboration.

Singapore Institute of Manufacturing Technology (SIMTech)
71 Nanyang Dr.
638075 Singapore
Phone: 65-6793-8383
E-mail Address: *ido@SIMTech.a-star.edu.sg*
Web Address: www.simtech.a-star.edu.sg
The Singapore Institute of Manufacturing Technology (SIMTech) has completed more than 880 projects with more than 410 companies, big and small, in the electronics, semiconductor, precision engineering, aerospace, automotive, marine, logistics and other sectors.

XLII. Manufacturing Associations-Machinery

Indian Machine Tool Manufacturers Association (IMTMA)
Plot No. 249 F, Phase IV
Udyog Vihar, Sector 18
Gurgaon, Haryana 122 015 India
Phone: 91-124-4014101
Fax: 91-124-4014108
E-mail Address: *imtma@imtma.in*
Web Address: www.imtma.in
Indian Machine Tool Manufacturers Association (IMTMA) has a membership of over 400 organizations of all sizes spread across the country. Membership of IMTMA specializes in the complete range of metalworking machine tools and manufacturing solutions, accessories for machines, as well as the varied range of cutting tools and tooling systems.

Korea Association of Machinery Industry (KOAMI)
KOAMI Bldg., 13-31
Yeouido-dong, Yeongdeungpo-gu
Seoul, 150-729 Korea
Phone: 82-2-369-7851
Fax: 82-2-369-7900
E-mail Address: *trade@koami.or.kr*
Web Address: www.koami.or.kr
The Korea Association of Machinery Industry (KOAMI) is the national trade organization for the Korean machinery industry.

National Tooling and Machining Association (NTMA)
9300 Livingston Rd.
Ft. Washington, MD 20744 US
Fax: 301-248-7104
Toll Free: 800-248-6862
E-mail Address: *info@ntma.org*
Web Address: www.ntma.org
The National Tooling and Machining Association (NTMA) helps members of the U.S. precision custom manufacturing industries achieve business success in a global economy through advocacy, advice, networking, information, programs and services.

XLIII. Metals & Steel Industry Associations

Chinese Society for Metals
Chinese Society for Metals
46 Dongsixi Dajie
Beijing, 100711 China
Phone: 86-10-65211206
Fax: 86-10-65124122
E-mail Address: *csmoffice@csm.org.cn*
Web Address: www.csm.org.cn
The Chinese Society for Metals is a non-profit organization that focuses on advancing science and technology in the metallurgical industry, materials science and engineering, and the professionals in these fields.

Society for Mining, Metallurgy and Exploration (SME)
8307 Shaffer Pkwy.
Littleton, CO 80127-4102 US
Phone: 303-973-9550
Fax: 303-973-3845
Toll Free: 800-763-3132
E-mail Address: *cs@smenet.org*
Web Address: www.smenet.org
The Society for Mining, Metallurgy and Exploration (SME) advances the worldwide mining and minerals community through information exchange and professional development.

XLIV. Nanotechnology Associations

Global Emerging Technology Institute (GETI)
106 Central Park S., Ste. 6D
New York, NY 10019 US
E-mail Address: *inquiries@getinet.org*
Web Address: www.getinet.org
GETI is a non-profit association active in promoting the development of nanotechnology and other emerging technologies. It has offices in New York City and Tokyo.

International Association of Nanotechnology (Anano)
1290 Parkmoor Ave.
San Jose, CA 95126 US
Phone: 408-280-6222
Fax: 408-280-6255
E-mail Address: *info@ianano.org*
Web Address: www.ianano.org
The International Association of Nanotechnology is a nonprofit organization that promotes research collaboration worldwide for the benefit of society.

XLV. Nanotechnology Resources

Center for Directed Assembly of Nanostructures
Rensselaer Polytechnic Institute
Nanoscale Science & Engineering Ctr., 110 8th St., 1st Fl. MRC
Troy, NY 12180 US
Phone: 518-276-8846
Fax: 518-276-6540
E-mail Address: *nanocenter@rpi.edu*
Web Address: www.rpi.edu/dept/nsec
The Center for Directed Assembly of Nanostructures focuses on learning to produce nanomaterials in controlled ways, incorporating them into polymer and ceramic composites and assembling them into complex structures. It is part of the Rensselaer Polytechnic Institute, and was one of the first six National Science Foundation Nanoscale Science and Engineering Centers (NSF NSEC) establihsed in 2001.

Indian Institute Of Technology - Roorkee
Roorkee
Uttarakhand, 247 667 India
Phone: 91-1332-285311
E-mail Address: *regis@iitr.ernet.in*
Web Address: www.iitr.ac.in
Indian Institute of Technology - Roorkee is among the foremost institutes in higher technological education and engineering in India for basic and applied research.

IndiaNano
IndiaCo Center, 4th Fl., Symphony, S. No. 210 A/1
Range Hills Road, Shivaji Nagar
Pune, Maharashtra 411 020 India
Phone: 91-20-25513254
Fax: 91-20-25513243
E-mail Address: *info@indianano.com*
Web Address: www.indianano.com
IndiaNano is a non-profit organization located in India and supported by academic and industry experts. It aims to develop collaboration in order to advance technologies, including nanotechnology.

Institute of Bioengineering and Nanotechnology, Singapore
31 Biopolis Way
The Nanos, 04-01
138669 Singapore
Phone: 65-6824-7000
Fax: 65-6478-9080
E-mail Address: *enquiry@ibn.a-star.edu.sg*
Web Address: www.ibn.a-star.edu.sg
As a scientific research institute, Institute of Bioengineering and Nanotechnology focuses its activities on developing the following key areas: developing a critical knowledge base in bioengineering and nanotechnology; generating new biomaterials, devices and processes; and producing and publishiing high-quality scientific research.

National Nanotechnology Initiative (NNI)
National Nanotechnology Coordination Office
4201 Wilson Blvd., Stafford II, Rm. 405
Arlington, VA 22230 US
Phone: 703-292-8626
Fax: 703-292-9312
E-mail Address: *info@nnco.nano.gov*
Web Address: www.nano.gov
The National Nanotechnology Initiative (NNI) is a federal R&D program established to coordinate the multiagency efforts in nanoscale science, engineering and technology. Twenty-six federal agencies participate in the NNI, of which 13 have an R&D budget for nanotechnology. Other federal organizations contribute with studies, applications of the results from those agencies performing R&D and other collaborations. The NNI is part of the National Nanotechnology Coordination Office within the Nanoscale Science Engineering and Technology (NSET) subcommittee of the National Science and Technology Council (NSTC).

XLVI. Patent Organizations-Global

World Intellectual Property Organization (WIPO)
34, chemin des Colombettes
Geneva 20, CH-1211 Switzerland
Phone: 41-22-338-9111
Fax: 41-22-733-54-28
E-mail Address: *publicinf@wipo.int*
Web Address: www.wipo.int
The WIPO has a United Nations mandate to assist organizations and companies in filing patents and other intellectual property data on a global basis. At its website, you can download free copies of its WIPO magazine, and you can search its international patent applications.

XLVII. Patent Resources

Patent Board (The)
20 N. Wacker Dr.
Chicago, IL 60606 US
Phone: 312-205-7000
Fax: 312-205-7001
E-mail Address: *info@patentboard.com*
Web Address: www.patentboard.com
The Patent Board is an independent provider of tools and metrics for patent analysis and intellectual property investing. Its services include technology landscape analysis, portfolio assessment and merger and acquisition due diligence.

Patent Law for Non-Lawyers
E-mail Address: *info@thinkbiotech.com*
Web Address: www.dnapatent.com/law

Patent Law for Non-Lawyers is an informative site detailing the patent process in the fields of biotechnology and engineering. The site assumes a working knowledge of the industry.

XLVIII. Payment, E-Commerce and Data Interchange Technology

International Center for Electronic Commerce (ICEC)
Technology Innovation Center of KAIST
Seoul Campus, 207-43, Cheongryang
Seoul, 130-012 Korea
Phone: 65-6-828-0230
E-mail Address: *icec@icec.net*
Web Address: www.icec.net
The International Center for Electronic Commerce (ICEC), based in Korea, is involved in the development of next-generation electronic commerce technologies and management schemes and establishing an international research consortium of e-commerce-related companies. It is part of the Graduate School of Management of the Korean Advanced Institute of Science & Technology (KAIST).

XLIX. Pharmaceutical Industry Associations (Drug Industry)

International Society of Pharmaceutical Engineers (ISPE)
3109 W. Dr. Martin Luther King, Jr. Blvd., Ste. 250
Tampa, FL 33607 US
Phone: 813-960-2105
Fax: 813-264-2816
E-mail Address: *ASK@ispe.org*
Web Address: www.ispe.org
The International Society of Pharmaceutical Engineers (ISPE) is a worldwide nonprofit society dedicated to educating and advancing pharmaceutical manufacturing professionals and the pharmaceutical industry.

L. Plastics Industry Associations

China Engineering Plastics Industry Association
19 E Beisanhaun Rd.
Lanxing Plaza, Rm 703
Beijing, 100084 China
Phone: 86-10-6441-3726
Fax: 86-10-6445-0969
E-mail Address: *cepia@126.com*
Web Address: www.plasticsnews.com
The China Engineering Plastics Industry Association promotes the plastics technologies in construction engineering.

China Plastics Processing Industry Association
6 East Chang'an Ave.
Beijing, 100740 China
Phone: 86-10-6512-2056
Fax: 86-10-6522-5254
E-mail Address: *ccpa@ccpia.com.cn*
Web Address: www.cppia.com.cn
The China Plastics Processing Industry Association promotes the industry which includes plastic pipe, injection molded products and other engineering plastics.

LI. Research & Development, Laboratories

Applied Research Laboratories (ARL)
Applied Research Laboratories
University of Texas at Austin, 10000 Burnet Rd.
Austin, TX 78758 US
Phone: 512-835-3200
Fax: 512-835-3259
E-mail Address: *WebContactUs@arlut.utexas.edu*
Web Address: www.arlut.utexas.edu
Applied Research Laboratories (ARL) at the University of Texas at Austin provides research programs dedicated to improving the military capability of the United States in applications of acoustics, electromagnetic and information technology.

Argonne National Laboratory, Nuclear Engineering Division (ANL)
9700 S. Cass Ave.
Argonne, IL 60439-4814 US
Phone: 630-252-4780
E-mail Address: *neinfo@anl.gov*
Web Address: www.td.anl.gov
The Argonne National Laboratory-Nuclear Engineering Division (ANL) is engaged in research and development in the applied nuclear technology fields. These focuses include nuclear-related technologies such as nonproliferation, environmental remediation, fusion power and new initiatives.

Battelle Memorial Institute
505 King Ave.
Columbus, OH 43201-2693 US
Phone: 614-424-5853
Toll Free: 800-201-2011
Web Address: www.battelle.org
Battelle Memorial Institute serves commercial and governmental customers in developing new technologies and products. The institute adds technology to systems and processes for manufacturers; pharmaceutical and agrochemical industries; trade associations; and government agencies supporting energy, the environment, health, national security and transportation.

Brookhaven National Laboratory (BNL)
P.O. Box 5000
Upton, NY 11973-5000 US
Phone: 631-344-8000
E-mail Address: *mrowe@bnl.gov*

Web Address: www.bnl.gov
Brookhaven National Laboratory (BNL) is a research facility funded by the Office of Science within the Department of Energy. BNL conducts research in the physical, biomedical and environmental sciences, as well as in energy technologies and national security.

China Academy of Building Research (CABR)
30 Bei San Huan Dong Lu
Beijing, 100013 China
Phone: 010-84272233
Fax: 010-84281369
E-mail Address: *office@cabr.com.cn*
Web Address: www.cabr.cn
CABR is responsible for the development and management of the major engineering construction and product standards of China and is also the largest comprehensive research and development institute in the building industry in China. Some related institutes include Institute of Earthquake Engineering, Institute of Building Fire Research, Institute of Building Environment and Energy Efficiency (Building Physics), Institute of Foundation Engineering as well as many others.

Commonwealth Scientific and Industrial Research Organization (CSRIO)
CSIRO Enquiries
Bag 10
Clayton South, Victoria 3169 Australia
Phone: 61-3-9545-2176
Fax: 61-3-9545-2175
E-mail Address: *enquiries@csiro.au*
Web Address: www.csiro.au
The Commonwealth Scientific and Industrial Research Organization (CSRIO) is Australia's national science agency and a leading international research agency. CSRIO performs research in Australia over a broad range of areas including agriculture, minerals and energy, manufacturing, communications, construction, health and the environment.

Computational Neurobiology Laboratory
The Salk Institute
10010 N. Torrey Pines Rd.
La Jolla, CA 92037 US
Phone: 858-453-4100
E-mail Address: *sejnowski@salk.edu*
Web Address: www.cnl.salk.edu
The Computational Neurobiology Laboratory at The Salk Institute strives to understand the computational resources of the brain from the biophysical to the systems levels.

Council of Scientific & Industrial Research (CSIR)
Anusandhan Bhawan, 2 Rafi Marg
New Delhi, 110 001 India
Phone: 011-23710618
Fax: 011-23713011
E-mail Address: *itweb@csir.res.in*
Web Address: www.csir.res.in
The Council of Scientific & Industrial Research (CSIR) is a government-funded organization that promotes research and development initiatives in India. It operates in the fields of energy, biotechnology, space, science and technology.

Daresbury Laboratory
Daresbury
Warrington, Cheshire WA4 4AD UK
Phone: 44-1925-603000
Fax: 44-1925-603100
E-mail Address: *enquires@cclrc.ac.uk*
Web Address:
www.scitech.ac.uk/About/Struc/Locs/DL/facs.aspx
Daresbury Laboratory, operated by the Science & Technology Facilities Council (STFC), is a strong resource in computational science and engineering. The STFC was formed in April 2007 from the merger of the Council for the Central Laboratory of the Research Councils (CCLRC) and the Particle Physics and Astronomy Council (PPARRC).

Electronics and Telecommunications Research Institute (ETRI)
138 Gajeongno
Yuseong-gu
Daejeon, 305-700 Korea
Phone: 82-42-860-6114
E-mail Address: *khchong@etri.re.kr*
Web Address: www.etri.re.kr
Established in 1976, ETRI is a non-profit government-funded research organization that promotes technological excellence. The research institute has successfully developed information technologies such as TDX-Exchange, High Density Semiconductor Microchips, Mini-Super Computer (TiCOM), and Digital Mobile Telecommunication System (CDMA). ETRI's focus is on information technologies, robotics, telecommunications, digital broadcasting and future technology strategies.

Hanford Nuclear Site
825 Jadwin Ave., Ste. 1
Richland, WA 99352 US
Phone: 509-376-7411
E-mail Address: *Webmaster@rl.gov*
Web Address: www.hanford.gov
The Hanford Nuclear Site is designed to solve critical problems related to the environment, energy production and use, U.S. economic competitiveness and national security.

Idaho National Laboratory (INL)
1765 North Yellowstone Hwy.
P.O. Box 1625
Idaho Falls, ID 83415 US
Phone: 208-526-0111
Toll Free: 866-495-7440

Web Address: www.inl.gov
Idaho National Laboratory (INL) is a multidisciplinary, multiprogram laboratory that specializes in developing nuclear energy with research concerning the environment, energy, science and national defense.

Los Alamos National Laboratory (LANL)
Bikini Atoll Rd., SM 30
P.O. Box 1663
Los Alamos, NM 87545 US
Phone: 505-665-4400
Fax: 505-665-4411
Toll Free: 888-841-8256
E-mail Address: *community@lanl.gov*
Web Address: www.lanl.gov
The Los Alamos National Laboratory (LANL), a national energy lab in New Mexico, was originally built as a work site for the team that designed the first atomic bomb during World War II. Currently, it provides a continual stream of research in physics and energy matters. Much of that research is put to use in the commercial sector.

MITRE Corporation
202 Burlington Rd.
Bedford, MA 01730-1420 US
Phone: 781-271-2000
Web Address: www.mitre.org
MITRE Corporation is a nonprofit engineering institution offering expertise in communications, information, space, environmental and aviation systems. It operates three federally funded research and development centers for the U.S. government.

National Renewable Energy Laboratory (NREL)
1617 Cole Blvd.
Golden, CO 80401-3393 US
Phone: 303-275-3000
E-mail Address: *public_affairs@nrel.gov*
Web Address: www.nrel.gov
The National Renewable Energy Laboratory (NREL) reduces nuclear danger, transfers applied environmental technology to government and non-government entities and forms economic and industrial alliances.

National Research Council Canada (NRC)
NRC Communications & Corp. Rel.
1200 Montreal Rd., Bldg. M-58
Ottawa, ON K1A 0R6 Canada
Phone: 613-993-9101
Fax: 613-952-9907
Toll Free: 877-672-2672
E-mail Address: *info@nrc-cnrc.gc.ca*
Web Address: www.nrc-cnrc.gc.ca
National Research Council Canada (NRC) is a government organization of 20 research institutes that carry out multidisciplinary research with partners in industries and sectors key to Canada's economic development.

National Science Council of Taiwan (NSC)
No. 106, HoPing E. Road, Sec.2
Taipei, 10622 Taiwan
Phone: 886-2-27377992
Fax: 886-2-27377566
Web Address: www.nsc.gov.tw
The National Science Council of Taiwan oversees government funding of research and development as well as national technology programs.

Oak Ridge National Laboratory (ORNL)
P.O. Box 2008
1 Bethel Valley Rd.
Oak Ridge, TN 37831 US
Phone: 865-574-4160
Fax: 865-574-0595
E-mail Address: *strohlhf@ornl.gov*
Web Address: www.ornl.gov
The Oak Ridge National Laboratory (ORNL) is a multiprogram science and technology laboratory managed for the U.S. Department of Energy by U.T.-Battelle, LLC. It conducts basic and applied research and development to create scientific knowledge and technological solutions.

Pacific Northwest National Laboratory (PNNL)
902 Battelle Blvd.
Richland, WA 99352 US
Phone: 509-375-2121
Toll Free: 888-375-7665
E-mail Address: *inquiry@pnl.gov*
Web Address: www.pnl.gov
The Pacific Northwest National Laboratory (PNNL) is a Department of Energy facility that conducts nanotechnology research.

Sandia National Laboratories
1515 Eubank SE
Albuquerque, NM 87123 US
Phone: 505-845-0011
E-mail Address: *webmaster@sandia.gov*
Web Address: www.sandia.gov
Sandia National Laboratories is a national security laboratory operated for the U.S. Department of Energy by the Sandia Corporation. It designs all -nuclear components for the nation's nuclear weapons and performs a wide variety of energy research and development projects.

Savannah River Site (SRS)
Washington Savannah River Company, LLC
2131 S. Centennial Avenue SE
Aiken, SC 29803 US
Phone: 803.952.9583
Fax: 803-952-9523
E-mail Address: *will.callicott@srs.gov*
Web Address: www.srs.gov
The Savannah River Site (SRS) is a nuclear fuel storage and production site that works to protect the people and the environment of the U.S. through safe, secure, cost-

effective management of the country's nuclear weapons stockpile and nuclear materials. While the site is owned by the U.S. Department of Energy, it is operated by Washington Savannah River Company, LLC (WSRC), a wholly-owned subsidiary of Washington Group International.

SRI International
333 Ravenswood Ave.
Menlo Park, CA 94025-3493 US
Phone: 650-859-2000
E-mail Address: *ellie.javadi@sri.com*
Web Address: www.sri.com
SRI International is a nonprofit organization offering a wide range of services, including engineering services, information technology, pure and applied physical sciences, product development, pharmaceutical discovery, biopharmaceutical discovery and policy issues. SRI conducts research for commercial and governmental customers.

LII. RFID Associations

EPCglobal Inc.
Rue Royale 29
Brussels, 1000 Belgium
Phone: 32 2 229 18 80
Fax: 32 2 217 43 47
E-mail Address: *info@gs1belu.org*
Web Address: www.epcglobalinc.org
EPCglobal Inc. is a global standards organization for the Electronic Product Code (EPC), which supports the use of RFID. It was initially developed by the Auto-ID Center, an academic research project at the Massachusetts Institute of Technology (MIT). Today, offices and affiliates of EPCglobal are based in nearly every nation of the world. The nonprofit organization is a joint venture between GS1, formerly known as EAN International, and GS1 US, formerly known as the Uniform Code Council. (Also see GS1 US (UCC) under Logistics and Supply Chain Associations.)

LIII. Robotics Associations

Laboratory Robotics Interest Group (LRIG)
1730 W. Circle Dr.
Martinsville, NJ 08836-2147 US
Phone: 732-302-1038
Fax: 732-875-0270
E-mail Address: *andy.zaayenga@lab-robotics.org*
Web Address: www.lab-robotics.org
Laboratory Robotics Interest Group (LRIG) is a membership group focused on the application of robotics in the laboratory.

Singapore Industrial Automation Association (SIAA)
71 Ubi Crescent 06-06
Excalibur Ctr.
408571 Singapore
Phone: 65-6749-1822
Fax: 65-6841-3986
E-mail Address: *secretariat@siaa.org*
Web Address: www.esiaa.com
The Singapore Industrial Automation Association (SIAA) is a non-profit organization which promotes the application of industrial automation with reference to business, technology & information services.

LIV. Satellite-Related Professional Organizations

Geospatial Information and Technology Association (GITA)
14456 E. Evans Ave.
Aurora, CO 80014-1409 US
Phone: 303-337-0513
Fax: 303-337-1001
E-mail Address: *info@gita.org*
Web Address: www.gita.org
The Geospatial Information and Technology Association (GITA) is an educational association for geospatial information and technology professionals.

Society of Satellite Professionals International (SSPI)
The New York Information Technology Ctr.
55 Broad St., 14th Fl.
New York, NY 10004 US
Phone: 212-809-5199
Fax: 212-825-0075
E-mail Address: *rbell@sspi.org*
Web Address: www.sspi.org
The Society of Satellite Professionals International (SSPI) is a nonprofit member-benefit society that serves satellite professionals worldwide throughout the span of their careers.

LV. Shipyard Industry Associations

Association of Singapore Marine Industries (ASMI)
20 Science Park Rd.
02-04/05 TeleTech Park
117674 Singapore
Phone: 65-6872-0030
Fax: 65-6872-5747
E-mail Address: *asmi@pacific.net.sg*
Web Address: www.asmi.com
The Association of Singapore Marine Industries (ASMI) is a non-profit trade association which promotes the interests of a wide cross-section of the Singapore ship repair, shipbuilding, rig building and marine industry in Singapore.

LVI. Software Industry Associations

Business Software Alliance (BSA)
1150 18th St. NW, Ste. 700
Washington, DC 20036 US
Phone: 202-872-5500
Fax: 202-872-5501
E-mail Address: *software@bsa.org*
Web Address: www.bsa.org
The Business Software Alliance (BSA) is a leading global software industry association. BSA educates consumers regarding software management, copyright protection, cyber security, trade, e-commerce and other internet-related issues.

Information Systems Security Association, Inc. (ISSA)
9220 SW Barbur Blvd., Ste. 119-333
Portland, OR 97219 US
Phone: 206-388-4584
Fax: 206-299-3366
Toll Free: 866-349-5818
E-mail Address: *editor@issa.org*
Web Address: www.issa.org
The Information Systems Security Association, Inc. (ISSA) is an international not-for-profit organization of information security professionals.

National Association of Software and Service Companies of India (NASSCOM)
International Youth Centre
Teen Murti Marg, Chanakyapuri
New Delhi, 110 021 India
Phone: 202-944-1973
Fax: 202-944-1970
E-mail Address: *in_pr@nasscom.in*
Web Address: www.nasscom.org
The National Association of Software and Service Companies (NASSCOM) is the trade body and chamber of commerce for the IT software and services industry in India. The association's 1,200 members consist of corporations located around the world involved in software development, software services, software products, IT-enabled/BPO services and e-commerce. Collectively, its members employ over 2 million people.

LVII. Software Industry Resources

Software Engineering Institute (SEI)-Carnegie Mellon
Customer Relations
4500 Fifth Ave.
Pittsburgh, PA 15213-2612 US
Phone: 412-268-5800
Fax: 412-268-6257
Toll Free: 888-201-4479
E-mail Address: *customer-relations@sei.cmu.edu*
Web Address: www.sei.cmu.edu
The Software Engineering Institute (SEI) is a federally funded research and development center at Carnegie Mellon University, sponsored by the U.S. Department of Defense through the Office of the Under Secretary of Defense for Acquisition, Technology, and Logistics [OUSD (AT&L)]. The SEI's core purpose is to help users make measured improvements in their software engineering capabilities.

LVIII. Supercomputing

Top 500 Supercomputer Sites
Prometeus GmbH
Fliederstr. 2
Waibstadt-Daisbach, D-74915 Germany
Phone: 49-7261-913-160
E-mail Address: *info@top500.org*
Web Address: www.top500.org
The Top 500 project was started in 1993 to provide a reliable basis for tracking and detecting trends in high-performance computing. Twice a year, a list of the sites operating the 500 most powerful computer systems is assembled and released. The Linpack benchmark is used as a performance measure for ranking the computer systems. The list contains a variety of information including system specifications and major application areas. The Top 500 web site is promoted by Prometeus GmbH.

LIX. Technology Transfer Associations

Association of University Technology Managers (AUTM)
111 Deer Lake Rd., Ste. 100
Deerfield, IL 60015 US
Phone: 847-559-0846
Fax: 847-480-9282
E-mail Address: *info@autm.net*
Web Address: www.autm.net
The Association of University Technology Managers (AUTM) is a non-profit professional association with membership of more than 3,600 intellectual property managers and business executives from 45 countries. The association’s mission is to advance the field of technology transfer, and enhance our ability to bring academic and non-profit research to people around the world.

LX. Telecommunications Industry Associations

Alliance for Telecommunications Industry Solutions (ATIS)
1200 G St. NW, Ste. 500
Washington, DC 20005 US
Phone: 202-628-6380
Fax: 202-393-5453
E-mail Address: *atispr@atis.org*
Web Address: www.atis.org

The Alliance for Telecommunications Industry Solutions (ATIS) is a U.S.-based body committed to rapidly developing and promoting technical and operations standards for the communications and related information technologies industry worldwide.

China Communications Standards Association
4 South 4th St., Zhongguancun
Haidian District
Beijing, 100190 China
Phone: 86-10-62302730
Fax: 86-10-62301849
Web Address: www.cwts.org
China Communications Standards Association is a nonprofit organization which works to standardize the field of communications technology across China.

European Telecommunications Standards Institute (ETSI)
ETSI Secretariat
650, route des Lucioles
Sophia-Antipolis Cedex, 06921 France
Phone: 33-4-92-94-42-00
Fax: 33-4-93-65-47-16
E-mail Address: *helpdesk@etsi.org*
Web Address: www.etsi.org
The European Telecommunications Standards Institute (ETSI) is a nonprofit organization whose mission is to produce the telecommunications standards that will be used throughout Europe.

Institute for Telecommunication Sciences (ITS)
325 Broadway
Boulder, CO 80305-3328 US
Phone: 303-497-5216
E-mail Address: *info@its.bldrdoc.gov*
Web Address: www.its.bldrdoc.gov
The Institute for Telecommunication Sciences (ITS) is the research and engineering branch of the National Telecommunications and Information Administration (NTIA), a division of the U.S. Department of Commerce (DOC).

International Telecommunications Union (ITU)
Place des Nations
Geneva 20, 1211 Switzerland
Phone: 41-22-730-5111
Fax: 41-22-733-7256
E-mail Address: *itumail@itu.int*
Web Address: www.itu.int
The International Telecommunications Union (ITU) is an international organization for the standardization of the radio and telecommunications industry. It is an agency of the United Nations (UN).

The International Communications Project
Intercomms Unit 2 Marine Action
Birdhill Industrial Estate
Birdhill, Co Tipperary Ireland
Phone: 353-86-108-3932
Fax: 353-61-749801
E-mail Address: *robert.alcock@intercomms.net*
Web Address: www.intercomms.net
International Communications (InterComms) is an authoritative policy, strategy and reference publication for the international telecommunications industry.

LXI. Telecommunications Resources

Infocomm Development Authority of Singapore (IDA)
8 Temasek Blvd. 14-00
Suntec Tower 3
038998 Singapore
Phone: 65-6211-0888
Fax: 65-6211-2222
E-mail Address: *info@ida.gov.sg*
Web Address: www.ida.com
The goal of the Infocomm Development Authority of Singapore (IDA) is to actively seek opportunities to grow the infocomm industry in both the domestic and international markets.

LXII. Temporary Staffing Firms

CDI Corporation
1717 Arch St., 35th Fl.
Philadelphia, PA 19103-2768 US
Phone: 215-569-2200
Fax: 215-569-1300
Toll Free: 800 996 7566
Web Address: www.cdicorp.com
CDI Corporation specializes in engineering and information technology staffing services. Company segments include CDI IT Solutions, specializing in information technology, CDI Engineering Solutions, specializing in engineering outsourcing services, AndersElite Limited, operating in the United Kingdom and Australia, and MRINetwork, specializing in executive recruitment.

Crystal Staffing Ltd.
23 Church St.
Boston, Lincolnshire PE21 6NW UK
Phone: 01205-358777
Fax: 01205-358797
E-mail Address: *crystalgroup@btconnect.com*
Web Address: www.crystalstaffing.ltd.uk
Crystal Staffing Group is a specialist recruiter in the provision of permanent, contract and temporary staffing throughout the UK within the technical, professional, engineering, construction, industrial, commercial and national sales sectors.

Glotel Inc.
30 S. Wacker Dr., Ste. 2800

Chicago, IL 60606 US
Phone: 312-612-7480
Fax: 312-715-0756
E-mail Address: *chicago@glotelinc.com*
Web Address: www.usa.glotel.com
Glotel is a global technology staffing and managed projects solutions company specializing in the placement of contract and permanent personnel within all areas of technology. Glotel has a network of 19 offices throughout Europe, the U.S. and Asia-Pacific.

Hays plc
141 Moorgate
London, EC2M 6TX UK
Phone: 0800-716026
E-mail Address: *customerservice@hays.com*
Web Address: www.hays.com
Hays is a global leader in specialist recruitment, placing professional candidates in permanent, temporary and interim positions with over 8,900 staff in 390 offices across 27 countries.

Hudson Highland Group, Inc.
560 Lexington Ave.
4th & 5th Fl.
New York, NY 10022 US
Phone: 212-351-7400
Fax: 917-256-8592
Web Address: www.hudson.com
Hudson Highland Group, Inc. provides permanent recruitment, contract and human resources consulting and inclusion solutions. Services range from single placements to total outsourced solutions. The company employs more than 3,300 professionals serving clients and candidates in more than 20 countries.

MPS Group, Inc.
1 Independent Dr.
Jacksonville, FL 32202 US
Phone: 904-360-2000
Fax: 904-360-2972
Web Address: www.mpsgroup.com
MPS Group is a leading provider of staffing, consulting, and human resource solutions with offices throughout the United States, Canada, the United Kingdom and continental Europe. Primary brands include Accounting Principals, Badenoch, Entegee Engineering Technical Group, Soliant Health and Modis International IT solutions

Pasona Group Inc. (Japan)
Otemachi-Nomura Bldg. 2-1-1 Otemachi, Chiyoda-ku
Tokyo, 100-0004 Japan
Phone: 03-6734-1100
Web Address: www.pasonagroup.co.jp
Pasona Inc. provides personnel services. Services offered range from temporary staffing/contracting, placement/recruiting, outplacement, to outsourcing and training.

Volt Information Sciences, Inc.
560 Lexington Ave., 15th Fl.
New York, NY 10022 US
Phone: 212-704-2400
Web Address: www.volt.com
Volt Information Sciences, Inc. maintains 300 temporary staffing offices in North America and in the U.K.

LXIII. U.S. Government Agencies

Federal Communications Commission (FCC)
445 12th St. SW
Washington, DC 20554 US
Fax: 866-418-0232
Toll Free: 888-225-5322
E-mail Address: *fccinfo@fcc.gov*
Web Address: www.fcc.gov
The Federal Communications Commission (FCC) is an independent U.S. government agency established by the Communications Act of 1934, and is responsible for regulating interstate and international communications by radio, television, wire, satellite and cable.

Federal Communications Commission (FCC)-Wireless Telecommunications Bureau
Federal Communications Commission
445 12th St. SW
Washington, DC 20554 US
Fax: 888-225-5322
Toll Free: 888-225-5322
E-mail Address: *fccinfo@fcc.gov*
Web Address: wireless.fcc.gov
The Federal Communications Commission (FCC)-Wireless Telecommunications Bureau handles nearly all FCC domestic wireless telecommunications programs and policies, including cellular and PCS phones, pagers and two-way radios. The bureau also regulates the use of radio spectrum for businesses, aircraft/ship operators and individuals.

National Aeronautics and Space Administration (NASA)
NASA Headquarters
Ste. 5K39
Washington, DC 20546-0001 US
Phone: 202-358-0001
Fax: 202-358-3469
E-mail Address: *public-inquiries@hq.nasa.gov*
Web Address: www.nasa.gov
The National Aeronautics and Space Administration (NASA) is the U.S. space agency, handling all space-related research and development.

National Institute of Standards and Technology (NIST)
100 Bureau Dr., Stop 1070

Gaithersburg, MD 20899-1070 US
Phone: 301-975-6478
E-mail Address: *inquiries@nist.gov*
Web Address: www.nist.gov
The National Institute of Standards and Technology (NIST) is an agency of the U.S. Department of Commerce's Technology Administration. It works with various industries to develop and apply technology, measurements and standards.

National Science Foundation (NSF)
4201 Wilson Blvd.
Arlington, VA 22230 US
Phone: 703-292-5111
Toll Free: 800-877-8339
E-mail Address: *info@nsf.gov*
Web Address: www.nsf.gov
The National Science Foundation (NSF) is an independent U.S. government agency responsible for promoting science and engineering. The foundation provides grants and funding for research.

U.S. Nuclear Regulatory Commission (NRC)
11555 Rockville Pike
Rockville, MD 20852 US
Phone: 301-415-7000
Fax: 301-415-3716
Toll Free: 800-368-5642
Web Address: www.nrc.gov
The U.S. Nuclear Regulatory Commission (NRC) is an independent agency established by Congress to ensure adequate protection of public health and safety, common defense and security and the environment in use of nuclear materials in the United States.

U.S. Patent and Trademark Office (PTO)
U.S. Patent and Trademark Office
Office of Public Affairs, P. O. Box 1450
Alexandria, VA 22313-1450 US
Phone: 571-272-1000
Fax: 571-273-8300
Toll Free: 800-786-9199
E-mail Address: *usptoinfo@uspto.gov*
Web Address: www.uspto.gov
The U.S. Patent and Trademark Office (PTO) administers patent and trademark laws for the U.S. and enables registration of patents and trademarks.

LXIV. Wireless & Cellular Industry Associations

Bluetooth Special Interest Group (SIG)
500 108th Ave. NE, Ste. 250
Bellevue, WA 98004 US
Phone: 425-691-3535
E-mail Address: *webmaster@bluetooth.com*
Web Address: www.bluetooth.com
The Bluetooth Special Interest Group (SIG) is a trade association comprised of leaders in the telecommunications, computing, automotive, industrial automation and network industries that is driving the development of Bluetooth wireless technology, a low cost short-range wireless specification for connecting mobile devices and bringing them to market.

CDMA Development Group (CDG)
575 Anton Blvd., Ste. 560
Costa Mesa, CA 92626 US
Phone: 714-545-5211
Fax: 714-545-4601
Toll Free: 888-800-2362
E-mail Address: *cdg@cdg.org*
Web Address: www.cdg.org
The CDMA Development Group (CDG) is composed of the world's leading CDMA service providers and manufacturers that have joined together to lead the adoption and evolution of CDMA wireless systems around the world.

Femto Forum
P.O. Box 23
Dursley, Gloucestershire GL11 5WA UK
Phone: 44-0845-644-5823
Fax: 44-0845-644-5824
E-mail Address: *info@femtoforum.org*
Web Address: www.femtoforum.org
The Femto Forum is a not-for-profit membership organisation founded in 2007 to promote femtocell deployment worldwide. Comprised of mobile operators, telecoms hardware and software vendors, content providers and innovative start-ups, the group's mission is to advance the development and adoption of femtocell products and services as the optimum technology for the provision of high-quality 2G/3G coverage and premium services within the residential and small to medium business markets.

Global System for Mobile Communication Association (GSMA)
1st Fl., Mid City Pl.
71 High Holborn
London, WC1V 6EA UK
Phone: 44-020-7759-2300
Fax: 44-020-7759-2301
E-mail Address: *info@gsm.org*
Web Address: www.gsmworld.com
The Global System for Mobile Communications Association (GSMA) is a global trade association representing more than 740 GSM mobile phone operators from 219 countries.

Wireless Communications Association International (WCA)
1333 H St. NW, Ste. 700 W.
Washington, DC 20005-4754 US
Phone: 202-452-7823
Fax: 202-452-0041

E-mail Address: *susan@wcai.com*
Web Address: www.wcai.com
The Wireless Communications Association International (WCA) is the principal nonprofit trade association representing the wireless broadband industry.

Chapter 4

THE ENGINEERING & RESEARCH 500: WHO THEY ARE AND HOW THEY WERE CHOSEN

Includes Indexes by Company Name, Industry & Location, And a Complete Table of Sales, Profits and Ranks

The companies chosen to be listed in PLUNKETT'S ENGINEERING & RESEARCH INDUSTRY ALMANAC comprise a unique list. THE ENGINEERING & RESEARCH 500 (the actual count is 503 companies) were chosen specifically for their dominance in the many facets of the engineering and research industry in which they operate. Complete information about each firm can be found in the "Individual Profiles," beginning at the end of this chapter. These profiles are in alphabetical order by company name.

THE ENGINEERING & RESEARCH 500 companies are from all parts of the United States, Asia, Canada, Europe and beyond. Essentially, THE ENGINEERING & RESEARCH 500 includes companies that are deeply involved in the technologies, services and trends that keep the entire industry forging ahead.

Simply stated, THE ENGINEERING & RESEARCH 500 contains the largest, most successful, fastest growing firms in engineering, research and related industries in the world. To be included in our list, the firms had to meet the following criteria:

1) Generally, these are corporations based in the U.S., however, the headquarters of 250 firms are located in other nations.
2) Prominence, or a significant presence, in engineering, research, engineering services, equipment and supporting fields. (See the following Industry Codes section for a complete list of types of businesses that are covered).
3) The companies in THE ENGINEERING & RESEARCH 500 do not have to be exclusively in the engineering and research field.
4) Financial data and vital statistics must have been available to the editors of this book, either directly from the company being written about or from outside sources deemed reliable and accurate by the editors. A small number of companies that we would like to have included are not listed because of a lack of sufficient, objective data.

INDEXES TO THE ENGINEERING & RESEARCH 500, AS FOUND IN THIS CHAPTER AND IN THE BACK OF THE BOOK:

INDUSTRY LIST, WITH CODES

This book refers to the following list of unique industry codes, based on the 1997 NAIC code system (NAIC is used by many analysts as a replacement for older SIC codes because NAIC is more specific to today's industry sectors). Companies profiled in this book are given a primary NAIC code, reflecting the main line of business of each firm.

Energy

Fuel Mining & Extraction

211111 Oil & Natural Gas Exploration & Production
213111 Petroleum-Drilling Oil & Gas Wells Support

Petroleum-Refining & Manufacturing

325110 Petrochemicals Manufacturing
325120 Industrial Gas Manufacturing

Energy

325188 Nuclear Fuels & Other Inorganic Chemicals

Financial Services

Banking, Credit & Finance

522220A Financing--Business

Health Care

Health Products, Manufacturing

325412 Drugs (Pharmaceuticals), Discovery & Manufacturing
325413 Diagnostic Services and Substances Manufacturing
325414 Biological Products, Manufacturing
339113 Medical/Dental/Surgical Equipment & Supplies, Manufacturing

InfoTech

Computers & Electronics Manufacturing

334110 Computer Networking & Related Equipment, Manufacturing
334111 Computer Hardware, Manufacturing
334112 Computer Storage Equipment & Misc Parts, Manufacturing
334119 Computer Accessories, Monitors, Printers Manufacturing
334310 Audio & Video Equipment, Consumer Electronics
334413 Semiconductors (Microchips)/Integrated Circuits/Components, Manufacturing
334419 Contract Electronics Manufacturing
334500 Instrument Manufacturing, including Measurement, Control, Test & Navigational

Electrical Equipment & Wire, Manufacturing

335921 Fiber Optic Cable & Electrical Wire

Software

511201 Computer Software, Accounting, Banking & Financial

511203 Computer Software, Sales & Customer Relationship Management

511204 Computer Software, Operating Systems, Languages & Development Tools

511207 Computer Software, Business Management & ERP

511208 Computer Software, Games & Entertainment

511209 Computer Software, Multimedia, Graphics & Publishing

511211 Computer Software, Security & Anti-Virus

511213 Computer Software, Telecom, Communications & VOIP

511214 Computer Software, Networking & Storage

511215 Computer Software, Product Lifecycle, Engineering, Design & CAD

Information & Data Processing Services

514199B Search Engine Portals

Information Services-Professional

541512 Consulting--Computer, Telecommunications & Internet

541512A Consulting--Information Systems & Applications Research

Manufacturing

Paper Products/Forest Products

322000 Forest Products/Paper, Manufacturing

Chemicals

325000 Chemicals, Manufacturing

Construction

326199 Building Products & Construction Materials in Plastic, Manufacturing

Primary Minerals

331000 Steel & Metals, Manufacturing

Machinery & Manufacturing Equipment

333000 Machinery, Manufacturing

333295 Semiconductor Manufacturing Equipment

333298 Fuel Cells Manufacturing

333313 Business Machines, Manufacturing

333314 Optical Instrument & Lens, Manufacturing

333410 Ventilation, Heating & Air-Conditioning Manufacturing

333611 Turbine & Turbine Generator Set Unit Manufacturing

Electrical Equipment, Appliances, Tools

335000 Electrical Equipment, Manufacturing

335313 Electrical Switches, Sensors, MEMS, Optomechanicals

Fabricated Metals

336350 Automobile Transmission & Power Train Parts Manufacturing

Retailing

Gasoline Stations

447110 Gasoline Stations

Services

Agriculture

115112 Agricultural Crop Production Support, Seeds, Fertilizers

Construction

230000 Construction Services

234000 Construction, Heavy & Civil Engineering

Consulting & Professional Services

541330 Engineering & Facilities Support Services

541620 Consulting--Environmental

541710 Research & Development-Physical, Engineering & Life Sciences

Management

551110 Management of Companies & Enterprises

Security Services

561610 Security, Protection, Armored Car & Investigation Services

Telecommunications

Telecommunications Equipment

334200 Communications Equipment, Manufacturing

334210 Telecommunications Equipment Manufacturing

334220 Radio & Wireless Communication, Manufacturing

Transportation

Transportation-Manufacturing of Equipment

336111 Automobiles, Manufacturing

336120 Trucks, RVs & Misc. Automotive, Manufacturing

336300 Automobile Parts Manufacturing

336600 Ship Manufacturing

Aerospace

336410 Aerospace & Aircraft Related Manufacturing

Truck

488490 Other Support Activities for Road Transportation

INDEX OF RANKINGS WITHIN INDUSTRY GROUPS

Company	Industry Code	2008 Sales (U.S. $ thousands)	Sales Rank	2008 Profits (U.S. $ thousands)	Profits Rank
Aerospace & Aircraft Related Manufacturing					
AIRBUS SAS	336410				
AVIALL INC	336410	2,000,000	22		
BAE SYSTEMS PLC	336410	23,931,600	8	2,538,000	6
BOEING COMPANY	336410	60,909,000	1	2,672,000	5
BOMBARDIER INC	336410	17,506,000	11	317,000	16
DASSAULT AVIATION SA	336410	4,684,520	19	466,420	13
EMBRAER BRASILIAN AVIATION	336410	6,335,000	17	388,700	14
EUROPEAN AERONAUTIC DEFENSE AND SPACE CO (EADS)	336410	57,301,500	3	2,115,110	8
GE AVIATION	336410	19,239,000	10	3,684,000	2
GENERAL DYNAMICS CORP	336410	29,300,000	7	2,459,000	7
GOODRICH CORPORATION	336410	7,062,000	16	681,000	11
GULFSTREAM AEROSPACE	336410	5,512,000	18		
HONEYWELL INTERNATIONAL	336410	36,556,000	5	2,792,000	4
ITT CORPORATION	336410	11,694,800	15	794,700	10
LEARJET INC	336410				
LOCKHEED MARTIN CORP	336410	42,731,000	4	3,217,000	3
NORTHROP GRUMMAN CORP	336410	33,887,000	6	-1,281,000	20
RAYTHEON CO	336410	23,174,000	9	1,672,000	9
ROLLSROYCE PLC	336410	13,323,400	14	-1,973,130	21
SAAB AB	336410				
SAFRAN SA	336410	13,666,700	13	206,410	18
SINGAPORE TECHNOLOGIES ENGINEERING LIMITED	336410	3,523,310	21	356,420	15
SPIRIT AEROSYSTEMS HOLDINGS INC	336410	3,772,000	20	265,000	17
TELEDYNE TECHNOLOGIES INC	336410	1,893,000	23	111,300	19
TEXTRON INC	336410	14,246,000	12	486,000	12
UNITED TECHNOLOGIES CORP	336410	58,681,000	2	4,689,000	1
Agricultural Crop Production Support, Seeds, Fertilizers					
MONSANTO CO	115112	11,365,000	2	2,024,000	1
SYNGENTA AG	115112	11,624,000	1	1,385,000	2
Audio & Video Equipment, Consumer Electronics					
PANASONIC CORPORATION	334310	93,428,320	2	2,905,150	3
PIONEER CORPORATION	334310	7,753,300	7	-179,900	6
ROYAL PHILIPS ELECTRONICS	334310	37,183,000	4	-262,000	7
SAMSUNG ELECTRONICS CO	334310	97,035,500	1	4,420,700	1
SANYO ELECTRIC COMPANY	334310	20,389,900	6	287,000	5
SHARP CORPORATION	334310	34,177,400	5	1,019,200	4
SONY CORPORATION	334310	88,714,100	3	3,694,400	2
Automobile Parts Manufacturing					
AISIN SEIKI CO LTD	336300	27,327,200	3	927,510	5
ARVINMERITOR INC	336300	7,167,000	14	-101,000	13
AUTOLIV INC	336300	6,473,200	18	164,700	9
CALSONIC KANSEI CORP	336300				

Company	Industry Code	2008 Sales (U.S. $ thousands)	Sales Rank	2008 Profits (U.S. $ thousands)	Profits Rank
CUMMINS INC	336300	14,342,000	9	755,000	6
DANA HOLDINGS CORP	336300	8,095,000	13	18,000	12
DELPHI CORP	336300	18,060,000	5	3,037,000	1
DENSO CORPORATION	336300	40,109,100	1	2,435,570	2
EATON CORP	336300	15,376,000	7	1,058,000	3
FAURECIA SA	336300	16,001,860	6	-765,810	20
FEDERAL MOGUL CORP	336300	6,865,600	15	-467,900	17
GEORG FISCHER LTD	336300	3,949,130	21	61,030	11
GKN PLC	336300	6,491,970	17	-158,740	14
JOHNSON CONTROLS INC	336300	38,062,000	2	979,000	4
LEAR CORP	336300	13,570,500	10	-689,900	19
MAGNA INTERNATIONAL INC	336300	23,704,000	4	71,000	10
MAGNETI MARELLI HOLDING	336300				
RHEINMETALL AG	336300	5,154,670	20	179,860	8
ROBERT BOSCH GMBH	336300				
TENNECO INC	336300	5,916,000	19	-415,000	16
TOYODA GOSEI CO LTD	336300	6,612,408	16	307,443	7
TRW AUTOMOTIVE HOLDINGS	336300	14,995,000	8	-779,000	21
VALEO	336300	11,365,800	11	-273,200	15
VISTEON CORPORATION	336300	9,544,000	12	-681,000	18
WANXIANG GROUP CORP	336300				
Automobile Transmission & Power Train Parts Manufacturing					
ZF FRIEDRICHSHAFEN AG	336350				
Automobiles, Manufacturing					
ADAM OPEL AG	336111				
ASTON MARTIN LAGONDA LTD	336111				
AUDI AG	336111	45,246,100	13	4,203,620	6
BMW (BAYERISCHE MOTOREN WERKE AG)	336111	59,737,500	11	517,660	14
BRILLIANCE CHINA AUTOMOTIVE HOLDINGS LTD	336111	1,634,500	23	-45,910	20
CHRYSLER LLC	336111				
DAIHATSU MOTOR CO LTD	336111	16,993,738	17	348,742	16
DAIMLER AG	336111	129,244,000	5	1,906,190	8
DONGFENG MOTOR CORP	336111				
FERRARI SPA	336111				
FIAT SPA	336111	80,147,000	8	2,322,890	7
FIRST AUTOMOTIVE GROUP CORPORATION	336111				
FORD MOTOR CO	336111	146,277,000	4	-14,672,000	23
FUJI HEAVY INDUSTRIES LTD (SUBARU)	336111	15,867,800	18	186,510	18
GENERAL MOTORS CORP (GM)	336111	148,979,000	3	-30,860,000	24
GM DAEWOO AUTO AND TECHNOLOGY CO	336111				
GROUP LOTUS PLC	336111				
HONDA MOTOR CO LTD	336111	119,801,000	6	5,989,000	4
HONDA OF AMERICA MFG INC	336111				
HYUNDAI MOTOR COMPANY	336111	60,240,800	10	648,030	13
ISUZU MOTORS LTD	336111	19,180,300	16	757,330	11
JAGUAR CARS LTD	336111				
KIA MOTORS CORPORATION	336111	12,501,100	20	86,990	19

Company	Industry Code	2008 Sales (U.S. $ thousands)	Sales Rank	2008 Profits (U.S. $ thousands)	Profits Rank
LAND ROVER	336111				
MAZDA MOTOR CORPORATION	336111	34,757,890	14	918,350	10
MITSUBISHI MOTORS CORP	336111	26,726,600	15	345,880	17
NISSAN MOTOR CO LTD	336111	108,242,000	7	4,823,000	5
PACCAR INC	336111	14,972,500	19	1,017,900	9
PININFARINA SPA	336111	711,720	24	-275,520	21
PORSCHE AUTOMOBIL HOLDING SE	336111	9,935,620	22	8,371,000	2
PSA PEUGEOT CITROEN SA	336111	73,365,900	9	-462,960	22
RENAULT SA	336111	47,578,900	12	754,140	12
SAIC-GM-WULING AUTOMOBILE COMPANY	336111				
SHANGHAI AUTOMOTIVE INDUSTRY CORP (SAIC)	336111				
SUZUKI MOTOR CORPORATION	336111				
TATA MOTORS LIMITED	336111	9,998,600	21	355,100	15
TOYOTA MOTOR CORPORATION	336111	262,394,000	1	17,146,000	1
VOLKSWAGEN AG	336111	150,559,000	2	6,201,850	3
VOLVO CAR CORPORATION	336111				
Biological Products, Manufacturing					
ALPHARMA INC	325414				
CSL LIMITED	325414	2,698,750	2	499,350	1
EISAI CO LTD	325414	7,304,620	1	-169,110	3
NOVOZYMES	325414	1,453,610	3	189,510	2
Building Products & Construction Materials in Plastic, Manufacturing					
LARSEN & TOUBRO LTD (L&T)	326199				
Business Machines, Manufacturing					
IKON OFFICE SOLUTIONS INC	333313				
PITNEY BOWES INC	333313	6,262,305	3	419,793	2
RICOH COMPANY LTD	333313	22,199,890	1	1,815,060	1
XEROX CORP	333313	17,608,000	2	230,000	3
Chemicals, Manufacturing					
AKZO NOBEL NV	325000	20,387,300	6	981,340	6
ALFA SAB DE CV	325000	10,637,000	14	-791,000	25
ARKEMA	325000	7,449,980	17	132,260	21
BASF AG	325000	83,990,800	1	3,925,610	1
BAYER AG	325000	43,536,000	3	2,273,480	3
BAYER CORP	325000				
CELANESE CORPORATION	325000	6,823,000	20	282,000	17
CIBA HOLDING AG	325000	5,205,560	23	-495,730	24
CLARIANT INTERNATIONAL LTD	325000	6,987,390	19	-32,030	23
DIC CORPORATION	325000	10,778,970	13	310,330	15
DOW CHEMICAL COMPANY (THE)	325000	57,514,000	2	579,000	11
DOW CORNING CORPORATION	325000	5,450,000	22	738,700	7
E I DU PONT DE NEMOURS & CO (DUPONT)	325000	30,529,000	4	2,007,000	4
EASTMAN CHEMICAL COMPANY	325000	6,726,000	21	346,000	14
EVONIK DEGUSSA	325000				
EVONIK INDUSTRIES AG	325000	21,002,200	5	377,100	13
HUNTSMAN CORPORATION	325000	10,215,000	15	609,000	10
KANEKA CORPORATION	325000	5,020,142	25	187,813	20

Company	Industry Code	2008 Sales (U.S. $ thousands)	Sales Rank	2008 Profits (U.S. $ thousands)	Profits Rank
LANXESS AG	325000	8,864,970	16	230,520	19
MITSUI CHEMICALS INC	325000	17,832,917	8	247,840	18
NITTO DENKO CORPORATION	325000	7,413,640	18	463,900	12
SASOL LIMITED	325000	15,618,000	9	2,828,000	2
SHIN ETSU CHEMICAL CO LTD	325000	13,763,650	10	1,835,800	5
SHOWA DENKO KK	325000	11,027,972	12	26,925	22
SOLVAY SA	325000	13,207,000	11	625,000	9
SUMITOMO CHEMICAL CO LTD	325000	18,929,424	7	629,634	8
TATE & LYLE PLC	325000	5,136,000	24	291,000	16
UNION CARBIDE CORPORATION	325000				
Communications Equipment, Manufacturing					
ARRIS GROUP INC	334200	1,144,565	3	-95,075	5
HARRIS CORPORATION	334200	5,311,000	2	444,200	2
L-3 COMMUNICATIONS HOLDINGS INC	334200	14,901,000	1	949,000	1
PLANTRONICS INC	334200	856,286	4	68,395	3
UNIDEN CORPORATION	334200	611,598	5	-74,768	4
Computer Accessories, Monitors, Printers Manufacturing					
ASUSTEK COMPUTER INC	334119				
AU OPTRONICS CORP	334119	12,520,800	3	638,000	5
CANON INC	334119	44,990,780	1	3,397,231	1
CHI MEI OPTOELECTRONICS	334119	9,074,200	6	1,085,100	2
LEXMARK INTERNATIONAL INC	334119	4,528,400	7	240,200	6
LG DISPLAY CO LTD	334119	12,410,800	4	829,320	3
LITE-ON TECHNOLOGY CORP	334119				
LOGITECH INTERNATIONAL SA	334119	2,370,496	10	231,026	7
MOLEX INC	334119	3,328,347	9	215,437	8
NVIDIA CORP	334119	4,097,860	8	797,645	4
SEIKO EPSON CORPORATION	334119	13,478,400	2	190,900	9
TPV TECHNOLOGY LTD	334119	9,247,020	5	97,580	10
Computer Hardware, Manufacturing					
ACER INC	334111	16,650,000	9	428,800	8
APPLE INC	334111	32,479,000	7	4,834,000	2
CASIO COMPUTER CO LTD	334111	6,274,700	12		
CRAY INC	334111	282,853	17	-31,346	14
DELL INC	334111	61,133,000	4	2,947,000	3
DIEBOLD INC	334111	3,170,080	15	88,583	13
DRS TECHNOLOGIES INC	334111	3,295,384	14	165,769	12
FUJITSU LIMITED	334111	53,308,650	5	481,070	7
FUJITSU-SIEMENS COMPUTER HOLDING COMPANY	334111				
HEWLETT-PACKARD CO (HP)	334111	118,364,000	1	8,329,000	1
HITACHI LTD	334111	113,390,020	2	-587,060	16
LENOVO GROUP LIMITED	334111	16,352,000	10	2,450,000	5
NCR CORPORATION	334111	5,315,000	13	228,000	10
NEC CORPORATION	334111	46,171,500	6	226,800	11
NINTENDO CO LTD	334111	16,724,230	8	2,573,426	4
PALM INC	334111	1,318,691	16	-105,419	15
SUN MICROSYSTEMS INC	334111	13,880,000	11	403,000	9

Company	Industry Code	2008 Sales (U.S. $ thousands)	Sales Rank	2008 Profits (U.S. $ thousands)	Profits Rank
TOSHIBA CORPORATION	334111	76,680,800	3	1,274,100	6
Computer Networking & Related Equipment, Manufacturing					
3COM CORP	334110	1,294,879	3	-228,841	4
CISCO SYSTEMS INC	334110	39,540,000	1	8,052,000	1
D-LINK CORPORATION	334110	1,087,000	4	100,200	3
JUNIPER NETWORKS INC	334110	3,572,376	2	511,749	2
Computer Software, Accounting, Banking & Financial					
INTUIT INC	511201	3,070,974	1	476,762	1
Computer Software, Business Management & ERP					
BMC SOFTWARE INC	511207	1,731,600	5	313,600	4
BUSINESS OBJECTS SA	511207				
CA INC	511207	4,277,000	3	500,000	3
CITRIX SYSTEMS INC	511207	1,583,354	6	178,276	5
COGNOS INC	511207				
COMPUWARE CORP	511207	1,229,611	7	134,394	7
ORACLE CORP	511207	22,430,000	1	5,521,000	1
SAP AG	511207	15,005,600	2	2,449,260	2
SAS INSTITUTE INC	511207	2,260,000	4		
SYBASE INC	511207	1,131,930	8	138,571	6
Computer Software, Electronic Games & Entertainment					
ACTIVISION BLIZZARD INC	511208	3,026,000	3	-233,000	4
ELECTRONIC ARTS INC	511208	3,665,000	2	-454,000	5
KONAMI CORP	511208	2,968,380	4	183,102	1
SEGA SAMMY HOLDINGS INC	511208	4,589,800	1	-524,700	6
TAKE-TWO INTERACTIVE SOFTWARE INC	511208	1,537,530	5	97,097	2
THQ INC	511208	1,030,467	6	-35,337	3
Computer Software, Multimedia, Graphics & Publishing					
ADOBE SYSTEMS INC	511209	3,579,889	1	871,814	1
Computer Software, Network Management, System Testing, & Storage					
BROCADE COMMUNICATIONS SYSTEMS INC	511214	1,466,937	1	167,070	1
NOVELL INC	511214	956,513	2	-8,745	2
TELCORDIA TECHNOLOGIES	511214				
Computer Software, Operating Systems, Languages & Development Tools					
MICROSOFT CORP	511204	60,420,000	1	17,681,000	1
Computer Software, Product Lifecycle, Engineering, Design & CAD					
AUTODESK INC	511215	2,171,900	1	356,200	1
CADENCE DESIGN SYSTEMS	511215	1,038,600	5	-1,854,000	7
DASSAULT SYSTEMES SA	511215	1,778,360	2	263,800	2
MENTOR GRAPHICS CORP	511215	789,101	6	-88,802	6
MSCSOFTWARE CORP	511215	254,386	7	-6,246	5
NAVTEQ CORPORATION	511215				
PARAMETRIC TECHNOLOGY	511215	1,070,330	4	79,702	4
SIEMENS PLM SOFTWARE	511215				
SYNOPSYS INC	511215	1,336,951	3	189,978	3
Computer Software, Sales & Customer Relationship Management					
ACXIOM CORP	511203	1,384,079	1	-7,780	1
Computer Software, Security & Anti-Virus					
MCAFEE INC	511211	1,600,065	2	172,209	2

Company	Industry Code	2008 Sales (U.S. $ thousands)	Sales Rank	2008 Profits (U.S. $ thousands)	Profits Rank
SYMANTEC CORP	511211	5,874,419	1	463,850	1
VERISIGN INC	511211	961,735	3	-374,692	3
Computer Software, Telecom, Communications & VOIP					
AMDOCS LTD	511213	3,162,096	1	378,906	1
COMVERSE TECHNOLOGY INC	511213				
Computer Storage Equipment & Misc. Parts, Manufacturing					
EMC CORP	334112	14,880,000	1	2,160,000	1
HITACHI GLOBAL STORAGE TECHNOLOGIES	334112				
IMATION CORP	334112	2,154,600	6	-33,300	6
NETAPP INC	334112	3,303,167	5	309,738	5
NIDEC CORPORATION	334112	7,407,186	4	410,780	4
QUANTUM CORP	334112	975,702	7	-60,234	7
SEAGATE TECHNOLOGY INC	334112	12,708,000	2	1,262,000	2
WESTERN DIGITAL CORP	334112	8,074,000	3	867,000	3
Construction Services					
JAIPRAKASH ASSOCIATES LTD	230000				
KUMHO INDUSTRIAL CO LTD	230000				
MICHAEL BAKER CORP	230000	699,395	1	29,154	1
TRC COMPANIES INC	230000	465,079	2	-109,149	2
Construction, Heavy & Civil Engineering					
ABENGOA SA	234000	4,134,360	20	393,080	12
ACCIONA SA	234000	17,094,300	9	626,280	5
AECOM TECHNOLOGY CORPORATION	234000	5,194,482	19	147,226	17
AECON GROUP INC	234000	1,492,630	26	47,160	22
AMEC PLC	234000	3,823,620	22	291,940	14
BALFOUR BEATTY PLC	234000	12,658,800	10	396,460	11
BARAN GROUP LTD	234000				
BECHTEL GROUP INC	234000	31,400,000	3		
BLACK & VEATCH HOLDING COMPANY	234000				
BOUYGUES SA	234000	43,264,900	1	1,985,160	2
BURNS & MCDONNELL	234000				
CAMP DRESSER & MCKEE INC	234000				
CHICAGO BRIDGE & IRON COMPANY NV	234000	5,944,981	15	-21,146	26
DAELIM INDUSTRIAL CO LTD	234000				
EMPRESAS ICA SA DE CV	234000	2,020,700	25	58,300	21
FLUOR CORP	234000	22,325,900	5	720,500	4
FOMENTO DE CONSTRUCCIONES Y CONTRATAS SA (FCC)	234000	18,563,200	8	446,330	8
FOSTER WHEELER AG	234000	6,854,290	13	526,620	6
GRANITE CONSTRUCTION INC	234000	2,674,244	23	122,404	19
GRUPO ACS	234000	19,320,500	6	1,769,040	3
GRUPO FERROVIAL SA	234000	18,672,700	7	43,600	23
GS ENGINEERING & CONSTRUCTION CORP	234000				
HDR INC	234000				
HOCHTIEF AG	234000	25,783,870	4	419,100	10
HYUNDAI ENGINEERING & CONSTRUCTION COMPANY LTD	234000	5,782,184	16	296,997	13
IMPREGILO SPA	234000	3,991,960	21	226,220	16

Company	Industry Code	2008 Sales (U.S. $ thousands)	Sales Rank	2008 Profits (U.S. $ thousands)	Profits Rank
JACOBS ENGINEERING GROUP INC	234000	11,252,159	11	420,742	9
LAYNE CHRISTENSEN COMPANY	234000	868,274	27	37,256	24
LOUIS BERGER GROUP INC (THE)	234000				
MATRIX SERVICE COMPANY	234000	731,301	28	21,414	25
MEADOW VALLEY CORPORATION	234000				
MWH GLOBAL INC	234000				
PARSONS BRINCKERHOFF INC	234000	2,343,117	24	73,882	20
PCL CONSTRUCTION GROUP INC	234000				
PERINI CORPORATION	234000	5,660,286	18	-75,140	27
RAILWORKS CORP	234000				
SEMBCORP INDUSTRIES LTD	234000	6,548,910	14	482,170	7
SHAW GROUP INC (THE)	234000	6,998,011	12	140,717	18
SNC-LAVALIN GROUP INC	234000	5,737,200	17	252,270	15
VINCI	234000	42,717,900	2	2,003,070	1
Consulting--Computer, Telecommunications & Internet					
ACCENTURE LTD	541512	25,313,826	3	1,691,751	2
AFFILIATED COMPUTER SERVICES INC	541512	6,160,550	9	329,010	7
ALTRAN TECHNOLOGIES SA	541512	2,234,170	18	15,440	13
ATOS ORIGIN SA	541512	7,107,800	8		
CAPGEMINI	541512	11,741,800	5	789,980	4
CGI GROUP INC	541512	3,073,080	14	242,770	9
COMPUTER SCIENCES CORPORATION (CSC)	541512	16,499,500	4	544,600	5
CSK HOLDINGS CORP	541512	2,397,000	17	12,700	14
ELECTRONIC DATA SYSTEMS CORP (EDS)	541512				
GETRONICS NV	541512				
IBM GLOBAL SERVICES	541512	58,892,000	2		
INTERNATIONAL BUSINESS MACHINES CORP (IBM)	541512	103,600,000	1	12,300,000	1
L-3 TITAN GROUP	541512				
LOGICA PLC	541512	5,322,940	10	57,710	12
NTT DATA CORP	541512	10,744,050	6	304,550	8
PEROT SYSTEMS CORP	541512	2,779,000	15	117,000	10
SAIC INC	541512	8,935,000	7	415,000	6
TATA CONSULTANCY SERVICES (TCS)	541512	4,597,100	13		
TIETOENATOR	541512	2,485,670	16	80,600	11
UNISYS CORP	541512	5,233,200	11	-130,100	15
WIPRO LTD	541512	4,933,000	12	806,000	3
Consulting--Environmental					
OYO CORPORATION	541620				
Consulting--Information Systems & Applications Research					
INDRAS SISTEMAS SA	541512A				
Contract Electronics Manufacturing					
ACCTON TECHNOLOGY CORP	334419				
BENCHMARK ELECTRONICS	334419	2,590,167	8	-135,632	9
CELESTICA INC	334419	7,678,200	5	-720,500	12
COMPAL ELECTRONICS INC	334419	11,937,700	4	372,550	3
CTS CORP	334419	691,707	10	29,886	6
FLEXTRONICS INTERNATIONAL	334419	27,558,135	2	-639,370	11

Company	Industry Code	2008 Sales (U.S. $ thousands)	Sales Rank	2008 Profits (U.S. $ thousands)	Profits Rank
HIGH TECH COMPUTER CORPORATION (HTC)	334419	4,528,650	7	851,180	2
HON HAI PRECISION INDUSTRY COMPANY LTD	334419	51,079,900	1	2,330,700	1
JABIL CIRCUIT INC	334419	12,779,703	3	133,892	4
KEY TRONIC CORP	334419	204,122	12	5,584	7
PLEXUS CORP	334419	1,841,622	9	84,144	5
SANMINA-SCI CORPORATION	334419	7,303,403	6	-486,349	10
TTM TECHNOLOGIES INC	334419	680,981	11	-35,270	8
Diagnostic Services and Substances Manufacturing					
AFFYMETRIX INC	325413	410,249	1	-307,919	1
Drugs (Pharmaceuticals), Discovery & Manufacturing					
ABBOTT LABORATORIES	325412	29,527,600	8	4,880,700	10
ALCON INC	325412	6,294,000	21	2,046,000	15
ALLERGAN INC	325412	4,339,700	25	578,600	22
ALTANA AG	325412	1,774,430	28	136,760	25
AMGEN INC	325412	15,003,000	14	4,196,000	12
ASTELLAS PHARMA INC	325412	9,726,000	19	1,774,000	18
ASTRAZENECA PLC	325412	31,601,000	7	6,130,000	7
BAYER SCHERING PHARMA AG	325412	14,243,900	15		
BIOGEN IDEC INC	325412	4,097,500	26	783,200	21
BRISTOL MYERS SQUIBB CO	325412	20,597,000	11	5,247,000	9
CHIRON CORP	325412				
ELI LILLY & COMPANY	325412	20,378,000	12	-2,071,900	27
FOREST LABORATORIES INC	325412	3,501,802	27	967,933	20
GENENTECH INC	325412	13,418,000	17	3,427,000	14
GENZYME CORP	325412	4,605,039	24	421,081	24
GILEAD SCIENCES INC	325412	5,335,750	22	2,011,154	16
GLAXOSMITHKLINE PLC	325412	36,127,200	6	10,594,000	2
JOHNSON & JOHNSON	325412	63,747,000	1	12,949,000	1
MERCK & CO INC	325412	23,850,300	9	7,808,400	5
MERCK KGAA	325412	10,000,300	18	501,600	23
MERCK SERONO SA	325412				
NOVARTIS AG	325412	41,459,000	4	8,233,000	3
NOVO-NORDISK AS	325412	8,239,030	20	1,744,460	19
PFIZER INC	325412	48,296,000	2	8,104,000	4
ROCHE HOLDING LTD	325412	41,676,500	3	7,803,000	6
SANOFI-AVENTIS SA	325412	36,751,700	5	5,721,790	8
SCHERING-PLOUGH CORP	325412	18,502,000	13	1,903,000	17
TAKEDA PHARMACEUTICAL COMPANY LTD	325412	13,748,020	16	3,554,540	13
UCB SA	325412	4,860,380	23	-58,040	26
WYETH	325412	22,833,908	10	4,417,833	11
Electrical Equipment, Manufacturing					
ABB LTD	335000	34,912,000	4	3,118,000	2
ALSTOM	335000	21,980,400	6	1,107,600	5
AREVA GROUP	335000	17,404,900	8	658,640	6
ATOMIC ENERGY OF CANADA LIMITED	335000	442,170	10	-228,860	9
BABCOCK & WILCOX COMPANY	335000				
BLACK & DECKER CORP	335000	6,086,100	9	293,600	8
BSST LLC	335000				

Company	Industry Code	2008 Sales (U.S. $ thousands)	Sales Rank	2008 Profits (U.S. $ thousands)	Profits Rank
GE ENERGY	335000	38,570,000	3		
MITSUBISHI ELECTRIC CORP	335000	40,498,200	2	1,579,800	4
SCHNEIDER ELECTRIC SA	335000	24,395,700	5	2,240,930	3
SIEMENS AG	335000	107,580,000	1	8,189,070	1
WESTINGHOUSE ELECTRIC CO	335000				
WHIRLPOOL CORP	335000	18,907,000	7	418,000	7
Electrical Switches, Sensors, MEMS, Optomechanicals					
ALPS ELECTRIC CO LTD	335313	6,926,600	1	44,200	1
Engineering & Facilities Support Services					
ABERTIS INFRAESTRUCTURAS SA	541330	4,883,650	5	820,360	1
AMEY PLC	541330				
ARCADIS NV	541330	2,277,630	6	83,350	8
ASC INCORPORATED	541330				
BIOS-BIOENERGIESYSTEME GMBH	541330				
CHIYODA CORPORATION	541330	6,035,600	4	96,410	7
ENGLOBAL CORP	541330	493,332	10	18,258	10
KBR INC	541330	11,581,000	1	319,000	3
KIMLEY-HORN AND ASSOCIATES INC	541330				
MCDERMOTT INTERNATIONAL	541330	6,572,423	3	429,302	2
SKIDMORE OWINGS & MERRILL	541330				
STV GROUP INC	541330				
TREVI-FINANZIARIA INDUSTRIALE SPA (TREVI GROUP)	541330	1,443,130	8	100,830	6
URS CORPORATION	541330	10,086,289	2	219,791	4
VSE CORP	541330	1,043,735	9	19,040	9
WS ATKINS PLC	541330	2,076,210	7	148,360	5
Fiber Optic Cable & Electrical Wire					
CORNING INC	335921	5,948,000	1	5,257,000	1
Financing--Business					
GENERAL ELECTRIC CO (GE)	522220A	182,515,000	1	17,410,000	1
Fuel Cells Manufacturing					
BALLARD POWER SYSTEMS	333298	59,580	2	34,079	1
FUELCELL ENERGY INC	333298	100,735	1	-93,357	2
Gasoline Stations					
DAESUNG INDUSTRIAL CO LTD	447110				
Industrial Gas Manufacturing					
AIR PRODUCTS & CHEMICALS	325120	10,415,000	1	910,000	1
Instrument Manufacturing, including Measurement, Control, Test & Navigational					
AGILENT TECHNOLOGIES INC	334500	5,774,000	2	693,000	2
EMERSON ELECTRIC CO	334500	24,807,000	1	2,412,000	1
ROCKWELL AUTOMATION INC	334500	5,697,800	3	577,600	3
Machinery, Manufacturing					
CATERPILLAR INC	333000	51,324,000	2	3,557,000	2
DEERE & CO	333000	28,438,000	3	2,053,000	3
ILLINOIS TOOL WORKS INC	333000	15,869,354	5	1,519,003	4
IMI PLC	333000	2,788,790	9	170,170	8
KAWASAKI HEAVY INDUSTRIES	333000	14,981,008	6	350,709	7
LINDE GROUP	333000	17,070,700	4	1,046,110	5

Company	Industry Code	2008 Sales (U.S. $ thousands)	Sales Rank	2008 Profits (U.S. $ thousands)	Profits Rank
MITSUBISHI CORP	333000	60,308,100	1	4,627,900	1
SMITHS GROUP PLC	333000	3,410,420	8	394,930	6
TEREX CORPORATION	333000	9,889,600	7	71,900	9
Management of Companies & Enterprises					
TATA GROUP	551110	62,500,000	1		
Medical/Dental/Surgical Equipment & Supplies, Manufacturing					
3M COMPANY	339113	25,269,000	1	3,460,000	1
BAUSCH & LOMB INC	339113				
BAXTER INTERNATIONAL INC	339113	12,348,000	4	2,014,000	4
BECKMAN COULTER INC	339113	3,098,900	12	194,000	11
BECTON DICKINSON & CO	339113	7,155,910	6	1,127,000	6
BOSTON SCIENTIFIC CORP	339113	8,050,000	5	-2,036,000	13
ESSILOR INTERNATIONAL SA	339113	4,096,023	9	518,010	7
GE HEALTHCARE	339113	17,392,000	2	2,851,000	2
HILL-ROM HOLDINGS INC	339113	1,507,700	13	115,800	12
HOSPIRA INC	339113	3,629,500	11	320,900	10
MEDTRONIC INC	339113	13,515,000	3	2,231,000	3
SIEMENS HEALTHCARE	339113				
SMITH & NEPHEW PLC	339113	3,801,000	10	377,000	9
ST JUDE MEDICAL INC	339113	4,363,251	8	384,327	8
STRYKER CORP	339113	6,718,200	7	1,147,800	5
Nuclear Fuels & Other Inorganic Chemicals					
BRITISH NUCLEAR FUELS PLC	325188				
Oil & Natural Gas Exploration & Production					
BP PLC	211111	365,700,000	3	21,666,000	4
CHEVRON CORPORATION	211111	273,005,000	5	23,931,000	3
CONOCOPHILLIPS COMPANY	211111	240,842,000	6	-16,998,000	13
ENI SPA	211111	145,792,000	9	12,884,900	8
EXXON MOBIL CORPORATION (EXXONMOBIL)	211111	459,579,000	1	45,220,000	1
LUKOIL (OAO)	211111	107,680,000	11	9,144,000	9
MARATHON OIL CORP	211111	77,193,000	14	3,528,000	11
PETROCHINA COMPANY	211111	156,490,000	8	18,503,200	6
PETROLEO BRASILEIRO SA (PETROBRAS)	211111	118,257,000	10	18,879,000	5
PETROLEOS MEXICANOS (PEMEX)	211111	98,200,000	13	-8,100,000	12
ROYAL DUTCH SHELL (SHELL GROUP)	211111	458,361,000	2	26,476,000	2
SAUDI ARAMCO (SAUDI ARABIAN OIL CO)	211111	280,000,000	4		
SHELL OIL CO	211111				
STATOILHYDRO ASA	211111	98,337,900	12	6,530,720	10
TOTAL SA	211111	213,742,000	7	14,117,800	7
Optical Instrument & Lens, Manufacturing					
AGFA-GEVAERT NV	333314	4,024,800	4	-221,680	3
EASTMAN KODAK CO	333314	9,416,000	2	-442,000	4
FUJIFILM HOLDINGS CORP	333314	24,484,400	1	1,043,540	1
LUXOTTICA GROUP SPA	333314	6,881,300	3	522,550	2
Other Support Activities for Road Transportation					
GLOBAL VIA INFRASTRUCTURES SA (GLOBALVIA)	488490				

Company	Industry Code	2008 Sales (U.S. $ thousands)	Sales Rank	2008 Profits (U.S. $ thousands)	Profits Rank
Petrochemicals Manufacturing					
EXXONMOBIL CHEMICAL	325110				
LYONDELLBASELL INDUSTRIES	325110				
Petroleum--Drilling Oil & Gas Wells Support					
BAKER HUGHES INC	213111	11,864,000	3	1,635,000	2
FMC TECHNOLOGIES INC	213111	4,550,900	5	361,300	5
HALLIBURTON COMPANY	213111	18,279,000	2	1,538,000	3
SCHLUMBERGER LIMITED	213111	27,163,000	1	5,435,000	1
TECHNIP	213111	9,898,940	4	592,770	4
Radio & Wireless Communication, Manufacturing					
LG ELECTRONICS INC	334220	36,220,000	2	1,560,000	2
LORAL SPACE & COMMUNICATIONS LTD	334220	869,398	6	-692,916	5
MOTOROLA INC	334220	30,146,000	3	-4,244,000	6
NOKIA CORPORATION	334220	66,957,600	1	9,284,190	1
SCIENTIFIC ATLANTA INC	334220				
SONY ERICSSON MOBILE COMMUNICATIONS AB	334220	14,980,380	5	-97,260	4
TELEFON AB LM ERICSSON (ERICSSON)	334220	26,120,660	4	1,412,940	3
Research & Development--Physical, Engineering & Life Sciences					
ALBANY MOLECULAR RESEARCH	541710	229,260	4	20,560	4
BASF FUTURE BUSINESS GMBH	541710				
BELL LABS	541710				
CH2M HILL COMPANIES LTD	541710				
CHEVRON TECHNOLOGY VENTURES	541710				
COVANCE INC	541710	1,827,067	1	196,760	1
DUPONT CENTRAL RESEARCH & DEVELOPMENT	541710				
FUJITSU LABORATORIES LTD	541710				
GE GLOBAL RESEARCH	541710				
HEWLETT-PACKARD QUANTUM SCIENCE RESEARCH	541710				
HITACHI HIGH TECHNOLOGIES AMERICA INC	541710				
HP LABS (HEWLETT-PACKARD LABORATORIES)	541710				
IBM RESEARCH	541710				
KODAK RESEARCH LABORATORIES	541710				
MOTOROLA LABS	541710				
NEC LABORATORIES AMERICA	541710				
PALO ALTO RESEARCH CENTER	541710				
PAREXEL INTERNATIONAL	541710	964,283	3	64,640	3
PHARMACEUTICAL PRODUCT DEVELOPMENT INC	541710	1,569,901	2	187,519	2
QUINTILES TRANSNATIONAL	541710				
ROSETTA INPHARMATICS LLC	541710				
SAMSUNG ADVANCED INSTITUTE OF TECHNOLOGY (SAIT)	541710				
SCHERING-PLOUGH RESEARCH INSTITUTE	541710				
SIEMENS CORPORATE TECHNOLOGY	541710				
TOSHIBA CORPORATE R&D CENTER	541710				

Company	Industry Code	2008 Sales (U.S. $ thousands)	Sales Rank	2008 Profits (U.S. $ thousands)	Profits Rank
Search Engine Portals					
GOOGLE INC	514199B	21,795,550	1	4,226,858	1
YAHOO! INC	514199B	7,208,502	2	424,298	2
Security, Protection, Armored Car & Investigation Services					
TYCO INTERNATIONAL LTD	561610	20,199,000	1	1,553,000	1
Semiconductor Manufacturing Equipment & Services					
ADVANCED SEMICONDUCTOR ENGINEERING INC	333295	2,779,400	2	181,310	2
APPLIED MATERIALS INC	333295	8,129,240	1	960,746	1
Semiconductors (Microchips)/Integrated Circuits/Components, Manufacturing					
ADVANCED MICRO DEVICES INC (AMD)	334413	5,808,000	8	-3,098,000	18
ALTERA CORP	334413	1,367,224	20	359,651	6
ANALOG DEVICES INC	334413	2,582,931	15	786,284	5
ATMEL CORP	334413	1,566,763	19	-27,209	12
BROADCOM CORP	334413	4,658,125	10	214,794	10
FREESCALE SEMICONDUCTOR	334413	5,226,000	9	-7,939,000	20
GEMALTO NV	334413	2,238,260	16	203,840	11
INFINEON TECHNOLOGIES AG	334413	6,084,000	6	-4,396,000	19
INTEL CORP	334413	37,586,000	1	5,292,000	1
LSI CORPORATION	334413	2,677,077	14	-622,253	13
MAXIM INTEGRATED PRODUCTS	334413	2,052,783	17	317,725	9
MICRON TECHNOLOGY INC	334413	5,841,000	7	-1,619,000	16
NATIONAL SEMICONDUCTOR	334413	1,885,900	18	332,300	7
QUALCOMM INC	334413	11,142,000	3	3,160,000	3
RENESAS TECHNOLOGY CORP	334413				
ROHM CO LTD	334413	3,734,100	11	319,300	8
SANDISK CORP	334413	3,351,352	12	-2,056,776	17
STMICROELECTRONICS NV	334413	9,842,000	5	-786,000	15
TAIWAN SEMICONDUCTOR MANUFACTURING CO LTD (TSMC)	334413	10,608,000	4	3,201,000	2
TEXAS INSTRUMENTS INC (TI)	334413	12,501,000	2	1,920,000	4
UNITED MICROELECTRONICS	334413	2,824,000	13	-681,000	14
Ship Manufacturing					
DAEWOO SHIPBUILDING & MARINE ENGINEERING CO LTD	336600				
Steel & Metals, Manufacturing					
CITIC PACIFIC LTD	331000	5,989,180	1	-1,633,670	1
Telecommunications Equipment Manufacturing					
ADC TELECOMMUNICATIONS	334210	1,456,400	9	-41,900	4
ALCATEL-LUCENT	334210	22,033,000	1	-6,710,830	9
AVAYA INC	334210				
BELDEN INC	334210	2,005,890	4	-361,027	6
HUAWEI TECHNOLOGIES CO	334210				
JDS UNIPHASE CORPORATION	334210	1,530,100	8	-21,700	3
NORTEL NETWORKS CORP	334210	10,421,000	2	-5,799,000	8
PANASONIC MOBILE COMMUNICATIONS CO LTD	334210				
TELLABS INC	334210	1,729,000	5	-930,000	7

Company	Industry Code	2008 Sales (U.S. $ thousands)	Sales Rank	2008 Profits (U.S. $ thousands)	Profits Rank
UTSTARCOM INC	334210	1,640,449	6	-150,316	5
VTECH HOLDINGS LIMITED	334210	1,552,000	7	228,900	2
ZTE CORPORATION	334210	6,470,650	3	330,520	1
Trucks, RVs & Misc. Automotive, Manufacturing					
AB VOLVO	336120	36,793,200	1	1,213,570	1
DAIMLER TRUCKS NORTH AMERICA LLC	336120				
Turbine & Turbine Generator Set Unit Manufacturing					
ENERCON GMBH	333611				
GAMESA CORPORACION TECNOLOGICA SA	333611	4,857,800	2	429,220	2
VESTAS WIND SYSTEMS A/S	333611	8,135,660	1	688,870	1
Ventilation, Heating & Air-Conditioning Manufacturing					
INGERSOLL-RAND CO LTD	333410	13,227,400	1	-2,567,400	1

ALPHABETICAL INDEX

CGI GROUP INC
CH2M HILL COMPANIES LTD
CHEVRON CORPORATION
CHEVRON TECHNOLOGY VENTURES
CHI MEI OPTOELECTRONICS
CHICAGO BRIDGE & IRON COMPANY NV
CHIRON CORP
CHIYODA CORPORATION
CHRYSLER LLC
CIBA HOLDING AG
CISCO SYSTEMS INC
CITIC PACIFIC LTD
CITRIX SYSTEMS INC
CLARIANT INTERNATIONAL LTD
COGNOS INC
COMPAL ELECTRONICS INC
COMPUTER SCIENCES CORPORATION (CSC)
COMPUWARE CORP
COMVERSE TECHNOLOGY INC
CONOCOPHILLIPS COMPANY
CORNING INC
COVANCE INC
CRAY INC
CSK HOLDINGS CORP
CSL LIMITED
CTS CORP
CUMMINS INC
DAELIM INDUSTRIAL CO LTD
DAESUNG INDUSTRIAL CO LTD
DAEWOO SHIPBUILDING & MARINE ENGINEERING CO LTD
DAIHATSU MOTOR CO LTD
DAIMLER AG
DAIMLER TRUCKS NORTH AMERICA LLC
DANA HOLDINGS CORPORATION
DASSAULT AVIATION SA
DASSAULT SYSTEMES SA
DEERE & CO
DELL INC
DELPHI CORP
DENSO CORPORATION
DIC CORPORATION
DIEBOLD INC
D-LINK CORPORATION
DONGFENG MOTOR CORPORATION
DOW CHEMICAL COMPANY (THE)
DOW CORNING CORPORATION
DRS TECHNOLOGIES INC
DUPONT CENTRAL RESEARCH & DEVELOPMENT
E I DU PONT DE NEMOURS & CO (DUPONT)
EASTMAN CHEMICAL COMPANY
EASTMAN KODAK CO
EATON CORP
EISAI CO LTD
ELECTRONIC ARTS INC
ELECTRONIC DATA SYSTEMS CORP (EDS)
ELI LILLY & COMPANY
EMBRAER BRASILIAN AVIATION COMPANY
EMC CORP
EMERSON ELECTRIC CO
EMPRESAS ICA SA DE CV
ENERCON GMBH
ENGLOBAL CORP
ENI SPA
ESSILOR INTERNATIONAL SA
EUROPEAN AERONAUTIC DEFENSE AND SPACE CO (EADS)
EVONIK DEGUSSA
EVONIK INDUSTRIES AG
EXXON MOBIL CORPORATION (EXXONMOBIL)
EXXONMOBIL CHEMICAL
FAURECIA SA
FEDERAL MOGUL CORP
FERRARI SPA
FIAT SPA
FIRST AUTOMOTIVE GROUP CORPORATION
FLEXTRONICS INTERNATIONAL LTD
FLUOR CORP
FMC TECHNOLOGIES INC
FOMENTO DE CONSTRUCCIONES Y CONTRATAS SA (FCC)
FORD MOTOR CO
FOREST LABORATORIES INC
FOSTER WHEELER AG
FREESCALE SEMICONDUCTOR INC
FUELCELL ENERGY INC
FUJI HEAVY INDUSTRIES LTD (SUBARU)
FUJIFILM HOLDINGS CORP
FUJITSU LABORATORIES LTD
FUJITSU LIMITED
FUJITSU-SIEMENS COMPUTER HOLDING COMPANY
GAMESA CORPORACION TECNOLOGICA SA
GE AVIATION
GE ENERGY
GE GLOBAL RESEARCH
GE HEALTHCARE
GEMALTO NV
GENENTECH INC
GENERAL DYNAMICS CORP
GENERAL ELECTRIC CO (GE)
GENERAL MOTORS CORP (GM)
GENZYME CORP
GEORG FISCHER LTD
GETRONICS NV
GILEAD SCIENCES INC
GKN PLC
GLAXOSMITHKLINE PLC
GLOBAL VIA INFRASTRUCTURES SA (GLOBALVIA)
GM DAEWOO AUTO AND TECHNOLOGY CO
GOODRICH CORPORATION
GOOGLE INC
GRANITE CONSTRUCTION INC
GROUP LOTUS PLC
GRUPO ACS

GRUPO FERROVIAL SA
GS ENGINEERING & CONSTRUCTION CORP
GULFSTREAM AEROSPACE CORP
HALLIBURTON COMPANY
HARRIS CORPORATION
HDR INC
HEWLETT-PACKARD CO (HP)
HEWLETT-PACKARD QUANTUM SCIENCE RESEARCH
HIGH TECH COMPUTER CORPORATION (HTC)
HILL-ROM HOLDINGS INC
HITACHI GLOBAL STORAGE TECHNOLOGIES
HITACHI HIGH TECHNOLOGIES AMERICA INC
HITACHI LTD
HOCHTIEF AG
HON HAI PRECISION INDUSTRY COMPANY LTD
HONDA MOTOR CO LTD
HONDA OF AMERICA MFG INC
HONEYWELL INTERNATIONAL INC
HOSPIRA INC
HP LABS (HEWLETT-PACKARD LABORATORIES)
HUAWEI TECHNOLOGIES CO LTD
HUNTSMAN CORPORATION
HYUNDAI ENGINEERING & CONSTRUCTION COMPANY LTD
HYUNDAI MOTOR COMPANY
IBM GLOBAL SERVICES
IBM RESEARCH
IKON OFFICE SOLUTIONS INC
ILLINOIS TOOL WORKS INC
IMATION CORP
IMI PLC
IMPREGILO SPA
INDRAS SISTEMAS SA
INFINEON TECHNOLOGIES AG
INGERSOLL-RAND COMPANY LIMITED
INTEL CORP
INTERNATIONAL BUSINESS MACHINES CORP (IBM)
INTUIT INC
ISUZU MOTORS LTD
ITT CORPORATION
JABIL CIRCUIT INC
JACOBS ENGINEERING GROUP INC
JAGUAR CARS LTD
JAIPRAKASH ASSOCIATES LIMITED
JDS UNIPHASE CORPORATION
JOHNSON & JOHNSON
JOHNSON CONTROLS INC
JUNIPER NETWORKS INC
KANEKA CORPORATION
KAWASAKI HEAVY INDUSTRIES LTD
KBR INC
KEY TRONIC CORP
KIA MOTORS CORPORATION
KIMBERLY-CLARK CORP
KIMLEY-HORN AND ASSOCIATES INC
KODAK RESEARCH LABORATORIES
KONAMI CORP
KUMHO INDUSTRIAL CO LTD
L-3 COMMUNICATIONS HOLDINGS INC
L-3 TITAN GROUP
LAND ROVER
LANXESS AG
LARSEN & TOUBRO LIMITED (L&T)
LAYNE CHRISTENSEN COMPANY
LEAR CORP
LEARJET INC
LENOVO GROUP LIMITED
LEXMARK INTERNATIONAL INC
LG DISPLAY CO LTD
LG ELECTRONICS INC
LINDE GROUP
LITE-ON TECHNOLOGY CORP
LOCKHEED MARTIN CORP
LOGICA PLC
LOGITECH INTERNATIONAL SA
LORAL SPACE & COMMUNICATIONS LTD
LOUIS BERGER GROUP INC (THE)
LSI CORPORATION
LUKOIL (OAO)
LUXOTTICA GROUP SPA
LYONDELLBASELL INDUSTRIES
MAGNA INTERNATIONAL INC
MAGNETI MARELLI HOLDING SPA
MARATHON OIL CORP
MATRIX SERVICE COMPANY
MAXIM INTEGRATED PRODUCTS INC
MAZDA MOTOR CORPORATION
MCAFEE INC
MCDERMOTT INTERNATIONAL INC
MEADOW VALLEY CORPORATION
MEDTRONIC INC
MENTOR GRAPHICS CORP
MERCK & CO INC
MERCK KGAA
MERCK SERONO SA
MICHAEL BAKER CORPORATION
MICRON TECHNOLOGY INC
MICROSOFT CORP
MITSUBISHI CORP
MITSUBISHI ELECTRIC CORPORATION
MITSUBISHI MOTORS CORP
MITSUI CHEMICALS INC
MOLEX INC
MONSANTO CO
MOTOROLA INC
MOTOROLA LABS
MSCSOFTWARE CORP
MWH GLOBAL INC
NATIONAL SEMICONDUCTOR CORP
NAVTEQ CORPORATION
NCR CORPORATION
NEC CORPORATION
NEC LABORATORIES AMERICA INC
NETAPP INC

NIDEC CORPORATION
NINTENDO CO LTD
NISSAN MOTOR CO LTD
NITTO DENKO CORPORATION
NOKIA CORPORATION
NORTEL NETWORKS CORP
NORTHROP GRUMMAN CORP
NOVARTIS AG
NOVELL INC
NOVO-NORDISK AS
NOVOZYMES
NTT DATA CORP
NVIDIA CORP
ORACLE CORP
OYO CORPORATION
PACCAR INC
PALM INC
PALO ALTO RESEARCH CENTER
PANASONIC CORPORATION
PANASONIC MOBILE COMMUNICATIONS CO LTD
PARAMETRIC TECHNOLOGY CORP
PAREXEL INTERNATIONAL CORP
PARSONS BRINCKERHOFF INC
PCL CONSTRUCTION GROUP INC
PERINI CORPORATION
PEROT SYSTEMS CORP
PETROCHINA COMPANY
PETROLEO BRASILEIRO SA (PETROBRAS)
PETROLEOS MEXICANOS (PEMEX)
PFIZER INC
PHARMACEUTICAL PRODUCT DEVELOPMENT INC
PININFARINA SPA
PIONEER CORPORATION
PITNEY BOWES INC
PLANTRONICS INC
PLEXUS CORP
PORSCHE AUTOMOBIL HOLDING SE
PSA PEUGEOT CITROEN SA
QUALCOMM INC
QUANTUM CORP
QUINTILES TRANSNATIONAL CORP
RAILWORKS CORP
RAYTHEON CO
RENAULT SA
RENESAS TECHNOLOGY CORP
RHEINMETALL AG
RICOH COMPANY LTD
ROBERT BOSCH GMBH
ROCHE HOLDING LTD
ROCKWELL AUTOMATION INC
ROHM CO LTD
ROLLSROYCE PLC
ROSETTA INPHARMATICS LLC
ROYAL DUTCH SHELL (SHELL GROUP)
ROYAL PHILIPS ELECTRONICS NV
SAAB AB
SAFRAN SA
SAIC INC
SAIC-GM-WULING AUTOMOBILE COMPANY
SAMSUNG ADVANCED INSTITUTE OF TECHNOLOGY (SAIT)
SAMSUNG ELECTRONICS CO LTD
SANDISK CORP
SANMINA-SCI CORPORATION
SANOFI-AVENTIS SA
SANYO ELECTRIC COMPANY LTD
SAP AG
SAS INSTITUTE INC
SASOL LIMITED
SAUDI ARAMCO (SAUDI ARABIAN OIL CO)
SCHERING-PLOUGH CORP
SCHERING-PLOUGH RESEARCH INSTITUTE
SCHLUMBERGER LIMITED
SCHNEIDER ELECTRIC SA
SCIENTIFIC ATLANTA INC
SEAGATE TECHNOLOGY INC
SEGA SAMMY HOLDINGS INC
SEIKO EPSON CORPORATION
SEMBCORP INDUSTRIES LTD
SHANGHAI AUTOMOTIVE INDUSTRY CORP (SAIC)
SHARP CORPORATION
SHAW GROUP INC (THE)
SHELL OIL CO
SHIN ETSU CHEMICAL CO LTD
SHOWA DENKO KK
SIEMENS AG
SIEMENS CORPORATE TECHNOLOGY
SIEMENS HEALTHCARE
SIEMENS PLM SOFTWARE
SINGAPORE TECHNOLOGIES ENGINEERING LIMITED
SKIDMORE OWINGS & MERRILL LLP
SMITH & NEPHEW PLC
SMITHS GROUP PLC
SNC-LAVALIN GROUP INC
SOLVAY SA
SONY CORPORATION
SONY ERICSSON MOBILE COMMUNICATIONS AB
SPIRIT AEROSYSTEMS HOLDINGS INC
ST JUDE MEDICAL INC
STATOILHYDRO ASA
STMICROELECTRONICS NV
STRYKER CORP
STV GROUP INC
SUMITOMO CHEMICAL CO LTD
SUN MICROSYSTEMS INC
SUZUKI MOTOR CORPORATION
SYBASE INC
SYMANTEC CORP
SYNGENTA AG
SYNOPSYS INC
TAIWAN SEMICONDUCTOR MANUFACTURING CO LTD (TSMC)
TAKEDA PHARMACEUTICAL COMPANY LTD
TAKE-TWO INTERACTIVE SOFTWARE INC
TATA CONSULTANCY SERVICES (TCS)

INDEX OF U.S. HEADQUARTERS LOCATION BY STATE

To help you locate members of the firms geographically, the city and state of the headquarters of each company are in the following index.

MSCSOFTWARE CORP; Santa Ana
NATIONAL SEMICONDUCTOR CORP; Santa Clara
NETAPP INC; Sunnyvale
NORTHROP GRUMMAN CORP; Los Angeles
NVIDIA CORP; Santa Clara
ORACLE CORP; Redwood Shores
PALM INC; Sunnyvale
PALO ALTO RESEARCH CENTER; Palo Alto
PLANTRONICS INC; Santa Cruz
QUALCOMM INC; San Diego
QUANTUM CORP; San Jose
SAIC INC; San Diego
SANDISK CORP; Milpitas
SANMINA-SCI CORPORATION; San Jose
SEAGATE TECHNOLOGY INC; Scotts Valley
SUN MICROSYSTEMS INC; Santa Clara
SYBASE INC; Dublin
SYMANTEC CORP; Cupertino
SYNOPSYS INC; Mountain View
TELEDYNE TECHNOLOGIES INCORPORATED; Thousand Oaks
THQ INC; Aguora Hills
TTM TECHNOLOGIES INC; Santa Ana
URS CORPORATION; San Francisco
UTSTARCOM INC; Alameda
VERISIGN INC; Mountain View
WESTERN DIGITAL CORP; Lake Forest
YAHOO! INC; Sunnyvale

COLORADO
CH2M HILL COMPANIES LTD; Englewood
MWH GLOBAL INC; Broomfield

CONNECTICUT
FUELCELL ENERGY INC; Danbury
GENERAL ELECTRIC CO (GE); Fairfield
PITNEY BOWES INC; Stamford
TEREX CORPORATION; Westport
TRC COMPANIES INC; Windsor
UNITED TECHNOLOGIES CORPORATION; Hartford
XEROX CORP; Norwalk

DELAWARE
DUPONT CENTRAL RESEARCH & DEVELOPMENT; Wilmington
E I DU PONT DE NEMOURS & CO (DUPONT); Wilmington

FLORIDA
CITRIX SYSTEMS INC; Fort Lauderdale
HARRIS CORPORATION; Melbourne
JABIL CIRCUIT INC; St. Petersburg

GEORGIA
ARRIS GROUP INC; Suwanee
GE ENERGY; Atlanta
GULFSTREAM AEROSPACE CORP; Savannah
SCIENTIFIC ATLANTA INC; Lawrenceville

IDAHO
MICRON TECHNOLOGY INC; Boise

ILLINOIS
ABBOTT LABORATORIES; Abbott Park
BAXTER INTERNATIONAL INC; Deerfield
BOEING COMPANY (THE); Chicago
CATERPILLAR INC; Peoria
DEERE & CO; Moline
HITACHI HIGH TECHNOLOGIES AMERICA INC; Schaumburg
HOSPIRA INC; Lake Forest
ILLINOIS TOOL WORKS INC; Glenview
MOLEX INC; Lisle
MOTOROLA INC; Schaumburg
MOTOROLA LABS; Schaumburg
NAVTEQ CORPORATION; Chicago
SKIDMORE OWINGS & MERRILL LLP; Chicago
TELLABS INC; Naperville
TENNECO INC; Lake Forest

INDIANA
CTS CORP; Elkhart
CUMMINS INC; Columbus
ELI LILLY & COMPANY; Indianapolis
HILL-ROM HOLDINGS INC; Batesville

KANSAS
BLACK & VEATCH HOLDING COMPANY; Overland Park
LAYNE CHRISTENSEN COMPANY; Mission Woods
LEARJET INC; Wichita
SPIRIT AEROSYSTEMS HOLDINGS INC; Wichita

KENTUCKY
LEXMARK INTERNATIONAL INC; Lexington

LOUISIANA
SHAW GROUP INC (THE); Baton Rouge

MARYLAND
BLACK & DECKER CORP; Towson
LOCKHEED MARTIN CORP; Bethesda

MASSACHUSETTS
3COM CORP; Marlborough
ANALOG DEVICES INC; Norwood
BIOGEN IDEC INC; Cambridge
BOSTON SCIENTIFIC CORP; Natick
CAMP DRESSER & MCKEE INC; Cambridge
EMC CORP; Hopkinton
GENZYME CORP; Cambridge
NOVELL INC; Waltham
PARAMETRIC TECHNOLOGY CORP; Needham
PAREXEL INTERNATIONAL CORP; Waltham
PERINI CORPORATION; Framingham
RAYTHEON CO; Waltham

MICHIGAN
ARVINMERITOR INC; Troy
ASC INCORPORATED; Southgate
CHRYSLER LLC; Auburn Hills
COMPUWARE CORP; Detroit
DELPHI CORP; Troy
DOW CHEMICAL COMPANY (THE); Midland
DOW CORNING CORPORATION; Midland
FEDERAL MOGUL CORP; Southfield
FORD MOTOR CO; Dearborn
GENERAL MOTORS CORP (GM); Detroit
LEAR CORP; Southfield
STRYKER CORP; Kalamazoo
TRW AUTOMOTIVE HOLDINGS CORP; Livonia
VISTEON CORPORATION; Van Buren Township
WHIRLPOOL CORP; Benton Harbor

MINNESOTA
3M COMPANY; St. Paul
ADC TELECOMMUNICATIONS INC; Eden Prairie
IMATION CORP; Oakdale
MEDTRONIC INC; Minneapolis
ST JUDE MEDICAL INC; St. Paul

MISSOURI
BELDEN INC; St. Louis
BURNS & MCDONNELL; Kansas City
EMERSON ELECTRIC CO; St. Louis
MONSANTO CO; St. Louis

NEBRASKA
HDR INC; Omaha

NEW JERSEY
ALPHARMA INC; Bridgewater
AVAYA INC; Basking Ridge
BECTON DICKINSON & CO; Franklin Lakes
BELL LABS; Murray Hill
COVANCE INC; Princeton
DRS TECHNOLOGIES INC; Parsippany
FOSTER WHEELER AG; Clinton
HONEYWELL INTERNATIONAL INC; Morristown
JOHNSON & JOHNSON; New Brunswick
LOUIS BERGER GROUP INC (THE); Morristown
MERCK & CO INC; Whitehouse Station
NEC LABORATORIES AMERICA INC; Princeton
SCHERING-PLOUGH CORP; Kenilworth
SCHERING-PLOUGH RESEARCH INSTITUTE; Kenilworth
TELCORDIA TECHNOLOGIES; Piscataway
WYETH; Madison

NEW YORK
ALBANY MOLECULAR RESEARCH; Albany
BAUSCH & LOMB INC; Rochester
BRISTOL MYERS SQUIBB CO; New York
CA INC; Islandia
COMVERSE TECHNOLOGY INC; New York
CORNING INC; Corning
EASTMAN KODAK CO; Rochester
FOREST LABORATORIES INC; New York
GE GLOBAL RESEARCH; Niskayuna
IBM GLOBAL SERVICES; Armonk
IBM RESEARCH; Yorktown Heights
INTERNATIONAL BUSINESS MACHINES CORP (IBM); Armonk
ITT CORPORATION; White Plains
KODAK RESEARCH LABORATORIES; Rochester
L-3 COMMUNICATIONS HOLDINGS INC; New York
LORAL SPACE & COMMUNICATIONS LTD; New York
PARSONS BRINCKERHOFF INC; New York
PFIZER INC; New York
RAILWORKS CORP; New York
TAKE-TWO INTERACTIVE SOFTWARE INC; New York

NORTH CAROLINA
GOODRICH CORPORATION; Charlotte
KIMLEY-HORN AND ASSOCIATES INC; Cary
LENOVO GROUP LIMITED; Morrisville
PHARMACEUTICAL PRODUCT DEVELOPMENT INC; Wilmington
QUINTILES TRANSNATIONAL CORP; Durham
SAS INSTITUTE INC; Cary

OHIO
DANA HOLDINGS CORPORATION; Toledo
DIEBOLD INC; North Canton
EATON CORP; Cleveland
GE AVIATION; Cincinnati
HONDA OF AMERICA MFG INC; Marysville
NCR CORPORATION; Dayton

OKLAHOMA
MATRIX SERVICE COMPANY; Tulsa

OREGON
DAIMLER TRUCKS NORTH AMERICA LLC; Portland
MENTOR GRAPHICS CORP; Wilsonville

PENNSYLVANIA
AIR PRODUCTS & CHEMICALS INC; Allentown
BAYER CORP; Pittsburgh
IKON OFFICE SOLUTIONS INC; Malvern
MICHAEL BAKER CORPORATION; Moon Township
STV GROUP INC; Douglassville
UNISYS CORP; Blue Bell
WESTINGHOUSE ELECTRIC COMPANY LLC; Monroeville

RHODE ISLAND
TEXTRON INC; Providence

INDEX OF NON-U.S. HEADQUARTERS LOCATION BY COUNTRY

VTECH HOLDINGS LIMITED; Hong Kong
WANXIANG GROUP CORPORATION; Hangzhou
ZTE CORPORATION; Shenzhen

DENMARK
NOVO-NORDISK AS; Bagsvaerd
NOVOZYMES; Bagsvaerd
VESTAS WIND SYSTEMS A/S; Randers

FINLAND
NOKIA CORPORATION; Espoo
TIETOENATOR; Helsinki

FRANCE
AIRBUS SAS; Blagnac
ALCATEL-LUCENT; Paris
ALSTOM; Levallois-Perret
ALTRAN TECHNOLOGIES SA; Levallois-Perret
AREVA GROUP; Paris
ARKEMA; Colombes
ATOS ORIGIN SA; Paris
BOUYGUES SA; Paris
BUSINESS OBJECTS SA; Levallois-Perret Cedex
CAPGEMINI; Paris
DASSAULT AVIATION SA; Paris
DASSAULT SYSTEMES SA; Velizy-Villacoublay
ESSILOR INTERNATIONAL SA; Charenton-le-Pont
FAURECIA SA; Nanterre
PSA PEUGEOT CITROEN SA; Paris
RENAULT SA; Boulogne Billancourt
SAFRAN SA; Paris
SANOFI-AVENTIS SA; Paris
SCHNEIDER ELECTRIC SA; Rucil-Malmaison
TECHNIP; Paris
TOTAL SA; Courbevoie
VALEO; Paris
VINCI; Rueil-Malmaison

GERMANY
ADAM OPEL AG; Russelsheim
ALTANA AG; Wesel
AUDI AG; Ingolstadt
BASF AG; Ludwigshafen
BASF FUTURE BUSINESS GMBH; Ludwigshafen
BAYER AG; Leverkusen
BAYER SCHERING PHARMA AG; Berlin
BMW (BAYERISCHE MOTOREN WERKE AG); Munich
DAIMLER AG; Stuttgart
ENERCON GMBH; Zurich
EVONIK DEGUSSA; Essen
EVONIK INDUSTRIES AG; Essen
HOCHTIEF AG; Essen
INFINEON TECHNOLOGIES AG; Neubiberg
LANXESS AG; Leverkusen
LINDE GROUP; Munich
MERCK KGAA; Darmstadt
PORSCHE AUTOMOBIL HOLDING SE; Stuttgart
RHEINMETALL AG; Dusseldorf
ROBERT BOSCH GMBH; Stuttgart
SAP AG; Walldorf
SIEMENS AG; Munich
SIEMENS CORPORATE TECHNOLOGY; Munich
SIEMENS HEALTHCARE; Erlangen
VOLKSWAGEN AG; Wolfsburg
ZF FRIEDRICHSHAFEN AG; Friedrichshafen

INDIA
JAIPRAKASH ASSOCIATES LIMITED; New Delhi
LARSEN & TOUBRO LIMITED (L&T); Mumbai
TATA CONSULTANCY SERVICES (TCS); Mumbai
TATA GROUP; Mumbai
TATA MOTORS LIMITED; Mumbai
WIPRO LTD; Bangalore

ISRAEL
BARAN GROUP LTD; Omer

ITALY
ENI SPA; Rome
FERRARI SPA; Modena
FIAT SPA; Turin
IMPREGILO SPA; Milan
LUXOTTICA GROUP SPA; Milan
MAGNETI MARELLI HOLDING SPA; Milano
PININFARINA SPA; Turin
TREVI-FINANZIARIA INDUSTRIALE SPA (TREVI GROUP); Cesena

JAPAN
AISIN SEIKI CO LTD; Kariya
ALPS ELECTRIC CO LTD; Tokyo
ASTELLAS PHARMA INC; Tokyo
CALSONIC KANSEI CORPORATION; Saitama
CANON INC; Tokyo
CASIO COMPUTER CO LTD; Tokyo
CHIYODA CORPORATION; Yokohama
CSK HOLDINGS CORP; Tokyo
DAIHATSU MOTOR CO LTD; Ikeda-city
DENSO CORPORATION; Kariya
DIC CORPORATION; Tokyo
EISAI CO LTD; Tokyo
FUJI HEAVY INDUSTRIES LTD (SUBARU); Tokyo
FUJIFILM HOLDINGS CORP; Tokyo
FUJITSU LABORATORIES LTD; Kawasaki-shi
FUJITSU LIMITED; Tokyo
HITACHI LTD; Tokyo
HONDA MOTOR CO LTD; Tokyo
ISUZU MOTORS LTD; Tokyo
KANEKA CORPORATION; Osaka
KAWASAKI HEAVY INDUSTRIES LTD; Chuo-ku, Kobe
KONAMI CORP; Tokyo
MAZDA MOTOR CORPORATION; Hiroshima
MITSUBISHI CORP; Tokyo
MITSUBISHI ELECTRIC CORPORATION; Tokyo

MITSUBISHI MOTORS CORP; Tokyo
MITSUI CHEMICALS INC; Tokyo
NEC CORPORATION; Tokyo
NIDEC CORPORATION; Kyoto
NINTENDO CO LTD; Kyoto
NISSAN MOTOR CO LTD; Tokyo
NITTO DENKO CORPORATION; Osaka
NTT DATA CORP; Tokyo
OYO CORPORATION; Tokyo
PANASONIC CORPORATION; Osaka
PANASONIC MOBILE COMMUNICATIONS CO LTD; Yokohama
PIONEER CORPORATION; Tokyo
RENESAS TECHNOLOGY CORP; Tokyo
RICOH COMPANY LTD; Tokyo
ROHM CO LTD; Kyoto
SANYO ELECTRIC COMPANY LTD; Osaka
SEGA SAMMY HOLDINGS INC; Tokyo
SEIKO EPSON CORPORATION; Nagano
SHARP CORPORATION; Osaka
SHIN ETSU CHEMICAL CO LTD; Tokyo
SHOWA DENKO KK; Tokyo
SONY CORPORATION; Tokyo
SUMITOMO CHEMICAL CO LTD; Tokyo
SUZUKI MOTOR CORPORATION; Shizuoka
TAKEDA PHARMACEUTICAL COMPANY LTD; Osaka
TOSHIBA CORPORATE R&D CENTER; Kawasaki-shi
TOSHIBA CORPORATION; Tokyo
TOYODA GOSEI CO LTD; Aichi
TOYOTA MOTOR CORPORATION; Aichi
UNIDEN CORPORATION; Tokyo

KOREA
DAELIM INDUSTRIAL CO LTD; Seoul
DAESUNG INDUSTRIAL CO LTD; Seoul
DAEWOO SHIPBUILDING & MARINE ENGINEERING CO LTD; Seoul
GM DAEWOO AUTO AND TECHNOLOGY CO; Incheon
GS ENGINEERING & CONSTRUCTION CORP; Seoul
HYUNDAI ENGINEERING & CONSTRUCTION COMPANY LTD; Seoul
HYUNDAI MOTOR COMPANY; Seoul
KIA MOTORS CORPORATION; Seoul
KUMHO INDUSTRIAL CO LTD; Seoul
LG DISPLAY CO LTD; Seoul
LG ELECTRONICS INC; Seoul
SAMSUNG ADVANCED INSTITUTE OF TECHNOLOGY (SAIT); Yonggin-si, Gyunggi-Do
SAMSUNG ELECTRONICS CO LTD; Seoul

MEXICO
ALFA SAB DE CV; San Pedro Garza Garcia
EMPRESAS ICA SA DE CV; Mexico City
PETROLEOS MEXICANOS (PEMEX); Colonia Huasteca

NORWAY
STATOILHYDRO ASA; Stavanger

RUSSIA
LUKOIL (OAO); Moscow

SAUDI ARABIA
SAUDI ARAMCO (SAUDI ARABIAN OIL CO); Dhahran

SINGAPORE
FLEXTRONICS INTERNATIONAL LTD; Singapore
SEMBCORP INDUSTRIES LTD; Singapore
SINGAPORE TECHNOLOGIES ENGINEERING LIMITED; Singapore

SOUTH AFRICA
SASOL LIMITED; Rosebank

SPAIN
ABENGOA SA; Seville
ABERTIS INFRAESTRUCTURAS SA; Barcelona
ACCIONA SA; Alcobendas
FOMENTO DE CONSTRUCCIONES Y CONTRATAS SA (FCC); Barcelona
GAMESA CORPORACION TECNOLOGICA SA; Vitoria
GLOBAL VIA INFRASTRUCTURES SA (GLOBALVIA); Madrid
GRUPO ACS; Madrid
GRUPO FERROVIAL SA; Madrid
INDRAS SISTEMAS SA; Madrid

SWEDEN
AB VOLVO; Goteborg
AUTOLIV INC; Stockholm
SAAB AB; Stockholm
TELEFON AB LM ERICSSON (ERICSSON); Stockholm
VOLVO CAR CORPORATION; Goteborg

SWITZERLAND
ABB LTD; Zurich
ALCON INC; Hunenberg
CIBA HOLDING AG; Basel
CLARIANT INTERNATIONAL LTD; Muttenz
GEORG FISCHER LTD; Schaffhausen
LOGITECH INTERNATIONAL SA; Romanel-sur-Morges
MERCK SERONO SA; Geneva 20
NOVARTIS AG; Basel
ROCHE HOLDING LTD; Basel
STMICROELECTRONICS NV; Plan-Les-Ouates
SYNGENTA AG; Basel

TAIWAN
ACCTON TECHNOLOGY CORP; Hsinchu
ACER INC; Taipei

INDEX BY REGIONS OF THE U.S. WHERE THE FIRMS HAVE LOCATIONS

BAYER CORP
BAYER SCHERING PHARMA AG
BECHTEL GROUP INC
BECKMAN COULTER INC
BECTON DICKINSON & CO
BELDEN INC
BENCHMARK ELECTRONICS INC
BIOGEN IDEC INC
BLACK & DECKER CORP
BLACK & VEATCH HOLDING COMPANY
BMC SOFTWARE INC
BMW (BAYERISCHE MOTOREN WERKE AG)
BOEING COMPANY (THE)
BOMBARDIER INC
BOSTON SCIENTIFIC CORP
BOUYGUES SA
BP PLC
BRISTOL MYERS SQUIBB CO
BRITISH NUCLEAR FUELS PLC
BROADCOM CORP
BROCADE COMMUNICATIONS SYSTEMS INC
BSST LLC
BURNS & MCDONNELL
BUSINESS OBJECTS SA
CA INC
CADENCE DESIGN SYSTEMS INC
CAMP DRESSER & MCKEE INC
CAPGEMINI
CATERPILLAR INC
CELESTICA INC
CGI GROUP INC
CH2M HILL COMPANIES LTD
CHEVRON CORPORATION
CHEVRON TECHNOLOGY VENTURES
CHI MEI OPTOELECTRONICS
CHICAGO BRIDGE & IRON COMPANY NV
CHIRON CORP
CHRYSLER LLC
CISCO SYSTEMS INC
CITRIX SYSTEMS INC
CLARIANT INTERNATIONAL LTD
COGNOS INC
COMPUTER SCIENCES CORPORATION (CSC)
COMPUWARE CORP
COMVERSE TECHNOLOGY INC
CONOCOPHILLIPS COMPANY
COVANCE INC
CRAY INC
CTS CORP
CUMMINS INC
DAIMLER AG
DAIMLER TRUCKS NORTH AMERICA LLC
DASSAULT SYSTEMES SA
DEERE & CO
DELL INC
DELPHI CORP
DENSO CORPORATION
DIC CORPORATION
DIEBOLD INC
D-LINK CORPORATION
DOW CORNING CORPORATION
DRS TECHNOLOGIES INC
E I DU PONT DE NEMOURS & CO (DUPONT)
EASTMAN KODAK CO
EATON CORP
ELECTRONIC ARTS INC
ELECTRONIC DATA SYSTEMS CORP (EDS)
ELI LILLY & COMPANY
EMC CORP
EMERSON ELECTRIC CO
ENGLOBAL CORP
ENI SPA
ESSILOR INTERNATIONAL SA
EXXON MOBIL CORPORATION (EXXONMOBIL)
FEDERAL MOGUL CORP
FERRARI SPA
FLEXTRONICS INTERNATIONAL LTD
FLUOR CORP
FMC TECHNOLOGIES INC
FORD MOTOR CO
FOSTER WHEELER AG
FUJI HEAVY INDUSTRIES LTD (SUBARU)
FUJIFILM HOLDINGS CORP
FUJITSU LABORATORIES LTD
FUJITSU LIMITED
FUJITSU-SIEMENS COMPUTER HOLDING COMPANY
GE AVIATION
GE ENERGY
GENENTECH INC
GENERAL DYNAMICS CORP
GENERAL ELECTRIC CO (GE)
GENERAL MOTORS CORP (GM)
GENZYME CORP
GEORG FISCHER LTD
GILEAD SCIENCES INC
GKN PLC
GLAXOSMITHKLINE PLC
GOODRICH CORPORATION
GOOGLE INC
GRANITE CONSTRUCTION INC
GROUP LOTUS PLC
GULFSTREAM AEROSPACE CORP
HALLIBURTON COMPANY
HARRIS CORPORATION
HDR INC
HEWLETT-PACKARD CO (HP)
HEWLETT-PACKARD QUANTUM SCIENCE RESEARCH
HILL-ROM HOLDINGS INC
HITACHI GLOBAL STORAGE TECHNOLOGIES
HITACHI HIGH TECHNOLOGIES AMERICA INC
HITACHI LTD
HOCHTIEF AG
HON HAI PRECISION INDUSTRY COMPANY LTD
HONDA MOTOR CO LTD

HONEYWELL INTERNATIONAL INC
HOSPIRA INC
HP LABS (HEWLETT-PACKARD LABORATORIES)
HUAWEI TECHNOLOGIES CO LTD
HUNTSMAN CORPORATION
HYUNDAI MOTOR COMPANY
IBM RESEARCH
IKON OFFICE SOLUTIONS INC
ILLINOIS TOOL WORKS INC
IMATION CORP
INFINEON TECHNOLOGIES AG
INGERSOLL-RAND COMPANY LIMITED
INTEL CORP
INTERNATIONAL BUSINESS MACHINES CORP (IBM)
INTUIT INC
ISUZU MOTORS LTD
ITT CORPORATION
JABIL CIRCUIT INC
JACOBS ENGINEERING GROUP INC
JAGUAR CARS LTD
JDS UNIPHASE CORPORATION
JOHNSON & JOHNSON
JOHNSON CONTROLS INC
JUNIPER NETWORKS INC
KAWASAKI HEAVY INDUSTRIES LTD
KEY TRONIC CORP
KIA MOTORS CORPORATION
KIMBERLY-CLARK CORP
KIMLEY-HORN AND ASSOCIATES INC
KONAMI CORP
L-3 COMMUNICATIONS HOLDINGS INC
L-3 TITAN GROUP
LAND ROVER
LAYNE CHRISTENSEN COMPANY
LEAR CORP
LEXMARK INTERNATIONAL INC
LG DISPLAY CO LTD
LITE-ON TECHNOLOGY CORP
LOCKHEED MARTIN CORP
LOGICA PLC
LOGITECH INTERNATIONAL SA
LORAL SPACE & COMMUNICATIONS LTD
LOUIS BERGER GROUP INC (THE)
LSI CORPORATION
LUXOTTICA GROUP SPA
MARATHON OIL CORP
MATRIX SERVICE COMPANY
MAXIM INTEGRATED PRODUCTS INC
MAZDA MOTOR CORPORATION
MCAFEE INC
MCDERMOTT INTERNATIONAL INC
MEADOW VALLEY CORPORATION
MEDTRONIC INC
MENTOR GRAPHICS CORP
MERCK & CO INC
MERCK KGAA
MICHAEL BAKER CORPORATION
MICRON TECHNOLOGY INC
MICROSOFT CORP
MITSUBISHI ELECTRIC CORPORATION
MITSUBISHI MOTORS CORP
MITSUI CHEMICALS INC
MOLEX INC
MONSANTO CO
MSCSOFTWARE CORP
MWH GLOBAL INC
NATIONAL SEMICONDUCTOR CORP
NCR CORPORATION
NEC CORPORATION
NEC LABORATORIES AMERICA INC
NETAPP INC
NIDEC CORPORATION
NINTENDO CO LTD
NISSAN MOTOR CO LTD
NITTO DENKO CORPORATION
NOKIA CORPORATION
NORTEL NETWORKS CORP
NORTHROP GRUMMAN CORP
NOVARTIS AG
NOVELL INC
NOVO-NORDISK AS
NOVOZYMES
NTT DATA CORP
NVIDIA CORP
ORACLE CORP
OYO CORPORATION
PACCAR INC
PALM INC
PALO ALTO RESEARCH CENTER
PANASONIC CORPORATION
PARAMETRIC TECHNOLOGY CORP
PAREXEL INTERNATIONAL CORP
PARSONS BRINCKERHOFF INC
PCL CONSTRUCTION GROUP INC
PERINI CORPORATION
PEROT SYSTEMS CORP
PFIZER INC
PHARMACEUTICAL PRODUCT DEVELOPMENT INC
PIONEER CORPORATION
PITNEY BOWES INC
PLANTRONICS INC
PLEXUS CORP
QUALCOMM INC
QUANTUM CORP
QUINTILES TRANSNATIONAL CORP
RAILWORKS CORP
RAYTHEON CO
RENESAS TECHNOLOGY CORP
RICOH COMPANY LTD
ROBERT BOSCH GMBH
ROCHE HOLDING LTD
ROCKWELL AUTOMATION INC
ROHM CO LTD
ROLLSROYCE PLC
ROSETTA INPHARMATICS LLC

ROYAL DUTCH SHELL (SHELL GROUP)
ROYAL PHILIPS ELECTRONICS NV
SAFRAN SA
SAIC INC
SAMSUNG ELECTRONICS CO LTD
SANDISK CORP
SANMINA-SCI CORPORATION
SANOFI-AVENTIS SA
SANYO ELECTRIC COMPANY LTD
SAP AG
SAS INSTITUTE INC
SASOL LIMITED
SCHERING-PLOUGH CORP
SCHERING-PLOUGH RESEARCH INSTITUTE
SCHLUMBERGER LIMITED
SCIENTIFIC ATLANTA INC
SEAGATE TECHNOLOGY INC
SEGA SAMMY HOLDINGS INC
SEIKO EPSON CORPORATION
SHARP CORPORATION
SHAW GROUP INC (THE)
SHELL OIL CO
SHOWA DENKO KK
SIEMENS AG
SIEMENS CORPORATE TECHNOLOGY
SIEMENS PLM SOFTWARE
SKIDMORE OWINGS & MERRILL LLP
SMITHS GROUP PLC
SNC-LAVALIN GROUP INC
SOLVAY SA
SONY CORPORATION
ST JUDE MEDICAL INC
STMICROELECTRONICS NV
STRYKER CORP
STV GROUP INC
SUN MICROSYSTEMS INC
SUZUKI MOTOR CORPORATION
SYBASE INC
SYMANTEC CORP
SYNGENTA AG
SYNOPSYS INC
TAIWAN SEMICONDUCTOR MANUFACTURING CO LTD (TSMC)
TAKEDA PHARMACEUTICAL COMPANY LTD
TATA CONSULTANCY SERVICES (TCS)
TECHNIP
TELCORDIA TECHNOLOGIES
TELEDYNE TECHNOLOGIES INCORPORATED
TELEFON AB LM ERICSSON (ERICSSON)
TELLABS INC
TENNECO INC
TEREX CORPORATION
TEXAS INSTRUMENTS INC (TI)
THQ INC
TIETOENATOR
TOSHIBA CORPORATION
TOTAL SA
TOYODA GOSEI CO LTD
TOYOTA MOTOR CORPORATION
TRC COMPANIES INC
TREVI-FINANZIARIA INDUSTRIALE SPA (TREVI GROUP)
TTM TECHNOLOGIES INC
TYCO INTERNATIONAL LTD
UNION CARBIDE CORPORATION
UNISYS CORP
UNITED MICROELECTRONICS CORP
UNITED TECHNOLOGIES CORPORATION
URS CORPORATION
UTSTARCOM INC
VERISIGN INC
VESTAS WIND SYSTEMS A/S
VINCI
VSE CORP
VTECH HOLDINGS LIMITED
WESTERN DIGITAL CORP
WESTINGHOUSE ELECTRIC COMPANY LLC
WHIRLPOOL CORP
WIPRO LTD
WS ATKINS PLC
WYETH
XEROX CORP
YAHOO! INC
ZF FRIEDRICHSHAFEN AG

SOUTHWEST

3COM CORP
3M COMPANY
AB VOLVO
ABBOTT LABORATORIES
ABERTIS INFRAESTRUCTURAS SA
ACCENTURE LTD
ACTIVISION BLIZZARD INC
ACXIOM CORP
ADVANCED MICRO DEVICES INC (AMD)
ADVANCED SEMICONDUCTOR ENGINEERING INC
AECOM TECHNOLOGY CORPORATION
AFFILIATED COMPUTER SERVICES INC
AIR PRODUCTS & CHEMICALS INC
ALCATEL-LUCENT
ALCON INC
ALPS ELECTRIC CO LTD
ALTERA CORP
ALTRAN TECHNOLOGIES SA
AMDOCS LTD
AMEC PLC
ANALOG DEVICES INC
APPLE INC
APPLIED MATERIALS INC
ARCADIS NV
ARKEMA
ARVINMERITOR INC
ASTON MARTIN LAGONDA LTD
ASTRAZENECA PLC
ATMEL CORP
ATOS ORIGIN SA

AUDI AG
AVIALL INC
BABCOCK & WILCOX COMPANY (THE)
BAE SYSTEMS PLC
BAKER HUGHES INC
BASF AG
BAXTER INTERNATIONAL INC
BAYER AG
BAYER CORP
BECHTEL GROUP INC
BECTON DICKINSON & CO
BENCHMARK ELECTRONICS INC
BIOS-BIOENERGIESYSTEME GMBH
BLACK & VEATCH HOLDING COMPANY
BMC SOFTWARE INC
BOEING COMPANY (THE)
BOMBARDIER INC
BOSTON SCIENTIFIC CORP
BP PLC
BRISTOL MYERS SQUIBB CO
BROADCOM CORP
BROCADE COMMUNICATIONS SYSTEMS INC
BURNS & MCDONNELL
BUSINESS OBJECTS SA
CA INC
CAMP DRESSER & MCKEE INC
CAPGEMINI
CATERPILLAR INC
CELANESE CORPORATION
CELESTICA INC
CGI GROUP INC
CH2M HILL COMPANIES LTD
CHEVRON CORPORATION
CHEVRON TECHNOLOGY VENTURES
CHICAGO BRIDGE & IRON COMPANY NV
CHIYODA CORPORATION
CHRYSLER LLC
CISCO SYSTEMS INC
CITRIX SYSTEMS INC
CLARIANT INTERNATIONAL LTD
COGNOS INC
COMPUTER SCIENCES CORPORATION (CSC)
COMPUWARE CORP
COMVERSE TECHNOLOGY INC
CONOCOPHILLIPS COMPANY
CORNING INC
COVANCE INC
CRAY INC
CTS CORP
CUMMINS INC
DAELIM INDUSTRIAL CO LTD
DAEWOO SHIPBUILDING & MARINE ENGINEERING CO LTD
DAIMLER AG
DEERE & CO
DELL INC
DELPHI CORP
DENSO CORPORATION
DIC CORPORATION
DIEBOLD INC
DOW CHEMICAL COMPANY (THE)
DRS TECHNOLOGIES INC
E I DU PONT DE NEMOURS & CO (DUPONT)
EASTMAN CHEMICAL COMPANY
EATON CORP
ELECTRONIC ARTS INC
ELECTRONIC DATA SYSTEMS CORP (EDS)
ELI LILLY & COMPANY
EMERSON ELECTRIC CO
ENGLOBAL CORP
ENI SPA
ESSILOR INTERNATIONAL SA
EXXON MOBIL CORPORATION (EXXONMOBIL)
EXXONMOBIL CHEMICAL
FEDERAL MOGUL CORP
FERRARI SPA
FLEXTRONICS INTERNATIONAL LTD
FLUOR CORP
FMC TECHNOLOGIES INC
FORD MOTOR CO
FOSTER WHEELER AG
FREESCALE SEMICONDUCTOR INC
FUJITSU LABORATORIES LTD
FUJITSU LIMITED
GE AVIATION
GE ENERGY
GEMALTO NV
GENERAL DYNAMICS CORP
GENERAL ELECTRIC CO (GE)
GENERAL MOTORS CORP (GM)
GENZYME CORP
GKN PLC
GLAXOSMITHKLINE PLC
GLOBAL VIA INFRASTRUCTURES SA (GLOBALVIA)
GOODRICH CORPORATION
GOOGLE INC
GRANITE CONSTRUCTION INC
GROUP LOTUS PLC
GRUPO FERROVIAL SA
GULFSTREAM AEROSPACE CORP
HALLIBURTON COMPANY
HARRIS CORPORATION
HDR INC
HEWLETT-PACKARD CO (HP)
HITACHI HIGH TECHNOLOGIES AMERICA INC
HITACHI LTD
HOCHTIEF AG
HON HAI PRECISION INDUSTRY COMPANY LTD
HONDA MOTOR CO LTD
HONEYWELL INTERNATIONAL INC
HOSPIRA INC
HUAWEI TECHNOLOGIES CO LTD
HUNTSMAN CORPORATION
IBM RESEARCH
IKON OFFICE SOLUTIONS INC

ILLINOIS TOOL WORKS INC
IMATION CORP
INGERSOLL-RAND COMPANY LIMITED
INTEL CORP
INTERNATIONAL BUSINESS MACHINES CORP (IBM)
INTUIT INC
ITT CORPORATION
JACOBS ENGINEERING GROUP INC
JAGUAR CARS LTD
JDS UNIPHASE CORPORATION
JOHNSON & JOHNSON
JOHNSON CONTROLS INC
JUNIPER NETWORKS INC
KANEKA CORPORATION
KAWASAKI HEAVY INDUSTRIES LTD
KBR INC
KEY TRONIC CORP
KIMBERLY-CLARK CORP
KIMLEY-HORN AND ASSOCIATES INC
L-3 COMMUNICATIONS HOLDINGS INC
L-3 TITAN GROUP
LAND ROVER
LANXESS AG
LAYNE CHRISTENSEN COMPANY
LEAR CORP
LINDE GROUP
LITE-ON TECHNOLOGY CORP
LOCKHEED MARTIN CORP
LOGICA PLC
LOUIS BERGER GROUP INC (THE)
LUXOTTICA GROUP SPA
LYONDELLBASELL INDUSTRIES
MARATHON OIL CORP
MATRIX SERVICE COMPANY
MAXIM INTEGRATED PRODUCTS INC
MAZDA MOTOR CORPORATION
MCAFEE INC
MCDERMOTT INTERNATIONAL INC
MEADOW VALLEY CORPORATION
MEDTRONIC INC
MENTOR GRAPHICS CORP
MERCK & CO INC
MICHAEL BAKER CORPORATION
MICRON TECHNOLOGY INC
MICROSOFT CORP
MITSUBISHI ELECTRIC CORPORATION
MITSUI CHEMICALS INC
MONSANTO CO
MOTOROLA INC
MOTOROLA LABS
MSCSOFTWARE CORP
MWH GLOBAL INC
NATIONAL SEMICONDUCTOR CORP
NEC CORPORATION
NIDEC CORPORATION
NISSAN MOTOR CO LTD
NOKIA CORPORATION
NORTEL NETWORKS CORP
NORTHROP GRUMMAN CORP
NOVELL INC
NVIDIA CORP
ORACLE CORP
PACCAR INC
PANASONIC CORPORATION
PARAMETRIC TECHNOLOGY CORP
PARSONS BRINCKERHOFF INC
PCL CONSTRUCTION GROUP INC
PERINI CORPORATION
PEROT SYSTEMS CORP
PETROLEO BRASILEIRO SA (PETROBRAS)
PFIZER INC
PHARMACEUTICAL PRODUCT DEVELOPMENT INC
PITNEY BOWES INC
QUALCOMM INC
QUINTILES TRANSNATIONAL CORP
RAILWORKS CORP
RAYTHEON CO
RICOH COMPANY LTD
ROBERT BOSCH GMBH
ROCHE HOLDING LTD
ROCKWELL AUTOMATION INC
ROHM CO LTD
ROLLSROYCE PLC
ROYAL DUTCH SHELL (SHELL GROUP)
ROYAL PHILIPS ELECTRONICS NV
SAFRAN SA
SAIC INC
SAMSUNG ELECTRONICS CO LTD
SANMINA-SCI CORPORATION
SANOFI-AVENTIS SA
SAP AG
SAS INSTITUTE INC
SASOL LIMITED
SAUDI ARAMCO (SAUDI ARABIAN OIL CO)
SCHERING-PLOUGH CORP
SCHLUMBERGER LIMITED
SCIENTIFIC ATLANTA INC
SEIKO EPSON CORPORATION
SHAW GROUP INC (THE)
SHELL OIL CO
SIEMENS AG
SIEMENS PLM SOFTWARE
SINGAPORE TECHNOLOGIES ENGINEERING LIMITED
SMITHS GROUP PLC
SNC-LAVALIN GROUP INC
SOLVAY SA
SONY CORPORATION
SPIRIT AEROSYSTEMS HOLDINGS INC
ST JUDE MEDICAL INC
STATOILHYDRO ASA
STMICROELECTRONICS NV
STRYKER CORP
STV GROUP INC
SUMITOMO CHEMICAL CO LTD

SUN MICROSYSTEMS INC
SYBASE INC
SYMANTEC CORP
SYNGENTA AG
SYNOPSYS INC
TATA CONSULTANCY SERVICES (TCS)
TECHNIP
TELCORDIA TECHNOLOGIES
TELEDYNE TECHNOLOGIES INCORPORATED
TELEFON AB LM ERICSSON (ERICSSON)
TELLABS INC
TEREX CORPORATION
TEXAS INSTRUMENTS INC (TI)
THQ INC
TIETOENATOR
TOSHIBA CORPORATION
TOTAL SA
TOYODA GOSEI CO LTD
TOYOTA MOTOR CORPORATION
TRC COMPANIES INC
TREVI-FINANZIARIA INDUSTRIALE SPA (TREVI GROUP)
TRW AUTOMOTIVE HOLDINGS CORP
TYCO INTERNATIONAL LTD
UNIDEN CORPORATION
UNION CARBIDE CORPORATION
UNISYS CORP
UNITED TECHNOLOGIES CORPORATION
URS CORPORATION
VERISIGN INC
VINCI
VISTEON CORPORATION
VSE CORP
WHIRLPOOL CORP
WIPRO LTD
WS ATKINS PLC
WYETH
XEROX CORP
YAHOO! INC
ZF FRIEDRICHSHAFEN AG
ZTE CORPORATION

MIDWEST

3COM CORP
3M COMPANY
AB VOLVO
ABBOTT LABORATORIES
ABENGOA SA
ACCENTURE LTD
ACTIVISION BLIZZARD INC
ACXIOM CORP
ADC TELECOMMUNICATIONS INC
ADVANCED MICRO DEVICES INC (AMD)
AECOM TECHNOLOGY CORPORATION
AFFILIATED COMPUTER SERVICES INC
AGFA-GEVAERT NV
AIR PRODUCTS & CHEMICALS INC
AIRBUS SAS
AKZO NOBEL NV
ALPHARMA INC
ALPS ELECTRIC CO LTD
ALTANA AG
ALTERA CORP
ALTRAN TECHNOLOGIES SA
AMDOCS LTD
AMEC PLC
ANALOG DEVICES INC
APPLE INC
ARCADIS NV
ARKEMA
ARRIS GROUP INC
ARVINMERITOR INC
ASC INCORPORATED
ASTELLAS PHARMA INC
ASTON MARTIN LAGONDA LTD
ASTRAZENECA PLC
ASUSTEK COMPUTER INC
ATMEL CORP
ATOS ORIGIN SA
AUDI AG
AUTOLIV INC
AVIALL INC
BABCOCK & WILCOX COMPANY (THE)
BAE SYSTEMS PLC
BAKER HUGHES INC
BALFOUR BEATTY PLC
BALLARD POWER SYSTEMS
BASF AG
BAXTER INTERNATIONAL INC
BAYER AG
BAYER CORP
BECHTEL GROUP INC
BECTON DICKINSON & CO
BELDEN INC
BENCHMARK ELECTRONICS INC
BLACK & VEATCH HOLDING COMPANY
BMC SOFTWARE INC
BOEING COMPANY (THE)
BOMBARDIER INC
BOSTON SCIENTIFIC CORP
BOUYGUES SA
BP PLC
BRISTOL MYERS SQUIBB CO
BRITISH NUCLEAR FUELS PLC
BROADCOM CORP
BROCADE COMMUNICATIONS SYSTEMS INC
BURNS & MCDONNELL
BUSINESS OBJECTS SA
CA INC
CADENCE DESIGN SYSTEMS INC
CALSONIC KANSEI CORPORATION
CAMP DRESSER & MCKEE INC
CANON INC
CAPGEMINI
CATERPILLAR INC
CELANESE CORPORATION

CELESTICA INC
CGI GROUP INC
CH2M HILL COMPANIES LTD
CHEVRON CORPORATION
CHICAGO BRIDGE & IRON COMPANY NV
CHIRON CORP
CHRYSLER LLC
CIBA HOLDING AG
CISCO SYSTEMS INC
CITRIX SYSTEMS INC
CLARIANT INTERNATIONAL LTD
COGNOS INC
COMPUTER SCIENCES CORPORATION (CSC)
COMPUWARE CORP
COMVERSE TECHNOLOGY INC
CONOCOPHILLIPS COMPANY
CORNING INC
COVANCE INC
CRAY INC
CSL LIMITED
CTS CORP
CUMMINS INC
DAIMLER AG
DAIMLER TRUCKS NORTH AMERICA LLC
DANA HOLDINGS CORPORATION
DASSAULT SYSTEMES SA
DEERE & CO
DELL INC
DELPHI CORP
DENSO CORPORATION
DIC CORPORATION
DIEBOLD INC
DOW CHEMICAL COMPANY (THE)
DOW CORNING CORPORATION
DRS TECHNOLOGIES INC
E I DU PONT DE NEMOURS & CO (DUPONT)
EASTMAN KODAK CO
EATON CORP
EISAI CO LTD
ELECTRONIC ARTS INC
ELECTRONIC DATA SYSTEMS CORP (EDS)
ELI LILLY & COMPANY
EMERSON ELECTRIC CO
ESSILOR INTERNATIONAL SA
EXXON MOBIL CORPORATION (EXXONMOBIL)
FAURECIA SA
FEDERAL MOGUL CORP
FERRARI SPA
FLEXTRONICS INTERNATIONAL LTD
FLUOR CORP
FMC TECHNOLOGIES INC
FORD MOTOR CO
FOREST LABORATORIES INC
FOSTER WHEELER AG
FUJI HEAVY INDUSTRIES LTD (SUBARU)
FUJIFILM HOLDINGS CORP
FUJITSU LIMITED
GE AVIATION
GE ENERGY
GE HEALTHCARE
GENERAL DYNAMICS CORP
GENERAL ELECTRIC CO (GE)
GENERAL MOTORS CORP (GM)
GENZYME CORP
GEORG FISCHER LTD
GKN PLC
GLAXOSMITHKLINE PLC
GOODRICH CORPORATION
GRANITE CONSTRUCTION INC
GROUP LOTUS PLC
GRUPO FERROVIAL SA
GULFSTREAM AEROSPACE CORP
HARRIS CORPORATION
HDR INC
HEWLETT-PACKARD CO (HP)
HILL-ROM HOLDINGS INC
HITACHI GLOBAL STORAGE TECHNOLOGIES
HITACHI HIGH TECHNOLOGIES AMERICA INC
HITACHI LTD
HOCHTIEF AG
HON HAI PRECISION INDUSTRY COMPANY LTD
HONDA MOTOR CO LTD
HONDA OF AMERICA MFG INC
HONEYWELL INTERNATIONAL INC
HOSPIRA INC
HUNTSMAN CORPORATION
HYUNDAI MOTOR COMPANY
IKON OFFICE SOLUTIONS INC
ILLINOIS TOOL WORKS INC
IMATION CORP
INFINEON TECHNOLOGIES AG
INGERSOLL-RAND COMPANY LIMITED
INTEL CORP
INTERNATIONAL BUSINESS MACHINES CORP (IBM)
INTUIT INC
ISUZU MOTORS LTD
ITT CORPORATION
JABIL CIRCUIT INC
JACOBS ENGINEERING GROUP INC
JAGUAR CARS LTD
JDS UNIPHASE CORPORATION
JOHNSON & JOHNSON
JOHNSON CONTROLS INC
JUNIPER NETWORKS INC
KAWASAKI HEAVY INDUSTRIES LTD
KIA MOTORS CORPORATION
KIMBERLY-CLARK CORP
KIMLEY-HORN AND ASSOCIATES INC
L-3 COMMUNICATIONS HOLDINGS INC
L-3 TITAN GROUP
LAND ROVER
LANXESS AG
LAYNE CHRISTENSEN COMPANY
LEAR CORP
LEARJET INC

LEXMARK INTERNATIONAL INC
LINDE GROUP
LOCKHEED MARTIN CORP
LOGICA PLC
LOUIS BERGER GROUP INC (THE)
LSI CORPORATION
LUXOTTICA GROUP SPA
MAGNA INTERNATIONAL INC
MAGNETI MARELLI HOLDING SPA
MARATHON OIL CORP
MATRIX SERVICE COMPANY
MAXIM INTEGRATED PRODUCTS INC
MAZDA MOTOR CORPORATION
MCAFEE INC
MCDERMOTT INTERNATIONAL INC
MEDTRONIC INC
MENTOR GRAPHICS CORP
MERCK & CO INC
MERCK KGAA
MICHAEL BAKER CORPORATION
MICRON TECHNOLOGY INC
MICROSOFT CORP
MITSUBISHI ELECTRIC CORPORATION
MITSUBISHI MOTORS CORP
MITSUI CHEMICALS INC
MOLEX INC
MONSANTO CO
MOTOROLA INC
MOTOROLA LABS
MSCSOFTWARE CORP
MWH GLOBAL INC
NATIONAL SEMICONDUCTOR CORP
NAVTEQ CORPORATION
NCR CORPORATION
NEC CORPORATION
NIDEC CORPORATION
NISSAN MOTOR CO LTD
NITTO DENKO CORPORATION
NOKIA CORPORATION
NORTEL NETWORKS CORP
NORTHROP GRUMMAN CORP
NOVELL INC
NOVOZYMES
NTT DATA CORP
ORACLE CORP
PACCAR INC
PANASONIC CORPORATION
PARAMETRIC TECHNOLOGY CORP
PARSONS BRINCKERHOFF INC
PCL CONSTRUCTION GROUP INC
PERINI CORPORATION
PEROT SYSTEMS CORP
PFIZER INC
PHARMACEUTICAL PRODUCT DEVELOPMENT INC
PITNEY BOWES INC
PLEXUS CORP
QUALCOMM INC
QUANTUM CORP
QUINTILES TRANSNATIONAL CORP
RAILWORKS CORP
RAYTHEON CO
RENESAS TECHNOLOGY CORP
RHEINMETALL AG
RICOH COMPANY LTD
ROBERT BOSCH GMBH
ROCHE HOLDING LTD
ROCKWELL AUTOMATION INC
ROHM CO LTD
ROLLSROYCE PLC
ROYAL DUTCH SHELL (SHELL GROUP)
ROYAL PHILIPS ELECTRONICS NV
SAFRAN SA
SAIC INC
SAMSUNG ELECTRONICS CO LTD
SANMINA-SCI CORPORATION
SANOFI-AVENTIS SA
SAP AG
SAS INSTITUTE INC
SASOL LIMITED
SCHERING-PLOUGH CORP
SCHLUMBERGER LIMITED
SEAGATE TECHNOLOGY INC
SEGA SAMMY HOLDINGS INC
SEIKO EPSON CORPORATION
SHANGHAI AUTOMOTIVE INDUSTRY CORP (SAIC)
SHARP CORPORATION
SHAW GROUP INC (THE)
SHELL OIL CO
SIEMENS AG
SIEMENS PLM SOFTWARE
SKIDMORE OWINGS & MERRILL LLP
SMITHS GROUP PLC
SOLVAY SA
SONY CORPORATION
SPIRIT AEROSYSTEMS HOLDINGS INC
ST JUDE MEDICAL INC
STMICROELECTRONICS NV
STRYKER CORP
STV GROUP INC
SUN MICROSYSTEMS INC
SYBASE INC
SYMANTEC CORP
SYNGENTA AG
SYNOPSYS INC
TAKEDA PHARMACEUTICAL COMPANY LTD
TATA CONSULTANCY SERVICES (TCS)
TATE & LYLE PLC
TELEDYNE TECHNOLOGIES INCORPORATED
TELLABS INC
TENNECO INC
TEREX CORPORATION
TEXAS INSTRUMENTS INC (TI)
THQ INC
TOYODA GOSEI CO LTD
TOYOTA MOTOR CORPORATION
TRC COMPANIES INC

TRW AUTOMOTIVE HOLDINGS CORP
TTM TECHNOLOGIES INC
TYCO INTERNATIONAL LTD
UCB SA
UNION CARBIDE CORPORATION
UNISYS CORP
UNITED TECHNOLOGIES CORPORATION
URS CORPORATION
UTSTARCOM INC
VALEO
VERISIGN INC
VINCI
VISTEON CORPORATION
VSE CORP
VTECH HOLDINGS LIMITED
WANXIANG GROUP CORPORATION
WESTINGHOUSE ELECTRIC COMPANY LLC
WHIRLPOOL CORP
WIPRO LTD
WS ATKINS PLC
WYETH
XEROX CORP
YAHOO! INC
ZF FRIEDRICHSHAFEN AG

SOUTHEAST

3COM CORP
3M COMPANY
AB VOLVO
ABERTIS INFRAESTRUCTURAS SA
ACCENTURE LTD
ACTIVISION BLIZZARD INC
ACXIOM CORP
ADVANCED MICRO DEVICES INC (AMD)
AECOM TECHNOLOGY CORPORATION
AFFILIATED COMPUTER SERVICES INC
AIR PRODUCTS & CHEMICALS INC
AIRBUS SAS
AKZO NOBEL NV
ALCON INC
ALFA SAB DE CV
ALPHARMA INC
ALPS ELECTRIC CO LTD
ALTERA CORP
AMDOCS LTD
AMEC PLC
AMGEN INC
ANALOG DEVICES INC
APPLE INC
ARCADIS NV
ARKEMA
ARRIS GROUP INC
ARVINMERITOR INC
ASTON MARTIN LAGONDA LTD
ASTRAZENECA PLC
ATMEL CORP
AUDI AG
AUTODESK INC
AVAYA INC
AVIALL INC
BABCOCK & WILCOX COMPANY (THE)
BAE SYSTEMS PLC
BAKER HUGHES INC
BALFOUR BEATTY PLC
BARAN GROUP LTD
BASF AG
BAUSCH & LOMB INC
BAXTER INTERNATIONAL INC
BAYER CORP
BECHTEL GROUP INC
BECKMAN COULTER INC
BECTON DICKINSON & CO
BELDEN INC
BENCHMARK ELECTRONICS INC
BLACK & DECKER CORP
BLACK & VEATCH HOLDING COMPANY
BMC SOFTWARE INC
BOEING COMPANY (THE)
BOMBARDIER INC
BOSTON SCIENTIFIC CORP
BP PLC
BRISTOL MYERS SQUIBB CO
BRITISH NUCLEAR FUELS PLC
BROADCOM CORP
BROCADE COMMUNICATIONS SYSTEMS INC
BURNS & MCDONNELL
BUSINESS OBJECTS SA
CA INC
CADENCE DESIGN SYSTEMS INC
CALSONIC KANSEI CORPORATION
CAMP DRESSER & MCKEE INC
CANON INC
CAPGEMINI
CATERPILLAR INC
CELESTICA INC
CGI GROUP INC
CH2M HILL COMPANIES LTD
CHEVRON CORPORATION
CHICAGO BRIDGE & IRON COMPANY NV
CHRYSLER LLC
CIBA HOLDING AG
CISCO SYSTEMS INC
CITRIX SYSTEMS INC
CLARIANT INTERNATIONAL LTD
COGNOS INC
COMPUTER SCIENCES CORPORATION (CSC)
COMPUWARE CORP
COMVERSE TECHNOLOGY INC
CONOCOPHILLIPS COMPANY
COVANCE INC
CSL LIMITED
CUMMINS INC
DAIMLER AG
DAIMLER TRUCKS NORTH AMERICA LLC
DANA HOLDINGS CORPORATION
DEERE & CO

DELL INC
DELPHI CORP
DENSO CORPORATION
DIEBOLD INC
DOW CHEMICAL COMPANY (THE)
DRS TECHNOLOGIES INC
E I DU PONT DE NEMOURS & CO (DUPONT)
EASTMAN CHEMICAL COMPANY
EASTMAN KODAK CO
EATON CORP
ELECTRONIC ARTS INC
ELECTRONIC DATA SYSTEMS CORP (EDS)
ELI LILLY & COMPANY
EMBRAER BRASILIAN AVIATION COMPANY
EMERSON ELECTRIC CO
ENGLOBAL CORP
ESSILOR INTERNATIONAL SA
EXXON MOBIL CORPORATION (EXXONMOBIL)
FAURECIA SA
FEDERAL MOGUL CORP
FERRARI SPA
FLEXTRONICS INTERNATIONAL LTD
FLUOR CORP
FMC TECHNOLOGIES INC
FOMENTO DE CONSTRUCCIONES Y CONTRATAS SA (FCC)
FORD MOTOR CO
FOSTER WHEELER AG
FUJIFILM HOLDINGS CORP
GE AVIATION
GE ENERGY
GENERAL DYNAMICS CORP
GENERAL ELECTRIC CO (GE)
GENERAL MOTORS CORP (GM)
GENZYME CORP
GEORG FISCHER LTD
GKN PLC
GLAXOSMITHKLINE PLC
GLOBAL VIA INFRASTRUCTURES SA (GLOBALVIA)
GOODRICH CORPORATION
GRANITE CONSTRUCTION INC
GROUP LOTUS PLC
GULFSTREAM AEROSPACE CORP
HALLIBURTON COMPANY
HARRIS CORPORATION
HDR INC
HEWLETT-PACKARD CO (HP)
HITACHI HIGH TECHNOLOGIES AMERICA INC
HITACHI LTD
HOCHTIEF AG
HONDA MOTOR CO LTD
HONEYWELL INTERNATIONAL INC
HUNTSMAN CORPORATION
HYUNDAI MOTOR COMPANY
IKON OFFICE SOLUTIONS INC
ILLINOIS TOOL WORKS INC
IMATION CORP
INDRAS SISTEMAS SA
INGERSOLL-RAND COMPANY LIMITED
INTEL CORP
INTERNATIONAL BUSINESS MACHINES CORP (IBM)
INTUIT INC
ITT CORPORATION
JABIL CIRCUIT INC
JACOBS ENGINEERING GROUP INC
JAGUAR CARS LTD
JDS UNIPHASE CORPORATION
JOHNSON & JOHNSON
JOHNSON CONTROLS INC
JUNIPER NETWORKS INC
KIA MOTORS CORPORATION
KIMBERLY-CLARK CORP
KIMLEY-HORN AND ASSOCIATES INC
L-3 COMMUNICATIONS HOLDINGS INC
L-3 TITAN GROUP
LAND ROVER
LANXESS AG
LAYNE CHRISTENSEN COMPANY
LEAR CORP
LINDE GROUP
LITE-ON TECHNOLOGY CORP
LOCKHEED MARTIN CORP
LOGICA PLC
LOUIS BERGER GROUP INC (THE)
LUXOTTICA GROUP SPA
MAGNA INTERNATIONAL INC
MARATHON OIL CORP
MAXIM INTEGRATED PRODUCTS INC
MAZDA MOTOR CORPORATION
MCAFEE INC
MCDERMOTT INTERNATIONAL INC
MEDTRONIC INC
MERCK & CO INC
MERCK KGAA
MICHAEL BAKER CORPORATION
MICRON TECHNOLOGY INC
MICROSOFT CORP
MITSUBISHI ELECTRIC CORPORATION
MOLEX INC
MONSANTO CO
MOTOROLA INC
MOTOROLA LABS
MSCSOFTWARE CORP
MWH GLOBAL INC
NATIONAL SEMICONDUCTOR CORP
NCR CORPORATION
NISSAN MOTOR CO LTD
NITTO DENKO CORPORATION
NOKIA CORPORATION
NORTEL NETWORKS CORP
NORTHROP GRUMMAN CORP
NOVELL INC
ORACLE CORP
PACCAR INC

PANASONIC CORPORATION
PARAMETRIC TECHNOLOGY CORP
PARSONS BRINCKERHOFF INC
PCL CONSTRUCTION GROUP INC
PERINI CORPORATION
PEROT SYSTEMS CORP
PFIZER INC
PHARMACEUTICAL PRODUCT DEVELOPMENT INC
PITNEY BOWES INC
PLEXUS CORP
QUALCOMM INC
QUINTILES TRANSNATIONAL CORP
RAILWORKS CORP
RAYTHEON CO
RICOH COMPANY LTD
ROBERT BOSCH GMBH
ROCHE HOLDING LTD
ROCKWELL AUTOMATION INC
ROHM CO LTD
ROLLSROYCE PLC
ROYAL DUTCH SHELL (SHELL GROUP)
ROYAL PHILIPS ELECTRONICS NV
SAAB AB
SAFRAN SA
SAIC INC
SAMSUNG ELECTRONICS CO LTD
SANMINA-SCI CORPORATION
SANOFI-AVENTIS SA
SAP AG
SAS INSTITUTE INC
SASOL LIMITED
SCHERING-PLOUGH CORP
SCIENTIFIC ATLANTA INC
SEAGATE TECHNOLOGY INC
SEGA SAMMY HOLDINGS INC
SEIKO EPSON CORPORATION
SHARP CORPORATION
SHAW GROUP INC (THE)
SHELL OIL CO
SIEMENS AG
SIEMENS PLM SOFTWARE
SINGAPORE TECHNOLOGIES ENGINEERING LIMITED
SMITH & NEPHEW PLC
SMITHS GROUP PLC
SOLVAY SA
SONY CORPORATION
SONY ERICSSON MOBILE COMMUNICATIONS AB
ST JUDE MEDICAL INC
STMICROELECTRONICS NV
STRYKER CORP
STV GROUP INC
SUN MICROSYSTEMS INC
SUZUKI MOTOR CORPORATION
SYBASE INC
SYMANTEC CORP
SYNGENTA AG
SYNOPSYS INC
TATA CONSULTANCY SERVICES (TCS)
TECHNIP
TELCORDIA TECHNOLOGIES
TELEDYNE TECHNOLOGIES INCORPORATED
TELLABS INC
TENNECO INC
TEREX CORPORATION
TEXAS INSTRUMENTS INC (TI)
TOYOTA MOTOR CORPORATION
TRC COMPANIES INC
TREVI-FINANZIARIA INDUSTRIALE SPA (TREVI GROUP)
TRW AUTOMOTIVE HOLDINGS CORP
TYCO INTERNATIONAL LTD
UCB SA
UNION CARBIDE CORPORATION
UNISYS CORP
UNITED TECHNOLOGIES CORPORATION
URS CORPORATION
UTSTARCOM INC
VALEO
VERISIGN INC
VINCI
VISTEON CORPORATION
VSE CORP
WESTINGHOUSE ELECTRIC COMPANY LLC
WHIRLPOOL CORP
WIPRO LTD
WS ATKINS PLC
WYETH
XEROX CORP
YAHOO! INC
ZF FRIEDRICHSHAFEN AG

NORTHEAST

3COM CORP
3M COMPANY
AB VOLVO
ABB LTD
ABBOTT LABORATORIES
ACCENTURE LTD
ACCIONA SA
ACCTON TECHNOLOGY CORP
ACTIVISION BLIZZARD INC
ADOBE SYSTEMS INC
ADVANCED MICRO DEVICES INC (AMD)
ADVANCED SEMICONDUCTOR ENGINEERING INC
AECOM TECHNOLOGY CORPORATION
AFFILIATED COMPUTER SERVICES INC
AGFA-GEVAERT NV
AGILENT TECHNOLOGIES INC
AIR PRODUCTS & CHEMICALS INC
AIRBUS SAS
AKZO NOBEL NV
ALBANY MOLECULAR RESEARCH
ALCATEL-LUCENT
ALFA SAB DE CV
ALPHARMA INC

ALPS ELECTRIC CO LTD
ALSTOM
ALTANA AG
ALTERA CORP
ALTRAN TECHNOLOGIES SA
AMDOCS LTD
AMEC PLC
AMGEN INC
ANALOG DEVICES INC
APPLE INC
ARCADIS NV
AREVA GROUP
ARKEMA
ARRIS GROUP INC
ARVINMERITOR INC
ASTELLAS PHARMA INC
ASTON MARTIN LAGONDA LTD
ASTRAZENECA PLC
ATMEL CORP
ATOMIC ENERGY OF CANADA LIMITED
AUDI AG
AUTODESK INC
AVAYA INC
AVIALL INC
BABCOCK & WILCOX COMPANY (THE)
BAE SYSTEMS PLC
BAKER HUGHES INC
BALLARD POWER SYSTEMS
BASF AG
BASF FUTURE BUSINESS GMBH
BAUSCH & LOMB INC
BAXTER INTERNATIONAL INC
BAYER AG
BAYER CORP
BAYER SCHERING PHARMA AG
BECHTEL GROUP INC
BECTON DICKINSON & CO
BELDEN INC
BELL LABS
BENCHMARK ELECTRONICS INC
BIOGEN IDEC INC
BLACK & DECKER CORP
BLACK & VEATCH HOLDING COMPANY
BMC SOFTWARE INC
BMW (BAYERISCHE MOTOREN WERKE AG)
BOEING COMPANY (THE)
BOMBARDIER INC
BOSTON SCIENTIFIC CORP
BOUYGUES SA
BP PLC
BRISTOL MYERS SQUIBB CO
BRITISH NUCLEAR FUELS PLC
BROADCOM CORP
BROCADE COMMUNICATIONS SYSTEMS INC
BURNS & MCDONNELL
BUSINESS OBJECTS SA
CA INC
CADENCE DESIGN SYSTEMS INC
CAMP DRESSER & MCKEE INC
CANON INC
CAPGEMINI
CASIO COMPUTER CO LTD
CATERPILLAR INC
CELANESE CORPORATION
CELESTICA INC
CGI GROUP INC
CH2M HILL COMPANIES LTD
CHEVRON CORPORATION
CHICAGO BRIDGE & IRON COMPANY NV
CHIRON CORP
CHRYSLER LLC
CIBA HOLDING AG
CISCO SYSTEMS INC
CITRIX SYSTEMS INC
CLARIANT INTERNATIONAL LTD
COGNOS INC
COMPUTER SCIENCES CORPORATION (CSC)
COMPUWARE CORP
COMVERSE TECHNOLOGY INC
CONOCOPHILLIPS COMPANY
CORNING INC
COVANCE INC
CSL LIMITED
CTS CORP
CUMMINS INC
DAEWOO SHIPBUILDING & MARINE
ENGINEERING CO LTD
DAIMLER AG
DAIMLER TRUCKS NORTH AMERICA LLC
DANA HOLDINGS CORPORATION
DASSAULT AVIATION SA
DASSAULT SYSTEMES SA
DEERE & CO
DELL INC
DELPHI CORP
DENSO CORPORATION
DIC CORPORATION
DIEBOLD INC
DOW CHEMICAL COMPANY (THE)
DOW CORNING CORPORATION
DRS TECHNOLOGIES INC
DUPONT CENTRAL RESEARCH & DEVELOPMENT
E I DU PONT DE NEMOURS & CO (DUPONT)
EASTMAN CHEMICAL COMPANY
EASTMAN KODAK CO
EATON CORP
EISAI CO LTD
ELECTRONIC ARTS INC
ELECTRONIC DATA SYSTEMS CORP (EDS)
ELI LILLY & COMPANY
EMC CORP
EMERSON ELECTRIC CO
ENI SPA
ESSILOR INTERNATIONAL SA
EUROPEAN AERONAUTIC DEFENSE AND SPACE
CO (EADS)

EVONIK DEGUSSA
EXXON MOBIL CORPORATION (EXXONMOBIL)
FEDERAL MOGUL CORP
FERRARI SPA
FLEXTRONICS INTERNATIONAL LTD
FLUOR CORP
FMC TECHNOLOGIES INC
FOMENTO DE CONSTRUCCIONES Y CONTRATAS SA (FCC)
FORD MOTOR CO
FOREST LABORATORIES INC
FOSTER WHEELER AG
FUELCELL ENERGY INC
FUJI HEAVY INDUSTRIES LTD (SUBARU)
FUJIFILM HOLDINGS CORP
FUJITSU LABORATORIES LTD
FUJITSU LIMITED
GAMESA CORPORACION TECNOLOGICA SA
GE AVIATION
GE ENERGY
GE GLOBAL RESEARCH
GEMALTO NV
GENERAL DYNAMICS CORP
GENERAL ELECTRIC CO (GE)
GENERAL MOTORS CORP (GM)
GENZYME CORP
GEORG FISCHER LTD
GETRONICS NV
GILEAD SCIENCES INC
GKN PLC
GLAXOSMITHKLINE PLC
GLOBAL VIA INFRASTRUCTURES SA (GLOBALVIA)
GOODRICH CORPORATION
GOOGLE INC
GRANITE CONSTRUCTION INC
GROUP LOTUS PLC
HARRIS CORPORATION
HDR INC
HEWLETT-PACKARD CO (HP)
HILL-ROM HOLDINGS INC
HITACHI HIGH TECHNOLOGIES AMERICA INC
HITACHI LTD
HOCHTIEF AG
HON HAI PRECISION INDUSTRY COMPANY LTD
HONDA MOTOR CO LTD
HONEYWELL INTERNATIONAL INC
HOSPIRA INC
HUAWEI TECHNOLOGIES CO LTD
HUNTSMAN CORPORATION
HYUNDAI ENGINEERING & CONSTRUCTION COMPANY LTD
HYUNDAI MOTOR COMPANY
IBM GLOBAL SERVICES
IBM RESEARCH
IKON OFFICE SOLUTIONS INC
ILLINOIS TOOL WORKS INC
INDRAS SISTEMAS SA
INFINEON TECHNOLOGIES AG
INGERSOLL-RAND COMPANY LIMITED
INTEL CORP
INTERNATIONAL BUSINESS MACHINES CORP (IBM)
INTUIT INC
ITT CORPORATION
JABIL CIRCUIT INC
JACOBS ENGINEERING GROUP INC
JAGUAR CARS LTD
JDS UNIPHASE CORPORATION
JOHNSON & JOHNSON
JOHNSON CONTROLS INC
JUNIPER NETWORKS INC
KANEKA CORPORATION
KAWASAKI HEAVY INDUSTRIES LTD
KBR INC
KIMBERLY-CLARK CORP
KIMLEY-HORN AND ASSOCIATES INC
KODAK RESEARCH LABORATORIES
L-3 COMMUNICATIONS HOLDINGS INC
L-3 TITAN GROUP
LAND ROVER
LANXESS AG
LAYNE CHRISTENSEN COMPANY
LEAR CORP
LENOVO GROUP LIMITED
LINDE GROUP
LOCKHEED MARTIN CORP
LOGICA PLC
LORAL SPACE & COMMUNICATIONS LTD
LOUIS BERGER GROUP INC (THE)
LUKOIL (OAO)
LUXOTTICA GROUP SPA
MAGNA INTERNATIONAL INC
MARATHON OIL CORP
MATRIX SERVICE COMPANY
MAXIM INTEGRATED PRODUCTS INC
MAZDA MOTOR CORPORATION
MCAFEE INC
MCDERMOTT INTERNATIONAL INC
MEDTRONIC INC
MERCK & CO INC
MERCK KGAA
MERCK SERONO SA
MICHAEL BAKER CORPORATION
MICRON TECHNOLOGY INC
MICROSOFT CORP
MITSUBISHI ELECTRIC CORPORATION
MITSUI CHEMICALS INC
MOLEX INC
MONSANTO CO
MOTOROLA INC
MOTOROLA LABS
MSCSOFTWARE CORP
MWH GLOBAL INC
NATIONAL SEMICONDUCTOR CORP
NCR CORPORATION

NEC CORPORATION
NEC LABORATORIES AMERICA INC
NETAPP INC
NIDEC CORPORATION
NISSAN MOTOR CO LTD
NITTO DENKO CORPORATION
NOKIA CORPORATION
NORTEL NETWORKS CORP
NORTHROP GRUMMAN CORP
NOVARTIS AG
NOVELL INC
NOVO-NORDISK AS
NOVOZYMES
NVIDIA CORP
ORACLE CORP
OYO CORPORATION
PACCAR INC
PALM INC
PANASONIC CORPORATION
PARAMETRIC TECHNOLOGY CORP
PAREXEL INTERNATIONAL CORP
PARSONS BRINCKERHOFF INC
PERINI CORPORATION
PEROT SYSTEMS CORP
PETROLEO BRASILEIRO SA (PETROBRAS)
PFIZER INC
PHARMACEUTICAL PRODUCT DEVELOPMENT INC
PITNEY BOWES INC
PLEXUS CORP
PSA PEUGEOT CITROEN SA
QUALCOMM INC
QUANTUM CORP
QUINTILES TRANSNATIONAL CORP
RAILWORKS CORP
RAYTHEON CO
RENESAS TECHNOLOGY CORP
RHEINMETALL AG
RICOH COMPANY LTD
ROBERT BOSCH GMBH
ROCHE HOLDING LTD
ROCKWELL AUTOMATION INC
ROHM CO LTD
ROLLSROYCE PLC
ROYAL DUTCH SHELL (SHELL GROUP)
ROYAL PHILIPS ELECTRONICS NV
SAFRAN SA
SAIC INC
SAMSUNG ELECTRONICS CO LTD
SANMINA-SCI CORPORATION
SANOFI-AVENTIS SA
SAP AG
SAS INSTITUTE INC
SASOL LIMITED
SAUDI ARAMCO (SAUDI ARABIAN OIL CO)
SCHERING-PLOUGH CORP
SCHERING-PLOUGH RESEARCH INSTITUTE
SCHLUMBERGER LIMITED
SEAGATE TECHNOLOGY INC
SEIKO EPSON CORPORATION
SHARP CORPORATION
SHAW GROUP INC (THE)
SHELL OIL CO
SHOWA DENKO KK
SIEMENS AG
SIEMENS CORPORATE TECHNOLOGY
SIEMENS HEALTHCARE
SIEMENS PLM SOFTWARE
SINGAPORE TECHNOLOGIES ENGINEERING LIMITED
SKIDMORE OWINGS & MERRILL LLP
SMITH & NEPHEW PLC
SMITHS GROUP PLC
SNC-LAVALIN GROUP INC
SOLVAY SA
SONY CORPORATION
SONY ERICSSON MOBILE COMMUNICATIONS AB
ST JUDE MEDICAL INC
STATOILHYDRO ASA
STMICROELECTRONICS NV
STRYKER CORP
STV GROUP INC
SUMITOMO CHEMICAL CO LTD
SUN MICROSYSTEMS INC
SYBASE INC
SYMANTEC CORP
SYNGENTA AG
SYNOPSYS INC
TAKEDA PHARMACEUTICAL COMPANY LTD
TAKE-TWO INTERACTIVE SOFTWARE INC
TATA CONSULTANCY SERVICES (TCS)
TATA GROUP
TELCORDIA TECHNOLOGIES
TELEDYNE TECHNOLOGIES INCORPORATED
TELEFON AB LM ERICSSON (ERICSSON)
TELLABS INC
TENNECO INC
TEREX CORPORATION
TEXAS INSTRUMENTS INC (TI)
TEXTRON INC
THQ INC
TIETOENATOR
TOSHIBA CORPORATE R&D CENTER
TOSHIBA CORPORATION
TOYOTA MOTOR CORPORATION
TRC COMPANIES INC
TREVI-FINANZIARIA INDUSTRIALE SPA (TREVI GROUP)
TRW AUTOMOTIVE HOLDINGS CORP
TTM TECHNOLOGIES INC
TYCO INTERNATIONAL LTD
UCB SA
UNION CARBIDE CORPORATION
UNISYS CORP
UNITED TECHNOLOGIES CORPORATION
URS CORPORATION
UTSTARCOM INC

INDEX OF FIRMS WITH INTERNATIONAL OPERATIONS

ATMEL CORP
ATOMIC ENERGY OF CANADA LIMITED
ATOS ORIGIN SA
AU OPTRONICS CORP
AUDI AG
AUTODESK INC
AUTOLIV INC
AVAYA INC
AVIALL INC
BABCOCK & WILCOX COMPANY (THE)
BAE SYSTEMS PLC
BAKER HUGHES INC
BALFOUR BEATTY PLC
BALLARD POWER SYSTEMS
BARAN GROUP LTD
BASF AG
BASF FUTURE BUSINESS GMBH
BAUSCH & LOMB INC
BAXTER INTERNATIONAL INC
BAYER AG
BAYER SCHERING PHARMA AG
BECHTEL GROUP INC
BECKMAN COULTER INC
BECTON DICKINSON & CO
BELDEN INC
BELL LABS
BENCHMARK ELECTRONICS INC
BIOGEN IDEC INC
BIOS-BIOENERGIESYSTEME GMBH
BLACK & DECKER CORP
BLACK & VEATCH HOLDING COMPANY
BMC SOFTWARE INC
BMW (BAYERISCHE MOTOREN WERKE AG)
BOEING COMPANY (THE)
BOMBARDIER INC
BOSTON SCIENTIFIC CORP
BOUYGUES SA
BP PLC
BRILLIANCE CHINA AUTOMOTIVE HOLDINGS LIMITED
BRISTOL MYERS SQUIBB CO
BRITISH NUCLEAR FUELS PLC
BROADCOM CORP
BROCADE COMMUNICATIONS SYSTEMS INC
BUSINESS OBJECTS SA
CA INC
CADENCE DESIGN SYSTEMS INC
CALSONIC KANSEI CORPORATION
CAMP DRESSER & MCKEE INC
CANON INC
CAPGEMINI
CASIO COMPUTER CO LTD
CATERPILLAR INC
CELANESE CORPORATION
CELESTICA INC
CGI GROUP INC
CH2M HILL COMPANIES LTD
CHEVRON CORPORATION
CHI MEI OPTOELECTRONICS
CHICAGO BRIDGE & IRON COMPANY NV
CHIRON CORP
CHIYODA CORPORATION
CHRYSLER LLC
CIBA HOLDING AG
CISCO SYSTEMS INC
CITIC PACIFIC LTD
CITRIX SYSTEMS INC
CLARIANT INTERNATIONAL LTD
COGNOS INC
COMPAL ELECTRONICS INC
COMPUTER SCIENCES CORPORATION (CSC)
COMPUWARE CORP
COMVERSE TECHNOLOGY INC
CONOCOPHILLIPS COMPANY
CORNING INC
COVANCE INC
CRAY INC
CSK HOLDINGS CORP
CSL LIMITED
CTS CORP
CUMMINS INC
DAELIM INDUSTRIAL CO LTD
DAESUNG INDUSTRIAL CO LTD
DAEWOO SHIPBUILDING & MARINE ENGINEERING CO LTD
DAIHATSU MOTOR CO LTD
DAIMLER AG
DAIMLER TRUCKS NORTH AMERICA LLC
DANA HOLDINGS CORPORATION
DASSAULT AVIATION SA
DASSAULT SYSTEMES SA
DEERE & CO
DELL INC
DELPHI CORP
DENSO CORPORATION
DIC CORPORATION
DIEBOLD INC
D-LINK CORPORATION
DONGFENG MOTOR CORPORATION
DOW CHEMICAL COMPANY (THE)
DOW CORNING CORPORATION
DRS TECHNOLOGIES INC
E I DU PONT DE NEMOURS & CO (DUPONT)
EASTMAN CHEMICAL COMPANY
EASTMAN KODAK CO
EATON CORP
EISAI CO LTD
ELECTRONIC ARTS INC
ELECTRONIC DATA SYSTEMS CORP (EDS)
ELI LILLY & COMPANY
EMBRAER BRASILIAN AVIATION COMPANY
EMC CORP
EMERSON ELECTRIC CO
EMPRESAS ICA SA DE CV
ENERCON GMBH
ENGLOBAL CORP

ENI SPA
ESSILOR INTERNATIONAL SA
EUROPEAN AERONAUTIC DEFENSE AND SPACE CO (EADS)
EVONIK DEGUSSA
EVONIK INDUSTRIES AG
EXXON MOBIL CORPORATION (EXXONMOBIL)
EXXONMOBIL CHEMICAL
FAURECIA SA
FEDERAL MOGUL CORP
FERRARI SPA
FIAT SPA
FIRST AUTOMOTIVE GROUP CORPORATION
FLEXTRONICS INTERNATIONAL LTD
FLUOR CORP
FMC TECHNOLOGIES INC
FOMENTO DE CONSTRUCCIONES Y CONTRATAS SA (FCC)
FORD MOTOR CO
FOREST LABORATORIES INC
FOSTER WHEELER AG
FREESCALE SEMICONDUCTOR INC
FUELCELL ENERGY INC
FUJI HEAVY INDUSTRIES LTD (SUBARU)
FUJIFILM HOLDINGS CORP
FUJITSU LABORATORIES LTD
FUJITSU LIMITED
FUJITSU-SIEMENS COMPUTER HOLDING COMPANY
GAMESA CORPORACION TECNOLOGICA SA
GE AVIATION
GE ENERGY
GE GLOBAL RESEARCH
GE HEALTHCARE
GEMALTO NV
GENENTECH INC
GENERAL DYNAMICS CORP
GENERAL ELECTRIC CO (GE)
GENERAL MOTORS CORP (GM)
GENZYME CORP
GEORG FISCHER LTD
GETRONICS NV
GILEAD SCIENCES INC
GKN PLC
GLAXOSMITHKLINE PLC
GLOBAL VIA INFRASTRUCTURES SA (GLOBALVIA)
GM DAEWOO AUTO AND TECHNOLOGY CO
GOODRICH CORPORATION
GOOGLE INC
GROUP LOTUS PLC
GRUPO ACS
GRUPO FERROVIAL SA
GS ENGINEERING & CONSTRUCTION CORP
GULFSTREAM AEROSPACE CORP
HALLIBURTON COMPANY
HARRIS CORPORATION
HDR INC
HEWLETT-PACKARD CO (HP)
HEWLETT-PACKARD QUANTUM SCIENCE RESEARCH
HIGH TECH COMPUTER CORPORATION (HTC)
HILL-ROM HOLDINGS INC
HITACHI GLOBAL STORAGE TECHNOLOGIES
HITACHI HIGH TECHNOLOGIES AMERICA INC
HITACHI LTD
HOCHTIEF AG
HON HAI PRECISION INDUSTRY COMPANY LTD
HONDA MOTOR CO LTD
HONEYWELL INTERNATIONAL INC
HOSPIRA INC
HP LABS (HEWLETT-PACKARD LABORATORIES)
HUAWEI TECHNOLOGIES CO LTD
HUNTSMAN CORPORATION
HYUNDAI ENGINEERING & CONSTRUCTION COMPANY LTD
HYUNDAI MOTOR COMPANY
IBM GLOBAL SERVICES
IBM RESEARCH
IKON OFFICE SOLUTIONS INC
ILLINOIS TOOL WORKS INC
IMATION CORP
IMI PLC
IMPREGILO SPA
INDRAS SISTEMAS SA
INFINEON TECHNOLOGIES AG
INGERSOLL-RAND COMPANY LIMITED
INTEL CORP
INTERNATIONAL BUSINESS MACHINES CORP (IBM)
INTUIT INC
ISUZU MOTORS LTD
ITT CORPORATION
JABIL CIRCUIT INC
JACOBS ENGINEERING GROUP INC
JAGUAR CARS LTD
JAIPRAKASH ASSOCIATES LIMITED
JDS UNIPHASE CORPORATION
JOHNSON & JOHNSON
JOHNSON CONTROLS INC
JUNIPER NETWORKS INC
KANEKA CORPORATION
KAWASAKI HEAVY INDUSTRIES LTD
KBR INC
KEY TRONIC CORP
KIA MOTORS CORPORATION
KIMBERLY-CLARK CORP
KODAK RESEARCH LABORATORIES
KONAMI CORP
KUMHO INDUSTRIAL CO LTD
L-3 COMMUNICATIONS HOLDINGS INC
L-3 TITAN GROUP
LAND ROVER
LANXESS AG
LARSEN & TOUBRO LIMITED (L&T)
LAYNE CHRISTENSEN COMPANY

LEAR CORP
LENOVO GROUP LIMITED
LEXMARK INTERNATIONAL INC
LG DISPLAY CO LTD
LG ELECTRONICS INC
LINDE GROUP
LITE-ON TECHNOLOGY CORP
LOCKHEED MARTIN CORP
LOGICA PLC
LOGITECH INTERNATIONAL SA
LORAL SPACE & COMMUNICATIONS LTD
LOUIS BERGER GROUP INC (THE)
LSI CORPORATION
LUKOIL (OAO)
LUXOTTICA GROUP SPA
LYONDELLBASELL INDUSTRIES
MAGNA INTERNATIONAL INC
MAGNETI MARELLI HOLDING SPA
MARATHON OIL CORP
MATRIX SERVICE COMPANY
MAXIM INTEGRATED PRODUCTS INC
MAZDA MOTOR CORPORATION
MCAFEE INC
MCDERMOTT INTERNATIONAL INC
MEDTRONIC INC
MENTOR GRAPHICS CORP
MERCK & CO INC
MERCK KGAA
MERCK SERONO SA
MICHAEL BAKER CORPORATION
MICRON TECHNOLOGY INC
MICROSOFT CORP
MITSUBISHI CORP
MITSUBISHI ELECTRIC CORPORATION
MITSUBISHI MOTORS CORP
MITSUI CHEMICALS INC
MOLEX INC
MONSANTO CO
MOTOROLA INC
MOTOROLA LABS
MSCSOFTWARE CORP
MWH GLOBAL INC
NATIONAL SEMICONDUCTOR CORP
NAVTEQ CORPORATION
NCR CORPORATION
NEC CORPORATION
NETAPP INC
NIDEC CORPORATION
NINTENDO CO LTD
NISSAN MOTOR CO LTD
NITTO DENKO CORPORATION
NOKIA CORPORATION
NORTEL NETWORKS CORP
NORTHROP GRUMMAN CORP
NOVARTIS AG
NOVELL INC
NOVO-NORDISK AS
NOVOZYMES
NTT DATA CORP
NVIDIA CORP
ORACLE CORP
OYO CORPORATION
PACCAR INC
PALM INC
PANASONIC CORPORATION
PANASONIC MOBILE COMMUNICATIONS CO LTD
PARAMETRIC TECHNOLOGY CORP
PAREXEL INTERNATIONAL CORP
PARSONS BRINCKERHOFF INC
PCL CONSTRUCTION GROUP INC
PEROT SYSTEMS CORP
PETROCHINA COMPANY
PETROLEO BRASILEIRO SA (PETROBRAS)
PETROLEOS MEXICANOS (PEMEX)
PFIZER INC
PHARMACEUTICAL PRODUCT DEVELOPMENT INC
PININFARINA SPA
PIONEER CORPORATION
PITNEY BOWES INC
PLANTRONICS INC
PLEXUS CORP
PORSCHE AUTOMOBIL HOLDING SE
PSA PEUGEOT CITROEN SA
QUALCOMM INC
QUANTUM CORP
QUINTILES TRANSNATIONAL CORP
RAILWORKS CORP
RAYTHEON CO
RENAULT SA
RENESAS TECHNOLOGY CORP
RHEINMETALL AG
RICOH COMPANY LTD
ROBERT BOSCH GMBH
ROCHE HOLDING LTD
ROCKWELL AUTOMATION INC
ROHM CO LTD
ROLLSROYCE PLC
ROYAL DUTCH SHELL (SHELL GROUP)
ROYAL PHILIPS ELECTRONICS NV
SAAB AB
SAFRAN SA
SAIC INC
SAIC-GM-WULING AUTOMOBILE COMPANY
SAMSUNG ADVANCED INSTITUTE OF TECHNOLOGY (SAIT)
SAMSUNG ELECTRONICS CO LTD
SANDISK CORP
SANMINA-SCI CORPORATION
SANOFI-AVENTIS SA
SANYO ELECTRIC COMPANY LTD
SAP AG
SAS INSTITUTE INC
SASOL LIMITED
SAUDI ARAMCO (SAUDI ARABIAN OIL CO)
SCHERING-PLOUGH CORP
SCHERING-PLOUGH RESEARCH INSTITUTE

SCHLUMBERGER LIMITED
SCHNEIDER ELECTRIC SA
SCIENTIFIC ATLANTA INC
SEAGATE TECHNOLOGY INC
SEGA SAMMY HOLDINGS INC
SEIKO EPSON CORPORATION
SEMBCORP INDUSTRIES LTD
SHANGHAI AUTOMOTIVE INDUSTRY CORP (SAIC)
SHARP CORPORATION
SHAW GROUP INC (THE)
SHELL OIL CO
SHIN ETSU CHEMICAL CO LTD
SHOWA DENKO KK
SIEMENS AG
SIEMENS CORPORATE TECHNOLOGY
SIEMENS HEALTHCARE
SIEMENS PLM SOFTWARE
SINGAPORE TECHNOLOGIES ENGINEERING LIMITED
SKIDMORE OWINGS & MERRILL LLP
SMITH & NEPHEW PLC
SMITHS GROUP PLC
SNC-LAVALIN GROUP INC
SOLVAY SA
SONY CORPORATION
SONY ERICSSON MOBILE COMMUNICATIONS AB
SPIRIT AEROSYSTEMS HOLDINGS INC
ST JUDE MEDICAL INC
STATOILHYDRO ASA
STMICROELECTRONICS NV
STRYKER CORP
SUMITOMO CHEMICAL CO LTD
SUN MICROSYSTEMS INC
SUZUKI MOTOR CORPORATION
SYBASE INC
SYMANTEC CORP
SYNGENTA AG
SYNOPSYS INC
TAIWAN SEMICONDUCTOR MANUFACTURING CO LTD (TSMC)
TAKEDA PHARMACEUTICAL COMPANY LTD
TAKE-TWO INTERACTIVE SOFTWARE INC
TATA CONSULTANCY SERVICES (TCS)
TATA GROUP
TATA MOTORS LIMITED
TATE & LYLE PLC
TECHNIP
TELCORDIA TECHNOLOGIES
TELEDYNE TECHNOLOGIES INCORPORATED
TELEFON AB LM ERICSSON (ERICSSON)
TELLABS INC
TENNECO INC
TEREX CORPORATION
TEXAS INSTRUMENTS INC (TI)
THQ INC
TIETOENATOR
TOSHIBA CORPORATE R&D CENTER
TOSHIBA CORPORATION
TOTAL SA
TOYODA GOSEI CO LTD
TOYOTA MOTOR CORPORATION
TPV TECHNOLOGY LTD
TREVI-FINANZIARIA INDUSTRIALE SPA (TREVI GROUP)
TRW AUTOMOTIVE HOLDINGS CORP
TTM TECHNOLOGIES INC
TYCO INTERNATIONAL LTD
UCB SA
UNIDEN CORPORATION
UNION CARBIDE CORPORATION
UNISYS CORP
UNITED MICROELECTRONICS CORP
UNITED TECHNOLOGIES CORPORATION
URS CORPORATION
UTSTARCOM INC
VALEO
VERISIGN INC
VESTAS WIND SYSTEMS A/S
VINCI
VISTEON CORPORATION
VOLKSWAGEN AG
VOLVO CAR CORPORATION
VSE CORP
VTECH HOLDINGS LIMITED
WANXIANG GROUP CORPORATION
WESTERN DIGITAL CORP
WESTINGHOUSE ELECTRIC COMPANY LLC
WHIRLPOOL CORP
WIPRO LTD
WS ATKINS PLC
WYETH
XEROX CORP
YAHOO! INC
ZF FRIEDRICHSHAFEN AG
ZTE CORPORATION

Individual Profiles
On Each Of
THE ENGINEERING & RESEARCH 500

3COM CORP

www.3com.com

Industry Group Code: 334110 **Ranks within this company's industry group:** Sales: 3 Profits: 4

Techology:		Medical/Drugs:		Engineering:		Transportation:		Chemicals/Petrochemicals:		Specialty:	
Computers:	Y	Manufacturer:		Design:		Aerospace:		Oil/Gas Products:		Special Services:	
Software:	Y	Contract Research:		Construction:		Automotive:		Chemicals:		Consulting:	
Communications:		Medical Services:		Eng. Services:		Shipping:		Oil/Chem. Svcs.:		Specialty Mgmt.:	
Electronics:		Labs:		Consulting:				Gases:		Products:	
Alternative Energy:		Bio. Services:						Other:		Other:	

TYPES OF BUSINESS:

Computer Networking Equipment
Support Services

BRANDS/DIVISIONS/AFFILIATES:

TippingPoint Technologies, Inc.
IntelliJack Switches
NBX
VCX
OfficeConnect
Huawei-3Com Co. Ltd.
X505
OfficeConnect

CONTACTS: *Note: Officers with more than one job title may be intentionally listed here more than once.*

Robert Mao, CEO
Ronald Sege, COO
Ronald Sege, Pres.
Jay Zager, CFO/Exec. VP
Eileen Nelson, Sr. VP-Human Resources
Neal D. Goldman, Chief Admin. Officer
Neal D. Goldman, Chief Legal Officer
Dan Beck, Sr. VP-Oper.
Gene Skayne, VP-Investor Rel.
Gene Skayne, Treas./VP-Finance
Shusheng Zheng, Exec. VP
Eric A. Benhamou, Chmn.
Tony Wang, VP-World Supply Chain

Phone: 508-323-5000 **Fax:** 508-323-1111
Toll-Free: 800-876-3266
Address: 350 Campus Dr., Marlborough, MA 01752-3064 US

GROWTH PLANS/SPECIAL FEATURES:

3Com Corp. provides voice, video and data networking products, in addition to technical support and maintenance services, for enterprises and public-sector organizations. The company's products enable customers to manage applications in a stable, secure, scalable network environment even when software is from multiple vendors. The company operates in three core segments: Huawei-3COM (H-3C), Data Voice Business Unit (DVBU) and Tipping Point. The H-3C segment provides services and products for networking, network security and network management to China. The DVBU segment designs and markets networking solutions targeted at customers in developed networking markets, and sells H3C-soruced networking gear worldwide. The tipping point segment offers a line of security products and firewalls, available to customers as overlaid and embedded security solutions. The company provides products and services for Internet Protocol (IP) telephony, such as telephony modules and Internet phones, and for networking, including routers, gateways and wired and wireless LAN switches. The firm's Global Technology Partner Program, 3ComOpen Network (3ComON), is a service designed to build and support a wide-array of third-party relationships with best-of-breed independent software and hardware vendors, systems integrators, service providers, consultants and the open source community. The program allows members the opportunity to create new services and solutions to manage, control and enhance their communications network infrastructures and expand their market reach.

Employees are offered health insurance and retirement plans, including a 401(k).

FINANCIALS: **Sales and profits are in thousands of dollars—add 000 to get the full amount. 2008 Note: Financial information for 2008 was not available for all companies at press time.**

2008 Sales: $1,294,879	2008 Profits: $-228,841	**U.S. Stock Ticker: COMS**
2007 Sales: $1,267,481	2007 Profits: $-88,589	**Int'l Ticker:** Int'l Exchange:
2006 Sales: $794,807	2006 Profits: $-100,675	Employees: 6,103
2005 Sales: $651,244	2005 Profits: $-195,686	Fiscal Year Ends: 5/31
2004 Sales: $698,884	2004 Profits: $-349,263	Parent Company:

SALARIES/BENEFITS:

Pension Plan: Y	ESOP Stock Plan:	Profit Sharing:	Top Exec. Salary: $617,500	Bonus: $895,464
Savings Plan: Y	Stock Purch. Plan: Y		Second Exec. Salary: $375,000	Bonus: $443,661

OTHER THOUGHTS:

Apparent Women Officers or Directors: 3
Hot Spot for Advancement for Women/Minorities: Y

LOCATIONS: ("Y" = Yes)

West:	Southwest:	Midwest:	Southeast:	Northeast:	International:
Y	Y	Y	Y	Y	Y

3M COMPANY

www.mmm.com

Industry Group Code: 339113 **Ranks within this company's industry group:** Sales: 1 Profits: 1

Techology:		Medical/Drugs:		Engineering:		Transportation:		Chemicals/Petrochemicals:		Specialty:	
Computers:		Manufacturer:	Y	Design:		Aerospace:		Oil/Gas Products:		Special Services:	
Software:	Y	Contract Research:		Construction:		Automotive:	Y	Chemicals:	Y	Consulting:	
Communications:	Y	Medical Services:		Eng. Services:		Shipping:		Oil/Chem. Svcs.:		Specialty Mgmt.:	
Electronics:	Y	Labs:		Consulting:				Gases:		Products:	Y
Alternative Energy:		Bio. Services:						Other:		Other:	

TYPES OF BUSINESS:

Health Care Products
Specialty Materials & Textiles
Industrial Products
Safety, Security & Protection Products
Display & Graphics Products
Consumer & Office Products
Electronics & Communications Products
Fuel-Cell Technology

BRANDS/DIVISIONS/AFFILIATES:

Aearo Technologies Inc
Les Entreprieses Solumed Inc
Quest Technologies Inc
ABRASIVOS SA
Financiere Burgienne
3M eStore

CONTACTS: *Note: Officers with more than one job title may be intentionally listed here more than once.*

George W. Buckley, CEO
George W. Buckley, Pres.
Patrick D. Campbell, CFO/Sr. VP
Robert D. MacDonald, Sr. VP-Mktg. & Sales
Angela S. Lalor, Sr. VP-Human Resources
Frederick J. Palensky, Exec. VP-R&D
Frederick J. Palensky, CTO
Marschall I. Smith, General Counsel/Sr. VP-Legal Affairs
Brad T. Sauer, Exec. VP-Health Care Bus.
H.C. Shin, Exec. VP-Industrial & Transportation Bus.
Joe E. Harlan, Exec. VP-Electro & Comm. Bus.
Moe S. Nozari, Exec. VP-Consumer & Office Bus.
George W. Buckley, Chmn.
Inge Thulin, Exec. VP-Int'l Oper.
John K. Woodworth, Sr. VP-Corp. Supply Chain Oper.

Phone: 651-733-1110 **Fax:** 651-733-9973
Toll-Free: 800-364-3577
Address: 3M Center, Bldg. 220-11W-02, St. Paul, MN 55144-1000 US

GROWTH PLANS/SPECIAL FEATURES:

3M Company is involved in the research, manufacturing and marketing of a variety of products. The firm is organized into six segments: health care; consumer and office; display and graphics; electronics and communications; industrial and transportation; and safety, security and protection. The health care segment's products include medical and surgical supplies, skin infection prevention products, pharmaceuticals, drug delivery systems, orthodontic products, health information systems and microbiology products. The consumer and office segment includes office supply, stationery, construction, home improvement, protective material and visual systems products. The display and graphics segment's products include optical film and lenses for electronic displays; touch screens and monitors; screen filters; reflective sheeting; and commercial graphics systems. The electronics and communications segment's products include packaging and interconnection devices (used in circuits); fluids used in computer chips; high-temperature and display tapes; pressure-sensitive tapes and resins; and products for telecommunications systems. The industrial and transportation segment's products include vinyl, polyester, tapes, a variety of non-woven abrasives, adhesives, specialty materials, supply chain execution software, filtration systems, paint finishing products, engineering fluids and components for catalytic converters. The safety, security and protection services segment provides products for personal protection, safety and security, energy control, commercial cleaning and protection, passports and secure cards. The company also maintains a 3M eStore, providing easy access to its line of industrial products. Recent acquisitions include Aearo Technologies Inc.; Les Entreprieses Solumed Inc.; Quest Technologies Inc.; ABRASIVOS S.A.; and Financiere Burgienne.

Employees are offered medical and dental insurance; health and dependent care reimbursement accounts; disability benefits; life insurance; domestic partner benefits; profit sharing; a management stock ownership program; a discount stock purchase plan; a 401(k) plan; tuition reimbursement; an employee assistance program; adoption assistance; group auto and home insurance; and discounts on company products.

FINANCIALS: **Sales and profits are in thousands of dollars—add 000 to get the full amount. 2008 Note: Financial information for 2008 was not available for all companies at press time.**

2008 Sales: $25,269,000	2008 Profits: $3,460,000	**U.S. Stock Ticker: MMM**
2007 Sales: $24,462,000	2007 Profits: $4,096,000	**Int'l Ticker:** Int'l Exchange:
2006 Sales: $22,923,000	2006 Profits: $3,851,000	Employees: 79,183
2005 Sales: $21,167,000	2005 Profits: $3,111,000	Fiscal Year Ends: 12/31
2004 Sales: $20,011,000	2004 Profits: $2,841,000	Parent Company:

SALARIES/BENEFITS:

Pension Plan:	ESOP Stock Plan: Y	Profit Sharing: Y	Top Exec. Salary: $1,670,000	Bonus: $4,521,495
Savings Plan: Y	Stock Purch. Plan: Y		Second Exec. Salary: $728,900	Bonus: $1,075,266

OTHER THOUGHTS:

Apparent Women Officers or Directors: 3
Hot Spot for Advancement for Women/Minorities: Y

LOCATIONS: ("Y" = Yes)

West:	Southwest:	Midwest:	Southeast:	Northeast:	International:
Y	Y	Y	Y	Y	Y

AB VOLVO

www.volvo.com

Industry Group Code: 336120 **Ranks within this company's industry group:** Sales: 1 Profits: 1

Techology:		Medical/Drugs:		Engineering:		Transportation:		Chemicals/Petrochemicals:		Specialty:	
Computers:		Manufacturer:		Design:		Aerospace:	Y	Oil/Gas Products:		Special Services:	Y
Software:		Contract Research:		Construction:		Automotive:	Y	Chemicals:		Consulting:	
Communications:		Medical Services:		Eng. Services:		Shipping:		Oil/Chem. Svcs.:		Specialty Mgmt.:	
Electronics:		Labs:		Consulting:				Gases:		Products:	
Alternative Energy:		Bio. Services:						Other:		Other:	

TYPES OF BUSINESS:

Truck Manufacturer
Engines
Buses
Aerospace Products
Construction Equipment
Financial Services
Intelligent Transport Systems
Overhaul & Repair Services

BRANDS/DIVISIONS/AFFILIATES:

Volvo Trucks
Renault Trucks
Nissan Diesel Motor Co Ltd
Mack Trucks Inc
Volvo Penta
Volvo Aero
Eicher Motors

CONTACTS: *Note: Officers with more than one job title may be intentionally listed here more than once.*

Leif Johansson, CEO
Leif Johansson, Pres.
Mikael Bratt, CFO/Sr. VP
Stefan Johnsson, Sr. VP-Human Resources & Bus. Units
Eva Persson, General Counsel/Sr. VP
Per Lojdquist, Sr. VP-Corp. Comm. & Brand Mgmt.
Stefano Chmielewski, Pres., Renault Trucks
Staffan Jufors, Pres., Volvo Truck Corp.
Hakan Karlsson, Pres., Volvo Bus Corp.
Dennis Slagle, Pres./CEO-Mack Trucks, Inc
Finn Johnsson, Chmn.
Par Ostberg, Head-Trucks, Asia

Phone: 46-31-66-10-67 **Fax:** 46-31-53-72-96
Toll-Free:
Address: Volvo Bergegards vag 1, Torslanda, Goteborg, SE-405 08 Sweden

GROWTH PLANS/SPECIAL FEATURES:

AB Volvo, also called the Volvo Group, is a world leader in the manufacture of automotive and other heavy machinery, namely trucks and buses, construction equipment and marine, industrial and aerospace components. The company has nine main remaining business areas: Volvo Trucks, Renault Trucks, Mack Trucks, Nissan Diesel, Buses, Construction Equipment, Volvo Penta, Volvo Aero and Financial Services. The firm also has six business units which support the business areas: Volvo 3P, Volvo Powertrain, Volvo Parts, Volvo Technology, Volvo Logistics and Volvo Information Technology. The 3P unit handles purchasing and product planning and development for the three truck businesses, Volvo, Renault and Mack, which mainly manufacture heavy-duty, long-haul trucks marketed in 130 countries worldwide. Powertrain supplies engine drivelines for Volvo's trucks, busses and Volvo Penta, an engine manufacturer whose engines are used in shipping, leisure boating, power plants and heavy equipment. The Parts unit supports aftermarket (often repair and replacement) activities; the Technology unit is mainly involved in R&D; and the Logistics and IT units offer their solutions worldwide. Volvo Aero constructs military engines, space propulsion components, commercial engines and land and marine gas turbines. It also offers services such as sales of spare parts for aircraft and aircraft engines; sales and leasing of aircraft and aircraft engines; and overhaul and repair. Volvo Financial Services covers customer financing, insurance, treasury, real estate and related services operations. In May 2008, the company entered into a joint venture with Indian vehicle manufacturer Eicher Motors for the production and sales of trucks and buses in India. In July 2008, Volvo Aero entered into joint ventures with aircraft engine manufacturers Pratt & Whitney and Rolls-Royce. Also in 2008, Volvo Buses announced plans to sell its body plant in Turku, Finland.

FINANCIALS: **Sales and profits are in thousands of dollars—add 000 to get the full amount. 2008 Note: Financial information for 2008 was not available for all companies at press time.**

2008 Sales: $36,793,200	2008 Profits: $1,213,570	**U.S. Stock Ticker: VOLV**
2007 Sales: $34,580,500	2007 Profits: $1,820,840	**Int'l Ticker: VOLV B** Int'l Exchange: Stockholm-SSE
2006 Sales: $44,002,000	2006 Profits: $2,765,600	Employees: 101,698
2005 Sales: $31,813,343	2005 Profits: $1,804,045	Fiscal Year Ends: 12/31
2004 Sales: $31,813,000	2004 Profits: $1,414,000	Parent Company:

SALARIES/BENEFITS:

Pension Plan: Y	ESOP Stock Plan:	Profit Sharing:	Top Exec. Salary: $1,788,558	Bonus: $8,650
Savings Plan:	Stock Purch. Plan:		Second Exec. Salary: $	Bonus: $

OTHER THOUGHTS:

Apparent Women Officers or Directors: 2
Hot Spot for Advancement for Women/Minorities: Y

LOCATIONS: ("Y" = Yes)

West:	Southwest:	Midwest:	Southeast:	Northeast:	International:
Y	Y	Y	Y	Y	Y

ABB LTD

www.abb.com

Industry Group Code: 335000 **Ranks within this company's industry group:** Sales: 4 Profits: 2

Techology:		Medical/Drugs:		Engineering:		Transportation:		Chemicals/Petrochemicals:		Specialty:	
Computers:		Manufacturer:		Design:	Y	Aerospace:		Oil/Gas Products:		Special Services:	
Software:		Contract Research:		Construction:	Y	Automotive:		Chemicals:		Consulting:	
Communications:		Medical Services:		Eng. Services:	Y	Shipping:		Oil/Chem. Svcs.:	Y	Specialty Mgmt.:	
Electronics:		Labs:		Consulting:	Y			Gases:		Products:	
Alternative Energy:		Bio. Services:						Other:	Y	Other:	

TYPES OF BUSINESS:

Diversified Engineering Services
Power Transmission & Distribution Systems
Control & Automation Technology Products
Industrial Robotics
Energy Trading Software

BRANDS/DIVISIONS/AFFILIATES:

Lummus Global
Vectek Electronics
Kuhlman Electric Corp.

CONTACTS: *Note: Officers with more than one job title may be intentionally listed here more than once.*

Joseph Hogan, CEO
Michel Demare, CFO
Gary Steel, Dir.-Human Resources
Peter Terwiesch, Head-Group R&D
Dinesh Paliwal, Pres., Global Markets & Tech.
Diane de Saint Victor, General Counsel
Ulrich Spiesshofer, Dir.-Corp. Dev.
Clarissa Haller, Head-Group Corp. Comm.
Michael Gerber, Head-Investor Rel.
Tom Sjoekvist, Dir.-Automation Prod. Div.
Bernhard Jucker, Dir.-Power Products Div.
Peter Leupp, Dir.-Power Systems Div.
Anders Jonsson, Dir.-Robotics Div.
Hubertus von Grunberg, Chmn.
John Walker, Head-Supply Chain Mgmt.

Phone: 41-43-317-7111 **Fax:** 41-43-317-4420
Toll-Free:
Address: Affolternstrasse 44, Zurich, CH-8050 Switzerland

GROWTH PLANS/SPECIAL FEATURES:

ABB, Ltd. is a global leader in power and automation technologies for utility and industrial companies. The company provides a broad range of products, systems, solutions and services that improve power grid reliability, increase industrial productivity and enhance energy efficiency. The firm operates in approximately 100 countries, and structures its global operations into four regions: Europe; the Americas; Asia and the Middle East and Africa. ABB divides its business into five divisions: power products; power systems; automation products; process automation; and robotics. The power products segment manufactures and sells high- and medium-voltage switchgear and apparatus, circuit breakers for various current and voltage levels and power and distribution transformers. The division's primary customers are utilities, distributors, wholesalers, installers and original equipment manufacturers (OEMs). The power systems division's solutions include engineering of grid systems, power generation systems, network management solutions and substations. This division also offers automation, control and protection systems and related services for power transmission and distribution networks, power plants and water pumping stations. The automation products segment offers low-voltage switchgear, breakers, switches, control products, DIN-rail components, enclosures, wiring accessories, instrumentation, drives, motors, generators and power electronics systems. The process automation segment offers plant automation and electrification, energy management, process and asset optimization, analytical measurement and telecommunication for such industries as metals and minerals; oil and gas; pharmaceuticals; pulp and paper; chemicals; and petrochemicals. The robotics segment designs, manufactures and commissions robots, services and modular manufacturing solutions for use in the automotive and manufacturing industries. In 2007, the company divested the remainder of its building systems business and its downstream oil and gas business, Lummus Global. In May 2008, ABB acquired Vectek Electronics, a power electronics business. In July 2008, the company agreed to acquire Kuhlman Electric Corp., a U.S.-based transformer company.

FINANCIALS: **Sales and profits are in thousands of dollars—add 000 to get the full amount. 2008 Note: Financial information for 2008 was not available for all companies at press time.**

2008 Sales: $34,912,000	2008 Profits: $3,118,000	**U.S. Stock Ticker: ABB**
2007 Sales: $29,183,000	2007 Profits: $3,757,000	**Int'l Ticker: ABBN** Int'l Exchange: Zurich-SWX
2006 Sales: $23,281,000	2006 Profits: $1,390,000	Employees: 120,000
2005 Sales: $20,964,000	2005 Profits: $735,000	Fiscal Year Ends: 12/31
2004 Sales: $18,158,000	2004 Profits: $177,000	Parent Company:

SALARIES/BENEFITS:

Pension Plan:	ESOP Stock Plan:	Profit Sharing:	Top Exec. Salary: $1,197,074	Bonus: $1,685,946
Savings Plan:	Stock Purch. Plan:		Second Exec. Salary: $769,282	Bonus: $900,245

OTHER THOUGHTS:

Apparent Women Officers or Directors: 2
Hot Spot for Advancement for Women/Minorities:

LOCATIONS: ("Y" = Yes)

West:	Southwest:	Midwest:	Southeast:	Northeast:	International:
				Y	Y

ABBOTT LABORATORIES

www.abbott.com

Industry Group Code: 325412 **Ranks within this company's industry group:** Sales: 8 Profits: 10

Techology:		Medical/Drugs:		Engineering:		Transportation:		Chemicals/Petrochemicals:		Specialty:	
Computers:		Manufacturer:	Y	Design:		Aerospace:		Oil/Gas Products:		Special Services:	
Software:		Contract Research:		Construction:		Automotive:		Chemicals:		Consulting:	
Communications:		Medical Services:		Eng. Services:		Shipping:		Oil/Chem. Svcs.:		Specialty Mgmt.:	
Electronics:		Labs:		Consulting:				Gases:		Products:	Y
Alternative Energy:		Bio. Services:	Y					Other:		Other:	

TYPES OF BUSINESS:

Pharmaceuticals Manufacturing
Nutritional Products
Diagnostics
Consumer Health Products
Medical & Surgical Devices
Pharmaceutical Products
Animal Health

BRANDS/DIVISIONS/AFFILIATES:

Abbott Medical Optics Inc
Prevacid
Lupix
Trilipix
Humira
Simcor
Glucerna
Ensure

CONTACTS: *Note: Officers with more than one job title may be intentionally listed here more than once.*

Miles D. White, CEO
Thomas C. Freyman, CFO
Stephen R. Fussell, Sr. VP-Human Resources
John M. Leonard, Sr. VP-R&D
John C. Landgraf, Sr. VP-Global Pharmaceutical Mgmt. & Supply
Laura J. Schumacher, General Counsel/Exec. VP/Corp. Sec.
Richard W. Ashley, Exec. VP-Corp. Dev.
Melissa Brotz, VP-External Comm.
Thomas C. Freyman, Exec. VP-Finance
James L. Tyree, Exec. VP-Pharmaceutical Products Group
Holger Liepmann, Exec. VP-Global Nutrition
John M. Capek, Exec. VP-Medical Devices
Michael J. Warmuth, Sr. VP-Diagnostics
Miles D. White, Chmn.
Olivier Bohuon, Sr. VP-Int'l Oper.

Phone: 847-937-6100	**Fax:** 847-937-9555
Toll-Free:	
Address: 100 Abbott Park Rd., Abbott Park, IL 60064-3500 US	

GROWTH PLANS/SPECIAL FEATURES:

Abbott Laboratories develops, manufactures and sells health care products and technologies ranging from pharmaceuticals to medical devices. The firm markets its products in more than 130 countries. The pharmaceutical segment deals with adult and pediatric conditions such as rheumatoid arthritis, HIV, epilepsy and manic depression. The diagnostic instruments and test segment deals with a range of medical tests to diagnose infectious diseases, cancer, diabetes and genetic conditions. Products include Humira for arthritis, Prevacid (Ogastro), a proton pump inhibitor for the short-term treatment of gastroesophageal reflux disease and Lupix for prostate cancer. The nutritional products segment offers consumer products such as Similac, Ensure, Glucerna and AdvantEdge, as well as medical nutritional products and feeding devices. The diagnostic products segment includes diagnostic systems and tests such as immunoassay, chemistry and hematology systems, which are manufactured, marketed and sold to blood banks, hospitals, commercial laboratories, physicians' offices and plasma protein therapeutic companies. The vascular products segment consists of coronary, endovascular and vessel closure devices, used in the treatment of vascular disease. These products are generally marketed and sold directly to hospitals from Abbot-owned distribution centers and public warehouses. The firm also produces a line of animal products such as anesthetics, wound care products and intravenous fluid therapy for the veterinary market. The company operates internationally in Europe, Asia, Africa, Latin and South America and the Middle East. In December 2008, Abbott received FDA approval for Trilipix, a cholesterol management medication. In February 2009, the company acquired Advanced Medical Optics which has been renamed Abbott Medical Optics Inc.

Employees are offered medical, dental and vision insurance; flexible spending accounts; child care solutions; an employee assistance program; legal referral services; a pension plan; a 401(k) plan; profit sharing; tuition assistance; travel accident insurance; long-term care insurance; and life insurance.

FINANCIALS: **Sales and profits are in thousands of dollars—add 000 to get the full amount. 2008 Note: Financial information for 2008 was not available for all companies at press time.**

2008 Sales: $29,527,600	2008 Profits: $4,880,700	**U.S. Stock Ticker: ABT**
2007 Sales: $25,914,200	2007 Profits: $3,606,300	**Int'l Ticker:** Int'l Exchange:
2006 Sales: $22,476,322	2006 Profits: $1,716,755	Employees: 69,000
2005 Sales: $22,337,808	2005 Profits: $3,372,065	Fiscal Year Ends: 12/31
2004 Sales: $19,680,016	2004 Profits: $3,235,851	Parent Company:

SALARIES/BENEFITS:

Pension Plan: Y	ESOP Stock Plan:	Profit Sharing: Y	Top Exec. Salary: $1,726,936	Bonus: $4,050,000
Savings Plan: Y	Stock Purch. Plan:		Second Exec. Salary: $951,771	Bonus: $1,287,000

OTHER THOUGHTS:

Apparent Women Officers or Directors: 5
Hot Spot for Advancement for Women/Minorities: Y

LOCATIONS: ("Y" = Yes)

West:	Southwest:	Midwest:	Southeast:	Northeast:	International:
Y	Y	Y		Y	Y

ABENGOA SA

www.abengoa.es

ndustry Group Code: 234000 **Ranks within this company's industry group:** Sales: 20 Profits: 12

echology:		Medical/Drugs:		Engineering:		Transportation:		Chemicals/Petrochemicals:		Specialty:	
omputers:		Manufacturer:		Design:	Y	Aerospace:		Oil/Gas Products:		Special Services:	Y
oftware:		Contract Research:		Construction:	Y	Automotive:		Chemicals:	Y	Consulting:	
ommunications:		Medical Services:		Eng. Services:	Y	Shipping:		Oil/Chem. Svcs.:	Y	Specialty Mgmt.:	
lectronics:		Labs:		Consulting:				Gases:		Products:	
lternative Energy:	Y	Bio. Services:						Other:	Y	Other:	Y

TYPES OF BUSINESS:

ioenergy Services
thanol Production
ecycling & Waste Management Services
ngineering Services
T Services
onstruction-Plants & Infrastructure
olar Energy Generation

BRANDS/DIVISIONS/AFFILIATES:

Hynergreen Technologies
Focus-Abengoa Foundation
Hospital of the Venerable Priests
HyGear BV

CONTACTS:

Note: Officers with more than one job title may be ntentionally listed here more than once.

elipe Benjumea Llorente, CEO
varo Polo Guerrero, Dir.-Human Resources
anuel Sanchez Ortega, Pres., IT Bus. Group
lfonso Gonzalez Dominguez, Pres., Eng. & Industrial Construction Group
.A. Jimenez-Velasco Mazario, Gen. Sec.
uan Carlos Jimenez Lora, Dir.-Investor Rel.
mando Sanchez Falcon, Dir.-Finance
avier Molina Montes, Pres., Environmental Svcs. Bus. Group
avier Salgado Leirado, Pres., Bioenergy Bus. Group
antiago Seage Medela, Pres., Solar Bus. Group
uis Fernandez Mateo, Dir.-Organization, Quality & Budgets
elipe Benjumea Llorente, Chmn.
lfonso Gonzalez Dominguez, Pres., Latin America Bus. Group

hone: 34-95-493-71-11 **Fax:** 34-95-493-70-12
oll-Free:
ddress: 2 Avenida de la Buhaira, Seville, 41018 Spain

GROWTH PLANS/SPECIAL FEATURES:

Abengoa S.A. is a Spanish technology company that offers products and services geared toward sustainable development. The company, which operates in over 70 countries, is divided into six business units: solar; bioenergy; environmental services; information technology; engineering and industrial construction; and the Focus-Abengoa Foundation. The solar business unit develops and applies solar technologies to achieve sustainable development and combat climate change, which intensifies weather extremes such as hurricanes, floods, droughts and desertification. The bioenergy unit produces bioethanol from vegetable products, which is used to manufacture a petrol additive or can be blended directly with petrol or gas oil. Environmental services focuses on aluminum, salt slag and zinc waste recycling, industrial waste management and cleaning and engineering. The information technology unit offers real-time solutions for energy, environment, traffic and transport sectors. The engineering and industrial construction unit engineers, constructs and maintains electrical and mechanical infrastructures, and also develops, constructs and operates industrial and power plants. The Focus-Abengoa Foundation is a restoration project that seeks to preserve the baroque art and Spanish heritage of the historic Hospital of the Venerable Priests. In March 2009, Abengoa subsidiary, Hynergreen Technologies acquired HyGear B.V. In 2008, the company was selected by the Private Investment Promotion Agency in Peru to construct a $250 mllllon transmlsslon llne ln Peru that wlll connect the towns of Carhuamayo, Paragsha, Conococha, Huallanca, Cajamarca, Cerro Corona and Carhuaquero.

FINANCIALS:

Sales and profits are in thousands of dollars—add 000 to get the full amount. 2008 Note: Financial information for 2008 was not available for all companies at press time.

2008 Sales: $4,134,360	2008 Profits: $393,080	**U.S. Stock Ticker: Private**
2007 Sales: $3,525,360	2007 Profits: $309,770	**Int'l Ticker:** Int'l Exchange:
2006 Sales: $4,198,150	2006 Profits: $343,690	Employees: 11,082
2005 Sales: $3,173,110	2005 Profits: $256,310	Fiscal Year Ends: 12/31
2004 Sales: $2,301,200	2004 Profits: $70,600	Parent Company:

SALARIES/BENEFITS:

ension Plan:	ESOP Stock Plan:	Profit Sharing:	Top Exec. Salary: $	Bonus: $
avings Plan:	Stock Purch. Plan:		Second Exec. Salary: $	Bonus: $

OTHER THOUGHTS:

pparent Women Officers or Directors: 3
ot Spot for Advancement for Women/Minorities: Y

LOCATIONS: ("Y" = Yes)

West:	Southwest:	Midwest:	Southeast:	Northeast:	International:
		Y			Y

ABERTIS INFRAESTRUCTURAS SA

www.abertis.com

Industry Group Code: 541330 **Ranks within this company's industry group:** Sales: 5 Profits: 1

Techology:		Medical/Drugs:		Engineering:		Transportation:		Chemicals/Petrochemicals:		Specialty:	
Computers:		Manufacturer:		Design:		Aerospace:		Oil/Gas Products:		Special Services:	
Software:		Contract Research:		Construction:		Automotive:		Chemicals:		Consulting:	
Communications:		Medical Services:		Eng. Services:		Shipping:		Oil/Chem. Svcs.:		Specialty Mgmt.:	Y
Electronics:		Labs:		Consulting:				Gases:		Products:	
Alternative Energy:		Bio. Services:						Other:		Other:	

TYPES OF BUSINESS:

Transport & Communications
Logistics Services
TV & Radio Broadcasting
Airport Operations
Parking Facilities Management
Motorway Construction & Management
Warehouses
Heavy Construction

BRANDS/DIVISIONS/AFFILIATES:

Saba
Tradia
Retevision
Abertis Logistica
Abertis Telecom
Desarrollo de Concesiones Aeroportuarias SA

CONTACTS: *Note: Officers with more than one job title may be intentionally listed here more than once.*

Salvador Alemany Mas, CEO
Jose Aljaro Navarro, CFO
Joan Rafel Herrero, Dir.-Personnel & Organization
Marta Casas, Dir.-Legal Svcs.
David Diaz Almazan, Dir.-Corp. Dev.
Antoni Brunet Mauri, Dir.-Corp. Comm.
Luis Subira Laborda, Dir.-Corp. Finance
Juan A. M. Padros, Company Sec.
Sergi Loughney Castells, Dir.-Institutional Rel.
Tobias Martinez Gimeno, Managing Dir.-Abertis Telecom
Manel Cruces Socasau, Managing Dir.-Toll Roads South America
Isidre Faine Casas, Chmn.
Jordi Graells Ferrandez, Managing Dir.-Toll Roads North America & Int'l

Phone: 34-932-305-000	**Fax:** 34-932-305-001
Toll-Free:	
Address: 12-20 Parc Logistic Ave., Barcelona, 08040 Spain	

GROWTH PLANS/SPECIAL FEATURES:

Abertis Infraestructuras S.A., a private transport and communications infrastructure management company based in Barcelona, is a leading Spain-based operator of motorways and car parks. The company, which is active in 17 countries in Europe, North America and South America, also offers logistics parks, telecommunications infrastructure and airport operation services. Abertis is the head of a number of business units made up of over 60 directly-managed or associate companies. The firm's motorways division, representing approximately 76% of revenues, directly manages a network of 3,320 kilometers of motorways, including 59% of all toll routes in Spain. Abertis manages an additional 5,400 kilometers of motorways through interests in Italy, the U.K., Argentina, Chile and Portugal. The company's car park division is headed by Saba and manages facilities in over 70 municipalities in Spain, Italy, Portugal, Chile, Morocco and Andorra. The company's logistics activities, headed by Abertis Logistica, consist of warehouses and offices in Spain and abroad. Industrial facilities under the firm's management total approximately 800,000 square meters and currently house the operations of more than 300 companies. Abertis Telecom, the company's telecommunications division, consists of two companies, Tradia and Retevision. Tradia's activities include provision of radio and TV signal broadcasting services and the renting of space for telecommunications operators. Retevision, which provides national coverage with its analog and digital network, focuses on audiovisual signal transportation and broadcasting. In the field of airport operations, the company operates directly in 16 airports in six countries, including the U.S., as well as providing airport-related consulting services. In March 2008, the firm completed its acquisition of Desarrollo de Concesiones Aeroportuarias, S.A., with stakes in 15 airports in Mexico, Jamaica, Chile and Columbia. In January 2009, Abertis announced that it would install a satellite-based toll system for heavy vehicles on a 2,000-kilometer road network in Slovakia.

FINANCIALS: **Sales and profits are in thousands of dollars—add 000 to get the full amount. 2008 Note: Financial information for 2008 was not available for all companies at press time.**

2008 Sales: $4,883,650	2008 Profits: $820,360	**U.S. Stock Ticker: ABE**
2007 Sales: $4,805,330	2007 Profits: $905,310	**Int'l Ticker: ABE** Int'l Exchange: Madrid-MCE
2006 Sales: $4,880,810	2006 Profits: $775,660	Employees: 11,894
2005 Sales: $2,257,200	2005 Profits: $609,800	Fiscal Year Ends: 12/31
2004 Sales: $2,031,200	2004 Profits: $637,400	Parent Company:

SALARIES/BENEFITS:

Pension Plan:	ESOP Stock Plan:	Profit Sharing:	Top Exec. Salary: $	Bonus: $
Savings Plan:	Stock Purch. Plan:		Second Exec. Salary: $	Bonus: $

OTHER THOUGHTS:

Apparent Women Officers or Directors: 2
Hot Spot for Advancement for Women/Minorities:

LOCATIONS: ("Y" = Yes)

West:	Southwest:	Midwest:	Southeast:	Northeast:	International:
	Y		Y		Y

ACCENTURE LTD

www.accenture.com

Industry Group Code: 541512 **Ranks within this company's industry group:** Sales: 3 Profits: 2

Techology:		Medical/Drugs:		Engineering:		Transportation:		Chemicals/Petrochemicals:		Specialty:	
Computers:		Manufacturer:		Design:		Aerospace:		Oil/Gas Products:		Special Services:	
Software:		Contract Research:		Construction:		Automotive:		Chemicals:		Consulting:	Y
Communications:		Medical Services:		Eng. Services:		Shipping:		Oil/Chem. Svcs.:		Specialty Mgmt.:	
Electronics:		Labs:		Consulting:				Gases:		Products:	
Alternative Energy:		Bio. Services:						Other:		Other:	

TYPES OF BUSINESS:

Technology Consulting Services
Computer Operations Outsourcing
Supply Chain Management
Technology Research
Software Development
Human Resources Consulting
Management Consulting
Research & Development

BRANDS/DIVISIONS/AFFILIATES:

Gestalt, LLC
Maxamine
SOPIA Corporation
AddVal Technology
ATAN
Accenture Mobility Operated Services

CONTACTS: *Note: Officers with more than one job title may be intentionally listed here more than once.*

William D. Green, CEO
Stephen J. Rohleder, COO
Pamela J. Craig, CFO
Roxanne Taylor, Chief Mktg. Officer
Jill B. Smart, Chief Human Resources Officer
Gianfranco Casati, Group CEO-Prod.
Douglas G. Scrivner, General Counsel/Corp. Sec./Compliance Officer
David C. Thomlinson, Sr. Managing Dir.-Geographic Strategy & Oper.
R. Timothy Breene, Chief Strategy & Corp. Dev. Officer
Roxanne Taylor, Chief Comm. Officer
David P. Rowland, Sr. VP-Finance
Karl-Heinz Floether, Group CEO-Systems Integration, Tech. & Delivery
Martin I. Cole, Group CEO-Comm. & High Tech.
Kevin M. Campbell, Group CEO-Outsourcing
Mark Foster, Group CEO-Mgmt. Consulting & Integrated Markets.
William D. Green, Chmn.
Diego Visconti, Chmn.-Int'l, Strategic Countries
Basilio Rueda, Sr. Managing Dir.-Global Delivery Network

Phone: 441-296-8262	**Fax:** 441-296-4245
Toll-Free:	
Address: Canon's Ct., 22 Victoria St., Hamilton, HM12 Bermuda	

GROWTH PLANS/SPECIAL FEATURES:

Accenture, Ltd. is a leading provider of management consulting, technology and outsourcing services, with operations in over 200 cities in 52 countries. The firm delivers services through five operating groups, which together comprise 17 industry groups. The operating groups are communications and high-tech; financial services; products; resources; and public services. Accenture's communications and high-tech group offers technology, consulting and systems integration to the electronics, communications and media industries. Its financial services group provides consulting and outsourcing strategies to the insurance, capital markets and banking industries. Accenture's products group serves the automotive; health and life sciences; consumer goods; industrial equipment; retail; and transportation and travel services industries. The company's resources group works with the chemicals; energy; forest products; metals and mining; and utilities industries. Finally, its public service group works with local, state, provincial and national governments in the areas of defense; revenue; human services; health; justice; and postal and education authorities. Accenture offers management consulting services including customer relationship management; supply chain management; human performance; finance and performance management; and strategy. The firm's systems integration and technology services include enterprise resource planning; service-oriented architecture; mobility solutions; Microsoft solutions; IT strategy and transformation services; enterprise architecture; infrastructure consulting services; research and development services; and e-commerce solutions. Accenture also offers outsourcing for business processes, applications and infrastructure needs. Clients include AT&T; Microsoft; Sony; Bank of America; and the U.S. Department of Commerce. During 2008, Accenture acquired defense consulting firm Gestalt, LLC; testing and optimization services provider Maxamine; consulting and IT solutions company SOPIA Corporation; shipment management services provider AddVal Technology; and Brazilian IT and automation solutions provider ATAN. In February 2009, the firm launched a global mobility business, Accenture Mobility Operated Services.

Accenture offers its employees flexible work arrangements and ongoing training and development resources.

FINANCIALS: Sales and profits are in thousands of dollars—add 000 to get the full amount. 2008 Note: Financial information for 2008 was not available for all companies at press time.

2008 Sales: $25,313,826	2008 Profits: $1,691,751	**U.S. Stock Ticker: ACN**
2007 Sales: $21,452,747	2007 Profits: $1,243,148	**Int'l Ticker:** Int'l Exchange:
2006 Sales: $18,228,366	2006 Profits: $973,329	Employees: 186,000
2005 Sales: $17,094,400	2005 Profits: $940,500	Fiscal Year Ends: 8/31
2004 Sales: $15,113,582	2004 Profits: $690,828	Parent Company:

SALARIES/BENEFITS:

Pension Plan:	ESOP Stock Plan:	Profit Sharing:	Top Exec. Salary: $1,237,121	Bonus: $1,939,526
Savings Plan:	Stock Purch. Plan:		Second Exec. Salary: $1,133,640	Bonus: $3,010,000

OTHER THOUGHTS:

Apparent Women Officers or Directors: 7
Hot Spot for Advancement for Women/Minorities: Y

LOCATIONS: ("Y" = Yes)

West:	Southwest:	Midwest:	Southeast:	Northeast:	International:
Y	Y	Y	Y	Y	Y

Note: Financial information, benefits and other data can change quickly and may vary from those stated here.

ACCIONA SA

www.acciona.es

Industry Group Code: 234000 **Ranks within this company's industry group:** Sales: 9 Profits: 5

Techology:		Medical/Drugs:		Engineering:		Transportation:		Chemicals/Petrochemicals:		Specialty:	
Computers:		Manufacturer:		Design:		Aerospace:		Oil/Gas Products:		Special Services:	Y
Software:		Contract Research:		Construction:	Y	Automotive:		Chemicals:		Consulting:	
Communications:		Medical Services:		Eng. Services:	Y	Shipping:	Y	Oil/Chem. Svcs.:		Specialty Mgmt.:	Y
Electronics:		Labs:		Consulting:	Y			Gases:		Products:	
Alternative Energy:	Y	Bio. Services:						Other:		Other:	

TYPES OF BUSINESS:

Heavy Construction
Infrastructure Services
Road Concessions
Logistics Services
Airport Services
Passenger Ferries
Urban & Environmental Services
Alternative Energy Production

BRANDS/DIVISIONS/AFFILIATES:

Acciona Infraestructuras SA
Acciona Concesiones SL
Trasmediterranea
Acciona Energia
CESA
Inmobiliaria Parque Reforma

CONTACTS: *Note: Officers with more than one job title may be intentionally listed here more than once.*

Jose M. E. Domecq, Pres.
Rafael M. Caracuel, Mgr.-Human Resources
Vicente S. P. Castillo, Mgr.-Legal
Carmen Becerril, Head- Corp Resources & Institutional Rel.
Juan A. S. Elegido, Mgr.-Logistics & Airport Svcs.
Jorge Vega-Penichet, Chmn.
Osvaldo Puccio, Exec. VP-Latin America

Phone: 34-91-663-28-50	**Fax:** 34-91-663-30-99
Toll-Free:	
Address: Ave. De Europa, 18, Parque Empresarial La Moreleja, Alcobendas, 28108 Spain	

GROWTH PLANS/SPECIAL FEATURES:

Acciona SA develops and manages infrastructure in Spain and internationally. Operations include road concessions; transport activities; hydraulic, maritime, underground and industrial works; operation of renewable energy; and general real estate. Acciona Infraestructuras SA, the company's chief infrastructure division, was recently restructured into three units: Strategic Analysis and R&D, which advises on which strategic lines to pursue and on identifying potential business opportunities; the International Division, which promotes, coordinates and monitors Acciona's internationalization process; and the Group Executive Director's Office for Corporate Development and Investor Relations, which plans, identifies, generates, negotiates and performs operations for corporate development. The company constructs bridges, highways, railway lines, airstrips, dams, ports, power plants, skyscrapers and more. Acciona Concesiones SL, the firm's road concessions division, controls the Madrid-Guadalajara Radial 2 toll road and the Tranvia Parla, a tramway in one of Madrid's suburbs, among others. In addition to Acciona's logistics services of road cargo transport, airport services, storage and distribution services, the company operates Trasmediterranea, a passenger ferry company. The urban and environmental division manages parking lots, solid waste treatment facilities, street cleaning companies, water supply and treatment plants and landscaping and funeral services providers. Acciona Energia, the firm's alternative energy division, engages in wind, hydroelectric, solar, biomass and cogeneration energy generation projects and develops biofuels for consumers. The company expects to obtain 70% of revenues from international markets within 10 years. In April 2008, Acciona acquired Inmobiliaria Parque Reforma in Mexico, a luxury residential property company created in 1997 by Acciona and Concord Group.

FINANCIALS: **Sales and profits are in thousands of dollars—add 000 to get the full amount. 2008 Note: Financial information for 2008 was not available for all companies at press time.**

2008 Sales: $17,094,300	2008 Profits: $626,280	**U.S. Stock Ticker: ANA**
2007 Sales: $10,734,400	2007 Profits: $1,282,240	**Int'l Ticker: ANA** Int'l Exchange: Madrid-MCE
2006 Sales: $7,418,400	2006 Profits: $452,500	Employees: 30,000
2005 Sales: $5,838,200	2005 Profits: $389,800	Fiscal Year Ends: 12/31
2004 Sales: $5,518,300	2004 Profits: $307,900	Parent Company:

SALARIES/BENEFITS:

Pension Plan:	ESOP Stock Plan:	Profit Sharing:	Top Exec. Salary: $	Bonus: $
Savings Plan:	Stock Purch. Plan:		Second Exec. Salary: $	Bonus: $

OTHER THOUGHTS:

Apparent Women Officers or Directors: 1
Hot Spot for Advancement for Women/Minorities:

LOCATIONS: ("Y" = Yes)

West:	Southwest:	Midwest:	Southeast:	Northeast:	International:
				Y	Y

ACCTON TECHNOLOGY CORP

www.accton.com

Industry Group Code: 334419 **Ranks within this company's industry group:** Sales: Profits:

Techology:		Medical/Drugs:		Engineering:		Transportation:		Chemicals/Petrochemicals:		Specialty:	
Computers:		Manufacturer:		Design:	Y	Aerospace:		Oil/Gas Products:		Special Services:	Y
Software:		Contract Research:		Construction:		Automotive:		Chemicals:		Consulting:	
Communications:	Y	Medical Services:		Eng. Services:		Shipping:		Oil/Chem. Svcs.:		Specialty Mgmt.:	
Electronics:	Y	Labs:		Consulting:				Gases:		Products:	Y
Alternative Energy:		Bio. Services:						Other:		Other:	Y

TYPES OF BUSINESS:

Networking Equipment
Technical & Communications Outsourcing
IP Network Switches
Semiconductors & Chipsets
Wireless Hardware
Online Portal
VoIP Hardware
Consumer Electronics

BRANDS/DIVISIONS/AFFILIATES:

Accton Wireless Broadband
SMC Networks
Arcadyan
Acute Corporation
Vodtel
Edge-Core
Mototech

CONTACTS: *Note: Officers with more than one job title may be intentionally listed here more than once.*

Anjie Huang, CEO
Samuel Chang, VP-Mktg. & Sales
Yimin Du, Chmn.

Phone: 886-3-577-0270	**Fax:** 886-3-578-0764
Toll-Free:	
Address: 1 Creation Rd. III, Science-Based Industrial Park, Hsinchu, 300 Taiwan	

GROWTH PLANS/SPECIAL FEATURES:

Accton Technology Corp., based in Taiwan, provides communications outsourcing services for original equipment manufactures (OEM) and original design manufacturers (ODM) and data communication for both personal and business needs. The firm's primary focus is Ethernet technology, however, the company's offers a variety of products including broadband products; network switches; network hubs; network cards; and wireless products. These products are marketed under the Edge-core and SMC Networks brand names. Accton's numerous subsidiaries include Acute Corporation, a designer of semiconductors; Vodtel, a VOIP hardware producer; Edge-Core, a provider of an integrated service platform; Accton Wireless Broadband Corp. or AWB, a provider of wireless infrastructure technology and advanced technology integration; and Mototech, a global ODM specialist in the broadband and data networking market. It also owns E-charity, an Internet platform for charitable works in Taiwan; url.com.tw, a Chinese-language online entertainment portal; and the Accton Arts Foundation, which encourages and funds artistic expression in and near science parks and corporations. Accton has operations in San Jose and Boston in the U.S.; Shanghai and Taiwan in China; the U.K.; and Japan. The company has plans to continue to expand its market reach within Europe, South America, China and India.

Accton offers employees a 10 month maternity leave and a three day paternity leave; a $3,000 salary incentive to encourage marriage; on-site child care; two month leave with pay for employees who have seven years of continuous service; birthday coupons; rooftop gardens; on-site coffee shops; and a health care center for employee use.

FINANCIALS: **Sales and profits are in thousands of dollars—add 000 to get the full amount. 2008 Note: Financial information for 2008 was not available for all companies at press time.**

2008 Sales: $	2008 Profits: $	**U.S. Stock Ticker:**
2007 Sales: $474,900	2007 Profits: $-7,800	**Int'l Ticker: 2345** Int'l Exchange: Taipei-TPE
2006 Sales: $469,160	2006 Profits: $ 690	Employees: 3,552
2005 Sales: $421,180	2005 Profits: $-9,190	Fiscal Year Ends: 12/31
2004 Sales: $629,500	2004 Profits: $-18,600	Parent Company:

SALARIES/BENEFITS:

Pension Plan:	ESOP Stock Plan:	Profit Sharing:	Top Exec. Salary: $	Bonus: $
Savings Plan:	Stock Purch. Plan:		Second Exec. Salary: $	Bonus: $

OTHER THOUGHTS:

Apparent Women Officers or Directors:
Hot Spot for Advancement for Women/Minorities:

LOCATIONS: ("Y" = Yes)

West:	Southwest:	Midwest:	Southeast:	Northeast:	International:
Y				Y	Y

ACER INC

www.acer.com.tw

Industry Group Code: 334111 **Ranks within this company's industry group:** Sales: 9 Profits: 8

Techology:		Medical/Drugs:		Engineering:		Transportation:		Chemicals/Petrochemicals:		Specialty:	
Computers:	Y	Manufacturer:		Design:		Aerospace:		Oil/Gas Products:		Special Services:	
Software:		Contract Research:		Construction:		Automotive:		Chemicals:		Consulting:	
Communications:		Medical Services:		Eng. Services:		Shipping:		Oil/Chem. Svcs.:		Specialty Mgmt.:	
Electronics:		Labs:		Consulting:				Gases:		Products:	
Alternative Energy:		Bio. Services:						Other:		Other:	

TYPES OF BUSINESS:

Computer Equipment Distribution
PCs & Accessories
Components
Software

BRANDS/DIVISIONS/AFFILIATES:

Pan Acer Group
Aspire
Veriton
Acer Ferrari
HiTRUST
Lottery Technology Services
TWP
Gateway, Inc.

CONTACTS: *Note: Officers with more than one job title may be intentionally listed here more than once.*

J. T. Wang, CEO
Gianfranco Lanci, Pres.
Hau Zhan, Dir.-Finance/Gen. Mgr.
J. T. Wang, Chmn.

Phone: 886-2-696-1234	**Fax:** 886-2-696-3535
Toll-Free:	
Address: 9F, 88 Hsin Tai Wu Rd., Sec. 1, Taipei, 221 Taiwan	

GROWTH PLANS/SPECIAL FEATURES:

Acer, Inc., a part of the Pan Acer Group, ranks among the world's top 10 branded PC manufacturers with a presence in over 100 countries. The company markets a full scope of branded IT products including PCs, servers, monitors, handheld devices, storage devices and projectors. The firm also supplies multiple brands of components, software and 3C products throughout China. Acer markets under several main brand names: Aspire, its consumer desktop and notebook PC brand name; TravelMate, its notebook-only brand name; and AcerPower and Veriton, its line of commercial PCs targeted for business users and MIS managers. The company's relationship with Ferrari has spawned the much sought after Acer Ferrari notebooks, which come in patented Ferrari red (the company recently launched Ferrari 500 and Ferrari 1000 models). The company has several subsidiaries, including Weblink, HiTRUST, Lottery Technology Services, TWP, Sertek and Apacer. It is aggressively expanding its markets on a global basis. The company recently began offering the Ferrari 4000, a new carbon-fiber notebook computer using the latest AMD-64 bit technology. In October 2007, the firm acquired Gateway, Inc. for $710 million. In late 2007, Acer announced it would begin selling Sun Microsystems server and storage products in Australia and New Zealand. The company's latest product is the Acer Aspire One, an ultraportable netbook featuring an 8.9-inch screen, wifi connectivity and up to a seven-hour battery life. Models are available with features such as solid state hard drives, 3G connectivity (through a partnership with AT&T), a choice of Linux or Windows XP operating systems and a wide range of colors. In March 2008, the company acquired smart handheld device manufacturer E-TEN.

FINANCIALS: **Sales and profits are in thousands of dollars—add 000 to get the full amount. 2008 Note: Financial information for 2008 was not available for all companies at press time.**

2008 Sales: $16,650,000	2008 Profits: $428,800	**U.S. Stock Ticker:**
2007 Sales: $14,070,000	2007 Profits: $310,170	**Int'l Ticker: 2353** Int'l Exchange: Taipei-TPE
2006 Sales: $11,320,000	2006 Profits: $313,470	Employees: 5,400
2005 Sales: $9,690,000	2005 Profits: $232,950	Fiscal Year Ends: 12/31
2004 Sales: $7,036,200	2004 Profits: $219,300	Parent Company:

SALARIES/BENEFITS:

Pension Plan: Y	ESOP Stock Plan:	Profit Sharing:	Top Exec. Salary: $	Bonus: $
Savings Plan:	Stock Purch. Plan:		Second Exec. Salary: $	Bonus: $

OTHER THOUGHTS:

Apparent Women Officers or Directors:
Hot Spot for Advancement for Women/Minorities:

LOCATIONS: ("Y" = Yes)

West:	Southwest:	Midwest:	Southeast:	Northeast:	International:
Y					Y

ACTIVISION BLIZZARD INC

www.activisionblizzard.com

Industry Group Code: 511208 **Ranks within this company's industry group:** Sales: 3 Profits: 4

Techology:		**Medical/Drugs:**		**Engineering:**		**Transportation:**		**Chemicals/Petrochemicals:**		**Specialty:**	
Computers:		Manufacturer:		Design:		Aerospace:		Oil/Gas Products:		Special Services:	
Software:	Y	Contract Research:		Construction:		Automotive:		Chemicals:		Consulting:	
Communications:		Medical Services:		Eng. Services:		Shipping:		Oil/Chem. Svcs.:		Specialty Mgmt.:	
Electronics:		Labs:		Consulting:				Gases:		Products:	
Alternative Energy:		Bio. Services:						Other:		Other:	

TYPES OF BUSINESS:

Video Games
Logistics Services

BRANDS/DIVISIONS/AFFILIATES:

Activision Publishing, Inc.
Blizzard Entertainment, Inc.
Vivendi Games
Bizarre Creations, Ltd.
FreeStyleGames
Budcat Creations
World of Warcraft
Guitar Hero

CONTACTS: *Note: Officers with more than one job title may be intentionally listed here more than once.*

Robert A. Kotick, CEO
Thomas Tippl, CFO
Brian Hodous, Chief Customer Officer
Ann Weiser, Chief Human Resources Officer
George Rose, Chief Legal Officer
Michael Griffith, CEO/Pres., Activision Publishing Inc.
Michael Morhaime, CEO/Pres., Blizzard Entertainment
Bruce Hack, Vice-Chmn./Chief Corp. Officer
Brian Kelly, Co-Chmn.
Rene Pennison, Co-Chmn.

Phone: 310-255-2000	**Fax:**
Toll-Free:	
Address: 3100 Ocean Park Blvd., Santa Monica, CA 90405 US	

GROWTH PLANS/SPECIAL FEATURES:

Activision Blizzard, Inc., formerly Activision, Inc., is a leading international publisher and distributor of interactive entertainment software and peripherals for a variety of game genres, operating through subsidiaries Activision Publishing and Blizzard Entertainment. The firm operates in four segments: Blizzard Entertainment, Inc. and its subsidiaries, which publish traditional games and online subscription-based games in the massively multiplayer online game (MMOG) category; Activision Publishing, which publishes interactive entertainment software and peripherals, including certain studios, assets and titles previously included in Vivendi Games' Sierra Entertainment; Activision Blizzard Distribution, which handles the distribution of interactive entertainment software and hardware products; and non-core exit operations. Activision Blizzard offers products that operate primarily on the Sony PlayStation 2, Sony PlayStation 3, Nintendo Wii, and Microsoft Xbox 360 console systems, Sony PlayStation Portable and Nintendo Dual Screen handheld devices, as well as PCs. Some of its most popular products include Guitar Hero, Call of Duty and Tony Hawk, as well as Spider-Man, James Bond, TRANSFORMERS, StarCraft, Diablo, and Warcraft franchise games, including World of Warcraft. Activision Blizzard maintains operations worldwide throughout North America, Europe and Asia. In September 2007, the company acquired video game developer Bizarre Creations Ltd. In July 2008, the company completed its merger with Vivendi Games and renaming as Activision Blizzard, Inc. Following this merger, the company restructured to operate through two subsidiaries, Activision Publishing and Blizzard Entertainment, formerly a subsidiary of Vivendi. In September 2008, Activision Blizzard acquired FreeStyleGames, a video game developer specializing in music-based games. In November 2008, the firm acquired Budcat Creations, a development studio focused on games for the Nintendo Wii and Nintendo DS systems.

The company offers its employees medical, dental and vision insurance, a college savings plan, tuition reimbursement, identity theft protection, home and auto insurance and group legal insurance, as well as company store discounts.

FINANCIALS: Sales and profits are in thousands of dollars—add 000 to get the full amount. 2008 Note: Financial information for 2008 was not available for all companies at press time.

2008 Sales: $3,026,000	2008 Profits: $-233,000	**U.S. Stock Ticker: ATVI**
2007 Sales: $1,349,000	2007 Profits: $179,000	**Int'l Ticker:** Int'l Exchange:
2006 Sales: $1,018,000	2006 Profits: $121,000	Employees: 7,000
2005 Sales: $1,405,857	2005 Profits: $135,057	Fiscal Year Ends: 12/31
2004 Sales: $947,656	2004 Profits: $77,715	Parent Company:

SALARIES/BENEFITS:

Pension Plan:	ESOP Stock Plan:	Profit Sharing:	Top Exec. Salary: $899,560	Bonus: $5,000,000
Savings Plan: Y	Stock Purch. Plan: Y		Second Exec. Salary: $875,387	Bonus: $5,000,000

OTHER THOUGHTS:

Apparent Women Officers or Directors: 2
Hot Spot for Advancement for Women/Minorities: Y

LOCATIONS: ("Y" = Yes)

West:	Southwest:	Midwest:	Southeast:	Northeast:	International:
Y	Y	Y	Y	Y	Y

ACXIOM CORP

www.acxiom.com

Industry Group Code: 511203 **Ranks within this company's industry group:** Sales: 1 Profits: 1

Techology:		Medical/Drugs:		Engineering:		Transportation:		Chemicals/Petrochemicals:		Specialty:	
Computers:		Manufacturer:		Design:		Aerospace:		Oil/Gas Products:		Special Services:	Y
Software:	Y	Contract Research:		Construction:		Automotive:		Chemicals:		Consulting:	Y
Communications:		Medical Services:		Eng. Services:		Shipping:		Oil/Chem. Svcs.:		Specialty Mgmt.:	
Electronics:		Labs:		Consulting:				Gases:		Products:	
Alternative Energy:		Bio. Services:						Other:		Other:	

TYPES OF BUSINESS:

Consumer Data Management
Consumer Databases
Consulting and Analytics
Risk Mitigation Services
CDI Technology
Consumer Privacy Solutions

BRANDS/DIVISIONS/AFFILIATES:

PersonicX
InfoBase-X
Acxiom Access-X Express
InsightIdentify
Acxiom Information Security Services (AISS)
Quinetix LLC
Acxiom Digital
Quinetix, LLC

CONTACTS: *Note: Officers with more than one job title may be intentionally listed here more than once.*

John A. Meyer, CEO
John A. Adams, COO/Exec. VP
John A. Meyer, Pres.
Christopher W. Wolf, CFO
Richard K. Howe, Sr. VP-Mktg.
Cindy K. Childers, Sr. VP-Human Resources
David R. Guzman, Sr. VP-IT Svcs.
Jerry C. Jones, Chief Legal Officer/Sr. VP
Cindy K. Childers, Corp. Comm.
Martin D. Sunde, Sr. VP
Michael Durham, Chmn.

Phone: 501-342-1000	**Fax:** 501-342-3913
Toll-Free: 800-322-9466	
Address: 1 Information Way, Little Rock, AR 72202 US	

GROWTH PLANS/SPECIAL FEATURES:

Acxiom Corp. is a customer information management firm offering 11 core products and services. Customer data integration (CDI) solutions include analyzing, optimizing, expanding and protecting a client's existing customer data. Data products include InfoBase-X, a database of U.S. telephone and consumer data; products that customize InfoBase-X such as PersonicX, which divides InfoBase into 70 segments based on demographics and consumer behavior; Acxiom Access-X Express, an data management tool for InfoBase; and others. Consulting and analytics solutions include diagnostic software, analytic consulting and other professional services to support existing customer information. Privacy services consist of privacy policy and compliance consultations. IT services include IT outsourcing, network management and other services, such as IT security. Direct marketing agency solutions include campaign and database management; direct mail and e-mail services; creative consultations; and CDI and analytics. Risk mitigation solutions include identification products to assist banks, investigators and credit unions prevent fraud loss and meet U.S.A. P.A.T.R.I.O.T. Act regulations, and investigation tools, as for debt collection or law enforcement agencies. Acxiom Information Security Services (AISS) provides criminal, civil and driving record background searches. Government solutions provides products that identify, locate and evaluates individuals for government service roles. Marketing-database solutions analyzes prospects and customers, designs, plans and manages campaigns and tracks results. Online Marketing Services assists clients in improving business through e-mail, search marketing and personalizing websites. Acxiom's clients are mostly of Fortune 1000 finance, insurance, information services, direct marketing, publishing, retail and telecommunications companies. Acquisitions of 2008 include the database marketing solutions division from ChoicePoint Inc; the direct marketing technology unit of Alvion, LLC; and Quinetix, LLC.

Employees are offered health, dental and vision insurance; a health savings account; a flexible spending account; an employee assistance program; short-and long-term disability; life insurance; pet insurance; education reimbursement assistance; adoption reimbursement assistance; and credit union.

FINANCIALS: **Sales and profits are in thousands of dollars—add 000 to get the full amount. 2008 Note: Financial information for 2008 was not available for all companies at press time.**

2008 Sales: $1,384,079	2008 Profits: $-7,780	**U.S. Stock Ticker: ACXM**
2007 Sales: $1,390,511	2007 Profits: $67,873	**Int'l Ticker:** Int'l Exchange:
2006 Sales: $1,328,773	2006 Profits: $61,775	Employees: 6,610
2005 Sales: $1,220,139	2005 Profits: $67,918	Fiscal Year Ends: 3/31
2004 Sales: $1,010,822	2004 Profits: $58,344	Parent Company:

SALARIES/BENEFITS:

Pension Plan:	ESOP Stock Plan:	Profit Sharing:	Top Exec. Salary: $715,998	Bonus: $700,000
Savings Plan: Y	Stock Purch. Plan: Y		Second Exec. Salary: $490,000	Bonus: $224,475

OTHER THOUGHTS:

Apparent Women Officers or Directors: 3
Hot Spot for Advancement for Women/Minorities: Y

LOCATIONS: ("Y" = Yes)

West:	Southwest:	Midwest:	Southeast:	Northeast:	International:
Y	Y	Y	Y		Y

ADAM OPEL AG

www.opel.com

Industry Group Code: 336111 **Ranks within this company's industry group:** Sales: Profits:

Techology:		Medical/Drugs:		Engineering:		Transportation:		Chemicals/Petrochemicals:		Specialty:	
Computers:		Manufacturer:		Design:		Aerospace:		Oil/Gas Products:		Special Services:	
Software:		Contract Research:		Construction:		Automotive:	Y	Chemicals:		Consulting:	
Communications:		Medical Services:		Eng. Services:		Shipping:		Oil/Chem. Svcs.:		Specialty Mgmt.:	
Electronics:		Labs:		Consulting:				Gases:		Products:	
Alternative Energy:		Bio. Services:						Other:		Other:	

TYPES OF BUSINESS:

Automobile Manufacturing
Alternative Fuel Vehicles

BRANDS/DIVISIONS/AFFILIATES:

Vauxhall
Agila
Corsa
Astra
Zafira
Vectra
Combo
Insignia

GROWTH PLANS/SPECIAL FEATURES:

Adam Opel AG (called Vauxhall in the U.K.), a European manufacturer of cars and trucks, has been a wholly-owned subsidiary of General Motors since 1929. Beginning with the manufacture of sewing machines and bikes, the company's founder, Adam Opel, began making automobiles in 1899. Accounting for approximately 78% of GM's European sales, Opel is GM's largest non-U.S. subsidiary. Opel's brand name models include the Antara, Astra, Corsa, Insignia, GT, Meriva, Signum, Tigra Twintop, Vectra, Vivaro and Zafira. The company also builds commercial vehicles, such as the Combo and Movano, and produces automotive components. Opel operates nine plants in six countries throughout Europe. In the interest of cutting down on carbon dioxide emissions, the company's Astra and Zafira product lines are powered with natural gas. Currently, fuel cells, noise reduction technologies and methods lowering fuel consumption are being explored. In June 2007, Opel introduced its new ecoFLEX model, which emits lower CO2 levels. In August 2008, the firm announced a new station wagon model, the Insignia Sports Tourer, to be unveiled at the Paris Auto Show.

CONTACTS:

Note: Officers with more than one job title may be intentionally listed here more than once.

Marco Molinari, Exec. Dir.-Finance
Hans H. Demant, Dir.-Eng.
Michael Hartwig, Dir.-European Mktg. Comm.
Hans H. Demant, Managing Dir.
Alain Visser, Chief Mktg. Officer-GM Europe
Carl-Peter Forster, Chmn.

Phone: 49-6142-66-7473 **Fax:** 49-6142-66-8205
Toll-Free:
Address: Postfach 1710, Russelsheim, 65423 Germany

FINANCIALS:

Sales and profits are in thousands of dollars—add 000 to get the full amount. 2008 Note: Financial information for 2008 was not available for all companies at press time.

2008 Sales: $	2008 Profits: $	**U.S. Stock Ticker: Subsidiary**
2007 Sales: $	2007 Profits: $	**Int'l Ticker:** Int'l Exchange:
2006 Sales: $	2006 Profits: $	Employees: 36,000
2005 Sales: $	2005 Profits: $	Fiscal Year Ends: 12/31
2004 Sales: $	2004 Profits: $	Parent Company: GENERAL MOTORS CORP (GM)

SALARIES/BENEFITS:

Pension Plan:	ESOP Stock Plan:	Profit Sharing:	Top Exec. Salary: $	Bonus: $
Savings Plan:	Stock Purch. Plan:		Second Exec. Salary: $	Bonus: $

OTHER THOUGHTS:

Apparent Women Officers or Directors:
Hot Spot for Advancement for Women/Minorities:

LOCATIONS: ("Y" = Yes)

West:	Southwest:	Midwest:	Southeast:	Northeast:	International:
					Y

ADC TELECOMMUNICATIONS INC

www.adc.com

Industry Group Code: 334210 **Ranks within this company's industry group:** Sales: 9 Profits: 4

Techology:		Medical/Drugs:		Engineering:		Transportation:		Chemicals/Petrochemicals:		Specialty:	
Computers:		Manufacturer:		Design:		Aerospace:		Oil/Gas Products:		Special Services:	
Software:		Contract Research:		Construction:		Automotive:		Chemicals:		Consulting:	
Communications:	Y	Medical Services:		Eng. Services:		Shipping:		Oil/Chem. Svcs.:		Specialty Mgmt.:	
Electronics:		Labs:		Consulting:				Gases:		Products:	
Alternative Energy:		Bio. Services:						Other:		Other:	

TYPES OF BUSINESS:

Telecommunications Equipment
Networking Systems
Broadband Connectivity Products
Equipment Services
Systems Integration

BRANDS/DIVISIONS/AFFILIATES:

OmniReach FTTX Infrastructure Solutions
Fiber Guide Raceway
Century Man Communication
RF Worx
DSX1/3
ADC Krone
LGC Wireless

CONTACTS: *Note: Officers with more than one job title may be intentionally listed here more than once.*

Robert E. Switz, CEO
Robert E. Switz, Pres.
James G. Mathews, CFO/VP
Hubert Shanne, VP-EMEA, Mktg. & Customer Service
Laura N. Owen, VP-Human Resources
Christopher Jurasek, CIO
Mike Day, CTO
Laura N. Owen, Chief Admin. Officer/VP
Jeffery D. Pflaum, General Counsel/Sec./VP
Mike Day, VP-Strategy
Mike Smith, Dir.-Corp. Comm.
Mark P. Borman, VP-Investor Rel./Treas.
Bradley V. Crary, VP-Tax
Kimberly Hartwell, VP-Americas Sales, Mktg. & Customer Service
Richard B. Parran, VP/Pres., Network Solutions
Patrick D. O'Brien, Pres., Connectivity Solutions
Steven G. Nemitz, VP/Controller
Robert E. Switz, Chmn.

Phone: 952-938-8080 **Fax:** 952-917-1717
Toll-Free: 800-366-3889
Address: 13625 Technology Dr., Eden Prairie, MN 55344 US

GROWTH PLANS/SPECIAL FEATURES:

ADC Telecommunications, Inc. is a provider of global network infrastructure products and services that enable the delivery of high-speed Internet, data, video and voice services to consumers and businesses worldwide. The company operates in three business segments: connectivity, network solutions and professional services. Connectivity is by far its largest segment, accounting for 77.2% of ADC's sales. ADC's connectivity devices are used in copper, coaxial, fiber-optic, wireless and broadcast communications networks. These products provide the physical interconnections between network components or access points into networks. These devices include DSX and DDF products, FTTX products, fiber distribution panels and frames, radio frequency digital management products, power distribution and protection panels, modular fiber-optic cable systems, structured cabling products and broadcast and entertainment products. ADC's network solutions services cover both in-building and outdoor services, and its wireline products (principally Soneplex and HiGain) enable communications service providers to deliver high capacity voice and data services over copper or optical facilities in the last mile/kilometer of communications networks. The company's professional services department helps operators plan, deploy and maintain networks, including cable, wireless and wireline networks. ADC serves markets such as broadcast and entertainment, global and local carriers, global original equipment manufacturers, government and wireless. ADC subsidiary ADC Krone is a global supplier of copper- and fiber-based connectivity solutions. In January 2008, the company completed its acquisition of Century Man Communication, a provider of communication distribution frame products in China. In July 2008, ADC announced a new version of its InterReach Fusion in-building cellular system designated for use by Canadian cellular providers.

FINANCIALS: Sales and profits are in thousands of dollars—add 000 to get the full amount. 2008 Note: Financial information for 2008 was not available for all companies at press time.

2008 Sales: $1,456,400	2008 Profits: $-41,900	**U.S. Stock Ticker: ADCT**
2007 Sales: $1,276,700	2007 Profits: $106,300	**Int'l Ticker:** Int'l Exchange:
2006 Sales: $1,231,900	2006 Profits: $65,700	Employees: 10,600
2005 Sales: $1,128,900	2005 Profits: $98,800	Fiscal Year Ends: 10/31
2004 Sales: $733,900	2004 Profits: $16,400	Parent Company:

SALARIES/BENEFITS:

Pension Plan:	ESOP Stock Plan:	Profit Sharing:	Top Exec. Salary: $742,415	Bonus: $673,205
Savings Plan:	Stock Purch. Plan:		Second Exec. Salary: $329,231	Bonus: $208,001

OTHER THOUGHTS:

Apparent Women Officers or Directors: 2
Hot Spot for Advancement for Women/Minorities: Y

LOCATIONS: ("Y" = Yes)

West:	Southwest:	Midwest:	Southeast:	Northeast:	International:
		Y			Y

ADOBE SYSTEMS INC

www.adobe.com

Industry Group Code: 511209 **Ranks within this company's industry group:** Sales: 1 Profits: 1

Techology:		Medical/Drugs:		Engineering:		Transportation:		Chemicals/Petrochemicals:		Specialty:	
Computers:		Manufacturer:		Design:		Aerospace:		Oil/Gas Products:		Special Services:	
Software:	Y	Contract Research:		Construction:		Automotive:		Chemicals:		Consulting:	
Communications:		Medical Services:		Eng. Services:		Shipping:		Oil/Chem. Svcs.:		Specialty Mgmt.:	
Electronics:		Labs:		Consulting:				Gases:		Products:	
Alternative Energy:		Bio. Services:						Other:		Other:	

TYPES OF BUSINESS:

Computer Software-Desktop & Publishing
Document Management Software
Photo Editing & Management Software
Graphic Design Software

BRANDS/DIVISIONS/AFFILIATES:

Adobe Acrobat
Adobe Flash Player
Adobe Photoshop
Adobe Creative Suite
Macromedia Flash SDK
Adobe Reader LE
Macromedia ColdFusion
Scene7 Inc

CONTACTS: *Note: Officers with more than one job title may be intentionally listed here more than once.*

Shantanu Narayen, CEO
Shantanu Narayen, Pres.
Mark Garrett, CFO/Exec. VP
Ann Lewnes, Sr. VP-Corp. Mktg. & Comm.
Donna Morris, Sr. VP-Human Resources
Naresh Gupta, Managing Dir.-R&D, India
Gerri Martin-Flickinger, CIO/Sr. VP
Kevin Lynch, CTO
Digby Horner, Sr. VP-Eng. Tech. Group
Karen Cottle, General Counsel/Corp. Sec./Sr. VP
Matt Thompson, Sr. VP-Worldwide Field Oper.
Paul Weiskopf, Sr. VP-Corp. Dev.
Kevin Burr, VP-Corp. Affairs & Comm.
Mike Saviage, VP-Investor Rel.
John E. Warnock, Co-Chmn.
Naresh Gupta, Sr. VP-Print & Classic Publishing Solutions Unit
John Loiacono, Sr. VP-Creative Solutions Bus. Unit
Charles M. Geschke, Co-Chmn.

Phone: 408-536-6000 **Fax:** 408-537-6000
Toll-Free: 800-833-6687
Address: 345 Park Ave., San Jose, CA 95110 US

GROWTH PLANS/SPECIAL FEATURES:

Adobe Systems, Inc. is one of the largest software companies in the world. It offers a line of creative, business and mobile software and services used by creative professionals, designers, knowledge workers, high-end consumers, original equipment manufacturers, developers and enterprises for creating, managing, delivering and engaging with content and experiences across multiple operating systems, devices and media. The company operates in five segments: creative solutions; knowledge worker solutions (KWS); enterprise and developer solutions (EDS); mobile and device solutions (MDS); and other. Creative Solutions focuses primarily on professional creative clients such as graphic designers, production artists, writers and photographers. Products include Adobe After Effects Professional; Adobe Audition; Adobe Photoshop; and Adobe Ultra. The KWS segment focuses on knowledge clients such as accountants, architects, educators, insurance underwriters and stock analysts. Products include Adobe Document Center and Adobe Acrobat Professional. The EDS segment works with corporate clients to make business processes more efficient and web applications more engaging for these firms. Products include Adobe LiveCycle Data Services ES and Adobe Output Designer. The MDS segment, though the continued relationships with organizations such as Verizon, Nokia and Sony/Ericsson, focuses on mobile devices. Products include Adobe Reader LE and Adobe Flash Lite. The other segment contains products and services that address market opportunities ranging from publishing to printing. In September 2008, the firm acquired YaWah ApS, a European imaging software provider. In May 2008, Adobe entered into agreement to purchase Overlook Center located in Waltham, Massachusetts.

Employees of the firm (based in the U.S.) are offered medical, dental and vision coverage; dependent and health care reimbursement accounts; home, auto and pet insurance; back-up child care; adoption assistance; commuter program; educational assistance program; employee discounts; a fitness program; and an employee assistance program.

FINANCIALS: **Sales and profits are in thousands of dollars—add 000 to get the full amount. 2008 Note: Financial information for 2008 was not available for all companies at press time.**

2008 Sales: $3,579,889	2008 Profits: $871,814	**U.S. Stock Ticker: ADBE**
2007 Sales: $3,157,881	2007 Profits: $723,807	**Int'l Ticker:** Int'l Exchange:
2006 Sales: $2,575,300	2006 Profits: $505,809	Employees: 6,959
2005 Sales: $1,966,321	2005 Profits: $602,839	Fiscal Year Ends: 11/30
2004 Sales: $1,666,581	2004 Profits: $450,398	Parent Company:

SALARIES/BENEFITS:

Pension Plan:	ESOP Stock Plan:	Profit Sharing: Y	Top Exec. Salary: $925,000	Bonus: $681,262
Savings Plan: Y	Stock Purch. Plan: Y		Second Exec. Salary: $575,000	Bonus: $376,925

OTHER THOUGHTS:

Apparent Women Officers or Directors: 5
Hot Spot for Advancement for Women/Minorities: Y

LOCATIONS: ("Y" = Yes)

West:	Southwest:	Midwest:	Southeast:	Northeast:	International:
Y				Y	Y

ADVANCED MICRO DEVICES INC (AMD)

www.amd.com

Industry Group Code: 334413 **Ranks within this company's industry group:** Sales: 8 Profits: 18

Techology:		Medical/Drugs:		Engineering:		Transportation:		Chemicals/Petrochemicals:		Specialty:	
Computers:	Y	Manufacturer:		Design:		Aerospace:		Oil/Gas Products:		Special Services:	
Software:		Contract Research:		Construction:		Automotive:		Chemicals:		Consulting:	
Communications:		Medical Services:		Eng. Services:		Shipping:		Oil/Chem. Svcs.:		Specialty Mgmt.:	
Electronics:		Labs:		Consulting:				Gases:		Products:	
Alternative Energy:		Bio. Services:						Other:		Other:	

TYPES OF BUSINESS:

Microprocessors
Semiconductors
Low-End PCs

BRANDS/DIVISIONS/AFFILIATES:

AMD Athlon 64 FX
AMD Athlon 64
ATI Avivo
AMD Radeon Xpress
ATI Radeon HD 2000
ATI Radeon X1000
AMD Sempron
AMD Opteron

CONTACTS: *Note: Officers with more than one job title may be intentionally listed here more than once.*

Dirk Meyer, CEO
Robert J. Rivet, COO/Exec. VP
Dirk Meyer, Pres.
Nigel Dessau, Chief Mktg. Officer/Sr. VP
Allen Sockwell, Sr. VP-Human Resources
Amhed Mahamoud, CIO/Sr. VP
Doug Grose, Sr. VP-Mfg.
Robert J. Rivet, Chief Admin. Officer
Thomas M. McCoy, Exec. VP-Legal Affairs
Thomas M. McCoy, Exec. VP-Corp. & Public Affairs
Richard Bergman, Sr. VP-Graphics Product Group
Gustavo Arenas, Chief Sales Officer/Sr. VP
Randy Allen, Sr. VP-Computing Solutions Group
Adrian Hartog, Pres., AMD Canada
Hector de J. Ruiz, Exec. Chmn.
Emilio Ghilardi, Sr. VP/Gen. Mgr.-EMEA
Douglas Grose, Sr. VP-Supply Chain

Phone: 408-749-4000 **Fax:** 408-749-4291
Toll-Free: 800-538-8450
Address: 1 AMD Pl., Sunnyvale, CA 94088-3453 US

GROWTH PLANS/SPECIAL FEATURES:

Advanced Micro Devices, Inc. (AMD) is a global semiconductor company that provides processing solutions for the computing, graphics and consumer electronics markets. It supplies semiconductors, 3D graphics; video and multimedia products; chipsets for PCs, including desktop and notebook PCs, professional workstations and servers; and products for consumer electronic devices such as mobile phones, digital TVs and game consoles. AMD has manufacturing operations in the U.S., Europe and Asia and sales offices throughout the U.S. The company operates through three segments: Computation Products; Graphics and Chipsets; and Consumer Electronics. AMD's computation products segment encompasses microprocessor products, servers and workstations, notebook PCs and desktop PCs. The Graphics and Chipsets segment consists of Discrete Desktop Products (consisting of its two major product series, ATI Radeon X1000 and the new ATI Radeon HD 2000 graphics processors), discrete notebook products (its ATI Mobility Radeon X1000 series), chipset products (motherboard solutions delivered through AMD's Radeon Xpress and Crossfire products) and home media PC products (such as its ATI Avivo technology which enables PCs to record and playback in HD). Prominent customers include Microsoft, Macintosh and Toshiba. In 2008, AMD sold its digital TV assets to Broadcom Corporation. In October 2008, the firm announced its intent to spin off its computer chip factories, with Advanced Technology Investment Company agreeing to contribute more than $8 billion in initial funding in exchange for a 55.6% stake in the new company.

Employees are offered health and dental insurance; disability plans; life insurance; business travel accident insurance; a profit sharing plan; a stock purchase plan; a 401(k) plan; an educational assistance program; and discounted tickets to movie theaters, sporting events and amusement parks.

FINANCIALS: Sales and profits are in thousands of dollars—add 000 to get the full amount. 2008 Note: Financial information for 2008 was not available for all companies at press time.

2008 Sales: $5,808,000
2007 Sales: $5,858,000
2006 Sales: $5,627,000
2005 Sales: $4,973,000
2004 Sales: $3,924,000

2008 Profits: $-3,098,000
2007 Profits: $-3,379,000
2006 Profits: $-166,000
2005 Profits: $165,000
2004 Profits: $91,000

U.S. Stock Ticker: AMD
Int'l Ticker: Int'l Exchange:
Employees: 14,700
Fiscal Year Ends: 12/31
Parent Company:

SALARIES/BENEFITS:

Pension Plan: ESOP Stock Plan: Profit Sharing: Y Top Exec. Salary: $1,124,000 Bonus: $
Savings Plan: Y Stock Purch. Plan: Y Second Exec. Salary: $695,000 Bonus: $

OTHER THOUGHTS:

Apparent Women Officers or Directors:
Hot Spot for Advancement for Women/Minorities:

LOCATIONS: ("Y" = Yes)

West:	Southwest:	Midwest:	Southeast:	Northeast:	International:
Y	Y	Y	Y	Y	Y

Note: Financial information, benefits and other data can change quickly and may vary from those stated here.

ADVANCED SEMICONDUCTOR ENGINEERING INC

www.aseglobal.com

Industry Group Code: 333295 **Ranks within this company's industry group:** Sales: 2 Profits: 2

Techology:		Medical/Drugs:		Engineering:		Transportation:		Chemicals/Petrochemicals:		Specialty:	
Computers:		Manufacturer:		Design:	Y	Aerospace:		Oil/Gas Products:		Special Services:	Y
Software:		Contract Research:		Construction:		Automotive:		Chemicals:		Consulting:	
Communications:		Medical Services:		Eng. Services:		Shipping:		Oil/Chem. Svcs.:		Specialty Mgmt.:	
Electronics:	Y	Labs:		Consulting:				Gases:		Products:	
Alternative Energy:		Bio. Services:						Other:		Other:	

TYPES OF BUSINESS:

Semiconductor Manufacturing
Semiconductor Packaging Services
Design & Testing Services

BRANDS/DIVISIONS/AFFILIATES:

ASE Group
Universal Scientific Industrial Co Ltd
ASE Electronics
Hung Ching
ISE Labs Inc
Global Advanced Packaging Technology Limited
Weihai Aimhigh Electronic Co Ltd
ASE Test

CONTACTS: *Note: Officers with more than one job title may be intentionally listed here more than once.*

Jason C. S. Chang, CEO
Tien Wu, COO
Richard H. P. Chang, Pres./Vice Chmn.
Joseph Tung, CFO/VP
Freddie Liu, VP-Investor Rel.
Jeffrey Chen, VP
Jason C. S. Chang, Chmn.

Phone: 886-7-361-7131 **Fax:** 886-7-361-4546

Toll-Free:

Address: 26 Chin 3rd Rd., Nantze Export Processing Zone, Kaohsiung, Taiwan

GROWTH PLANS/SPECIAL FEATURES:

Advanced Semiconductor Engineering, Inc. (ASE) is a leading provider of semiconductor packaging, also called assembly, which is the process of turning bare semiconductors into finished semiconductors. ASE semiconductor assembly products are available in a variety of formats, including dual-in-line packages, quad packages, ball-grid arrays (BGAs), pin grid arrays (PGAs), chip scale packages (CSPs), system-in-package (SiPs), flip chips and lead-free packages. These assemblies are used to connect the integrated circuit, or die, to the printed circuit board, thus enabling reliable chip testing. ASE provides services at all stages of the semiconductor manufacturing process except circuit design and wafer fabrication. Its service capabilities include front-end engineering testing, which is the testing of prototypes that takes place before volume production, including software development, electrical verification, reliability analysis and failure analysis; wafer probing, testing each chip on a wafer for defects packaging; and final testing, which makes sure that the product is functional before being sent to customers. Company affiliates include Universal Scientific Industrial Co. Ltd., which provides design manufacturing services; ASE Electronics, a supplier of substrates and packaging material; Hung Ching, a company engaged in the development and management of commercial, residential and industrial real estate properties in Taiwan; and U.S.-based ISE Labs, Inc. a front-end engineering test firm. Some of ASE's customers include Microsoft Corporation; ATI Technologies, Inc.; Freescale Semiconductor, Inc.; VIA Technologies, Inc.; and Advanced Micro Devices. In January 2007, the firm acquired Shanghai-based Global Advanced Packaging Technology Limited (GAPT) for approximately $60 million. GAPT provides packaging and testing services. In May 2008, AES acquired Weihai Aimhigh Electronic Co. Ltd. from Aimhigh Global Corp. and TCC Steel. In June 2008, the company announced its acquisition of all the remaining shares of semiconductor testing company ASE Test that it did not already own, making ASE Test a wholly-owned subsidiary of the company.

FINANCIALS: **Sales and profits are in thousands of dollars—add 000 to get the full amount. 2008 Note: Financial information for 2008 was not available for all companies at press time.**

2008 Sales: $2,779,400	2008 Profits: $181,310	**U.S. Stock Ticker: ASX**
2007 Sales: $2,977,540	2007 Profits: $358,050	**Int'l Ticker: 2311** Int'l Exchange: Taipei-TPE
2006 Sales: $3,081,400	2006 Profits: $534,400	Employees: 26,977
2005 Sales: $2,602,942	2005 Profits: $-146,135	Fiscal Year Ends: 12/31
2004 Sales: $2,330,432	2004 Profits: $130,401	Parent Company:

SALARIES/BENEFITS:

Pension Plan:	ESOP Stock Plan:	Profit Sharing:	Top Exec. Salary: $	Bonus: $
Savings Plan:	Stock Purch. Plan:		Second Exec. Salary: $	Bonus: $

OTHER THOUGHTS:

Apparent Women Officers or Directors:

Hot Spot for Advancement for Women/Minorities:

LOCATIONS: ("Y" = Yes)

West:	Southwest:	Midwest:	Southeast:	Northeast:	International:
Y	Y			Y	Y

AECOM TECHNOLOGY CORPORATION

www.aecom.com

Industry Group Code: 234000 **Ranks within this company's industry group:** Sales: 19 Profits: 17

Techology:		Medical/Drugs:		Engineering:		Transportation:		Chemicals/Petrochemicals:		Specialty:	
Computers:		Manufacturer:		Design:	Y	Aerospace:		Oil/Gas Products:		Special Services:	Y
Software:		Contract Research:		Construction:	Y	Automotive:		Chemicals:		Consulting:	Y
Communications:		Medical Services:		Eng. Services:	Y	Shipping:		Oil/Chem. Svcs.:		Specialty Mgmt.:	Y
Electronics:		Labs:		Consulting:	Y			Gases:		Products:	
Alternative Energy:		Bio. Services:						Other:		Other:	

TYPES OF BUSINESS:

Engineering & Design Services
Transportation Projects
Environmental Projects
Power & Mining Support
Consulting
Economic Development Consulting

BRANDS/DIVISIONS/AFFILIATES:

AGS
CTE
DMJM Aviation
Faber Maunsell
Tecsult, Inc
Boyle Engineering
Totten Sims Hubicki Associates
Earth Tech Inc

CONTACTS: *Note: Officers with more than one job title may be intentionally listed here more than once.*

John M. Dionisio, CEO
James R. Royer, COO/Exec. VP
John M. Dionisio, Pres.
Michael S. Burke, CFO/Sr. VP
Robert Kelleher, Chief Human Capital Officer
Raul Cruz, CIO/Sr. VP
Stephanie Hunter, Chief Admin. Officer
Eric Chen, General Counsel
Robert L. Costello, Exec. VP-Global Oper.
Jane Chmielinski, CEO-Corp. Dev.
Paul J. Gennaro, Jr., Chief Comm. Officer
Paul J. Gennaro, Jr., Sr. VP-Investor Rel.
Eric Chen, Sr. VP-Finance
John L. Kinley, CEO-Canada
Glenn R. Robson, Chief Strategy Officer/Sr. VP-Finance
Frederick W. Werner, CEO-U.S.
Jane Chmielinski, CEO-Corp. Dev.
Richard G. Newman, Chmn.
Anthony C. K. Shum, CEO-Hong Kong, China & Asia

Phone: 213-593-8000 **Fax:** 213-593-8730
Toll-Free:
Address: 555 S. Flower St., Ste. 3700, Los Angeles, CA 90071-2300 US

GROWTH PLANS/SPECIAL FEATURES:

AECOM Technology Corporation is a global engineering and design company engaged in facility, transportation, environment and specialty engineering projects for corporate, institutional and government clients. Certain specialized services are available in mining, power, international development, and operations and maintenance. The firm's facility design and construction projects encompass land development assignments and a wide variety of building projects. Transportation services include feasibility studies, planning, design, engineering, construction management and asset management for transit and rail, highway, bridge, port, harbor and airport projects. AECOM offers water resource, wastewater, wet weather, hazardous waste management and other environmental engineering services. The power sector offers design, construction management and commissioning services. The company operates largely through a network of subsidiaries, including AGS, AECOM's government services arm; CTE, an infrastructure engineering firm (with a wastewater treatment plant in Antarctica); DMJM Aviation, the firm's flagship aviation design and construction management company; Faber Maunsell, a European engineering consultancy firm; Metcalf & Eddy, an environmental engineering group; UMA, a Canadian division; Hayes, Seay, Mattern & Mattern, Inc., an architectural and engineering firm that merged into AECOM in January 2007; and PADCO, a firm that promotes sustainable economic development in more than 100 countries. AECOM Austin, another subsidiary, is devoted to serving engineering and development clients in a variety of sectors, including pharmaceutical, industrial and aviation companies. Recent acquisitions include Earth Tech, Inc., a business unit of Tyco International Ltd; Totten Sims Hubicki Associates, a Canadian engineering firm; Boyle Engineering, a company that specializes in the water sector; and Tecsult, Inc. an international engineering firm based in Quebec.

Employees are offered health, life and disability insurance, as well as retirement benefits.

FINANCIALS: **Sales and profits are in thousands of dollars—add 000 to get the full amount. 2008 Note: Financial information for 2008 was not available for all companies at press time.**

2008 Sales: $5,194,482	2008 Profits: $147,226	**U.S. Stock Ticker: ACM**
2007 Sales: $4,237,270	2007 Profits: $100,297	**Int'l Ticker:** Int'l Exchange:
2006 Sales: $3,421,492	2006 Profits: $53,686	Employees: 43,000
2005 Sales: $2,395,340	2005 Profits: $53,814	Fiscal Year Ends: 9/30
2004 Sales: $2,012,000	2004 Profits: $50,400	Parent Company:

SALARIES/BENEFITS:

Pension Plan: Y	ESOP Stock Plan:	Profit Sharing:	Top Exec. Salary: $956,543	Bonus: $2,000,000
Savings Plan: Y	Stock Purch. Plan: Y		Second Exec. Salary: $918,090	Bonus: $1,700,000

OTHER THOUGHTS:

Apparent Women Officers or Directors: 2
Hot Spot for Advancement for Women/Minorities: Y

LOCATIONS: ("Y" = Yes)

West:	Southwest:	Midwest:	Southeast:	Northeast:	International:
Y	Y	Y	Y	Y	Y

Note: Financial information, benefits and other data can change quickly and may vary from those stated here.

AECON GROUP INC

www.aecon.com

Industry Group Code: 234000 **Ranks within this company's industry group:** Sales: 26 Profits: 22

Techology:		Medical/Drugs:		Engineering:		Transportation:		Chemicals/Petrochemicals:		Specialty:	
Computers:		Manufacturer:		Design:	Y	Aerospace:		Oil/Gas Products:		Special Services:	
Software:		Contract Research:		Construction:	Y	Automotive:		Chemicals:		Consulting:	
Communications:		Medical Services:		Eng. Services:	Y	Shipping:		Oil/Chem. Svcs.:		Specialty Mgmt.:	
Electronics:		Labs:		Consulting:				Gases:		Products:	
Alternative Energy:		Bio. Services:						Other:		Other:	

TYPES OF BUSINESS:

Construction
Infrastructure Development
Utility Systems
Steam Power Generation
Engineering
Materials Fabrication

BRANDS/DIVISIONS/AFFILIATES:

Aecon Concessions
Aecon Buildings
Aecon Civil & Utilities
Aecon Industrial
Aecon Atlantic
Aecon Group Ltee
Innovative Steam Technologies, Inc.
Aecon Constructors

CONTACTS: *Note: Officers with more than one job title may be intentionally listed here more than once.*

John M. Beck, CEO
Scott C. Balfour, Pres.
Scott C. Balfour, CFO
Mitch Patten, VP-Human Resources
Andy DeHaan, VP-IT
L. Brian Swartz, Sr. VP-Legal & Commercial Svcs.
Mitch Patten, VP-Corp. Affairs
Gerard A. Kelly, Sr. VP-Finance
Terrance L. McKibbon, CEO-Aecon Infrastructure
Paul P. Koenderman, CEO-Aecon Industrial Group/Exec. VP
Mike Archambault, VP-Safety & Loss Control
Robert McDonald, Pres., Aecon Buildings
John M. Beck, Chmn.

Phone: 416-293-7004 **Fax:** 416-754-8736
Toll-Free: 877-232-2677
Address: 20 Carlson Ct., Ste. 800, Toronto, ON M9W 7K6 Canada

GROWTH PLANS/SPECIAL FEATURES:

Aecon Group, Inc., formerly Aecon Enterprises, is one of Canada's largest construction and infrastructure development companies. The firm operates in four principal segments: Buildings, Infrastructure, Industrial and Concessions. The Buildings segment specializes in the construction and renovation of commercial, institutional and multi-family residential buildings, including hospitals, office buildings, airport terminals, entertainment facilities, schools, embassies, retail complexes and high-rise condominium buildings. The Infrastructure segment includes all aspects of the construction of both public and private infrastructure, including roads and highways, dams, tunnels, bridges, airports, marine facilities, transit systems and hydroelectric power projects. The Industrial segment encompasses all of Aecon's industrial construction and manufacturing activities including in-plant construction and module assembly in the energy, manufacturing, petrochemical, steel and automotive sectors. Activities within the Concessions segment include the development, financing and operation of infrastructure projects by way of build-operate-transfer, build-own-operate-transfer and other public-private partnership contract structures. The company operates through eight subsidiaries: Aecon Atlantic; Aecon Buildings, a commercial building construction business; Aecon Civil and Utilities; Aecon Concessions; Aecon Constructors; Aecon Industrial, which offers a single-source solution for multi-trade industrial construction and fabrication projects; Innovative Steam Technologies, Inc., which designs and manufactures the firm's patented Once-Through Heat Recovery Steam Generators (OTSG's) for the industrial and power generation sectors; and Aecon Group Ltee., a Quebec-based construction company with expertise primarily in civil buildings and industrial construction. In December 2007 Aecon acquired construction and materials company Leo Alarie and Sons Limited, along with all of its assets, including its equipment fleet, land, pits and quarries, as well as selected construction and mining contracts.

FINANCIALS: **Sales and profits are in thousands of dollars—add 000 to get the full amount. 2008 Note: Financial information for 2008 was not available for all companies at press time.**

2008 Sales: $1,492,630	2008 Profits: $47,160	**U.S. Stock Ticker:**
2007 Sales: $1,187,260	2007 Profits: $38,410	**Int'l Ticker: ARE** Int'l Exchange: Toronto-TSX
2006 Sales: $1,091,000	2006 Profits: $11,300	Employees: 1,979
2005 Sales: $972,000	2005 Profits: $- 954	Fiscal Year Ends: 12/31
2004 Sales: $832,100	2004 Profits: $-34,500	Parent Company:

SALARIES/BENEFITS:

Pension Plan:	ESOP Stock Plan:	Profit Sharing:	Top Exec. Salary: $	Bonus: $
Savings Plan:	Stock Purch. Plan:		Second Exec. Salary: $	Bonus: $

OTHER THOUGHTS:

Apparent Women Officers or Directors:
Hot Spot for Advancement for Women/Minorities:

LOCATIONS: ("Y" = Yes)

West:	Southwest:	Midwest:	Southeast:	Northeast:	International:
Y					Y

AFFILIATED COMPUTER SERVICES INC

www.acs-inc.com

Industry Group Code: 541512 **Ranks within this company's industry group:** Sales: 9 Profits: 7

Techology:		Medical/Drugs:		Engineering:		Transportation:		Chemicals/Petrochemicals:		Specialty:	
Computers:		Manufacturer:		Design:		Aerospace:		Oil/Gas Products:		Special Services:	Y
Software:	Y	Contract Research:		Construction:		Automotive:		Chemicals:		Consulting:	
Communications:		Medical Services:		Eng. Services:		Shipping:		Oil/Chem. Svcs.:		Specialty Mgmt.:	
Electronics:		Labs:		Consulting:				Gases:		Products:	
Alternative Energy:		Bio. Services:						Other:		Other:	

TYPES OF BUSINESS:

IT Consulting
Loan Processing Services
Systems Integration
Human Resources Services
IT Outsourcing
Business Process Outsourcing

BRANDS/DIVISIONS/AFFILIATES:

Grupo Multivoice

CONTACTS:

Note: Officers with more than one job title may be intentionally listed here more than once.

Lynn Blodgett, CEO
Tom Burlin, COO/Exec. VP
Lynn Blodgett, Pres.
Kevin Kyser, CFO/Exec. VP
Lora Villarreal, Chief People Officer/Exec. VP
Tasos Tsolakis, CIO
Skip Stitt, Chief Admin. Officer
Tas Panos, General Counsel/Exec. VP
John Rexford, Exec. VP-Corp. Dev.
Ann Vezina, Exec. VP/Pres., Commercial Solutions
Tom Blodgett, Exec. VP/Pres., Bus. Process Solutions
Derrell James, Exec. VP/Pres., ITO Svcs.
Michael Huerta, Exec. VP/Pres., Transportation Solutions
Darwin Deason, Chmn.

Phone: 214-841-6111 **Fax:** 214-823-9369
Toll-Free:
Address: 2828 N. Haskell Ave., Bldg. 1, Dallas, TX 75204 US

GROWTH PLANS/SPECIAL FEATURES:

Affiliated Computer Services, Inc. (ACS) is a provider of business process outsourcing and IT (information technology) services to commercial and government clients. The company operates in two segments: government and commercial. Through the commercial segment, which generates approximately 60% of its revenues, ACS provides business process outsourcing, systems integration services and consulting services to a variety of commercial clients. The commercial segment is focused on markets including communications and consumer goods; healthcare; transportation; consumer goods and services; and financial services, which includes education services. ACS' solutions for the commercial segment include IT services; human capital management; finance and accounting; customer care; transaction processing; payment services; and commercial education. Services in the government market, which represents approximately 40% of the company's revenues, include technology and business process based services with a focus on transaction processing, child support payment processing, electronic toll collection, traffic violations processing, program management services (such as Medicaid fiscal agent services) and student loan processing services. While ACS serves customers in over 100 countries, approximately 92% of its revenue for 2008 was derived from domestic clients. In December 2008, the company acquired Grupo Multivoice, an Argentina based provider of customer care services.

ACS offers its employees medical, dental, vision, life and disability insurance.

FINANCIALS:

Sales and profits are in thousands of dollars—add 000 to get the full amount. 2008 Note: Financial information for 2008 was not available for all companies at press time.

2008 Sales: $6,160,550	2008 Profits: $329,010	**U.S. Stock Ticker: ACS**
2007 Sales: $5,772,479	2007 Profits: $253,090	**Int'l Ticker:** Int'l Exchange:
2006 Sales: $5,353,661	2006 Profits: $358,806	Employees: 65,000
2005 Sales: $4,351,159	2005 Profits: $409,569	Fiscal Year Ends: 6/30
2004 Sales: $4,106,393	2004 Profits: $521,728	Parent Company:

SALARIES/BENEFITS:

Pension Plan:	ESOP Stock Plan:	Profit Sharing:	Top Exec. Salary: $923,911	Bonus: $1,772,856
Savings Plan: Y	Stock Purch. Plan:		Second Exec. Salary: $750,000	Bonus: $1,127,025

OTHER THOUGHTS:

Apparent Women Officers or Directors: 3
Hot Spot for Advancement for Women/Minorities: Y

LOCATIONS: ("Y" = Yes)

West:	Southwest:	Midwest:	Southeast:	Northeast:	International:
Y	Y	Y	Y	Y	Y

Note: Financial information, benefits and other data can change quickly and may vary from those stated here.

AFFYMETRIX INC

www.affymetrix.com

Industry Group Code: 325413 **Ranks within this company's industry group:** Sales: 1 Profits: 1

Techology:		Medical/Drugs:		Engineering:		Transportation:		Chemicals/Petrochemicals:		Specialty:	
Computers:	Y	Manufacturer:	Y	Design:		Aerospace:		Oil/Gas Products:		Special Services:	
Software:	Y	Contract Research:		Construction:		Automotive:		Chemicals:		Consulting:	
Communications:		Medical Services:		Eng. Services:		Shipping:		Oil/Chem. Svcs.:		Specialty Mgmt.:	
Electronics:		Labs:		Consulting:				Gases:		Products:	Y
Alternative Energy:		Bio. Services:	Y					Other:		Other:	

TYPES OF BUSINESS:

Chips-Genetics
DNA Array Technology
Genomics

BRANDS/DIVISIONS/AFFILIATES:

GeneChip
CustomExpress
CustomSeq
USB Corporation
Panomics, Inc.

CONTACTS:

Note: Officers with more than one job title may be intentionally listed here more than once.

Kevin M. King, CEO
Kevin M. King, Pres.
John C. Batty, CFO
Rick Runkel, General Counsel
John C. Batty, Exec. VP-Finance
Stephen P. A. Fodor, Chmn.

Phone: 408-731-5000	**Fax:** 408-731-5441
Toll-Free: 888-362-2447	
Address: 3420 Central Expwy., Santa Clara, CA 95051 US	

GROWTH PLANS/SPECIAL FEATURES:

Affymetrix, Inc. develops, manufactures, sells and services consumables and systems for genetic analysis in the life sciences and clinical healthcare markets. The firm sells its products directly to pharmaceutical, biotechnology, agrichemical, diagnostics and consumer products companies, as well as academic research centers, government research laboratories, private foundation laboratories and clinical reference laboratories, in North America and Europe. The company also sells its products through life science supply specialists acting as authorized distributors in Latin America, India and the Middle East and Asia Pacific regions. Affymetrix markets products for two principal applications: monitoring of gene or exon expression levels and investigation of genetic variation. Its catalogue GeneChip expression arrays are available for the study of human, rat, mouse and a range of other mammalian and model organisms. Human, mouse and rat exon analysis arrays are also available. The firm's integrated GeneChip microarray platform includes disposable DNA probe arrays consisting of nucleic acid sequences set out in an ordered, high density pattern; certain reagents for use with the probe arrays; a scanner and other instruments used to process the probe arrays; and software to analyze and manage genomic or genetic information obtained from the probe arrays. Additionally, the company markets CustomExpress and CustomSeq products, which enable its customers to design their own custom GeneChip expression arrays or a sequence of arrays for organisms of interest to them. In January 2008, Affymetrix acquired USB Corporation, an Ohio-based developer of molecular biology and biochemical reagent products. In December 2008, Affymetrix acquired Panomics, Inc., a provider of assay products for a variety of low- to mid-plex genetic, protein and cellular analysis applications.

Affymetrix offers its employees a tuition assistance plan, health fitness membership discounts, a lunch program, a family resources program, domestic partner benefits, reimbursement accounts and medical, dental, vision, life and disability insurance.

FINANCIALS:

Sales and profits are in thousands of dollars—add 000 to get the full amount. 2008 Note: Financial information for 2008 was not available for all companies at press time.

2008 Sales: $410,249	2008 Profits: $-307,919	**U.S. Stock Ticker: AFFX**
2007 Sales: $371,320	2007 Profits: $12,593	**Int'l Ticker:** Int'l Exchange:
2006 Sales: $355,317	2006 Profits: $-13,704	Employees: 1,128
2005 Sales: $367,602	2005 Profits: $65,787	Fiscal Year Ends: 12/31
2004 Sales: $345,962	2004 Profits: $47,608	Parent Company:

SALARIES/BENEFITS:

Pension Plan:	ESOP Stock Plan:	Profit Sharing:	Top Exec. Salary: $630,673	Bonus: $635,000
Savings Plan: Y	Stock Purch. Plan:		Second Exec. Salary: $432,692	Bonus: $500,000

OTHER THOUGHTS:

Apparent Women Officers or Directors: 1
Hot Spot for Advancement for Women/Minorities: Y

LOCATIONS: ("Y" = Yes)

West:	Southwest:	Midwest:	Southeast:	Northeast:	International:
Y					Y

AGFA-GEVAERT NV

www.agfa.com

Industry Group Code: 333314 **Ranks within this company's industry group:** Sales: 4 Profits: 3

Techology:		Medical/Drugs:		Engineering:		Transportation:		Chemicals/Petrochemicals:		Specialty:	
Computers:	Y	Manufacturer:		Design:		Aerospace:		Oil/Gas Products:		Special Services:	
Software:		Contract Research:		Construction:		Automotive:		Chemicals:		Consulting:	
Communications:		Medical Services:		Eng. Services:		Shipping:		Oil/Chem. Svcs.:		Specialty Mgmt.:	
Electronics:		Labs:		Consulting:				Gases:		Products:	
Alternative Energy:		Bio. Services:						Other:		Other:	

TYPES OF BUSINESS:

Imaging Equipment
Commercial Printing Equipment & Products
Image Publishing Software
Consumer Photographic Products
Medical Imaging Systems
X-Ray Films

BRANDS/DIVISIONS/AFFILIATES:

Agfa Graphics
Agfa HealthCare
Agfa Materials

CONTACTS: *Note: Officers with more than one job title may be intentionally listed here more than once.*

Jo Cornu, CEO
Jo Cornu, Pres.
Kris Hoornaert, CFO
Werner Vanderhaege, General Counsel/Corp. Sec.
Albert Follens, VP
Luc Delagaye, Pres., Agfa Materials
Christian Reinaudo, Pres., Agfa HealthCare
Stefaan Vanhooren, Pres., Agfa Graphics
Julien De Wilde, Chmn.

Phone: 32-3-444-2111 **Fax:** 32-3-444-4485
Toll-Free:
Address: Septestraat 27, Mortsel, B-2640 Belgium

GROWTH PLANS/SPECIAL FEATURES:

Agfa-Gevaert N.V. (Agfa) is a leading imaging equipment company that develops, produces and markets analog and digital systems, and IT solutions, primarily for the printing industry and the healthcare sector. Agfa has three main divisions: Agfa Graphics, Agfa HealthCare, and Agfa Materials. The Graphics division provides pre-press services for printing, such as scanning images and designing layouts for anything from books and magazines to billboards and CDs. In addition, the company's commercial printing systems provide commercial, newspaper and packaging printers including computer-to-film and computer-to-plate systems, as well as equipment and consumables. Agfa also supplies digital proofing systems, large-format printing, digital inkjet presses and the professional software that controls the entire prepress process. As the first company to provide X-ray films to the market, Agfa HealthCare has grown to supply both analog and digital imaging solutions as well as diagnosis and communications equipment. The company's digital networks and information systems streamline the distribution, storage and management of digital images and optimize the workflow of the entire hospital organization. The Agfa Materials division provides film-based products for the business-to-business market, such as motion picture film, microfilm, and film for non-destructive testing. The company also provides solutions for aerial photography, printed circuit boards, identification cards and many other applications.

FINANCIALS: Sales and profits are in thousands of dollars—add 000 to get the full amount. 2008 Note: Financial information for 2008 was not available for all companies at press time.

2008 Sales: $4,024,800	2008 Profits: $-221,680	**U.S. Stock Ticker:**
2007 Sales: $4,357,990	2007 Profits: $55,750	**Int'l Ticker: AGFB** Int'l Exchange: Brussels-Euronext
2006 Sales: $4,486,900	2006 Profits: $19,800	Employees: 14,014
2005 Sales: $4,003,052	2005 Profits: $-21,774	Fiscal Year Ends: 10/31
2004 Sales: $4,552,104	2004 Profits: $-174,194	Parent Company:

SALARIES/BENEFITS:

Pension Plan:	ESOP Stock Plan:	Profit Sharing:	Top Exec. Salary: $173,052	Bonus: $6,000
Savings Plan:	Stock Purch. Plan:		Second Exec. Salary: $164,023	Bonus: $115,269

OTHER THOUGHTS:

Apparent Women Officers or Directors:
Hot Spot for Advancement for Women/Minorities:

LOCATIONS: ("Y" = Yes)

West:	Southwest:	Midwest:	Southeast:	Northeast:	International:
		Y		Y	Y

Note: Financial information, benefits and other data can change quickly and may vary from those stated here.

AGILENT TECHNOLOGIES INC

www.agilent.com

Industry Group Code: 334500 **Ranks within this company's industry group:** Sales: 2 Profits: 2

Techology:		Medical/Drugs:		Engineering:		Transportation:		Chemicals/Petrochemicals:		Specialty:	
Computers:		Manufacturer:	Y	Design:		Aerospace:		Oil/Gas Products:		Special Services:	
Software:	Y	Contract Research:		Construction:		Automotive:		Chemicals:		Consulting:	
Communications:	Y	Medical Services:		Eng. Services:		Shipping:		Oil/Chem. Svcs.:		Specialty Mgmt.:	
Electronics:	Y	Labs:	Y	Consulting:				Gases:		Products:	Y
Alternative Energy:		Bio. Services:						Other:		Other:	

TYPES OF BUSINESS:

Test Equipment
Communications Test Equipment
Integrated Circuits Test Equipment
Optoelectronics Test Equipment
Image Sensors
Bioinstrumentation
Software Products
Informatics Products

BRANDS/DIVISIONS/AFFILIATES:

Agilent Technologies Laboratories
Particle Sizing Systems
RVM Scientific Inc
TILL Photonics GmbH
Stratagene Corp.

CONTACTS: *Note: Officers with more than one job title may be intentionally listed here more than once.*

William P. Sullivan, CEO
William P. Sullivan, Pres.
Adrian T. Dillon, CFO
Jean M. Halloran, Sr. VP-Human Resources
Darlene J. S. Solomon, CTO/VP-Agilent Laboratories
Adrian T. Dillon, Exec. VP-Admin.
D. Craig Nordlund, General Counsel/Sec./Sr. VP
Amy Flores, Mgr.-Public Rel.
Rodney Gonsalves, Dir.-Investor Rel.
Adrian T. Dillon, Exec. VP-Finance
Gooi Soon Chai, VP/Gen. Mgr.-Electronic Instruments
Ron Nersesian, VP/Gen. Mgr.-Wireless
Nick Roelofs, VP/Gen. Mgr.-Life Sciences Solutions
David Churchill, VP/Gen. Mgr.-Network & Digital Solutions
James G. Cullen, Chmn.

Phone: 408-345-8886 **Fax:** 408-345-8474
Toll-Free: 877-424-4536
Address: 5301 Stevens Creek Blvd., Santa Clara, CA 95051 US

GROWTH PLANS/SPECIAL FEATURES:

Agilent Technologies, Inc. is a diversified technology company with two main business segments: Electronic Measurement and Bio-analytical Measurement. The Electronic Measurement business operates in two markets. Its products for the communications testing market include testing equipment for fiber optic networks; broadband and data networks; and wireless communications and microwave networks. It also assists in installing, activating and maintaining optical, wireless, wireline and large-company networks. Supplying the aerospace, defense, computer and semiconductor industries, its offerings for the general purpose testing market include general purpose instruments, including voltmeters and signal generators; modular instruments and test software used as reconfigurable testing platforms; digital design products, including complex high-speed servers and logic analyzers; high-frequency electronic design automation software tools used to construct computer simulations; parametric test instruments and systems for semiconductor wafers; and electronic manufacturing test products such as automated x-ray inspection and in-circuit testing products. The Bio-analytical Measurement business serves two main life sciences markets: Pharmaceuticals, biotech, contract research and contract manufacturing; and academic and government institutions. It also serves five main chemical analysis markets: petroleum and chemicals; the environment; forensics and homeland security; bio-agriculture and food safety; and materials science. Its main product categories are gas chromatography, liquid chromatography, mass spectrometry, microfluidics, microarrays, atomic force microscopy, PCR (Polymerase Chain Reaction) instrumentation, software and informatics. It also supplies consumables and related bioagents. Agilent conducts centralized research for both segments through Agilent Technologies Laboratories, based in Santa Clara, California. In 2008, the company acquired Particle Sizing Systems, a particle measuring instruments manufacturer; RVM Scientific Inc, a manufacturer of direct heating/cooling systems for gas chromatography capillary columns; and TILL Photonics GmbH, a developer and manufacturer of microscopy products.

Employees are offered medical, dental and vision insurance; life insurance; disability coverage; an employee and family assistance plan; and adoption assistance.

FINANCIALS: Sales and profits are in thousands of dollars—add 000 to get the full amount. 2008 Note: Financial information for 2008 was not available for all companies at press time.

2008 Sales: $5,774,000	2008 Profits: $693,000	**U.S. Stock Ticker: A**
2007 Sales: $5,420,000	2007 Profits: $638,000	**Int'l Ticker:** Int'l Exchange:
2006 Sales: $4,973,000	2006 Profits: $3,307,000	Employees: 19,400
2005 Sales: $4,685,000	2005 Profits: $327,000	Fiscal Year Ends: 10/31
2004 Sales: $4,556,000	2004 Profits: $369,000	Parent Company:

SALARIES/BENEFITS:

Pension Plan: Y	ESOP Stock Plan:	Profit Sharing:	Top Exec. Salary: $986,667	Bonus: $1,305,563
Savings Plan: Y	Stock Purch. Plan: Y		Second Exec. Salary: $699,996	Bonus: $627,775

OTHER THOUGHTS:

Apparent Women Officers or Directors: 3
Hot Spot for Advancement for Women/Minorities: Y

LOCATIONS: ("Y" = Yes)

West:	Southwest:	Midwest:	Southeast:	Northeast:	International:
Y				Y	Y

Note: Financial information, benefits and other data can change quickly and may vary from those stated here.

AIR PRODUCTS & CHEMICALS INC

www.airproducts.com

Industry Group Code: 325120 **Ranks within this company's industry group:** Sales: 1 Profits: 1

Techology:		Medical/Drugs:		Engineering:		Transportation:		Chemicals/Petrochemicals:		Specialty:	
Computers:		Manufacturer:	Y	Design:		Aerospace:		Oil/Gas Products:		Special Services:	Y
Software:		Contract Research:		Construction:		Automotive:		Chemicals:	Y	Consulting:	
Communications:		Medical Services:	Y	Eng. Services:		Shipping:		Oil/Chem. Svcs.:	Y	Specialty Mgmt.:	
Electronics:		Labs:		Consulting:				Gases:	Y	Products:	
Alternative Energy:		Bio. Services:						Other:		Other:	

TYPES OF BUSINESS:

Industrial Gases & Chemicals
Respiratory Therapy & Home Medical Equipment
Specialty Resins
Hydrogen Refinery
Natural Gas Liquefaction
Semiconductor Materials

BRANDS/DIVISIONS/AFFILIATES:

Air Products Asia
Air Products Europe
Air Products Japan
Harvest Energy Technology Inc
Goar Allison & Associates Inc
CryoService Limited

CONTACTS: *Note: Officers with more than one job title may be intentionally listed here more than once.*

John McGlade, CEO
John McGlade, Pres.
Paul Huck, CFO/Sr. VP
Lynn Minella, Sr. VP-Human Resources & Comm.
Stephen Jones, General Counsel/Corp. Sec./Sr. VP
Nelson Squires, Dir.-Investor Rel.
Michael Crocco, Controller/VP
Scott Sherman, VP-Tonnage Gases, Equipment & Energy
Robert Dixon, Sr. VP/Gen Mgr.-Merchant Gases
Patricia A. Mattimore, VP/Gen. Mgr.-Performance Materials
John Marsland, VP-Bus. Svcs.
John McGlade, Chmn.

Phone: 610-481-4911	**Fax:** 610-481-5900
Toll-Free:	
Address: 7201 Hamilton Blvd., Allentown, PA 18195-1501 US	

GROWTH PLANS/SPECIAL FEATURES:

Air Products and Chemicals, Inc. serves global technology, energy, industrial and healthcare customers. Products and services include atmospheric gases; process and specialty gases; performance materials; and equipment and services. The company is one of the world's largest suppliers of hydrogen and helium and has built leading positions in growth markets such as semiconductor materials, refinery hydrogen, natural gas liquefaction, and advanced coatings and adhesives. The firm conducts business under four segments: merchant gasses; tonnage gases; electronics and performance materials; and equipment. The merchant gasses segment sells industrial gases such as oxygen, nitrogen, argon, hydrogen and helium, as well as certain medical and specialty gases. The segment also includes healthcare products such as respiratory therapies, home medical equipment and infusion services. These products are provided to patients in their homes, primarily in Europe. Tonnage gases provides hydrogen, carbon monoxide, nitrogen, oxygen and syngas, primarily to the petroleum refining, chemical and metallurgical industries worldwide. Electronics and performance materials provides solutions to a broad range of global industries through chemical synthesis, analytical technology, process engineering and surface science. The equipment and energy segment designs and manufactures cryogenic and gas processing equipment for air separation; hydrocarbon recovery; and purification, natural gas liquefaction and helium distribution. The company has majority or wholly-owned foreign subsidiaries that operate in Canada, 17 European countries, 10 Asian countries and four Latin American countries. International subsidiaries include Air Products Asia, Air Products Europe and Air Products Japan. Recent acquisitions include Harvest Energy Technology, Inc. a developer of hydrogen generation technology; Goar, Allison & Associates Inc, a process engineering company, and a majority interest in CryoService Limited.

Employees are offered medical and dental coverage; life insurance; disability insurance; educational assistance; flexible spending accounts; access to an onsite fitness center; credit union membership; discounts on personal purchases; and an onsite health unit.

FINANCIALS: Sales and profits are in thousands of dollars—add 000 to get the full amount. 2008 Note: Financial information for 2008 was not available for all companies at press time.

2008 Sales: $10,415,000	2008 Profits: $910,000	**U.S. Stock Ticker: APD**
2007 Sales: $9,148,000	2007 Profits: $1,036,000	**Int'l Ticker:** Int'l Exchange:
2006 Sales: $7,885,000	2006 Profits: $723,400	Employees: 21,100
2005 Sales: $7,673,000	2005 Profits: $711,700	Fiscal Year Ends: 9/30
2004 Sales: $7,031,900	2004 Profits: $604,100	Parent Company:

SALARIES/BENEFITS:

Pension Plan: Y	ESOP Stock Plan:	Profit Sharing: Y	Top Exec. Salary: $1,000,000	Bonus: $2,002,000
Savings Plan: Y	Stock Purch. Plan:		Second Exec. Salary: $575,000	Bonus: $696,000

OTHER THOUGHTS:

Apparent Women Officers or Directors: 5
Hot Spot for Advancement for Women/Minorities: Y

LOCATIONS: ("Y" = Yes)

West:	Southwest:	Midwest:	Southeast:	Northeast:	International:
Y	Y	Y	Y	Y	Y

AIRBUS SAS

www.airbus.com/en

Industry Group Code: 336410 **Ranks within this company's industry group:** Sales: Profits:

Techology:		Medical/Drugs:		Engineering:		Transportation:		Chemicals/Petrochemicals:		Specialty:	
Computers:		Manufacturer:		Design:		Aerospace:	Y	Oil/Gas Products:		Special Services:	
Software:		Contract Research:		Construction:		Automotive:		Chemicals:		Consulting:	
Communications:		Medical Services:		Eng. Services:		Shipping:		Oil/Chem. Svcs.:		Specialty Mgmt.:	
Electronics:		Labs:		Consulting:				Gases:		Products:	
Alternative Energy:		Bio. Services:						Other:		Other:	

TYPES OF BUSINESS:

Aircraft Manufacturer
Commercial Aircraft
Military Aircraft

BRANDS/DIVISIONS/AFFILIATES:

Airbus China
EADS
Airbus North America
Airbus Japan
A330
A380
A350 XWB
A400M

CONTACTS: *Note: Officers with more than one job title may be intentionally listed here more than once.*

Thomas Enders, CEO
Fabrice Bregier, COO
Thomas Enders, Pres.
Harald Wilhelm, CFO
Thierry Baril, Exec. VP-Human Resources
Patrick Gavin, Exec. VP-Eng.
Gerald Weber, Exec. VP-Oper.
John Leahy, COO-Customers
Tom Williams, Exec. VP-Programmes
Glen S. Fukushima, CEO/Pres., Airbus Japan K.K.
Allan McArtor, Chmn.- Airbus Americas, Inc.
Laurence Barron, Pres., Airbus China
Klaus Richter, Exec. VP-Procurement

Phone: 33-5-61-93-33-33 **Fax:** 33-5-61-93-49-55
Toll-Free:
Address: 1 Rond Point Maurice Bellonte, Blagnac, 31707 France

GROWTH PLANS/SPECIAL FEATURES:

Airbus SAS, a subsidiary of European Aeronautic Defense and Space Company (EADS), competes head-to-head with Boeing in the commercial aircraft sector. Airbus's single-aisle and wide-body jets have capacities ranging from 100 to over 500 passengers. The firm maintains 160 field sites around the globe, 16 production facilities in Europe, engineering and sales locations in North America, sales and customer support centers in Japan and China and a joint engineering center in Russia with Kaskol. Subsidiaries include Airbus North America, Airbus China and Airbus Japan. The firm also holds a 64% share in Airbus Military SL, a company responsible for the A400M, a military aircraft used in nine countries. The firm's A380 jumbo jet model, with 525 seats, burns 17% less fuel per seat than today's largest aircraft. The craft is also significantly quieter than other large aircraft. The A350 XWB, an extra wide body plane designed to compete with the new high-efficiency Boeing 787, is slated for availability in 2013, has seating capacities ranging from 270-350. Airbus recently announced plans to cut 10,000 European jobs by 2011. In February 2009, the company introduced a new freight and cargo business unit to house its freighter aircraft production and to support the passenger-to-cargo conversions of its jetliners. The firm recently signed a lucrative $35 billion contract with the U.S. Air Force for the production of 179 KC-45A tankers, replacing the military's KC-135 aircraft that have performed the country's vital military air-to-air refueling missions for more than 40 years.

There are 85 different nationalities represented and over 20 languages spoken among Airbus employees. English is the company's working language.

FINANCIALS: Sales and profits are in thousands of dollars—add 000 to get the full amount. 2008 Note: Financial information for 2008 was not available for all companies at press time.

2008 Sales: $	2008 Profits: $	**U.S. Stock Ticker: Subsidiary**
2007 Sales: $	2007 Profits: $	**Int'l Ticker:** Int'l Exchange:
2006 Sales: $35,528,500	2006 Profits: $	Employees: 47,600
2005 Sales: $28,642,457	2005 Profits: $	Fiscal Year Ends: 12/31
2004 Sales: $27,280,000	2004 Profits: $	Parent Company: EUROPEAN AERONAUTIC DEFENSE AND SPACE CO (EADS)

SALARIES/BENEFITS:

Pension Plan:	ESOP Stock Plan:	Profit Sharing:	Top Exec. Salary: $	Bonus: $
Savings Plan:	Stock Purch. Plan:		Second Exec. Salary: $	Bonus: $

OTHER THOUGHTS:

Apparent Women Officers or Directors:
Hot Spot for Advancement for Women/Minorities:

LOCATIONS: ("Y" = Yes)

West:	Southwest:	Midwest:	Southeast:	Northeast:	International:
		Y	Y	Y	Y

Note: Financial information, benefits and other data can change quickly and may vary from those stated here.

AISIN SEIKI CO LTD

www.aisin.co.jp

Industry Group Code: 336300 **Ranks within this company's industry group:** Sales: 3 Profits: 5

Techology:		Medical/Drugs:		Engineering:		Transportation:		Chemicals/Petrochemicals:		Specialty:	
Computers:		Manufacturer:		Design:		Aerospace:		Oil/Gas Products:		Special Services:	
Software:		Contract Research:		Construction:		Automotive:	Y	Chemicals:		Consulting:	
Communications:		Medical Services:		Eng. Services:		Shipping:		Oil/Chem. Svcs.:		Specialty Mgmt.:	
Electronics:		Labs:		Consulting:				Gases:		Products:	
Alternative Energy:		Bio. Services:						Other:		Other:	

TYPES OF BUSINESS:

Automobile Parts Manufacturing
Sewing & Embroidery Machines
Air Conditioners
Hospital & Biotechnology Equipment
Lasers & Laser Imaging Technology

BRANDS/DIVISIONS/AFFILIATES:

Aisin Kyushu Casting Co., Ltd.
Toyota Motor Corporation

CONTACTS:

Note: Officers with more than one job title may be intentionally listed here more than once.

Yasuhito Yamauchi, Pres.
Norio Oku, Exec. VP
Shunichi Nakamura, Exec. VP
Fumio Fujimori, Exec. VP
Takeshi Kawata, Exec. VP
Kanshiro Toyoda, Chmn.

Phone: 81-566-24-8441	**Fax:** 81-566-24-8817
Toll-Free:	
Address: 2-1, Asahi-machi, Kariya, 448-8650 Japan	

GROWTH PLANS/SPECIAL FEATURES:

Aisin Seiki Co., Ltd., an affiliate of Toyota Motor, primarily manufactures auto parts. It operates through three business units: Automotive parts and systems; life and energy products; and new business areas. The automotive unit, which generated almost 96% of the firm's 2008 sales, manufactures drivetrain, brake, chassis, body and engine products. Specific products include transmissions, clutches, suspension systems, power seats, oil pumps and exhaust manifolds. This unit also produces information products, such as parking assist systems, lane departure warning systems, front and side monitors, GPS antenna and daytime running light computers; and casting products, such as cast iron, resin moldings and aluminum die cast products. Its customers include Japanese manufacturers Toyota, Suzuki, Mitsubishi, Isuzu, Yamaha, Honda, Nissan and Mazda, as well as Daimler, Chrysler, GM, Ford, Volvo, Hyundai/Kia, Audi and BMW. The company also sells its automotive parts as aftermarket products. The life and energy products unit manufactures life and amenity related products, including home sewing and embroidery machines; energy system products, such as air conditioners and vacuum devices; and welfare products including reclining beds, electric wheelchairs and electric lifters. Lastly, the new business areas unit develops the firm's automotive experience into new areas, including fiber optic lasers, biotechnology and laser imaging technology. During 2008, drivetrain products generated 43.4% of sales; brake & chassis products, 19.8%; body products, 17.7%; engine products, 9.6%; information products, 5.4%; and other, including life & energy products, 4.1%. Aisin has 75 consolidated subsidiaries in Japan and 84 outside of Japan, mainly in North America and Asia, with additional locations in Europe, South America and Australia. Aisin has developed what it calls its Fourth Environmental Action Plan, being implemented from 2007-2011, to bring the company closer to its zero emissions goal. In August 2007, the firm established Aisin Kyushu Casting Co., Ltd., to produce engine components.

FINANCIALS:

Sales and profits are in thousands of dollars—add 000 to get the full amount. 2008 Note: Financial information for 2008 was not available for all companies at press time.

2008 Sales: $27,327,200	2008 Profits: $927,510	**U.S. Stock Ticker:**
2007 Sales: $23,786,100	2007 Profits: $668,900	**Int'l Ticker: 7259** Int'l Exchange: Tokyo-TSE
2006 Sales: $21,205,900	2006 Profits: $611,000	Employees: 61,300
2005 Sales: $18,290,700	2005 Profits: $467,200	Fiscal Year Ends: 3/31
2004 Sales: $15,195,300	2004 Profits: $328,700	Parent Company:

SALARIES/BENEFITS:

Pension Plan:	ESOP Stock Plan:	Profit Sharing:	Top Exec. Salary: $	Bonus: $
Savings Plan:	Stock Purch. Plan:		Second Exec. Salary: $	Bonus: $

OTHER THOUGHTS:

Apparent Women Officers or Directors:
Hot Spot for Advancement for Women/Minorities:

LOCATIONS: ("Y" = Yes)

West:	Southwest:	Midwest:	Southeast:	Northeast:	International:
					Y

AKZO NOBEL NV

www.akzonobel.com

Industry Group Code: 325000 **Ranks within this company's industry group:** Sales: 6 Profits: 6

Techology:		Medical/Drugs:		Engineering:		Transportation:		Chemicals/Petrochemicals:		Specialty:	
Computers:		Manufacturer:	Y	Design:		Aerospace:		Oil/Gas Products:		Special Services:	
Software:		Contract Research:		Construction:		Automotive:		Chemicals:	Y	Consulting:	
Communications:		Medical Services:		Eng. Services:		Shipping:		Oil/Chem. Svcs.:		Specialty Mgmt.:	
Electronics:		Labs:	Y	Consulting:				Gases:		Products:	
Alternative Energy:		Bio. Services:						Other:		Other:	

TYPES OF BUSINESS:

Specialty Chemicals
Coatings
Decorative Paints

BRANDS/DIVISIONS/AFFILIATES:

Imperial Chemical Industries PLC
Nippon Kayaku, Kayaku Akzo Co Ltd
LII Europe
Sikkens
Dulux
Hammerite

CONTACTS: *Note: Officers with more than one job title may be intentionally listed here more than once.*

Hanz Wijers, CEO
Keith Nichols, CFO
Jennifer Midura, Dir.-Corp. Strategy
Leif Darner, Mgr.-Performance Coatings
Rob Frohn, Mgr.-Specialty Chemicals
Tex Gunning, Dir.-Decorative Paints
Maarten van den Bergh, Chmn.

Phone: 31-20-502-7555 **Fax:** 31-20-502-7666
Toll-Free:
Address: Strawinskylaan 2555, Amsterdam, 1077 ZZ The Netherlands

GROWTH PLANS/SPECIAL FEATURES:

Akzo Nobel N.V. produces paints, coatings and chemicals, and operates in over 80 countries. The company's operations are divided into three segments: Decorative Paints, Performance Coatings and Specialty Chemicals. The Decorative Paints division includes paint, lacquer and varnish products, as well as adhesives, and floor leveling compounds. Brands consist of Sikkens, Dulux and Hammerite. The segment has offices in the U.K., Continental Europe, the Americas and Asia. Akzo Nobel's Performance Coatings division makes a variety of chemical products including powder, wood, coil, and marine coatings; tile and wood adhesives; and a line of car refinishes. The company's Specialty Chemicals division produces pulp and paper chemicals; polymer chemicals such as metal alkyls and suspending agents; surfactants used in hair and skincare products; base chemicals such as salt and chlor-alkali products used in the manufacture of glass and plastics; and functional chemicals used in toothpaste, ice cream and flame retardants. In April 2008, the company sold its Adhesives and Electronic Materials business. In December of the same year, Akzo Nobel acquired a 75% stake in Kayaku Akzo Co. Ltd., its Japanese joint venture with Nippon Kayaku. In January 2009, the firm acquired LII Europe.

FINANCIALS: **Sales and profits are in thousands of dollars—add 000 to get the full amount. 2008 Note: Financial information for 2008 was not available for all companies at press time.**

2008 Sales: $20,387,300
2007 Sales: $18,481,000
2006 Sales: $15,836,300
2005 Sales: $20,540,000
2004 Sales: $17,187,000

2008 Profits: $981,340
2007 Profits: $12,770,600
2006 Profits: $1,821,700
2005 Profits: $1,518,400
2004 Profits: $1,159,000

U.S. Stock Ticker:
Int'l Ticker: AKZA Int'l Exchange: Amsterdam-Euronext
Employees: 42,600
Fiscal Year Ends: 12/31
Parent Company:

SALARIES/BENEFITS:

Pension Plan: ESOP Stock Plan: Profit Sharing: Top Exec. Salary: $ Bonus: $
Savings Plan: Stock Purch. Plan: Second Exec. Salary: $ Bonus: $

OTHER THOUGHTS:

Apparent Women Officers or Directors: 2
Hot Spot for Advancement for Women/Minorities:

LOCATIONS: ("Y" = Yes)

West:	Southwest:	Midwest:	Southeast:	Northeast:	International:
		Y	Y	Y	Y

ALBANY MOLECULAR RESEARCH

www.amriglobal.com

Industry Group Code: 541710 **Ranks within this company's industry group:** Sales: 4 Profits: 4

Techology:		Medical/Drugs:		Engineering:		Transportation:		Chemicals/Petrochemicals:		Specialty:	
Computers:		Manufacturer:	Y	Design:		Aerospace:		Oil/Gas Products:		Special Services:	
Software:		Contract Research:	Y	Construction:		Automotive:		Chemicals:	Y	Consulting:	
Communications:		Medical Services:		Eng. Services:		Shipping:		Oil/Chem. Svcs.:		Specialty Mgmt.:	
Electronics:		Labs:	Y	Consulting:				Gases:		Products:	
Alternative Energy:		Bio. Services:	Y					Other:		Other:	

TYPES OF BUSINESS:

Contract Drug Discovery & Development
Custom Biotech & Genomic Research
Chemistry Research
Manufacturing Services
Consulting Services
Analytical Chemistry Services

BRANDS/DIVISIONS/AFFILIATES:

CONTACTS: *Note: Officers with more than one job title may be intentionally listed here more than once.*

Thomas E. D'Ambra, CEO
Thomas E. D'Ambra, Pres.
Mark T. Frost, CFO
W. Steven (Steve) Jennings, Sr. VP-Sales & Mktg.
Brian D. Russell, VP-Human Resources
Bruce J. Sargent, VP-Discovery R&D
Harold Meckler, VP-Science & Tech.
Steven R. Hagen, VP-Pharmaceutical Dev. & Mfg.
W. Steven (Steve) Jennings, Sr. VP-Bus. Dev.
Peter Jerome, Dir.-Investor Rel.
Mark T. Frost, Treas.
Michael P. Trova, Sr. VP-Chemistry
Richard A. Saffee, Gen. Mgr.-Large Scale Mfg.
Thomas E. D'Ambra, Chmn.
Michael D. Ironside, Dir.-Global Project Mgmt.

Phone: 518-464-0279 **Fax:** 518-512-2020
Toll-Free:
Address: 21 Corporate Cir., P.O. Box 15098, Albany, NY 12212-5098 US

GROWTH PLANS/SPECIAL FEATURES:

Albany Molecular Research, Inc. (AMRI) is a chemistry-based drug discovery and development company, focusing on applications for new small-molecule and prescription drugs. It derives revenue from discovering then licensing new compounds with commercial potential for service fees, milestone and royalty payments. Some of the products of this research led to the development of the active ingredient (fexofenadine HCl) for a non-sedating antihistamine marketed by Sanofi-Aventis S.A. as Allegra in the U.S. and as Telfast outside the U.S. Since its launch in 1995, AMRI has earned more than $367.3 million in royalty and milestone revenue from this product. The firm has also licensed the rights to develop and commercialize two chemicals (amine neurotransmitter reuptake inhibitors) from Bristol-Myers Squibb Company (BMS). In addition to developing its own drugs, AMRI has increasingly acted as a custom research and development source for the pharmaceutical, genomic and biotechnology industries. It provides contract services across the entire product development cycle, from lead discovery to commercial manufacturing. The company's services allow pharmaceutical companies to outsource their chemistry departments in order to pursue a greater number of drug discovery and development opportunities. An integral part of these contract operations consists of several facilities in India and Singapore, which were launched as part of a strategic move to globalize its services. The firm also has domestic research facilities in Albany, Syracuse and Rensselaer, New York as well as in Bothell, Washington. In February 2008, AMRI acquired a custom pilot scale intermediaries manufacturing firm, FineKem Laboratories Pvt. Limited, based in Aurangabad, India. In June 2008, the first BMS-licensed chemical, indicated for treating depression, entered Phase I clinical trials in Canada. In September 2008, the second chemical, a novel cancer treatment, entered preclinical trials, and subsequent positive test results moved the chemical into Phase I trials by October 2008.

FINANCIALS: Sales and profits are in thousands of dollars—add 000 to get the full amount. 2008 Note: Financial information for 2008 was not available for all companies at press time.

2008 Sales: $229,260 | 2008 Profits: $20,560
2007 Sales: $192,511 | 2007 Profits: $8,936
2006 Sales: $179,807 | 2006 Profits: $2,183
2005 Sales: $183,906 | 2005 Profits: $16,321
2004 Sales: $169,527 | 2004 Profits: $-11,691

U.S. Stock Ticker: AMRI
Int'l Ticker: Int'l Exchange:
Employees: 1,357
Fiscal Year Ends: 12/31
Parent Company:

SALARIES/BENEFITS:

Pension Plan: | ESOP Stock Plan: | Profit Sharing: | Top Exec. Salary: $416,514 | Bonus: $30,660
Savings Plan: Y | Stock Purch. Plan: Y | | Second Exec. Salary: $293,808 | Bonus: $39,390

OTHER THOUGHTS:

Apparent Women Officers or Directors: 2
Hot Spot for Advancement for Women/Minorities:

LOCATIONS: ("Y" = Yes)

West:	Southwest:	Midwest:	Southeast:	Northeast:	International:
Y				Y	Y

ALCATEL-LUCENT

www.alcatel-lucent.com

Industry Group Code: 334210 **Ranks within this company's industry group:** Sales: 1 Profits: 9

Techology:		Medical/Drugs:		Engineering:		Transportation:		Chemicals/Petrochemicals:		Specialty:	
Computers:		Manufacturer:		Design:		Aerospace:		Oil/Gas Products:		Special Services:	Y
Software:		Contract Research:		Construction:		Automotive:		Chemicals:		Consulting:	Y
Communications:	Y	Medical Services:		Eng. Services:		Shipping:		Oil/Chem. Svcs.:		Specialty Mgmt.:	
Electronics:		Labs:		Consulting:				Gases:		Products:	
Alternative Energy:		Bio. Services:						Other:		Other:	

TYPES OF BUSINESS:

Telecommunications Equipment Manufacturer
Telecommunications Software & Information Systems
Digital Switching Equipment
Optical Networking Equipment
Cable & Fiber Manufacturing
Mobile Messaging & Payment Solutions
Satellite Manufacturing
Consulting Services

BRANDS/DIVISIONS/AFFILIATES:

Lucent Technologies Inc
Motive Inc
CDMA2000
WiMAX
Bell Labs
Alcatel USA Inc
Thales SA

CONTACTS: *Note: Officers with more than one job title may be intentionally listed here more than once.*

Ben Verwaayen, CEO
Paul Tufano, CFO
Tim Krause, Chief Mktg. Officer
Claire Pedini, Sr. VP-Human Resources
Martin Lehnich, Head-IT
Steve Reynolds, General Counsel
Helle Kristoffersen, VP-Corp. Strategy
Claire Pedini, Sr. VP-Corp. Comm.
Sean Dolan, Pres., Asia Pacific & China
Robert Vrij, Pres., Americas
Michel Rahier, Head-Carrier Business Group
Andy Williams, Head-Services Business Group
Philippe Camus, Chmn.
Adolfo Hernandez, Pres., EMEA

Phone: 33-1-40-76-10-10	**Fax:** 33-1-40-76-14-00
Toll-Free:	
Address: 54 rue de la Boetie, Paris, 75008 France	

GROWTH PLANS/SPECIAL FEATURES:

Alcatel-Lucent provides solutions that enable service providers, enterprises and governments worldwide, to deliver voice, data and video communication services to end-users. As a leader in fixed, mobile and converged broadband networking, IP technologies, applications and services, Alcatel-Lucent offers end-to-end solutions that enable communications services for residential, business and mobile customers. The company has three reporting segments: Carriers, (broken up into wireline, wireless and convergence), Enterprise and Services. The wireless business group is a supplier of wireless communications solutions including CDMA2000 and GSM/EDGE for 2G; UMTS and HSPA for 3G; and LTE and WiMAX technologies for 4G. The wireline business group focuses on access, IP and optics and is a market leader in broadband access, triple play/IPTV networks and IP routing. The convergence business group offers service providers end-to-end core, multimedia and IMS solutions centered on the convergence of voice, video, wireless, wireline and data on next-generation IP networks. The Enterprise business group offers products, software and services designed for multimedia sharing through unified communications and contact centers, IP address and performance management software, IP telephony and security solutions. The Services business group supports some of the world's largest service providers with services categories including consultation, design, integration, deployment, operation and maintenance. Alcatel-Lucent runs Bell Laboratories, a leading technology development laboratory in the communications sector. Bell Laboratories also conducts research, develops prototype devices and commercializes new business concepts in nanotechnology. In October 2008, Alcatel-Lucent's subsidiary Lucent Technologies acquired Motive, Inc., a provider of service management software for broadband and mobile data services, for approximately $67.8 million. In December 2008, the company sold its stake in defense electronics firm Thales SA to Dassault Aviation, in a transaction valued at $2.24 billion.

FINANCIALS: **Sales and profits are in thousands of dollars—add 000 to get the full amount. 2008 Note: Financial information for 2008 was not available for all companies at press time.**

2008 Sales: $22,033,000	2008 Profits: $-6,710,830	**U.S. Stock Ticker: ALU**
2007 Sales: $24,350,000	2007 Profits: $-4,810,000	**Int'l Ticker: CGE** Int'l Exchange: Paris-Euronext
2006 Sales: $16,410,600	2006 Profits: $-175,040	Employees: 58,000
2005 Sales: $15,547,000	2005 Profits: $904,000	Fiscal Year Ends: 12/31
2004 Sales: $15,314,641	2004 Profits: $665,172	Parent Company:

SALARIES/BENEFITS:

Pension Plan:	ESOP Stock Plan:	Profit Sharing:	Top Exec. Salary: $	Bonus: $
Savings Plan:	Stock Purch. Plan:		Second Exec. Salary: $	Bonus: $

OTHER THOUGHTS:

Apparent Women Officers or Directors: 6
Hot Spot for Advancement for Women/Minorities: Y

LOCATIONS: ("Y" = Yes)

West:	Southwest:	Midwest:	Southeast:	Northeast:	International:
Y	Y			Y	Y

ALCON INC

www.alcon.com

Industry Group Code: 325412 **Ranks within this company's industry group:** Sales: 21 Profits: 15

Techology:		Medical/Drugs:		Engineering:		Transportation:		Chemicals/Petrochemicals:		Specialty:	
Computers:		Manufacturer:	Y	Design:		Aerospace:		Oil/Gas Products:		Special Services:	
Software:		Contract Research:		Construction:		Automotive:		Chemicals:		Consulting:	
Communications:		Medical Services:		Eng. Services:		Shipping:		Oil/Chem. Svcs.:		Specialty Mgmt.:	
Electronics:		Labs:	Y	Consulting:				Gases:		Products:	
Alternative Energy:		Bio. Services:						Other:		Other:	

TYPES OF BUSINESS:

Eye Care Products
Ophthalmic Products & Equipment
Contact Lens Care Products
Surgical Instruments

BRANDS/DIVISIONS/AFFILIATES:

Opti-Free
Patanol
AcrySof
Systane
WaveLight AG
Alcon Surgical
William C. Conner Research Center
Nestle Corporation

CONTACTS: *Note: Officers with more than one job title may be intentionally listed here more than once.*

Cary Rayment, CEO
Cary Rayment, Pres.
Richard J. Croarkin, CFO/Sr. VP
Kevin J. Buehler, Chief Mktg. Officer
Sabri Markabi, Sr. VP-R&D
Ed McGough, Sr. VP-Tech.
Ed McGough, Sr. VP-Global Mfg.
Elaine E. Whitbeck, General Counsel/Chief Legal Officer
Cary Rayment, Chmn.

Phone: 41-41-785-8888	**Fax:**
Toll-Free:	
Address: Bosch 69, Hunenberg, CH-6331 Switzerland	

GROWTH PLANS/SPECIAL FEATURES:

Alcon, Inc. is one of the world's largest eye care product companies. The firm manages its business through two business segments: Alcon United States and Alcon International. Its portfolio spans three key ophthalmic categories: pharmaceutical, surgical and consumer eye care products. The divisions develop, manufacture and market ophthalmic pharmaceuticals, surgical equipment and devices, contact lens care products and other consumer eye care products that treat diseases and conditions of the eye. Alcon maintains manufacturing plants, laboratories and offices in 75 countries and offers its products and services in over 180 countries. The firm holds approximately 4,500 global patents and 3,200 pending patent applications. The company makes more than 10,000 unique products, including prescription and over-the-counter drugs, contact lens solutions, surgical instruments, intraocular lenses and office systems for ophthalmologists. Its brand names include Patanol solution for eye allergies, AcrySof intraocular lenses, Systane lubricant drops for dry eye and the Opti-Free system for contact lens care. Alcon's research and development headquarters houses the 400,000 square-foot William C. Conner Research Center in Texas. The firm also has research and development laboratories in California, Florida, Switzerland and Spain. Alcon Surgical creates implantable lenses, viscoelastics and medical tools specifically made for ocular surgeons, including instruments for cataract removal and absorbable sutures. Sales of glaucoma products account for 35.9% of total pharmaceutical sales. Nestle Corporation owns 77% of the firm. In 2008, the firm agreed to be acquired from Nestle SA by Novartis AG for $39 billion. In September 2008, Alcon announced plans to build an additional 74,000 square foot manufacturing facility in West Virginia.

Alcon matches employee contributions to a 401(k) up to 5% of total compensation. In addition, it offers employees a retirement plan and total company combined contributions to the Alcon 401(k) and the Alcon Retirement Plan can be as much as 12%.

FINANCIALS: Sales and profits are in thousands of dollars—add 000 to get the full amount. 2008 Note: Financial information for 2008 was not available for all companies at press time.

2008 Sales: $6,294,000	2008 Profits: $2,046,000	**U.S. Stock Ticker: ACL**
2007 Sales: $5,599,600	2007 Profits: $1,586,400	**Int'l Ticker:** Int'l Exchange:
2006 Sales: $4,896,600	2006 Profits: $1,348,100	Employees: 14,500
2005 Sales: $4,368,500	2005 Profits: $931,000	Fiscal Year Ends: 12/31
2004 Sales: $3,913,600	2004 Profits: $871,800	Parent Company:

SALARIES/BENEFITS:

Pension Plan: Y	ESOP Stock Plan:	Profit Sharing:	Top Exec. Salary: $1,083,333	Bonus: $1,250,000
Savings Plan: Y	Stock Purch. Plan:		Second Exec. Salary: $627,341	Bonus: $430,000

OTHER THOUGHTS:

Apparent Women Officers or Directors: 2
Hot Spot for Advancement for Women/Minorities: Y

LOCATIONS: ("Y" = Yes)

West:	Southwest:	Midwest:	Southeast:	Northeast:	International:
Y	Y		Y		Y

ALFA SAB DE CV

www.alfa.com.mx

Industry Group Code: 325000 **Ranks within this company's industry group:** Sales: 14 Profits: 25

Techology:		Medical/Drugs:		Engineering:		Transportation:		Chemicals/Petrochemicals:		Specialty:	
Computers:		Manufacturer:		Design:		Aerospace:		Oil/Gas Products:		Special Services:	
Software:		Contract Research:		Construction:		Automotive:	Y	Chemicals:	Y	Consulting:	
Communications:	Y	Medical Services:		Eng. Services:		Shipping:		Oil/Chem. Svcs.:		Specialty Mgmt.:	
Electronics:		Labs:		Consulting:				Gases:		Products:	Y
Alternative Energy:		Bio. Services:						Other:		Other:	

TYPES OF BUSINESS:

Petrochemicals
Synthetic Fibers
Frozen Food
Aluminum Automobile Components
Telecommunications Services

BRANDS/DIVISIONS/AFFILIATES:

Alpek
Sigma
Nemak
Onexa
Braedt, S.A.

CONTACTS: *Note: Officers with more than one job title may be intentionally listed here more than once.*

Dionisio G. Medina, CEO
Alejandro M. Elizondo, CFO
Angel Casan, Dir.-Human Resources & Corp. Affairs
Armando G. Sada, Sr. VP-Dev.
Enrique F. Rodriguez, VP-Corp. Comm.
Raul G. Casas, Mgr.-Investor Rel.
Mario H. Paez, Pres., Sigma
Jose Valdez, Pres., Alpek
Manuel Rivera, Pres., Nemak
Alfonso Gonzalez, Dir.-Strategic Projects
Dionisio G. Medina, Chmn.

Phone: 52-81-8748-1111 **Fax:** 52-81-8748-2552
Toll-Free:
Address: Avenida Gomez Morin Sur 1111, Colonia Carrizalejo, San Pedro Garza Garcia, 66254 Mexico

GROWTH PLANS/SPECIAL FEATURES:

ALFA S.A.B. de C.V. is one of the world's largest producers of aluminum cylinder heads, one of the top two worldwide producers of PTA (Purified Terephthalic Acid, used to produce polyester) and one of Mexico's leaders in refrigerated and frozen food. The firm operates in four business groups: Alpek, which is engaged in the production of petrochemicals and synthetic fibers; Sigma, which offers refrigerated and frozen food; Nemak, which is engaged in the production of aluminum auto components; and Alestra, which is primarily a provider of broadband telecommunications services under the AT&T brand name. The company runs 17 production facilities in the Americas, Europe and Asia. In recent years, Nemak expanded its aluminum cylinder head operations to China. The market for its products extends to over 40 countries. The firm has alliances and joint ventures with over 20 businesses internationally, including ConAgra, Ford, BP and BASF. In May 2008, Sigma opened a processed meats plant in Seminole, Oklahoma. In July 2008, Sigma entered a definitive agreement to acquire Braedt, S.A., a Peruvian company that distributes and produces processed meats.

FINANCIALS: **Sales and profits are in thousands of dollars—add 000 to get the full amount. 2008 Note: Financial information for 2008 was not available for all companies at press time.**

2008 Sales: $10,637,000 | 2008 Profits: $-791,000
2007 Sales: $9,570,000 | 2007 Profits: $317,000
2006 Sales: $7,081,100 | 2006 Profits: $525,500
2005 Sales: $6,214,000 | 2005 Profits: $587,000
2004 Sales: $5,069,000 | 2004 Profits: $540,000

U.S. Stock Ticker:
Int'l Ticker: ALFAA Int'l Exchange: Mexico City-BMV
Employees: 50,695
Fiscal Year Ends: 12/31
Parent Company:

SALARIES/BENEFITS:

Pension Plan: ESOP Stock Plan: Profit Sharing: Top Exec. Salary: $ Bonus: $
Savings Plan: Stock Purch. Plan: Second Exec. Salary: $ Bonus: $

OTHER THOUGHTS:

Apparent Women Officers or Directors:
Hot Spot for Advancement for Women/Minorities:

LOCATIONS: ("Y" = Yes)

West:	Southwest:	Midwest:	Southeast:	Northeast:	International:
			Y	Y	Y

ALLERGAN INC

www.allergan.com

Industry Group Code: 325412 **Ranks within this company's industry group:** Sales: 25 Profits: 22

Techology:		Medical/Drugs:		Engineering:		Transportation:		Chemicals/Petrochemicals:		Specialty:	
Computers:		Manufacturer:	Y	Design:		Aerospace:		Oil/Gas Products:		Special Services:	
Software:		Contract Research:		Construction:		Automotive:		Chemicals:		Consulting:	
Communications:		Medical Services:		Eng. Services:		Shipping:		Oil/Chem. Svcs.:		Specialty Mgmt.:	
Electronics:		Labs:		Consulting:				Gases:		Products:	
Alternative Energy:		Bio. Services:						Other:		Other:	

TYPES OF BUSINESS:

Pharmaceutical Development
Eye Care Supplies
Dermatological Products
Neuromodulator Products
Obesity Intervention Products
Urologic Products
Medical Aesthetics

BRANDS/DIVISIONS/AFFILIATES:

Restasis
Lumigan
Optive
Refresh
Botox
Sanctura XR
Aczone
Spectrum Pharmaceuticals, Inc.

CONTACTS: *Note: Officers with more than one job title may be intentionally listed here more than once.*

David Pyott, CEO
F. Michael Ball, Pres.
Jeffrey L. Edwards, CFO
Dianne Dyer-Bruggeman, Exec. VP-Human Resources
Scott M. Whitcup, Exec. VP-R&D
Raymond H. Diradoorian, Exec. VP-Global Tech. Oper.
Douglas S. Ingram, Chief Admin. Officer/Chief Ethics Officer
Douglas S. Ingram, General Counsel/Corp. Sec./Exec. VP
Jeffrey L. Edwards, Exec. VP-Bus. Dev.
Jeffrey L. Edwards, Exec. VP-Finance
David Pyott, Chmn.

Phone: 714-246-4500 **Fax:** 714-246-6987
Toll-Free: 800-433-8871
Address: 2525 Dupont Dr., Irvine, CA 92612 US

GROWTH PLANS/SPECIAL FEATURES:

Allergan, Inc. is a technology-driven global health care company that develops and commercializes specialty pharmaceutical products, biologics and medical devices for the ophthalmic, neurological, medical aesthetics, medical dermatology, breast aesthetics, obesity intervention, urological and other specialty markets in more than 100 countries. The company focuses on treatments for chronic dry eye, glaucoma, retinal disease, psoriasis, acne, movement disorders, neuropathic pain and genitourinary diseases. The company operates in two segments: specialty pharmaceuticals and medical devices. The specialty pharmaceuticals segment includes eye care products, such as Restasis ophthalmic emulsion, Lumigan ophthalmic solution, Optive lubricant eye drops and the Refresh line of artificial tears; Botox, used in the treatment of neuromuscular disorders, pain management, the temporary improvement of wrinkles and for certain other therapeutic and aesthetic indications; skin care products, principally tazarotene products in cream and gel formulations for the treatment of acne, facial wrinkles and psoriasis, marketed under the name Tazorac; eyelash growth products; and urologics products, including Sanctura XR, a medication for overactive bladder. The medical devices segment includes breast implants for augmentation, revision and reconstructive surgery; obesity intervention products, including the Lap-Band, an adjustable gastric banding system, and the Orbera intragastric balloon system; and facial aesthetics products, including the Juvederm line of dermal filler products. In July 2008, the company completed the acquisition of the Aczone Gel 5% product, a topical treatment for acne vulgaris, from QLT, Inc. In October 2008, Allergan signed a collaboration agreement with Spectrum Pharmaceuticals, Inc. for the development of apaziquone, currently being investigated for the treatment of non-muscle invasive bladder cancer.

The firm offers employees benefits including a 401(k) plan; a defined benefit retirement contribution; adoption assistance; education assistance; before-tax flex dollars and flexible spending accounts; backup child care; an employee credit union; an employee assistance program; dependent scholarship awards; and U.S. savings bond deductions.

FINANCIALS: **Sales and profits are in thousands of dollars—add 000 to get the full amount. 2008 Note: Financial information for 2008 was not available for all companies at press time.**

2008 Sales: $4,339,700	2008 Profits: $578,600	**U.S. Stock Ticker: AGN**
2007 Sales: $3,879,000	2007 Profits: $499,300	**Int'l Ticker:** Int'l Exchange:
2006 Sales: $3,010,100	2006 Profits: $-127,400	Employees: 7,886
2005 Sales: $2,319,200	2005 Profits: $403,900	Fiscal Year Ends: 12/31
2004 Sales: $2,045,600	2004 Profits: $377,100	Parent Company:

SALARIES/BENEFITS:

Pension Plan: Y	ESOP Stock Plan:	Profit Sharing:	Top Exec. Salary: $1,293,076	Bonus: $2,244,800
Savings Plan: Y	Stock Purch. Plan:		Second Exec. Salary: $627,115	Bonus: $634,600

OTHER THOUGHTS:

Apparent Women Officers or Directors: 3
Hot Spot for Advancement for Women/Minorities: Y

LOCATIONS: ("Y" = Yes)

West:	Southwest:	Midwest:	Southeast:	Northeast:	International:
Y					Y

ALPHARMA INC

www.alpharma.com

Industry Group Code: 325414 **Ranks within this company's industry group:** Sales: Profits:

Techology:		Medical/Drugs:		Engineering:		Transportation:		Chemicals/Petrochemicals:		Specialty:	
Computers:		Manufacturer:	Y	Design:		Aerospace:		Oil/Gas Products:		Special Services:	
Software:		Contract Research:		Construction:		Automotive:		Chemicals:		Consulting:	
Communications:		Medical Services:		Eng. Services:		Shipping:		Oil/Chem. Svcs.:		Specialty Mgmt.:	
Electronics:		Labs:		Consulting:				Gases:		Products:	Y
Alternative Energy:		Bio. Services:						Other:		Other:	

TYPES OF BUSINESS:

Drugs-Animal Health
Human Pharmaceuticals
Animal Feed Additives

BRANDS/DIVISIONS/AFFILIATES:

KADIAN
FLECTOR
BMD
ALBAC
3-NITRO
HISTOSTAT
BIO-COX
King Pharmaceuticals Inc

CONTACTS: *Note: Officers with more than one job title may be intentionally listed here more than once.*

Dean J. Mitchell, CEO
Dean J. Mitchell, Pres.
Jeffrey S. Campbell, CFO/Exec. VP
Peter Watts, Exec. VP-Human Resources
Ronald N. Warner, Chief Scientific Officer/Exec. VP
Thomas J. Spellman III, General Counsel/Exec. VP/Sec.
Peter Watts, Exec. VP-Comm.
R. Scott Shively, Sr. VP-Pharmaceuticals Commercial Oper.
Carol A. Wrenn, Pres., Animal Health
Peter G. Tombros, Chmn.

Phone: 908-566-3800 **Fax:** 908-566-4137
Toll-Free: 866-322-2525
Address: 440 U.S. Highway 22 East, Bridgewater, NJ 08807 US

GROWTH PLANS/SPECIAL FEATURES:

Alpharma, Inc. is a multinational pharmaceutical company that manufactures specialty and proprietary human pharmaceutical and animal health products. The company operates in two business segments, pharmaceuticals and animal health. The pharmaceuticals unit, which is focused on prescription pain management, markets two branded products: KADIAN, which is a morphine sulfate sustained release capsule, and FLECTOR, a prescription topical non-steroidal anti-inflammatory patch that delivers anti-inflammatory and analgesic effects of diclofenac epolamine and is indicated for the topical treatment of acute pain due to minor strains, sprains, and contusions. Both of these drugs are manufactured by third parties. Alpharma's animal health segment is a leading provider of animal feed additives and water soluble therapeutics for poultry and livestock. This division markets over 100 products, which are organized into three main lines: antibiotics, anticoccidials and antibacterials. Key products include BMD, a feed additive that promotes growth and feed efficiency, as well as prevents or treats diseases in poultry and swine; ALBAC, a feed additive for poultry, swine and calves; BIO-COX, which prevents coccidiosis in poultry; and 3-NITRO and HISTOSTAT feed grade antibacterials. Animal products are manufactured by the firm at several plant locations across the U.S., China and Norway as well as by third parties. In April 2008, the firm sold its active pharmaceutical division to 3i for $395 million. This division formerly produced active pharmaceutical ingredients (APIs), marketing and selling 14 APIs, including fermentation-based APIs and one chemically synthesized API. These products were used primarily by third parties in the manufacture of finished dose pharmaceuticals. In November 2008, the company agreed to be acquired by King Pharmaceuticals Inc. for roughly $1.6 billion.

Alpharma offers employees benefits including medical, dental, prescription and vision coverage; life and disability insurance; paid time off; and tuition reimbursement.

FINANCIALS: **Sales and profits are in thousands of dollars—add 000 to get the full amount. 2008 Note: Financial information for 2008 was not available for all companies at press time.**

2008 Sales: $	2008 Profits: $	**U.S. Stock Ticker: ALO**
2007 Sales: $722,425	2007 Profits: $-13,581	**Int'l Ticker:** Int'l Exchange:
2006 Sales: $653,828	2006 Profits: $82,544	Employees: 2,000
2005 Sales: $553,617	2005 Profits: $133,769	Fiscal Year Ends: 12/31
2004 Sales: $513,329	2004 Profits: $-314,737	Parent Company:

SALARIES/BENEFITS:

Pension Plan:	ESOP Stock Plan:	Profit Sharing:	Top Exec. Salary: $646,923	Bonus: $845,000
Savings Plan: Y	Stock Purch. Plan: Y		Second Exec. Salary: $436,762	Bonus: $212,000

OTHER THOUGHTS:

Apparent Women Officers or Directors: 1
Hot Spot for Advancement for Women/Minorities:

LOCATIONS: ("Y" = Yes)

West:	Southwest:	Midwest:	Southeast:	Northeast:	International:
Y		Y	Y	Y	Y

Note: Financial information, benefits and other data can change quickly and may vary from those stated here.

ALPS ELECTRIC CO LTD

www.alps.com

Industry Group Code: 335313 **Ranks within this company's industry group:** Sales: 1 Profits: 1

Techology:		Medical/Drugs:		Engineering:		Transportation:		Chemicals/Petrochemicals:		Specialty:	
Computers:		Manufacturer:		Design:		Aerospace:		Oil/Gas Products:		Special Services:	
Software:		Contract Research:		Construction:		Automotive:	Y	Chemicals:		Consulting:	
Communications:	Y	Medical Services:		Eng. Services:		Shipping:		Oil/Chem. Svcs.:		Specialty Mgmt.:	
Electronics:	Y	Labs:		Consulting:				Gases:		Products:	Y
Alternative Energy:		Bio. Services:						Other:		Other:	

TYPES OF BUSINESS:

Electronic Components Manufacturing
Automotive Parts Manufacturing

BRANDS/DIVISIONS/AFFILIATES:

Haptic Commander
GlidePoint
Avnet Electronics Marketing

CONTACTS: *Note: Officers with more than one job title may be intentionally listed here more than once.*

Masataka Kataoka, Pres.
Takahide Sato, Sr. Managing Dir.
Yozo Yasuoka, Sr. Managing Dir.
Hideharu Kogashira, Managing Dir.
Seishi Kai, Managing Dir.

Phone: 81-3-3726-1211 **Fax:** 81-2-3278-1741
Toll-Free:
Address: 1-7 Yukigaya Otsuka-cho, Ota-Ku, Tokyo, 145-8501 Japan

GROWTH PLANS/SPECIAL FEATURES:

Alps Electric Co., Ltd. is primarily engaged in the manufacture and sale of electronic components, specializing in electronics development and miniaturization. Alps operates through four divisions: the Mechatronics Devices Division, the Automotive Products Division, the Communication Devices Division and the Peripheral Products Division. The Mechatronics Devices Division manufactures human-to-machine interface components, such as switches, variable resistors, sensors and connectors, which are used in automotive components; information and communication devices; and home appliances. The Automotive Products Division develops on-board electronics and safety and comfort systems for automotive applications. One of its propriety systems, the Haptic Commander unit, incorporates modules to control various switches, air-conditioning units and passive keyless entry systems. The Communication Devices Division utilizes high-frequency circuits and other technologies to develop products for high-definition digital equipment, broadcast systems and other communications products, including optical communications equipment and cameras for mobile phones. The Peripheral Products Division develops human-to-machine input and output devices, such as keyboards, remote controls, touch sensors, printers and power-saving LCDs. The firm's GlidePoint device is used primarily in the touch pads of laptop PCs and uses electrostatic detection technology to detect the movement of a fingertip. GlidePoint is additionally used in the touch pads of TV remote control units and mobile phone sensor keys. In February 2008, Avnet Electronics Marketing, part of the Avnet, Inc., agreed to distribute Alps' full line of products worldwide.

FINANCIALS: **Sales and profits are in thousands of dollars—add 000 to get the full amount. 2008 Note: Financial information for 2008 was not available for all companies at press time.**

2008 Sales: $6,926,600	2008 Profits: $44,200	**U.S. Stock Ticker: APELY.PK**
2007 Sales: $7,081,300	2007 Profits: $49,200	**Int'l Ticker: 6770** Int'l Exchange: Tokyo-TSE
2006 Sales: $7,096,100	2006 Profits: $188,700	Employees: 32,869
2005 Sales: $6,436,300	2005 Profits: $163,200	Fiscal Year Ends: 3/31
2004 Sales: $5,862,592	2004 Profits: $160,293	Parent Company:

SALARIES/BENEFITS:

Pension Plan:	ESOP Stock Plan:	Profit Sharing:	Top Exec. Salary: $	Bonus: $
Savings Plan:	Stock Purch. Plan:		Second Exec. Salary: $	Bonus: $

OTHER THOUGHTS:

Apparent Women Officers or Directors:
Hot Spot for Advancement for Women/Minorities:

LOCATIONS: ("Y" = Yes)

West:	Southwest:	Midwest:	Southeast:	Northeast:	International:
Y	Y	Y	Y	Y	Y

Note: Financial information, benefits and other data can change quickly and may vary from those stated here.

ALSTOM

www.alstom.com

Industry Group Code: 335000 **Ranks within this company's industry group:** Sales: 6 Profits: 5

Techology:		**Medical/Drugs:**		**Engineering:**		**Transportation:**		**Chemicals/Petrochemicals:**		**Specialty:**	
Computers:		Manufacturer:		Design:		Aerospace:		Oil/Gas Products:		Special Services:	
Software:	Y	Contract Research:		Construction:		Automotive:		Chemicals:		Consulting:	
Communications:	Y	Medical Services:		Eng. Services:		Shipping:	Y	Oil/Chem. Svcs.:		Specialty Mgmt.:	
Electronics:		Labs:		Consulting:				Gases:		Products:	
Alternative Energy:	Y	Bio. Services:						Other:		Other:	

TYPES OF BUSINESS:

Equipment-Electric Power Distribution
Energy & Transport Infrastructure
Power Plant Machinery
Rail Transport Services
Rail Transport Manufacturing
Technical Consulting & Power Plant Refurbishment

BRANDS/DIVISIONS/AFFILIATES:

Alstom Power
Alstom Transport
Transmashholding
Ecotecnia
Wuhan Boiler Company Ltd.
Power Systems Mfg.
Qingdao Sizhou

CONTACTS: *Note: Officers with more than one job title may be intentionally listed here more than once.*

Patrick Kron, CEO
Henri Poupart-Lafarge, CFO
Patrick Dubert, Sr. VP-Human Resources
Philippe Joubert, Exec. VP/Pres., Power Systems Sector
Philippe Mellier, Exec. VP/Pres., Transport Sector
Walter Graenicher, Pres., Power Service Sector
Patrick Kron, Chmn.

Phone: 33-1-41-49-20-00 **Fax:** 33-1-41-49-24-85
Toll-Free:
Address: 3 Ave. Andre Malraux, Levallois-Perret, 92309 France

GROWTH PLANS/SPECIAL FEATURES:

ALSTOM, which operates in 70 countries, is a world leader in integrated power plant, power production services and air quality control systems. The company divides its operations into two segments: power generation, through Alstom Power, and rail transport, through Alstom Transport. Alstom Power designs, manufactures, supplies and services products and systems for the power generation sector and industrial markets. Its products and services include boilers, turbines (gas, hydroelectric and steam), turbogenerators and generators, air quality control systems, product retrofitting, control systems, refurbishment of existing plants and maintenance and service, such as spare parts, consultancy and technical support for power plant operation. Alstom Power also provides turnkey solutions for gas and coal-fired power plants, hydroelectric power plants, conventional islands for nuclear power plants and wind farms. Alstom Transport develops and markets a complete range of systems, equipment and service in the railway market. Alstom offers rolling stock for high speed and very high speed trains, regional and commuter trains, locomotives, freight cars, metros, trams and tram-trains. In November 2007, Alstom acquired Spanish wind turbine company Ecotecnia for approximately $511.5 million. Other recent acquisitions include Wuhan Boiler Company Ltd., Qingdao Sizhou and Power Systems Mfg. In October 2008, Alstom Transport and the Russian firm Transmashholding (TMH) agreed to a strategic partnership and the future creation of a joint venture for the manufacture of freight and passenger locomotives.

FINANCIALS: **Sales and profits are in thousands of dollars—add 000 to get the full amount. 2008 Note: Financial information for 2008 was not available for all companies at press time.**

2008 Sales: $21,980,400	2008 Profits: $1,107,600	**U.S. Stock Ticker:**
2007 Sales: $21,880,300	2007 Profits: $686,800	**Int'l Ticker: ALSO** Int'l Exchange: Paris-Euronext
2006 Sales: $20,656,000	2006 Profits: $275,700	Employees: 76,000
2005 Sales: $19,896,800	2005 Profits: $-967,100	Fiscal Year Ends: 3/31
2004 Sales: $20,535,000	2004 Profits: $-2,200,000	Parent Company:

SALARIES/BENEFITS:

Pension Plan:	ESOP Stock Plan:	Profit Sharing:	Top Exec. Salary: $	Bonus: $
Savings Plan:	Stock Purch. Plan:		Second Exec. Salary: $	Bonus: $

OTHER THOUGHTS:

Apparent Women Officers or Directors: 1
Hot Spot for Advancement for Women/Minorities:

LOCATIONS: ("Y" = Yes)

West:	Southwest:	Midwest:	Southeast:	Northeast:	International:
				Y	Y

ALTANA AG

www.altana.com

Industry Group Code: 325412 **Ranks within this company's industry group:** Sales: 28 Profits: 25

Techology:		Medical/Drugs:		Engineering:		Transportation:		Chemicals/Petrochemicals:		Specialty:	
Computers:		Manufacturer:		Design:		Aerospace:		Oil/Gas Products:		Special Services:	
Software:		Contract Research:		Construction:		Automotive:		Chemicals:	Y	Consulting:	
Communications:		Medical Services:		Eng. Services:		Shipping:		Oil/Chem. Svcs.:		Specialty Mgmt.:	
Electronics:		Labs:		Consulting:				Gases:		Products:	Y
Alternative Energy:		Bio. Services:						Other:		Other:	

TYPES OF BUSINESS:

Specialty Chemical Manufacturing
Imaging Products
Electrical Insulation
Coatings

BRANDS/DIVISIONS/AFFILIATES:

BYK Additives & Instruments
ECKART Effect Pigments
ELANTAS Electrical Insulation
ACTEGA Coatings & Sealants
BYK-Chemie
BYK-Gardner
Dick Peters BV
BYK USA Inc

CONTACTS:

Note: Officers with more than one job title may be intentionally listed here more than once.

Matthias L. Wolfgruber, CEO
Martin Babilas, CFO
Roland Peter, Pres., Additives & Instruments Div.
Christoph Schlunken, Pres., Effect Pigments Div.
Wolfgang Schutt, Pres., Electrical Insulation Div.
Guido Forstbach, Pres., Coatings & Sealants Div.
Fritz Frohlich, Chmn.

Phone: 49-281-670-8	**Fax:** 49-281-670-376
Toll-Free:	
Address: Abelstrasse 43, Wesel, 46483 Germany	

GROWTH PLANS/SPECIAL FEATURES:

Altana AG is an international chemicals company that develops, manufactures and markets products for a range of targeted, highly specialized applications. The company serves customers in the coatings, paint and plastics, printing, cosmetics, electrical and electronics industries. The firm operates through four divisions: BYK Additives & Instruments; ECKART Effect Pigments; ELANTAS Electrical Insulation; and ACTEGA Coatings & Sealants. BYK Additives & Instruments offers a range of chemical additives, produced by subsidiary BYK-Chemie, that help to improve and regulate the quality and processability of coatings and plastics. This division also offers testing and measuring equipment, produced by subsidiary BYK-Gardner, allowing manufacturers to predetermine the color, gloss and other physical properties of paints and plastics products. ECKART Effect Pigments develops and produces metallic effect and pearlescent pigments, as well as gold-bronze and zinc pigments, used to produce certain optical effects in paints, inks, cosmetics and coatings. ELANTAS Electrical Insulation produces insulating materials used in electrical and electronics applications, including electric motors, household appliances, cars, generators, transformers, capacitors, televisions, computers, wind mills, circuit boards and sensors. ACTEGA Coatings & Sealants develops and produces specialty coatings and sealants used primarily by the graphic arts and packaging industries. These products, which include sealants for glass bottles and metal cans as well as coatings for flexible packaging, help to regulate the physical properties of packaging, preserve the freshness of contents and contribute to the overall appearance of packaged goods. The full Altana group consists of approximately 42 operational companies and 46 research laboratories worldwide. Sales outside of Germany account for approximately 83% of annual revenues, with products sold in over 100 countries. In November 2008, Altana announced that it would acquire Dick Peters BV, the wax additives business of Swiss chemicals firm Clariant, for approximately $22.4 million.

FINANCIALS:

Sales and profits are in thousands of dollars—add 000 to get the full amount. 2008 Note: Financial information for 2008 was not available for all companies at press time.

2008 Sales: $1,774,430	2008 Profits: $136,760	**U.S. Stock Ticker:**
2007 Sales: $1,825,660	2007 Profits: $171,790	**Int'l Ticker: ALT** Int'l Exchange: Frankfurt-Euronext
2006 Sales: $2,039,470	2006 Profits: $89,500	Employees: 4,646
2005 Sales: $1,405,400	2005 Profits: $679,100	Fiscal Year Ends: 12/31
2004 Sales: $4,013,500	2004 Profits: $529,200	Parent Company:

SALARIES/BENEFITS:

Pension Plan:	ESOP Stock Plan:	Profit Sharing:	Top Exec. Salary: $	Bonus: $
Savings Plan:	Stock Purch. Plan:		Second Exec. Salary: $	Bonus: $

OTHER THOUGHTS:

Apparent Women Officers or Directors: 1
Hot Spot for Advancement for Women/Minorities:

LOCATIONS: ("Y" = Yes)

West:	Southwest:	Midwest:	Southeast:	Northeast:	International:
		Y		Y	Y

ALTERA CORP

www.altera.com

Industry Group Code: 334413 **Ranks within this company's industry group:** Sales: 20 Profits: 6

Techology:		Medical/Drugs:		Engineering:		Transportation:		Chemicals/Petrochemicals:		Specialty:	
Computers:	Y	Manufacturer:		Design:		Aerospace:		Oil/Gas Products:		Special Services:	
Software:	Y	Contract Research:		Construction:		Automotive:		Chemicals:		Consulting:	
Communications:		Medical Services:		Eng. Services:		Shipping:		Oil/Chem. Svcs.:		Specialty Mgmt.:	
Electronics:		Labs:		Consulting:				Gases:		Products:	
Alternative Energy:		Bio. Services:						Other:		Other:	

TYPES OF BUSINESS:

Programmable Logic Devices
Development System Software
System-On-A-Programmable-Chip (SOPC) Devices
CMOS Semiconductor PDLs

BRANDS/DIVISIONS/AFFILIATES:

HardCopy
Stratix
Cyclone
APEX
FLEX
Mercury
MAX+PLUS II
Excalibur

CONTACTS: *Note: Officers with more than one job title may be intentionally listed here more than once.*

John P. Daane, CEO
John P. Daane, Pres.
Timothy R. Morse, CFO/Sr. VP
Jordan S. Plofsky, Sr. VP-Mktg.
Kevin H. Lyman, Sr. VP-Human Resources
Misha Burich, Sr. VP-R&D
Lance M. Lissner, CIO
William Y. Hata, VP-Eng.
Katherine Schuelke, General Counsel/VP/Corp. Sec.
William Y. Hata, VP-World Oper.
Lance Lissner, Sr. VP-Bus. Dev.
Scott Wylie, VP-Investor Rel.
Timothy R. Morse, Sr. VP-Finance
Todd Scott, Sr. Dir.-Broadcast & Consumer Bus.
George A. Papa, Sr. VP-Worldwide Sales
John P. Daane, Chmn.

Phone: 408-544-7000 **Fax:** 408-544-6403
Toll-Free: 800-767-3753
Address: 101 Innovation Dr., San Jose, CA 95134 US

GROWTH PLANS/SPECIAL FEATURES:

Altera Corporation is a world leader in system-on-a-programmable-chip (SOPC) technology. The company designs, manufactures and markets high-performance, high-density programmable logic devices (PLDs), HardCopy devices, pre-defined design building blocks known as intellectual property cores and associated development tools. Founded in 1983, Altera was one of the first suppliers of complementary metal oxide semiconductor (CMOS) PLDs and is currently a global leader in this market. The company's PLDs consist of field-programmable arrays and complex programmable logic devices, which are semiconductor integrated circuits, manufactured as standard chips, that its customers program to perform desired logic functions within their electronic systems. The firm offers a broad range of general-purpose PLDs that present unique features as well as differing densities and performance specifications for implementing particular applications. Programmable logic's primary advantage is that it allows for quicker design cycles, meeting customers' needs for quick time-to-market. Altera's HardCopy devices allow its customers to move from a PLD to a low-cost, high-volume, non-programmable implementation of their designs. The company operates in a wide variety of segments, such as telecommunications, data communication, electronic data processing, computer and storage products and industrial applications.

Employees are offered medical, dental and vision coverage; an employee assistance program; a child and elder care counseling and referral service; life insurance; short and long-term disability; flexible spending account; a 401(k) plan; a retirement plan; accidental death and dismemberment coverage; business travel accident insurance; employee stock purchase plan; legal services; auto, home and pet insurance; and educational reimbursement.

FINANCIALS: **Sales and profits are in thousands of dollars—add 000 to get the full amount. 2008 Note: Financial information for 2008 was not available for all companies at press time.**

2008 Sales: $1,367,224	2008 Profits: $359,651	**U.S. Stock Ticker: ALTR**
2007 Sales: $1,263,548	2007 Profits: $290,023	**Int'l Ticker:** Int'l Exchange:
2006 Sales: $1,285,535	2006 Profits: $323,236	Employees: 2,760
2005 Sales: $1,123,739	2005 Profits: $278,829	Fiscal Year Ends: 12/31
2004 Sales: $1,016,364	2004 Profits: $275,111	Parent Company:

SALARIES/BENEFITS:

Pension Plan: Y	ESOP Stock Plan:	Profit Sharing:	Top Exec. Salary: $700,027	Bonus: $1,493,805
Savings Plan: Y	Stock Purch. Plan: Y		Second Exec. Salary: $375,014	Bonus: $266,102

OTHER THOUGHTS:

Apparent Women Officers or Directors: 1
Hot Spot for Advancement for Women/Minorities:

LOCATIONS: ("Y" = Yes)

West:	Southwest:	Midwest:	Southeast:	Northeast:	International:
Y	Y	Y	Y	Y	Y

ALTRAN TECHNOLOGIES SA

www.altran.com

Industry Group Code: 541512 **Ranks within this company's industry group:** Sales: 18 Profits: 13

Techology:		Medical/Drugs:		Engineering:		Transportation:		Chemicals/Petrochemicals:		Specialty:	
Computers:		Manufacturer:		Design:		Aerospace:	Y	Oil/Gas Products:		Special Services:	Y
Software:		Contract Research:		Construction:		Automotive:	Y	Chemicals:		Consulting:	Y
Communications:		Medical Services:		Eng. Services:	Y	Shipping:		Oil/Chem. Svcs.:		Specialty Mgmt.:	
Electronics:		Labs:		Consulting:	Y			Gases:		Products:	
Alternative Energy:		Bio. Services:						Other:		Other:	Y

TYPES OF BUSINESS:

Consulting-Technology & Engineering
Research
Management Consulting
Automotive Consulting
Motor Sports Consulting

BRANDS/DIVISIONS/AFFILIATES:

Altran Foundation
Altran Technologies Korea
Altran Europe
Acsience
Altran GmbH & Co KG
Altran India
Altran Solutions Corp
Altran Technologies UK

CONTACTS: *Note: Officers with more than one job title may be intentionally listed here more than once.*

Yves de Chaisemartin, CEO
Gerald Berge, CFO
Pascal Brier, VP
Frederic Grard, VP
Cyril Roger, VP
Yves de Chaisemartin, Chmn.
Patrick Dauga, Exec. Dir.-Americas

Phone: 33-1-46-17-46-17	**Fax:** 33-1-46-17-46-18
Toll-Free:	
Address: 2 rue Paul Vaillant-Couturier, Levallois-Perret, 92300 France	

GROWTH PLANS/SPECIAL FEATURES:

Altran Technologies, based in France, is a leader in global technology consulting, structured around three business segments and six practice focuses. The three business segments are technology and innovation consulting, accounting for nearly half of the firm's revenues; organization and information systems consulting, accounting for a third of revenues; and strategy and management consulting, representing the remainder of annual revenues. The six practice areas are aerospace and defense; automotive and transports; energy and industry; financial services; healthcare; and telecoms and media. The company derives roughly 43% of its revenues from activities in France, but it has operations in many European countries, Asia and Brazil, as well as locations in the U.S. The majority of Altran's business is done with companies in the aerospace, automotive and telecommunications fields, but it also works with companies in the banking, energy, electronics and biotechnology industries. The company operates research laboratories in Cambridge, U.K. and Boston, Massachusetts. Altran works on an integral basis with companies, assisting them in areas such as the development and implementation of science and technology and the design of new products, as well as by providing advice on how to streamline business and manufacturing through the use of technology. The company is an official partner in the Solar Impulse project, which has been working to develop a solar-powered aircraft capable of long-range flight, with initial test flights of the aircraft scheduled for 2009.

FINANCIALS: **Sales and profits are in thousands of dollars—add 000 to get the full amount. 2008 Note: Financial information for 2008 was not available for all companies at press time.**

2008 Sales: $2,234,170	2008 Profits: $15,440	**U.S. Stock Ticker: ALTKF.PK**
2007 Sales: $2,154,690	2007 Profits: $29,250	**Int'l Ticker: ALT** Int'l Exchange: Paris-Euronext
2006 Sales: $2,347,700	2006 Profits: $5,900	Employees: 16,152
2005 Sales: $2,252,100	2005 Profits: $ 400	Fiscal Year Ends: 12/31
2004 Sales: $1,935,100	2004 Profits: $-2,900	Parent Company:

SALARIES/BENEFITS:

Pension Plan:	ESOP Stock Plan:	Profit Sharing:	Top Exec. Salary: $1,025,591	Bonus: $
Savings Plan: Y	Stock Purch. Plan:		Second Exec. Salary: $1,025,591	Bonus: $

OTHER THOUGHTS:

Apparent Women Officers or Directors:
Hot Spot for Advancement for Women/Minorities:

LOCATIONS: ("Y" = Yes)

West:	Southwest:	Midwest:	Southeast:	Northeast:	International:
Y	Y	Y		Y	Y

AMDOCS LTD

www.amdocs.com

Industry Group Code: 511213 **Ranks within this company's industry group:** Sales: 1 Profits: 1

Techology:		Medical/Drugs:		Engineering:		Transportation:		Chemicals/Petrochemicals:		Specialty:	
Computers:		Manufacturer:		Design:		Aerospace:		Oil/Gas Products:		Special Services:	Y
Software:	Y	Contract Research:		Construction:		Automotive:		Chemicals:		Consulting:	
Communications:		Medical Services:		Eng. Services:		Shipping:		Oil/Chem. Svcs.:		Specialty Mgmt.:	
Electronics:		Labs:		Consulting:				Gases:		Products:	
Alternative Energy:		Bio. Services:						Other:		Other:	

TYPES OF BUSINESS:

Software-Customer Services & Business Operations
Customer Relationship Management Software
Billing Management Software
Directory Publishing Systems
Technical & Support Services
Managed Services

BRANDS/DIVISIONS/AFFILIATES:

Exchange Applications, Inc.
Cramer, Amdocs OSS Division
Amdocs Enabler
Amdocs ClarifyCRM
DST Innovis, Inc.
Changing Worlds Ltd
Qpass
Jacobs Rimell Ltd

CONTACTS: *Note: Officers with more than one job title may be intentionally listed here more than once.*

Dov Baharav, CEO
Dov Baharav, Pres.
Tamar Rapaport-Dagim, CFO/Sr. VP
Harel Kodesh, Chief Prod. Officer
James Liang, Chief Strategy Officer/Sr. VP
Anthony Piniella, Dir.-Corp. Comm.
Thomas G. O'Brien, VP-Investor Rel.
Thomas G. O'Brien, Treas.
Holly Rossetti, Dir.-Global Public Rel.
Guy Dubois, Exec. VP/Head-Product Bus. Group
Bruce K. Anderson, Chmn.

Phone: 44-1481-728-444 **Fax:**
Toll-Free:
Address: Tower Hill House, Ste. 5, Le Bordage, St. Peter Port, Guernsey, GY1 3QT Channel Islands

GROWTH PLANS/SPECIAL FEATURES:

Amdocs, Ltd. provides software products and services primarily to tier one and tier two communications companies worldwide, offering an integrated approach to customer management. Its product offerings consist of billing and customer relationship management (CRM) systems and directory sales and publishing systems for publishers of both traditional and Internet-based directories, as well as system implementation, integration, support and maintenance services. The CRM segment includes the Amdocs Enabler and Amdocs ClarifyCRM products. Amdocs Enabler is a billing service for next generation voice, wireless, data and content services. Amdocs ClarifyCRM is a CRM document management system. The firm also offers managed services, which include modernization and consolidation, operation of data centers, purchase and management of hardware assets, billing operations and application support. The solutions provided by the company are designed to support a variety of lines of business including wireline, cable and satellite and a range of communications services including video, data, Internet protocol, electronic and mobile commerce. In December 2008, the firm acquired Changing Worlds Ltd. for $60 million. Changing Worlds offers mobile service providers personalization and intelligent portal solutions. In April 2008, the firm announced it acquired Jacobs Rimell, Ltd., a provider of fulfillment solutions for the broadband cable industry, for $45 million.

FINANCIALS: **Sales and profits are in thousands of dollars—add 000 to get the full amount. 2008 Note: Financial information for 2008 was not available for all companies at press time.**

2008 Sales: $3,162,096	2008 Profits: $378,906	**U.S. Stock Ticker: DOX**
2007 Sales: $2,836,173	2007 Profits: $364,937	**Int'l Ticker:** Int'l Exchange:
2006 Sales: $2,480,050	2006 Profits: $318,636	Employees: 12,000
2005 Sales: $2,038,621	2005 Profits: $288,636	Fiscal Year Ends: 9/30
2004 Sales: $1,773,700	2004 Profits: $234,900	Parent Company:

SALARIES/BENEFITS:

Pension Plan: Y	ESOP Stock Plan:	Profit Sharing:	Top Exec. Salary: $	Bonus: $
Savings Plan:	Stock Purch. Plan: Y		Second Exec. Salary: $	Bonus: $

OTHER THOUGHTS:

Apparent Women Officers or Directors: 1
Hot Spot for Advancement for Women/Minorities:

LOCATIONS: ("Y" = Yes)

West:	Southwest:	Midwest:	Southeast:	Northeast:	International:
Y	Y	Y	Y	Y	Y

AMEC PLC

www.amec.com

Industry Group Code: 234000 **Ranks within this company's industry group:** Sales: 22 Profits: 14

Techology:		Medical/Drugs:		Engineering:		Transportation:		Chemicals/Petrochemicals:		Specialty:	
Computers:		Manufacturer:		Design:	Y	Aerospace:		Oil/Gas Products:		Special Services:	Y
Software:		Contract Research:		Construction:	Y	Automotive:		Chemicals:		Consulting:	
Communications:		Medical Services:		Eng. Services:	Y	Shipping:		Oil/Chem. Svcs.:		Specialty Mgmt.:	Y
Electronics:		Labs:		Consulting:	Y			Gases:		Products:	
Alternative Energy:		Bio. Services:						Other:		Other:	

TYPES OF BUSINESS:

Architectural & Engineering Services
Commercial & Heavy Construction
Environmental Services
Infrastructure Projects
IT Services
Support & Maintenance Services
Consulting
Communications Systems

BRANDS/DIVISIONS/AFFILIATES:

Stevenson & Associates SRL
Hydrosphere Resource Consultants, Inc.
Applied Environmental Research Centre
OEST Associates, Inc.
AllDeco, s.r.o.
Performance Improvements Group (PI) Limited
Bower Damberger Rolseth Engineering Limited
Geomatrix Consultants, Inc.

CONTACTS: *Note: Officers with more than one job title may be intentionally listed here more than once.*

Samir Brikho, CEO
Neil Bruce, COO
Ian McHoul, CFO
Ron Lee, Dir.-Human Resources
Michael Blacker, General Counsel
Didier Pfleger, COO
Francois-Philippe Champagne, Dir.-Strategic Dev.
Sue Scholes, Dir.-Comm.
Sue Scholes, Dir.-Investor Rel.
Roger Jinks, Pres., Earth & Environmental Div.
Jock Green-Armytage, Chmn.

Phone: 44-20-7539-5800	Fax: 44-20-7539-5900
Toll-Free:	
Address: 76 - 78 Old St., London, EC1V 9RU UK	

GROWTH PLANS/SPECIAL FEATURES:

AMEC plc, headquartered in London, is a global engineering and construction management firm with operations in more than 30 countries worldwide. Its operations are divided into four segments: oil and gas; environmental; nuclear; and power and utilities. Oil and gas services include design, delivery, commissioning and decommissioning of oil and gas facilities, surface mining and oil sands engineering services, as well as minerals and metals mining consultancy, design and project management. Environmental services include consultancy and engineering, as well as specialty services such as environmental assessment, materials testing, specialty water services and clean-up. The company's nuclear service areas include new build, the licensing, regulatory and project support; reactor support, life time extension and asset performance improvement; clean up, specialist decommissioning and waste management services; and nuclear defense, engineering and technical services. The power and utilities sector includes engineering; project management; risk and reputation management; environmental impact assessments and sustainable solutions, for the Americas and Europe; and a Power Training School. The firm serves a range of industries including oil and gas, power, transportation, mining, food and pharmaceuticals and defense, among others. Customers include ExxonMobil, BP, Kuwait Oil Company, Syncrude, Shell, Bruce Power, British Energy and various local and national governments. Recent acquisitions include Bower Damberger Rolseth Engineering Limited; Geomatrix Consultants, Inc.; AllDeco, s.r.o.; and OEST Associates, Inc. In January 2009, the company acquired Performance Improvements Group (PI) Limited, a U.K.-based asset optimization consultancy services company. In February 2009, the company formed a joint venture with Black Cat Engineering & Construction to offer asset support services to the oil, gas and petrochemical sectors in Qatar.

FINANCIALS: **Sales and profits are in thousands of dollars—add 000 to get the full amount. 2008 Note: Financial information for 2008 was not available for all companies at press time.**

2008 Sales: $3,823,620	2008 Profits: $291,940	**U.S. Stock Ticker:**
2007 Sales: $3,456,570	2007 Profits: $505,240	**Int'l Ticker: AMEC** Int'l Exchange: London-LSE
2006 Sales: $3,112,410	2006 Profits: $321,569	Employees: 21,479
2005 Sales: $8,564,860	2005 Profits: $145,910	Fiscal Year Ends: 12/31
2004 Sales: $8,070,980	2004 Profits: $130,141	Parent Company:

SALARIES/BENEFITS:

Pension Plan:	ESOP Stock Plan:	Profit Sharing:	Top Exec. Salary: $	Bonus: $
Savings Plan:	Stock Purch. Plan:		Second Exec. Salary: $	Bonus: $

OTHER THOUGHTS:

Apparent Women Officers or Directors: 3
Hot Spot for Advancement for Women/Minorities: Y

LOCATIONS: ("Y" = Yes)

West:	Southwest:	Midwest:	Southeast:	Northeast:	International:
Y	Y	Y	Y	Y	Y

AMEY PLC

www.amey.co.uk

Industry Group Code: 541330 **Ranks within this company's industry group:** Sales: Profits:

Techology:		Medical/Drugs:		Engineering:		Transportation:		Chemicals/Petrochemicals:		Specialty:	
Computers:		Manufacturer:		Design:	Y	Aerospace:		Oil/Gas Products:		Special Services:	
Software:		Contract Research:		Construction:		Automotive:		Chemicals:		Consulting:	Y
Communications:		Medical Services:		Eng. Services:		Shipping:		Oil/Chem. Svcs.:		Specialty Mgmt.:	Y
Electronics:		Labs:		Consulting:				Gases:		Products:	
Alternative Energy:		Bio. Services:						Other:		Other:	

TYPES OF BUSINESS:

Engineering Services
Facilities Management
Design Services
Consulting Services
Asset Management
Infrastructure Services
Highway Design Services
IT Services

BRANDS/DIVISIONS/AFFILIATES:

Incident Support Unit
AmeySECO
Network Rail
Hampshire Highways
Hertfordshire Highways

CONTACTS:

Note: Officers with more than one job title may be intentionally listed here more than once.

Mel Ewell, CEO
Chris Webster, COO
Andrew Nelson, Group Dir.-Finance
Valerie Hughes-D'Aeth, Dir.-Human Resources
Wayne Robertson, Head-Legal
John Pilkington, Dir.-Strategic Dev.
Keith Cottrell, Managing Dir.-Amey Ventures
Keith Sexton, Dir.-Health, Safety, Environment & Quality
Chris Fenton, Managing Dir.-Ventures & Tube Svcs.
Richard Mottram, Chmn.

Phone: 44-18-6571-3100 **Fax:** 44-18-6571-3357
Toll-Free:
Address: The Sherard Bldg., Edmund Halley Rd., Oxford, OX4 4DQ UK

GROWTH PLANS/SPECIAL FEATURES:

Amey plc, a subsidiary of the Spanish Grupo Ferrovial, provides business and infrastructure support services through 200 locations across the U.K. and Ireland. The company identifies its services as belonging to the following four areas: transport systems, school and youth support, community development and public services. In the transport systems division, Amey offers design and advisory services, such as feasibility studies, technical surveys and environmental assessments; ensures the delivery and renewal of road and rail infrastructure; provides management services; and designs, provides and manages transport information solutions across the road and rail networks. Amey's tube lines division holds a 30-year contract to upgrade and maintain London's Jubilee, Northern and Piccadilly lines. The properties administered by this division include 100 stations, 200 miles of track and 255 subway trains. Amey designs and builds schools and colleges, manages school facilities, implements new technology in school management solutions and provides education improvement consultation services. In the vein of community development, the company designs and manages public spaces, consults with local and government organizations to improve community services, and works to maximize community resources through community centers. The firm's public services division includes financing services, managing estates, business support services and transportation solutions. In early 2008, Amey secured contracts with the Home Office, Hampshire Highways and Hertfordshire Highways, compositely worth about $1.6 billion.

FINANCIALS:

Sales and profits are in thousands of dollars—add 000 to get the full amount. 2008 Note: Financial information for 2008 was not available for all companies at press time.

2008 Sales: $	2008 Profits: $	**U.S. Stock Ticker: Subsidiary**
2007 Sales: $	2007 Profits: $	**Int'l Ticker:** Int'l Exchange:
2006 Sales: $2,613,130	2006 Profits: $127,413	Employees: 7,500
2005 Sales: $2,122,990	2005 Profits: $91,985	Fiscal Year Ends: 12/31
2004 Sales: $1,699,953	2004 Profits: $37,148	Parent Company: GRUPO FERROVIAL SA

SALARIES/BENEFITS:

Pension Plan: Y	ESOP Stock Plan:	Profit Sharing:	Top Exec. Salary: $	Bonus: $
Savings Plan:	Stock Purch. Plan:		Second Exec. Salary: $	Bonus: $

OTHER THOUGHTS:

Apparent Women Officers or Directors: 2
Hot Spot for Advancement for Women/Minorities:

LOCATIONS: ("Y" = Yes)

West:	Southwest:	Midwest:	Southeast:	Northeast:	International:
					Y

AMGEN INC

www.amgen.com

Industry Group Code: 325412 **Ranks within this company's industry group:** Sales: 14 Profits: 12

Techology:		Medical/Drugs:		Engineering:		Transportation:		Chemicals/Petrochemicals:		Specialty:	
Computers:		Manufacturer:	Y	Design:		Aerospace:		Oil/Gas Products:		Special Services:	
Software:		Contract Research:		Construction:		Automotive:		Chemicals:		Consulting:	
Communications:		Medical Services:		Eng. Services:		Shipping:		Oil/Chem. Svcs.:		Specialty Mgmt.:	
Electronics:		Labs:	Y	Consulting:				Gases:		Products:	
Alternative Energy:		Bio. Services:						Other:		Other:	

TYPES OF BUSINESS:

Drugs-Diversified
Oncology Drugs
Nephrology Drugs
Inflammation Drugs
Neurology Drugs
Metabolic Drugs

BRANDS/DIVISIONS/AFFILIATES:

Aranesp
EPOGEN
Neulasta
NEUPOGEN
Enbrel

CONTACTS:

Note: Officers with more than one job title may be intentionally listed here more than once.

Kevin W. Sharer, CEO
Kevin W. Sharer, Pres.
Robert A. Bradway, CFO/Exec. VP
Brian McNamee, Sr. VP-Human Resources
Roger M. Perlmutter, Exec. VP-R&D
Thomas J. (Tom) Flanagan, CIO/Sr. VP
David J. Scott, General Counsel/Sr. VP/Corp. Sec.
Fabrizio Bonanni, Exec. VP-Oper.
David Beier, Sr. VP-Corp. Affairs & Global Gov't
Anna Richo, Sr. VP/Chief Compliance Officer
Kevin W. Sharer, Chmn.
George J. Morrow, Exec. VP-Global Commercial Oper.

Phone: 805-447-1000	**Fax:** 805-447-1010
Toll-Free:	
Address: 1 Amgen Center Dr., Thousand Oaks, CA 91320-1799 US	

GROWTH PLANS/SPECIAL FEATURES:

Amgen, Inc. is a global biotechnology company that develops, manufactures and markets human therapeutics based on cellular and molecular biology. Its products are used for treatment in the fields of supportive cancer care, nephrology and inflammation. Amgen's primary products include Aranesp, EPOGEN, Neulasta, NEUPOGEN and Enbrel, which together represent 94% of the company's sales. Aranesp and EPOGEN stimulate the production of red blood cells to treat anemia and belong to a class of drugs referred to as erythropoiesis-stimulating agents. Aranesp is used for the treatment of anemia both in supportive cancer care and in nephrology. EPOGEN is used to treat anemia associated with chronic renal failure. Neulasta and NEUPOGEN selectively stimulate the production of neutrophils, one type of white blood cell that helps the body fight infections. ENBREL inhibits tumor necrosis factor (TNF), a substance induced in response to inflammatory and immunological responses, such as rheumatoid arthritis and psoriasis. Amgen maintains sales and marketing forces primarily in the U.S., Europe and Canada, and markets its products to healthcare providers including physicians, dialysis centers, hospitals and pharmacies. Amgen focuses its research and development efforts in the core areas of oncology, inflammation, bone, metabolic disorders and neuroscience, taking a modality-independent approach to drug discovery by choosing the best possible approach to block a specific disease process before considering the type of drug that may be required to pursue that approach. In September 2008, Biovitrum AB acquired the marketed biologic therapeutic products Kepivance and Stemgen from Amgen and obtained a worldwide exclusive license from the firm for Kineret.

Amgen offers its employees an education reimbursement plan, a Long Term Incentive program and medical, prescription, vision and dental benefits.

FINANCIALS:

Sales and profits are in thousands of dollars—add 000 to get the full amount. 2008 Note: Financial information for 2008 was not available for all companies at press time.

2008 Sales: $15,003,000	2008 Profits: $4,196,000	**U.S. Stock Ticker: AMGN**
2007 Sales: $14,771,000	2007 Profits: $3,166,000	**Int'l Ticker:** Int'l Exchange:
2006 Sales: $14,268,000	2006 Profits: $2,950,000	Employees: 17,500
2005 Sales: $12,430,000	2005 Profits: $3,674,000	Fiscal Year Ends: 12/31
2004 Sales: $10,550,000	2004 Profits: $2,363,000	Parent Company:

SALARIES/BENEFITS:

Pension Plan:	ESOP Stock Plan:	Profit Sharing:	Top Exec. Salary: $1,547,308	Bonus: $1,530,000
Savings Plan: Y	Stock Purch. Plan: Y		Second Exec. Salary: $961,858	Bonus: $640,000

OTHER THOUGHTS:

Apparent Women Officers or Directors: 2
Hot Spot for Advancement for Women/Minorities: Y

LOCATIONS: ("Y" = Yes)

West:	Southwest:	Midwest:	Southeast:	Northeast:	International:
Y			Y	Y	Y

ANALOG DEVICES INC

www.analog.com

Industry Group Code: 334413 **Ranks within this company's industry group:** Sales: 15 Profits: 5

Techology:		Medical/Drugs:		Engineering:		Transportation:		Chemicals/Petrochemicals:		Specialty:	
Computers:	Y	Manufacturer:		Design:		Aerospace:		Oil/Gas Products:		Special Services:	
Software:		Contract Research:		Construction:		Automotive:		Chemicals:		Consulting:	
Communications:		Medical Services:		Eng. Services:		Shipping:		Oil/Chem. Svcs.:		Specialty Mgmt.:	
Electronics:		Labs:		Consulting:				Gases:		Products:	
Alternative Energy:		Bio. Services:						Other:		Other:	

TYPES OF BUSINESS:

Integrated Circuits-Analog & Digital
MEMS Products
DSP Products
Accelerometers & Gyroscopes

BRANDS/DIVISIONS/AFFILIATES:

CONTACTS: *Note: Officers with more than one job title may be intentionally listed here more than once.*

Jerald G. Fishman, CEO
Jerald G. Fishman, Pres.
Joseph E. McDonough, CFO/VP-Finance
Vincent Roche, VP-Worldwide Sales
William Matson, VP-Human Resources
Samuel H. Fuller, VP-R&D
Robert R. Marshall, VP-Worldwide Mfg.
Margaret K. Seif, General Counsel/VP/Sec.
Keith Rutherford, VP-Comm. Bus. Dev.
Mindy Kohl, Dir.-Investor Rel.
William A. Martin, Treas./Dir.-Mergers & Acquisitions
Thomas Wessel, VP-European Sales & Mktg.
Dennis Dempsey, VP/Gen. Mgr.-Limerick Mfg.
Mark Norton, VP/Gen. Mgr.-Mfg.
Alex Glass, VP-Global Acct.
Ray Stata, Chmn.
Howard Cheng, VP-Asia
Gerry Dundon, VP-Planning & Supply Chain Logistics

Phone: 781-329-4700 **Fax:** 781-461-4482
Toll-Free: 800-262-5643
Address: 1 Technology Way, P.O. Box 9106, Norwood, MA 02062 US

GROWTH PLANS/SPECIAL FEATURES:

Analog Devices, Inc. (ADI) designs, manufactures and markets a broad line of high-performance analog, mixed-signal and digital signal processing (DSP) integrated circuits (ICs). Its principal products are used in a wide variety of electronic equipment, including industrial process control, factory automation systems, smart munitions, base stations, central office equipment, wireless telephones, computers, cars, CAT scanners, digital cameras and DVD players. The company's product portfolio includes several thousand analog ICs, with as many as several hundred customers per design. ADI's analog technology base also includes an advanced IC technology known in the industry as surface micromachining, which is used to produce micro-electromechanical systems (MEMS) semiconductor products. The firm's MEMS product portfolio includes accelerometers used to sense acceleration and gyroscopes used to sense position. The majority of the ADI's current revenue from micromachined products comes from accelerometers used by automotive manufacturers in airbag applications. These accelerometers are also used in the IBM ThinkPad to protect the hard drives from drops and falls. The company offers both general-purpose and application-specific DSP products. Its application-specific DSP products typically include analog and DSP technology, with the DSPs preprogrammed to execute software for applications such as wireless telecommunications or image processing. ADI's customers include Dell, Alcatel, Lucent, Ericsson, Siemens, Sony, Philips, Ford and Volkswagen. The firm has manufacturing facilities in the U.S., Ireland and the Philippines. The company has approximately 1,300 U.S. patents and nearly 550 non-provisional pending U.S. patent applications. In 2008, Analog Devices sold its cellular handset radio and baseband chipset operations to MediaTek, Inc. for $350 million. Additionally, the firm sold its CPU voltage regulation and PC thermal monitoring business to ON Semiconductor Corporation for $184 million.

The company offers its employees medical, dental and vision coverage; life insurance; dependant and health care spending accounts; a retirement plan; and an education assistance plan.

FINANCIALS: **Sales and profits are in thousands of dollars—add 000 to get the full amount. 2008 Note: Financial information for 2008 was not available for all companies at press time.**

2008 Sales: $2,582,931 — 2008 Profits: $786,284
2007 Sales: $2,464,721 — 2007 Profits: $496,907
2006 Sales: $2,250,100 — 2006 Profits: $549,482
2005 Sales: $2,037,154 — 2005 Profits: $414,787
2004 Sales: $2,633,800 — 2004 Profits: $570,738

U.S. Stock Ticker: ADI
Int'l Ticker: Int'l Exchange:
Employees: 9,000
Fiscal Year Ends: 10/31
Parent Company:

SALARIES/BENEFITS:

Pension Plan: Y | ESOP Stock Plan: | Profit Sharing: | Top Exec. Salary: $948,838 | Bonus: $1,317,632
Savings Plan: | Stock Purch. Plan: | Second Exec. Salary: $386,019 | Bonus: $250,830

OTHER THOUGHTS:

Apparent Women Officers or Directors: 1
Hot Spot for Advancement for Women/Minorities: Y

LOCATIONS: ("Y" = Yes)

West:	Southwest:	Midwest:	Southeast:	Northeast:	International:
Y	Y	Y	Y	Y	Y

APPLE INC

www.apple.com

Industry Group Code: 334111 **Ranks within this company's industry group:** Sales: 7 Profits: 2

Techology:		Medical/Drugs:		Engineering:		Transportation:		Chemicals/Petrochemicals:		Specialty:	
Computers:	Y	Manufacturer:		Design:		Aerospace:		Oil/Gas Products:		Special Services:	Y
Software:	Y	Contract Research:		Construction:		Automotive:		Chemicals:		Consulting:	
Communications:		Medical Services:		Eng. Services:		Shipping:		Oil/Chem. Svcs.:		Specialty Mgmt.:	
Electronics:		Labs:		Consulting:				Gases:		Products:	Y
Alternative Energy:		Bio. Services:						Other:		Other:	

TYPES OF BUSINESS:

Computer Hardware-PCs
Software
Computer Accessories
Retail Stores
Portable Music Players
Online Music Sales
Cellular Phones
Home Entertainment Software & Systems

BRANDS/DIVISIONS/AFFILIATES:

Apple Computer Inc
MacBook Pro
Xserve
Mac OS X
Intel
iPod
iPhone
Safari

CONTACTS: *Note: Officers with more than one job title may be intentionally listed here more than once.*

Steve P. Jobs, CEO
Timothy D. Cook, COO
Peter Oppenheimer, CFO/Sr. VP
Philip W. Schiller, Sr. VP-Worldwide Prod. Mktg.
Bertrand Serlet, Sr. VP-Software Eng.
Daniel Cooperman, General Counsel/Sr. VP/Sec.
Ronald B. Johnson, Sr. VP-Retail
Jonathan Ive, Sr. VP-Industrial Design
Sina Tamaddon, Sr. VP-Applications
Tony Fadell, Sr. VP-iPod Div.
Bill Campbell, Chmn.

Phone: 408-996-1010	**Fax:** 408-974-2113
Toll-Free: 800-275-2273	
Address: 1 Infinite Loop, Cupertino, CA 95014 US	

GROWTH PLANS/SPECIAL FEATURES:

Apple, Inc. designs, manufactures and markets personal computers, portable digital music players and mobile communication devices; and sells a variety of related software, services, peripherals and networking solutions. The company's hardware products include the MacBook and MacBook Pro notebook computers; Mac Pro and iMac desktop computers; Mac minis; and Xserve servers and Xserve RAID Storage Systems. The firm's Mac products feature Intel microprocessors, Mac OS X Leopard operating systems and iLife software. Software products include Mac OS X; iLife '08; iWork '08; Logic Studio; and FileMaker Pro. Additional products include the iSight digital video cameras; the iPod line of portable digital music players and accessories; the iPhone, with touch controls, phone, iPod, and Internet services; Final Cut Studio, a high-definition video production suite of applications; and the iTunes digital entertainment management software for MP3 music files, television shows and movies. Peripheral products include printers, storage devices, memory, still cameras, widescreen flat panel displays and Apple TV, which plays iTunes content wirelessly. The firm operates over 215 retail stores in Canada, China, Japan, the U.K., the U.S., Australia and Italy. Apple's retail stores average $4,000 in sales per square foot per year. The iPod has sold over 100 million units; iTunes has sold over 5 billion songs and rents and sells over 50,000 movies daily. In 2008, the company released upgraded versions of the Mac Pro, MacBook and MacBook Pro, iMac, iPod, iPhone, and introduced new products such as the MacBook Air notebook computer, which is less than an inch thick; Time Capsule, a wireless backup appliance for Mac computers; and MobileMe internet service for mobile Apple products. In June 2008, Apple previewed Mac OS X Snow Leopard for 2009. In July 2008, Apple released the iPhone 3G, available in 22 countries, selling 1 million units in three days.

FINANCIALS: **Sales and profits are in thousands of dollars—add 000 to get the full amount. 2008 Note: Financial information for 2008 was not available for all companies at press time.**

2008 Sales: $32,479,000	2008 Profits: $4,834,000	**U.S. Stock Ticker: AAPL**
2007 Sales: $24,006,000	2007 Profits: $3,496,000	**Int'l Ticker:** Int'l Exchange:
2006 Sales: $19,315,000	2006 Profits: $1,989,000	Employees: 35,100
2005 Sales: $13,931,000	2005 Profits: $1,328,000	Fiscal Year Ends: 9/30
2004 Sales: $8,279,000	2004 Profits: $266,000	Parent Company:

SALARIES/BENEFITS:

Pension Plan:	ESOP Stock Plan:	Profit Sharing:	Top Exec. Salary: $700,014	Bonus: $700,000
Savings Plan: Y	Stock Purch. Plan: Y		Second Exec. Salary: $600,012	Bonus: $600,000

OTHER THOUGHTS:

Apparent Women Officers or Directors:
Hot Spot for Advancement for Women/Minorities:

LOCATIONS: ("Y" = Yes)

West:	Southwest:	Midwest:	Southeast:	Northeast:	International:
Y	Y	Y	Y	Y	Y

APPLIED MATERIALS INC

www.appliedmaterials.com

Industry Group Code: 333295 **Ranks within this company's industry group:** Sales: 1 Profits: 1

Techology:		Medical/Drugs:		Engineering:		Transportation:		Chemicals/Petrochemicals:		Specialty:	
Computers:	Y	Manufacturer:		Design:		Aerospace:		Oil/Gas Products:		Special Services:	
Software:		Contract Research:		Construction:		Automotive:		Chemicals:		Consulting:	
Communications:		Medical Services:		Eng. Services:		Shipping:		Oil/Chem. Svcs.:		Specialty Mgmt.:	
Electronics:		Labs:		Consulting:				Gases:		Products:	Y
Alternative Energy:		Bio. Services:						Other:		Other:	

TYPES OF BUSINESS:

Semiconductor Manufacturing Equipment
Solar Cells
Photovoltaics (PV)

BRANDS/DIVISIONS/AFFILIATES:

Nanomanufacturing
Silicon Systems Group
Dainippon Screen
Sokudo Company
Brooks Software
HCT Shaping Systems SA
Kachina
Baccini SpA

CONTACTS: *Note: Officers with more than one job title may be intentionally listed here more than once.*

Michael R. Splinter, CEO
Michael R. Splinter, Pres.
George S. Davis, CFO/Sr. VP
Franz Janker, Exec. VP-Sales & Mktg.
Jeannette Liebman, VP-Global Human Resources
Chris Eberspacher, Head-R&D, Solar Bus. Group
Ron Kifer, CIO/VP
Mark R. Pinto, CTO/Sr. VP/Gen. Mgr.-Energy & Environment
Joseph J. Sweeney, General Counsel/Corp. Sec./Sr. VP
Randhir Thakur, Sr. VP/Gen. Mgr.-Strategic Oper.
George Alajajian, VP/Oper. Mgr.-Corp. Bus. Dev.
Yvonne Weatherford, VP/Controller
Manfred Kerschbaum, Sr. VP/Gen. Mgr.-Applied Global Svcs.
Thomas St. Dennis, Sr. VP/Gen. Mgr.-Silicon Systems Group
Gilad Almogy, Sr. VP/Gen. Mgr.-Display & Thin Solar Products
Raymond Leubner, VP-Global Materials Oper.
James C. Morgan, Chmn.

Phone: 408-727-5555 **Fax:** 408-748-9943
Toll-Free: 800-882-0373
Address: 3050 Bowers Ave., Santa Clara, CA 95054 US

GROWTH PLANS/SPECIAL FEATURES:

Applied Materials, Inc. (AMI), a global leader in the semiconductor industry, provides solutions for the global semiconductor, flat panel display, solar and related industries, with a portfolio of equipment, service and software products. The firm operates in 11 principle regions including Canada, China, Europe, India, Israel, Japan, Korea, Malaysia, Singapore, Taiwan and the U.S. AMI operates in four reportable segments: Silicon, Fab Solutions, Display, and Adjacent Technologies. The Silicon segment develops, manufactures and sells a wide range of manufacturing equipment used to fabricate semiconductor chips or integrated circuits. Most chips are built on a silicon wafer base and include a variety of circuit components, such as transistors and other devices, that are connected by multiple layers of wiring (interconnects). The Fab Solutions segment provides products and services designed to improve the performance and productivity and reduce the environmental impact of the fab operations of semiconductor, LCD and solar cell manufacturers. The Display segment designs, manufactures and sells and services equipment to fabricate thin film transistor LCDs for televisions, computer displays and other consumer-oriented electronic applications. The Adjacent Technologies segment provides manufacturing solutions for the generation and conservation of energy. AMI's solutions utilize Nanomanufacturing, or the production of ultra-small structures, including the engineering of thin layers of film onto substrates. The company is investing heavily to become a world leader in PV cell technology for the creation of electricity from the sun's rays. Its focus is on raising the efficiency of the manufacturing process while raising the output of the cells. In July 2008, the company announced the release of Applied E3, a software package designed to improve productivity and reduce the cost of semiconductors, flat panel display and photovoltaic solar cell manufacturing. In July 2008, the firm began an expansion project of its Taiwan Manufacturing Center. Total cost of the expansion is approximately $17 million.

FINANCIALS: Sales and profits are in thousands of dollars—add 000 to get the full amount. 2008 Note: Financial information for 2008 was not available for all companies at press time.

2008 Sales: $8,129,240	2008 Profits: $960,746	**U.S. Stock Ticker: AMAT**
2007 Sales: $9,734,856	2007 Profits: $1,710,196	**Int'l Ticker:** Int'l Exchange:
2006 Sales: $9,167,014	2006 Profits: $1,516,663	Employees: 15,410
2005 Sales: $6,991,823	2005 Profits: $1,209,900	Fiscal Year Ends: 10/31
2004 Sales: $8,013,053	2004 Profits: $1,351,303	Parent Company:

SALARIES/BENEFITS:

Pension Plan:	ESOP Stock Plan:	Profit Sharing:	Top Exec. Salary: $945,000	Bonus: $1,622,329
Savings Plan:	Stock Purch. Plan:		Second Exec. Salary: $542,308	Bonus: $856,625

OTHER THOUGHTS:

Apparent Women Officers or Directors: 6
Hot Spot for Advancement for Women/Minorities: Y

LOCATIONS: ("Y" = Yes)

West:	Southwest:	Midwest:	Southeast:	Northeast:	International:
Y	Y				Y

ARCADIS NV

www.arcadis-global.com

Industry Group Code: 541330 **Ranks within this company's industry group:** Sales: 6 Profits: 8

Techology:		Medical/Drugs:		Engineering:		Transportation:		Chemicals/Petrochemicals:		Specialty:	
Computers:		Manufacturer:		Design:	Y	Aerospace:		Oil/Gas Products:		Special Services:	
Software:		Contract Research:		Construction:	Y	Automotive:		Chemicals:		Consulting:	
Communications:		Medical Services:		Eng. Services:	Y	Shipping:		Oil/Chem. Svcs.:		Specialty Mgmt.:	Y
Electronics:		Labs:		Consulting:	Y			Gases:		Products:	
Alternative Energy:		Bio. Services:						Other:		Other:	

TYPES OF BUSINESS:

Engineering Services
Consulting Services
Project Management
Environmental Services
Infrastructure Construction Management
Power Generation Facilities
Industrial & Residential Development

BRANDS/DIVISIONS/AFFILIATES:

ARCADIS Geraghty & Miller Inc
HOMOLA Projectmanagement AG
Bessent, Hammack & Ruckman Inc
Logos Engenharia
Eurolatina
Arcadis Euroconsult
HL-Service Management GmbH

CONTACTS: *Note: Officers with more than one job title may be intentionally listed here more than once.*

Harrie L. J. Noy, Exec. Chmn.
Ben A. van der Klift, CFO
Tom W. Haak, Dir.-Human Resources
Anja M. Van Bergen-van Kruijsbergen, General Counsel/Corp. Sec.
Joost Slloten, Investor Rel. Officer
Craig E. Eisen, Dir.-Mergers & Acquisitions
C. Michiel Jaski, Member-Exec. Board
Friedrich M.T. Schneider, Member-Exec. Board
Rijnhard W. F. van Tets, Chmn.
Steven B. Blake, CEO-Arcadis U.S.

Phone: 31-26-377-8911 **Fax:** 31-26-351-5235
Toll-Free:
Address: Nieuwe Stationsstraat 10, Arnhem, 6800 LE The Netherlands

GROWTH PLANS/SPECIAL FEATURES:

Arcadis N.V., based in the Netherlands, is an international provider of consulting, engineering and project management services for infrastructure, environment and facilities. The company develops, designs, implements, maintains and operates projects for private and public sector clients through three activity divisions: Infrastructure, which accounts for 41% of Arcadis' business; Environment, which accounts for 36%; and Buildings, which accounts for 23%. The infrastructure division consults, designs and manages the construction of infrastructure projects, including railroads, highways, airports, harbors, waterways, dikes and retention ponds. The company also develops utilities for rail signaling, safety, communications and energy supply; constructs bridges and tunnels; and develops small power plants, wind farms and hydroelectric facilities. In addition, the infrastructure division designs and develops new industrial parks and residential areas and oversees the redevelopment of old sites. The environment division provides consulting on environmental policy for companies and governments; conducts environmental impact assessments; and supports environmental management and environmentally conscious engineering practices. The division provides soil and groundwater contamination testing and develops cost-effective solutions for the remediation of contaminated soil and water. Lastly, the buildings division develops and maintains buildings, including offices, stores, commercial properties, schools, museums, prisons, stadiums and railway stations. To carry out the activities of these divisions, Arcadis works from its strong home market positions in Europe, the U.S. and South America, with approximately 200 locations in 100 countries. The firm is also seeking to expand into new markets, with select offices in the Middle East, Japan and China. In July 2008, the company acquired SET, an Italian firm specializing in environmental consulting.

Arcadis offers its U.S. employees benefits including medical, dental and vision coverage; flexible spending accounts; an employee assistance program; a 401(k) plan; a discount stock purchase plan; and life and AD&D insurance.

FINANCIALS: **Sales and profits are in thousands of dollars—add 000 to get the full amount. 2008 Note: Financial information for 2008 was not available for all companies at press time.**

2008 Sales: $2,277,630	2008 Profits: $83,350	**U.S. Stock Ticker: ARCAY**
2007 Sales: $2,235,000	2007 Profits: $81,260	**Int'l Ticker: ARCAD** Int'l Exchange: Amsterdam
2006 Sales: $1,825,000	2006 Profits: $66,460	Employees: 13,171
2005 Sales: $873,000	2005 Profits: $41,200	Fiscal Year Ends: 12/31
2004 Sales: $786,400	2004 Profits: $25,200	Parent Company:

SALARIES/BENEFITS:

Pension Plan:	ESOP Stock Plan:	Profit Sharing:	Top Exec. Salary: $	Bonus: $
Savings Plan: Y	Stock Purch. Plan: Y		Second Exec. Salary: $	Bonus: $

OTHER THOUGHTS:

Apparent Women Officers or Directors:
Hot Spot for Advancement for Women/Minorities:

LOCATIONS: ("Y" = Yes)

West:	Southwest:	Midwest:	Southeast:	Northeast:	International:
Y	Y	Y	Y	Y	Y

AREVA GROUP

www.arevagroup.com

Industry Group Code: 335000 **Ranks within this company's industry group:** Sales: 8 Profits: 6

Techology:		Medical/Drugs:		Engineering:		Transportation:		Chemicals/Petrochemicals:		Specialty:	
Computers:		Manufacturer:		Design:		Aerospace:		Oil/Gas Products:		Special Services:	
Software:		Contract Research:		Construction:		Automotive:		Chemicals:		Consulting:	
Communications:		Medical Services:		Eng. Services:		Shipping:		Oil/Chem. Svcs.:		Specialty Mgmt.:	
Electronics:		Labs:		Consulting:				Gases:		Products:	
Alternative Energy:	Y	Bio. Services:						Other:		Other:	

TYPES OF BUSINESS:

Nuclear Power Generation Equipment
Nuclear Power Plant Design, Construction & Maintenance
Electrical Transmission & Distribution Products
Electrical & Electronic Interconnect Systems
Uranium Mining & Processing
Forged Steel Equipment

BRANDS/DIVISIONS/AFFILIATES:

AREVA T&D
AREVA NC
AREVA NP
Commissariat a l'Energie Atomique (CEA)
UraMin
RM Consultants, Ltd.
Nokian Capacitors, Ltd.
Koblitz

CONTACTS: *Note: Officers with more than one job title may be intentionally listed here more than once.*

Anne Lauvergeon, CEO
Gerald Arbola, COO
Alain Pierre-Raynaud, CFO
Philippe Vivien, Sr. Exec. VP-Human Resources
Isabelle Coupey, VP-Investor Rel. & Financial Comm.
Didier Benedetti, COO-AREVA NC, Research
Luc Oursel, Pres./CEO-AREVA NP
Tom Christopher, CEO-AREVA, Inc.
Frederic Lemoine, Chmn.-Supervisory Board

Phone: 33-1-34-96-00-00	**Fax:** 33-1-34-96-00-01
Toll-Free:	
Address: 33 rue La Fayette, Paris, 75442 France	

GROWTH PLANS/SPECIAL FEATURES:

AREVA Group was created through the merger of AREVA T&D, COGEMA and FRAMATOME ANP, which combined the French Government's interests in several nuclear power and information technology businesses. The CEA (Commissariat a l'Energie Atomique), the French atomic energy commission, owns 79% of the company. The firm has manufacturing facilities in over 43 countries and a sales network in over 100 countries. AREVA operates in four divisions: front-end; reactors and services; back-end; and transmission and distribution (T&D). Through the front-end division and wholly-owned subsidiary AREVA NC, the company provides uranium ore exploration, mining, concentration, conversion and enrichment, as well as nuclear fuel design and fabrication. The reactors and services division offers design and construction services for nuclear reactors and other non-carbon dioxide emitting power generation systems. Through AREVA NP, which is 66%-owned by AREVA and 34%-owned by Siemens, the firm offers the design and construction of nuclear power plants and research reactors, instrumentation and control, modernization and maintenance services, components manufacture and the supply of nuclear fuel. The back-end division provides treatment and recycling of used fuel, as well as cleanup of nuclear facilities and nuclear logistics. The T&D division and wholly-owned subsidiary AREVA T&D supply products, systems and services for all stages in the transfer of electricity, from the generator to the large end-user. In January 2008, AREVA's T&D division agreed to acquire Nokian Capacitors, Ltd., to reinforce its position in the ultra high-voltage market. Also in January, AREVA acquired a 70% stake in Koblitz, a provider of renewable source power generation solutions. In April 2008, AREVA acquired RM Consultants, Ltd., a nuclear safety consulting company. Later that year, AREVA sold its 30% stake in wind turbine manufacturer Repower. The company is also proposing to build a $2 billion centrifuge enrichment plant in Idaho that could break ground by 2010.

FINANCIALS: **Sales and profits are in thousands of dollars—add 000 to get the full amount. 2008 Note: Financial information for 2008 was not available for all companies at press time.**

2008 Sales: $17,404,900	2008 Profits: $658,640	**U.S. Stock Ticker: ARVCF**
2007 Sales: $15,768,900	2007 Profits: $1,166,500	**Int'l Ticker: CEI** Int'l Exchange: Paris-Euronext
2006 Sales: $14,331,600	2006 Profits: $856,200	Employees: 75,414
2005 Sales: $14,196,300	2005 Profits: $1,303,400	Fiscal Year Ends: 12/31
2004 Sales: $15,152,700	2004 Profits: $583,800	Parent Company:

SALARIES/BENEFITS:

Pension Plan:	ESOP Stock Plan:	Profit Sharing:	Top Exec. Salary: $500,264	Bonus: $
Savings Plan:	Stock Purch. Plan:		Second Exec. Salary: $380,364	Bonus: $

OTHER THOUGHTS:

Apparent Women Officers or Directors: 1
Hot Spot for Advancement for Women/Minorities: Y

LOCATIONS: ("Y" = Yes)

West:	Southwest:	Midwest:	Southeast:	Northeast:	International:
				Y	Y

ARKEMA

www.arkema.com

Industry Group Code: 325000 **Ranks within this company's industry group:** Sales: 17 Profits: 21

Techology:		Medical/Drugs:		Engineering:		Transportation:		Chemicals/Petrochemicals:		Specialty:	
Computers:		Manufacturer:		Design:		Aerospace:		Oil/Gas Products:		Special Services:	
Software:		Contract Research:		Construction:		Automotive:		Chemicals:	Y	Consulting:	
Communications:		Medical Services:		Eng. Services:		Shipping:		Oil/Chem. Svcs.:		Specialty Mgmt.:	
Electronics:		Labs:		Consulting:				Gases:		Products:	Y
Alternative Energy:		Bio. Services:						Other:		Other:	

TYPES OF BUSINESS:

Chemicals, Manufacturing
Vinyl Products
Industrial Chemicals
Performance Products
Plexiglas
Agrochemicals
Nanomaterials

BRANDS/DIVISIONS/AFFILIATES:

Nakan
Alphacan
Ceca
Lacovyl
Aqua Keep
Rilsan
Plexiglas
Oxford Performance Materials Inc

CONTACTS: *Note: Officers with more than one job title may be intentionally listed here more than once.*

Thierry Le Henaff, CEO
Thierry Lemonnier, CFO
Michel Delaborde, Exec. VP-Human Resources
Alain Devic, Exec. VP-Industrial Oper.
Bernard Boyer, Exec. VP-Strategy
Michel Delaborde, Exec. VP-Corp. Comm.
Otto Takken, Exec. VP-Vinyl Prod.
Marc Schuller, Exec. VP-Industrial Chemicals
Pierre Chanoine, Exec. VP-Performance Prod.
Thierry Le Henaff, Chmn.

Phone: 33-1-49-00-80-80 **Fax:** 33-1-49-00-83-96
Toll-Free:
Address: 420, rue d'Estienne d'Orves, Colombes, 92705 France

GROWTH PLANS/SPECIAL FEATURES:

Arkema, formerly the chemical branch of TOTAL S.A., is a leading chemical company with operations in three divisions: Vinyl Products, Industrial Chemicals and Performance Products. The vinyl products division manufactures chlorochemicals such as caustic soda, chlorine and polyvinyl chloride (PVC) as well as various vinyl compounds and, through its Alphacan business unit, pipes and profiles. Brands produced by this division include Lacovyl, for cosmetic and pharmaceutical packaging; Nakan, for instrument panel coating and medical equipment; Lucobay, for windows and shutters; and Bactivel, for bleaches and disinfectants. The industrial chemicals division produces acrylics, fluorochemicals, hydrogen peroxide and thiochemicals such as sulfides and odorizers for natural gas. Brands produced by this division include Forane, for refrigeration, air conditioning and as a blowing agent for insulating foam; Albone, for textile and pulp bleaching, chemical synthesis and water treatment; Aquakeep, a super-absorbent material for diapers; and Altuglas and Plexiglas, for furniture, automotive and noise barriers. The performance products division manufactures specialty chemicals through its Ceca business unit. Brands in this division include Rilsan, an additive for anti-corrosion coating, brake circuits, pipes and automotive fuels; Luperox, a polymerization agent used in producing packaging plastics, hoses and gaskets; Pebax, used in athletic shoes, toy manufacturing, watch making and automobiles; and Kynar, a protective coating for the construction, chemical engineering and petrochemical industries. The company has 60 manufacturing facilities in Europe, as well as 20 manufacturing facilities in North America and 15 in Asia. The firm also has six research centers in France, the U.S. and Japan. In 2008, the company sold its Urea Formaldehyde Resins business to the American company Hexion. In December 2008, the firm announced plans to acquire the organic peroxide business of U.S.-based GEO Specialty Chemicals. In February 2009, Arkema acquired Oxford Performance Materials, Inc., an American company specializing in polyketone-based thermoplastic materials.

FINANCIALS: **Sales and profits are in thousands of dollars—add 000 to get the full amount. 2008 Note: Financial information for 2008 was not available for all companies at press time.**

2008 Sales: $7,449,980
2007 Sales: $7,505,530
2006 Sales: $7,739,000
2005 Sales: $6,762,400
2004 Sales: $7,092,800

2008 Profits: $132,260
2007 Profits: $161,350
2006 Profits: $
2005 Profits: $
2004 Profits: $

U.S. Stock Ticker:
Int'l Ticker: AKE Int'l Exchange: Paris-Euronext
Employees: 15,000
Fiscal Year Ends: 12/31
Parent Company:

SALARIES/BENEFITS:

Pension Plan: ESOP Stock Plan: Profit Sharing: Top Exec. Salary: $ Bonus: $
Savings Plan: Stock Purch. Plan: Second Exec. Salary: $ Bonus: $

OTHER THOUGHTS:

Apparent Women Officers or Directors:
Hot Spot for Advancement for Women/Minorities:

LOCATIONS: ("Y" = Yes)

West:	Southwest:	Midwest:	Southeast:	Northeast:	International:
Y	Y	Y	Y	Y	Y

Note: Financial information, benefits and other data can change quickly and may vary from those stated here.

ARRIS GROUP INC

www.arrisi.com

Industry Group Code: 334200 **Ranks within this company's industry group:** Sales: 3 Profits: 5

Techology:		Medical/Drugs:		Engineering:		Transportation:		Chemicals/Petrochemicals:		Specialty:	
Computers:		Manufacturer:		Design:		Aerospace:		Oil/Gas Products:		Special Services:	
Software:		Contract Research:		Construction:		Automotive:		Chemicals:		Consulting:	
Communications:	Y	Medical Services:		Eng. Services:		Shipping:		Oil/Chem. Svcs.:		Specialty Mgmt.:	
Electronics:		Labs:		Consulting:				Gases:		Products:	
Alternative Energy:		Bio. Services:						Other:		Other:	

TYPES OF BUSINESS:

Communications Equipment-Cable Systems
Optical & Radio Frequency Transmission Equipment
Internet Access Products
Support & Testing Products

BRANDS/DIVISIONS/AFFILIATES:

Broadband Communications Systems
Access, Transport and Supplies
Media & Communications Systems
Madison River Communications Corp
YourBroadbandStore.com
C-COR Inc

CONTACTS: *Note: Officers with more than one job title may be intentionally listed here more than once.*

Robert J. (Bob) Stanzione, CEO
Robert J. (Bob) Stanzione, Pres.
David B. Potts, CFO/Exec. VP
Ronald M. (Ron) Coppock, Pres., Worldwide Sales & Mktg.
David B. Potts, CIO
Lawrence Margolis, Exec. VP-Admin.
Lawrence Margolis, General Counsel/Corp. Sec.
Lawrence A. Margolis, Exec. VP-Strategic Planning
James A. Bauer, Dir.-Investor Rel.
Marc C. Geraci, Treas./VP
James D. Lakin, Pres., Broadband
Bryant K. Isaacs, Pres., New Bus. Ventures
Robert (Bob) Puccini, Pres., TeleWire Supply
Robert J. (Bob) Stanzione, Chmn.

Phone: 770-473-2000 **Fax:** 770-622-8750
Toll-Free: 800-469-6569
Address: 3871 Lakefield Dr., Suwanee, GA 30024 US

GROWTH PLANS/SPECIAL FEATURES:

Arris Group, Inc. is a global telecommunications technology company specializing in integrated broadband network solutions that include products, systems and software for content and operations management and professional services. Arris develops, manufactures and supplies cable telephony, video and high-speed data equipment. In addition, the firm is a leading supplier of infrastructure products used by cable system operators to build-out and maintain hybrid fiber-coaxial (HFC) networks. It provides products and equipment principally to cable system operators and, more specifically, to multiple system operators (MSOs). Arris' products enable MSOs and other broadband service providers to deliver a full range of integrated voice, video and high-speed data services to their subscribers. The company operates in three segments: Broadband Communications Systems (BCS); Access, Transport and Supplies (ATS); and Media & Communications Systems (MCS). Its BCS product offerings include VoIP (Voice over Internet Protocol) and high speed data products; video and IP (Internet Protocol) headend products; and constant bit rate telephony products. ATS products include HFC plant equipment products and infrastructure products for fiber optic or coaxial networks built under or above ground. Arris' MCS products include content and operations management systems, operations management systems and fixed mobile convergence networks. The company maintains domestic sales offices in Colorado, Georgia and Pennsylvania and international sales offices in Argentina, Chile, Hong Kong, Japan, the Netherlands and Spain. The firm's two largest customers are Comcast and Time Warner Cable, which generated 39.8% and 10.7% of its sales for 2007, respectively. In April 2007, the company acquired Madison River Communications Corp. for approximately $830 million. In September 2007, Arris created YourBroadbandStore.com, a retail website providing professional grade telecommunications products. In December 2007, the company acquired C-COR, Inc., a provider of integrated access and management platforms, for approximately $730 million.

FINANCIALS: **Sales and profits are in thousands of dollars—add 000 to get the full amount. 2008 Note: Financial information for 2008 was not available for all companies at press time.**

2008 Sales: $1,144,565	2008 Profits: $-95,075	**U.S. Stock Ticker: ARRS**
2007 Sales: $992,194	2007 Profits: $98,340	**Int'l Ticker:** Int'l Exchange:
2006 Sales: $891,551	2006 Profits: $142,287	Employees: 1,992
2005 Sales: $680,417	2005 Profits: $51,483	Fiscal Year Ends: 12/31
2004 Sales: $490,041	2004 Profits: $-28,396	Parent Company:

SALARIES/BENEFITS:

Pension Plan:	ESOP Stock Plan:	Profit Sharing:	Top Exec. Salary: $687,500	Bonus: $763,000
Savings Plan:	Stock Purch. Plan:		Second Exec. Salary: $368,125	Bonus: $245,000

OTHER THOUGHTS:

Apparent Women Officers or Directors:
Hot Spot for Advancement for Women/Minorities:

LOCATIONS: ("Y" = Yes)

West:	Southwest:	Midwest:	Southeast:	Northeast:	International:
Y		Y	Y	Y	Y

Note: Financial information, benefits and other data can change quickly and may vary from those stated here.

ARVINMERITOR INC

www.arvinmeritor.com

Industry Group Code: 336300 **Ranks within this company's industry group:** Sales: 14 Profits: 13

Techology:		**Medical/Drugs:**		**Engineering:**		**Transportation:**		**Chemicals/Petrochemicals:**		**Specialty:**	
Computers:		Manufacturer:		Design:		Aerospace:		Oil/Gas Products:		Special Services:	
Software:		Contract Research:		Construction:		Automotive:	Y	Chemicals:		Consulting:	
Communications:		Medical Services:		Eng. Services:		Shipping:		Oil/Chem. Svcs.:		Specialty Mgmt.:	
Electronics:		Labs:		Consulting:				Gases:		Products:	
Alternative Energy:		Bio. Services:						Other:		Other:	

TYPES OF BUSINESS:

Auto Parts Manufacturer
Drivetrain Systems & Components
Exhaust Systems
Braking Systems
Driveline Systems & Axles
Undercarriage Systems
Roof & Door Systems

BRANDS/DIVISIONS/AFFILIATES:

Commercial Vehicle Systems
Light Vehicle Systems
OnGuard

CONTACTS: *Note: Officers with more than one job title may be intentionally listed here more than once.*

Charles McClure, CEO
Charles McClure, Pres.
Jeffrey Craig, CFO/Sr. VP
Vernon Baker, General Counsel/Sr. VP
Mary Lehmann, Sr. VP-Strategic Initiatives
Lin Cummins, Sr. VP-Comm.
Mary Lehmann, Treas.
Carsten Reinhardt, Sr. VP/Pres., Commercial Vehicle Systems
James Donion, Exec. VP
Charles McClure, Chmn.

Phone: 248-435-1000	**Fax:** 248-435-1393
Toll-Free:	
Address: 2135 W. Maple Rd., Troy, MI 48084 US	

GROWTH PLANS/SPECIAL FEATURES:

ArvinMeritor, Inc., headquartered in Troy, Michigan, is a global supplier of a broad range of integrated systems, modules and components serving light vehicle, commercial truck, trailer and specialty original equipment manufacturers and certain aftermarkets. The company operates approximately 82 manufacturing facilities in 22 countries, participates in 21 joint ventures in 12 of these countries and serves its customers through two businesses: Light vehicle systems (LVS) and commercial vehicle systems (CVS). The LVS segment supplies body systems, chassis systems and wheel products for passenger cars, all-terrain vehicles (ATVs), light trucks and sport utility vehicles (SUVs). CVS supplies drivetrain systems and components, including axles and drivelines, braking systems, suspension systems and ride control products for medium- and heavy-duty trucks, trailers and specialty vehicles. CVS also operates a joint venture with Volvo for the manufacturing of truck axles. North America represents 46% of the company's sales; Europe, 32%, South America, 12%; and Asia Pacific, 10%. One of the firm's most recent products, OnGuard, is a radar-based adaptive cruise control system with active braking for commercial vehicles in North America. In May 2008, the firm announced that it would spin off its automotive parts unit into a new company called Arvin Innovation, Inc. The new company will be publically traded and have 42 facilities in 16 countries, with its headquarters in Detroit. International business will account for 65% of the new company's revenue. In July 2008, ArvinMeritor agreed to acquire Trucktechnic, a Belgian remanufacturer and distributor of commercial vehicle disc and foundation brakes.

Employees are offered medical, dental, vision and life insurance; a disability income plan; adoption assistance; and educational assistance.

FINANCIALS: **Sales and profits are in thousands of dollars—add 000 to get the full amount. 2008 Note: Financial information for 2008 was not available for all companies at press time.**

2008 Sales: $7,167,000	2008 Profits: $-101,000	**U.S. Stock Ticker: ARM**
2007 Sales: $6,449,000	2007 Profits: $-219,000	**Int'l Ticker:** Int'l Exchange:
2006 Sales: $6,415,000	2006 Profits: $-175,000	Employees: 19,800
2005 Sales: $6,371,000	2005 Profits: $12,000	Fiscal Year Ends: 9/30
2004 Sales: $7,887,000	2004 Profits: $-42,000	Parent Company:

SALARIES/BENEFITS:

Pension Plan: Y	ESOP Stock Plan:	Profit Sharing:	Top Exec. Salary: $1,120,833	Bonus: $2,743,000
Savings Plan: Y	Stock Purch. Plan:		Second Exec. Salary: $696,900	Bonus: $1,017,383

OTHER THOUGHTS:

Apparent Women Officers or Directors: 4
Hot Spot for Advancement for Women/Minorities: Y

LOCATIONS: ("Y" = Yes)

West:	Southwest:	Midwest:	Southeast:	Northeast:	International:
Y	Y	Y	Y	Y	Y

ASC INCORPORATED

www.ascglobal.com

Industry Group Code: 541330 **Ranks within this company's industry group:** Sales: Profits:

Techology:		Medical/Drugs:		Engineering:		Transportation:		Chemicals/Petrochemicals:		Specialty:	
Computers:		Manufacturer:		Design:		Aerospace:		Oil/Gas Products:		Special Services:	
Software:		Contract Research:		Construction:		Automotive:	Y	Chemicals:		Consulting:	
Communications:		Medical Services:		Eng. Services:		Shipping:		Oil/Chem. Svcs.:		Specialty Mgmt.:	
Electronics:		Labs:		Consulting:				Gases:		Products:	
Alternative Energy:		Bio. Services:						Other:		Other:	

TYPES OF BUSINESS:

Specialty Car Manufacturing
Automobile Design Services

BRANDS/DIVISIONS/AFFILIATES:

Questor Funds
Halo
Image
Buzz
Saleen Incorporated

CONTACTS:
Note: Officers with more than one job title may be intentionally listed here more than once.

Paul Wilbur, CEO
Paul Wilbur, Pres.
John Carson, CFO
Steven Laurain, VP-Sales
Steven Laurain, VP-Eng.
Mike Lingo, VP-Oper.
John Carson, Treas.
Mark Trostle, Pres., Creative Svcs.
Marques B. McCammon, Gen. Manager-ASC West Coast Design & Tech. Center
Dennis Kneale, Manager-Lexington Plant

Phone: 734-285-4911	**Fax:** 734-246-2735
Toll-Free:	
Address: 1 ASC Center, Southgate, MI 48195 US	

GROWTH PLANS/SPECIAL FEATURES:

ASC, Inc., an acronym standing for American Specialty Cars, is a firm based in Southgate, Michigan that helps carmakers design, engineer and manufacture high-image low-volume specialty vehicles. The company capitalizes on the recent trend away from standard vehicles towards more personalized, higher-end vehicles. Beyond its modeling and prototyping services, ASC boast manufacturing capabilities that range from body framing to multi-panel open air systems. The firm produces vehicles under the Halo, Image and Buzz platforms. The Halo and Image platforms focus on new, low-volume, high-performance vehicles designed to grab the attention of consumers. Buzz models are special versions of existing nameplates, capitalizing on what consumers are already doing in the aftermarket. The company was involved in developing models such as the Dodge Ram SportSide Concept, Chevrolet SSR, the Buick GNX and the Pontiac Vibe GTR. ASC has manufacturing facilities in Michigan and Kentucky. The firm is privately held by Questor Funds. In 2007, the firm came together with Saleen Incorporated as sister companies operating out of common facilities.

FINANCIALS:
Sales and profits are in thousands of dollars—add 000 to get the full amount. 2008 Note: Financial information for 2008 was not available for all companies at press time.

2008 Sales: $	2008 Profits: $	**U.S. Stock Ticker: Private**
2007 Sales: $	2007 Profits: $	**Int'l Ticker:** Int'l Exchange:
2006 Sales: $	2006 Profits: $	Employees: 1,221
2005 Sales: $	2005 Profits: $	Fiscal Year Ends:
2004 Sales: $493,000	2004 Profits: $	Parent Company:

SALARIES/BENEFITS:

Pension Plan:	ESOP Stock Plan:	Profit Sharing:	Top Exec. Salary: $	Bonus: $
Savings Plan:	Stock Purch. Plan:		Second Exec. Salary: $	Bonus: $

OTHER THOUGHTS:

Apparent Women Officers or Directors:
Hot Spot for Advancement for Women/Minorities:

LOCATIONS: ("Y" = Yes)

West:	Southwest:	Midwest:	Southeast:	Northeast:	International:
		Y			

ASTELLAS PHARMA INC

www.astellas.com

Industry Group Code: 325412 **Ranks within this company's industry group:** Sales: 19 Profits: 18

Techology:		Medical/Drugs:		Engineering:		Transportation:		Chemicals/Petrochemicals:		Specialty:	
Computers:		Manufacturer:	Y	Design:		Aerospace:		Oil/Gas Products:		Special Services:	Y
Software:		Contract Research:		Construction:		Automotive:		Chemicals:		Consulting:	
Communications:		Medical Services:		Eng. Services:		Shipping:		Oil/Chem. Svcs.:		Specialty Mgmt.:	
Electronics:		Labs:		Consulting:				Gases:		Products:	
Alternative Energy:		Bio. Services:						Other:		Other:	

TYPES OF BUSINESS:

Drugs, Manufacturing
Immunological Pharmaceuticals
Over-the-Counter Products
Reagents
Genomic Research
Venture Capital
Drug Licensing

BRANDS/DIVISIONS/AFFILIATES:

Yamanouchi Pharmaceutical Co., Ltd.
Fujisawa Pharmaceutical Co., Ltd.
Prograf
Lipitor
Harnal
Flomax
Micardis
Astellas Venture Management, LLC

CONTACTS: *Note: Officers with more than one job title may be intentionally listed here more than once.*

Masafumi Nogimori, CEO
Masafumi Nogimori, Pres.
Yasuo Ishii, Chief Sales & Mktg. Officer/Exec. VP
Hirofumi Onosaka, Sr. Corp. Officer
Hitoshi Ohta, Sr. Corp. Officer
Iwaki Miyazaki, Sr. Corp. Officer
Katsuro Yamada, Sr. Corp. Officer
Toichi Takenaka, Chmn.
Yoshihiko Hatanaka, CEO/Pres., Astellas Pharma U.S., Inc.

Phone: 81-3-3244-3000 **Fax:** 81-3-3244-3272
Toll-Free:
Address: 2-3-11 Nihonbashi-Honcho, Chuo-ku, Tokyo, 103-8411 Japan

GROWTH PLANS/SPECIAL FEATURES:

Astellas Pharma, Inc. is one of the largest pharmaceuticals manufacturers in Japan. It was formed from the recent merger of Yamanouchi Pharmaceutical Co., Ltd. and Fujisawa Pharmaceutical Co., Ltd. In addition to developing its own pharmaceuticals, Astellas pursues in-licensing and co-promotion agreements with biotechnology firms and a host of other pharmaceutical companies such as Pfizer, Inc. Nearly all of Astellas's sales relate to pharmaceuticals, led by Prograf, which is used as an immunosuppressant in conjunction with organ transplantation. Other products target needs in dermatology, urology, gastrointestinal disorders, immunology, infectious diseases, psychiatry and cardiology. Some of the firm's main products include Lipitor (developed by Pfizer) for high cholesterol; Micardis (co-promoted with Nippon Boehringer Ingelheim), a hypertension treatment; Myslee, an insomnia treatment co-promoted with sanofi-aventis S.A.; Seroquel, an antipsychotic; Gaster, for peptic ulcers and gastritis; fungal infection treatments AmBisome and Mycamine; overactive bladder treatment VESIcare; and Harnal for symptoms caused by enlarged prostates. Harnal is marketed by Boehringer Ingelheim Pharmaceuticals, Inc. in the U.S. under the name Flomax. Besides developing its own drugs or marketing drugs developed by others, the firm maintains Los Altos, CA-based subsidiary Astellas Venture Management, LLC, which is engaged in investing in biotechnology companies, starting with $30 million in initial capitalization. Astellas has 24 subsidiaries and affiliates in Europe; 11 in North America; seven in Asia; and three manufacturing subsidiaries in Japan. Geographically, Japan accounted for 51% of 2008 sales; Europe, 25%; North America, 22%; and Asia, 2%. In January 2009, the firm announced its intention to acquired CV Therapeutics, Inc. for $1.1 billion.

FINANCIALS: **Sales and profits are in thousands of dollars—add 000 to get the full amount. 2008 Note: Financial information for 2008 was not available for all companies at press time.**

2008 Sales: $9,726,000 | 2008 Profits: $1,774,000
2007 Sales: $9,114,200 | 2007 Profits: $1,299,700
2006 Sales: $8,705,700 | 2006 Profits: $1,026,200
2005 Sales: $4,425,800 | 2005 Profits: $333,800
2004 Sales: $4,839,100 | 2004 Profits: $568,500

U.S. Stock Ticker: ALPMF.PK
Int'l Ticker: 4503 Int'l Exchange: Tokyo-TSE
Employees: 7,453
Fiscal Year Ends: 3/31
Parent Company:

SALARIES/BENEFITS:

Pension Plan: Y | ESOP Stock Plan: | Profit Sharing: | Top Exec. Salary: $ | Bonus: $
Savings Plan: | Stock Purch. Plan: | | Second Exec. Salary: $ | Bonus: $

OTHER THOUGHTS:

Apparent Women Officers or Directors: 1
Hot Spot for Advancement for Women/Minorities:

LOCATIONS: ("Y" = Yes)

West:	Southwest:	Midwest:	Southeast:	Northeast:	International:
Y		Y		Y	Y

ASTON MARTIN LAGONDA LTD

www.astonmartin.com

Industry Group Code: 336111 **Ranks within this company's industry group:** Sales: Profits:

Techology:		Medical/Drugs:		Engineering:		Transportation:		Chemicals/Petrochemicals:		Specialty:	
Computers:		Manufacturer:		Design:		Aerospace:		Oil/Gas Products:		Special Services:	
Software:		Contract Research:		Construction:		Automotive:	Y	Chemicals:		Consulting:	
Communications:		Medical Services:		Eng. Services:		Shipping:		Oil/Chem. Svcs.:		Specialty Mgmt.:	
Electronics:		Labs:		Consulting:				Gases:		Products:	
Alternative Energy:		Bio. Services:						Other:		Other:	

TYPES OF BUSINESS:

Automobile Manufacturing
Sports Cars
Antique Vehicle Maintenance & Restoration
Clothing & Fashion Accessories
Automobile Racing

BRANDS/DIVISIONS/AFFILIATES:

Lagonda
DBS
DB9
V8 Vantage
DBR9
V8 Vantage Roadster
Collection (The)
Prodrive Ltd.

CONTACTS: *Note: Officers with more than one job title may be intentionally listed here more than once.*

Ulrich Bez, CEO
Marek Reichman, Dir.-Design
Kingsley Riding-Felce, Dir.-Works Svc. & Customer Rel.
Robin Brundle, Managing Dir.-Aston Martin Racing
Ulrich Bez, Chmn.

Phone: 44-1926-644644 **Fax:** 44-1926-644733
Toll-Free:
Address: Banbury Rd., Gaydon, Warwickshire CV35 0DB UK

GROWTH PLANS/SPECIAL FEATURES:

Aston Martin Lagonda, Ltd., formerly a subsidiary of Ford Motor Company, is a small British firm with more than 90 years of experience in building high-performance sports cars. Its current models, the DBS, DB9 Coupe and DB9 Volante, and the V8 Vantage Roadster and V8 Vantage Coupe, are all built by hand and retail for between $113,000 and $265,000. In addition, subsidiary Aston Martin Racing manufactures a line of DBR9 racing cars in partnership with Prodrive Ltd., a British motorsport and vehicle technology company. Aston Martin operates a headquarters production facility in Gaydon, Warwickshire in the U.K. with a production capacity of 5,000 vehicles per year. The firm offers a wide variety of customization options and a performance driving course. It can collect and deliver cars for servicing at its Newport Pagnell, Buckinghamshire facility from anywhere in Europe, and will send service teams to any location in the world if necessary. The company operates a Heritage team dedicated to providing obsolete parts for repair of its older model and antique Aston Martin and Lagonda cars. The firm also markets The Collection, a line of clothing, luggage and fashion accessories. The Aston Martin Racing division sponsors competitive drivers and a dedicated team. In recent news, Aston Martin announced a plan to expand its production and sales network over the next five or so years. In March 2007, Ford announced the sale of Aston Martin to a group led by former racer David Richards for $931 million. The deal was completed in the second quarter of 2007. In late 2007, the company opened a new design studio at its Gaydon headquarters. In 2008, Aston Martin Racing unveiled its GT2 racing car, with is based on the V8 Vantage but can run on E85 bioethanol.

FINANCIALS: **Sales and profits are in thousands of dollars—add 000 to get the full amount. 2008 Note: Financial information for 2008 was not available for all companies at press time.**

2008 Sales: $	2008 Profits: $	**U.S. Stock Ticker: Private**
2007 Sales: $515,400	2007 Profits: $	**Int'l Ticker:** Int'l Exchange:
2006 Sales: $	2006 Profits: $	Employees: 916
2005 Sales: $	2005 Profits: $	Fiscal Year Ends: 12/31
2004 Sales: $	2004 Profits: $	Parent Company:

SALARIES/BENEFITS:

Pension Plan:	ESOP Stock Plan:	Profit Sharing:	Top Exec. Salary: $	Bonus: $
Savings Plan:	Stock Purch. Plan:		Second Exec. Salary: $	Bonus: $

OTHER THOUGHTS:

Apparent Women Officers or Directors:
Hot Spot for Advancement for Women/Minorities:

LOCATIONS: ("Y" = Yes)

West:	Southwest:	Midwest:	Southeast:	Northeast:	International:
Y	Y	Y	Y	Y	Y

ASTRAZENECA PLC

www.astrazeneca.com

Industry Group Code: 325412 **Ranks within this company's industry group:** Sales: 7 Profits: 7

Techology:		Medical/Drugs:		Engineering:		Transportation:		Chemicals/Petrochemicals:		Specialty:	
Computers:		Manufacturer:	Y	Design:		Aerospace:		Oil/Gas Products:		Special Services:	
Software:		Contract Research:		Construction:		Automotive:		Chemicals:		Consulting:	
Communications:		Medical Services:		Eng. Services:		Shipping:		Oil/Chem. Svcs.:		Specialty Mgmt.:	
Electronics:		Labs:		Consulting:				Gases:		Products:	
Alternative Energy:		Bio. Services:	Y					Other:		Other:	

TYPES OF BUSINESS:

Drugs-Diversified
Pharmaceutical Research & Development

BRANDS/DIVISIONS/AFFILIATES:

Nexium
Seroquel
Crestor
Arimidex
Symbicort
Pulmicort
AstraTech
Aptium Oncology

CONTACTS:

Note: Officers with more than one job title may be intentionally listed here more than once.

David R. Brennan, CEO
Simon Lowth, CFO
Tony Zook, Exec. VP-Global Mktg.
Lynn Tetrault, Exec. VP-Human Resources & Corp. Affairs
Jan Lundberg, Exec. VP-Discovery Research
Jeff Pott, General Counsel
David Smith, Exec. VP-Oper.
Anders Ekblom, Exec. VP-Dev.
Tony Zook, Pres., MedImmune
Tony Zook, CEO-North America
Louis Schweitzer, Chmn.
Bruno Angelici, Exec. VP-Europe/Japan/Asia Pacific/Rest of World

Phone: 44-20-7304-5000	**Fax:** 44-20-7304-5151
Toll-Free:	
Address: 15 Stanhope Gate, London, W1Y 6LN UK	

GROWTH PLANS/SPECIAL FEATURES:

AstraZeneca plc is a leading global pharmaceutical company that discovers, develops, manufactures and markets prescription pharmaceuticals, biologics and vaccines for the treatment or prevention of diseases in such areas of healthcare as cardiovascular, gastrointestinal, infection, neuroscience, oncology and respiratory and inflammation. The company is the result of the merger of the Zeneca Group with Astra. The firm invests over $5 billion annually in research and development and enjoys sales in over 100 countries. It operates 26 manufacturing sites in 18 countries and 17 major research centers in eight countries. AstraZeneca's cardiovascular products include Seloken ZOK, Crestor, Atacand, Plendil, Zestril and Tenormin. The firm's gastrointestinal products include Nexium, Entocort and Prilosec. Merrem, its primary infection product, is an antibiotic for serious hospital-acquired infections. AstraZeneca's neuroscience offering includes Zomig, a migraine treatment; anesthetics Diprivan and Xylocaine; Naropin, a long-acting anesthetic; and Seroquel for the treatment of schizophrenia and bipolar mania. AstraZeneca's cancer treatments include Casodex for prostate cancer; Zoladex; Armidex and Faslodex for breast cancer; Iressa for lung cancer; and Nolvadex. The firm's respiratory and inflammation brands include Pulmicort, Symbicort, Rhinocort, Accolate and Oxis. Nexium, Seroquel, Crestor, Arimidex, Symbicort, Pulmicort, Casodex, Atacand, Synagis, Prilosec and Zoladex all have sales in excess of $1 billion. Subsidiary AstraTech is engaged in the research, development, manufacture and marketing of medical devices and implants. Another subsidiary, Aptium Oncology, is a leading provider of outpatient oncology management and consulting services in the U.S., with full-service outpatient comprehensive cancer centers in California, Florida and New York. In February 2008, AstraZeneca formed Albireo, a joint venture with Nomura Phase4 Ventures, for the development of treatments for gastrointestinal disorders. In November 2008, the firm sold its Nordic over-the-counter portfolio to GlaxoSmithKline.

FINANCIALS:

Sales and profits are in thousands of dollars—add 000 to get the full amount. 2008 Note: Financial information for 2008 was not available for all companies at press time.

2008 Sales: $31,601,000	2008 Profits: $6,130,000	**U.S. Stock Ticker: AZN**
2007 Sales: $29,559,000	2007 Profits: $5,627,000	**Int'l Ticker: AZN** Int'l Exchange: London-LSE
2006 Sales: $26,475,000	2006 Profits: $6,063,000	Employees: 65,000
2005 Sales: $23,950,000	2005 Profits: $3,881,000	Fiscal Year Ends: 12/31
2004 Sales: $21,426,000	2004 Profits: $3,813,000	Parent Company:

SALARIES/BENEFITS:

Pension Plan:	ESOP Stock Plan:	Profit Sharing:	Top Exec. Salary: $1,191,000	Bonus: $588,000
Savings Plan:	Stock Purch. Plan:		Second Exec. Salary: $732,000	Bonus: $347,000

OTHER THOUGHTS:

Apparent Women Officers or Directors: 4
Hot Spot for Advancement for Women/Minorities: Y

LOCATIONS: ("Y" = Yes)

West:	Southwest:	Midwest:	Southeast:	Northeast:	International:
Y	Y	Y	Y	Y	Y

ASUSTEK COMPUTER INC

www.asus.com

Industry Group Code: 334119 **Ranks within this company's industry group:** Sales: Profits:

Techology:		Medical/Drugs:		Engineering:		Transportation:		Chemicals/Petrochemicals:		Specialty:	
Computers:	Y	Manufacturer:		Design:		Aerospace:		Oil/Gas Products:		Special Services:	
Software:		Contract Research:		Construction:		Automotive:		Chemicals:		Consulting:	
Communications:	Y	Medical Services:		Eng. Services:		Shipping:		Oil/Chem. Svcs.:		Specialty Mgmt.:	
Electronics:	Y	Labs:		Consulting:				Gases:		Products:	
Alternative Energy:		Bio. Services:						Other:		Other:	

TYPES OF BUSINESS:

Computer Components & Accessories
Motherboards
Networking Devices
Wireless Communication Products
Smart Phones

BRANDS/DIVISIONS/AFFILIATES:

Kinsus Interconnect Technology
A7G Notebook Series
Mobility Radeon X1600
W1 Carbon Notebook Series
ASUS-Lamborghini Notebook
Eee PC
Pegatron Technology
Unihan Technology

CONTACTS: *Note: Officers with more than one job title may be intentionally listed here more than once.*

Chongtang Shi, Gen. Mgr.
Weiming Zhang, Dir.-Finance
Jingru Wu, Head-Acct.
Zixian Tong, Vice Chmn./Deputy General Mgr.
Hongchang Hong, Deputy General Mgr.
Zhenlai Shen, Deputy General Mgr.
Shichang Xu, Deputy General Mgr.
Chongtang Shi, Chmn.

Phone: 886-02-28943447 **Fax:** 886-02-28967761
Toll-Free:
Address: No. 150, Li-Te Rd., 4 Fl., Peitou, 112 Taiwan

GROWTH PLANS/SPECIAL FEATURES:

ASUSTeK Computer, Inc. participates in the 3C industry (computing, consumer electronics and communications). The company manufactures PCs, broadband modems, digital home phones, graphic cards, LCD monitors, mobile phones, motherboards, networking equipment, notebook computers, storage devices, PC components, PDAs and server equipment. ASUSTeK boasts a world-class research and design team, high-capacity manufacturing capabilities (recently shipping over 50 million motherboards in a single year), industry-leading products and services, and competitive material costs. Subsidiary Kinsus Interconnect Technology produces IC substrates. The company often acts as a third-party producer of computer equipment for names such as Hewlett-Packard and IBM. ASUSTeK notebooks were the first TCO'99-certified notebooks worldwide. The requirements for this certification include radiation emission control, energy (battery consumption), ecology (environment friendly) and ergonomics. ASUSTeK has won over 1,600 awards from IT media and organizations such as BusinessWeek, who has ranked the firm amongst its InfoTech 100 for nine straight years, and the Wall Street Journal, who ranked Asus number one for best quality products in Taiwan. The company has also received Taiwan's National Award of Excellence presented by the Ministry of Economics Affairs, as well as Germany's Industrie Forum (iF) Gold Award for industrial design excellence. One of the company's latest and more successful products, the Eee PC, is 7-inch solid-state minimalist laptop PC featuring built-in wifi connectivity, Intel processors and Linux/Windows XP compatibility. The company announced plans to ship over 1 million units and to introduce a desktop version in 2008. In recent news, AsusTeK announced plans to divide its operations, creating two new companies to handle its contract manufacturing services, Pegatron Technology and Unihan Technology. In 2008, the firm introduced a terabyte notebook, its new Eee PC desktop version, and its My Cinema card, which allows an individual to display satellite, digital or analog television on a PC. In 2009, the firm announced plans to partner with GPS maker Garmin to build a line of enhanced cellular phones to be branded Garmin-Asus.

FINANCIALS: **Sales and profits are in thousands of dollars—add 000 to get the full amount. 2008 Note: Financial information for 2008 was not available for all companies at press time.**

2008 Sales: $
2007 Sales: $22,660,800
2006 Sales: $16,807,000
2005 Sales: $11,551,700
2004 Sales: $

2008 Profits: $
2007 Profits: $828,700
2006 Profits: $576,600
2005 Profits: $458,300
2004 Profits: $

U.S. Stock Ticker:
Int'l Ticker: 2357 Int'l Exchange: Taipei-TPE
Employees: 58,000
Fiscal Year Ends: 12/31
Parent Company:

SALARIES/BENEFITS:

Pension Plan: ESOP Stock Plan: Profit Sharing: Top Exec. Salary: $ Bonus: $
Savings Plan: Stock Purch. Plan: Second Exec. Salary: $ Bonus: $

OTHER THOUGHTS:

Apparent Women Officers or Directors:
Hot Spot for Advancement for Women/Minorities:

LOCATIONS: ("Y" = Yes)

West:	Southwest:	Midwest:	Southeast:	Northeast:	International:
Y		Y			Y

Note: Financial information, benefits and other data can change quickly and may vary from those stated here.

ATMEL CORP

www.atmel.com

Industry Group Code: 334413 **Ranks within this company's industry group:** Sales: 19 Profits: 12

Techology:		Medical/Drugs:		Engineering:		Transportation:		Chemicals/Petrochemicals:		Specialty:	
Computers:		Manufacturer:		Design:		Aerospace:	Y	Oil/Gas Products:		Special Services:	
Software:		Contract Research:		Construction:		Automotive:	Y	Chemicals:		Consulting:	
Communications:		Medical Services:		Eng. Services:		Shipping:		Oil/Chem. Svcs.:		Specialty Mgmt.:	
Electronics:	Y	Labs:		Consulting:				Gases:		Products:	
Alternative Energy:		Bio. Services:						Other:		Other:	

TYPES OF BUSINESS:

Semiconductor Manufacturing
Non-Volatile Memory & Logic Integrated Circuits
Mixed-Signal Semiconductors
RF Semiconductors
Microcontrollers
Military & Aerospace Products

BRANDS/DIVISIONS/AFFILIATES:

Atmel Finance, Inc.
Atmel Semiconductor Corp.
Atmel Asia, Ltd.
Atmel FSC, Inc.
Atmel Korea, Ltd.
Atmel U.K., Ltd.
SiliconCITV
e2v Technologies PLC

CONTACTS: *Note: Officers with more than one job title may be intentionally listed here more than once.*

Steven Laub, CEO
Steven Laub, Pres.
Stephen Cumming, CFO
Ken Kwong, VP-Corp. Mktg.
John Klinestiver, VP-Human Resources
Tom Wasilczyk, CIO/VP-IT
Tom Roff, VP-Worldwide Mfg.
Patrick Reutens, Chief Legal Officer/VP
Walter Lifsey, Sr. VP-Worldwide Oper.
Robert Pursel, Dir.-Investor Rel.
Stephen Cumming, VP-Finance
Bernard Pruniaux, VP/Managing Dir.-Atmel Rousset SAS
Robert McConnell, VP/Gen. Mgr.-RF & Automotive Bus. Unit
Michel Thouvenin, VP-European Sales
Tsung-Ching Wu, Exec. VP
David Sugishita, Chmn.
Yang Chiah Yee, Pres,. Sales-Asia Pacific

Phone: 408-441-0311 **Fax:** 408-436-4314
Toll-Free:
Address: 2325 Orchard Pkwy., San Jose, CA 95131 US

GROWTH PLANS/SPECIAL FEATURES:

Atmel Corporation designs, manufactures and markets advanced semiconductors, non-volatile memory, mixed-signal and radio frequency (RF) integrated circuits (ICs). The company operates through four business segments: application specific integrated circuit (ASIC); microcontrollers; nonvolatile memories; and RF and automotive. The company produces a full range of chips including application-specific ICs, memory, microcontrollers and programmable logic. Atmel's semiconductors are used in applications in a variety of markets, including security, automotive, industrial, multimedia, imaging, military and aerospace. Atmel devotes substantial resources to research and development. The ASIC segment provides semi-custom, single customer integrated circuits for the telecommunications, consumer, banking and military markets. The microcontrollers segment offers a variety of proprietary and standard microcontrollers, which mostly contain embedded nonvolatile memory; and military and aerospace application specific products. The nonvolatile memories section provides serial and parallel interface programmable read only memories and serial and parallel flash memories for use in a variety of applications. The RF and automotive division includes radio frequency and analog circuits for the telecommunications, automotive and industrial markets. In March 2008, Atmel acquired Quantum Research Group Ltd. In September of the same year, the firm agreed to sell its wafer fabrication operation in Heilbronn, Germany to Tejas Silicon Holdings (UK) Limited. This sale reflects the company's restructuring efforts to move to a fab-lite manufacturing model with increased utilization of third-party foundry capacity. When the restructuring is complete, the firm's focus will be on microcontrollers, security-based products, RF and automotive products.

Employees are offered health, dental and vision insurance; life insurance; disability plans; a flexible benefits account; an employee assistance program; a 401(k) plan; an employee stock purchase plan; and tuition reimbursement.

FINANCIALS: **Sales and profits are in thousands of dollars—add 000 to get the full amount. 2008 Note: Financial information for 2008 was not available for all companies at press time.**

2008 Sales: $1,566,763	2008 Profits: $-27,209	**U.S. Stock Ticker: ATML**
2007 Sales: $1,639,237	2007 Profits: $47,885	**Int'l Ticker:** Int'l Exchange:
2006 Sales: $1,670,887	2006 Profits: $14,650	Employees: 7,400
2005 Sales: $1,561,107	2005 Profits: $-32,898	Fiscal Year Ends: 12/31
2004 Sales: $1,649,722	2004 Profits: $-2,434	Parent Company:

SALARIES/BENEFITS:

Pension Plan:	ESOP Stock Plan:	Profit Sharing:	Top Exec. Salary: $706,731	Bonus: $968,333
Savings Plan: Y	Stock Purch. Plan: Y		Second Exec. Salary: $479,577	Bonus: $428,563

OTHER THOUGHTS:

Apparent Women Officers or Directors:
Hot Spot for Advancement for Women/Minorities:

LOCATIONS: ("Y" = Yes)

West:	Southwest:	Midwest:	Southeast:	Northeast:	International:
Y	Y	Y	Y	Y	Y

ATOMIC ENERGY OF CANADA LIMITED

www.aecl.ca

Industry Group Code: 335000 **Ranks within this company's industry group:** Sales: 10 Profits: 9

Techology:		Medical/Drugs:		Engineering:		Transportation:		Chemicals/Petrochemicals:		Specialty:	
Computers:		Manufacturer:		Design:	Y	Aerospace:		Oil/Gas Products:		Special Services:	
Software:		Contract Research:		Construction:	Y	Automotive:		Chemicals:		Consulting:	
Communications:		Medical Services:		Eng. Services:	Y	Shipping:		Oil/Chem. Svcs.:		Specialty Mgmt.:	
Electronics:		Labs:		Consulting:				Gases:		Products:	
Alternative Energy:	Y	Bio. Services:						Other:		Other:	

TYPES OF BUSINESS:

Nuclear Reactor Design
Nuclear Waste Management
Research & Laboratories
Medical Isotopes & Diagnostics

BRANDS/DIVISIONS/AFFILIATES:

CANDU
MACSTOR
MAPLE
Team CANDU
Chalk River Laboratories

CONTACTS: *Note: Officers with more than one job title may be intentionally listed here more than once.*

Hugh MacDiarmid, CEO
Ken Petrunik, COO/Exec. VP
Hugh MacDiarmid, Pres.
Michael Robins, CFO/Sr. VP
Ala Alizadeh, VP-Mktg.
Beth Medhurst, Sr. VP-Human Resources
William Kupferschmidt, VP-R&D
Andre Robillard, CIO/VP
Jerry Hopwood, VP-Reactor Dev.
Allan A. Hawryluk, General Counsel/Corp. Sec./Sr. VP
Wayne Inch, VP-Oper.
Ala Alizadeh, VP-Bus. Dev.
Bill Pilkington, Sr. VP/Chief Nuclear Officer
Greg Sayer, VP-Compliance, Corp. Oversight & Regulatory Affair
Ron Cullen, VP-New Build & Construction
Michael Ingram, VP-CANDU Projects & Svcs.
Glenna Carr, Chmn.

Phone: 905-823-9040 **Fax:** 905-823-7565
Toll-Free: 866-513-2325
Address: 2251 Speakman Dr., Mississauga, ON L5K 1B2 Canada

GROWTH PLANS/SPECIAL FEATURES:

Atomic Energy of Canada, Ltd. (AECL) is a global technology and engineering company that provides research and development, nuclear services, design, engineering, construction management, specialist technology, waste management and decommissioning to the nuclear industry. The company constructs CANada Deuterium Uranium (CANDU) nuclear power plants and provides reactor services and technical support to operating CANDU reactors. AECL also designs and builds MACSTOR (Modular Air Cooled Storage) used-fuel storage facilities. The company operates MAPLE reactors, dedicated to the production of medical isotopes. Approximately 48 CANDU reactors are in use or under construction on four continents; reactors of this type supply approximately 15% of Canada's electricity. AECL operates nuclear laboratories that perform research; produce isotopes used in nuclear medicine and other applications; store and manage nuclear wastes; and decommission nuclear facilities. The NRU research reactor at AECL's Chalk River Laboratories has been the primary source of radio-isotopes produced for use in nuclear medicine. Canada is the world's leading supplier of medical isotopes used to diagnose, prevent and treat disease in over 80 countries and produces 75% of the world's supply of Cobalt-60 used to sterilize 40% of the world's disposable medical supplies. AECL's research reactors are also used for neutron beam research, inspection tools, nuclear power industry support and other research and training. Team CANDU, formed by AECL and four leading nuclear technology and engineering companies (Babcock & Wilcox Canada, General Electric Canada, Hitachi Canada Ltd. and SNC-Lavalin Nuclear Inc.) plan to develop a turn key service and competitive solutions for building ne nuclear power plants in Ontario. In January 2008, the firm announced plans to join with the Nuclear Power Institute of China to further the development of low uranium consumption CANDU technologies in China.

The company offers its employees health and dental care; a travel plan; disability income protection; and a pension plan.

FINANCIALS: **Sales and profits are in thousands of dollars—add 000 to get the full amount. 2008 Note: Financial information for 2008 was not available for all companies at press time.**

2008 Sales: $442,170 | 2008 Profits: $-228,860
2007 Sales: $549,728 | 2007 Profits: $11,760
2006 Sales: $324,060 | 2006 Profits: $50,270
2005 Sales: $302,671 | 2005 Profits: $18,180
2004 Sales: $379,600 | 2004 Profits: $1,800

U.S. Stock Ticker: Government-Owned
Int'l Ticker: Int'l Exchange:
Employees: 4,728
Fiscal Year Ends: 3/31
Parent Company:

SALARIES/BENEFITS:

Pension Plan: Y | ESOP Stock Plan: | Profit Sharing: | Top Exec. Salary: $ | Bonus: $
Savings Plan: | Stock Purch. Plan: | | Second Exec. Salary: $ | Bonus: $

OTHER THOUGHTS:

Apparent Women Officers or Directors: 7
Hot Spot for Advancement for Women/Minorities: Y

LOCATIONS: ("Y" = Yes)

West:	Southwest:	Midwest:	Southeast:	Northeast:	International:
				Y	Y

ATOS ORIGIN SA

www.atosorigin.com

Industry Group Code: 541512 **Ranks within this company's industry group:** Sales: 8 Profits:

Techology:		**Medical/Drugs:**		**Engineering:**		**Transportation:**		**Chemicals/Petrochemicals:**		**Specialty:**	
Computers:	Y	Manufacturer:		Design:		Aerospace:		Oil/Gas Products:		Special Services:	Y
Software:		Contract Research:		Construction:		Automotive:		Chemicals:		Consulting:	Y
Communications:		Medical Services:		Eng. Services:		Shipping:		Oil/Chem. Svcs.:		Specialty Mgmt.:	
Electronics:		Labs:		Consulting:				Gases:		Products:	
Alternative Energy:		Bio. Services:						Other:		Other:	

TYPES OF BUSINESS:

IT Consulting
Business Process Outsourcing
Payment Solutions
e-Commerce Consulting
Supply Chain Management
Customer Relationship Management
Product Lifecycle Management
Web Design

BRANDS/DIVISIONS/AFFILIATES:

Atos Consulting
Atos Worldline
AtosEuronext
Banksys
Bank Card Company

CONTACTS: *Note: Officers with more than one job title may be intentionally listed here more than once.*

Thierry Breton, CEO
Eric Guilhou, Sr. Exec. VP-Human Resources
Eric Guilhou, Sr. Exec. VP-IT
Eric Guilhou, Sr. Exec. VP-Legal
Eric Guilhou, Sr. Exec. VP-Finance
Thierry Breton, Chmn.
Eric Guilhou, Sr. Exec. VP-Purchasing

Phone: 33-1-55-91-20-00 **Fax:** 33-1-55-91-20-05
Toll-Free:
Address: Tour les Mirroirs- Bat C, 18 Ave. d'Alsace, Paris, 92926 France

GROWTH PLANS/SPECIAL FEATURES:

Atos Origin SA is an international consulting firm that performs information technology (IT) services for its clients. Through subsidiary Atos Consulting, the company provides consulting, systems integration and managed operations resources in more than 40 countries worldwide. The company's other divisions create IT strategies and design information systems to suit clients' needs. In addition to system design, Atos builds infrastructure itself and provides outsourcing services, including system operation, web design, support and upgrading. Through Atos Worldline, the company offers business process outsourcing (BPO), payment solutions for cashless transfers and multi-channel contact services, all on a global basis. AtosEuronext, a joint venture between Atos Origin and the Euronext stock exchange, is a leading provider of IT solutions to the European financial services industry. The company also has an enterprise alliance agreement with TIS, Inc., a Japanese IT provider. By an agreement with the International Olympic Committee, Atos Origin will provide IT support for the next two Olympic Games, and has previously provided support to the 2008 events in Beijing, Athens in 2004 and Torino, Italy in 2006. Its role is to assume primary responsibility for IT consulting, systems integration, operations management, information security and software applications development at the Olympic events. Other subsidiaries include Banksys and Bank Card Company.

FINANCIALS: **Sales and profits are in thousands of dollars—add 000 to get the full amount. 2008 Note: Financial information for 2008 was not available for all companies at press time.**

2008 Sales: $7,107,800
2007 Sales: $9,251,500
2006 Sales: $8,527,100
2005 Sales: $8,625,100
2004 Sales: $6,332,280

2008 Profits: $
2007 Profits: $76,200
2006 Profits: $-417,800
2005 Profits: $371,900
2004 Profits: $146,325

U.S. Stock Ticker:
Int'l Ticker: ATO Int'l Exchange: Paris-Euronext
Employees: 51,704
Fiscal Year Ends: 12/31
Parent Company:

SALARIES/BENEFITS:

Pension Plan:	ESOP Stock Plan:	Profit Sharing:	Top Exec. Salary: $	Bonus: $1,008,406
Savings Plan:	Stock Purch. Plan:		Second Exec. Salary: $990,926	Bonus: $990,926

OTHER THOUGHTS:

Apparent Women Officers or Directors: 1
Hot Spot for Advancement for Women/Minorities:

LOCATIONS: ("Y" = Yes)

West:	Southwest:	Midwest:	Southeast:	Northeast:	International:
	Y	Y			Y

AU OPTRONICS CORP

www.auo.com

Industry Group Code: 334119 **Ranks within this company's industry group:** Sales: 3 Profits: 5

Techology:		Medical/Drugs:		Engineering:		Transportation:		Chemicals/Petrochemicals:		Specialty:	
Computers:	Y	Manufacturer:		Design:		Aerospace:		Oil/Gas Products:		Special Services:	
Software:		Contract Research:		Construction:		Automotive:		Chemicals:		Consulting:	
Communications:		Medical Services:		Eng. Services:		Shipping:		Oil/Chem. Svcs.:		Specialty Mgmt.:	
Electronics:		Labs:		Consulting:				Gases:		Products:	
Alternative Energy:		Bio. Services:						Other:		Other:	

TYPES OF BUSINESS:

Liquid Crystal Display Panels
Information Technology Displays
Television Displays
Consumer Product Displays

BRANDS/DIVISIONS/AFFILIATES:

Unipac Optoelectronics Corporation
Acer Display
Qisda Corp.

CONTACTS: *Note: Officers with more than one job title may be intentionally listed here more than once.*

Lai-Juh Chen, CEO
Lai-Juh Chen, COO
Lai-Juh Chen, Pres.
Max Cheng, CFO/VP
M.J. Chen, VP-Exec. Human Resources Div.
Michael Tsai, VP/Gen. Mgr.-IT Display Bus. Group
Fang-Chen Luo, CTO/VP
Fwu-Chyi Hsiang, Exec. VP-Global Oper. Unit
Chun-Ting Liu, Sr. VP/Gen. Mgr.-Consumer Prod. Display Bus. Group
Kuen-Yao Lee, Chmn.

Phone: 886-3-500-8899 **Fax:** 886-3-563-7608
Toll-Free:
Address: 1 Li-Hsin Rd. 2, Hsinchu Science Park, Hsinchu, 30078 Taiwan

GROWTH PLANS/SPECIAL FEATURES:

AU Optronics (AUO), a Taiwanese company, designs, manufactures, assembles and markets thin-film transistor liquid crystal display (TFT-LCD) panels. The firm holds approximately 9.58% of Qisda Corp. (formerly BenQ Corp.), one of AUO's major customer's. AUO's screens are bought by original equipment manufacturing service providers, companies that design and assemble products based on customer specifications; and are used in monitor applications, notebook PCs, mobile phones, LCD TVs, Internet appliances, car display/portable DVD applications and general industrial applications. These panels offer clear images for laptops, cellular phones, digital cameras, personal digital assistants (PDAs) and other portable technologies. Major customers include Qisda; TPV Electronics (Fujian) Company Limited; and Proview Optronics (Shenzhen) Co. Ltd. In January 2007, the firm reorganized its business operations into three groups. The information technology display group covers applications such as desktop, notebook and general displays. The television displays group covers applications such as LCD television. The consumer products display group covers applications such as audio-video displays and mobile device displays. In September 2007, the company opened a new manufacturing facility in Xiamen, China. In May 2008, AUO introduced the first curved-screen display for mobile-device technology. In October 2008, the firm introduced new energy-saving technologies for LCD panels. Also in October, the company introduced image and fingerprint scanning technology for mobile devices.

AUO offers its employees a benefits package that includes an on-site wellness center, company cafeteria, fitness facilities, on-site convenience store, coffee shop, juice bar, bakery, meridian and acupuncture therapy, free shuttle bus and employee dormitories.

FINANCIALS: **Sales and profits are in thousands of dollars—add 000 to get the full amount. 2008 Note: Financial information for 2008 was not available for all companies at press time.**

2008 Sales: $12,520,800	2008 Profits: $638,000	**U.S. Stock Ticker: AUO**
2007 Sales: $14,810,000	2007 Profits: $1,740,000	**Int'l Ticker: 2409** Int'l Exchange: Taipei-TPE
2006 Sales: $8,993,764	2006 Profits: $279,024	Employees: 41,010
2005 Sales: $6,687,190	2005 Profits: $479,850	Fiscal Year Ends: 12/31
2004 Sales: $5,072,000	2004 Profits: $828,000	Parent Company:

SALARIES/BENEFITS:

Pension Plan: Y	ESOP Stock Plan:	Profit Sharing: Y	Top Exec. Salary: $	Bonus: $
Savings Plan:	Stock Purch. Plan:		Second Exec. Salary: $	Bonus: $

OTHER THOUGHTS:

Apparent Women Officers or Directors:
Hot Spot for Advancement for Women/Minorities:

LOCATIONS: ("Y" = Yes)

West:	Southwest:	Midwest:	Southeast:	Northeast:	International:
					Y

Note: Financial information, benefits and other data can change quickly and may vary from those stated here.

AUDI AG

www.audi.com

Industry Group Code: 336111 **Ranks within this company's industry group:** Sales: 13 Profits: 6

Techology:		Medical/Drugs:		Engineering:		Transportation:		Chemicals/Petrochemicals:		Specialty:	
Computers:		Manufacturer:		Design:		Aerospace:		Oil/Gas Products:		Special Services:	
Software:		Contract Research:		Construction:		Automotive:	Y	Chemicals:		Consulting:	
Communications:		Medical Services:		Eng. Services:		Shipping:		Oil/Chem. Svcs.:		Specialty Mgmt.:	
Electronics:	Y	Labs:		Consulting:				Gases:		Products:	
Alternative Energy:		Bio. Services:						Other:		Other:	

TYPES OF BUSINESS:

Automobile Manufacturing
Luxury & Sports Cars
Automobile Customization & Accessories
Engine Manufacturing
Automotive Electronics

BRANDS/DIVISIONS/AFFILIATES:

Audi
Audi Hungaria Motor Kft
Quattro Gmbh
Automobili Lamborghini Holding, SpA
Lamborghini
AUTOGERMA SpA
Q7
Volkswagen AG

CONTACTS: *Note: Officers with more than one job title may be intentionally listed here more than once.*

Rupert Stadler, Chmn.-Mgmt. Board
Axel Strotbek, Dir.-Finance & Organization
Peter Schwarzenbauer, Dir.-Mktg. & Sales
Werner Widuckel, Dir.-Human Resources
Michael Dick, Dir.-Tech. Dev.
Frank Dreves, Dir.-Production
Martin Winterkorn, Chmn.
Ulf Berkenhagen, Dir.-Purchasing

Phone: 49-841-89-40300 **Fax:** 49-841-89-30900
Toll-Free:
Address: Postfach 100457, Ingolstadt, D-85045 Germany

GROWTH PLANS/SPECIAL FEATURES:

Audi AG, a publically listed subsidiary of Volkswagen AG, is a German firm that designs and manufactures high-end luxury cars. The company operates through three main subsidiaries: Audi Hungaria Motor Kft.; Automobili Lamborghini Holding, S.p.A.; and Quattro GmbH. Audi Hungaria Motor Kft., based in Gyor, Hungary, develops and builds engines for Audi, other Volkswagen Group companies and third parties. In addition, this subsidiary produces the Audi TT Coupe and TT Roadster lines of vehicles. Automobili Lamborghini Holding, S.p.A. builds the Lamborghini brand of high-end sports cars, which includes the Gallardo Coupe, Gallardo Spyder, Murcielago LP640 Coupe and Murcielago LP640 Roadster. Additionally, this subsidiary oversees AUTOGERMA S.p.A., which sells Audi and Volkswagen vehicles in Italy. Quattro GmbH, based in Neckarsulm, Germany, designs and manufactures the RS range of vehicles as well as the Avant model. This subsidiary also runs customization operations. Formed in Germany in 1932 from the combination of four separate auto manufacturers, Audi now has production facilities in Germany, Italy, Hungary, Brazil and China, manufacturing over 1 million cars per year. The company also owns and operates various consolidated sales subsidiaries such as Audi Australia Pty Ltd.; Audi Japan K.K.; Audi Volkswagen Korea Ltd.; and Audi Volkswagen Middle East Fze.

FINANCIALS: **Sales and profits are in thousands of dollars—add 000 to get the full amount. 2008 Note: Financial information for 2008 was not available for all companies at press time.**

2008 Sales: $45,246,100	2008 Profits: $4,203,620	**U.S. Stock Ticker: Subsidiary**
2007 Sales: $49,417,000	2007 Profits: $2,431,400	**Int'l Ticker:** Int'l Exchange:
2006 Sales: $45,778,700	2006 Profits: $1,974,200	Employees: 53,347
2005 Sales: $39,088,800	2005 Profits: $1,211,300	Fiscal Year Ends: 12/31
2004 Sales: $33,426,000	2004 Profits: $1,184,300	Parent Company: VOLKSWAGEN AG

SALARIES/BENEFITS:

Pension Plan:	ESOP Stock Plan:	Profit Sharing:	Top Exec. Salary: $	Bonus: $
Savings Plan:	Stock Purch. Plan:		Second Exec. Salary: $	Bonus: $

OTHER THOUGHTS:

Apparent Women Officers or Directors:
Hot Spot for Advancement for Women/Minorities:

LOCATIONS: ("Y" = Yes)

West:	Southwest:	Midwest:	Southeast:	Northeast:	International:
Y	Y	Y	Y	Y	Y

AUTODESK INC

www.autodesk.com

Industry Group Code: 511215 **Ranks within this company's industry group:** Sales: 1 Profits: 1

Techology:		Medical/Drugs:		Engineering:		Transportation:		Chemicals/Petrochemicals:		Specialty:	
Computers:		Manufacturer:		Design:		Aerospace:		Oil/Gas Products:		Special Services:	
Software:	Y	Contract Research:		Construction:		Automotive:		Chemicals:		Consulting:	
Communications:		Medical Services:		Eng. Services:		Shipping:		Oil/Chem. Svcs.:		Specialty Mgmt.:	
Electronics:		Labs:		Consulting:				Gases:		Products:	
Alternative Energy:		Bio. Services:						Other:		Other:	

TYPES OF BUSINESS:

Computer Software-Design & Drafting
Computer Assisted Design Software
Mapping & Infrastructure Management Technology
Film & Media Production Software

BRANDS/DIVISIONS/AFFILIATES:

AutoCAD
AutoCAD LT
Hanna Strategies Inc
3D Geo GmbH
Softimage
ALGOR Inc
Alias Systems Corp

CONTACTS: *Note: Officers with more than one job title may be intentionally listed here more than once.*

Carl Bass, CEO
Carl Bass, Pres.
Carl Bass, Interim CFO
Ken Bado, Exec. VP-Sales & Svcs.
Jan Becker, Sr. VP-Human Resources
Jay Bhatt, Sr. VP-Architecture, Eng. & Construction
Robert Kross, Sr. VP-Mfg.
Pascal Di Fronzo, General Counsel/Corp. Sec./Sr. VP
Moonhie Chin, Sr. VP-Oper.
Moonhie Chin, Sr. VP-Strategic Planning
Jan Becker, Sr. VP-Corp. Real Estate
Chris Bradshaw, Chief Mktg. Officer/Sr. VP
Amar Hanspal, Sr. VP-Platform Solutions & Emerging Business
Marc Petit, Sr. VP-Media & Entertainment
Carol Bartz, Chmn.

Phone: 415-507-5000	**Fax:** 415-507-5100
Toll-Free:	
Address: 111 McInnis Pkwy., San Rafael, CA 94903 US	

GROWTH PLANS/SPECIAL FEATURES:

Autodesk, Inc. is one of the world's leading design software and services companies, offering products and solutions to customers in the architectural, engineering, construction, manufacturing, geospatial mapping and digital media markets. The firm provides a broad range of integrated and interoperable design software, Internet services, wireless development platforms and point-of-location applications. The company is organized into two operating segments: the Design Solutions Segment and the Media and Entertainment Segment. The Design segment, accounting for 87% of 2008 revenues, sells software products and services to professionals who design, build, manage and own building projects. The principal products sold by this segment are AutoCAD and AutoCAD LT (2D design products), as well as such 3D model products as AutoCAD Civil 3D. The Media segment, accounting for 12% of 2008 revenues, sells products to post-production facilities and creative professionals for projects such as feature films, interactive game production and interactive web streaming. The firm's products are sold both directly to customers and through resellers and distributors. The company also sells mapping and infrastructure management technologies to public and private users. The firm acquired Hanna Strategies, Inc., an engineering services and software development firm, in January 2008. In September 2008, the company acquired 3D Geo GmbH, a privately-held German maker of intelligent 3D urban modeling software. In November 2008, Autodesk acquired Softimage, a developer of 3D technology for the film, television and games markets, for approximately $35 million. In December 2008, the company announced plans to acquire ALGOR, Inc., a provider of analysis and simulation software, for approximately $34 million.

The company offers a paid six-week sabbatical every four years. Autodesk also offers employees adoption assistance to offset the cost of adopting a child, along with medical, dental, life and AD&D insurance.

FINANCIALS: **Sales and profits are in thousands of dollars—add 000 to get the full amount. 2008 Note: Financial information for 2008 was not available for all companies at press time.**

2008 Sales: $2,171,900	2008 Profits: $356,200	**U.S. Stock Ticker: ADSK**
2007 Sales: $1,839,800	2007 Profits: $289,700	**Int'l Ticker:** Int'l Exchange:
2006 Sales: $1,537,200	2006 Profits: $333,600	Employees: 7,300
2005 Sales: $1,238,900	2005 Profits: $221,100	Fiscal Year Ends: 1/31
2004 Sales: $951,643	2004 Profits: $120,316	Parent Company:

SALARIES/BENEFITS:

Pension Plan:	ESOP Stock Plan:	Profit Sharing:	Top Exec. Salary: $783,333	Bonus: $800,000
Savings Plan: Y	Stock Purch. Plan: Y		Second Exec. Salary: $500,000	Bonus: $

OTHER THOUGHTS:

Apparent Women Officers or Directors: 4
Hot Spot for Advancement for Women/Minorities: Y

LOCATIONS: ("Y" = Yes)

West:	Southwest:	Midwest:	Southeast:	Northeast:	International:
Y			Y	Y	Y

AUTOLIV INC

www.autoliv.com

Industry Group Code: 336300 **Ranks within this company's industry group:** Sales: 18 Profits: 9

Techology:		Medical/Drugs:		Engineering:		Transportation:		Chemicals/Petrochemicals:		Specialty:	
Computers:		Manufacturer:		Design:		Aerospace:		Oil/Gas Products:		Special Services:	
Software:		Contract Research:		Construction:		Automotive:	Y	Chemicals:		Consulting:	
Communications:		Medical Services:		Eng. Services:		Shipping:		Oil/Chem. Svcs.:		Specialty Mgmt.:	
Electronics:		Labs:		Consulting:				Gases:		Products:	
Alternative Energy:		Bio. Services:						Other:		Other:	

TYPES OF BUSINESS:

Automotive Safety Products Manufacturing
Seat Belts
Airbags
Seat Components
Steering Wheels
Child Seats
Safety Electronics
Anti-Whiplash Systems

BRANDS/DIVISIONS/AFFILIATES:

Inflatable Curtain
Anti-Whiplash Seat
Active Hood
Pedestrian Protection Airbag
Bumper Airbag
Front Edge Airbag
Autoliv AB
Autoliv ASP, Inc.

CONTACTS: *Note: Officers with more than one job title may be intentionally listed here more than once.*

Jan Carlson, CEO
Benoit Marsaud, COO/VP
Jan Carlson, Pres.
Magnus Lindquist, CFO/VP
Hans-Goran Patring, VP-Human Resources
Jan Olsson, VP-Research
Steve Fredin, VP-Eng.
Benoit Marsaud, VP-Mfg.
Mike Anderson, Acting VP-Legal Affairs/General Counsel/Sec.
Mats Odman, VP-Corp. Comm.
Svante Mogefors, VP-Quality
Lars Westerberg, Chmn.
Benoit Marsaud, Pres., Autoliv Europe
Halvar Jonzon, VP-Purchasing

Phone: 46-8-587-20-600	**Fax:** 46-8-411-7025
Toll-Free:	
Address: Klarabergsviadukten 70, Section E, Stockholm, SE-107 24 Sweden	

GROWTH PLANS/SPECIAL FEATURES:

Autoliv, Inc. develops, manufactures and produces automotive safety equipment and systems. Autoliv is the result of a merger of two companies, which continue as the company's primary subsidiaries: Autoliv AB and Autoliv ASP, Inc. Swedish-based Autoliv AB produces restraint systems; steering wheels, seatbelts and seatbelt pretensioners; frontal and side-impact airbags; and seat subsystems. Indiana-based Autoliv ASP, Inc. provides air bag inflators; modules and airbag cushions; seatbelts; and steering wheels. Autoliv's customers include all the leading automobile manufacturers in the world, with the majority of sales in Europe, the U.S. and Japan. The firm has 80 plants in 29 countries, 21 crash tracks and 13 technical centers in 13 countries. In 2007, 65% of the firm's sales consisted of airbags and associated products and 35% consisted of seatbelts and associated products. Autoliv invented the world's first side-impact airbag, the Inflatable Curtain for head protection in side impacts and the Anti-Whiplash Seat. New products include a side impact airbag mounted on the door of the vehicle for rollover protection; a fixed-hub steering wheel optimizing the orientation of the driver airbag for head and abdomen protection; a night vision system which uses an infrared camera installed on the front of the car to project on a display in front of the driver; and the pedestrian protection system. Utilizing the Active Hood, which raises instantly when a sensor system placed in the front bumper is triggered, and the Pedestrian Protection Airbag, a pair of airbags installed near the front windshield, the pedestrian protection system reduces the chances of pedestrian fatality in a car-to-pedestrian impact at 25 mph from nearly 100% to less than 15%. In June 2007, the company introduced two new airbags: the Bumper Airbag for SUV-to-passenger car impacts and the Front Edge Airbag for and SUV-to-pedestrian impacts.

FINANCIALS: **Sales and profits are in thousands of dollars—add 000 to get the full amount. 2008 Note: Financial information for 2008 was not available for all companies at press time.**

2008 Sales: $6,473,200	2008 Profits: $164,700	**U.S. Stock Ticker: ALV**
2007 Sales: $6,769,000	2007 Profits: $287,900	**Int'l Ticker: ALIV** Int'l Exchange: Stockholm-SSE
2006 Sales: $6,118,000	2006 Profits: $402,300	Employees: 34,000
2005 Sales: $6,204,900	2005 Profits: $292,600	Fiscal Year Ends: 12/31
2004 Sales: $6,143,900	2004 Profits: $320,000	Parent Company:

SALARIES/BENEFITS:

Pension Plan:	ESOP Stock Plan:	Profit Sharing:	Top Exec. Salary: $701,172	Bonus: $353,953
Savings Plan:	Stock Purch. Plan:		Second Exec. Salary: $661,765	Bonus: $285,882

OTHER THOUGHTS:

Apparent Women Officers or Directors:
Hot Spot for Advancement for Women/Minorities:

LOCATIONS: ("Y" = Yes)

West:	Southwest:	Midwest:	Southeast:	Northeast:	International:
Y		Y			Y

AVAYA INC

www.avaya.com

Industry Group Code: 334210 **Ranks within this company's industry group:** Sales: Profits:

Techology:		Medical/Drugs:		Engineering:		Transportation:		Chemicals/Petrochemicals:		Specialty:	
Computers:		Manufacturer:		Design:		Aerospace:		Oil/Gas Products:		Special Services:	
Software:	Y	Contract Research:		Construction:		Automotive:		Chemicals:		Consulting:	
Communications:	Y	Medical Services:		Eng. Services:		Shipping:		Oil/Chem. Svcs.:		Specialty Mgmt.:	
Electronics:		Labs:		Consulting:				Gases:		Products:	
Alternative Energy:		Bio. Services:						Other:		Other:	

TYPES OF BUSINESS:

Telecommunications Systems
Telecommunications Software
Consulting Services
CRM Products
Networking Systems & Software
Systems Planning & Integration
Network Maintenance, Management & Security Services

BRANDS/DIVISIONS/AFFILIATES:

Avaya Labs
Ubiquity Software Corporation plc
Silver Lake Partners
TPG Capital
TPG (Texas Pacific Group)

CONTACTS: *Note: Officers with more than one job title may be intentionally listed here more than once.*

Charles Giancarlo, CEO
Charles Giancarlo, Pres.
Thomas Manley, CFO
Jocelyne J. Attal, Chief Mktg. Officer
Roger Gaston, Sr. VP-Human Resources
Karyn Mashima, Sr. VP-Tech. & Strategy
Pamela F. Craven, Chief Admin. Officer
Jim Chirico, Sr. VP-Oper.
Todd Abbott, Sr. VP/Pres., Field Oper.
Jeremy Butt, VP-Worldwide Channels

Phone: 908-953-6000 **Fax:** 908-953-7609
Toll-Free: 866-462-8292
Address: 211 Mt. Airy Rd., Basking Ridge, NJ 07920 US

GROWTH PLANS/SPECIAL FEATURES:

Avaya, Inc. is a leading global provider of communications systems and applications for businesses of all sizes and government organizations. The company's products and services fall into four categories: communications enabled business processes; contact centers; IP telephony; services; and unified communications. Avaya offers voice, converged voice and data, customer relationship management (CRM), messaging, multi-service networking and structured cabling products and services. Multi-service networking products support infrastructures that carry voice, video and data traffic over any protocols supported by the Internet on local area and wide area data networks. Structured cabling systems are flexible networks designed to connect phones, workstations, personal computers, local area networks and other devices through a building or across one or more campuses. The firm supports its customers with comprehensive global service offerings, including remote diagnostics testing, installation, on-site repair and maintenance. Avaya has its own research facilities, Avaya Labs, where research and development professionals develop new offerings. Additionally, a small group of the company's scientists concentrate on investigating the basic technologies needed for converged communications. In February 2007, Avaya acquired Ubiquity Software Corporation plc for $144 million. In October 2007, Avaya was acquired by private equity firms Silver Lake Partners and TPG Capital, the global buyout group of TPG (Texas Pacific Group), for $8.3 blllion.

Avaya offers its employees tuition assistance; short term incentive plans; employee discounts; a mortgage program; academic scholarship awards for undergraduate students; reimbursement accounts; and medical, dental, disability and life insurance.

FINANCIALS: **Sales and profits are in thousands of dollars—add 000 to get the full amount. 2008 Note: Financial information for 2008 was not available for all companies at press time.**

2008 Sales: $	2008 Profits: $	**U.S. Stock Ticker: Private**
2007 Sales: $5,100,000	2007 Profits: $	**Int'l Ticker:** Int'l Exchange:
2006 Sales: $5,148,000	2006 Profits: $201,000	Employees: 18,525
2005 Sales: $4,902,000	2005 Profits: $921,000	Fiscal Year Ends: 9/30
2004 Sales: $4,069,000	2004 Profits: $296,000	Parent Company:

SALARIES/BENEFITS:

Pension Plan:	ESOP Stock Plan:	Profit Sharing:	Top Exec. Salary: $940,000	Bonus: $975,250
Savings Plan: Y	Stock Purch. Plan:		Second Exec. Salary: $536,905	Bonus: $584,269

OTHER THOUGHTS:

Apparent Women Officers or Directors: 3
Hot Spot for Advancement for Women/Minorities: Y

LOCATIONS: ("Y" = Yes)

West:	Southwest:	Midwest:	Southeast:	Northeast:	International:
Y			Y	Y	Y

AVIALL INC

www.aviall.com

Industry Group Code: 336410 **Ranks within this company's industry group:** Sales: 22 Profits:

Techology:		Medical/Drugs:		Engineering:		Transportation:		Chemicals/Petrochemicals:		Specialty:	
Computers:		Manufacturer:		Design:		Aerospace:	Y	Oil/Gas Products:		Special Services:	
Software:		Contract Research:		Construction:		Automotive:		Chemicals:		Consulting:	Y
Communications:		Medical Services:		Eng. Services:		Shipping:		Oil/Chem. Svcs.:		Specialty Mgmt.:	Y
Electronics:		Labs:		Consulting:				Gases:		Products:	
Alternative Energy:		Bio. Services:						Other:		Other:	

TYPES OF BUSINESS:

Aerospace Parts Distribution
E-Commerce-Aerospace Parts
E-Business Services-Aerospace, Defense, Marine
Aftermarket Services

BRANDS/DIVISIONS/AFFILIATES:

Aviall Services
Inventory Locator Service LLC
Internet Business Applications, Inc.
Aerospace Repairable Management System

CONTACTS: *Note: Officers with more than one job title may be intentionally listed here more than once.*

Paul E. Fulchino, CEO
Paul E. Fulchino, Pres.
Colin M. Cohen, CFO/Sr. VP
Terry Scott, Sr. VP-Sales & Mktg.
Jeffrey J. Murphy, Sr. VP-Human Resources
Joe Lacik, VP-Info. Svcs.
Jeffrey J. Murphy, General Counsel/Sr. VP-Law/Corp. Sec.
Charley Kienzle, Sr. VP-Oper.
Colin M. Cohen, Sr. VP/Treas.
Dan Komnenovich, COO/Pres., Aviall Svcs., Inc.
Bruce Langsen, Pres., Inventory Locator Svc., LLC
Jacque Collier, VP/Controller
Lou Koch, VP-Human Resources
Paul E. Fulchino, Chmn.

Phone: 972-586-1000 **Fax:** 972-586-1361
Toll-Free: 800-284-2551
Address: 2750 Regent Blvd., Dallas Fort Worth Airport, TX 75261-9048 US

GROWTH PLANS/SPECIAL FEATURES:

Aviall, Inc. is a provider of aftermarket supply-chain management services for companies in the aerospace, defense and marine industries. The company manages two main business units: Aviall Services and Inventory Locator Service LLC. Aviall Services is an independent provider of new aerospace parts and aftermarket services. The unit markets and distributes products for more than 225 manufacturers and offers approximately 1,000,000 catalog items from customer service centers in North America, Europe and Asia. The subsidiary's customer service centers are served by an automated central distribution facility in Dallas, Texas. In addition, Aviall Services offers aviation batteries, hoses, wheels, brakes and oxygen. The firm's other unit, Inventory Locator Service LLC (ILS), provides information and global e-commerce services through its online marketplace. Through a subscription, users can buy and sell commercial parts, equipment and services through a database containing more than 50 million line items and more than 5 billion parts. In addition, the subsidiary provides e-business services and consulting for the aviation, marine and defense industries. The company owns Internet Business Applications, Inc. including its inventory management software, Aerospace Repairable Management System, or ARMS.

Aviall offers its employees a comprehensive benefits package that includes child and health care flexible spending accounts, a defined-benefit pension plan, a 401(k) savings plan, an educational assistance plan, internal job posting policy, credit union membership and an employee assistance program.

FINANCIALS: Sales and profits are in thousands of dollars—add 000 to get the full amount. 2008 Note: Financial information for 2008 was not available for all companies at press time.

2008 Sales: $2,000,000 — 2008 Profits: $
2007 Sales: $2,000,000 — 2007 Profits: $
2006 Sales: $1,500,000 — 2006 Profits: $
2005 Sales: $1,295,201 — 2005 Profits: $56,531
2004 Sales: $1,164,003 — 2004 Profits: $43,169

U.S. Stock Ticker: Subsidiary
Int'l Ticker: Int'l Exchange:
Employees: 1,009
Fiscal Year Ends: 12/31
Parent Company: BOEING COMPANY (THE)

SALARIES/BENEFITS:

Pension Plan: Y — ESOP Stock Plan: — Profit Sharing: — Top Exec. Salary: $542,380 — Bonus: $371,234
Savings Plan: Y — Stock Purch. Plan: — Second Exec. Salary: $332,991 — Bonus: $242,578

OTHER THOUGHTS:

Apparent Women Officers or Directors: 1
Hot Spot for Advancement for Women/Minorities:

LOCATIONS: ("Y" = Yes)

West:	Southwest:	Midwest:	Southeast:	Northeast:	International:
Y	Y	Y	Y	Y	Y

BABCOCK & WILCOX COMPANY (THE)

www.babcock.com

Industry Group Code: 335000 **Ranks within this company's industry group:** Sales: Profits:

Techology:		Medical/Drugs:		Engineering:		Transportation:		Chemicals/Petrochemicals:		Specialty:	
Computers:		Manufacturer:		Design:		Aerospace:		Oil/Gas Products:		Special Services:	
Software:		Contract Research:		Construction:	Y	Automotive:		Chemicals:		Consulting:	
Communications:		Medical Services:		Eng. Services:	Y	Shipping:		Oil/Chem. Svcs.:		Specialty Mgmt.:	
Electronics:		Labs:		Consulting:				Gases:		Products:	
Alternative Energy:	Y	Bio. Services:						Other:		Other:	

TYPES OF BUSINESS:

Power Generation Systems
Steam Generators
Environmental Equipment
Engineering & Construction Services
Power Plants
Emissions Reduction Equipment
Waste-to-Energy & Biomass Energy Systems
Boiler Cleaning Equipment

BRANDS/DIVISIONS/AFFILIATES:

McDermott International
Babcock & Wilcox Nuclear Power Generation Group
Babcock & Wilcox Power Generation Group
Babcock & Wilcox Technical Services Group
Babcock & Wilcox Nuclear Operations Group
Intech
Delta Power Services LLC
Nuclear Fuel Services, Inc.

CONTACTS: *Note: Officers with more than one job title may be intentionally listed here more than once.*

Brandon Berthards, CEO
Richard Killion, COO
Richard Killion, Pres.
Michael J. McCann, Dir.-Human Capital Dev.
Richard W. Loving, Dir.-Admin.
Michael J. Grady, Associate General Counsel/VP
John D. Krueger, VP-Bus. Dev. & Planning
Sharyn McCaulley, Mgr.-Employee Comm. & Public Rel.
David S. Black, VP/Controller
Brandon C. Bethards, Pres., B&W Power Generation Group
S. Robert Cochran, Pres., B&W Tech. Svcs. Group
Winfred D. Nash, Pres., B&W Nuclear Oper. Group
Richard E. Reimels, Pres., B&W Nuclear Power Generation Group

Phone: 434-522-6800	**Fax:**
Toll-Free:	
Address: 800 Main St., 4th Fl., Lynchburg, VA 24505 US	

GROWTH PLANS/SPECIAL FEATURES:

The Babcock and Wilcox Company (B&W), which functions as the power generation systems segment of McDermott International, designs, supplies and services power generation systems and associated equipment. The company's products include steam generators for electric power generation and industrial process heating; nuclear plant components, such as pressurizers and reactor vessels; environmental protection equipment; auxiliary steam generation components, such as air heaters, burners and control systems; and replacement parts for steam generators and other equipment. B&W upgrades, services and replaces parts for existing power plants, pulp and paper mills and industrial applications. In November 2007, the company reorganized its structure and renamed its primary subsidiaries. This move included the creation of a new commercial nuclear power subsidiary, Babcock & Wilcox Nuclear Power Generation Group, Inc. Other subsidiaries include Babcock & Wilcox Power Generation Group, Inc.; Babcock & Wilcox Technical Services Group, Inc.; and Babcock & Wilcox Nuclear Operations Group, Inc. The firm has international facilities in Denmark, Canada and China. In May 2007, B&W received a contract to design, supply and erect a 600-megawatt net coal-fired boiler and environmental control equipment for the Southwestern Electric Power Company. In October 2007, the company received a contract to build a new 220-megawatt coal-fired boiler and selective catalytic reduction system for Public Power Generation Agency. In July 2008, Babcock & Wilcox Power Generation Group, Inc. began construction of a 7,500-square-foot facility to study carbon dioxide capture technology. Also in July 2008, B&W acquired the Intech group of companies, which serve the nuclear service market, and Delta Power Services LLC, an operation and maintenance services provider. In August 2008, B&W agreed to acquire Nuclear Fuel Services, Inc., a specialty nuclear fuels and related services company.

Employee benefits include medical, dental and vision coverage; 401(k); tuition reimbursement; career development programs; retirement plan; and employee assistance program.

FINANCIALS: Sales and profits are in thousands of dollars—add 000 to get the full amount. 2008 Note: Financial information for 2008 was not available for all companies at press time.

2008 Sales: $	2008 Profits: $	**U.S. Stock Ticker: Subsidiary**
2007 Sales: $	2007 Profits: $	**Int'l Ticker:** Int'l Exchange:
2006 Sales: $	2006 Profits: $	Employees: 10,996
2005 Sales: $	2005 Profits: $	Fiscal Year Ends: 12/31
2004 Sales: $1,370,000	2004 Profits: $	Parent Company: MCDERMOTT INTERNATIONAL INC

SALARIES/BENEFITS:

Pension Plan: Y	ESOP Stock Plan:	Profit Sharing:	Top Exec. Salary: $	Bonus: $
Savings Plan: Y	Stock Purch. Plan:		Second Exec. Salary: $	Bonus: $

OTHER THOUGHTS:

Apparent Women Officers or Directors: 2
Hot Spot for Advancement for Women/Minorities:

LOCATIONS: ("Y" = Yes)

West:	Southwest:	Midwest:	Southeast:	Northeast:	International:
Y	Y	Y	Y	Y	Y

BAE SYSTEMS PLC

www.baesystems.com

Industry Group Code: 336410 **Ranks within this company's industry group:** Sales: 8 Profits: 6

Techology:		Medical/Drugs:		Engineering:		Transportation:		Chemicals/Petrochemicals:		Specialty:	
Computers:		Manufacturer:		Design:	Y	Aerospace:	Y	Oil/Gas Products:		Special Services:	Y
Software:		Contract Research:		Construction:		Automotive:	Y	Chemicals:		Consulting:	Y
Communications:	Y	Medical Services:		Eng. Services:		Shipping:	Y	Oil/Chem. Svcs.:		Specialty Mgmt.:	
Electronics:	Y	Labs:		Consulting:				Gases:		Products:	Y
Alternative Energy:		Bio. Services:						Other:		Other:	

TYPES OF BUSINESS:

Aerospace & Defense Manufacturing
Military Vehicles
Military Aircraft
Naval Vessels & Submarines
Satellite Manufacturing
Electronic Systems
Advanced Materials & Technologies
Security & Surveillance Technology

BRANDS/DIVISIONS/AFFILIATES:

Integrated System Technologies
Military Air Solutions
BAE Systems Australia
CS&S International
Detica

CONTACTS: *Note: Officers with more than one job title may be intentionally listed here more than once.*

Ian King, CEO
Walt Havenstein, COO
George Rose, Group Dir.-Finance
Fiona Davies, Chief of Staff
Phillip Bramwell, Group Dir.-Legal
Mike O'Callaghan, Dir.-Oper.
Richard J. Millies, VP-Bus. Dev. & Int'l Strategy
Lucy R. Fitch, VP-Corp. Comm.
Linda Hudson, Pres., Land & Armaments
Walt Havenstein, Pres., BAE Systems, Inc.
Mike Heffron, Pres., Electronics, Intelligence & Support
Richard Olver, Chmn.
Julian Scopes, Pres., BAE SystemsIndia

Phone: 44-1252-373-232	**Fax:** 44-1252-383-000
Toll-Free:	
Address: 6 Carlton Gardens, London, SW1Y 5AD UK	

GROWTH PLANS/SPECIAL FEATURES:

BAE Systems plc is involved in a wide variety of operations in the aerospace and defense industries. The firm is the largest defense provider in Europe and among the top ten in the U.S. BAE Systems has six home markets: Australia, Saudi Arabia, South Africa, Sweden, the U.K. and the U.S. The company has several business groups. The Electronics, Intelligence & Support group provides defense and aerospace systems, sub-systems and services. It comprises three operating groups: Electronics, Integrated Solutions and Customer Solutions. The Land & Armaments business group is a leader in the design, development, production, through-life support and upgrade of armored combat vehicles; tactical wheeled vehicles; naval guns; missile launchers; artillery systems; and intelligent munitions. The Integrated System Technologies business offers advanced mission-critical solutions and homeland security. Military Air Solutions designs, manufactures and supplies military air capabilities. BAE also does business through its subsidiaries like Detica, which offers governments and corporate clients intelligence collection, security maintenance and risk management; and CS&S International, which manages business opportunities in the Middle East. In January 2008, BAE signed a five-year deal with UK Sport to provide mathematical engineering expertise to athletes in Britain's premier championship/Olympic sports. In March 2008, the company sold its flight systems business to Calspan Corporation in 2008. In April 2008, BAE acquired 1ST Dynamics, a South African producer of turrets and weapons stations. In June 2008, the firm acquired MTC Technologies, Inc., service provider to the U.S. military and intelligence agencies; BAE also acquired Tenix Defence, which has been incorporated into BAE Systems Australia. In July 2008, BAE partnered with Lockheed Martin to develop Extended Range Munitions for the U.S. Navy. In December 2008, the firm acquired Tenix Toll Defence Logistics Pty Ltd., also incorporating it into BAE Systems Australia.

FINANCIALS: **Sales and profits are in thousands of dollars—add 000 to get the full amount. 2008 Note: Financial information for 2008 was not available for all companies at press time.**

2008 Sales: $23,931,600	2008 Profits: $2,538,000	**U.S. Stock Ticker: BAESY.PK**
2007 Sales: $20,540,900	2007 Profits: $1,323,550	**Int'l Ticker: BA** Int'l Exchange: London-LSE
2006 Sales: $24,150,500	2006 Profits: $3,209,500	Employees: 106,400
2005 Sales: $18,957,100	2005 Profits: $954,800	Fiscal Year Ends: 12/31
2004 Sales: $17,518,800	2004 Profits: $-899,500	Parent Company:

SALARIES/BENEFITS:

Pension Plan: Y	ESOP Stock Plan:	Profit Sharing: Y	Top Exec. Salary: $	Bonus: $
Savings Plan:	Stock Purch. Plan:		Second Exec. Salary: $	Bonus: $

OTHER THOUGHTS:

Apparent Women Officers or Directors: 3
Hot Spot for Advancement for Women/Minorities: Y

LOCATIONS: ("Y" = Yes)

West:	Southwest:	Midwest:	Southeast:	Northeast:	International:
Y	Y	Y	Y	Y	Y

BAKER HUGHES INC

www.bakerhughes.com

Industry Group Code: 213111 **Ranks within this company's industry group:** Sales: 3 Profits: 2

Techology:		Medical/Drugs:		Engineering:		Transportation:		Chemicals/Petrochemicals:		Specialty:	
Computers:		Manufacturer:		Design:		Aerospace:		Oil/Gas Products:	Y	Special Services:	
Software:		Contract Research:		Construction:		Automotive:		Chemicals:	Y	Consulting:	
Communications:		Medical Services:		Eng. Services:		Shipping:		Oil/Chem. Svcs.:	Y	Specialty Mgmt.:	
Electronics:		Labs:		Consulting:				Gases:		Products:	
Alternative Energy:		Bio. Services:						Other:		Other:	

TYPES OF BUSINESS:

Oil & Gas Drilling Support Services
Specialty Chemicals
Process Equipment
Geophysical Services
Drilling Fluids
Drill Bits

BRANDS/DIVISIONS/AFFILIATES:

Baker Atlas
Baker Hughes INTEQ
Baker Hughes Drilling Fluids
Hughes Christensen
Tricone
Baker Oil Tools
Baker Petrolite
Centrilift

CONTACTS: *Note: Officers with more than one job title may be intentionally listed here more than once.*

Chad C. Deaton, CEO
James R. Clark, COO
James R. Clark, Pres.
Peter Ragauss, CFO/Sr. VP
Didier Charreton, VP-Human Resources
Joe Vandevier, Dir.-Tech.
David H. Barr, Group Pres., Completions & Production
Alan R. Crain, Jr., General Counsel/Sr. VP
David E. Emerson, VP-Corp. Dev.
Gary R. Flaharty, Dir.-Investor Rel.
Alan J. Keifer, Controller/VP
Martin S. Craighead, Group Pres., Drilling & Evaluation
Paul S. Butero, VP/Pres., INTEQ
Gary G. Rich, VP/Pres., Hughes Christensen Company
Richard Williams, VP/Pres., Baker Hughes Drilling Fluids
Chad C. Deaton, Chmn.
Tayo Akinokun, Country Dir.-Nigeria

Phone: 713-439-8600 **Fax:** 713-439-8699
Toll-Free: 888-408-4244
Address: 2929 Allen Pkwy., Ste. 2100, Houston, TX 77019-2118 US

GROWTH PLANS/SPECIAL FEATURES:

Baker Hughes, Inc. is engaged in the oilfield and process industries, through its two main segments: drilling and evaluation; and completion and production. The drilling and evaluation segment includes subsidiary Baker Atlas, a premier provider of downhole well logging technology and services, including advanced formation evaluation, production and reservoir engineering and petrophysical and geophysical data acquisition services. The division also provides perforating and completion technologies, pipe recovery and data management, processing and analysis. Baker Hughes INTEQ, another subsidiary, is a major supplier of real-time drilling and evaluation services to the oil and gas industry, providing drilling technologies, drilling fluid systems, coring, subsurface surveying and other services. Baker Hughes Drilling Fluids provides drilling and completion fluids and related services, fluids environmental services and drill-in fluids. Hughes Christensen is a leading manufacturer and marketer of Tricone roller cone drill bits and polycrystalline diamond compact fixed cutter bits for the worldwide oil, gas, mining and geothermal industries. Baker Hughes' completion and production segment includes Baker Oil Tools, a provider of downhole completion, workover and fishing equipment and services, with product lines including packers, flow control equipment and sand control systems. Baker Petrolite provides oilfield specialty chemicals and integrated chemical technology solutions for petroleum production, transportation and refining. Centrilift is a market leader for oilfield electric submersible pumping systems and downhole oil/water separation technology. As of July 2008, Baker Hughes operated 3,436 rigs worldwide. In April 2008, the firm acquired Gaffney, Cline & Associates and GeoMechanics International, both reservoir consulting firms to enhance the company's reservoir engineering, technical and managerial advisory services and reservoir geomechanics portfolios.

Baker Hughes offers its employees a benefits package that includes flexible spending accounts, tuition reimbursement and an employee assistance program. The company generally promotes from within.

FINANCIALS: Sales and profits are in thousands of dollars—add 000 to get the full amount. 2008 Note: Financial information for 2008 was not available for all companies at press time.

2008 Sales: $11,864,000	2008 Profits: $1,635,000	**U.S. Stock Ticker: BHI**
2007 Sales: $10,428,200	2007 Profits: $1,513,900	**Int'l Ticker:** Int'l Exchange:
2006 Sales: $9,027,400	2006 Profits: $2,419,000	Employees: 39,800
2005 Sales: $7,185,500	2005 Profits: $878,400	Fiscal Year Ends: 12/31
2004 Sales: $6,079,600	2004 Profits: $528,600	Parent Company:

SALARIES/BENEFITS:

Pension Plan:	ESOP Stock Plan:	Profit Sharing:	Top Exec. Salary: $1,082,692	Bonus: $1,092,717
Savings Plan: Y	Stock Purch. Plan: Y		Second Exec. Salary: $683,461	Bonus: $390,229

OTHER THOUGHTS:

Apparent Women Officers or Directors: 3
Hot Spot for Advancement for Women/Minorities: Y

LOCATIONS: ("Y" = Yes)

West:	Southwest:	Midwest:	Southeast:	Northeast:	International:
Y	Y	Y	Y	Y	Y

BALFOUR BEATTY PLC

www.balfourbeatty.com

Industry Group Code: 234000 **Ranks within this company's industry group:** Sales: 10 Profits: 11

Techology:		Medical/Drugs:		Engineering:		Transportation:		Chemicals/Petrochemicals:		Specialty:	
Computers:		Manufacturer:		Design:		Aerospace:		Oil/Gas Products:		Special Services:	
Software:		Contract Research:		Construction:	Y	Automotive:		Chemicals:		Consulting:	
Communications:		Medical Services:		Eng. Services:	Y	Shipping:		Oil/Chem. Svcs.:		Specialty Mgmt.:	Y
Electronics:		Labs:		Consulting:				Gases:		Products:	
Alternative Energy:		Bio. Services:						Other:		Other:	

TYPES OF BUSINESS:

Heavy Construction
Engineering Services
Railway Services
Property Management
Utility & Roadway Infrastructure Management

BRANDS/DIVISIONS/AFFILIATES:

Heery International
Balfour Beatty Construction U.S.
Balfour Beatty Rail, Inc.
Balfour Beatty Capital Projects
Dean & Dyball
Blackpool International Airport
Colledge Trundle and Hall Limited
Schreck-Mieves

CONTACTS: *Note: Officers with more than one job title may be intentionally listed here more than once.*

Ian P. Tyler, CEO
Andrew McNaughton, COO
Paul Raby, Dir.-Human Resources
Andy Rose, Managing Dir.-Eng.
Chris Vaughan, General Counsel/Corp. Sec.
Peter Zinkin, Dir.-Planning & Dev.
Duncan Magrath, Dir.-Finance
Anthony Rabin, Deputy CEO
Manfred Leger, Managing Dir.-Railroad Bus.
Brian Osborne, Managing Dir.-Utilities, Road & Facilities Mgmt.
Mike Peasland, Managing Dir.-UK Building Construction & Building
David John, Chmn.

Phone: 44-20-7216-6800	**Fax:** 44-20-7216-6902
Toll-Free:	
Address: 130 Wilton Rd., London, SW1V 1LQ UK	

GROWTH PLANS/SPECIAL FEATURES:

Balfour Beatty plc provides engineering, construction and financial services for rail, road, power and building projects worldwide. Balfour operates through numerous subsidiaries, dividing its enterprises into four categories: building, engineering, rail and investments. The building division largely focuses on public sector projects such as schools, hospitals and public housing. In the U.S., subsidiary Heery International provides architectural, engineering and program management services for education, health care, government, sports and aviation projects. Balfour Beatty also conducts U.S. operations via Balfour Beatty Construction U.S. In its specialist engineering business, the company provides design, construction, project management, strengthening, testing, civil engineering and other services for overhead transmission lines, gas and water utility contracting and road management and maintenance. The firm's rail division provides design, construction, project management, maintenance, track renewal, specialist plant, product, system, power and signaling services to the rail industry. Balfour performs these operations in the U.S. through subsidiary Balfour Beatty Rail, Inc. As part of this division's operations, Balfour holds responsibility for maintenance and upgrade of two-thirds of London's Underground system. Through its investments division, the company does a small amount of business promoting, managing and investing in privately funded infrastructure and accommodation projects for the transport, health care and education sectors in the U.K. Overseas, Balfour maintains its investment services through operating company Balfour Beatty Capital Projects. Acquisitions in 2008 include Schreck-Mieves, a German rail engineering group; Barnhart, a Californian construction management company; Colledge Trundle and Hall Limited, a specialist in the design and installation of automatic energy control systems for buildings; Blackpool International Airport; Dean & Dyball, a U.K. regional contractor; and the military PPP accommodation business of GMH Communities Trust, a U.S. real estate investment trust. In January 2009, the company acquired an interest in a military housing project near Lackland Air Force Base in San Antonio, Texas

FINANCIALS: **Sales and profits are in thousands of dollars—add 000 to get the full amount. 2008 Note: Financial information for 2008 was not available for all companies at press time.**

2008 Sales: $12,658,800	2008 Profits: $396,460	**U.S. Stock Ticker:**
2007 Sales: $9,494,480	2007 Profits: $230,530	**Int'l Ticker: BBY** Int'l Exchange: London-LSE
2006 Sales: $8,936,980	2006 Profits: $497,270	Employees: 27,351
2005 Sales: $7,642,340	2005 Profits: $587,570	Fiscal Year Ends: 12/31
2004 Sales: $6,739,800	2004 Profits: $391,000	Parent Company:

SALARIES/BENEFITS:

Pension Plan:	ESOP Stock Plan:	Profit Sharing:	Top Exec. Salary: $818,024	Bonus: $275,189
Savings Plan:	Stock Purch. Plan:		Second Exec. Salary: $591,768	Bonus: $39,457

OTHER THOUGHTS:

Apparent Women Officers or Directors:
Hot Spot for Advancement for Women/Minorities:

LOCATIONS: ("Y" = Yes)

West:	Southwest:	Midwest:	Southeast:	Northeast:	International:
Y		Y	Y		Y

Note: Financial information, benefits and other data can change quickly and may vary from those stated here.

BALLARD POWER SYSTEMS

www.ballard.com

Industry Group Code: 333298 **Ranks within this company's industry group:** Sales: 2 Profits: 1

Techology:		Medical/Drugs:		Engineering:		Transportation:		Chemicals/Petrochemicals:		Specialty:	
Computers:		Manufacturer:		Design:		Aerospace:		Oil/Gas Products:		Special Services:	
Software:		Contract Research:		Construction:		Automotive:		Chemicals:		Consulting:	
Communications:		Medical Services:		Eng. Services:		Shipping:		Oil/Chem. Svcs.:		Specialty Mgmt.:	
Electronics:		Labs:		Consulting:				Gases:		Products:	
Alternative Energy:	Y	Bio. Services:						Other:		Other:	

TYPES OF BUSINESS:

Fuel Cells Manufacturing
Automotive Parts Manufacturing
Carbon Products
Residential Cogeneration Fuel Cells

BRANDS/DIVISIONS/AFFILIATES:

EBARA BALLARD
Ballard Power Systems Corp.
Ballard Material Products, Inc.
Ballard Generation Systems, Inc.

CONTACTS: *Note: Officers with more than one job title may be intentionally listed here more than once.*

John W. Sheridan, CEO
John W. Sheridan, Pres.
David S. Smith, CFO
William Foulds, VP-Sales
Glenn Kumoi, VP-Human Resources
Christopher Guzy, CTO/VP
Glenn Kumoi, Chief Legal Officer
Christopher Guzy, VP-Oper.
Noordin Nanji, VP-Strategy & Dev.
William Foulds, Pres., Ballard Material Products Div.

Phone: 604-454-0900	**Fax:** 604-412-4700
Toll-Free:	
Address: 9000 Glenlyon Pkwy., Burnaby, BC V5J 5J8 Canada	

GROWTH PLANS/SPECIAL FEATURES:

Ballard Power Systems is a world leader in developing, manufacturing and marketing zero-emission hydrogen fuel cells. The company's fuel cells are primarily used in transportation, electricity generation and portable power products, but are also used for residential cogeneration and backup power applications. The fuel cell combines hydrogen obtained from methanol, natural gas, petroleum or renewable sources and oxygen from the air to generate electricity. The only emission as a result of this reaction is pure water. Subsidiary Ballard Material Products manufactures carbon products, including fabrics, fiber papers and laminates. Ballard is currently partnering with global giants, including DaimlerChrysler and Ford, to commercialize its fuel cell technology, and has supplied fuel cell products to Honda, Nissan, Volkswagen, Yamaha, Cinergy and Coleman Powermate. Ballard also is part-owner of Ebara Ballard Corporation, a Japanese joint venture owned by Ballard and EBARA Corporation. In April 2008, the company entered a joint venture with The Raymond Corporation to research lift vehicles with the intention of converting all Raymond lift trucks to Ballard's Mark9 SSL(TM) fuel cell product technology.

FINANCIALS: **Sales and profits are in thousands of dollars—add 000 to get the full amount. 2008 Note: Financial information for 2008 was not available for all companies at press time.**

2008 Sales: $59,580	2008 Profits: $34,079	**U.S. Stock Ticker: BLDP**
2007 Sales: $65,532	2007 Profits: $57,302	**Int'l Ticker: BLD** Int'l Exchange: Toronto-TSX
2006 Sales: $49,823	2006 Profits: $-181,137	Employees: 500
2005 Sales: $42,248	2005 Profits: $-86,983	Fiscal Year Ends: 12/31
2004 Sales: $73,040	2004 Profits: $-175,407	Parent Company:

SALARIES/BENEFITS:

Pension Plan:	ESOP Stock Plan:	Profit Sharing:	Top Exec. Salary: $	Bonus: $
Savings Plan:	Stock Purch. Plan:		Second Exec. Salary: $	Bonus: $

OTHER THOUGHTS:

Apparent Women Officers or Directors:
Hot Spot for Advancement for Women/Minorities:

LOCATIONS: ("Y" = Yes)

West:	Southwest:	Midwest:	Southeast:	Northeast:	International:
		Y		Y	Y

BARAN GROUP LTD

www.barangroup.com

Industry Group Code: 234000 **Ranks within this company's industry group:** Sales: Profits:

Techology:		Medical/Drugs:		Engineering:		Transportation:		Chemicals/Petrochemicals:		Specialty:	
Computers:		Manufacturer:		Design:	Y	Aerospace:		Oil/Gas Products:		Special Services:	
Software:	Y	Contract Research:		Construction:	Y	Automotive:		Chemicals:		Consulting:	Y
Communications:	Y	Medical Services:		Eng. Services:	Y	Shipping:		Oil/Chem. Svcs.:		Specialty Mgmt.:	Y
Electronics:	Y	Labs:	Y	Consulting:	Y			Gases:		Products:	
Alternative Energy:		Bio. Services:						Other:		Other:	

TYPES OF BUSINESS:

Civil Engineering
Technology Development
Telecommunications

BRANDS/DIVISIONS/AFFILIATES:

Nes Pan
Industrial Centers E.O.D. Ltd.
Baran Advanced Technologies Ltd.
Tefen

CONTACTS:

Note: Officers with more than one job title may be intentionally listed here more than once.

Meir Dor, Acting CEO
Sasson Shilo, CFO/Sr. VP
Avigdor Kaner, VP-Human Resources
Aviv Cohen, Sr. VP-Tech. & Investments Div.
Yossi Ron, Sr. VP-Eng. & Projects Div.
Haim Assael, General Counsel
Elhanan Abramov, Sr. VP-Bus. Dev.
Abel Raviv, Head-Comm.
Saar Bracha, Sr. VP-Telecommunications Div.
Adrian Hillel, Sr. VP/Pres. Oil & Petrochemical Div.
Aviv Cohen, Sr. VP/Gen Mgr.-Holding Group
Meir Dor, Chmn.
Israel Gotman, Pres., Russian Div.

Phone: 972-8-6200200 **Fax:** 972-8-6200201
Toll-Free:
Address: Baran House, 8 Omarim St., Industrial Park, Omer, 84965 Israel

GROWTH PLANS/SPECIAL FEATURES:

Baran Group, Ltd. is an Israeli engineering firm that operates in three segments: communications; engineering and projects; and technology and investments. The company offers project services at any level from feasibility studies and planning, detailed engineering, procurement, construction management and technology development to complete turnkey project and facility management. In the communications segment, Baran performs network infrastructure deployment, telecommunications equipment installation and other projects related to wireless, wireless data and broadband networks throughout North America, Europe, South Africa and the Asia-Pacific. The engineering and projects division provides construction management and supervision services for civil infrastructure, large buildings projects and project management services for governmental sectors and institutions. Baran specializes in the transportation industry, with additional expertise in the fields of chemical engineering; oil refining; petrochemicals; natural gas; energy and power; microelectronics; water treatment; and instrumentation and control. The engineering segment has offices in Israel and Eastern Europe. Baran's technology and investments division develops and produces proprietary products and technologies including a cashless, paperless and wireless in-vehicle parking management system; button switches based on piezo-electric crystals; and importation, marketing and distribution of raw materials for the Israeli feed industry. Subsidiaries include Nes Pan, an international real estate company; Industrial Centers E.O.D. Ltd., providing raw materials for livestock feed; Baran Advanced Technologies Ltd., developing, producing and marketing weatherproof, durable keyboards for harsh environments; and Tefen, an international management consulting firm.

FINANCIALS:

Sales and profits are in thousands of dollars—add 000 to get the full amount. 2008 Note: Financial information for 2008 was not available for all companies at press time.

2008 Sales: $	2008 Profits: $	**U.S. Stock Ticker: BRANF.PK**
2007 Sales: $327,996	2007 Profits: $34,237	**Int'l Ticker: BRAN** Int'l Exchange: Tel Aviv-TASE
2006 Sales: $246,473	2006 Profits: $2,538	Employees: 1,700
2005 Sales: $118,542	2005 Profits: $-22,916	Fiscal Year Ends: 12/31
2004 Sales: $	2004 Profits: $	Parent Company:

SALARIES/BENEFITS:

Pension Plan:	ESOP Stock Plan:	Profit Sharing:	Top Exec. Salary: $	Bonus: $
Savings Plan:	Stock Purch. Plan:		Second Exec. Salary: $	Bonus: $

OTHER THOUGHTS:

Apparent Women Officers or Directors: 2
Hot Spot for Advancement for Women/Minorities:

LOCATIONS: ("Y" = Yes)

West:	Southwest:	Midwest:	Southeast:	Northeast:	International:
			Y		Y

BASF AG

www.basf.com

Industry Group Code: 325000 **Ranks within this company's industry group:** Sales: 1 Profits: 1

Techology:		Medical/Drugs:		Engineering:		Transportation:		Chemicals/Petrochemicals:		Specialty:	
Computers:		Manufacturer:	Y	Design:		Aerospace:		Oil/Gas Products:	Y	Special Services:	
Software:		Contract Research:		Construction:		Automotive:		Chemicals:	Y	Consulting:	
Communications:		Medical Services:		Eng. Services:		Shipping:		Oil/Chem. Svcs.:		Specialty Mgmt.:	
Electronics:		Labs:		Consulting:				Gases:	Y	Products:	Y
Alternative Energy:		Bio. Services:						Other:	Y	Other:	Y

TYPES OF BUSINESS:

Chemicals Manufacturing
Agricultural Products
Oil & Gas Production
Plastics
Coatings
Nanotechnology Research
Nutritional Products
Agricultural Biotechnology

BRANDS/DIVISIONS/AFFILIATES:

Wintershall AG
Orgamol SA
BASF Catalysts LLC
Johnson Polymer
CropDesign
Hansa Chemie International
Sorex Holdings Ltd

CONTACTS:

Note: Officers with more than one job title may be intentionally listed here more than once.

Jurgen Hambrect, CEO
Kurt W. Bock, CFO
Harald Schwager, Exec. Dir.-Human Resources
Stefan Marcinowski, Exec. Dir.-Research Planning
Kurt W. Bock, Exec. Dir.-Info. Svcs.
Stefan Marcinowski, Exec. Dir.-Corp. Eng.
Magdalena Moll, Sr. VP-Investor Rel.
Kurt W. Bock, Exec. Dir.-Finance
Andreas Kreimeyer, Exec. Dir.-Performance Chemicals
John Feldmann, Exec. Dir.-Oil & Gas
Stefan Marcinowski, Exec. Dir.-Inorganics & Petrochemicals
Peter Oakley, Dir.-Agricultural Prod.
Juergen Hambrecht, Chmn.
Martin Brudermueller, Exec. Dir.-APAC
Hans-Ulrich Engel, Exec. Dir.-Procurement & Logistics

Phone: 49-621-60-0 **Fax:** 49-621-60-42525
Toll-Free:
Address: 38 Carl-Bosch St., Ludwigshafen, 67056 Germany

GROWTH PLANS/SPECIAL FEATURES:

BASF is a chemical manufacturing company that operates 330 production facilities in 38 countries and serves customers in more than 170 countries. Around 21% of BASF sales are made to North American industries. The firm operates in six business segments: chemicals; plastics; performance products; agricultural solutions; functional solutions; and oil and gas. The chemicals segment manufactures inorganic, petrochemical and intermediate chemicals for the pharmaceutical, construction, textile and automotive industries. The plastics segment primarily manufactures polystyrene, styrenics and performance polymers for the manufacturing and packaging industries. The performance polymers segment produces pigments, inks, printing supplies, coatings and polymers for the automotive, oil, packaging, textile, detergent, sanitary care, construction and chemical industries. The firm's agricultural solutions segment produces and markets genetically engineered plants, nutritional supplements, herbicides, fungicides and insecticides for use in agriculture, public health and pest control. The functional solutions segment develops automotive and industrial catalysts; construction chemicals; and coatings and refinishes for automotive and construction markets. The oil and gas segment is operated through BASF subsidiary Wintershall AG, which focuses on petroleum and natural gas exploration and production in North America, Asia, Europe, the Middle East and Africa. BASF also employs chemical nanotechnology in pigments that are used to color coatings, paints and plastics; and sunscreen. BASF is one of the world's leading R&D firms, with 8,000 employees working in research in 70 sites worldwide, employing a research budget of $1.3 billion Euros yearly. In September 2008, the firm agreed to acquire specialty chemicals maker Ciba Holding AG. In December of the same year, the company acquired Sorex Holdings Ltd., a manufacturer of branded chemical and other products for pest management.

U.S. employees are offered medical, dental and vision insurance; life insurance; disability coverage; an employee savings plan; tuition reimbursement; auto and home insurance; adoption assistance; and a preferred supplier discount.

FINANCIALS:

Sales and profits are in thousands of dollars—add 000 to get the full amount. 2008 Note: Financial information for 2008 was not available for all companies at press time.

2008 Sales: $83,990,800	2008 Profits: $3,925,610	**U.S. Stock Ticker: BF**
2007 Sales: $78,122,600	2007 Profits: $5,479,950	**Int'l Ticker: BAS** Int'l Exchange: Frankfurt-Euronext
2006 Sales: $69,448,400	2006 Profits: $4,575,330	Employees: 96,924
2005 Sales: $52,080,500	2005 Profits: $3,663,700	Fiscal Year Ends: 12/31
2004 Sales: $51,572,600	2004 Profits: $2,550,700	Parent Company:

SALARIES/BENEFITS:

Pension Plan:	ESOP Stock Plan:	Profit Sharing:	Top Exec. Salary: $	Bonus: $
Savings Plan:	Stock Purch. Plan:		Second Exec. Salary: $	Bonus: $

OTHER THOUGHTS:

Apparent Women Officers or Directors: 1
Hot Spot for Advancement for Women/Minorities:

LOCATIONS: ("Y" = Yes)

West:	Southwest:	Midwest:	Southeast:	Northeast:	International:
Y	Y	Y	Y	Y	Y

BASF FUTURE BUSINESS GMBH

www.basf-fb.de/en

Industry Group Code: 541710 **Ranks within this company's industry group:** Sales: Profits:

Techology:		**Medical/Drugs:**		**Engineering:**		**Transportation:**		**Chemicals/Petrochemicals:**		**Specialty:**	
Computers:		Manufacturer:		Design:		Aerospace:		Oil/Gas Products:		Special Services:	
Software:		Contract Research:		Construction:		Automotive:		Chemicals:	Y	Consulting:	
Communications:		Medical Services:		Eng. Services:		Shipping:		Oil/Chem. Svcs.:		Specialty Mgmt.:	
Electronics:	Y	Labs:		Consulting:				Gases:		Products:	Y
Alternative Energy:	Y	Bio. Services:						Other:		Other:	Y

TYPES OF BUSINESS:

Chemistry & Materials Research
Nanotechnology Research
Organic Photovoltaic Materials
Organic LEDs
Waste Heat Recovery
Probiotics

BRANDS/DIVISIONS/AFFILIATES:

BASF AG
LNCO-1

CONTACTS:

Note: Officers with more than one job title may be intentionally listed here more than once.

Thomas Weber, Managing Dir.
Tilo Habicher, Dir.-Health & Environmental Tech.
Joachim Roesch, Dir.-Energy & Organic Electronics
Marcos Gomez, Sr. Mgr.-Antimicrobial Prod.
Georg Degen, Sr. Mgr.-Magnetocalorics

Phone: 49-621-60-76811	**Fax:** 49-621-60-76818
Toll-Free:	
Address: 4 Gartenweg, Gebaude Z 025, Ludwigshafen, 67063 Germany	

GROWTH PLANS/SPECIAL FEATURES:

BASF Future Business GmbH, a subsidiary of BASF AG, strives to discover new business areas for the BASF group, focuses on chemicals-related new materials and technologies. It currently runs nine projects. The organic light-emitting diodes (OLEDs) project uses organic semiconductor materials to create thin films that could be used as luminescent wallpapers or lighting panels. OLEDs promise to be more energy efficient than conventional lighting. The metal organic frameworks (MOF) project has developed various nanoscale cubes, sold under the Basolite brand, that offer huge surface areas in a small volume of material, on the order of several football fields' area per gram of Basolite MOF material. These nanocubes can utilize their immense surface area and open structure to absorb, store and release specific chemicals for various applications. The Li-ion batteries project is developing cathode materials for specific applications, such as for hybrid electric vehicles or telecommunications back-up power systems. Its first product is the high energy density nanocrystalline material called LNCO-1. The organic photovoltaics project uses organic semiconductor material to create solar panels that require less energy to produce and possess higher photochemical and thermal stability as well as better light-absorption properties than conventional materials. The thermoelectrics project is developing semiconductor materials to efficiently create electricity from waste heat produced by automobiles, power plants or industrial processes. The magnetocalorics project is developing magnetic-based cooling systems that promise to have less ecological impact and consume less energy than conventional refrigerants in air conditioners and refrigerators. The pro-t-action project is developing probiotic microorganisms for oral hygiene and personal and skin care products. The printed electronics project is developing new inks capable of printing semiconductor circuitry on paper and plastics. Lastly, the antimicrobial materials project develops new dental cosmetics products, wound management materials (bandages and gels) and sanitizers for medical devices and equipment.

FINANCIALS:

Sales and profits are in thousands of dollars—add 000 to get the full amount. 2008 Note: Financial information for 2008 was not available for all companies at press time.

2008 Sales: $	2008 Profits: $	**U.S. Stock Ticker: Subsidiary**
2007 Sales: $	2007 Profits: $	**Int'l Ticker:** Int'l Exchange:
2006 Sales: $	2006 Profits: $	Employees:
2005 Sales: $	2005 Profits: $	Fiscal Year Ends: 12/31
2004 Sales: $	2004 Profits: $	Parent Company: BASF AG

SALARIES/BENEFITS:

Pension Plan:	ESOP Stock Plan:	Profit Sharing:	Top Exec. Salary: $	Bonus: $
Savings Plan:	Stock Purch. Plan:		Second Exec. Salary: $	Bonus: $

OTHER THOUGHTS:

Apparent Women Officers or Directors: 1
Hot Spot for Advancement for Women/Minorities: Y

LOCATIONS: ("Y" = Yes)

West:	Southwest:	Midwest:	Southeast:	Northeast:	International:
				Y	Y

BAUSCH & LOMB INC

www.bausch.com

Industry Group Code: 339113 **Ranks within this company's industry group:** Sales: Profits:

Techology:		Medical/Drugs:		Engineering:		Transportation:		Chemicals/Petrochemicals:		Specialty:	
Computers:		Manufacturer:	Y	Design:		Aerospace:		Oil/Gas Products:		Special Services:	
Software:		Contract Research:		Construction:		Automotive:		Chemicals:		Consulting:	
Communications:		Medical Services:		Eng. Services:		Shipping:		Oil/Chem. Svcs.:		Specialty Mgmt.:	
Electronics:		Labs:	Y	Consulting:				Gases:		Products:	
Alternative Energy:		Bio. Services:						Other:		Other:	

TYPES OF BUSINESS:

Supplies-Eye Care
Contact Lens Products
Ophthalmic Pharmaceuticals
Surgical Products

BRANDS/DIVISIONS/AFFILIATES:

Alrex
Warburg Pincus LLC
Eyeonics Inc
Ocuvite
Lotemax
Alrex
PreserVision
Zyoptic

CONTACTS: *Note: Officers with more than one job title may be intentionally listed here more than once.*

Gerald M. Ostrov, CEO
Brian J. Harris, CFO/Corp. VP
Paul H. Sartori, Corp. VP- Human Resources
Alan H. Farnsworth, CIO/Sr. VP-IT
John W. Sheets, Jr., CTO/Corp. VP
A Robert D. Bailey, General Counsel/Corp. VP
Michael Gowen, Exec. VP-Global Bus. Oper. & Process Excellence
Paul H. Sartori, Corp. VP-Public Affairs
J. Andy Corley, Corp. VP/Global Pres., Surgical Products
David N. Edwards, Pres., Asia Pacific Region/Corp. VP
Stuart Heap, Global Pres., Vision Care/Corp. VP
Flemming Ornskov, Global Pres., Pharmaceuticals/Corp. VP
Gerald M. Ostrov, Chmn.
John H. Brown, Pres., EMEA/Corp. VP

Phone: 585-338-6000 **Fax:**
Toll-Free: 800-344-8815
Address: 1 Bausch & Lomb Pl., Rochester, NY 14604-2701 US

GROWTH PLANS/SPECIAL FEATURES:

Bausch & Lomb, Inc. (B&L), a subsidiary of Warburg Pincus LLC, is a world leader in the development, marketing and manufacturing of eye care products. The firm's products are marketed in more than 100 countries and in five categories: contact lenses; lens care; pharmaceuticals; cataract and vitreoretinal surgery; and refractive surgery. In its contact lens category, B&L's product portfolio includes traditional, planned replacement disposable, daily disposable, continuous wear, toric soft contact lenses and rigid gas-permeable materials. The firm's lens care products include multi-purpose solutions, enzyme cleaners and saline solutions. The firm's pharmaceuticals include generic and branded prescription ophthalmic pharmaceuticals, ocular vitamins, over-the-counter medications and vision accessories. Key pharmaceutical trademarks of the firm are Bausch & Lomb, Alrex, Liposic, Lotemax, Ocuvite, PreserVision and Zylet. B&L's cataract and vitreoretinal division offers a broad line of intraocular lenses and delivery systems, as well as the Millennium and Stellaris lines of phacoemulsification equipment used in the extraction of the patient's natural lens during cataract surgery. The company's refractive surgery products include lasers and diagnostic equipment used in the LASIK surgical procedure under the brand Zyoptic. B&L's global operations include research and development units on six continents and operating offices in over 43 countries. In February 2008, B&L completed the acquisition of Eyeonics, Inc., a company specializing in ophthalmic medical devices based in Aliso Viejo, California.

The firm offers employees medical and dental coverage; various work/life programs; a vacation buy/sell program; domestic partner benefits; flexible spending accounts; and education reimbursement.

FINANCIALS: **Sales and profits are in thousands of dollars—add 000 to get the full amount. 2008 Note: Financial information for 2008 was not available for all companies at press time.**

2008 Sales: $	2008 Profits: $	**U.S. Stock Ticker: Private**
2007 Sales: $	2007 Profits: $	**Int'l Ticker:** Int'l Exchange:
2006 Sales: $2,293,400	2006 Profits: $	Employees: 13,700
2005 Sales: $2,353,800	2005 Profits: $19,200	Fiscal Year Ends: 12/31
2004 Sales: $2,233,500	2004 Profits: $153,900	Parent Company: WARBURG PINCUS LLC

SALARIES/BENEFITS:

Pension Plan:	ESOP Stock Plan:	Profit Sharing:	Top Exec. Salary: $1,100,000	Bonus: $
Savings Plan:	Stock Purch. Plan:		Second Exec. Salary: $410,001	Bonus: $295,000

OTHER THOUGHTS:

Apparent Women Officers or Directors: 1
Hot Spot for Advancement for Women/Minorities: Y

LOCATIONS: ("Y" = Yes)

West:	Southwest:	Midwest:	Southeast:	Northeast:	International:
Y			Y	Y	Y

BAXTER INTERNATIONAL INC

www.baxter.com

Industry Group Code: 339113 **Ranks within this company's industry group:** Sales: 4 Profits: 4

Techology:		Medical/Drugs:		Engineering:		Transportation:		Chemicals/Petrochemicals:		Specialty:	
Computers:		Manufacturer:	Y	Design:		Aerospace:		Oil/Gas Products:		Special Services:	
Software:	Y	Contract Research:	Y	Construction:		Automotive:		Chemicals:		Consulting:	
Communications:		Medical Services:	Y	Eng. Services:		Shipping:		Oil/Chem. Svcs.:		Specialty Mgmt.:	
Electronics:		Labs:		Consulting:				Gases:		Products:	
Alternative Energy:		Bio. Services:	Y					Other:		Other:	

TYPES OF BUSINESS:

Medical Equipment Manufacturing
Supplies-Intravenous & Renal Dialysis Systems
Medication Delivery Products & IV Fluids
Biopharmaceutical Products
Plasma Collection & Processing
Vaccines
Software
Contract Research

BRANDS/DIVISIONS/AFFILIATES:

Medication Delivery
BioScience
Renal
Colleague CX
Enlightened
ADVATE
RenalSoft HD
ARTISS

CONTACTS: *Note: Officers with more than one job title may be intentionally listed here more than once.*

Robert L. Parkinson, Jr., CEO
Robert L. Parkinson, Jr., Pres.
Robert M. Davis, CFO/VP
Jeanne K. Mason, VP-Human Resources
Norbert G. Riedel, Chief Scientific Officer/VP
Karenann Terrell, CIO/VP
J. Michael Gatling, VP-Mfg.
Susan R. Lichtenstein, General Counsel/VP
Michael J. Baughman, Controller/VP
Joy A. Amundson, VP/Pres., Bioscience
Bruce McGillivray, Pres., Renal/VP
Peter J. Arduini, Pres., Medication Delivery/VP
Gerald Lema, Pres., Asia Pacific/VP
Robert L. Parkinson, Jr., Chmn.
John J. Greisch, Pres., Int'l/VP

Phone: 847-948-2000	**Fax:** 847-948-3642
Toll-Free: 800-422-9837	
Address: 1 Baxter Pkwy., Deerfield, IL 60015-4625 US	

GROWTH PLANS/SPECIAL FEATURES:

Baxter International, Inc. manufactures and markets products for the treatment of hemophilia, immune disorders, cancer, infectious diseases, kidney disease, trauma and other chronic and acute medical conditions, offering expertise in medical devices, pharmaceuticals and biotechnology. Baxter markets its offerings to hospitals; clinical and medical research labs; blood and blood dialysis centers; rehab facilities; nursing homes; doctor's offices; and patients undergoing supervised home care. The firm has manufacturing facilities in 26 countries and offers products and services in 100 countries. Baxter operates in three segments: Medication Delivery, its largest sector, which provides a range of intravenous solutions and specialty products that are used in combination for fluid replenishment, nutrition therapy, pain management, antibiotic therapy and chemotherapy; BioScience, which develops biopharmaceuticals, biosurgery products, vaccines, blood collection, processing and storage products and technologies; and Renal, which develops products and provides services to treat end-stage kidney disease. Products include the Colleague CX infusion pump; the Enlightened bar-coding system for flexible IV containers; ADVATE, a coagulant for hemophilia patients; and RenalSoft HD, a software module for the management of prescription, therapy and monitoring information relating to patients suffering from kidney failure. In addition, the company provides the following services: BioLife Plasma Services, a plasma collection and processing business; BioPharma Solutions, biotechnology; Global Technical Services, providing instrument service and support for devices manufactured and marketed by Baxter; Renal Clinical Helpline; Renal Services, an education and research operation; and Training and Education, a portfolio of interactive clinical web sites. In March 2008, the company received FDA approval of ARTISS, a slow-setting fibrin sealant for the use of adhering skin grafts in burn patients.

Employees are offered medical and dental insurance; vision care discounts; health and dependent care reimbursement accounts; an educational assistance program; credit union membership; adoption reimbursement; an employee assistance program; a 401(k) plan; and a stock purchase plan.

FINANCIALS: **Sales and profits are in thousands of dollars—add 000 to get the full amount. 2008 Note: Financial information for 2008 was not available for all companies at press time.**

2008 Sales: $12,348,000	2008 Profits: $2,014,000	**U.S. Stock Ticker: BAX**
2007 Sales: $11,263,000	2007 Profits: $1,707,000	**Int'l Ticker:** Int'l Exchange:
2006 Sales: $10,378,000	2006 Profits: $1,397,000	Employees: 48,500
2005 Sales: $9,849,000	2005 Profits: $956,000	Fiscal Year Ends: 12/31
2004 Sales: $9,509,000	2004 Profits: $388,000	Parent Company:

SALARIES/BENEFITS:

Pension Plan:	ESOP Stock Plan:	Profit Sharing:	Top Exec. Salary: $1,296,153	Bonus: $3,000,000
Savings Plan: Y	Stock Purch. Plan: Y		Second Exec. Salary: $595,165	Bonus: $1,089,050

OTHER THOUGHTS:

Apparent Women Officers or Directors: 6
Hot Spot for Advancement for Women/Minorities: Y

LOCATIONS: ("Y" = Yes)

West:	Southwest:	Midwest:	Southeast:	Northeast:	International:
Y	Y	Y	Y	Y	Y

BAYER AG

www.bayer.com

Industry Group Code: 325000 **Ranks within this company's industry group:** Sales: 3 Profits: 3

Techology:		**Medical/Drugs:**		**Engineering:**		**Transportation:**		**Chemicals/Petrochemicals:**		**Specialty:**	
Computers:		Manufacturer:	Y	Design:		Aerospace:		Oil/Gas Products:		Special Services:	
Software:		Contract Research:		Construction:		Automotive:		Chemicals:	Y	Consulting:	
Communications:		Medical Services:		Eng. Services:		Shipping:		Oil/Chem. Svcs.:		Specialty Mgmt.:	
Electronics:		Labs:		Consulting:				Gases:		Products:	Y
Alternative Energy:		Bio. Services:						Other:		Other:	

TYPES OF BUSINESS:

Chemicals Manufacturing
Pharmaceuticals
Animal Health Products
Synthetic Materials
Crop Science
Plant Biotechnology
Health Care Products

BRANDS/DIVISIONS/AFFILIATES:

Bayer Corp
Bayer CropScience
Bayer HealthCare
Bayer MaterialScience
Bayer Business Services
Bayer Technology Services
Currenta GmbH & Co.
Bayer Schering Pharma AG

CONTACTS: *Note: Officers with more than one job title may be intentionally listed here more than once.*

Werner Wenning, Chmn.-Mgmt. Board
Klaus Kuhn, Dir.-Finance
Richard Pott, Dir.-Human Resources
Wolfgang Plischke, Dir.-Innovation
Wolfgang Plischke, Dir.-Tech.
Richard Pott, Dir.-Strategy
Michael Schade, Head.-Comm.
Alexander Rosar, Head-Investor Rel.
Wolfgang Plischke, Dir.-Environment
A.J. Higgins, Chmn.-Bayer Health Care
F. Berschauer, Chmn.-Bayer Crop Sciences
P. Thomas, Chmn.-Bayer Material Science
Manfred Schneider, Chmn.-Supervisory Board
Klaus Kuhn, Dir.-EMEA

Phone: 49-214-30-1 **Fax:** 49-214-30-66328
Toll-Free: 800-269-2377
Address: Bayerwerk Gebaeude W11, Leverkusen, D-51368 Germany

GROWTH PLANS/SPECIAL FEATURES:

The Bayer Group is a German holding company encompassing over 300 consolidated subsidiaries on five continents. The company has five business segments: Bayer HealthCare, Bayer CropScience, Bayer MaterialScience, Bayer Business Services and Bayer Technology Services. The Bayer HealthCare segment develops, produces and markets products for the prevention, diagnosis and treatment of human and animal diseases. Bayer CropScience is active in the areas of chemical crop protection and seed treatment, non-agricultural pest and weed control and plant biotechnology. Bayer MaterialScience develops, manufactures and markets polyurethane, polycarbonate, cellulose derivatives and special metals products. Bayer Business Services offers IT infrastructure and applications, procurement and logistics, human resources and management services. Bayer Technology Services offers process development, process and plant engineering, construction and optimization services. Bayer also operates the Currenta GmbH & Co. joint venture with Lanxess AG. Currenta offers utility supply, waste management, infrastructure, safety, security, analytics and vocational training services to the chemical industry. In March 2008, the firm acquired the over-the-counter (OTC) brand portfolio of Sagmel, Inc. In April 2008, the company acquired the remaining shares of BaySystems BUFA Polyurethane GmbH & Co. In July 2008, Bayer acquired Maxygen's hemophilia program assets. Also in July 2008, Bayer acquired the Western OTC cough and cold portfolio of Topsun Science and Technology Qidong Gaitianli Pharmaceutical Co., Ltd. In September 2008, the company acquired all outstanding shares of Bayer Schering Pharma AG, making it a wholly-owned subsidiary of Bayer. In March 2009, the company sold its Thermoplastics Testing Center to Underwriters Laboratories, Inc.

Bayer offers its employees deferred compensation, a defined benefit pension fund, sports amenities, flexible work schedules and a varied program of cultural events.

FINANCIALS: **Sales and profits are in thousands of dollars—add 000 to get the full amount. 2008 Note: Financial information for 2008 was not available for all companies at press time.**

2008 Sales: $43,536,000	2008 Profits: $2,273,480	**U.S. Stock Ticker: BAY**
2007 Sales: $42,831,100	2007 Profits: $6,230,580	**Int'l Ticker: BAY GR** Int'l Exchange: Frankfurt-Euronext
2006 Sales: $38,710,400	2006 Profits: $2,249,950	Employees: 108,600
2005 Sales: $32,662,374	2005 Profits: $1,902,517	Fiscal Year Ends: 12/31
2004 Sales: $27,731,937	2004 Profits: $816,045	Parent Company:

SALARIES/BENEFITS:

Pension Plan: Y	ESOP Stock Plan:	Profit Sharing:	Top Exec. Salary: $862,878	Bonus: $1,640,607
Savings Plan: Y	Stock Purch. Plan: Y		Second Exec. Salary: $499,286	Bonus: $935,368

OTHER THOUGHTS:

Apparent Women Officers or Directors:
Hot Spot for Advancement for Women/Minorities:

LOCATIONS: ("Y" = Yes)

West:	Southwest:	Midwest:	Southeast:	Northeast:	International:
Y	Y	Y		Y	Y

Note: Financial information, benefits and other data can change quickly and may vary from those stated here.

BAYER CORP

www.bayerus.com

Industry Group Code: 325000 **Ranks within this company's industry group:** Sales: Profits:

Techology:		Medical/Drugs:		Engineering:		Transportation:		Chemicals/Petrochemicals:		Specialty:	
Computers:		Manufacturer:	Y	Design:		Aerospace:		Oil/Gas Products:		Special Services:	
Software:		Contract Research:		Construction:		Automotive:		Chemicals:	Y	Consulting:	
Communications:		Medical Services:		Eng. Services:		Shipping:		Oil/Chem. Svcs.:		Specialty Mgmt.:	
Electronics:		Labs:		Consulting:				Gases:		Products:	Y
Alternative Energy:		Bio. Services:						Other:		Other:	

TYPES OF BUSINESS:

Chemicals Manufacturing
Animal Health Products
Over-the-Counter Drugs
Diagnostic Products
Coatings, Adhesives & Sealants
Polyurethanes & Plastics
Herbicides, Fungicides & Insecticides

BRANDS/DIVISIONS/AFFILIATES:

Bayer
Bayer HealthCare AG
Bayer MaterialSciences, LLC
Bayer CropScience, LP
Aleve
BREEZE
BaySystems
Alka-Seltzer Plus

CONTACTS: *Note: Officers with more than one job title may be intentionally listed here more than once.*

Gregory S. Babe, CEO
Gregory S. Babe, Pres.
Willy Scherf, CFO
Joyce Burgess, Dir.-Human Resources
Claudio Abreu, CIO
George J. Lykos, Chief Legal Officer
Mark Ryan, Chief Comm. Officer
Andreas Beier, Chief Acct. Officer
Arthur Higgins, Chmn.-Bayer HealthCare AG
Gregory Babe, Bayer MaterialScience LLC
William Buckner, CEO/Pres., Bayer CropScience, LP
Timothy Roseberry, Chief Procurement Officer/VP-Corp. Materials Mgmt.

Phone: 412-777-2000	**Fax:** 412-777-2034
Toll-Free:	
Address: 100 Bayer Rd., Pittsburgh, PA 15205-9741 US	

GROWTH PLANS/SPECIAL FEATURES:

Bayer Corporation is the U.S. subsidiary of chemical and pharmaceutical giant Bayer AG. The company operates through four subsidiaries: Bayer HealthCare; Bayer MaterialScience; Bayer Corporate and Business Services; and Bayer CropScience. Bayer HealthCare operates through five divisions: pharmaceuticals, consumer care, diagnostics, diabetes care and animal health. Its animal health products include vaccines and other preventative measures for farm and domestic animals. Its consumer care products include analgesics (Aleve and Bayer); cold and cough treatments (Alka-Seltzer Plus and Talcio); digestive relief products (Alka-Mints and Phillips' Milk of Magnesia); topical skin preparations (Domeboro and Bactine); and vitamins (One-A-Day and Flintstones). The diabetes care division is a leader in self-test blood glucose diagnostic systems, and has recently released the BREEZE product family that offers alternate site testing and automatic coding and requires smaller blood samples. Bayer HealthCare's diagnostics division, now called Siemens Medical Solutions Diagnostics, produces diagnostic systems for critical and intensive care, hematology, urinalysis, immunology, clinical chemistry and molecular testing. The Advia Centaur system is used for the diagnosis of diseases like cancer, cardiovascular diseases, allergies and infections; the Versant and Trugent brands of assays are used for the detection of HIV and hepatitis virus. Bayer's MaterialScience segment produces coatings, adhesives and sealant raw materials; polyurethanes; and plastics. Bayer CropScience makes products directed toward crop protection, environmental science and bioscience, which include herbicides, fungicides and insecticides. Bayer Corporate and Business Services provides business services to the aforementioned Bayer subsidiaries, such as administration, technology services, mergers/acquisitions and internal auditing. In March 2008, Bayer MaterialScience introduced Makrolon LED2245, a polycarbonate resin designed specifically for high-brightness LED applications.

FINANCIALS: **Sales and profits are in thousands of dollars—add 000 to get the full amount. 2008 Note: Financial information for 2008 was not available for all companies at press time.**

2008 Sales: $	2008 Profits: $	**U.S. Stock Ticker: Subsidiary**
2007 Sales: $	2007 Profits: $	**Int'l Ticker:** Int'l Exchange:
2006 Sales: $10,262,800	2006 Profits: $	Employees: 17,200
2005 Sales: $8,747,200	2005 Profits: $	Fiscal Year Ends: 12/31
2004 Sales: $11,504,000	2004 Profits: $	Parent Company: BAYER AG

SALARIES/BENEFITS:

Pension Plan:	ESOP Stock Plan:	Profit Sharing:	Top Exec. Salary: $	Bonus: $
Savings Plan: Y	Stock Purch. Plan: Y		Second Exec. Salary: $	Bonus: $

OTHER THOUGHTS:

Apparent Women Officers or Directors: 1
Hot Spot for Advancement for Women/Minorities:

LOCATIONS: ("Y" = Yes)

West:	Southwest:	Midwest:	Southeast:	Northeast:	International:
Y	Y	Y	Y	Y	

BAYER SCHERING PHARMA AG

www.bayerscheringpharma.de

Industry Group Code: 325412 **Ranks within this company's industry group:** Sales: 15 Profits:

Techology:		Medical/Drugs:		Engineering:		Transportation:		Chemicals/Petrochemicals:		Specialty:	
Computers:		Manufacturer:	Y	Design:		Aerospace:		Oil/Gas Products:		Special Services:	
Software:		Contract Research:		Construction:		Automotive:		Chemicals:		Consulting:	
Communications:		Medical Services:	Y	Eng. Services:		Shipping:		Oil/Chem. Svcs.:		Specialty Mgmt.:	
Electronics:		Labs:	Y	Consulting:				Gases:		Products:	
Alternative Energy:		Bio. Services:	Y					Other:		Other:	

TYPES OF BUSINESS:

Pharmaceuticals Discovery, Development & Manufacturing
Gynecology & Andrology Treatments
Contraceptives
Cancer Treatments
Multiple Sclerosis Treatments
Circulatory Disorder Treatments
Diagnostic & Radiopharmaceutical Agents
Proteomics

BRANDS/DIVISIONS/AFFILIATES:

Schering AG
Angeliq
Yasmin
Menostar
Betaferon
Fludara
Leukine
Zevalin

CONTACTS: *Note: Officers with more than one job title may be intentionally listed here more than once.*

Andreas Busch, Chmn.-Exec. Board
Werner Baumann, Member-Exec. Board, Human Resources
Ulrich Koestlin, Member-Exec. Board
Kemal Malik, Member-Exec. Board
Gunnar Riemann, Member-Exec. Board
Andreas Busch, Member-Exec. Board
Werner Wenning, Chmn.-Supervisory Board

Phone: 49-30-468-1111 **Fax:** 49-30-468-15305
Toll-Free:
Address: Mullerstrasse 178, Berlin, 13353 Germany

GROWTH PLANS/SPECIAL FEATURES:

Bayer Schering Pharma AG, formerly Schering AG, is a major global research-based pharmaceutical company that operates through subsidiaries in more than 100 countries. The firm concentrates its activities on four business areas: women's healthcare, specialty medicine, general medicine and diagnostic imaging. Schering's women's health products include birth control pills (Yasmin), hormone therapy (Angeliq and Menostar) and other contraceptives for women (Mirena). The firm's specialty medicine unit focuses on cancer, central nervous system disease and age related eye disease treatments. The division recently introduced the drug Fludara to provide treatment for chronic lymphocytic leukemia, a variety of leukemia. Another product, Leukine, is a drug administered to treat the immune system weakened by chemotherapy. Zevalin is a readioimmunotherapy for follicular B-cell non-Hodgkin's lymphoma approved for use in E.U. countries, and MabCampath/Campath is a chemotherapy drug often used on those patients who do not respond to traditional chemotherapy. Schering has contributed to the body of research on multiple sclerosis (MS) through its Beyond and Benefit studies. Its Betaferon drug reduces the frequency of MS episodes significantly. The general medicine segment focuses on anti-infective treatments, men's health care and cardiovascular, metabolic and thromboembolic diseases. Schering's diagnostics imaging products include a range of contrast media, such as Magnevist, a general MRI contrast agent and Gadovist, a central nervous system MRI contrast agent. The company is a subsidiary of Bayer A.G. In December 2008, the company signed an agreement with ProStrakan Group plc to market the ProStrakan's testosterone gel, Tostrex, in Canadam Latin America, Africa, Asia and the Middle East. In February 2009, the company announced plans to invest in the formation of a research and development facility in Beijing.

FINANCIALS: **Sales and profits are in thousands of dollars—add 000 to get the full amount. 2008 Note: Financial information for 2008 was not available for all companies at press time.**

2008 Sales: $14,243,900	2008 Profits: $	**U.S. Stock Ticker: Subsidiary**
2007 Sales: $5,806,500	2007 Profits: $1,980,100	**Int'l Ticker:** Int'l Exchange:
2006 Sales: $8,471,600	2006 Profits: $3,495,700	Employees: 25,000
2005 Sales: $7,802,800	2005 Profits: $909,900	Fiscal Year Ends: 12/31
2004 Sales: $6,647,000	2004 Profits: $677,000	Parent Company: BAYER AG

SALARIES/BENEFITS:

Pension Plan: Y	ESOP Stock Plan:	Profit Sharing:	Top Exec. Salary: $	Bonus: $
Savings Plan:	Stock Purch. Plan:		Second Exec. Salary: $	Bonus: $

OTHER THOUGHTS:

Apparent Women Officers or Directors:
Hot Spot for Advancement for Women/Minorities:

LOCATIONS: ("Y" = Yes)

West:	Southwest:	Midwest:	Southeast:	Northeast:	International:
Y				Y	Y

BECHTEL GROUP INC

www.bechtel.com

Industry Group Code: 234000 **Ranks within this company's industry group:** Sales: 3 Profits:

Techology:		**Medical/Drugs:**		**Engineering:**		**Transportation:**		**Chemicals/Petrochemicals:**		**Specialty:**	
Computers:		Manufacturer:		Design:	Y	Aerospace:		Oil/Gas Products:		Special Services:	Y
Software:		Contract Research:		Construction:	Y	Automotive:		Chemicals:		Consulting:	
Communications:		Medical Services:		Eng. Services:	Y	Shipping:		Oil/Chem. Svcs.:		Specialty Mgmt.:	Y
Electronics:		Labs:		Consulting:	Y			Gases:		Products:	
Alternative Energy:		Bio. Services:						Other:		Other:	

TYPES OF BUSINESS:

Engineering, Construction & Project Management Services
Civic Engineering
Outsourcing
Financial Services
Atomic Propulsion Systems Engineering
Airport Construction
Electric Power Plant Construction
Nuclear Power Plant Construction

BRANDS/DIVISIONS/AFFILIATES:

Bechtel Systems & Infrastructure, Inc.
Bechtel Power Corp.

CONTACTS: *Note: Officers with more than one job title may be intentionally listed here more than once.*

Riley P. Bechtel, CEO
Bill Dudley, COO
Bill Dudley, Pres.
Peter Dawson, CFO
John MacDonald, Dir.-Human Resources
Geir Ramleth, Dir.-Info. Systems
Geir Ramleth, Dir.-Tech.
Tom Patterson, Mgr.-Eng.
Judith Miller, General Counsel
Jim Jackson, Pres., Oil, Gas & Chemicals
Mike Adams, Pres., Civil
Scott Ogilvie, Pres., Bechtel Systems & Infrastructure, Inc.
Andy Greig, Pres., Mining & Metals
Riley P. Bechtel, Chmn.
Eli Smith, Mgr.-Contracts & Procurement

Phone: 415-768-1234	**Fax:** 415-768-9038
Toll-Free:	
Address: 50 Beale St., San Francisco, CA 94105-1895 US	

GROWTH PLANS/SPECIAL FEATURES:

Bechtel Group, Inc., founded in 1906 by Warren A. Bechtel, is one of the world's largest engineering companies. The privately-owned firm offers engineering, construction and project management services, with a broad project portfolio including road and rail systems, airports and seaports, nuclear power plants, petrochemical facilities, mines, defense and aerospace facilities, environmental cleanup projects, telecommunication networks, pipelines and oil fields development. The firm has participated in such notable endeavors as the construction of the Hoover Dam, the creation of the Bay Area Rapid Transit system in San Francisco, the massive James Bay Hydroelectric Project in Quebec and the quelling of oil field fires in Kuwait following the Persian Gulf War. Bechtel also constructed the Trans-Alaska Oil Pipeline, covering 800 miles between the Prudhoe Bay oil field and Valdez. In recent years, Bechtel has been awarded two multi-million dollar contracts by the U.S. Agency for International Development for the repair and reconstruction of Iraq's infrastructure. Bechtel has also been contracted to develop the New Doha International Airport in Qatar. An 11-year, multi-billion-dollar project, the new airport will be designed to accommodate six Airbus A380-800's, the largest passenger aircraft in the world. In February 2008, the company began construction of a 5.2 million-metric-ton-per-year liquified natural gas (LNG) train, with marine loading facilities and storage for LNG, liquefied petroleum gas in Angola; In July 2008, the firm signed a $200 million construction, engineering, and procurement agreement with Rio Tinto Alcan in Kitimat, British Columbia for the Kitmat Smelter modernization project. In December 2008, the company entered a $40 million front end engineering design (FEED) for the downstream components of Gladstone LNG in Queensland, Australia. In January 2009, the firm and American Municipal Power-Ohio, Inc are collaborating to construct an electric generation facility in Meigs County, Ohio.

FINANCIALS: **Sales and profits are in thousands of dollars—add 000 to get the full amount. 2008 Note: Financial information for 2008 was not available for all companies at press time.**

2008 Sales: $31,400,000	2008 Profits: $	**U.S. Stock Ticker: Private**
2007 Sales: $27,000,000	2007 Profits: $	**Int'l Ticker:** Int'l Exchange:
2006 Sales: $20,500,000	2006 Profits: $	Employees: 42,500
2005 Sales: $18,600,000	2005 Profits: $	Fiscal Year Ends: 12/31
2004 Sales: $17,400,000	2004 Profits: $	Parent Company:

SALARIES/BENEFITS:

Pension Plan:	ESOP Stock Plan:	Profit Sharing:	Top Exec. Salary: $	Bonus: $
Savings Plan:	Stock Purch. Plan:		Second Exec. Salary: $	Bonus: $

OTHER THOUGHTS:

Apparent Women Officers or Directors: 2
Hot Spot for Advancement for Women/Minorities: Y

LOCATIONS: ("Y" = Yes)

West:	Southwest:	Midwest:	Southeast:	Northeast:	International:
Y	Y	Y	Y	Y	Y

BECKMAN COULTER INC

www.beckmancoulter.com

Industry Group Code: 339113 **Ranks within this company's industry group:** Sales: 12 Profits: 11

Techology:		Medical/Drugs:		Engineering:		Transportation:		Chemicals/Petrochemicals:		Specialty:	
Computers:		Manufacturer:	Y	Design:		Aerospace:		Oil/Gas Products:		Special Services:	
Software:		Contract Research:		Construction:		Automotive:		Chemicals:		Consulting:	
Communications:		Medical Services:		Eng. Services:		Shipping:		Oil/Chem. Svcs.:		Specialty Mgmt.:	
Electronics:		Labs:		Consulting:				Gases:		Products:	
Alternative Energy:		Bio. Services:						Other:		Other:	

TYPES OF BUSINESS:

Equipment-Laboratory Instruments
Chemistry Systems
Genetic Analysis/Nucleic Acid Testing
Biomedical Research Supplies
Immunoassay Systems
Cellular Systems
Discovery & Automation Systems

BRANDS/DIVISIONS/AFFILIATES:

UniCel DxC 880i Sychrom Access Clinical System
GemomeLab GeXP
Solid Phase Reversible Immobilization (SPRI)
ProteomeLab
CyAn ADP Analyzer
Optima MAX-MP
Vi-Cell
Q-Prep Workstation

CONTACTS: *Note: Officers with more than one job title may be intentionally listed here more than once.*

Scott Garrett, CEO
Scott Garrett, Pres.
Charlie Slacik, CFO
Bob Hurley, Sr. VP-Human Resources
Russ Bell, Chief Scientific Officer/Sr. VP
Charlie Slacik, Sr. VP-IT
Arnie Pinkston, General Counsel/Sr. VP/Corp. Sec.
Paul Glyer, Sr. VP-Strategy & Bus. Dev.
Bob Hurley, Sr. VP-Comm.
Paul Glyer, Sr. VP-Investor Rel.
Carolyn D. Beaver, Chief Acct. Officer/Controller/VP
Russ Bell, Sr. VP
Bob Kleinert, Exec. VP-Worldwide Commercial Oper.
Mike Whelan, Group VP-High Sensitivity Testing Group
Cynthia Collins, Group VP-Cellular Business Group
Scott Garrett, Chmn.
Pam Miller, Sr. VP-Supply Chain Mgmt.

Phone: 714-871-4848	**Fax:** 714-773-8283
Toll-Free: 800-233-4685	
Address: 4300 N. Harbor Blvd., Fullerton, CA 92834-3100 US	

GROWTH PLANS/SPECIAL FEATURES:

Beckman Coulter, Inc. develops, manufactures and markets biomedical testing instrument systems, tests, and supplies that automate complex biomedical tests. Spanning the biomedical testing continuum, from pioneering medical research and clinical trials to laboratory diagnostics and point-of-care testing, the company installed base of over 200,000 systems provides essential biomedical information to enhance health care around the world. The firm's predominate customer base includes hospital clinical laboratories, physicians' offices, group practices, commercial reference laboratories, universities, medical research laboratories, pharmaceutical companies and biotechnology firms. Based on profitability, the company has four focus segments: chemistry systems, immunoassay systems, cellular systems, and discovery and automation systems. The firm's revenue is about evenly distributed inside and outside the United States. Sales to clinical laboratories represent nearly 83% of its total revenue, with the balance coming from the life sciences markets. About 78% of the company's total revenue is generated by the sale of supplies, test kits, services and operating-type lease payments. Central laboratories of mid- to large-size hospitals represent its most significant customer group. Beckman also obtained the rights to acquire the worldwide diagnostics assets of Nephromics.

The company offers health benefits, paid vacations and holidays, tuition assistance and savings and retirement plans.

FINANCIALS: **Sales and profits are in thousands of dollars—add 000 to get the full amount. 2008 Note: Financial information for 2008 was not available for all companies at press time.**

2008 Sales: $3,098,900	2008 Profits: $194,000	**U.S. Stock Ticker: BEC**
2007 Sales: $2,761,300	2007 Profits: $211,300	**Int'l Ticker:** Int'l Exchange:
2006 Sales: $2,528,500	2006 Profits: $186,900	Employees: 11,000
2005 Sales: $2,443,800	2005 Profits: $150,600	Fiscal Year Ends: 12/31
2004 Sales: $2,408,300	2004 Profits: $210,900	Parent Company:

SALARIES/BENEFITS:

Pension Plan: Y	ESOP Stock Plan:	Profit Sharing:	Top Exec. Salary: $837,969	Bonus: $826,440
Savings Plan: Y	Stock Purch. Plan:		Second Exec. Salary: $476,827	Bonus: $

OTHER THOUGHTS:

Apparent Women Officers or Directors: 3
Hot Spot for Advancement for Women/Minorities: Y

LOCATIONS: ("Y" = Yes)

West:	Southwest:	Midwest:	Southeast:	Northeast:	International:
Y			Y		Y

BECTON DICKINSON & CO

www.bd.com

Industry Group Code: 339113 **Ranks within this company's industry group:** Sales: 6 Profits: 6

Techology:		Medical/Drugs:		Engineering:		Transportation:		Chemicals/Petrochemicals:		Specialty:	
Computers:		Manufacturer:	Y	Design:		Aerospace:		Oil/Gas Products:		Special Services:	
Software:		Contract Research:		Construction:		Automotive:		Chemicals:		Consulting:	Y
Communications:		Medical Services:		Eng. Services:		Shipping:		Oil/Chem. Svcs.:		Specialty Mgmt.:	
Electronics:		Labs:		Consulting:				Gases:		Products:	
Alternative Energy:		Bio. Services:						Other:		Other:	

TYPES OF BUSINESS:

Medical Equipment-Injection/Infusion
Drug Delivery Systems
Infusion Therapy Products
Diabetes Care Products
Surgical Products
Microbiology Products
Diagnostic Products
Consulting Services

BRANDS/DIVISIONS/AFFILIATES:

Becton Dickinson Medical
Becton Dickinson Biosciences
Becton Dickinson Diagnostics
Vacutainer
Hypak
Cytopeia
BD BACTEC FX Blood Culture System

CONTACTS: *Note: Officers with more than one job title may be intentionally listed here more than once.*

Edward J. Ludwig, CEO
Vincent A. Forlenza, Pres.
David V. Elkins, CFO/Exec. VP
Donna M. Boles, Sr. VP-Human Resources
Scott P. Bruder, CTO/Sr. VP
Jeffrey S. Sherman, General Counsel/Sr. VP
Richard K. Berman, Treas./VP
Gary M. Cohen, Exec. VP
William A. Kozy, Exec. VP
A. John Hanson, Exec. VP
Mark H. Borofsky, VP-Taxes
Edward J. Ludwig, Chmn.

Phone: 201-847-6800	**Fax:** 201-847-6475
Toll-Free: 800-284-6845	
Address: 1 Becton Dr., Franklin Lakes, NJ 07417-1880 US	

GROWTH PLANS/SPECIAL FEATURES:

Becton, Dickinson & Company (BD) manufactures and sells a broad line of medical supplies, devices and diagnostic systems used by health care professionals, medical research institutions and the general public. The company operates in three segments: medical, biosciences and diagnostics. The medical segment offers hypodermic products, specially designed devices for diabetes care; prefillable drug delivery systems; and infusion therapy products. It also offers anesthesia and surgical products; ophthalmic surgery devices; critical care systems; elastic support products; and thermometers. The biosciences segment offers industrial microbiology products; cellular analysis systems; research; and clinical reagents for cellular and nucleic acid analysis; cell culture labware and growth media; hematology instruments; and other diagnostic systems, including immunodiagnostic test kits. The diagnostics segment offers specimen collection products and services, consulting services and customized, automated barcode systems for patient identification and point-of-care data capture. Two of BD's most popular products are Hypak prefillable syringes and Vacutainer blood-collection products. Outside of the U.S., BD's products are manufactured and sold in Europe, Japan, Mexico, Asia Pacific, Canada and Brazil. In May 2008, the company acquired Cytopeia, a developer and marketer of advanced flow cytometry cell sorting instrument. In June 2008, the firm launched the BD BACTEC FX Blood Culture System for detecting infections in the bloodstream.

FINANCIALS: Sales and profits are in thousands of dollars—add 000 to get the full amount. 2008 Note: Financial information for 2008 was not available for all companies at press time.

2008 Sales: $7,155,910	2008 Profits: $1,127,000	**U.S. Stock Ticker: BDX**
2007 Sales: $6,359,700	2007 Profits: $890,000	**Int'l Ticker:** Int'l Exchange:
2006 Sales: $5,738,000	2006 Profits: $752,300	Employees: 28,300
2005 Sales: $5,340,800	2005 Profits: $722,300	Fiscal Year Ends: 9/30
2004 Sales: $4,934,745	2004 Profits: $467,402	Parent Company:

SALARIES/BENEFITS:

Pension Plan: Y	ESOP Stock Plan:	Profit Sharing:	Top Exec. Salary: $1,059,846	Bonus: $1,526,179
Savings Plan: Y	Stock Purch. Plan:		Second Exec. Salary: $667,162	Bonus: $675,000

OTHER THOUGHTS:

Apparent Women Officers or Directors: 6
Hot Spot for Advancement for Women/Minorities: Y

LOCATIONS: ("Y" = Yes)

West:	Southwest:	Midwest:	Southeast:	Northeast:	International:
Y	Y	Y	Y	Y	Y

BELDEN INC

www.belden.com

Industry Group Code: 334210 **Ranks within this company's industry group:** Sales: 4 Profits: 6

Techology:		Medical/Drugs:		Engineering:		Transportation:		Chemicals/Petrochemicals:		Specialty:	
Computers:		Manufacturer:		Design:		Aerospace:	Y	Oil/Gas Products:		Special Services:	
Software:		Contract Research:		Construction:		Automotive:	Y	Chemicals:		Consulting:	
Communications:	Y	Medical Services:		Eng. Services:		Shipping:		Oil/Chem. Svcs.:		Specialty Mgmt.:	
Electronics:	Y	Labs:		Consulting:				Gases:		Products:	
Alternative Energy:		Bio. Services:						Other:		Other:	

TYPES OF BUSINESS:

Cable & Wire Systems Manufacturing & Retail
Electronic Products
Broadcasting Equipment
Aerospace & Automotive Electronics
Enclosures

BRANDS/DIVISIONS/AFFILIATES:

Belden CDT, Inc.
LTK Wiring Co., Ltd.
Hirschmann Automation and Control GmbH
Lumberg Automation Components

CONTACTS: *Note: Officers with more than one job title may be intentionally listed here more than once.*

John S. Stroup, CEO
John S. Stroup, Pres.
Gray G. Benoist, CFO/VP-Finance
Peter Sheehan, Global VP-Sales & Mktg.
Cathy O. Staples, VP-Human Resources
Louis Pace, Pres., Specialty Prod./VP-Oper.
Richard Kirschner, VP-Mfg.
Kevin L. Bloomfield, General Counsel/Corp. Sec./VP
Denis Suggs, VP-Oper./Pres., Belden Americas
Daniel Krawczyk, VP-Bus. Dev.
Stephen H. Johnson, Treas.
Naresh Kumra, Pres., Belden Asia/Pacific
Peter Leung, VP/Gen. Mgr.-LTK Wiring
John S. Norman, Controller/Chief Acct. Officer
Bryan C. Cressey, Chmn.
Wolfgang Babel, Pres., Belden EMEA/VP-Oper.

Phone: 314-854-8000 **Fax:** 314-854-8001
Toll-Free: 800-235-3361
Address: 7701 Forsyth Blvd., Ste. 800, St. Louis, MO 63105 US

GROWTH PLANS/SPECIAL FEATURES:

Belden, Inc., formerly known as Belden CDT, Inc., designs, manufactures and markets signal transmission solutions, including cable, connectivity and active components, for mission-critical applications in markets ranging from industrial automation to data centers, broadcast studios and aerospace. The company changed its name in May 2007. Belden produces and sells thousands of different cable products within various cable configurations, such as copper cables, including shielded and unshielded twisted pair cables, coaxial cables, stranded cables and ribbon cables; fiber optic cables; and composite cable configurations. The company produces and sells its connectors, including patch panels and interconnect hardware, primarily for industrial and data networking applications. Connectors are also sold as part of an end-to-end structures cabling solution. Other products sold by Belden include Industrial Ethernet switches, wireless networking access points and switches; cabinets, enclosures, racks, raceways and ties for organizing and managing cable; and tubing and sleeving products to protect and organize wire and cable. It also designs and manufactures electronic control systems for mobile cranes and other load-bearing equipment. Belden operates through four segments: Belden Americas, which generates approximately 43% of its consolidated revenues; Specialty Products, which generates 12%; Europe, which generates 30%; and Asia Pacific, which generates 15%. With manufacturing facilities in Canada, Mexico, China and Europe, approximately 55% of the company's sales were generated outside the U.S. in 2007. In March 2007, Belden acquired LTK Wiring Co., Ltd., a leading manufacturer of electronic cable for the China market, for $195 million. Also in March, the company acquired Hirschmann Automation and Control GmbH for $260 million. In April 2007, Belden acquired Lumberg Automation Components, a supplier of industrial connectors, high performance cord-sets and field bus communication components for factory automation machinery. In March 2008, Belden announced plans to cease production activities at its plant in Manchester, Connecticut.

FINANCIALS: **Sales and profits are in thousands of dollars—add 000 to get the full amount. 2008 Note: Financial information for 2008 was not available for all companies at press time.**

2008 Sales: $2,005,890	2008 Profits: $-361,027	**U.S. Stock Ticker: BDC**
2007 Sales: $2,032,841	2007 Profits: $137,123	**Int'l Ticker:** Int'l Exchange:
2006 Sales: $1,495,811	2006 Profits: $65,935	Employees: 8,200
2005 Sales: $1,352,131	2005 Profits: $47,558	Fiscal Year Ends: 12/31
2004 Sales: $966,174	2004 Profits: $15,189	Parent Company:

SALARIES/BENEFITS:

Pension Plan:	ESOP Stock Plan:	Profit Sharing:	Top Exec. Salary: $600,000	Bonus: $1,497,600
Savings Plan:	Stock Purch. Plan:		Second Exec. Salary: $373,568	Bonus: $330,500

OTHER THOUGHTS:

Apparent Women Officers or Directors: 3
Hot Spot for Advancement for Women/Minorities: Y

LOCATIONS: ("Y" = Yes)

West:	Southwest:	Midwest:	Southeast:	Northeast:	International:
Y		Y	Y	Y	Y

BELL LABS

www.alcatel-lucent.com/wps/portal/BellLabs

Industry Group Code: 541710 **Ranks within this company's industry group:** Sales: Profits:

Techology:		Medical/Drugs:		Engineering:		Transportation:		Chemicals/Petrochemicals:		Specialty:	
Computers:	Y	Manufacturer:		Design:	Y	Aerospace:		Oil/Gas Products:		Special Services:	
Software:	Y	Contract Research:		Construction:		Automotive:		Chemicals:		Consulting:	
Communications:	Y	Medical Services:		Eng. Services:		Shipping:		Oil/Chem. Svcs.:		Specialty Mgmt.:	
Electronics:		Labs:		Consulting:				Gases:		Products:	
Alternative Energy:		Bio. Services:						Other:		Other:	Y

TYPES OF BUSINESS:

Research & Development-Communications
Physical Science
Computer Science & Software
Mathematics Research
Optical & Wireless Networking Technologies
Nanotechnology Research

BRANDS/DIVISIONS/AFFILIATES:

Alcatel-Lucent
WaveStar ITM-SC
Base Station Router
IMS Service Enhancement Layer

CONTACTS: *Note: Officers with more than one job title may be intentionally listed here more than once.*

Jeong Kim, Pres.
Rod C. Alferness, Chief Scientist

Phone: 908-582-8500	**Fax:** 908-508-2576
Toll-Free:	
Address: 600 Mountain Ave., Murray Hill, NJ 07974 US	

GROWTH PLANS/SPECIAL FEATURES:

Bell Labs is the research and development subsidiary of the telecommunications manufacturer Alcatel-Lucent. Winner of six Nobel prizes, it designs products and services at the forefront of communications technology and conducts fundamental research in the following fields: physical technologies; computer science and software; mathematical/algorithmic sciences; optical and wireless networking; security solutions; and government research. The physical technologies department is involved in materials research, optical physics and nanotechnology. Computer science and software includes research on systems networking, service infrastructure and convergence application. Mathematical/Algorithmic research involves fundamental mathematics of networks and systems, statistics/data mining and scientific computing. The wireless networking department is involved in software, mobile and internet research; economic analysis; network planning; and business modeling. The optical networking research department studies fiber optic broadband networking, optical routers, high frequency electronics and photonic device fabrication. Bell's security solutions provide virus prevention and general infrastructure protection. The government research division focuses on the needs of its government clients, specializing in nanotechnology, network reliability/security and laser communications. Its current projects include novel cooling technology, a more environmentally friendly form of liquid cooling; soundless speech technology for public cell phone conversations; and advancements in firewall efficiency. Other products include the IMS Service Enhancement Layer, which simplifies and speeds up delivery services; WaveStar ITM-SC, an optical transport management program; and Base Station Router, which simplifies 3G mobile networks into a single network.

FINANCIALS: **Sales and profits are in thousands of dollars—add 000 to get the full amount. 2008 Note: Financial information for 2008 was not available for all companies at press time.**

2008 Sales: $	2008 Profits: $	**U.S. Stock Ticker: Subsidiary**
2007 Sales: $	2007 Profits: $	**Int'l Ticker:** Int'l Exchange:
2006 Sales: $	2006 Profits: $	Employees: 7,500
2005 Sales: $	2005 Profits: $	Fiscal Year Ends: 12/31
2004 Sales: $	2004 Profits: $	Parent Company: ALCATEL-LUCENT

SALARIES/BENEFITS:

Pension Plan:	ESOP Stock Plan:	Profit Sharing:	Top Exec. Salary: $	Bonus: $
Savings Plan:	Stock Purch. Plan:		Second Exec. Salary: $	Bonus: $

OTHER THOUGHTS:

Apparent Women Officers or Directors:
Hot Spot for Advancement for Women/Minorities:

LOCATIONS: ("Y" = Yes)

West:	Southwest:	Midwest:	Southeast:	Northeast:	International:
				Y	Y

BENCHMARK ELECTRONICS INC

www.bench.com

Industry Group Code: 334419 **Ranks within this company's industry group:** Sales: 8 Profits: 9

Techology:		Medical/Drugs:		Engineering:		Transportation:		Chemicals/Petrochemicals:		Specialty:	
Computers:		Manufacturer:		Design:	Y	Aerospace:		Oil/Gas Products:		Special Services:	Y
Software:		Contract Research:		Construction:		Automotive:		Chemicals:		Consulting:	
Communications:		Medical Services:		Eng. Services:	Y	Shipping:		Oil/Chem. Svcs.:		Specialty Mgmt.:	
Electronics:	Y	Labs:		Consulting:				Gases:		Products:	
Alternative Energy:		Bio. Services:						Other:		Other:	

TYPES OF BUSINESS:

Contract Manufacturing-Printed Circuit Boards
Design & Engineering

BRANDS/DIVISIONS/AFFILIATES:

Pemstar, Inc.

CONTACTS:

Note: Officers with more than one job title may be intentionally listed here more than once.

Cary T. Fu, CEO
Gayla J. Delly, Pres.
Donald F. Adam, CFO
Kenneth S. Barrow, Sec.

Phone: 979-849-6550	**Fax:** 979-848-5270
Toll-Free:	
Address: 3000 Technology Dr., Angleton, TX 77515 US	

GROWTH PLANS/SPECIAL FEATURES:

Benchmark Electronics, Inc. provides contract-manufacturing services for complex printed circuit boards and related electronics systems and subsystems. Benchmark primarily serves original equipment manufacturers (OEMs) of computers and related products for business enterprises, medical devices, industrial control equipment, testing and instrumentation products, and telecommunications equipment. The firm provides comprehensive and integrated design and manufacturing services, from initial product design to volume production and direct order fulfillment. In addition, the company offers specialized engineering services including product design, printed circuit board layout, prototyping and test development. Substantially all of Benchmark's manufacturing services are provided on a turnkey basis (though some are provided on consignment), whereby it purchases customer-specified components from its suppliers, assembles the components on finished printed circuit boards, performs post-production testing and provides production process and testing documentation. Benchmark offers flexible, just-in-time delivery programs allowing product shipments to be closely coordinated with customer inventory requirements. In addition to traditional manufacturing technologies, the company also provides its customers with a comprehensive set of advanced solutions, including pin-through-hole, surface mount, chip-on-board, fine pitch and ball grid array. The firm has 20 manufacturing facilities worldwide, operating a total of 144 surface mount production lines, where electrical components are soldered directly onto printed circuit boards. Benchmark operates domestic facilities in Alabama, Minnesota, New Hampshire, North Dakota, Oregon and Texas, totaling approximately 1.4 million square feet. Operations outside the U.S., totaling 1.3 million square feet, include Brazil, China, Ireland, Malaysia, Mexico, the Netherlands, Romania, Singapore and Thailand, providing international customers with a combination of strategic regional locations and global procurement capabilities. In 2007, the firm acquired Pemstar, Inc., a provider of engineering, design and manufacturing services, for $300 million. In 2008, Benchmark partnered with Silicon Graphics, Inc., to help create NASA's new Pleiades supercomputer system.

FINANCIALS:

Sales and profits are in thousands of dollars—add 000 to get the full amount. 2008 Note: Financial information for 2008 was not available for all companies at press time.

2008 Sales: $2,590,167	2008 Profits: $-135,632	**U.S. Stock Ticker: BHE**
2007 Sales: $2,915,919	2007 Profits: $93,282	**Int'l Ticker:** Int'l Exchange:
2006 Sales: $2,907,304	2006 Profits: $111,677	Employees: 10,522
2005 Sales: $2,257,225	2005 Profits: $80,589	Fiscal Year Ends: 12/31
2004 Sales: $2,001,340	2004 Profits: $70,991	Parent Company:

SALARIES/BENEFITS:

Pension Plan:	ESOP Stock Plan:	Profit Sharing:	Top Exec. Salary: $622,136	Bonus: $207,358
Savings Plan:	Stock Purch. Plan:		Second Exec. Salary: $440,000	Bonus: $110,000

OTHER THOUGHTS:

Apparent Women Officers or Directors: 1
Hot Spot for Advancement for Women/Minorities:

LOCATIONS: ("Y" = Yes)

West:	Southwest:	Midwest:	Southeast:	Northeast:	International:
Y	Y	Y	Y	Y	Y

BIOGEN IDEC INC

www.biogenidec.com

Industry Group Code: 325412 **Ranks within this company's industry group:** Sales: 26 Profits: 21

Techology:		Medical/Drugs:		Engineering:		Transportation:		Chemicals/Petrochemicals:		Specialty:	
Computers:		Manufacturer:	Y	Design:		Aerospace:		Oil/Gas Products:		Special Services:	
Software:		Contract Research:		Construction:		Automotive:		Chemicals:		Consulting:	
Communications:		Medical Services:		Eng. Services:		Shipping:		Oil/Chem. Svcs.:		Specialty Mgmt.:	
Electronics:		Labs:		Consulting:				Gases:		Products:	
Alternative Energy:		Bio. Services:						Other:		Other:	

TYPES OF BUSINESS:

Drugs-Immunology, Neurology & Oncology
Autoimmune & Inflammatory Disease Treatments
Drugs-Multiple Sclerosis
Drugs-Cancer

BRANDS/DIVISIONS/AFFILIATES:

AVONEX
TYSABRI
RITUXAN
FUMADERM

CONTACTS: *Note: Officers with more than one job title may be intentionally listed here more than once.*

James C. Mullen, CEO
Hans Peter Hasler, COO
James C. Mullen, Pres.
Paul J. Clancy, CFO/Exec. VP
Craig Eric Schneier, Exec. VP-Human Resources
Cecil Pickett, Pres., R&D
Robert A. Hamm, Exec. VP-Tech. & Pharmaceutical Oper.
Susan H. Alexander, General Counsel/Exec. VP/Corp. Sec.
Mark C. Wiggins, Exec. VP-Corp. & Bus. Dev.
Craig Eric Schneier, Exec. VP-Corp. Comm. & Public Affairs
Michael F. MacLean, Chief Acct. Officer/Sr. VP/Controller
John M. Dunn, Exec. VP-New Ventures
Bruce R. Ross, Chmn.

Phone: 617-679-2000	**Fax:** 617-679-2617
Toll-Free:	
Address: 14 Cambridge Ctr., Cambridge, MA 02142-1481 US	

GROWTH PLANS/SPECIAL FEATURES:

Biogen IDEC, Inc. is a biotechnology company that develops, manufactures and markets therapeutic pharmaceuticals in the fields of immunology, neurology and oncology. Biogen currently has four approved products: AVONEX, which is designed to treat relapsing forms of multiple sclerosis (MS) and is used by 135,000 patients globally; TYSABRI, which is approved for the treatment of relapsing forms of MS and in the U.S. is approved to treat moderate to severe active Crohn's disease; RITUXAN, which is globally approved for the treatment of relapsed or refractory low-grade or follicular, CD20-positive, B-cell non-Hodgkin's lymphomas (NHLs); and FUMADERM, which acts as an immunomodulator and is approved in Germany for the treatment of severe psoriasis. RITUXAN, in combination with methotrexate, is also approved to reduce signs and symptoms in adult patients with moderately-to-severely active rheumatoid arthritis who have had an inadequate response to one or more tumor necrosis factor antagonist therapies. The company is working with Genentech and Roche on the development of RITUXAN in additional oncology and other indications. In addition to its approved drugs, the firm currently has 15 drugs under development, including drugs in the company's core areas of focus as well as in the new therapeutic areas of cardiovascular disease and hemophilia. Biogen also generates revenue by licensing drugs it has developed to other companies, including Schering-Plough, Merck and GlaxoSmithKline.

Biogen offers employees medical, dental and vision insurance; tuition reimbursement; commuter benefits; discounts on health clubs and local events; flexible spending accounts; and an employee assistance program.

FINANCIALS: **Sales and profits are in thousands of dollars—add 000 to get the full amount. 2008 Note: Financial information for 2008 was not available for all companies at press time.**

2008 Sales: $4,097,500	2008 Profits: $783,200	**U.S. Stock Ticker: BIIB**
2007 Sales: $3,171,600	2007 Profits: $638,172	**Int'l Ticker:** Int'l Exchange:
2006 Sales: $2,683,049	2006 Profits: $217,511	Employees: 4,700
2005 Sales: $2,422,500	2005 Profits: $160,711	Fiscal Year Ends: 12/31
2004 Sales: $2,211,562	2004 Profits: $25,086	Parent Company:

SALARIES/BENEFITS:

Pension Plan:	ESOP Stock Plan:	Profit Sharing:	Top Exec. Salary: $1,142,308	Bonus: $1,943,500
Savings Plan: Y	Stock Purch. Plan: Y		Second Exec. Salary: $512,692	Bonus: $267,800

OTHER THOUGHTS:

Apparent Women Officers or Directors: 3
Hot Spot for Advancement for Women/Minorities: Y

LOCATIONS: ("Y" = Yes)

West:	Southwest:	Midwest:	Southeast:	Northeast:	International:
Y				Y	Y

Note: Financial information, benefits and other data can change quickly and may vary from those stated here.

BIOS-BIOENERGIESYSTEME GMBH

www.bios-bioenergy.at

Industry Group Code: 541330 **Ranks within this company's industry group:** Sales: Profits:

Techology:		Medical/Drugs:		Engineering:		Transportation:		Chemicals/Petrochemicals:		Specialty:	
Computers:		Manufacturer:		Design:	Y	Aerospace:		Oil/Gas Products:		Special Services:	Y
Software:	Y	Contract Research:		Construction:		Automotive:		Chemicals:		Consulting:	
Communications:		Medical Services:		Eng. Services:	Y	Shipping:		Oil/Chem. Svcs.:		Specialty Mgmt.:	
Electronics:		Labs:		Consulting:				Gases:		Products:	
Alternative Energy:	Y	Bio. Services:						Other:		Other:	

TYPES OF BUSINESS:

Biomass Plant Design & Development
Research Services
Software Development

BRANDS/DIVISIONS/AFFILIATES:

Austrian Bio Energy Centre
BIOSTROM Erzeugungs GmbH

CONTACTS:

Note: Officers with more than one job title may be intentionally listed here more than once.

Ingwald Obernberger, Managing Dir.
Robert Scharler, Project Mgr.-R&D
Thomas Barnthaler, Project Eng.
Thomas Brunner, Project Eng.
Friedrich Biedermann, Project Mgr.
Gerold Thek, Scientist
Werner Kanzian, Chemist

Phone: 43-316-481-300	**Fax:** 43-316-481-300-4
Toll-Free:	
Address: Inffeldgasse 21B, Graz, A-8010 Austria	

GROWTH PLANS/SPECIAL FEATURES:

BIOS-BIOENERGYSYSTEME GmbH (BIOS) is an internationally recognized team of engineers that research, develop, design and optimize plants for heat and power production from biomass fuels. The company provides solutions that cover the entire field of thermal biomass utilization (combustion, gasification, and combined heat and power systems). BIOS operates in eight working fields: engineering; QM-biomass heating plants; plant monitoring; analyses and measurements; expertise; research and development; CFD simulations; and software development. The company develops energy master plans and feasibility studies to creates detailed plans and the realizations of plants. The firm is an industrial partner of the Austrian Bio Energy Centre (ABEC), as well as a shareholder with a 26% stake. ABEC is a research center founded under the Kplus program that brings together expertise from various areas of research, such as biomass composting, biomass gasification, process development, chemistry and environmental science. Research is conducted in the field of alternative energy sources, with the main emphasis on the generation of energy using biomass. The company is also a shareholder in BIOSTROM Erzeugungs GmbH, a biomass co-generation heating plant in Vorarlberg, Austria that burns waste wood and has an electric capacity of 1,100 kilowatts, a thermal capacity of 6.2 megawatts and a chilling capacity of 2.4 megawatts.

FINANCIALS:

Sales and profits are in thousands of dollars—add 000 to get the full amount. 2008 Note: Financial information for 2008 was not available for all companies at press time.

2008 Sales: $	2008 Profits: $	**U.S. Stock Ticker: Private**
2007 Sales: $	2007 Profits: $	**Int'l Ticker:** Int'l Exchange:
2006 Sales: $3,300	2006 Profits: $	Employees: 27
2005 Sales: $	2005 Profits: $	Fiscal Year Ends:
2004 Sales: $	2004 Profits: $	Parent Company:

SALARIES/BENEFITS:

Pension Plan:	ESOP Stock Plan:	Profit Sharing:	Top Exec. Salary: $	Bonus: $
Savings Plan:	Stock Purch. Plan:		Second Exec. Salary: $	Bonus: $

OTHER THOUGHTS:

Apparent Women Officers or Directors: 2
Hot Spot for Advancement for Women/Minorities:

LOCATIONS: ("Y" = Yes)

West:	Southwest:	Midwest:	Southeast:	Northeast:	International:
	Y				Y

BLACK & DECKER CORP

www.bdk.com

Industry Group Code: 335000 **Ranks within this company's industry group:** Sales: 9 Profits: 8

Techology:		Medical/Drugs:		Engineering:		Transportation:		Chemicals/Petrochemicals:		Specialty:	
Computers:		Manufacturer:		Design:		Aerospace:		Oil/Gas Products:		Special Services:	
Software:		Contract Research:		Construction:		Automotive:		Chemicals:		Consulting:	
Communications:		Medical Services:		Eng. Services:		Shipping:		Oil/Chem. Svcs.:		Specialty Mgmt.:	
Electronics:		Labs:		Consulting:				Gases:		Products:	Y
Alternative Energy:		Bio. Services:						Other:		Other:	

TYPES OF BUSINESS:

Power Tools & Accessories Manufacturer
Residential Security Hardware
Household Appliances
Home Improvement Products
Fastening & Assembly Systems
Plumbing Products

BRANDS/DIVISIONS/AFFILIATES:

DeWALT
Dustbuster
Price Pfister
Kwikset
SnakeLight
Vector Products, Inc.
Porter-Cable
Emhart Teknologies

CONTACTS:

Note: Officers with more than one job title may be intentionally listed here more than once.

Nolan D. Archibald, CEO
Nolan D. Archibald, Pres.
Michael D. Mangan, CFO/Sr. VP
Paul F. McBride, Sr. VP-Human Resources & Corp. Initiatives
Charles E. Fenton, General Counsel/Sr. VP
Les. H. Ireland, VP/Pres., Commercial Oper.
James R. Raskin, VP-Bus. Dev.
Mark M. Rothleitner, VP-Investor Rel.
Christina M. McMullen, Controller/VP
James T. Caudill, VP/Pres., Hardware & Home Improvement Group
Bruce W. Brooks, VP/Pres., Consumer Products Group
Natalie A. Shields, Corp. Sec./VP
Michael A. Tyll, VP/Pres., Fastening & Assembly Systems Group
Nolan D. Archibald, Chmn.
Les H. Ireland, VP/Pres., EMEA

Phone: 410-716-3900 **Fax:** 410-716-2933
Toll-Free: 800-544-6986
Address: 701 E. Joppa Rd., Towson, MD 21286 US

GROWTH PLANS/SPECIAL FEATURES:

The Black & Decker Corp. is a global manufacturer and marketer of power tools and accessories; hardware and home improvement products; and technology-based fastening systems. The firm is also a global supplier of engineered fastening and assembly systems. The company's products and services are marketed in over 100 countries in hardware and home improvement stores around the globe. Black & Decker operates in three business segments: power tools and accessories; hardware and home improvement; and fastening and assembly systems with these business segments comprising approximately 73%, 15%, and 12%, respectively, of the corporation's sales. The power tools and accessories segment includes consumer and industrial power tools and accessories; lawn and garden tools; electric cleaning; automotive; lightning products; and product services. In addition, the power pools and accessories segment has responsibility for the sale of security hardware to customers in Mexico, Central America, the Caribbean, and South America; for the sale of plumbing products to customers outside of the U.S. and Canada; and for sales of household products, principally in Europe and Brazil. The hardware and home improvement segment includes security hardware such as locksets keying systems and exit devices; general hardware products including hinges, door stops and kick plates; decorative hardware such as cabinet hardware, switchplates and door pulls; and plumbing products. This section of the company is also responsible for producing faucets. The fastening and assembly systems group manufactures and sells an array of metal and plastic fasteners and engineered fastening systems for commercial applications. The company's product names include DeWALT and Black and Decker, as well as Price Pfister plumbing products, Kwikset security hardware, Emhart fastening systems, Dustbuster vacuum cleaners and SnakeLight flashlights.

FINANCIALS:

Sales and profits are in thousands of dollars—add 000 to get the full amount. 2008 Note: Financial information for 2008 was not available for all companies at press time.

2008 Sales: $6,086,100	2008 Profits: $293,600	**U.S. Stock Ticker: BDK**
2007 Sales: $6,563,200	2007 Profits: $518,100	**Int'l Ticker:** Int'l Exchange:
2006 Sales: $6,447,300	2006 Profits: $486,100	Employees: 22,100
2005 Sales: $6,523,700	2005 Profits: $5,352,100	Fiscal Year Ends: 12/31
2004 Sales: $5,398,400	2004 Profits: $445,600	Parent Company:

SALARIES/BENEFITS:

Pension Plan:	ESOP Stock Plan:	Profit Sharing:	Top Exec. Salary: $1,500,000	Bonus: $1,750,000
Savings Plan:	Stock Purch. Plan:		Second Exec. Salary: $602,083	Bonus: $465,000

OTHER THOUGHTS:

Apparent Women Officers or Directors: 4
Hot Spot for Advancement for Women/Minorities: Y

LOCATIONS: ("Y" = Yes)

West:	Southwest:	Midwest:	Southeast:	Northeast:	International:
Y			Y	Y	Y

BLACK & VEATCH HOLDING COMPANY

www.bv.com

Industry Group Code: 234000 **Ranks within this company's industry group:** Sales: Profits:

Techology:		Medical/Drugs:		Engineering:		Transportation:		Chemicals/Petrochemicals:		Specialty:	
Computers:		Manufacturer:		Design:	Y	Aerospace:		Oil/Gas Products:		Special Services:	Y
Software:		Contract Research:		Construction:	Y	Automotive:		Chemicals:		Consulting:	Y
Communications:		Medical Services:		Eng. Services:	Y	Shipping:		Oil/Chem. Svcs.:	Y	Specialty Mgmt.:	
Electronics:		Labs:		Consulting:	Y			Gases:		Products:	
Alternative Energy:		Bio. Services:						Other:		Other:	

TYPES OF BUSINESS:

Construction, Heavy & Civil Engineering
Infrastructure & Energy Services
Environmental & Hydrologic Engineering
Consulting Services
IT Services
Power Plant Engineering and Construction
LNG and Gas Processing Plant Engineering

BRANDS/DIVISIONS/AFFILIATES:

BV Solutions Group, Inc.
Fortegra
B&V China
B&V Corporation
B&V Construction, Inc.
B&V Europe
BV Solutions Group, Inc.
B&V International Co.

CONTACTS: *Note: Officers with more than one job title may be intentionally listed here more than once.*

Leonard C. Rodman, CEO
Leonard C. Rodman, Pres.
Karen L. Daniel, CFO
John G. Voeller, CTO
Howard G. Withey, Chief Admin. Officer
John G. Voeller, Chief Knowledge Officer
Leonard C. Rodman, Chmn.

Phone: 913-458-2000	**Fax:** 913-458-2934
Toll-Free:	
Address: 11401 Lamar Ave., Overland Park, KS 66211 US	

GROWTH PLANS/SPECIAL FEATURES:

Black & Veatch Holding Company (B&V) is a leading engineering, consulting and construction company specializing in infrastructure development for the energy, water and telecommunications, federal, management consulting and environmental markets. The company is employee-owned and operates over 100 offices worldwide. B&V provides its clients with conceptual and preliminary engineering services, engineering design, procurement, construction, financial management, asset management, information technology, environmental, security design and consulting, and management consulting services. The firm's energy market services include energy engineering and construction services for cogeneration, coal, nuclear and renewable energy sources; energy services, such as asset optimization, strategic market analysis, asset valuation and asset addition; gas, oil and chemical construction and consulting services for natural gas processing, sulfur recovery, LNG, petroleum refining, petrochemicals and cogeneration; and power delivery services for substations, overhead transmission, underground transmission, power system studies and distributed generation. B&V's water sector provides a broad range of water and environmental study, consulting, design, design-build and construction management services to utilities, agencies and industrial clients in the Americas, Europe and Asia Pacific. It develops water treatment facilities, distribution systems for potable water and wastewater collection systems and provides water reclamation and reuse consulting services. The company's information market services include telecommunications services, such as wireless, wireline, A&E services, integrated networks and federal and state government networks, as well as offerings through BV Solutions Group, Inc., a wholly-owned IT service provider subsidiary. It also provides enterprise consulting services, including strategic and process solutions for the water and energy industries, and comprehensive engineering, procurement, construction management and program management services to the U.S. Federal Government. In March 2008, the firm signed a contract with the Fuzhou Municipality to proved consulting services for the Fuzhou Environmental Improvement Project in Mainland China. In December 2008, the company opened a new office in Milwaukee, Wisconsin.

FINANCIALS: **Sales and profits are in thousands of dollars—add 000 to get the full amount. 2008 Note: Financial information for 2008 was not available for all companies at press time.**

2008 Sales: $	2008 Profits: $	**U.S. Stock Ticker: Private**
2007 Sales: $3,200,000	2007 Profits: $	**Int'l Ticker:** Int'l Exchange:
2006 Sales: $1,800,000	2006 Profits: $	Employees: 9,600
2005 Sales: $1,600,000	2005 Profits: $	Fiscal Year Ends: 12/31
2004 Sales: $1,350,000	2004 Profits: $	Parent Company:

SALARIES/BENEFITS:

Pension Plan:	ESOP Stock Plan:	Profit Sharing:	Top Exec. Salary: $	Bonus: $
Savings Plan:	Stock Purch. Plan:		Second Exec. Salary: $	Bonus: $

OTHER THOUGHTS:

Apparent Women Officers or Directors: 2
Hot Spot for Advancement for Women/Minorities: Y

LOCATIONS: ("Y" = Yes)

West:	Southwest:	Midwest:	Southeast:	Northeast:	International:
Y	Y	Y	Y	Y	Y

Note: Financial information, benefits and other data can change quickly and may vary from those stated here.

BMC SOFTWARE INC

www.bmc.com

Industry Group Code: 511207 **Ranks within this company's industry group:** Sales: 5 Profits: 4

Techology:		Medical/Drugs:		Engineering:		Transportation:		Chemicals/Petrochemicals:		Specialty:	
Computers:		Manufacturer:		Design:		Aerospace:		Oil/Gas Products:		Special Services:	Y
Software:	Y	Contract Research:		Construction:		Automotive:		Chemicals:		Consulting:	Y
Communications:		Medical Services:		Eng. Services:		Shipping:		Oil/Chem. Svcs.:		Specialty Mgmt.:	
Electronics:		Labs:		Consulting:				Gases:		Products:	
Alternative Energy:		Bio. Services:						Other:		Other:	

TYPES OF BUSINESS:

Computer Software-Mainframe Related
Systems Management Software
e-Business Software
Consulting & Training Services

BRANDS/DIVISIONS/AFFILIATES:

BMC Atrium
Emprisa Networks
BladeLogic, Inc.
ITM Software
Remedy Corp

CONTACTS: *Note: Officers with more than one job title may be intentionally listed here more than once.*

Robert E. Beauchamp, CEO
Stephen B. Solcher, CFO/Sr. VP
John McMahon, Sr. VP-Worldwide Sales & Svcs.
Michael Vescuso, Sr. VP-Admin.
Denise Clolery, General Counsel/Sr. VP/Corp. Sec.
Steve Goddard, Sr. VP-Bus. Oper.
Jim Grant, Sr. VP-Strategy & Corp. Dev.
Derrick Vializ, VP-Investor Rel.
T. Cory Bleuer, Chief Acct. Officer/Controller/VP
Dev Ittycheria, Pres., Enterprise Service Management
William D. Miller, Pres., Mainframe Service Management
Robert E. Beauchamp, Chmn.

Phone: 713-918-8800 **Fax:** 713-918-8000
Toll-Free: 800-841-2031
Address: 2101 Citywest Blvd., Houston, TX 77042-2827 US

GROWTH PLANS/SPECIAL FEATURES:

BMC Software, Inc. is one of the world's largest software vendors. The company provides system and service management solutions primarily for large companies. Its software products spans enterprise systems, applications, databases and IT process management. The company operates in two software business segments. Its Enterprise Service Management (ESM) segment consists of the company's non-mainframe and non-job scheduling solutions, including its core Business Service Management (BSM) products. Products in this segment address a variety of IT management issues, including service support, service assurance and service automation. Also included is the firm's BMC Atrium software package, which helps provide centralized coordination and execution of IT processes. The company's Mainframe Service Management (MSM) segment creates products that address the IT requirements for mainframe systems, operations and data management, with particular focus on streamlining mainframe operations in order to reduce costs and manage large amounts of data without affecting the availability of critical business applications. MSM products are organized into three areas: data management, infrastructure management and enterprise scheduling and output management. The company also operates a professional services segment, consisting of a worldwide team of software consultants who provide implementation, integration and education services related to its products. The company's customers include manufacturers, telecommunications companies, financial service providers, educational institutions, retailers, distributors, hospitals, government agencies and channel partners, distributors and system integrators. Approximately 15,000 companies worldwide use BMC products, including 99% of the Forbes Global 100 and over 85% of the Fortune 500 companies. In October 2007, BMC Software acquired privately held Emprisa Networks, a provider of network compliance, change and configuration management. In April 2008, the company acquired BladeLogic, Inc., a provider of data center automation software, for approximately $854 million. In June 2008, BMC completed its acquisition of ITM Software, a provider of business management software to IT organizations.

FINANCIALS: **Sales and profits are in thousands of dollars—add 000 to get the full amount. 2008 Note: Financial information for 2008 was not available for all companies at press time.**

2008 Sales: $1,731,600	2008 Profits: $313,600	**U.S. Stock Ticker: BMC**
2007 Sales: $1,580,400	2007 Profits: $215,900	**Int'l Ticker:** Int'l Exchange:
2006 Sales: $1,498,400	2006 Profits: $102,000	Employees: 5,800
2005 Sales: $1,463,000	2005 Profits: $75,300	Fiscal Year Ends: 3/31
2004 Sales: $1,418,700	2004 Profits: $-26,800	Parent Company:

SALARIES/BENEFITS:

Pension Plan:	ESOP Stock Plan:	Profit Sharing:	Top Exec. Salary: $950,000	Bonus: $4,328,869
Savings Plan:	Stock Purch. Plan:		Second Exec. Salary: $475,000	Bonus: $1,482,822

OTHER THOUGHTS:

Apparent Women Officers or Directors: 1
Hot Spot for Advancement for Women/Minorities: Y

LOCATIONS: ("Y" = Yes)

West:	Southwest:	Midwest:	Southeast:	Northeast:	International:
Y	Y	Y	Y	Y	Y

Note: Financial information, benefits and other data can change quickly and may vary from those stated here.

BMW (BAYERISCHE MOTOREN WERKE AG)

www.bmw.com

Industry Group Code: 336111 **Ranks within this company's industry group:** Sales: 11 Profits: 14

Techology:		Medical/Drugs:		Engineering:		Transportation:		Chemicals/Petrochemicals:		Specialty:	
Computers:		Manufacturer:		Design:		Aerospace:		Oil/Gas Products:		Special Services:	Y
Software:	Y	Contract Research:		Construction:		Automotive:	Y	Chemicals:		Consulting:	Y
Communications:		Medical Services:		Eng. Services:		Shipping:		Oil/Chem. Svcs.:		Specialty Mgmt.:	
Electronics:		Labs:		Consulting:				Gases:		Products:	
Alternative Energy:		Bio. Services:						Other:		Other:	

TYPES OF BUSINESS:

Automobile Manufacturing
Financial Services
Motorcycles
Software
Consulting Services
Fleet Management
IT Solutions
Engines

BRANDS/DIVISIONS/AFFILIATES:

MINI
Rolls-Royce Motor Cars
Softlab GmbH
Bavaria Wirtschaftsagentur GmbH
BMW M
BMW Car IT
BMW Motoren
Alphabet Fuhrparkmanagement

CONTACTS: *Note: Officers with more than one job title may be intentionally listed here more than once.*

Norbert Reithoffer, CEO
Ian Robertson, Dir.-Sales & Mktg.
Harald Kruger, Dir.-Human Resources & Industrial Rel.
Frank-Peter Arndt, Chief Prod. Officer
Klaus Draeger, Dir.-Dev.
Friedrich Eichiner, Chief Corp. & Brand Dev. Officer
Manfred Schoch, Deputy Chmn.
Stefan Quandt, Deputy Chmn.
Konrad Gottinger, Deputy Chmn.
Joachim Milberg, Chmn.
Herbert Diess, Chief Purchasing & Supplier Network Officer

Phone: 49-89-382-0 **Fax:** 49-89-382-2-44-18
Toll-Free:
Address: Petuelring 130, Munich, D-80788 Germany

GROWTH PLANS/SPECIAL FEATURES:

BMW (Bayerische Motoren Werke AG), based in Munich, Germany, is one of the leading vehicle manufacturers in Europe, with brands including the BMW line. The company operates in three primary business segments: automobiles, which generates 79.5% of revenues; motorcycles, 2.1%; and financial services, 18.4%. The company's automobile models include the 1 Series; the 3 Series coupe, sedan, convertible and compact; the 5 Series sedan and touring; the 6 Series coupe and convertible; the 7 Series sedan; the M3 coupe and convertible; the X3 and X5 sport utilities; and the Z4 roadster. In addition, BMW produces the MINI brand of cars (One, Cooper, Cooper D, Cooper S and Cabrio) and Rolls-Royce Motor Cars. The BMW brand motorcycles include the K 1200 GT, K 1200 R, R 1200 S, R 1200 GS, F 800 S, F 800 ST, G 650 Xcountry Scramble, G 650 Xchallenge Hard-Enduro and G 650 Xmoto. It also produces related motorcycle apparel, such as leather suits, gloves and boots. The financial services segment manages a range of vehicle related financial services including financing and leasing, asset management, dealer financing and company car pools. Other group activities include the following. Softlab GmbH offers IT consulting, systems integration and software. Bavaria Wirtschaftsagentur GmbH provides insurance and other services to the firm. BMW M develops high-performance sports cars. BMW Car IT is a think tank for automobile IT development and software. BMW Technik works to develop innovative automobile technologies. BKK BMW provides health care to group employees. BMW Motoren manufactures engines. Lastly, subsidiary Alphabet Fuhrparkmanagement manages car fleets. In 2008, the company entered into talks with Fiat Group to manufacture common parts and components for the MINI and Alfa Romeo vehicles.

FINANCIALS: **Sales and profits are in thousands of dollars—add 000 to get the full amount. 2008 Note: Financial information for 2008 was not available for all companies at press time.**

2008 Sales: $59,737,500	2008 Profits: $517,660	**U.S. Stock Ticker:**
2007 Sales: $65,125,700	2007 Profits: $1,596,130	**Int'l Ticker: BMW** Int'l Exchange: Frankfurt-Euronext
2006 Sales: $64,644,400	2006 Profits: $3,791,700	Employees: 106,575
2005 Sales: $55,254,700	2005 Profits: $2,651,600	Fiscal Year Ends: 12/31
2004 Sales: $60,472,900	2004 Profits: $3,030,800	Parent Company:

SALARIES/BENEFITS:

Pension Plan:	ESOP Stock Plan:	Profit Sharing:	Top Exec. Salary: $645,853	Bonus: $
Savings Plan:	Stock Purch. Plan:		Second Exec. Salary: $528,425	Bonus: $

OTHER THOUGHTS:

Apparent Women Officers or Directors: 1
Hot Spot for Advancement for Women/Minorities:

LOCATIONS: ("Y" = Yes)

West:	Southwest:	Midwest:	Southeast:	Northeast:	International:
Y				Y	Y

Note: Financial information, benefits and other data can change quickly and may vary from those stated here.

BOEING COMPANY (THE)

www.boeing.com

Industry Group Code: 336410 **Ranks within this company's industry group:** Sales: 1 Profits: 5

Techology:		Medical/Drugs:		Engineering:		Transportation:		Chemicals/Petrochemicals:		Specialty:	
Computers:		Manufacturer:		Design:		Aerospace:	Y	Oil/Gas Products:		Special Services:	Y
Software:		Contract Research:		Construction:		Automotive:		Chemicals:		Consulting:	
Communications:	Y	Medical Services:		Eng. Services:		Shipping:		Oil/Chem. Svcs.:		Specialty Mgmt.:	
Electronics:		Labs:		Consulting:				Gases:		Products:	
Alternative Energy:		Bio. Services:						Other:		Other:	

TYPES OF BUSINESS:

Commercial Aircraft Manufacturing
Aerospace Technology & Manufacturing
Military Aircraft
Satellite Manufacturing
Communications Products & Services
Air Traffic Management Technology
Financing Services
Research & Development

BRANDS/DIVISIONS/AFFILIATES:

Boeing Business Jets
787 Dreamliner
Integrated Defense Systems
Boeing Capital
Phantom Works
AH-64D Apache
F-15 Eagle

CONTACTS: *Note: Officers with more than one job title may be intentionally listed here more than once.*

W. James McNerney, Jr., CEO
W. James McNerney, Jr., Pres.
James A. Bell, CFO/Exec. VP
Richard Stephens, Sr. VP-Human Resources
John J. Tracy, CTO/Sr. VP-Eng. & Oper. Bus. Unit
Richard Stephens, Sr. VP-Admin.
J. Michael Luttig, General Counsel/Sr. VP
Michael J. Cave, Sr. VP-Bus. Dev. & Strategy
Thomas J. Downey, Sr. VP-Comm.
James F. Albaugh, CEO/Pres., Integrated Defense Systems/Exec. VP
Scott E. Carson, CEO/Pres., Commercial Airplanes/Exec. VP
Timothy Keating, Sr. VP-Public Policy
Wanda K. Denson-Low, Sr. VP-Office of Internal Governance
W. James McNerney, Jr., Chmn.
Shephard W. Hill, Pres., Boeing Int'l

Phone: 312-544-2000	Fax: 312-544-2082
Toll-Free:	
Address: 100 N. Riverside, Chicago, IL 60606 US	

GROWTH PLANS/SPECIAL FEATURES:

The Boeing Co. is one of the world's major aerospace firms. The company operates in three segments: commercial airplanes (CA); integrated defense systems, which is comprised of precision engagement and mobility systems (PE&MS), network and space systems (N&SS) and support systems; and Boeing Capital Corp. CA develops, produces and markets commercial jet aircraft and provides related support services. The family of jet aircraft includes the 737 Next-Generation narrow-body model and the 747, 767, 777 and the new 787 Dreamliner wide-body models. The division also offers aviation support, aircraft modifications, training, maintenance documents and technical advice to commercial customers worldwide. The integrated defense systems segment researches, develops, produces, modifies and supports products and related systems and services such as military aircraft, including fighters, transports, tankers and helicopters; missiles; space systems; missile defense systems; satellites and satellite launch vehicles; and communications, information and battle management systems. The PE&MS subdivision oversees precision engagement and mobility products and services. The N&SS subdivision provides products and services to assist customers in transforming operations through network integration, intelligence and surveillance systems, communications and space exploration. The support systems subdivision is engaged in operations, maintenance, and logistics support functions for military platforms. Boeing Capital Corp. provides financing to CA customers. Boeing's other businesses include Connection by Boeing, a high speed broadband communications business; and Engineering, Operations and Technology, a research and development organization. The 787 Dreamliner is Boeing's exciting, new-generation aircraft. It is manufactured of extremely light components that, combined with advanced technology jet engines, will enable the aircraft to enjoy very high fuel efficiency. It will seat 210-250 passengers, with a maximum range of 9,266 miles. The aircraft's first deliveries have been pushed back to 2009 due to production complications. In January 2009, the company announced plans to eliminate 10,000 jobs by the end of the year.

The company offers its employees health, disability and life insurance; and an employee assistance program.

FINANCIALS: Sales and profits are in thousands of dollars—add 000 to get the full amount. 2008 Note: Financial information for 2008 was not available for all companies at press time.

2008 Sales: $60,909,000	2008 Profits: $2,672,000	**U.S. Stock Ticker: BA**
2007 Sales: $66,387,000	2007 Profits: $4,074,000	**Int'l Ticker:** Int'l Exchange:
2006 Sales: $61,530,000	2006 Profits: $2,215,000	Employees: 162,200
2005 Sales: $53,621,000	2005 Profits: $2,572,000	Fiscal Year Ends: 12/31
2004 Sales: $51,400,000	2004 Profits: $1,872,000	Parent Company:

SALARIES/BENEFITS:

Pension Plan: Y	ESOP Stock Plan:	Profit Sharing:	Top Exec. Salary: $1,800,077	Bonus: $4,266,500
Savings Plan: Y	Stock Purch. Plan:		Second Exec. Salary: $896,303	Bonus: $1,537,900

OTHER THOUGHTS:

Apparent Women Officers or Directors: 3
Hot Spot for Advancement for Women/Minorities: Y

LOCATIONS: ("Y" = Yes)

West:	Southwest:	Midwest:	Southeast:	Northeast:	International:
Y	Y	Y	Y	Y	Y

Note: Financial information, benefits and other data can change quickly and may vary from those stated here.

BOMBARDIER INC

www.bombardier.com

Industry Group Code: 336410 **Ranks within this company's industry group:** Sales: 11 Profits: 16

Techology:		Medical/Drugs:		Engineering:		Transportation:		Chemicals/Petrochemicals:		Specialty:	
Computers:		Manufacturer:		Design:		Aerospace:	Y	Oil/Gas Products:		Special Services:	Y
Software:		Contract Research:		Construction:		Automotive:		Chemicals:		Consulting:	
Communications:		Medical Services:		Eng. Services:		Shipping:		Oil/Chem. Svcs.:		Specialty Mgmt.:	
Electronics:		Labs:		Consulting:				Gases:		Products:	Y
Alternative Energy:		Bio. Services:						Other:		Other:	

TYPES OF BUSINESS:

Aircraft Manufacturing
Railway Vehicles & Equipment
Business, Passenger & Civil Aircraft
Jet Leasing & Charters
Railroad Car Leasing & Management
Amphibious Aircraft

BRANDS/DIVISIONS/AFFILIATES:

Learjet Inc
Challenger
skyjet.com
Bombardier Aerospace
Bombardier Transportation

CONTACTS:

Note: Officers with more than one job title may be intentionally listed here more than once.

Pierre Beaudoin, CEO
Pierre Beaudoin, Pres.
Pierre Alary, CFO/Sr. VP
John Paul Macdonald, Sr. VP-Human Resources
Daniel Desjardins, General Counsel/Sr. VP
Richard C. Bradeen, Sr. VP-Strategy, Corp. Audit Svcs. & Risk
Isabelle Rondeau, Dir.-Comm.
Shirley Chénier, Sr. Dir.-Investor Rel.
John Paul Macdonald, Sr. VP-Public Affairs
Guy C. Hachey, COO/Pres., Bombardier Aerospace
André Navarri, COO/Pres., Bombardier Transportation
Roger Carle, Corp. Sec.
Jean-Louis Fontaine, Chmn.

Phone: 514-861-9481	**Fax:** 514-861-7053
Toll-Free:	
Address: 800 Rene-Levesque Blvd. W., Montreal, QC H3B 1Y8 Canada	

GROWTH PLANS/SPECIAL FEATURES:

Bombardier, Inc. is a diversified manufacturer with operations in rail transportation and aerospace, including jet aircraft. Through its aerospace division, Bombardier Aerospace, the company is one of the largest producers of regional jet passenger aircraft, civil aircraft and business jets in the world, with production sites in Canada, the U.S., Northern Ireland and Mexico. Its business aircraft include the Learjet and Challenger models. Bombardier also offers business jet leases and business jet charter services, in part through skyjet.com. In addition, this division provides defense services, including fleet management and aviation training management. The firm also makes multi-role amphibious aircraft, suitable for tasks such as forest-fire fighting, maritime surveillance, search and rescue and utility transport. The company's transportation division, Bombardier Transportation, is one of the world's largest producers of railway vehicles and equipment, with operations in 35 countries, approximately 42 production sites and 22 service centers. This unit also produces monorail systems, light rail transit systems, rapid transit systems and propulsion and controls technology, among other products. The transportation segment offers rail services including rail vehicles such as monorails, light rail vehicles, commuter/regional trains; propulsion and controls, which is a complete product for applications that range from trolley busses to freights locomotives; bogies, which is a product portfolio for the whole range of rail vehicles; services, such as vehicle refurbishment and modernization and fleet maintenance; total transit systems, which is custom transportation system solutions; and rail control solutions, which offers signaling solutions for mass transit. Bombardier's capital division offers railroad car leasing and management. In 2008, the U.S. represented 51% of the firm's total revenue, which is an 18% increase from sales in 2007.

FINANCIALS:

Sales and profits are in thousands of dollars—add 000 to get the full amount. 2008 Note: Financial information for 2008 was not available for all companies at press time.

2008 Sales: $17,506,000	2008 Profits: $317,000	**U.S. Stock Ticker: BBD**
2007 Sales: $14,816,000	2007 Profits: $268,000	**Int'l Ticker: BBD.B** Int'l Exchange: Toronto-TSX
2006 Sales: $14,726,000	2006 Profits: $249,000	Employees: 60,000
2005 Sales: $15,546,000	2005 Profits: $-85,000	Fiscal Year Ends: 1/31
2004 Sales: $15,508,000	2004 Profits: $-85,000	Parent Company:

SALARIES/BENEFITS:

Pension Plan:	ESOP Stock Plan:	Profit Sharing:	Top Exec. Salary: $1,166,673	Bonus: $1,004,926
Savings Plan:	Stock Purch. Plan:		Second Exec. Salary: $1,050,000	Bonus: $393,750

OTHER THOUGHTS:

Apparent Women Officers or Directors:
Hot Spot for Advancement for Women/Minorities:

LOCATIONS: ("Y" = Yes)

West:	Southwest:	Midwest:	Southeast:	Northeast:	International:
Y	Y	Y	Y	Y	Y

BOSTON SCIENTIFIC CORP

www.bostonscientific.com

Industry Group Code: 339113 **Ranks within this company's industry group:** Sales: 5 Profits: 13

Techology:		Medical/Drugs:		Engineering:		Transportation:		Chemicals/Petrochemicals:		Specialty:	
Computers:		Manufacturer:	Y	Design:		Aerospace:		Oil/Gas Products:		Special Services:	
Software:		Contract Research:		Construction:		Automotive:		Chemicals:		Consulting:	
Communications:		Medical Services:	Y	Eng. Services:		Shipping:		Oil/Chem. Svcs.:		Specialty Mgmt.:	
Electronics:		Labs:		Consulting:				Gases:		Products:	
Alternative Energy:		Bio. Services:						Other:		Other:	

TYPES OF BUSINESS:

Supplies-Surgery
Interventional Medical Products
Catheters
Guide wires
Stents
Oncology Research

BRANDS/DIVISIONS/AFFILIATES:

LATITUDE Patient Management
Synchro2 Guidewires
Afocus Steerable Diagnostic Catheter
Inquiry H-Curve Steerable Diagnostic Catheter
EndoVive
LeVeen Needle Electrode
ALTRUA
PROENCY

CONTACTS:

Note: Officers with more than one job title may be intentionally listed here more than once.

James R. Tobin, CEO
Paul A. LaViolette, COO
James R. Tobin, Pres.
Samuel R. Leno, CFO/Exec. VP-Finance
William F. McConnell, Jr., VP-Sales, Mktg. & Bus. Strategy
Lucia Luce Quinn, Exec. VP-Human Resources
Donald S. Baim, Chief Medical & Scientific Officer/Exec. VP
Samuel R. Leno, Exec. VP-Info. Systems
Timothy Pratt, General Counsel/Sec./Exec. VP
Kenneth J. Pucel, Exec. VP-Oper.
Jim Gilbert, Exec. VP-Strategy & Bus. Dev.
Paul Donovan, Sr. VP-Corp. Comm.
Jeffrey D. Capello, Controller/Chief Acct. Officer/Sr, VP
Stephen F. Moreci, Sr. VP/Group Pres., Endosurgery
Fredericus A. Colen, Exec. VP/Group Pres., CRM
William H. Kucheman, Sr. VP/Group Pres., Cardiovascular
Michael Onuscheck, Sr. VP/Group Pres., Neuromodulation
Peter M. Nicholas, Chmn.
David McFaul, Sr. VP-Int'l

Phone: 508-650-8000	**Fax:** 508-650-8923
Toll-Free: 888-272-1001	
Address: 1 Boston Scientific Pl., Natick, MA 01760-1537 US	

GROWTH PLANS/SPECIAL FEATURES:

Boston Scientific Corp., with operations in over 45 countries, manufactures minimally invasive medical devices intended as an alternative to major surgical procedures that reduces risk, trauma, cost, procedure time and the need for aftercare. The company's products are used in a wide range of interventional medical applications, including cardiology; oncology; gastroenterology; vascular surgery; neurovascular therapy; radiology; urology; and pain management. Products include AFocus and Inquiry H-Curve Steerable Diagnostic Catheters; LIVIAN Cardiac Resynchronization Therapy Defibrillator; ALTRUA pacemakers; EndoVive feeding tubes; WallFlex stents; TLC retractor; Synchro2 Guidewires; and LeVeen Needle Electrode. Stents account for 20% of sales. Recent product developments include drug-eluting stents, which have been proven more effective than bare metal stents; the LATITUDE Patient Management system which allows clinicians to store information from a patient's implanted cardiac device into GE Healthcare's Centricity Electronic Medical Record. In January 2008, the firm sold its auditory business and drug pump development program to previous shareholders of Boston Scientific's subsidiary, Advanced Bionics; it also sold its Vascular and Cardiac Surgery businesses to Getinge Group for $750 million. In February 2008, Boston Scientific launched PROENCY European registry to compare different coronary stents, and sold its Venous Access and Fluid Management businesses to Avista Capital Partners. In March 2008, the company sold subsidiary Boston Scientific Santa Rosa Corp. to TV2 Holding Company for $30 million. In April 2008, the firm signed a licensing agreement with Surgi-Vision, Inc., to develop/market MRI-safe cardiac devices. In May 2008, Boston Scientific acquired CryoCor, Inc., for approximately $17.6 million. In June 2008, the company agreed to sell various venture fund and company investments to secondary investment firms Saints Capital and Paul Capital Partners. In January 2009, Boston Scientific acquired Labcoat Ltd., a drug-eluting stent developer. In March 2009, the company released TAXUS Liberte, a drug-eluding stent, in Japan.

FINANCIALS:

Sales and profits are in thousands of dollars—add 000 to get the full amount. 2008 Note: Financial information for 2008 was not available for all companies at press time.

2008 Sales: $8,050,000	2008 Profits: $-2,036,000	**U.S. Stock Ticker: BSX**
2007 Sales: $8,357,000	2007 Profits: $-495,000	**Int'l Ticker:** Int'l Exchange:
2006 Sales: $7,821,000	2006 Profits: $-3,577,000	Employees: 24,800
2005 Sales: $6,283,000	2005 Profits: $628,000	Fiscal Year Ends: 12/31
2004 Sales: $5,624,000	2004 Profits: $1,062,000	Parent Company:

SALARIES/BENEFITS:

Pension Plan:	ESOP Stock Plan: Y	Profit Sharing:	Top Exec. Salary: $959,805	Bonus: $710,867
Savings Plan: Y	Stock Purch. Plan:		Second Exec. Salary: $716,274	Bonus: $640,886

OTHER THOUGHTS:

Apparent Women Officers or Directors: 5
Hot Spot for Advancement for Women/Minorities: Y

LOCATIONS: ("Y" = Yes)

West:	Southwest:	Midwest:	Southeast:	Northeast:	International:
Y	Y	Y	Y	Y	Y

BOUYGUES SA

www.bouygues.fr

Industry Group Code: 234000 **Ranks within this company's industry group:** Sales: 1 Profits: 2

Techology:		Medical/Drugs:		Engineering:		Transportation:		Chemicals/Petrochemicals:		Specialty:	
Computers:		Manufacturer:		Design:		Aerospace:		Oil/Gas Products:		Special Services:	Y
Software:		Contract Research:		Construction:	Y	Automotive:		Chemicals:		Consulting:	
Communications:	Y	Medical Services:		Eng. Services:		Shipping:		Oil/Chem. Svcs.:		Specialty Mgmt.:	
Electronics:		Labs:		Consulting:				Gases:		Products:	
Alternative Energy:		Bio. Services:						Other:		Other:	

TYPES OF BUSINESS:

Construction & Telecommunications
Construction
Road Building
Property Development
Precasting
Cellular Phone Service
Media Operation
Research & Development

BRANDS/DIVISIONS/AFFILIATES:

Bouygues Construction
Bouygues Immobilier
Bouygues Telecom
Bouygues e-Lab
Bouygues Travaux Publics
TF1
Colas
ALSTOM

CONTACTS: *Note: Officers with more than one job title may be intentionally listed here more than once.*

Martin Bouygues, CEO
Philippe Marien, CFO
Jean-Claude Tostivin, Sr. VP-Human Resources
Alain Pouyat, Exec. VP-Info. Systems
Alain Pouyat, Exec. VP-New Tech.
Jean-Claude Tostivin, Sr. VP-Admin.
Jean-Francois Guillemin, Corp. Sec.
Lionel Verdouck, Sr. VP-Cash Mgmt. & Finance
Olivier Poupart-Lafarge, Deputy CEO
Olivier Bouygues, Deputy CEO
Nonce Paolini, CEO-TF1
Martin Bouygues, Chmn.

Phone: 33-1-44-20-10-00	**Fax:** 33-1-44-20-12-42
Toll-Free:	
Address: 32 Ave. Hoche, Paris, 75378 France	

GROWTH PLANS/SPECIAL FEATURES:

Buoygues SA, based in Paris, France, was founded in 1952 and originally committed to the building sector, property development and industrial precasting. Operating through its subsidiaries, the firm now primarily serves two distinct areas: construction and telecoms/media. Company subsidiaries working within the construction sector include Bouygues Construction, dedicated to electrical contracting and civil works; Bouygues Immobilier, committed to property development; and Colas, dedicated to building roads. Subsidiaries serving the telecoms/media branch include TF1 and Buoygues Telecom. The firm also maintains the Bouygues e-Lab, a research and development city which supports all areas of the company with innovations in their particular fields and in the digital technologies sector. Current research projects include acoustics, vibration and energy performance for the Construction sector; strategic marketing and the development of new products for the Immobilier sector; various asphalts and mixing processes for the Colas sector; television capabilities on mobile phones as well as high-definition TV for the TF1 sector; and mobile videos, broadband innovations and contactless applications for the Telecom sector. The firm maintains operations in Europe, Central and South America, North America, Asia, the Middle East and Africa.

FINANCIALS: **Sales and profits are in thousands of dollars—add 000 to get the full amount. 2008 Note: Financial information for 2008 was not available for all companies at press time.**

2008 Sales: $43,264,900	2008 Profits: $1,985,160	**U.S. Stock Ticker:**
2007 Sales: $39,131,900	2007 Profits: $1,819,840	**Int'l Ticker: EN** Int'l Exchange: Paris-Euronext
2006 Sales: $36,022,600	2006 Profits: $2,157,970	Employees: 115,441
2005 Sales: $32,714,700	2005 Profits: $1,415,920	Fiscal Year Ends: 12/31
2004 Sales: $28,393,300	2004 Profits: $1,520,950	Parent Company:

SALARIES/BENEFITS:

Pension Plan:	ESOP Stock Plan:	Profit Sharing:	Top Exec. Salary: $	Bonus: $
Savings Plan:	Stock Purch. Plan:		Second Exec. Salary: $	Bonus: $

OTHER THOUGHTS:

Apparent Women Officers or Directors: 2
Hot Spot for Advancement for Women/Minorities:

LOCATIONS: ("Y" = Yes)

West:	Southwest:	Midwest:	Southeast:	Northeast:	International:
Y		Y		Y	Y

BP PLC

www.bp.com

Industry Group Code: 211111 **Ranks within this company's industry group:** Sales: 3 Profits: 4

Techology:		Medical/Drugs:		Engineering:		Transportation:		Chemicals/Petrochemicals:		Specialty:	
Computers:		Manufacturer:		Design:		Aerospace:		Oil/Gas Products:	Y	Special Services:	
Software:		Contract Research:		Construction:		Automotive:		Chemicals:	Y	Consulting:	
Communications:		Medical Services:		Eng. Services:		Shipping:		Oil/Chem. Svcs.:	Y	Specialty Mgmt.:	
Electronics:		Labs:		Consulting:				Gases:	Y	Products:	
Alternative Energy:	Y	Bio. Services:						Other:	Y	Other:	

TYPES OF BUSINESS:

Oil & Gas Exploration & Production
Refining
Renewable & Alternative Energy
Lubricants
Natural Gas
Photovoltaic Modules
Gas Stations & Convenience Stores

BRANDS/DIVISIONS/AFFILIATES:

BP Energy
Aral
am/pm
ARCO
Castrol
TNK-BP
BP Solar
BP Alternative Energy

CONTACTS: *Note: Officers with more than one job title may be intentionally listed here more than once.*

Tony Hayward, CEO
Byron Grote, CFO
Iain Conn, Chief Exec.-Mktg. & Refining
Sally Bott, Dir.-Human Resources
Andy Inglis, Exec. Dir.-Exploration & Prod.
Rupert Bondy, Group General Counsel
Fergus MacLeod, Dir.-Investor Rel.
Iain Conn, CEO-Refining & Mktg. Unit
Vivienne Cox, Exec. VP/CEO-Alternative Energy
Lamar McKay, Exec. VP/Pres./Chmn.-BP America
Steve Westwell, Exec. VP/Group Chief-Staff
Peter D. Sutherland, Chmn.

Phone: 44-2074-96-40-00	**Fax:** 44-20-7496-4570
Toll-Free:	
Address: 1 St. James's Sq., London, SW1Y 4PD UK	

GROWTH PLANS/SPECIAL FEATURES:

BP plc is one of the world's largest integrated oil companies, with reserves of 17.8 billion barrels of oil and gas equivalent. Its core brands include BP Energy, Aral petrol, am/pm convenience stores, ARCO gasoline, Castrol automotive lubricants and Wild Bean Cafe. The company operates through three segments: Exploration and Production (E&P); Refining and Marketing (R&M); and Alternative Energy. E&P manages BP's upstream activities, including oil and gas exploration, development and production; and midstream activities, including crude oil and natural gas pipelines, processing and export terminals and liquefied natural gas (LNG) processing facilities. R&M focuses on refining, marketing, supplying, trading and transporting crude oil and petroleum products (including gasoline, gasoil, marine and aviation fuels, heating fuels, liquefied petroleum gas, lubricants and bitumen) to wholesale and retail customers. BP owns, fully or partly, 17 refineries and operates over 28,500 gas stations under the BP, Amoco and ARCO names. Alternative Energy processes and markets ethane, propane, butanes and pentanes extracted from natural gas. This also includes the shipping and trading of LNG, along with the funding and building of regasification facilities and gas import terminals. With regard to renewables, BP focuses on developing and manufacturing technologies related to solar, wind and hydrogen power through its BP Alternative Energy subsidiary. It operates the company's BP Solar subsidiary, a leading manufacturer of photovoltaic modules and systems. In July 2008, the company acquired the Whiting Clean Energy facility, a 525 megawatt (MW) cogeneration power plant in Indiana, for $210 million from NiSource Inc. In February 2009, the company formed a 50-50 joint venture with Verenium Corporation to produce and market cellulosic ethanol from non-food feedstocks.

U.S. employees are offered medical and dental insurance; short-and long-term disability coverage; life insurance; a 401(k) plan; a pension plan; relocation and family assistance; an adoption assistance plan; and educational assistance.

FINANCIALS: **Sales and profits are in thousands of dollars—add 000 to get the full amount. 2008 Note: Financial information for 2008 was not available for all companies at press time.**

2008 Sales: $365,700,000	2008 Profits: $21,666,000	**U.S. Stock Ticker: BP**
2007 Sales: $288,951,000	2007 Profits: $21,169,000	**Int'l Ticker: BP** Int'l Exchange: London-LSE
2006 Sales: $270,602,000	2006 Profits: $22,286,000	Employees: 92,000
2005 Sales: $243,948,000	2005 Profits: $22,632,000	Fiscal Year Ends: 12/31
2004 Sales: $194,919,000	2004 Profits: $17,262,000	Parent Company:

SALARIES/BENEFITS:

Pension Plan: Y	ESOP Stock Plan:	Profit Sharing:	Top Exec. Salary: $1,842,150	Bonus: $2,394,890
Savings Plan: Y	Stock Purch. Plan:		Second Exec. Salary: $1,372,044	Bonus: $2,056,519

OTHER THOUGHTS:

Apparent Women Officers or Directors: 9
Hot Spot for Advancement for Women/Minorities: Y

LOCATIONS: ("Y" = Yes)

West:	Southwest:	Midwest:	Southeast:	Northeast:	International:
Y	Y	Y	Y	Y	Y

BRILLIANCE CHINA AUTOMOTIVE HOLDINGS LIMITED

www.brillianceauto.com

Industry Group Code: 336111 **Ranks within this company's industry group:** Sales: 23 Profits: 20

Techology:		Medical/Drugs:		Engineering:		Transportation:		Chemicals/Petrochemicals:		Specialty:	
Computers:		Manufacturer:		Design:		Aerospace:		Oil/Gas Products:		Special Services:	
Software:		Contract Research:		Construction:		Automotive:	Y	Chemicals:		Consulting:	
Communications:		Medical Services:		Eng. Services:		Shipping:		Oil/Chem. Svcs.:		Specialty Mgmt.:	
Electronics:		Labs:		Consulting:				Gases:		Products:	
Alternative Energy:		Bio. Services:						Other:		Other:	

TYPES OF BUSINESS:

Automobile Manufacturing
Minibus Manufacturing
Engine & Components Manufacturing

BRANDS/DIVISIONS/AFFILIATES:

Shenyang Brilliance JinBei Automobile Co., Ltd.
Zhonghua
Junjie
Kubao
JinBei
Granse
Mianyang Xinchen Engine Co., Ltd.
Ningbo Yuming Machinery Industrial Co.

CONTACTS: *Note: Officers with more than one job title may be intentionally listed here more than once.*

Qi Yumin, CEO
Qi Yumin, Pres.
Lei Xiaoyang, CFO
Lam Yee Wah Eva, Company Sec.
Huang Yu, Head-Financial Dept./Group Mgr.-Financial
Wu Xiao An, Chmn.

Phone: 852-2523-7227 | **Fax:** 852-2526-8472
Toll-Free:
Address: Chater House, 8 Connaught Rd Central, Stes 1602-05, Hong Kong, K3 00000 China

GROWTH PLANS/SPECIAL FEATURES:

Brilliance China Automotive Holdings Limited (Brilliance) is one of the leading manufacturers of autos and passenger vehicles in the Chinese market. Its principle business consists of the manufacture and sale of minibuses and sedans through 51%-owned subsidiary Shenyang Brilliance JinBei Automobile Co., Ltd. (Shenyang Automotive). The firm's sedans, based on Mitsubishi engine technology, are sold in China under the Zhonghua, Kubao, Junjie and Zunchi brands. Zhonghua was the firm's first sedan. The Zunchi is a later revision of the Zhonghua, and is a mid-range sedan designed for government institutions, as well as private use. It can be modified for use as a taxi or police car. The Kubao, launched in September 2007, is a coupe model jointly designed by Porsche and Shenyang Automotive. Brilliance's minibus designs, based off Toyota's HIACE and GRANVIA minibuses, are sold in China under the JinBei and Granse brand names. Minibus configurations range from 8-15-passenger models, with additional specialty designs for police and ambulance use. Brilliance has a 49.5%-owned joint venture with BMW Holding that uses facilities in Shenyang to produce and sell BMW 3-series and 5-series sedans in China. The firm's distribution network includes 197 minibus distributors, 217 sedan distributors and 90 BMW distributors, as well as service centers. During 2007, the firm sold over 73,400 minibuses, 213,500 sedans and 32,100 BMW sedans. The Zhonghua brand accounted for 50% of the firm's sedan sales, followed by the Junjie brand, at 34%; Zunchi, 15.7%; and Kubao, 0.3%. Besides manufacturing vehicles, Brilliance produces automotive components, including window moldings, axles and stamped parts, through holdings in 50%-owned Shenyang Xinguang Brilliance Automobile Engine Co., Ltd.; 50%-owned Mianyang Xinchen Engine Co., Ltd.; 51%-owned Ningbo Yuming Machinery Industrial Co.; and related companies. The company is also engaged in the manufacture of gasoline engines for minibuses, sedans, SUVs and light trucks.

FINANCIALS: **Sales and profits are in thousands of dollars—add 000 to get the full amount. 2008 Note: Financial information for 2008 was not available for all companies at press time.**

2008 Sales: $1,634,500	2008 Profits: $-45,910	**U.S. Stock Ticker: BCAHY.PK**
2007 Sales: $2,067,100	2007 Profits: $14,190	**Int'l Ticker: 1114** Int'l Exchange: Hong Kong-HKEX
2006 Sales: $1,531,770	2006 Profits: $-58,200	Employees: 11,670
2005 Sales: $677,600	2005 Profits: $-154,300	Fiscal Year Ends: 12/31
2004 Sales: $790,300	2004 Profits: $ 100	Parent Company:

SALARIES/BENEFITS:

Pension Plan: Y	ESOP Stock Plan:	Profit Sharing:	Top Exec. Salary: $	Bonus: $
Savings Plan:	Stock Purch. Plan:		Second Exec. Salary: $	Bonus: $

OTHER THOUGHTS:

Apparent Women Officers or Directors: 2
Hot Spot for Advancement for Women/Minorities: Y

LOCATIONS: ("Y" = Yes)

West:	Southwest:	Midwest:	Southeast:	Northeast:	International:
					Y

Note: Financial information, benefits and other data can change quickly and may vary from those stated here.

BRISTOL MYERS SQUIBB CO

www.bms.com

Industry Group Code: 325412 **Ranks within this company's industry group:** Sales: 11 Profits: 9

Techology:		Medical/Drugs:		Engineering:		Transportation:		Chemicals/Petrochemicals:		Specialty:	
Computers:		Manufacturer:	Y	Design:		Aerospace:		Oil/Gas Products:		Special Services:	
Software:		Contract Research:		Construction:		Automotive:		Chemicals:		Consulting:	
Communications:		Medical Services:		Eng. Services:		Shipping:		Oil/Chem. Svcs.:		Specialty Mgmt.:	
Electronics:		Labs:		Consulting:				Gases:		Products:	
Alternative Energy:		Bio. Services:						Other:		Other:	

TYPES OF BUSINESS:

Drugs-Diversified
Medical Imaging Products
Nutritional Products

BRANDS/DIVISIONS/AFFILIATES:

Plavix
Enfamil
Reyataz
Ixempra
Sprycel
Abilify
Orencia
Kosan Biosciences Incorporated

CONTACTS:

Note: Officers with more than one job title may be intentionally listed here more than once.

James M. Cornelius, CEO
Lamberto Andreotti, COO
Lamberto Andreotti, Pres.
Jean-Marc Huet, CFO/Exec. VP
Anthony McBride, Sr. VP-Human Resources
Elliott Sigal, Chief Scientific Officer/Pres., R&D/Exec. VP
Carlo de Notaristefani, Pres., Tech. Oper. & Global Support Functions
Sandra Leung, General Counsel/Corp. Sec./Sr. VP
Robert T. Zito, Chief Comm. Officer/Sr. VP-Corp. & Bus. Comm.
Anthony C. Hooper, Pres., Americas
John E. Celentano, Pres., Emerging Markets & Asia Pacific
Brian Daniels, Sr. VP-Global Dev. & Medical Affairs
James M. Cornelius, Chmn.
Beatrice Cazala, Pres., Europe & Global Commercialization
Quentin Roach, Chief Procurement Officer/Sr. VP

Phone: 212-546-4000	**Fax:** 212-546-4020
Toll-Free:	
Address: 345 Park Ave., New York, NY 10154 US	

GROWTH PLANS/SPECIAL FEATURES:

Bristol-Myers Squibb Co. discovers, develops, licenses, manufactures, markets, distributes and sells pharmaceuticals and other health care related products. It operates in two segments: Pharmaceuticals and Nutritionals. The pharmaceuticals segment, accounting for 86% of net sales, manufactures drugs across multiple therapeutic classes, including cardiovascular; virology, including immunodeficiency virus infection; oncology; affective and other psychiatric disorders; and immunoscience. Products include Plavix, Avapro/Avalide, Reyataz, Sprycel and Ixempra. These products are manufactured in the U.S. and Puerto Rico and 11 foreign countries. The nutritionals segment, through Mead Johnson, manufactures, markets, distributes and sells infant formulas and other nutritional products, including the entire line of Enfamil products. Nutritional products are generally sold by wholesalers and retailers and are promoted primarily to health care professionals. In 2008, the FDA approved Orencia for the treatment of moderate-to-severe Polyarticular Juvenile Idiopathic Arthritis, as well as Abilify, for the add-on treatment to Lithium or Valproate in the acute treatment of manic episodes of Bipolar disorder. In July 2008, the company acquired Kosan Biosciences Incorporated for $190 million. In August 2008, the firm completed the divestment of ConvaTec to Nordic Capital Fund VII and Avista Capital Partners.

Employees are offered medical and dental insurance; health care reimbursement accounts; a pension plan; a 401(k) plan; short-and long-term disability coverage; life insurance; travel accident insurance; an employee assistance plan; and adoption assistance.

FINANCIALS:

Sales and profits are in thousands of dollars—add 000 to get the full amount. 2008 Note: Financial information for 2008 was not available for all companies at press time.

2008 Sales: $20,597,000	2008 Profits: $5,247,000	**U.S. Stock Ticker: BMY**
2007 Sales: $18,193,000	2007 Profits: $2,165,000	**Int'l Ticker:** Int'l Exchange:
2006 Sales: $16,208,000	2006 Profits: $1,585,000	Employees: 42,000
2005 Sales: $18,605,000	2005 Profits: $3,000,000	Fiscal Year Ends: 12/31
2004 Sales: $19,380,000	2004 Profits: $2,388,000	Parent Company:

SALARIES/BENEFITS:

Pension Plan: Y	ESOP Stock Plan:	Profit Sharing:	Top Exec. Salary: $1,352,115	Bonus: $3,283,301
Savings Plan: Y	Stock Purch. Plan:		Second Exec. Salary: $1,098,637	Bonus: $1,866,344

OTHER THOUGHTS:

Apparent Women Officers or Directors: 2
Hot Spot for Advancement for Women/Minorities: Y

LOCATIONS: ("Y" = Yes)

West:	Southwest:	Midwest:	Southeast:	Northeast:	International:
Y	Y	Y	Y	Y	Y

BRITISH NUCLEAR FUELS PLC

www.bnfl.com

Industry Group Code: 325188 **Ranks within this company's industry group:** Sales: Profits:

Techology:		Medical/Drugs:		Engineering:		Transportation:		Chemicals/Petrochemicals:		Specialty:	
Computers:		Manufacturer:		Design:		Aerospace:		Oil/Gas Products:		Special Services:	Y
Software:		Contract Research:		Construction:		Automotive:		Chemicals:		Consulting:	
Communications:		Medical Services:		Eng. Services:		Shipping:		Oil/Chem. Svcs.:		Specialty Mgmt.:	
Electronics:		Labs:		Consulting:				Gases:		Products:	
Alternative Energy:	Y	Bio. Services:						Other:		Other:	

TYPES OF BUSINESS:

Nuclear Decommissioning & Clean-Up
Nuclear Fuel, Equipment & Services
Nuclear Fuel Disposal & Recycling
Transportation Services
Nuclear Plant Design Services

BRANDS/DIVISIONS/AFFILIATES:

British Nuclear Group
BNG America
Nexia Solutions
Sellafield Ltd.
British Nuclear Group Project Services

CONTACTS: *Note: Officers with more than one job title may be intentionally listed here more than once.*

Michael Parker, CEO
David Bonser, Group Dir.-Human Resources
John Edwards, Group Dir.-Finance
Gordon Campbell, Chmn.

Phone: 44-1925-83-20-00	**Fax:** 44-1925-822-711
Toll-Free:	
Address: 1100 Daresbury Park, Warrington, WA4 4GB UK	

GROWTH PLANS/SPECIAL FEATURES:

British Nuclear Fuels plc (BNFL) is the holding company for Sellafield Ltd. (which includes Capenhurst and Calder Hall sites), British Nuclear Group Project Services and Nexia Solutions. BNFL provides the overriding strategic guidance and corporate governance for the BNFL Group. The company's British Nuclear Group (BNG) companies primarily conduct decommissioning and nuclear cleanup projects under government contract, as well as in Continental and Eastern Europe, Russia and the U.S. (d.b.a. BNG America). BNFL's activities cover nuclear site decommissioning and clean-up as well as technology services and solutions across the nuclear fuel cycle. Nuclear fuel is manufactured primarily in the U.S., the U.K. and Sweden. Sellafield is responsible for the delivery of contracts on behalf of the NDA; its activities cover remediation, decommissioning, clean-up, as well as reprocessing plant operations, Mox fuel fabrication, waste management and effluent treatment. Project Services is a specialist decommissioning and remediation company providing core technical engineering expertise to help meet NDA requirements as well as operating as a key contracting business to nuclear customers worldwide. Nexia Solutions provides nuclear technology services and solutions, including nuclear research, development and scientific services to customers. In 2007, the firm sold its Reactor Sites Management Company to Energy Solutions. The firm is also pursuing the sale of BNG, though no concrete action has yet been taken.

FINANCIALS: **Sales and profits are in thousands of dollars—add 000 to get the full amount. 2008 Note: Financial information for 2008 was not available for all companies at press time.**

2008 Sales: $	2008 Profits: $	**U.S. Stock Ticker: Private**
2007 Sales: $	2007 Profits: $	**Int'l Ticker:** Int'l Exchange:
2006 Sales: $	2006 Profits: $	Employees: 10,000
2005 Sales: $	2005 Profits: $	Fiscal Year Ends: 3/31
2004 Sales: $4,571,800	2004 Profits: $-354,200	Parent Company:

SALARIES/BENEFITS:

Pension Plan:	ESOP Stock Plan:	Profit Sharing:	Top Exec. Salary: $539,148	Bonus: $105,259
Savings Plan:	Stock Purch. Plan:		Second Exec. Salary: $516,683	Bonus: $100,597

OTHER THOUGHTS:

Apparent Women Officers or Directors:
Hot Spot for Advancement for Women/Minorities:

LOCATIONS: ("Y" = Yes)

West:	Southwest:	Midwest:	Southeast:	Northeast:	International:
Y		Y	Y	Y	Y

BROADCOM CORP

www.broadcom.com

Industry Group Code: 334413 **Ranks within this company's industry group:** Sales: 10 Profits: 10

Techology:		Medical/Drugs:		Engineering:		Transportation:		Chemicals/Petrochemicals:		Specialty:	
Computers:		Manufacturer:		Design:		Aerospace:		Oil/Gas Products:		Special Services:	
Software:		Contract Research:		Construction:		Automotive:		Chemicals:		Consulting:	
Communications:	Y	Medical Services:		Eng. Services:		Shipping:		Oil/Chem. Svcs.:		Specialty Mgmt.:	
Electronics:		Labs:		Consulting:				Gases:		Products:	
Alternative Energy:		Bio. Services:						Other:		Other:	

TYPES OF BUSINESS:

Integrated Circuits-Broadband Transmission
Communications Products

BRANDS/DIVISIONS/AFFILIATES:

Sunext Design, Inc.

CONTACTS:

Note: Officers with more than one job title may be intentionally listed here more than once.

Scott A. McGregor, CEO
Scott A. McGregor, Pres.
Eric K. Brandt, CFO/Sr. VP
Kenneth E. Venner, CIO/Sr. VP
Neil Y. Kim, Sr. VP-Central Eng.
Arthur Chong, General Counsel/Sec./Sr. VP
Robert L. Tirva, Corp. Controller/Principal Acct. Officer/VP
Scott A. Bibaud, Sr. VP/Gen. Mgr.-Mobile Platforms Group
Daniel A. Marotta, Sr. VP/Gen. Mgr.-Broadband Comm. Group
Robert A. Rango, Sr. VP/Gen. Mgr.-Wireless Connectivity Group
Nariman Yousefi, Sr. VP/Gen. Mgr.-Enterprise Networking Group
Thomas F. Laqatta, Sr. VP-Worldwide Sales

Phone: 949-926-5000	**Fax:** 949-926-5203
Toll-Free:	
Address: 5300 California Ave., Irvine, CA 92617-3038 US	

GROWTH PLANS/SPECIAL FEATURES:

Broadcom Corp. is a developer of semiconductors for wired and wireless communications. The company's products enable the delivery of voice, data and multimedia to and throughout the home, office and mobile environment. Broadcom produces highly integrated silicon chips and software solutions to manufacturers of computing and networking equipment, digital entertainment products, broadband access products and mobile devices. The firm's products target the broadband communications, enterprise networking and mobile and wireless markets. In the broadband communications market, products incorporating Broadcom's solutions include broadband cable modems and residential gateways; cable modem termination systems and central office DSL applications; cable, satellite and IP set-top boxes, media servers and digital converters; high-definition digital televisions; high-definition Blu-ray Disc players and recorders; and personal video recorders. In the enterprise networking markets, products incorporating the firm's solutions include servers; workstations; desktop and notebook computers; service provider metro equipment; switches, hubs and routers; network interface cards; and virtual private networks and security appliances. In the mobile and wireless market, products incorporating Broadcom's solutions include wireless-enabled laptop and desktop computers; home broadband gateways; printers; Voice over Internet Protocol (VoIP) phones; handheld media devices; personal navigation devices; and home gaming and entertainment systems. In March 2008, Broadcom acquired Sunext Design, Inc., which will contribute technology for the development of a Blu-ray DVD disk platform. In October 2008, the firm acquired AMD's digital television business.

Broadcom offers its employees tuition reimbursement, credit union membership, an employee assistance program, flexible spending accounts, health care benefits, disability programs and dental and vision care plans.

FINANCIALS:

Sales and profits are in thousands of dollars—add 000 to get the full amount. 2008 Note: Financial information for 2008 was not available for all companies at press time.

2008 Sales: $4,658,125	2008 Profits: $214,794	**U.S. Stock Ticker: BRCM**
2007 Sales: $3,776,395	2007 Profits: $213,342	**Int'l Ticker:** Int'l Exchange:
2006 Sales: $3,667,818	2006 Profits: $379,041	Employees: 7,402
2005 Sales: $2,670,788	2005 Profits: $367,089	Fiscal Year Ends: 12/31
2004 Sales: $2,400,610	2004 Profits: $173,185	Parent Company:

SALARIES/BENEFITS:

Pension Plan:	ESOP Stock Plan:	Profit Sharing:	Top Exec. Salary: $639,231	Bonus: $321,750
Savings Plan: Y	Stock Purch. Plan: Y		Second Exec. Salary: $297,173	Bonus: $118,800

OTHER THOUGHTS:

Apparent Women Officers or Directors: 1
Hot Spot for Advancement for Women/Minorities:

LOCATIONS: ("Y" = Yes)

West:	Southwest:	Midwest:	Southeast:	Northeast:	International:
Y	Y	Y	Y	Y	Y

BROCADE COMMUNICATIONS SYSTEMS INC

www.brocade.com

Industry Group Code: 511214 **Ranks within this company's industry group:** Sales: 1 Profits: 1

Techology:		Medical/Drugs:		Engineering:		Transportation:		Chemicals/Petrochemicals:		Specialty:	
Computers:		Manufacturer:		Design:		Aerospace:		Oil/Gas Products:		Special Services:	
Software:	Y	Contract Research:		Construction:		Automotive:		Chemicals:		Consulting:	
Communications:		Medical Services:		Eng. Services:		Shipping:		Oil/Chem. Svcs.:		Specialty Mgmt.:	
Electronics:	Y	Labs:		Consulting:				Gases:		Products:	
Alternative Energy:		Bio. Services:						Other:		Other:	

TYPES OF BUSINESS:

Data Storage Equipment
Storage Area Networking (SAN) Equipment
SAN Management Software
IT Infrastructure Management Software

BRANDS/DIVISIONS/AFFILIATES:

Brocade Fabric Operating System
Fabric OS
McDATA Corporation
Silverback Systems, Inc.
Strategic Business Systems
Foundry Networks, Inc.

CONTACTS: *Note: Officers with more than one job title may be intentionally listed here more than once.*

Michael Klayko, CEO
Richard Deranleau, CFO
Tom Buiocchi, VP-Worldwide Mktg.
Bonnie Helton, VP-Human Resources
Raymond Lee, VP-IT
Dave Stevens, CTO
Tyler Wall, General Counsel/Corp. Sec./VP
Raymond Lee, VP-Oper.
T. J. Grewal, VP-Corp. Dev.
Richard Deranleau, VP-Finance
Hugues Meyrath, VP-Worldwide Svcs.
Luc Moyen, VP/Gen. Mgr.-Server Div.
Guru Pangal, VP-Files Div.
Ian Whiting, VP/Gen. Mgr.-Data Center Infrastructure Div.
Dave House, Chmn.

Phone: 408-333-8000 **Fax:** 408-333-8101
Toll-Free:
Address: 1745 Technology Dr., San Jose, CA 95110 US

GROWTH PLANS/SPECIAL FEATURES:

Brocade Communication Systems, Inc. is a leading supplier of data center networking hardware and software products and services that help enterprises connect and manage their information. The company is organized into four operating units: the data center infrastructure (DCI) unit; the server edge and storage (SES) unit; the services, support and solutions (S3) unit; and the files unit. The DCI unit encompasses the Brocade family of Storage Area Network (SAN) infrastructure products and solutions, including directors, switches, routers, fabric-based software applications and distance/extension products, as well as management applications and utilities to centralize data management. The SES unit includes the firm's host bus adapters (HBAs) and Intelligent Server Adapter initiatives, as well as SAN switch modules for bladed servers and embedded switches for blade servers. The S3 unit includes consulting and support services for designing, implementing, deploying and managing data center enterprise solutions, as well as post-contract customer support. The files unit includes the Brocade Fabric Operating System, which includes both software and hardware offerings for effectively managing file data and storage resources. The Brocade Fabric Operating System (Fabric OS) is the operating system that provides the core infrastructure for deploying storage networks and serves as the foundation for the company's products. Brocade products and services are marketed, sold and supported worldwide through distribution partners, including original equipment manufacturers (OEMs), distributors, systems integrators, value-added resellers (VARs) and by Brocade directly. In 2007, Brocade acquired McDATA Corporation and Silverback Systems, Inc. In March 2008, the company agreed to acquire Strategic Business Systems, a provider of IT professional services. In July 2008, Brocade agreed to acquire Foundry Networks, Inc.

Brocade offers its employees an education reimbursement program, flexible spending accounts, an employee assistance program, a fitness center, paternity leave and medical, dental, vision, life and business travel accident insurance.

FINANCIALS: **Sales and profits are in thousands of dollars—add 000 to get the full amount. 2008 Note: Financial information for 2008 was not available for all companies at press time.**

2008 Sales: $1,466,937	2008 Profits: $167,070	**U.S. Stock Ticker: BRCD**
2007 Sales: $1,236,863	2007 Profits: $76,872	**Int'l Ticker:** Int'l Exchange:
2006 Sales: $750,592	2006 Profits: $67,629	Employees: 2,834
2005 Sales: $574,120	2005 Profits: $43,121	Fiscal Year Ends: 10/31
2004 Sales: $596,265	2004 Profits: $-32,015	Parent Company:

SALARIES/BENEFITS:

Pension Plan:	ESOP Stock Plan:	Profit Sharing:	Top Exec. Salary: $605,000	Bonus: $1,299,314
Savings Plan: Y	Stock Purch. Plan: Y		Second Exec. Salary: $375,840	Bonus: $372,365

OTHER THOUGHTS:

Apparent Women Officers or Directors:
Hot Spot for Advancement for Women/Minorities:

LOCATIONS: ("Y" = Yes)

West:	Southwest:	Midwest:	Southeast:	Northeast:	International:
Y	Y	Y	Y	Y	Y

BSST LLC

www.bsst.com

Industry Group Code: 335000 **Ranks within this company's industry group:** Sales: Profits:

Techology:		Medical/Drugs:		Engineering:		Transportation:		Chemicals/Petrochemicals:		Specialty:	
Computers:		Manufacturer:		Design:	Y	Aerospace:		Oil/Gas Products:		Special Services:	
Software:		Contract Research:		Construction:		Automotive:		Chemicals:		Consulting:	
Communications:		Medical Services:		Eng. Services:		Shipping:		Oil/Chem. Svcs.:		Specialty Mgmt.:	
Electronics:	Y	Labs:		Consulting:				Gases:		Products:	
Alternative Energy:	Y	Bio. Services:						Other:		Other:	

TYPES OF BUSINESS:

Thermoelectric Systems Manufacturing

BRANDS/DIVISIONS/AFFILIATES:

Amerigon, Inc.
Herman Miller, Inc.

CONTACTS:

Note: Officers with more than one job title may be intentionally listed here more than once.

Lon E. Bell, CEO
Lon E. Bell, Pres.
Sandra Grouf, CFO
Sandra Grouf, CIO

Phone: 626-815-7400	**Fax:** 626-815-7441
Toll-Free:	
Address: 5462 Irwindale Ave., Irwindale, CA 91706 US	

GROWTH PLANS/SPECIAL FEATURES:

BSST LLC is the research and development subsidiary of Amerigon, Inc. The firm develops more efficient thermoelectric systems and products for its parent company. The firm focuses on the following applications: personal microclimate conditioning of individuals; thermal management solutions for electronic components and assemblies in confined spaces; and commercially and militarily viable thermal to electrical energy conversion. As of December 2007, BSST holds nine U.S. patents, one foreign patent, eleven pending U.S. patents and thirty-two pending foreign patents. In 2007, BSST received a Phase 3 Program by the U.S. Department of Energy (DOE) for completing the second phase of its Automotive Waste Heat Recovery Program. This four phase program, developed in partnership with Visteon Corporation, BMW of North America, Marlow Industries, the DOE's National Renewable Energy Laboratory and Jet Propulsion Laboratory/California Institute of Technology, is seeking a viable thermoelectric-based vehicle waste heat recovery and power generation system to improve internal combustion vehicle efficiency. In June 2007, the firm partnered with Herman Miller, Inc. to develop the thermoelectric device (TED) based thermal components for Herman Miller's C2 Climate Control device, a personal heating and cooling system.

FINANCIALS:

Sales and profits are in thousands of dollars—add 000 to get the full amount. 2008 Note: Financial information for 2008 was not available for all companies at press time.

2008 Sales: $	2008 Profits: $	**U.S. Stock Ticker: Subsidiary**
2007 Sales: $	2007 Profits: $	**Int'l Ticker:** Int'l Exchange:
2006 Sales: $	2006 Profits: $	Employees:
2005 Sales: $	2005 Profits: $	Fiscal Year Ends:
2004 Sales: $	2004 Profits: $	Parent Company: AMERIGON INC

SALARIES/BENEFITS:

Pension Plan:	ESOP Stock Plan:	Profit Sharing:	Top Exec. Salary: $222,000	Bonus: $45,500
Savings Plan:	Stock Purch. Plan:		Second Exec. Salary: $	Bonus: $

OTHER THOUGHTS:

Apparent Women Officers or Directors: 1
Hot Spot for Advancement for Women/Minorities:

LOCATIONS: ("Y" = Yes)

West:	Southwest:	Midwest:	Southeast:	Northeast:	International:
Y					

BURNS & MCDONNELL

www.burnsmcd.com

Industry Group Code: 234000 **Ranks within this company's industry group:** Sales: Profits:

Techology:		Medical/Drugs:		Engineering:		Transportation:		Chemicals/Petrochemicals:		Specialty:	
Computers:		Manufacturer:		Design:	Y	Aerospace:		Oil/Gas Products:		Special Services:	
Software:		Contract Research:		Construction:	Y	Automotive:		Chemicals:		Consulting:	Y
Communications:		Medical Services:		Eng. Services:	Y	Shipping:		Oil/Chem. Svcs.:		Specialty Mgmt.:	
Electronics:		Labs:		Consulting:	Y			Gases:		Products:	
Alternative Energy:		Bio. Services:						Other:		Other:	

TYPES OF BUSINESS:

Engineering
Construction
Consulting
Environmental Consulting
Architecture & Design
Energy Transmission

BRANDS/DIVISIONS/AFFILIATES:

CONTACTS:

Note: Officers with more than one job title may be intentionally listed here more than once.

Greg Graves, CEO
Greg Graves, Pres.
Mark Taylor, CFO
Joe Brooks, Dir.-Corp. Mktg.
G. William Quatman, General Counsel/VP
Mark Taylor, VP/Treas.
Rick Keeler, VP/Gen. Mgr.-Healthcare & Res. Facilities Group
Ray Kowalik, Pres./Gen. Mgr.-Energy Group
David Yeamans, Pres./Gen. Mgr.-Aviation & Facilities Group
John E. Nobles, Pres./Gen. Mgr.-Process & Industrial Group
Greg Graves, Chmn.

Phone: 816-333-9400	**Fax:** 816-822-3412
Toll-Free:	
Address: 9400 Ward Pkwy., Kansas City, MO 64114 US	

GROWTH PLANS/SPECIAL FEATURES:

Burns & McDonnell provides engineering, architectural, construction, environmental and consulting services across the U.S. and worldwide. The company divides its businesses into 10 global practice units and an operations division. The Aviation and Facilities unit designs and constructs airport terminals; military facilities; aerospace manufacturing facilities; runways and airfield infrastructure; and aviation support facilities, such as control towers, cargo warehouses and aircraft hangars. The Business and Technology Services unit provides business consulting services, such as project development, analysis and forecasting; energy services; and information technology services such as planning, engineering and design, procurement, maintenance and facility management. The Construction/Design-Build unit provides design through post-construction services to companies in the power, process, aviation, infrastructure and commercial industries. The Energy unit is focused on sustainability in construction and renovation, with projects ranging from the construction of baseload coal-fired power generation plants and high-voltage transmission networks to comprehensive energy system overhauls. The Environmental unit's services include hazardous waste remediation, solid waste management and emergency response. The Environmental Studies and Permitting unit offers permitting, ecology, studies and land management services. The Healthcare and Research Facilities unit constructs hospitals, laboratories and research facilities, and offers additional planning, management and landscape architecture services. The Infrastructure unit is focused on water and transportation projects, providing collection system construction, wastewater and watershed management and water distribution services. The Process and Industrial unit designs manufacturing plants, refineries, warehouses and assembly facilities. The Transmission and Distribution unit includes the construction of transportation infrastructure and facilities and electrical energy transmission services. Burns & McDonnell's customers include companies in a wide variety of industries, including the energy, environmental, government and defense, healthcare, manufacturing, security, transportation, construction, telecommunications and water and wastewater markets.

The company is 100% employee-owned through its employee stock ownership plan.

FINANCIALS:

Sales and profits are in thousands of dollars—add 000 to get the full amount. 2008 Note: Financial information for 2008 was not available for all companies at press time.

2008 Sales: $	2008 Profits: $	**U.S. Stock Ticker: Private**
2007 Sales: $	2007 Profits: $	**Int'l Ticker:** Int'l Exchange:
2006 Sales: $	2006 Profits: $	Employees: 2,850
2005 Sales: $	2005 Profits: $	Fiscal Year Ends: 12/31
2004 Sales: $	2004 Profits: $	Parent Company:

SALARIES/BENEFITS:

Pension Plan:	ESOP Stock Plan: Y	Profit Sharing:	Top Exec. Salary: $	Bonus: $
Savings Plan: Y	Stock Purch. Plan:		Second Exec. Salary: $	Bonus: $

OTHER THOUGHTS:

Apparent Women Officers or Directors:
Hot Spot for Advancement for Women/Minorities:

LOCATIONS: ("Y" = Yes)

West:	Southwest:	Midwest:	Southeast:	Northeast:	International:
Y	Y	Y	Y	Y	

Note: Financial information, benefits and other data can change quickly and may vary from those stated here.

BUSINESS OBJECTS SA

www.businessobjects.com

Industry Group Code: 511207 **Ranks within this company's industry group:** Sales: Profits:

Techology:		Medical/Drugs:		Engineering:		Transportation:		Chemicals/Petrochemicals:		Specialty:	
Computers:		Manufacturer:		Design:		Aerospace:		Oil/Gas Products:		Special Services:	
Software:	Y	Contract Research:		Construction:		Automotive:		Chemicals:		Consulting:	
Communications:		Medical Services:		Eng. Services:		Shipping:		Oil/Chem. Svcs.:		Specialty Mgmt.:	
Electronics:		Labs:		Consulting:				Gases:		Products:	
Alternative Energy:		Bio. Services:						Other:		Other:	

TYPES OF BUSINESS:

Software-Corporate Data
Enterprise Decision Support Software

BRANDS/DIVISIONS/AFFILIATES:

BusinessObjects
WebIntelligence
BusinessObjects XI
BusinessObjects Labs
BusinessObjects Press
Inxight Software, Inc.
SAP AG

CONTACTS:

Note: Officers with more than one job title may be intentionally listed here more than once.

John Schwarz, CEO
Benoit Fouilland, CFO/Sr. VP
Jonathan Becher, Sr. VP-Mktg.
David Swanson, Sr. VP/Chief Human Resources Officer
Jackie Magno, CIO/VP
Herve Couturier, VP-Prod.
Jim Tolonen, VP-Admin.
David Kennedy, Sr. VP/General Counsel/Corp. Sec.
Greg Wolfe, Exec. VP-Oper.
Tom Schroeder, Group VP-Strategic Customer Programs
Jim Tolonen, Sr. VP-Finance
Scott Bajtos, Sr. VP-Worldwide Customer Assurance
Janet Wood, Sr. VP-Global Partnerships & Sales Enablement
Mark Doll, Sr. VP/General Mgr.-Global Svcs. & EPM
Bernard Liautaud, Chmn.
Maurizio Carli, Sr. VP/General Mgr.-EMEA

Phone: 33-1-41-25-21-21 **Fax:** 33-1-41-25-31-00
Toll-Free: 866-681-3435
Address: 157-159, Rue Anatole France, Levallois-Perret Cedex, 92309 France

GROWTH PLANS/SPECIAL FEATURES:

Business Objects S.A., a subsidiary of SAP AG, develops, markets and supports integrated enterprise business intelligence software. Business intelligence software allows users to access, analyze and share information derived from a variety of sources and enhances the decision-making process of a business by providing key information and analysis. The software also enables users to direct queries to databases using representations of information that are understandable by non-technical end users. Data retrieved by these queries can then be analyzed using various tools, and reports can be produced to present the results of the analysis. The company has led the charge into Internet applications in its industry, allowing clients to strengthen relationships with customers, partners and suppliers over the web. Its products are used by groups that range in size from 20 to 20,000 people. Its principal product, BusinessObjects, is an integrated reporting, query, analysis, performance management and data integration platform, operates on Windows and UNIX client/server operating systems and is interoperable with most major databases. BusinessObjects XI is the newest version of the firm's core product. XI provides the industry's most expansive query, reporting and analysis, advanced analytic applications, the best connectivity to packaged applications and the most integrated business intelligence suite. Another product, WebIntelligence, duplicates many of the BusinessObjects functions for the Internet environment. The company has 43,000 clients in 80 countries, including 82% of the Fortune 500. The firm maintains two headquarters, one in Paris, France and the other in San Jose, California. In July 2007, the firm acquired Inxight Software, Inc., a provider of business intelligence software. In February 2008, the firm was acquired by SAP AG.

Business Objects maintains employee sport teams, activity clubs, volunteer programs, fitness centers and classes, bike storage and company rec-rooms.

FINANCIALS:

Sales and profits are in thousands of dollars—add 000 to get the full amount. 2008 Note: Financial information for 2008 was not available for all companies at press time.

2008 Sales: $	2008 Profits: $	**U.S. Stock Ticker: Subsidiary**
2007 Sales: $	2007 Profits: $	**Int'l Ticker:** Int'l Exchange:
2006 Sales: $1,253,760	2006 Profits: $75,364	Employees: 5,402
2005 Sales: $1,077,151	2005 Profits: $92,625	Fiscal Year Ends: 12/31
2004 Sales: $925,631	2004 Profits: $47,123	Parent Company: SAP AG

SALARIES/BENEFITS:

Pension Plan:	ESOP Stock Plan: Y	Profit Sharing:	Top Exec. Salary: $627,701	Bonus: $679,023
Savings Plan: Y	Stock Purch. Plan:		Second Exec. Salary: $339,000	Bonus: $132,422

OTHER THOUGHTS:

Apparent Women Officers or Directors: 3
Hot Spot for Advancement for Women/Minorities: Y

LOCATIONS: ("Y" = Yes)

West:	Southwest:	Midwest:	Southeast:	Northeast:	International:
Y	Y	Y	Y	Y	Y

CA INC

www.ca.com

Industry Group Code: 511207 **Ranks within this company's industry group:** Sales: 3 Profits: 3

Techology:		Medical/Drugs:		Engineering:		Transportation:		Chemicals/Petrochemicals:		Specialty:	
Computers:		Manufacturer:		Design:		Aerospace:		Oil/Gas Products:		Special Services:	
Software:	Y	Contract Research:		Construction:		Automotive:		Chemicals:		Consulting:	
Communications:		Medical Services:		Eng. Services:		Shipping:		Oil/Chem. Svcs.:		Specialty Mgmt.:	
Electronics:		Labs:		Consulting:				Gases:		Products:	
Alternative Energy:		Bio. Services:						Other:		Other:	

TYPES OF BUSINESS:

Computer Software-Diversified
Enterprise Management Software
Security Software
Storage Software
Application Development Software
Business Intelligence Software
Application Life Cycle Management
Consulting Services

BRANDS/DIVISIONS/AFFILIATES:

CA Ideal
Asentinel
CA Netman
Eurekify
IDFocus LLC

CONTACTS:

Note: Officers with more than one job title may be intentionally listed here more than once.

John Swainson, CEO
Michael J. Christenson, COO
Michael J. Christenson, Pres.
Nancy Cooper, CFO/Exec. VP
Donald Friedman, Chief Mktg. Officer/Exec. VP
Andrew Goodman, Exec. VP-Worldwide Human Resources
Alan F. Nugent, CTO/Exec. VP
James E. Bryant, Exec. VP/Chief Admin. Officer
Amy F. Olli, General Counsel/Exec. VP
Jacob Lamm, Exec. VP-Strategy & Corp. Dev.
Joseph Doncheski, VP-Investor Rel.
Kenneth V. Handal, Exec. VP/Global Risk & Compliance/Corp. Sec.
George Fischer, Exec. VP/Gen. Mgr.-Worldwide Sales
Ajei Gopal, Exec. VP-Prod. & Tech. Group
John Ruthven, Exec. VP-Worldwide Sales Oper.
William E. McCracken, Chmn.

Phone: 631-342-6000 **Fax:** 631-342-6800
Toll-Free: 800-225-5224
Address: 1 Computer Associates Plaza, Islandia, NY 11749 US

GROWTH PLANS/SPECIAL FEATURES:

CA, Inc., formerly Computer Associates International, Inc., designs, markets and licenses computer software products that allow businesses to run and manage critical aspects of their information technology operations and that allow data center managers and programmers to automate their daily functions. The company seeks to unify and simplify complex IT environments, serving the needs of systems management, networks, security, storage, applications and databases simultaneously, and in an integrated fashion. CA offers software products designed to operate with all major hardware platforms and operating systems. The company does not operate in separate business segments, but does maintain 16 focus areas known as capability solutions: CA Project & Portfolio Management; CA IT Asset Management; CA IT Client Management; CA Information Governance; CA Service Level & Catalog Management; CA Change, Configuration and Release Management; CA Service Desk Management; CA Application Performance Management; CA Service Availability Management; CA Network & Voice Management; CA Dynamic & Virtual Systems Management; CA Workload Automation; CA Database Management; CA Recovery Management; CA Identity & Access Management; CA Security Information Management; and CA Threat Management. CA's brands include CA Ideal, a database repository; the Asentinel telecom expense management software; and CA Netman, which consolidates all data center administrative functions into a single system. CA is headquartered in the U.S., with 150 offices in over 45 countries. The company serves approximately 99% of Fortune 1000 companies, as well as government entities, educational institutions and thousands of other companies in diverse industries worldwide. In early 2008, CA announced plans to cut 20% of its workforce, approximately 2,800 jobs, as part of an ongoing restructuring process. In October 2008, the company acquired IDFocus LLC and its identity management technology, ACE. In November 2008, CA announced its acquisition of Eurekify, a provider of identity and role management software.

FINANCIALS:

Sales and profits are in thousands of dollars—add 000 to get the full amount. 2008 Note: Financial information for 2008 was not available for all companies at press time.

2008 Sales: $4,277,000	2008 Profits: $500,000	**U.S. Stock Ticker: CA**
2007 Sales: $3,943,000	2007 Profits: $118,000	**Int'l Ticker:** Int'l Exchange:
2006 Sales: $3,772,000	2006 Profits: $159,000	Employees: 13,700
2005 Sales: $3,583,000	2005 Profits: $24,000	Fiscal Year Ends: 3/31
2004 Sales: $3,332,000	2004 Profits: $-28,000	Parent Company:

SALARIES/BENEFITS:

Pension Plan:	ESOP Stock Plan:	Profit Sharing:	Top Exec. Salary: $1,000,000	Bonus: $2,152,500
Savings Plan: Y	Stock Purch. Plan: Y		Second Exec. Salary: $762,500	Bonus: $1,377,600

OTHER THOUGHTS:

Apparent Women Officers or Directors: 4
Hot Spot for Advancement for Women/Minorities: Y

LOCATIONS: ("Y" = Yes)

West:	Southwest:	Midwest:	Southeast:	Northeast:	International:
Y	Y	Y	Y	Y	Y

CADENCE DESIGN SYSTEMS INC

www.cadence.com

Industry Group Code: 511215 **Ranks within this company's industry group:** Sales: 5 Profits: 7

Techology:		Medical/Drugs:		Engineering:		Transportation:		Chemicals/Petrochemicals:		Specialty:	
Computers:		Manufacturer:		Design:		Aerospace:		Oil/Gas Products:		Special Services:	
Software:	Y	Contract Research:		Construction:		Automotive:		Chemicals:		Consulting:	
Communications:		Medical Services:		Eng. Services:		Shipping:		Oil/Chem. Svcs.:		Specialty Mgmt.:	
Electronics:		Labs:		Consulting:				Gases:		Products:	
Alternative Energy:		Bio. Services:						Other:		Other:	

TYPES OF BUSINESS:

Software-Electronic Design Automation
Training & Support Services
Design & Methodology Services

BRANDS/DIVISIONS/AFFILIATES:

Incisive Functional Verification Platform
Encounter Digital IC Design Platform
Virtuoso Custom Design Platform
AllegroSystem Interconnect Platform
Invarium, Inc.
Clear Shape Technologies, Inc.

CONTACTS: *Note: Officers with more than one job title may be intentionally listed here more than once.*

Lip-Bu Tan, CEO
Lip-Bu Tan, Pres.
Kevin S. Palatnik, CFO/Sr. VP
Craig Johnson, Corp. VP-Mktg. & Strategy & Bus. Dev.
Tina Jones, Sr. VP-Global Human Resources
Ted Vucurevich, Sr. VP-Advanced R&D
Ted Vucurevich, CTO
Jim Cowie, General Counsel/Corp. Sec./Sr. VP
Thomas Cooley, Sr. VP-Worldwide Field Oper.
Charlie Huang, Sr. VP/Chief Strategy Officer
Chi-Ping Hsu, Sr. VP-R&D, Implementation Prod. Group
Nimish Modi, Sr. VP-R&D, Front End Group
John B. Shoven, Chmn.
Ryoichi Kawashima, Pres., Japan

Phone: 408-943-1234 **Fax:** 408-943-0513
Toll-Free: 800-746-6223
Address: 2655 Seely Rd., Bldg. 5, San Jose, CA 95134-1931 US

GROWTH PLANS/SPECIAL FEATURES:

Cadence Design Systems, Inc. (Cadence) is a leading provider of electronic design automation (EDA) technology and engineering services. Cadence licenses, sells and leases its hardware technology and provides design and methodology services throughout the world to help manage and accelerate electronics products development processes. The company's products and services are used by leading global electronics companies to design and develop complex integrated circuits (ICs) and personal and commercial electronics systems. Cadence combines its design technologies into platforms for four major design activities: functional verification, digital IC design, custom IC design and system interconnect. The four Cadence design platforms are Incisive functional verification, Encounter digital IC design, Virtuoso custom design and Allegro system interconnect. The company additionally augments its platform product offerings with a set of design for manufacturing (DFM) products that service both the digital and custom IC design flows. Cadence offers a number of fee-based services, including Internet, classroom and custom educational courses; and engineering services and reusable design technologies to aid customers with the design of complex ICs. The company sells software using subscription and term licenses, as well as perpetual licenses for customers who prefer to have the right to use the technology continuously without time restriction. In July 2007, the company acquired Invarium, Inc., a developer of advanced lithography-modeling and pattern-synthesis technology. In August 2007, Cadence acquired Clear Shape Technologies, Inc., a DFM technology company specializing in design-side solutions to minimize yield loss for advanced ICs. In March 2008, the firm opened a new research and development center in Zhangjiang, China to expand the semiconductor industry in China.

FINANCIALS: **Sales and profits are in thousands of dollars—add 000 to get the full amount. 2008 Note: Financial information for 2008 was not available for all companies at press time.**

2008 Sales: $1,038,600	2008 Profits: $-1,854,000	**U.S. Stock Ticker: CDNS**
2007 Sales: $1,615,013	2007 Profits: $296,252	**Int'l Ticker:** Int'l Exchange:
2006 Sales: $1,483,895	2006 Profits: $142,592	Employees: 4,900
2005 Sales: $1,329,192	2005 Profits: $49,343	Fiscal Year Ends: 12/31
2004 Sales: $1,197,480	2004 Profits: $74,474	Parent Company:

SALARIES/BENEFITS:

Pension Plan:	ESOP Stock Plan:	Profit Sharing:	Top Exec. Salary: $1,000,000	Bonus: $1,513,594
Savings Plan: Y	Stock Purch. Plan: Y		Second Exec. Salary: $500,000	Bonus: $1,206,499

OTHER THOUGHTS:

Apparent Women Officers or Directors: 1
Hot Spot for Advancement for Women/Minorities: Y

LOCATIONS: ("Y" = Yes)

West:	Southwest:	Midwest:	Southeast:	Northeast:	International:
Y		Y	Y	Y	Y

Note: Financial information, benefits and other data can change quickly and may vary from those stated here.

CALSONIC KANSEI CORPORATION

www.calsonickansei.co.jp

Industry Group Code: 336300 **Ranks within this company's industry group:** Sales: Profits:

Techology:		Medical/Drugs:		Engineering:		Transportation:		Chemicals/Petrochemicals:		Specialty:	
Computers:		Manufacturer:		Design:		Aerospace:		Oil/Gas Products:		Special Services:	
Software:		Contract Research:		Construction:		Automotive:	Y	Chemicals:		Consulting:	
Communications:		Medical Services:		Eng. Services:		Shipping:		Oil/Chem. Svcs.:		Specialty Mgmt.:	
Electronics:		Labs:		Consulting:				Gases:		Products:	
Alternative Energy:		Bio. Services:						Other:		Other:	

TYPES OF BUSINESS:

Automobile Parts Manufacturing
Modular Assemblies
Retail Parts & Accessories
Industrial & Construction Equipment

BRANDS/DIVISIONS/AFFILIATES:

Calsonic Corporation
Kansei Corporation
CK Sales
Calsonic Kansei (Shanghai) Corporation
Calsonic Kansei North America, Inc.
Nissan Motor Co Ltd
Calsonic Romania S.R.L.
Motherson Sumi Systems Limited

CONTACTS: *Note: Officers with more than one job title may be intentionally listed here more than once.*

Bunsei Kure, CEO
Bunsei Kure, COO
Bunsei Kure, Pres.
Keiji Nakanishi, Exec. VP/Sr. Exec. Gen. Mgr.-Sales Div.
Shuji Yamagata, Sr. Exec. Gen. Mgr.-R&D Div.
Shuji Yamagata, Sr. Exec. Gen. Mgr.-Prod. Div./Exec. VP
Akira Fujisaki, Sr. Exec. Gen. Mgr.-Prod. Eng. Center
Takashi Hayashi, Sr. Exec. Gen. Mgr.-Corp. Dev. Div.
Toru Yokoyama, Sr. VP/Sr. Exec. Gen. Mgr.-Accounting Div.
Masaharu Sato, Sr. Exec. Gen. Mgr.-Prod. Div/Exec. VP
Kiyoto Shinohara, Sr. Managing Dir./Exec. VP
Akiyo Tsurushima, Sr. Exec. Gen. Mgr.-Main Dev. Unit
Hiroshi Kondo, Sr. Exec. Gen. Mgr.-Mktg. Group
Itaru Koeda, Chmn.
Kiyoto Shinohara, Pres., Calsonic Kansei North America
Masaharu Sato, Sr. Exec. Gen. Mgr.-Purchasing Div.

Phone: 81-3-660-2202 **Fax:**
Toll-Free:
Address: 2-1917 Nissin-cho, Kita-ku, Saitama, 164-8602 Japan

GROWTH PLANS/SPECIAL FEATURES:

Calsonic Kansei Corporation, founded in 1938 as Nihon Radiator Manufacturing Co., Ltd., is a manufacturer of automotive parts and accessories, with a particular focus on integrated modular assemblies such as cockpits, front-ends and exhaust systems. With over 50 manufacturing centers across North America, Europe, China and Asia, Calsonic Kansei has 29 consolidated subsidiaries in its global network. Modules offer automakers reduced costs and lighter composite weights and provide drivers with engineered efficiencies that increase ease of use and comfort. Calsonic Kansei's cockpit modules integrate instrument panels, air conditioning systems, airbags, electric controls, audio systems, steering columns and other related components in one consolidated unit. Other modules in production and development include front-end modules that combine in one unit a radiator, condenser, internal air cooler, oil cooler, radiator core support, engine fan shroud, as well as headlamps and a bumper reinforcement assembly. Other Calsonic Kansei automotive components and products include air conditioners, exhaust systems and keyless entry devices. The company's CK Sales division sells retail automotive parts and accessories, as well as electronic toll collection devices. Calsonic Kansei additionally markets industrial and construction equipment including control units, instrument clusters, radiators and mufflers. Calsonic Kansei is a consolidated subsidiary of Nissan Motor. The firm recently held a groundbreaking ceremony for its new headquarters and Research and Development Center in Kita-ku, Saitama City, which were completed in 2008. Also in 2008, the firm reorganized the operating structure of the firm in keeping with new environmental standards, thus establishing a new logistics division, government affairs office, engineering center, compliance division and product quality group.

FINANCIALS: **Sales and profits are in thousands of dollars—add 000 to get the full amount. 2008 Note: Financial information for 2008 was not available for all companies at press time.**

2008 Sales: $	2008 Profits: $	**U.S. Stock Ticker: Subsidiary**
2007 Sales: $6,727,400	2007 Profits: $1,500	**Int'l Ticker:** Int'l Exchange:
2006 Sales: $6,868,700	2006 Profits: $184,600	Employees: 15,613
2005 Sales: $6,247,980	2005 Profits: $167,940	Fiscal Year Ends: 3/31
2004 Sales: $5,861,300	2004 Profits: $76,100	Parent Company: NISSAN MOTOR CO LTD

SALARIES/BENEFITS:

Pension Plan:	ESOP Stock Plan:	Profit Sharing:	Top Exec. Salary: $	Bonus: $
Savings Plan:	Stock Purch. Plan:		Second Exec. Salary: $	Bonus: $

OTHER THOUGHTS:

Apparent Women Officers or Directors:
Hot Spot for Advancement for Women/Minorities:

LOCATIONS: ("Y" = Yes)

West:	Southwest:	Midwest:	Southeast:	Northeast:	International:
		Y	Y		Y

CAMP DRESSER & MCKEE INC

www.cdm.com

Industry Group Code: 234000 **Ranks within this company's industry group:** Sales: Profits:

Techology:		Medical/Drugs:		Engineering:		Transportation:		Chemicals/Petrochemicals:		Specialty:	
Computers:		Manufacturer:		Design:	Y	Aerospace:		Oil/Gas Products:		Special Services:	Y
Software:	Y	Contract Research:		Construction:	Y	Automotive:		Chemicals:		Consulting:	Y
Communications:		Medical Services:		Eng. Services:	Y	Shipping:		Oil/Chem. Svcs.:		Specialty Mgmt.:	Y
Electronics:		Labs:		Consulting:	Y			Gases:		Products:	
Alternative Energy:		Bio. Services:						Other:		Other:	

TYPES OF BUSINESS:

Engineering & Construction
Water Management
Environmental Services
Design Services
Information Management & Technology
Consulting
Facilities Design
Geotechnical Services

BRANDS/DIVISIONS/AFFILIATES:

CDM
CDM International Inc
CDM Constructors Inc
CDM Federal Programs Corporation
CDM Consult Holding AG

CONTACTS: *Note: Officers with more than one job title may be intentionally listed here more than once.*

Richard D. Fox, CEO
John D. Manning, COO
John D. Manning, Pres.
William S. Howard, CTO/Exec. VP
Paul G. Camell, Chief Admin. Officer
Paul R. Brown, Exec. VP-Global Market Dev.
John L. Roberts, Exec. VP
Paul G. Camell, Exec. VP-Mergers & Acquisitions
Richard D. Fox, Chmn.

Phone: 617-452-6000 **Fax:** 617-452-8000
Toll-Free:
Address: 1 Cambridge Pl., 50 Hampshire St., Cambridge, MA 02139 US

GROWTH PLANS/SPECIAL FEATURES:

Camp Dresser & McKee, Inc. (CDM) provides services in engineering, consulting, construction and operations. The company has four operating units: client services - Europe, Middle East and Africa; federal services; industrial services; public services - North America east & Latin America; and public services - North America west/central & Asia. Supporting these units are the consulting services; engineering services; construction services; and the operations services. Consulting services include architecture; asset, energy and program management; environmental management systems; information management and technology; management consulting; security; and sustainable development. Engineering services include 3D design; automation and instrumentation; and civil, electrical, geotechnical, mechanical, process and structural engineering. Construction services include constructability and value engineering reviews; cost estimating; design-build and alternative delivery methods; engineering services during construction; general contracting; procurement; and project controls. Operations services include contract management; contract operations; operations and maintenance; and operations optimization. CDM's work has involved solid waste and wastewater purification facilities; municipal data management systems; airports, dams, harbors and bridges; a wildlife refuge; major universities; municipal railways; and sports facilities. The firm has three subsidiaries: CDM International, Inc., offering CDM's full range of services in Europe, Latin America, the Middle East and Asia; CDM Constructors, Inc., providing design, construction, remediation, general contracting and equipment fabrication services worldwide; and CDM Federal Programs Corporation, offering environmental management services for the EPA, Department of Energy, Department of Defense and other U.S. government agencies. Additionally, CDM owns a majority interest in geotechnical and environmental consulting and design firm, CDM Consult Holding AG, in Germany.

Employees of CDM receive medical, dental and vision plans; life insurance; spouse and domestic partner benefits; a commuter program; flexible spending accounts; an employee assistance program; and tuition assistance.

FINANCIALS: Sales and profits are in thousands of dollars—add 000 to get the full amount. 2008 Note: Financial information for 2008 was not available for all companies at press time.

2008 Sales: $	2008 Profits: $	**U.S. Stock Ticker: Private**
2007 Sales: $	2007 Profits: $	**Int'l Ticker:** Int'l Exchange:
2006 Sales: $	2006 Profits: $	Employees: 3,530
2005 Sales: $	2005 Profits: $	Fiscal Year Ends: 12/31
2004 Sales: $	2004 Profits: $	Parent Company:

SALARIES/BENEFITS:

Pension Plan:	ESOP Stock Plan:	Profit Sharing: Y	Top Exec. Salary: $	Bonus: $
Savings Plan: Y	Stock Purch. Plan:		Second Exec. Salary: $	Bonus: $

OTHER THOUGHTS:

Apparent Women Officers or Directors:
Hot Spot for Advancement for Women/Minorities:

LOCATIONS: ("Y" = Yes)

West:	Southwest:	Midwest:	Southeast:	Northeast:	International:
Y	Y	Y	Y	Y	Y

CANON INC

www.canon.com

Industry Group Code: 334119 **Ranks within this company's industry group:** Sales: 1 Profits: 1

Techology:		Medical/Drugs:		Engineering:		Transportation:		Chemicals/Petrochemicals:		Specialty:	
Computers:	Y	Manufacturer:		Design:	Y	Aerospace:		Oil/Gas Products:		Special Services:	
Software:		Contract Research:		Construction:		Automotive:		Chemicals:		Consulting:	
Communications:	Y	Medical Services:		Eng. Services:		Shipping:		Oil/Chem. Svcs.:		Specialty Mgmt.:	
Electronics:	Y	Labs:		Consulting:				Gases:		Products:	Y
Alternative Energy:		Bio. Services:						Other:		Other:	

TYPES OF BUSINESS:

Business Machines-Copiers
Printers & Scanners
Semiconductor Production Equipment
Cameras, Film & Digital
Optics & Lenses
X-Ray Equipment
Fax Machines
Photovoltaic Cells

BRANDS/DIVISIONS/AFFILIATES:

Bubble Jet
Tokki Corporation
SED Inc
Canon Ecology Industry Inc
Canon Marketing Japan Inc
Canon Information Systems Co Ltd
Matsushita Electric Industrial Co Ltd
Hitachi Ltd

CONTACTS: *Note: Officers with more than one job title may be intentionally listed here more than once.*

Fujio Mitarai, CEO
Tsuneji Uchida, COO
Tsuneji Uchida, Pres.
Akiyoshi Moroe, Managing Dir.-Human Resources Mgmt.
Seijiro Sekine, Dir.-Info. & Comm. Systems
Shigeyuki Matsumoto, Managing Dir.-Device Tech. Dev.
Tetsuro Tahara, Dir.-Global Mfg. & Logistics
Nobuyoshi Tanaka, Senior Managing Dir.-Legal
Kunio Watanabe, Managing Dir.-Corp. Planning Dev.
Akiyoshi Moroe, Managing Dir.-External Rel.
Masahiro Osawa, Managing Dir.-Finance & Acct.
Toshizo Tanaka, VP-Policy & Economy Research
Yoroku Adachi, Pres./CEO-Canon U.S.A. Inc.
Yasuo Mitsuhashi, CEO-Peripheral Prod. Oper.
Junji Ichikawa, CEO-Optical Prod. Oper.
Fujio Mitarai, Chmn.
Ryoichi Bamba, Pres./CEO- Canon Europe Ltd.
Shunji Onda, Dir.-Global Procurement

Phone: 81-3-3758-2111 **Fax:** 81-3-5482-5135
Toll-Free:
Address: 30-2, Shimomaruko 3-chome, Ohta-ku, Tokyo, 146-8501 Japan

GROWTH PLANS/SPECIAL FEATURES:

Canon, Inc. manufactures copiers, printers, computer peripherals, digital and film cameras and semiconductor production equipment. The company operates in five segments: business information products; office imaging products; computer peripherals; cameras; and optical products and other products. The business information products group includes document scanners, electronic calculators and dictionaries and computer information products. The office imaging products segment manufactures, markets and services a wide range of monochrome-networked and personal-use multifunctional devices (MFDs), full-color copying machines and office color MFDs. The computer peripherals segment includes laser printers, inkjet printers and scanners. The next operating segment, cameras, consists of film and digital cameras, lenses and liquid crystal display (LCD) projectors. The company's flagship camera products are the Digital ELPH and the EOS Rebel cameras. Canon's last line of business, optical products and others, includes semiconductor exposure systems, broadcasting equipment, medical equipment and LCD exposure systems. These products include x-ray equipment; medical image recording equipment; semiconductor steppers and aligners; and television camera lenses. In early 2008, the firm agreed to acquire a 24.9% stake in a wholly-owned Hitachi subsidiary that produces LCD panels. The agreement follows an LCD business alliance between Canon, Hitachi and Matsushita Electric Industrial Co., Ltd., formed in December 2007. In July 2008, Canon announced that it would build a $176.8 million camera production plant near Nagasaki, with production scheduled to begin in December 2009. In September 2008, the company acquired San Francisco-based NEWCAL Industries, an independent reseller of document and print solutions, including imaging hardware and software. Also in September, the firm announced plans to build a $20 million facility in Taiwan to produce SLR (single-lens reflex) camera lenses. In November 2008, subsidiary Canon Electronics acquired Asia Pacific System Research Co., Ltd.

FINANCIALS: **Sales and profits are in thousands of dollars—add 000 to get the full amount. 2008 Note: Financial information for 2008 was not available for all companies at press time.**

2008 Sales: $44,990,780	2008 Profits: $3,397,231	**U.S. Stock Ticker: CAJ**
2007 Sales: $43,179,800	2007 Profits: $4,705,400	**Int'l Ticker: 7751** Int'l Exchange: Tokyo-TSE
2006 Sales: $34,930,748	2006 Profits: $3,826,261	Employees: 166,980
2005 Sales: $31,836,000	2005 Profits: $3,257,000	Fiscal Year Ends: 12/31
2004 Sales: $33,344,700	2004 Profits: $3,301,400	Parent Company:

SALARIES/BENEFITS:

Pension Plan: Y	ESOP Stock Plan:	Profit Sharing:	Top Exec. Salary: $	Bonus: $
Savings Plan:	Stock Purch. Plan: Y		Second Exec. Salary: $	Bonus: $

OTHER THOUGHTS:

Apparent Women Officers or Directors:
Hot Spot for Advancement for Women/Minorities:

LOCATIONS: ("Y" = Yes)

West:	Southwest:	Midwest:	Southeast:	Northeast:	International:
		Y	Y	Y	Y

CAPGEMINI

www.capgemini.com

Industry Group Code: 541512 **Ranks within this company's industry group:** Sales: 5 Profits: 4

Techology:		Medical/Drugs:		Engineering:		Transportation:		Chemicals/Petrochemicals:		Specialty:	
Computers:		Manufacturer:		Design:		Aerospace:		Oil/Gas Products:		Special Services:	Y
Software:		Contract Research:		Construction:		Automotive:		Chemicals:		Consulting:	Y
Communications:		Medical Services:		Eng. Services:		Shipping:		Oil/Chem. Svcs.:		Specialty Mgmt.:	Y
Electronics:		Labs:		Consulting:				Gases:		Products:	
Alternative Energy:		Bio. Services:						Other:		Other:	

TYPES OF BUSINESS:

Management Consulting
IT Consulting
Outsourcing Services
Professional Staffing Services
Design & Development Services

BRANDS/DIVISIONS/AFFILIATES:

Sogeti

CONTACTS:

Note: Officers with more than one job title may be intentionally listed here more than once.

Paul Hermelin, CEO
Serge Kampf, Pres.
Nicolas Dufourcq, CFO
Philippe Grangeon, Dir.-Mktg.
Alain Donzeaud, Dir.-Human Resources
Bernard Helders, Dir.-Mfg., Retail & Dist.
Alain Donzeaud, Corp. Sec.
Jean-Pierre Durant des Aulnois, Dir.-Oper. Control
Pierre-Yves Cros, Dir.-Strategy
Philippe Grangeon, Dir.-Comm.
Manuel C. d'Oliveira, Dir.-Investor Rel.
Bertrand Lavayssiere, Financial Svcs.
Colette Lewiner, Energy, Utilities & Chemical
Salil Parekh, CEO-India Oper.
Luc-Francois Salvador, Dir.-Local Professional Svcs, Sogeti
Hubert Giraud, Dir.-Bus. Process Outsourcing
Serge Kampf, Chmn.
Henk Broeders, Dir.-Continental Europe & Asia Pacific
Francois Hucher, Dir.-Global Delivery

Phone: 33-1-47-54-50-00	**Fax:** 33-1-47-54-50-86
Toll-Free:	
Address: Place de l'Etoile, 11 rue de Tilsitt, Paris, 75017 France	

GROWTH PLANS/SPECIAL FEATURES:

Capgemini, is one of the world's largest international management consulting and information technology (IT) services firms. Based in Paris, with offices in 32 countries, the firm's services are organized into four main divisions: outsourcing, 36.6% of total revenues; technology services, 38.5%; consulting, 8.7%; and local professional services, 16.2%. The outsourcing division offers applications management, infrastructure management and business process outsourcing. The technology division, which employs a large portion of Capgemini's workforce, provides application development, systems architecture design, systems integration and infrastructure services. The company's consulting division specializes in customer relationship management, finance, employee transformation, supply chain and organizational transformation. The local professional services division, operating under the Sogeti brand name, connects local professionals to companies in need of help in software development, applications management, hardware management and network management. Capgemini primarily earns revenues in France (22.6%), the U.K. and Ireland (25.6%), North America (19.8%) and the Benelux countries (13.4%). Operations are conducted in six main industry groups: manufacturing, retail and distribution, 28% of revenues; energy and utilities, 13%; financial services, 17%; public sector, 26%; telecommunications, media and entertainment, 9%; and other, 7%. Capgemini maintains alliances with top technology companies to provide accelerated systems development and integration services to its clients. Technology partners include Oracle, Microsoft, Sun Systems, IBM, Intel, Cisco Systems and HP. The firm joined with Nokia and Oracle in creating the Managed Mobility Services Collaboration, aimed at providing cost-effective, scalable enterprise-wide mobility applications and services, including configuration, security and call center and asset management. In 2008, Capgemini agreed to acquire Empire s.r.o., a private Czech IT services and consulting company and its subsidiary Sophia Solutions s.r.o. Also in 2008, the company acquired Getronics PinkRoccade Business Application Services BV from Getronics Nederland N.V.

Employees are offered medical, dental and life insurance; disability coverage; auto and home owners insurance; employee assistance programs; and adoption assistance.

FINANCIALS:

Sales and profits are in thousands of dollars—add 000 to get the full amount. 2008 Note: Financial information for 2008 was not available for all companies at press time.

2008 Sales: $11,741,800	2008 Profits: $789,980	**U.S. Stock Ticker:**
2007 Sales: $11,732,300	2007 Profits: $664,600	**Int'l Ticker: CAPP** Int'l Exchange: Paris-Euronext
2006 Sales: $12,243,000	2006 Profits: $465,900	Employees: 91,621
2005 Sales: $11,056,900	2005 Profits: $224,200	Fiscal Year Ends: 12/31
2004 Sales: $8,128,161	2004 Profits: $-463,780	Parent Company:

SALARIES/BENEFITS:

Pension Plan:	ESOP Stock Plan:	Profit Sharing: Y	Top Exec. Salary: $1,165,078	Bonus: $40,777
Savings Plan: Y	Stock Purch. Plan:		Second Exec. Salary: $	Bonus: $

OTHER THOUGHTS:

Apparent Women Officers or Directors: 3
Hot Spot for Advancement for Women/Minorities: Y

LOCATIONS: ("Y" = Yes)

West:	Southwest:	Midwest:	Southeast:	Northeast:	International:
Y	Y	Y	Y	Y	Y

Note: Financial information, benefits and other data can change quickly and may vary from those stated here.

CASIO COMPUTER CO LTD

www.world.casio.com

Industry Group Code: 334111 **Ranks within this company's industry group:** Sales: 12 Profits:

Techology:		Medical/Drugs:		Engineering:		Transportation:		Chemicals/Petrochemicals:		Specialty:	
Computers:		Manufacturer:		Design:		Aerospace:		Oil/Gas Products:		Special Services:	
Software:		Contract Research:		Construction:		Automotive:		Chemicals:		Consulting:	
Communications:	Y	Medical Services:		Eng. Services:		Shipping:		Oil/Chem. Svcs.:		Specialty Mgmt.:	
Electronics:	Y	Labs:		Consulting:				Gases:		Products:	
Alternative Energy:		Bio. Services:						Other:		Other:	

TYPES OF BUSINESS:

Electronics & Computer Manufacturing
Timepieces
Mobile Network Solutions
Cellular Phones
Electronic Music Instruments
LCDs
Digital Cameras
Factory Automation Equipment

BRANDS/DIVISIONS/AFFILIATES:

Yamagata Casio Co Ltd
Kochi Casio Co Ltd
Casio Techno Co Ltd
Casio Hitachi Mobile Communications Co Ltd
Mexico Marketing S de R L de CV
LLC Casio

CONTACTS: *Note: Officers with more than one job title may be intentionally listed here more than once.*

Kazuo Kashio, CEO
Kazuo Kashio, Pres.
Yukio Kashio, Exec. VP
Fumitsune Murakami, Sr. Managing Dir.
Yozo Suzuki, Sr. Managing Dir.
Akira Kashio, Managing Dir.
Toshio Kashio, Chmn.

Phone: 03-5334-4111 **Fax:**
Toll-Free:
Address: 6-2, Hon-machi 1-chome, Shibuya-ku, Tokyo, 151-8543 Japan

GROWTH PLANS/SPECIAL FEATURES:

Casio Computer Co., Ltd. makes a wide range of consumer electronics products, timepieces, mobile network solutions (MNS), system equipment, electronic components and other equipment. Its consumer electronics products include calculators, electronic dictionaries, label printers, digital cameras and electronic musical instruments, such as keyboards. Timepieces include digital watches, analog watches and clocks. Casio's MNS include cellular phones and handy devices, such as mobile PCs, pocket computers and PDAs. The firm's system equipment products include cash registers, office computers, data projectors and page printers. Electronic components include LCDs, bump processing consignments, carrier tape and TCP assembly and processing consignments. Other products include molds and factory automation products. Consumer electronics accounted for approximately 36.9% of the firm's 2007 sales; MNS, 27.6%; timepieces, 12.6%; electronic components, 10.1%; system equipment, 7.8%; and others, 5%. Its key products are cell phones, electronic dictionaries, digital cameras and timepieces. The firm has eight domestic subsidiaries, including Yamagata Casio Co., Ltd., which manufactures electronic timepieces, digital cameras and cell phones; Kochi Casio Co., Ltd., which manufactures LCDs; and Casio Techno Co., Ltd., which provides customer service for the firm's products. Internationally, it has 10 Asian subsidiaries, located in Korea, Taiwan, Hong Kong, China, India, Singapore and Thailand; three North American subsidiaries, in the U.S. and Canada; and six European subsidiaries, in the U.K., Germany, France, the Netherlands, Norway and Spain. Casio recently celebrated a milestone after selling its one billionth electronic calculator. In June 2007, domestic subsidiary Casio Hitachi Mobile Communications Co., Ltd. began supplying a second cell phone, the G'zOne TYPE-S, to Verizon Wireless. Its first phone was the G'zOne TYPE-V. Both are water and shock resistant, but the Type-S sports a hands-free, Bluetooth microphone.

FINANCIALS: **Sales and profits are in thousands of dollars—add 000 to get the full amount. 2008 Note: Financial information for 2008 was not available for all companies at press time.**

2008 Sales: $6,274,700
2007 Sales: $5,264,100
2006 Sales: $4,934,900
2005 Sales: $5,197,600
2004 Sales: $4,955,700

2008 Profits: $
2007 Profits: $213,200
2006 Profits: $201,900
2005 Profits: $200,200
2004 Profits: $134,200

U.S. Stock Ticker: CSIOY.PK
Int'l Ticker: 6952 Int'l Exchange: Tokyo-TSE
Employees: 13,202
Fiscal Year Ends: 3/31
Parent Company:

SALARIES/BENEFITS:

Pension Plan:	ESOP Stock Plan:	Profit Sharing:	Top Exec. Salary: $	Bonus: $
Savings Plan:	Stock Purch. Plan:		Second Exec. Salary: $	Bonus: $

OTHER THOUGHTS:

Apparent Women Officers or Directors:
Hot Spot for Advancement for Women/Minorities:

LOCATIONS: ("Y" = Yes)

West:	Southwest:	Midwest:	Southeast:	Northeast:	International:
				Y	Y

CATERPILLAR INC

www.cat.com

Industry Group Code: 333000 **Ranks within this company's industry group:** Sales: 2 Profits: 2

Techology:		Medical/Drugs:		Engineering:		Transportation:		Chemicals/Petrochemicals:		Specialty:	
Computers:		Manufacturer:		Design:		Aerospace:		Oil/Gas Products:		Special Services:	Y
Software:		Contract Research:		Construction:		Automotive:	Y	Chemicals:		Consulting:	
Communications:		Medical Services:		Eng. Services:		Shipping:		Oil/Chem. Svcs.:		Specialty Mgmt.:	
Electronics:		Labs:		Consulting:				Gases:		Products:	Y
Alternative Energy:		Bio. Services:						Other:		Other:	

TYPES OF BUSINESS:

Machinery-Earth Moving & Agricultural
Engines
Financing
Fuel Cell Manufacturing
Turbine Engines
Engine & Equipment Remanufacturing
Supply Chain Services

BRANDS/DIVISIONS/AFFILIATES:

Solar Turbines
Caterpillar Remanufacturing Services
Progress Rail Services, Inc.
Eurenov S.A.S.
Blount
Lovat, Inc.

CONTACTS: *Note: Officers with more than one job title may be intentionally listed here more than once.*

James W. Owens, CEO
David B. Burritt, CFO/VP
Sidney C. Banwart, VP-Human Svcs.
John S. Heller, CIO/VP
Tana L. Utley, CTO/VP
James B. Buda, General Counsel/VP/Corp. Sec.
Kevin E. Colgan, Treas.
Mark Pflederer, VP/Gen. Mgr.-Mining & Construction Equipment
Thomas A. Gales, VP-Latin America Div.
Bradley M. Halverson, Controller
Steven L. Fisher, VP-Remanufacturing Div.
James W. Owens, Chmn.
Michael J. Baunton, VP-EMEA
Daniel M. Murphy, VP-Global Purchasing

Phone: 309-675-1000 **Fax:** 309-675-4332
Toll-Free:
Address: 100 NE Adams St., Peoria, IL 61629 US

GROWTH PLANS/SPECIAL FEATURES:

Caterpillar, Inc. manufactures construction equipment. The company's three principal lines of business are machinery, engines and financial products. The machinery segment designs, manufactures and markets construction, mining, agricultural and forestry machinery, including track and wheel tractors, track and wheel loaders, pipe layers, motor graders, wheel tractor-scrapers, track and wheel excavators, backhoe loaders, mining shovels, log skidders, log loaders, off-highway trucks, articulated trucks, paving products, telescopic handlers, skid steer loaders and parts. The engines segment designs, manufactures and markets engines for Caterpillar machinery; electric power generation systems; on-highway vehicles and locomotives; marine, petroleum, construction, industrial, agricultural and other applications; and related parts. Caterpillar also manufactures fuel cells, designed to incorporate ethanol, methanol, natural gas, propane, methane, hydrogen and biomass fuels. The firm's Solar Turbines subsidiary is a world leader in industrial gas turbine power system engines. The financial products segment provides financing to customers and dealers for the purchase and lease of Caterpillar and other equipment, financing approximately 64% of equipment sold. Caterpillar has a network 53 U.S. dealers and 128 outside of the U.S. Worldwide, these dealers serve 182 countries and operate 3,645 places of business, including 1,606 dealer rental outlets. More than half of the company's sales are to overseas customers. Caterpillar's logistics business provides supply chain services to Caterpillar and over 65 other companies worldwide. The firm's mid-term goal is to grow to $50 billion in annual revenue by 2010, largely through expansion of financing and engine remanufacturing. Operations in China are also targeted for rapid growth. Caterpillar also holds Progress Rail Services, a remanufacturer of locomotives and railcars. In April 2007, the company finished the acquisition of Eurenov S.A.S., a remanufacturer of engines, transmissions and components. In November 2007, Caterpillar acquired Blount's Forestry Division. In March 2008, the firm acquired Lovat, Inc., which manufactures tunnel boring machines. In January 2009, the company announced plans to lay off approximately 5,000 employees.

FINANCIALS: **Sales and profits are in thousands of dollars—add 000 to get the full amount. 2008 Note: Financial information for 2008 was not available for all companies at press time.**

2008 Sales: $51,324,000
2007 Sales: $44,958,000
2006 Sales: $41,517,000
2005 Sales: $36,339,000
2004 Sales: $30,306,000

2008 Profits: $3,557,000
2007 Profits: $3,541,000
2006 Profits: $3,537,000
2005 Profits: $2,854,000
2004 Profits: $2,035,000

U.S. Stock Ticker: CAT
Int'l Ticker: Int'l Exchange:
Employees: 97,444
Fiscal Year Ends: 12/31
Parent Company:

SALARIES/BENEFITS:

Pension Plan: Y ESOP Stock Plan: Profit Sharing: Top Exec. Salary: $1,512,504 Bonus: $4,742,998
Savings Plan: Y Stock Purch. Plan: Second Exec. Salary: $826,177 Bonus: $1,979,081

OTHER THOUGHTS:

Apparent Women Officers or Directors: 7
Hot Spot for Advancement for Women/Minorities: Y

LOCATIONS: ("Y" = Yes)

West:	Southwest:	Midwest:	Southeast:	Northeast:	International:
Y	Y	Y	Y	Y	Y

Note: Financial information, benefits and other data can change quickly and may vary from those stated here.

CELANESE CORPORATION

www.celanese.com

Industry Group Code: 325000 **Ranks within this company's industry group:** Sales: 20 Profits: 17

Techology:		Medical/Drugs:		Engineering:		Transportation:		Chemicals/Petrochemicals:		Specialty:	
Computers:		Manufacturer:		Design:		Aerospace:		Oil/Gas Products:		Special Services:	
Software:		Contract Research:		Construction:		Automotive:		Chemicals:	Y	Consulting:	
Communications:		Medical Services:		Eng. Services:		Shipping:		Oil/Chem. Svcs.:		Specialty Mgmt.:	
Electronics:		Labs:		Consulting:				Gases:		Products:	Y
Alternative Energy:		Bio. Services:						Other:		Other:	

TYPES OF BUSINESS:

Manufacturing-Basic Chemicals
Acetyl Products
Technical & High-Performance Polymers
Sweeteners & Sorbates

BRANDS/DIVISIONS/AFFILIATES:

AT Plastics
Nutrinova

CONTACTS:

Note: Officers with more than one job title may be intentionally listed here more than once.

David N. Weidman, CEO
Steven Sterin, CFO/Sr. VP
Christopher W. Jensen, Controller/VP
Sandra Beach Lin, Exec. VP/Pres., Ticona
Doug Madden, Exec. VP/Pres., Acetate, AT Plastics & Emulsions
David N. Weidman, Chmn.

Phone: 972-443-4000 **Fax:** 972-443-8519
Toll-Free:
Address: 1601 W. LBJ Freeway., Dallas, TX 75234-6034 US

GROWTH PLANS/SPECIAL FEATURES:

Celanese Corporation produces a line of industrial chemicals and advanced materials. It is one of the world's largest producers of acetyl products, which are intermediate chemicals for nearly all major industries, as well as a leading producer of high-performance engineered polymers. The company operates through four segments: advanced engineered materials, consumer specialties, industrial specialties, acetyl intermediates. The advanced engineered materials segment develops, produces and supplies high-performance technical polymers for application in automotive and electronics products, as well as other consumer and industrial applications. The primary products of advanced engineered materials are polyacetyl products (POM) and ultra-high molecular weight polyethylene (GUR), as well as liquid crystal polymers (LCP). POM is used in a broad range of products including automotive components, electronics and appliances. GUR is used in battery separators, conveyor belts, filtration equipment, coatings and medical devices. The consumer specialties segment consists of the acetate products business and the nutrinova business, which serve the filtration and food end markets. The industrial specialties segment includes the emulsions, PVOH and AT Plastics businesses, with major end-use markets including paints, coatings, adhesives, building products, textiles, paper and automotive parts. The acetyl intermediates segment produces and supplies acetyl products, including acetic acid, vinyl acetate monomer (VAM), acetic anhydride and acetate esters. These products are generally used as starting materials for colorants, paints, adhesives, coatings, medicines and other products. For 2008, 28% of the firm's total sales came from North America; 43% from Europe and Africa; 26% from Asia and Australia; and 3% from South America. In February 2009, the company announced plans to shut down its VAM production unit in Cangrejera, Mexico.

Celanese offers its employees medical, dental and vision plans; flexible spending accounts; an employee assistance program; education reimbursement; adoption and legal assistance; Six Sigma training; and a 401(k) plan.

FINANCIALS:

Sales and profits are in thousands of dollars—add 000 to get the full amount. 2008 Note: Financial information for 2008 was not available for all companies at press time.

2008 Sales: $6,823,000	2008 Profits: $282,000	**U.S. Stock Ticker: CE**
2007 Sales: $6,444,000	2007 Profits: $426,000	**Int'l Ticker:** Int'l Exchange:
2006 Sales: $6,656,000	2006 Profits: $406,000	Employees: 8,350
2005 Sales: $6,033,000	2005 Profits: $277,000	Fiscal Year Ends: 12/31
2004 Sales: $3,718,000	2004 Profits: $-253,000	Parent Company:

SALARIES/BENEFITS:

Pension Plan: Y	ESOP Stock Plan:	Profit Sharing:	Top Exec. Salary: $900,000	Bonus: $44,133,244
Savings Plan: Y	Stock Purch. Plan:		Second Exec. Salary: $735,000	Bonus: $14,632,804

OTHER THOUGHTS:

Apparent Women Officers or Directors: 2
Hot Spot for Advancement for Women/Minorities:

LOCATIONS: ("Y" = Yes)

West:	Southwest:	Midwest:	Southeast:	Northeast:	International:
	Y	Y		Y	Y

Note: Financial information, benefits and other data can change quickly and may vary from those stated here.

CELESTICA INC

www.celestica.com

Industry Group Code: 334419 **Ranks within this company's industry group:** Sales: 5 Profits: 12

Techology:		Medical/Drugs:		Engineering:		Transportation:		Chemicals/Petrochemicals:		Specialty:	
Computers:		Manufacturer:		Design:		Aerospace:		Oil/Gas Products:		Special Services:	Y
Software:		Contract Research:		Construction:		Automotive:		Chemicals:		Consulting:	
Communications:		Medical Services:		Eng. Services:		Shipping:		Oil/Chem. Svcs.:		Specialty Mgmt.:	
Electronics:		Labs:		Consulting:				Gases:		Products:	
Alternative Energy:		Bio. Services:						Other:		Other:	

TYPES OF BUSINESS:

Contract Electronics Manufacturing
Printed Circuit Assemblies
Manufacturing Support Services
Product Design
Distribution Services
Regulatory Compliance Services

BRANDS/DIVISIONS/AFFILIATES:

CONTACTS: *Note: Officers with more than one job title may be intentionally listed here more than once.*

Craig H. Muhlhauser, CEO
Craig H. Muhlhauser, Pres.
Paul Nicoletti, CFO/Exec. VP
Betty DelBianco, Sr. VP-Human Resources
Mary Gendron, CIO/Sr. VP
Betty DelBianco, Chief Admin. Officer
Betty DelBianco, Chief Legal Officer/Corp. Sec.
John Peri, Exec. VP-Global Oper.
Darren Myers, Sr. VP/Corp. Controller
Mike Andrade, Sr. VP/Gen. Mgr.-North America
Mike McCaughey, Sr. VP/Gen. Mgr.-Comm. Market Segment
Rob Sellers, Sr. VP/Gen. Mgr.-Enterprise & Consumer Markets
Peter Lindgren, Sr. VP/Gen. Mgr.-Growth & Emerging Markets Segment
Robert Crandall, Chmn.
John Boucher, Exec. VP-Supply Chain/Chief Procurement Officer

Phone: 416-448-5800 **Fax:** 416-448-4810
Toll-Free:
Address: 12 Concorde Place, 5th Fl., Toronto, ON M3C 3R8 Canada

GROWTH PLANS/SPECIAL FEATURES:

Celestica, Inc. is a leading provider of electronics manufacturing services (EMS). The company, based in Canada, operates a global network of approximately 30 manufacturing and design facilities worldwide, with operations in Asia, Europe and the Americas. It provides a broad range of services to original equipment manufacturers (OEMs), including supply chain management, design, prototyping, product assembly and test, systems assembly, product assurance, failure analysis, logistics, product upgrades and repair. Celestica primarily supports OEMs in the communications, computing, industrial, aerospace and defense sectors. The firm's objective is to assist its customers in overcoming manufacturing challenges related to cost, quality, time-to-market and rapidly changing technologies. It offers end-to-end services covering entire product lifecycles, from design to fulfillment and after-market services. Additionally, the company offers Green Services, which help customers comply with various international environmental regulations. Celestica's clientele includes over 100 OEMs, such as IBM, Avaya, Cisco Systems, Hewlett Packard, Motorola, Alcatel-Lucent, Research in Motion and Sun Microsystems. Its products and services contribute to the completion of various end products, including networking, wireless, telecommunications and computing equipment; handheld communications devices; peripherals; storage devices; servers; medical products; audio-visual equipment, including flat-panel televisions; printers and related supplies; gaming products; aerospace and defense electronics such as in-flight entertainment and guidance systems; and a range of industrial electronic equipment. In March 2008, the company announced that it would collaborate with Microsoft on the design of the BEE3, the Berkeley Emulation Engine 3rd version, intended to help companies more efficiently conduct computer architecture research.

FINANCIALS: **Sales and profits are in thousands of dollars—add 000 to get the full amount. 2008 Note: Financial information for 2008 was not available for all companies at press time.**

2008 Sales: $7,678,200
2007 Sales: $8,070,400
2006 Sales: $8,811,700
2005 Sales: $8,471,000
2004 Sales: $8,839,800

2008 Profits: $-720,500
2007 Profits: $-13,700
2006 Profits: $-150,600
2005 Profits: $-46,800
2004 Profits: $-854,100

U.S. Stock Ticker: CLS
Int'l Ticker: CLS Int'l Exchange: Toronto-TSX
Employees: 38,000
Fiscal Year Ends: 12/31
Parent Company:

SALARIES/BENEFITS:

Pension Plan: Y
Savings Plan:
ESOP Stock Plan:
Stock Purch. Plan:
Profit Sharing:
Top Exec. Salary: $714,286 Bonus: $
Second Exec. Salary: $687,500 Bonus: $

OTHER THOUGHTS:

Apparent Women Officers or Directors: 2
Hot Spot for Advancement for Women/Minorities: Y

LOCATIONS: ("Y" = Yes)

West:	Southwest:	Midwest:	Southeast:	Northeast:	International:
Y	Y	Y	Y	Y	Y

Note: Financial information, benefits and other data can change quickly and may vary from those stated here.

CGI GROUP INC

www.cgi.com

Industry Group Code: 541512 **Ranks within this company's industry group:** Sales: 14 Profits: 9

Techology:		Medical/Drugs:		Engineering:		Transportation:		Chemicals/Petrochemicals:		Specialty:	
Computers:		Manufacturer:		Design:		Aerospace:		Oil/Gas Products:		Special Services:	
Software:	Y	Contract Research:		Construction:		Automotive:		Chemicals:		Consulting:	Y
Communications:		Medical Services:		Eng. Services:		Shipping:		Oil/Chem. Svcs.:		Specialty Mgmt.:	Y
Electronics:		Labs:		Consulting:				Gases:		Products:	
Alternative Energy:		Bio. Services:						Other:		Other:	

TYPES OF BUSINESS:

IT Consulting
Systems Management Services
Systems Development & Integration
Business Process Outsourcing

BRANDS/DIVISIONS/AFFILIATES:

CONTACTS:

Note: Officers with more than one job title may be intentionally listed here more than once.

Michael E. Roach, CEO
Michael E. Roach, Pres.
David Anderson, CFO/Exec. VP
Luc Pinard, Chief Tech. & Quality Officer/Exec. VP
Andre J. Bourque, Chief Legal Officer/Exec. VP
John G. Campbell, Sr. VP/General Manager-Comm. Svcs.
Andre Imbeau, Exec. Vice-Chmn./Corp. Sec.
Daniel Rocheleau, Chief Bus. Eng. Officer/Exec. VP
Donna Morea, Pres., U.S. & India
Serge Godin, Exec. Chmn.
Joseph I. Saliba, Pres., Europe & Australia

Phone: 514-841-3200 **Fax:** 514-841-3299
Toll-Free:
Address: 1130 Sherbrooke St. W., 7th Fl., Montreal, QC H3A 2M8 Canada

GROWTH PLANS/SPECIAL FEATURES:

CGI Group, Inc. based in Canada, is one of the largest independent information technology (IT) services companies in the world with more than 100 offices in 16 countries. The firm offers its services to clients in a variety of sectors, including financial services, telecommunications, government, healthcare, utilities, retail, distribution and manufacturing. The company offers its clients four primary types of services: systems integration and consulting, technology management, application management and business process services. CGI's systems integration and consulting services provide a full range of IT management, consulting and implementation services that cover the entire enterprise environment. The company's technology management services allow clients to delegate partial or complete responsibility for their IT functions to the firm. CGI's application management services provide day-to-day maintenance and updating of a client's business applications. The firm's business process services help streamline client operations through management back-office business processes and transactions. CGI's outsourcing contracts include the following services: development and integration of new projects and applications; application maintenance and support; facilities management (data centers, call centers, network and desktop services); and business processing for the financial services sector, including payroll services, document management and finance and administration services. The company has business alliances with BEA Systems, Bell, Microsoft, Oracle, SAP, Sun Microsystems and IBM. In 2007, the company combined its U.S. Insurance Business Services Division with its Insurance System Integration and Consulting practice. In July 2008, CGI sold its Canadian claims adjusting and risk management services business to the privately-held Shumka Group.

CGI provides its employees with various benefits, including a profit sharing plan, an employee stock purchase plan, group insurance and counseling services.

FINANCIALS:

Sales and profits are in thousands of dollars—add 000 to get the full amount. 2008 Note: Financial information for 2008 was not available for all companies at press time.

2008 Sales: $3,073,080	2008 Profits: $242,770	**U.S. Stock Ticker: GIB**
2007 Sales: $3,768,390	2007 Profits: $240,020	**Int'l Ticker: GIB** Int'l Exchange: Toronto-TSX
2006 Sales: $2,962,550	2006 Profits: $124,830	Employees: 26,000
2005 Sales: $3,173,600	2005 Profits: $186,400	Fiscal Year Ends: 9/30
2004 Sales: $2,574,500	2004 Profits: $174,300	Parent Company:

SALARIES/BENEFITS:

Pension Plan:	ESOP Stock Plan:	Profit Sharing: Y	Top Exec. Salary: $754,000	Bonus: $
Savings Plan:	Stock Purch. Plan:		Second Exec. Salary: $649,029	Bonus: $

OTHER THOUGHTS:

Apparent Women Officers or Directors: 3
Hot Spot for Advancement for Women/Minorities: Y

LOCATIONS: ("Y" = Yes)

West:	Southwest:	Midwest:	Southeast:	Northeast:	International:
Y	Y	Y	Y	Y	Y

Note: Financial information, benefits and other data can change quickly and may vary from those stated here.

CH2M HILL COMPANIES LTD

www.ch2m.com

Industry Group Code: 541710 **Ranks within this company's industry group:** Sales: Profits:

Techology:		Medical/Drugs:		Engineering:		Transportation:		Chemicals/Petrochemicals:		Specialty:	
Computers:		Manufacturer:		Design:	Y	Aerospace:		Oil/Gas Products:		Special Services:	Y
Software:		Contract Research:		Construction:	Y	Automotive:		Chemicals:		Consulting:	Y
Communications:		Medical Services:		Eng. Services:	Y	Shipping:		Oil/Chem. Svcs.:		Specialty Mgmt.:	Y
Electronics:		Labs:		Consulting:	Y			Gases:		Products:	
Alternative Energy:		Bio. Services:						Other:		Other:	

TYPES OF BUSINESS:

Engineering Services-Consultation
Environmental Engineering & Consulting
Nuclear Management Services
Water & Electrical Utility Services
Decommissioning & Decontamination
Facilities Design & Construction
Project Financing & Procurement
Nanotechnology Research

BRANDS/DIVISIONS/AFFILIATES:

Operations Management International
CH2M HILL Canada, Ltd.
Lockwood Greene
Industrial Design and Construction
CH2M-IDC China
Wade & Assoicates, Inc.
Goldston Engineering, Inc.
VECO

CONTACTS: *Note: Officers with more than one job title may be intentionally listed here more than once.*

Lee A. McIntire, CEO
Catherine Santee, CFO
Donald S. Evans, Chief Mktg. Officer
Bob Allen, Chief Human Resource Officer/Sr. VP
John Corsi, Dir.-Corp. Comm.
Gary Higdem, Pres., CH2M HILL Energy & Chemicals
Mike McKelvy, Pres., CH2M HILL Industrial
Robert G. Card, Pres., CH2M HILL Government, Environment, Nuclear
Ralph R. Peterson, Chmn.
Thomas G. Searle, Pres., CH2M HILL Int'l

Phone: 303-771-0900	**Fax:** 720-286-9250
Toll-Free: 888-242-6445	
Address: 9191 S. Jamaica St., Englewood, CO 80112 US	

GROWTH PLANS/SPECIAL FEATURES:

CH2M HILL Companies, Ltd. is an employee-owned firm that offers engineering, consulting, design, construction, procurement, operations, maintenance and program and project management services to clients in the public and private sectors. CH2M HILL conducts business in more than 80 countries. The company's environmental services division offers its clients ecological and natural resource damage assessments, environmental consulting for remediation projects and treatment systems for properties that have been contaminated by toxic or radioactive waste. The nuclear services segment manages the decontamination and demolition of weapons production facilities and designs nuclear waste treatment and handling facilities. CH2M HILL's Operations Management International subsidiary provides water, wastewater and electrical utility services to private and public clients. CH2M HILL Canada, Ltd. is the Canadian division of the company. Lockwood Greene is a major engineering and construction firm focused on national and multinational industrial and power clients worldwide. Industrial Design and Construction (IDC) is a high-technology facilities design, construction, maintenance and operations company serving process-intensive technology clients. IDC also has interests in nanotechnology research and manufacturing. CH2M-IDC China provides full-service solution to manufacturing companies that are building or have plants in China. In March 2008, the company acquired Goldston Engineering, Inc., a Texas based engineering solutions provider w. Details of the transaction were not disclosed.

In 2009, CH2M HILL was ranked 84 on FORTUNE Magazine's 12th annual list of the100 Best Companies to Work For.

FINANCIALS: **Sales and profits are in thousands of dollars—add 000 to get the full amount. 2008 Note: Financial information for 2008 was not available for all companies at press time.**

2008 Sales: $	2008 Profits: $	**U.S. Stock Ticker: Private**
2007 Sales: $4,376,200	2007 Profits: $	**Int'l Ticker:** Int'l Exchange:
2006 Sales: $4,000,000	2006 Profits: $	Employees: 22,000
2005 Sales: $3,152,200	2005 Profits: $81,600	Fiscal Year Ends: 12/31
2004 Sales: $2,715,400	2004 Profits: $32,300	Parent Company:

SALARIES/BENEFITS:

Pension Plan:	ESOP Stock Plan:	Profit Sharing:	Top Exec. Salary: $	Bonus: $
Savings Plan:	Stock Purch. Plan:		Second Exec. Salary: $	Bonus: $

OTHER THOUGHTS:

Apparent Women Officers or Directors: 4
Hot Spot for Advancement for Women/Minorities: Y

LOCATIONS: ("Y" = Yes)

West:	Southwest:	Midwest:	Southeast:	Northeast:	International:
Y	Y	Y	Y	Y	Y

Note: Financial information, benefits and other data can change quickly and may vary from those stated here.

CHEVRON CORPORATION

www.chevron.com

Industry Group Code: 211111 **Ranks within this company's industry group:** Sales: 5 Profits: 3

Techology:		Medical/Drugs:		Engineering:		Transportation:		Chemicals/Petrochemicals:		Specialty:	
Computers:		Manufacturer:		Design:		Aerospace:		Oil/Gas Products:	Y	Special Services:	
Software:		Contract Research:		Construction:		Automotive:		Chemicals:	Y	Consulting:	
Communications:		Medical Services:		Eng. Services:		Shipping:		Oil/Chem. Svcs.:	Y	Specialty Mgmt.:	
Electronics:		Labs:		Consulting:				Gases:		Products:	
Alternative Energy:		Bio. Services:						Other:	Y	Other:	

TYPES OF BUSINESS:

Oil & Gas Exploration & Production
Power Generation
Petrochemicals
Gasoline Retailing
Coal Mining
Fuel & Oil Additives
Convenience Stores
Pipelines

BRANDS/DIVISIONS/AFFILIATES:

Texaco
Youngs Creek Mining Company LLC
Chevron Phillips Chemical Company
Caltex

CONTACTS: *Note: Officers with more than one job title may be intentionally listed here more than once.*

David J. O'Reilly, CEO
Patricia E. Yarrington, CFO/VP
Joe W. Laymon, VP-Human Resources
John E. Bethancourt, Exec. VP-Tech. & Svcs.
Charles A. James, General Counsel/VP
John S. Watson, Exec. VP-Strategy & Dev.
Jim Aleveras, Gen. Mgr.-Corp. Investor Rel.
Mark A. Humphrey, Comptroller/VP
Michael (Mike) K. Wirth, Exec. VP-Global Downstream
George L. Kirkland, Exec. VP-Global Upstream & Gas
John D. Gass, Pres. Global Gas/VP
Charles A. Taylor, VP-Health, Environment & Safety
David J. O'Reilly, Chmn.

Phone: 925-842-1000 **Fax:** 925-842-3530
Toll-Free:
Address: 6001 Bollinger Canyon Rd., San Ramon, CA 94583 US

GROWTH PLANS/SPECIAL FEATURES:

Chevron Corp. is an integrated energy company that conducts refining, marketing and transportation operations and, to a lesser degree, chemical operations, mining operations and power generation. The company conducts business activities in the U.S. and approximately 180 other countries. Refining operations maintains a refining network capable of processing 2.1 million barrels of crude oil per day. Marketing operations operates primarily under the brands Chevron, Texaco and Caltex. In the U.S., the company markets under the Chevron and Texaco brands. The company supplies directly or through retailers and marketers approximately 9,700 Chevron- and Texaco-branded motor vehicle retail outlets. Outside the U.S., the firm supplies approximately 15,300 branded service stations, including affiliates. Transportation operations maintains the Chevron owned and operated system of crude oil, refined products, chemicals, natural gas liquids and natural gas pipelines in the U.S. The company also has direct or indirect interests in other U.S. and international pipelines. Chemical operations include the manufacturing and marketing of fuel and lubricating oil additives and commodity petrochemicals through Chevron Phillips Chemical Company (CPChem), a joint venture company. CPChem operates manufacturing and research facilities in eight countries. Mining operations produces and markets coal and molybdenum. The firm owns three coal mines and controls a 50% interest in Youngs Creek Mining Company LLC. The power generation business develops and operates commercial power projects and has interests in 13 power assets through joint ventures in the U.S. and Asia. The company manages the production of more than 2,300 megawatts (MW) of electricity at 11 facilities it owns through joint ventures. Additionally, Chevron operates gas-fired cogeneration facilities that use waste heat recovery to produce additional electricity or to support industrial thermal hosts.

Chevron offers employees medical and dental insurance; domestic partner benefits; a retirement plan; tuition reimbursement; flexible work schedules; and fitness centers and/or memberships.

FINANCIALS: **Sales and profits are in thousands of dollars—add 000 to get the full amount. 2008 Note: Financial information for 2008 was not available for all companies at press time.**

2008 Sales: $273,005,000	2008 Profits: $23,931,000	**U.S. Stock Ticker: CVX**
2007 Sales: $220,904,000	2007 Profits: $18,688,000	**Int'l Ticker:** Int'l Exchange:
2006 Sales: $210,118,000	2006 Profits: $17,138,000	Employees: 67,000
2005 Sales: $198,200,000	2005 Profits: $14,099,000	Fiscal Year Ends: 12/31
2004 Sales: $155,300,000	2004 Profits: $13,328,000	Parent Company:

SALARIES/BENEFITS:

Pension Plan: Y	ESOP Stock Plan:	Profit Sharing:	Top Exec. Salary: $1,650,000	Bonus: $3,600,000
Savings Plan: Y	Stock Purch. Plan:		Second Exec. Salary: $985,417	Bonus: $1,500,000

OTHER THOUGHTS:

Apparent Women Officers or Directors: 3
Hot Spot for Advancement for Women/Minorities: Y

LOCATIONS: ("Y" = Yes)

West:	Southwest:	Midwest:	Southeast:	Northeast:	International:
Y	Y	Y	Y	Y	Y

Note: Financial information, benefits and other data can change quickly and may vary from those stated here.

CHEVRON TECHNOLOGY VENTURES

www.chevron.com/ctv

Industry Group Code: 541710 **Ranks within this company's industry group:** Sales: Profits:

Techology:		Medical/Drugs:		Engineering:		Transportation:		Chemicals/Petrochemicals:		Specialty:	
Computers:		Manufacturer:		Design:		Aerospace:		Oil/Gas Products:		Special Services:	Y
Software:		Contract Research:		Construction:		Automotive:		Chemicals:		Consulting:	
Communications:		Medical Services:		Eng. Services:		Shipping:		Oil/Chem. Svcs.:		Specialty Mgmt.:	
Electronics:		Labs:		Consulting:				Gases:		Products:	
Alternative Energy:		Bio. Services:						Other:		Other:	Y

TYPES OF BUSINESS:

Venture Capital
Power & Energy Investments
Diversified Technology Investments
Venture Capital
Hydrogen Energy Technology
Wind Farming Technology
Nanofilms
Biodiesel

BRANDS/DIVISIONS/AFFILIATES:

Chevron Corp
Magic Earth
Vacuum Resid Slurry Hydrocracking

CONTACTS: *Note: Officers with more than one job title may be intentionally listed here more than once.*

Trond Unneland, Managing Exec.
Colleen Mazza, Bus. Support
Mike Brooks, Venture Exec.
John Hanten, Venture Exec.
Don Riley, Venture Exec.
Richard Pardoe, Principal

Phone: 713-954-6803	**Fax:** 713-954-6016
Toll-Free:	
Address: 3901 Briarpark Rd., Houston, TX 77042-5301 US	

GROWTH PLANS/SPECIAL FEATURES:

Chevron Technology Ventures (CTV) is the branch of Chevron Corp. that invests in and commercializes new technologies through a corporate venture capital model. The firm's investments fall into four main business units: Venture capital (early-stage companies offering valuable technologies); biofuels (developing technologies engaged in large-scale commercial production and distribution of non-food biofuels); hydrogen (which entails five hydrogen demonstration fueling facilities in the U.S. and staying abreast of hydrogen technology developments); and emerging energy (which is focused on reducing the company's carbon footprint and running business operations more cost-effectively through the use and development of renewable energy systems). Investment areas of interest which are represented in each of these business categories are vast, including fuel processing and deepwater production, fuel additives and lubricants, biofuels, solar and wind power, advanced ceramics and polymers, networking infrastructures and nanotechnologies. Chevron is engaged in a number of partnerships and associations in an effort to help bring new energy systems to the market, including California Fuel Cell Partnership, National Hydrogen Association and the World Fuel Cell. To facilitate innovation within Chevron and to create additional value, the company also invests in internal ventures, such as business models created by employees which may have market potential beyond Chevron. Once development milestones are achieved, the commercialization effort may be spun off as an independent company or maintained internally. Magic Earth, for example, is an internal Chevron venture which provides the industry with three-dimensional visualization technology for oil and gas exploration and production. In 2008, the Chevron announced plans to build a pre-commercial plant at its refinery in Pascagoula, Mississippi, to test and further develop its breakthrough, heavy-oil upgrading technology, Vacuum Resid Slurry Hydrocracking (VRSH). The technology holds the potential to increase yields of gasoline, diesel and jet fuel from heavy and ultra-heavy crude oils at substantial levels.

FINANCIALS: **Sales and profits are in thousands of dollars—add 000 to get the full amount. 2008 Note: Financial information for 2008 was not available for all companies at press time.**

2008 Sales: $	2008 Profits: $	**U.S. Stock Ticker: Subsidiary**
2007 Sales: $5,600	2007 Profits: $	**Int'l Ticker:** Int'l Exchange:
2006 Sales: $5,600	2006 Profits: $	Employees: 80
2005 Sales: $	2005 Profits: $	Fiscal Year Ends: 12/31
2004 Sales: $	2004 Profits: $	Parent Company: CHEVRON CORPORATION

SALARIES/BENEFITS:

Pension Plan:	ESOP Stock Plan:	Profit Sharing:	Top Exec. Salary: $	Bonus: $
Savings Plan:	Stock Purch. Plan:		Second Exec. Salary: $	Bonus: $

OTHER THOUGHTS:

Apparent Women Officers or Directors: 1
Hot Spot for Advancement for Women/Minorities:

LOCATIONS: ("Y" = Yes)

West:	Southwest:	Midwest:	Southeast:	Northeast:	International:
Y	Y				

Note: Financial information, benefits and other data can change quickly and may vary from those stated here.

CHI MEI OPTOELECTRONICS

www.cmo.com.tw

Industry Group Code: 334119 **Ranks within this company's industry group:** Sales: 6 Profits: 2

Techology:		Medical/Drugs:		Engineering:		Transportation:		Chemicals/Petrochemicals:		Specialty:	
Computers:		Manufacturer:		Design:		Aerospace:		Oil/Gas Products:		Special Services:	
Software:		Contract Research:		Construction:		Automotive:		Chemicals:		Consulting:	
Communications:		Medical Services:		Eng. Services:		Shipping:		Oil/Chem. Svcs.:		Specialty Mgmt.:	
Electronics:	Y	Labs:		Consulting:				Gases:		Products:	
Alternative Energy:		Bio. Services:						Other:		Other:	

TYPES OF BUSINESS:

Computer Accessories-Flat-Panel LCDs
OLED Displays
LCD Televisions
Medical Display Panels
Color Filters

BRANDS/DIVISIONS/AFFILIATES:

Ningbo Chi Mei Optoelectronics Ltd.
Nanhai Chi Mei Optoelectronics Ltd.
iZ3D, LLC

CONTACTS:

Note: Officers with more than one job title may be intentionally listed here more than once.

Jau-Yang Ho, Pres.
Chun-Hua Hsu, Sr. VP-Mktg. & Sales
Chung-Tsun Yen, Sr. VP-Eng. Tech.
Jyh-Chau Wang, VP-Mfg.
Jack Lin, Sr. VP-Admin.
Robert Chen, Sr. VP-Intellectual Property & Legal Affairs
Loreta Chen, Media Rel. Contact
Sophia Luke, Investor Rel. Contact
Jack Lin, Sr. VP-Finance
Biing-Seng Wu, Exec. VP
Yao-Tung Chen, VP-Mfg.
Chen-Lung Kuo, VP-Sales & Mktg.
Ching-Siang Liao, Chmn.

Phone: 886-6-505-1888	**Fax:**
Toll-Free:	
Address: No. 3 Sec. 1 Huanshi Rd., S. Taiwan Science Park, Sinshih Township, 74147 Taiwan	

GROWTH PLANS/SPECIAL FEATURES:

Chi Mei Optoelectronics (CMO), established in 1998, manufactures thin-film transistor liquid-crystal display (TFT-LCD) flat-panel displays, used in notebook computers, desktop monitors and LCD TVs. Its 13 flat-panel PC monitors come in seven sizes, ranging from 15.6- to 26-inch models, while its 13 notebook panels come in 10 sizes, ranging from 8.9- 18.4-inch models. The firm's 15 LCD TV panels come in 11 sizes ranging from the 18.5-inch to the recently released 52-inch and 57-inch models, which are some of the largest LCD TV panels on the market. CMO creates 14 medical display panels in six sizes, from 18.1- 30-inch models, with five of the 14 panels offering color displays. Its 11 special-application displays come in six sizes, ranging from 7- to 15.4-inch models. These displays are often used gaming machines, kiosks, vehicle and avionics displays, cash registers and digital signage. Lastly, CMO also offers 27 audio-visual (AV) and mobile device displays, in sizes ranging from 1.77- to 10.4-inch models. The company also manufactures color filters and is currently developing organic light-emitting diode (OLED) displays. CMO operates eight manufacturing facilities, primarily located near the company's headquarters, and one sales office, located in Taipei. It has two subsidiaries on the Chinese mainland: Ningbo Chi Mei Optoelectronics Ltd.; and Nanhai Chi Mei Optoelectronics Ltd. CMO also maintains six international subsidiaries, headquartered in Japan, Singapore, the U.S., the U.K., the Netherlands and Germany. Additionally, the firm maintains a joint venture in the U.S. with Neurol Optics, LLC, called iZ3D, LLC. This joint venture develops and markets iZ3D products for the electronic entertainment market and for commercial and professional visualization applications.

CMO offers employees health insurance, free clinic visits, on-site psychiatric counseling, a recreational center, various employee lounges, subsidized travel, family services, educational assistance, free meals, employee housing and a company commuter bus.

FINANCIALS:

Sales and profits are in thousands of dollars—add 000 to get the full amount. 2008 Note: Financial information for 2008 was not available for all companies at press time.

2008 Sales: $9,074,200	2008 Profits: $1,085,100	**U.S. Stock Ticker:**
2007 Sales: $5,724,400	2007 Profits: $106,300	**Int'l Ticker: 3009** Int'l Exchange: Taipei-TPE
2006 Sales: $4,806,600	2006 Profits: $241,400	Employees: 15,000
2005 Sales: $3,537,200	2005 Profits: $515,700	Fiscal Year Ends: 12/31
2004 Sales: $3,206,200	2004 Profits: $537,600	Parent Company:

SALARIES/BENEFITS:

Pension Plan: Y	ESOP Stock Plan:	Profit Sharing: Y	Top Exec. Salary: $	Bonus: $
Savings Plan:	Stock Purch. Plan:		Second Exec. Salary: $	Bonus: $

OTHER THOUGHTS:

Apparent Women Officers or Directors: 2
Hot Spot for Advancement for Women/Minorities: Y

LOCATIONS: ("Y" = Yes)

West:	Southwest:	Midwest:	Southeast:	Northeast:	International:
Y					Y

CHICAGO BRIDGE & IRON COMPANY NV

www.cbiepc.com

Industry Group Code: 234000 **Ranks within this company's industry group:** Sales: 15 Profits: 26

Techology:		Medical/Drugs:		Engineering:		Transportation:		Chemicals/Petrochemicals:		Specialty:	
Computers:		Manufacturer:		Design:	Y	Aerospace:		Oil/Gas Products:		Special Services:	
Software:		Contract Research:		Construction:	Y	Automotive:		Chemicals:		Consulting:	
Communications:		Medical Services:		Eng. Services:	Y	Shipping:		Oil/Chem. Svcs.:	Y	Specialty Mgmt.:	
Electronics:		Labs:		Consulting:	Y			Gases:		Products:	
Alternative Energy:		Bio. Services:						Other:		Other:	

TYPES OF BUSINESS:

Heavy Construction & Civil Engineering
Specialty Engineering & Procurement Services
Liquid & Gas Storage Facilities
Maintenance & Support Services

BRANDS/DIVISIONS/AFFILIATES:

John Brown Hydrocarbons Ltd.
CB&I Howe-Baker
CB&I TPA
CB&I Matrix
ABB Lummus Global, Inc.
ABB Oil & Gas Europe B.V.

CONTACTS: *Note: Officers with more than one job title may be intentionally listed here more than once.*

Phillip K. Asheman, CEO
Phillip K. Asheman, Pres.
Ronald A. Ballschmiede, CFO/Exec. VP
David P. Bordages, VP-Human Resources
David P. Bordages, VP-Admin.
David A. Delman, Chief Legal Officer/General Counsel/Sec.
John W. Redmon, Exec. VP-Oper.
Mark Coscio, VP-Corp. Planning
Jerry H. Ballengee, Chmn.
Ronald E. Blum, Exec. VP-Global Bus. Dev.

Phone: 31-70-373-2010	**Fax:**
Toll-Free:	
Address: Oostduinlaan 75, Hoofddorp, The Hague, 2596JJ The Netherlands	

GROWTH PLANS/SPECIAL FEATURES:

Chicago Bridge & Iron Company N.V. (CB&I), a global engineering, procurement and construction (EPC) company, provides specialty construction for liquid and gas storage facilities. Company operations include over 80 offices, warehouses and other facilities on six continents. CB&I offers conceptual design, engineering, procurement, fabrication, field construction, mechanical installation and commissioning, serving customers in the oil and gas; petrochemical and chemical; power; water and wastewater; and metals and mining industries. Projects include hydrocarbon processing plants, liquid natural gas (LNG) terminals and peak shaving plants, offshore structures, pipelines, bulk liquid terminals and water storage and treatment facilities. The company provides complete service, from the initial design and engineering through procurement and construction and maintenance. The company also offers a range of complementary products and services including low temperature or cryogenic tanks and systems, primarily used by petroleum, chemical, petrochemical, natural gas and power generation companies to store, transport and handle liquefied gases; pressure vessels for use in petroleum, chemical and petrochemical storage and as digesters in the pulp and paper and wastewater treatment industries; and specialty structures including iron and aluminum processing facilities and hydroelectric structures. CB&I operates through several subsidiaries including: CB&I Howe-Baker, which provides oil and gas engineering services; CBI TPA, which provides engineering and services for sulfur reduction and removal projects; CB&I Matrix, which offers services for unit projects; and John Brown Hydrocarbons Ltd., which provides for offshore, onshore, pipeline and refining industries.

The firm offers its U.S. employees medical, dental and vision plans; employee and dependent life insurance options; a 401(k) plan; profit sharing; a stock purchase program; and an educational assistance plan.

FINANCIALS: Sales and profits are in thousands of dollars—add 000 to get the full amount. 2008 Note: Financial information for 2008 was not available for all companies at press time.

2008 Sales: $5,944,981	2008 Profits: $-21,146	**U.S. Stock Ticker: CBI**
2007 Sales: $4,363,492	2007 Profits: $165,640	**Int'l Ticker: BDZ** Int'l Exchange: Frankfurt-Euronext
2006 Sales: $3,125,307	2006 Profits: $116,968	Employees: 18,818
2005 Sales: $2,257,517	2005 Profits: $15,977	Fiscal Year Ends: 12/31
2004 Sales: $1,897,200	2004 Profits: $65,900	Parent Company:

SALARIES/BENEFITS:

Pension Plan:	ESOP Stock Plan:	Profit Sharing: Y	Top Exec. Salary: $720,000	Bonus: $1,185,840
Savings Plan: Y	Stock Purch. Plan: Y		Second Exec. Salary: $450,000	Bonus: $886,171

OTHER THOUGHTS:

Apparent Women Officers or Directors:
Hot Spot for Advancement for Women/Minorities:

LOCATIONS: ("Y" = Yes)

West:	Southwest:	Midwest:	Southeast:	Northeast:	International:
Y	Y	Y	Y	Y	Y

CHIRON CORP

www.chiron.com

Industry Group Code: 325412 **Ranks within this company's industry group:** Sales: Profits:

Techology:		Medical/Drugs:		Engineering:		Transportation:		Chemicals/Petrochemicals:		Specialty:	
Computers:		Manufacturer:		Design:		Aerospace:		Oil/Gas Products:		Special Services:	
Software:		Contract Research:		Construction:		Automotive:		Chemicals:		Consulting:	
Communications:		Medical Services:	Y	Eng. Services:		Shipping:		Oil/Chem. Svcs.:		Specialty Mgmt.:	
Electronics:		Labs:	Y	Consulting:				Gases:		Products:	
Alternative Energy:		Bio. Services:	Y					Other:		Other:	

TYPES OF BUSINESS:

Pharmaceuticals Discovery & Development
Biopharmaceuticals
Vaccines
Blood Screening Assays

BRANDS/DIVISIONS/AFFILIATES:

Novartis AG
Vaccines and Diagnostics
Gen-Probe
PROCLEIX
ZymeQuest

CONTACTS: *Note: Officers with more than one job title may be intentionally listed here more than once.*

Gene Walther, Pres.

Phone: 510-655-8730	**Fax:** 510-655-9910
Toll-Free:	
Address: 4560 Horton St., Emeryville, CA 94608-2916 US	

GROWTH PLANS/SPECIAL FEATURES:

Chiron Corp., the blood screening business of Novartis AG's Vaccines and Diagnostics division, develops tools, products and services focused on preventing transfusion-transmitted infection. The company was acquired by Novartis in April 2006. Chiron's transcription-mediated amplification (TMA) products are designed to simplify nucleic acid testing (NAT) by enabling simultaneous detection of multiple viruses within a single tube. TMA technology was developed by Gen-Probe, Chiron's NAT innovation partner. TMA begins by preparing samples for testing by lysing the viruses to release genetic material, a process which involves no pretreatment or handling, thus reducing the risk of contamination. Capture probes hybridize internal control (IC) and viral nucleic acids and bind them to magnetic particles, and then the unbound material is washed away. A DNA copy of the target nucleic acid is created using reverse transcriptase and RNA is synthesized using RNA polymerase. The newly synthesized RNA can then reenter the TMA process and serve as further amplification templates. With this process, billions of copies can potentially be created in under an hour. Simultaneous detection of both IC- and viral-encoded RNA is enabled by dual kinetic assay (DKA) technology, which produces a flash of light for IC-encoded RNA, and a long glow for viral-encoded RNA. Chiron's TMA products include instruments, software and assays, sold under the PROCLEIX brand. Chiron is currently developing an enhanced immunoassay for the detection of abnormal prions (protein particles) in blood and blood products that are associated with variant Creuzfeldt-Jakob Disease, a rare, degenerative and fatal brain disorder believed to be developed by consuming cattle products contaminated with mad-cow disease (bovine spongiform encephalopathy). With its partner ZymeQuest, Chiron is also developing a system to convert A, B and AB red blood cells to enzyme-converted, universally transfusable group O red blood cells. Chiron also offers its clients NAT training and support.

FINANCIALS: Sales and profits are in thousands of dollars—add 000 to get the full amount. 2008 Note: Financial information for 2008 was not available for all companies at press time.

2008 Sales: $	2008 Profits: $	**U.S. Stock Ticker: Subsidiary**
2007 Sales: $	2007 Profits: $	**Int'l Ticker:** Int'l Exchange:
2006 Sales: $	2006 Profits: $	Employees: 5,500
2005 Sales: $1,921,000	2005 Profits: $187,000	Fiscal Year Ends: 12/31
2004 Sales: $1,723,355	2004 Profits: $78,917	Parent Company: NOVARTIS AG

SALARIES/BENEFITS:

Pension Plan:	ESOP Stock Plan:	Profit Sharing:	Top Exec. Salary: $800,000	Bonus: $897,293
Savings Plan: Y	Stock Purch. Plan:		Second Exec. Salary: $552,461	Bonus: $1,500,000

OTHER THOUGHTS:

Apparent Women Officers or Directors:
Hot Spot for Advancement for Women/Minorities:

LOCATIONS: ("Y" = Yes)

West:	Southwest:	Midwest:	Southeast:	Northeast:	International:
Y		Y		Y	Y

CHIYODA CORPORATION

www.chiyoda-corp.com

Industry Group Code: 541330 **Ranks within this company's industry group:** Sales: 4 Profits: 7

Techology:		Medical/Drugs:		Engineering:		Transportation:		Chemicals/Petrochemicals:		Specialty:	
Computers:		Manufacturer:		Design:	Y	Aerospace:		Oil/Gas Products:		Special Services:	
Software:		Contract Research:		Construction:	Y	Automotive:		Chemicals:		Consulting:	Y
Communications:		Medical Services:		Eng. Services:	Y	Shipping:		Oil/Chem. Svcs.:	Y	Specialty Mgmt.:	Y
Electronics:		Labs:		Consulting:	Y			Gases:		Products:	
Alternative Energy:		Bio. Services:						Other:		Other:	

TYPES OF BUSINESS:

Engineering & Construction Services
Plant Lifecycle Engineering
Computer-Aided Engineering
Risk Management
Pollution Prevention Systems
Industrial Equipment-Online Procurement
Mining

BRANDS/DIVISIONS/AFFILIATES:

Chiyoda Advanced Solutions Corporation
Eureka
Biofiner
CTG Engineering Method
Thoroughbred 121 FGD Process
Chiyoda International Corporation

CONTACTS: *Note: Officers with more than one job title may be intentionally listed here more than once.*

Takashi Kubota, CEO
Takashi Kubota, Pres.
Hiroshi Shibata, CFO/Exec. VP
Sumio Nakashima, Dir.-Tech.
Sumio Nakashima, Dir.-Eng.
Takaharu Saegusa, Sr. Exec. Officer-Strategy & Planning
Toshiyuki Ohnuma, Dir.-Finance
Nobuyasu Kamei, Exec. VP-CSR Div.
Tsuyoshi Kakizaki, Gen. Mgr.-Petroleum & Chemical Project Div.
Eisaku Yamashita, Dir.-Domestic Project Oper.
Nobuo Seki, Chmn.
Madoka Koda, Dir.-Int'l Project Oper.
Atsuo Minamoto, Dir.-Logistics

Phone: 81-45-506-7105	**Fax:** 81-45-503-0200
Toll-Free:	
Address: 2-12-1, Tsurumichuo, 2-Chome, Tsurumi-ku, Yokohama, 230-8601 Japan	

GROWTH PLANS/SPECIAL FEATURES:

Chiyoda Corporation is a Japanese engineering firm that operates in the hydrocarbon, engineering, environmental preservation, metal and mining, architecture and automotive industries. Many of the firm's activities involve facilities that prevent disasters, improve the environment and control pollution. Chiyoda provides comprehensive engineering services that range from feasibility studies of design to maintenance, engineering, procurement, construction and start-up assistance. The firm's Eureka process provides a process of producing clean fuel from heavy residual materials. The first Eureka unit was installed in Japan over 20 years ago and is still in operation. Chiyoda has also developed many environmental preservation and pollution prevention systems, such as Biofiner, the CTG Engineering Method and the Thoroughbred 121 FGD Process. The company offers petroleum refining firms the ability to procure construction materials, equipment and spare parts through its Internet procurement service, called I-MOR. Through Chiyoda Advanced Solutions Corporation, the firm provides technological support for engineering projects, including computer-aided engineering analysis and plant lifecycle engineering and risk management. The firm's U.S. activities are overseen by Chiyoda International Corporation, headquartered in Houston, Texas. The company has offices in countries throughout the world, including Indonesia, the U.K., the U.S., the Philippines, the United Arab Emirates, China, Germany, Malaysia, the Netherlands, Nigeria, Saudi Arabia, Singapore, Thailand, Qatar, India and Iran. The company has 16 consolidated subsidiaries and five associated companies. In November 2008, the company announced that it would perform front-end engineering design services on a polycrystalline silicon plant to be built in Malaysia, on behalf of Tokuyama Corporation. The plant is scheduled to begin operations in 2012.

FINANCIALS: **Sales and profits are in thousands of dollars—add 000 to get the full amount. 2008 Note: Financial information for 2008 was not available for all companies at press time.**

2008 Sales: $6,035,600	2008 Profits: $96,410	**U.S. Stock Ticker:**
2007 Sales: $4,800,500	2007 Profits: $233,000	**Int'l Ticker: 6366** Int'l Exchange: Tokyo-TSE
2006 Sales: $3,869,700	2006 Profits: $192,100	Employees: 2,947
2005 Sales: $2,649,800	2005 Profits: $127,300	Fiscal Year Ends: 3/31
2004 Sales: $1,957,700	2004 Profits: $62,900	Parent Company:

SALARIES/BENEFITS:

Pension Plan:	ESOP Stock Plan:	Profit Sharing:	Top Exec. Salary: $	Bonus: $
Savings Plan:	Stock Purch. Plan:		Second Exec. Salary: $	Bonus: $

OTHER THOUGHTS:

Apparent Women Officers or Directors:
Hot Spot for Advancement for Women/Minorities:

LOCATIONS: ("Y" = Yes)

West:	Southwest:	Midwest:	Southeast:	Northeast:	International:
	Y				Y

CHRYSLER LLC

www.chryslerllc.com

Industry Group Code: 336111 **Ranks within this company's industry group:** Sales: Profits:

Techology:		Medical/Drugs:		Engineering:		Transportation:		Chemicals/Petrochemicals:		Specialty:	
Computers:		Manufacturer:		Design:		Aerospace:		Oil/Gas Products:		Special Services:	
Software:		Contract Research:		Construction:		Automotive:	Y	Chemicals:		Consulting:	
Communications:		Medical Services:		Eng. Services:		Shipping:		Oil/Chem. Svcs.:		Specialty Mgmt.:	
Electronics:		Labs:		Consulting:				Gases:		Products:	
Alternative Energy:		Bio. Services:						Other:		Other:	

TYPES OF BUSINESS:

Auto Manufacturing
Research & Development
Nanotechnology-Coatings
Light Truck Manufacturing
Financial Services

BRANDS/DIVISIONS/AFFILIATES:

Chrysler Financial Services, Inc.
Chrysler Group
Cerberus Capital Management LP
Jeep
Mopar
Dodge Ram
Jeep Grand Cherokee
Dodge

CONTACTS: *Note: Officers with more than one job title may be intentionally listed here more than once.*

Robert Nardelli, CEO
James Press, Co-Pres./Vice Chmn.
Ronald E. Kolka, CFO/Sr. VP
Steven Landry, Exec. VP-Sales, North America
Frank Ewasyshyn, Exec. VP-Mfg.
Thomas W. La Sorda, Co-Pres./Vice Chmn.
Robert Nardelli, Chmn.
Michael Manley, Exec. VP-Int'l Sales, Mktg. & Bus. Dev.
John P. Campi, Exec. VP-Procurement

Phone: 248-576-5741 **Fax:** 248-576-4742
Toll-Free: 800-992-1997
Address: 1000 Chrysler Dr., Auburn Hills, MI 48326-2766 US

GROWTH PLANS/SPECIAL FEATURES:

Chrysler LLC, formerly part of DaimlerChrysler Corp., manufactures, assembles and sells automobiles under the brands Chrysler, Jeep and Dodge, at facilities in the U.S., Canada and Mexico. It also provides parts and accessories marketed under the Mopar brand name. Chrysler's most popular models include the Chrysler Crossfire sedan, PT Cruiser and Town and Country minivan; the Dodge Neon sedan, Caliber and Durango SUVs and Dakota and Ram pick-ups; and Jeep's Wrangler, Grand Cherokee and Liberty. The company also produces luxury cars, such as the Chrysler Imperial; performance and sports cars like the Dodge Razor and the Dodge Viper; and specialized Jeeps as the Hurricane, the Rescue and the Gladiator. The firm is engaged in automotive-related research and is developing nanotechnologies to reduce air pollution while improving overall fuel-use efficiency. In addition to the production of cars, the firm also offers financing and leasing for customers through the Chrysler Financial Services, Inc. In May 2007, private equity firm Cerberus Capital Management LP agreed to buy an 80.1% stake in DaimlerChrysler AG's North American operations, including DaimlerChrysler Canada and DaimlerChrysler Corp., for $7.41 billion. Over the mid-term, in an effort to increase profits, Chrysler plans to cut the 30 different models it makes by as much as 30% to 50%. In addition, it plans consolidate and downsize its dealer network. By the end of 2008, Chrysler was dramatically reducing production amid slumping sales. Chrysler received $4 billion in bailout funds from the U.S. government, and hopes to receive an additional $5 billion. In January 2009, Chrysler entered into a tentative alliance agreement with Fiat. The alliance would give Fiat a 35% stake in Chrysler while giving Chrysler access to Fiat small car engineering and technology. If the alliance is successful, Chrysler could quickly be building cars based on Fiat designs for sale in the U.S. and abroad.

FINANCIALS: **Sales and profits are in thousands of dollars—add 000 to get the full amount. 2008 Note: Financial information for 2008 was not available for all companies at press time.**

2008 Sales: $	2008 Profits: $	**U.S. Stock Ticker: Private**
2007 Sales: $49,000,000	2007 Profits: $1,623,443	**Int'l Ticker:** Int'l Exchange:
2006 Sales: $63,294,342	2006 Profits: $	Employees: 72,000
2005 Sales: $67,336,201	2005 Profits: $	Fiscal Year Ends: 12/31
2004 Sales: $66,505,640	2004 Profits: $	Parent Company: CHRYSLER HOLDING LLC

SALARIES/BENEFITS:

Pension Plan:	ESOP Stock Plan:	Profit Sharing:	Top Exec. Salary: $	Bonus: $
Savings Plan: Y	Stock Purch. Plan:		Second Exec. Salary: $	Bonus: $

OTHER THOUGHTS:

Apparent Women Officers or Directors:
Hot Spot for Advancement for Women/Minorities:

LOCATIONS: ("Y" = Yes)

West:	Southwest:	Midwest:	Southeast:	Northeast:	International:
Y	Y	Y	Y	Y	Y

CIBA HOLDING AG

www.cibasc.com

Industry Group Code: 325000 **Ranks within this company's industry group:** Sales: 23 Profits: 24

Techology:		Medical/Drugs:		Engineering:		Transportation:		Chemicals/Petrochemicals:		Specialty:	
Computers:		Manufacturer:		Design:		Aerospace:		Oil/Gas Products:		Special Services:	
Software:	Y	Contract Research:		Construction:		Automotive:		Chemicals:	Y	Consulting:	
Communications:		Medical Services:		Eng. Services:		Shipping:		Oil/Chem. Svcs.:		Specialty Mgmt.:	
Electronics:		Labs:		Consulting:				Gases:		Products:	
Alternative Energy:		Bio. Services:						Other:		Other:	

TYPES OF BUSINESS:

Specialty Chemicals
Coatings
Plastic Additives
Dyes, Pigments, Stabilizers & Whitening Products
Water & Paper Treatment Products

BRANDS/DIVISIONS/AFFILIATES:

Ciba Colorviz Color Presenter
Coating Effects
Plastic Additives
Water & Paper Treatments

CONTACTS: *Note: Officers with more than one job title may be intentionally listed here more than once.*

Brendan Cummins, CEO
Andreas Tuerk, Chief Mktg. Officer
Mark Wright, Head-Human Resources
Michael Loechle, Head-Admin. & Group Svcs.
Tim Schlange, Chief Strategy Officer
Caroline Scherb, Head-Group Comm.
Markus Mayer, Head-Internal Audit
Martin Riediker, Chief Innovation Officer
Thomas Engelhardt, Head-Coating Effects
James McCummiskey, Head-Water & Paper Treatment
Armin Meyer, Chmn.
Franz Killer, Head-Procurement & Technical Oper.

Phone: 41-61-636-11-11	**Fax:** 41-61-636-12-12
Toll-Free:	
Address: Klybeckstrasse 141, Basel, CH-4002 Switzerland	

GROWTH PLANS/SPECIAL FEATURES:

CIBA Holding AG is an international specialty chemicals manufacturer that sells its products in over 120 countries worldwide. The company produces specialty chemicals through three business segments: coating effects; plastic additives; and water and paper treatments. The coating effects segment offers pigments, pigment preparations, special dyes, algicides, antioxidants, corrosion inhibitors, dye stabilizers and optical brighteners for the coatings, synthetic fibers, imaging and inks, electronic materials and plastics markets. It also produces organic pigments and functional dyes for information storage, photo-initiators that harness light to drive chemical reactions; and light stabilizers, which protect materials from light-driven degradation. The plastic additives segment produces products for the plastics, rubber, lubricants, home and fabric care and personal care industries. Its products generate materials with better stability and added improvements in performance and cost-efficiency during the development process of many industrial and consumer products. The water and paper treatment segment provides products, services and expertise to the agriculture, mining and oil, water treatment, detergents and hygiene industries. Its products include flocculants, coagulants and retention aids that improve the separation of solid/liquid mixtures. The segment also produces colorants, whiteners, fluorochemicals and color formers that enhance the appearance and quality of paper. In March 2008, the firm introduced Ciba Colorviz Color Presenter software that aids color communication between designers and color producers. In the same month, the company developed a long-lifetime phosphorescent material for use in power-efficient OLEDs (semiconductors that emit light in a diffuse way to form an area light source). In September 2008, the firm agreed to be acquired by chemicals giant BASF in a deal valued at about $3 billion. That same month, the company acquired the photoinitiator business of the Lamberti Group.

FINANCIALS: Sales and profits are in thousands of dollars—add 000 to get the full amount. 2008 Note: Financial information for 2008 was not available for all companies at press time.

2008 Sales: $5,205,560	2008 Profits: $-495,730	**U.S. Stock Ticker:**
2007 Sales: $6,457,800	2007 Profits: $234,600	**Int'l Ticker: CIBN** Int'l Exchange: Zurich-SWX
2006 Sales: $6,288,500	2006 Profits: $-40,600	Employees: 13,319
2005 Sales: $5,974,700	2005 Profits: $-253,400	Fiscal Year Ends: 12/31
2004 Sales: $6,158,000	2004 Profits: $273,000	Parent Company:

SALARIES/BENEFITS:

Pension Plan:	ESOP Stock Plan:	Profit Sharing:	Top Exec. Salary: $	Bonus: $
Savings Plan:	Stock Purch. Plan:		Second Exec. Salary: $	Bonus: $

OTHER THOUGHTS:

Apparent Women Officers or Directors: 2
Hot Spot for Advancement for Women/Minorities:

LOCATIONS: ("Y" = Yes)

West:	Southwest:	Midwest:	Southeast:	Northeast:	International:
		Y	Y	Y	Y

Note: Financial information, benefits and other data can change quickly and may vary from those stated here.

CISCO SYSTEMS INC

www.cisco.com

Industry Group Code: 334110 **Ranks within this company's industry group:** Sales: 1 Profits: 1

Techology:		Medical/Drugs:		Engineering:		Transportation:		Chemicals/Petrochemicals:		Specialty:	
Computers:	Y	Manufacturer:		Design:		Aerospace:		Oil/Gas Products:		Special Services:	
Software:	Y	Contract Research:		Construction:		Automotive:		Chemicals:		Consulting:	
Communications:	Y	Medical Services:		Eng. Services:		Shipping:		Oil/Chem. Svcs.:		Specialty Mgmt.:	
Electronics:		Labs:		Consulting:				Gases:		Products:	
Alternative Energy:		Bio. Services:						Other:		Other:	

TYPES OF BUSINESS:

Computer Networking Equipment
Routers & Switches
Adapters & Hubs
Server Virtualization Software
Data Storage Products
Security Products
Servers
Unified Communications Systems

BRANDS/DIVISIONS/AFFILIATES:

Scientific Atlanta Inc
Cognio Inc
Navini Networks Inc
Pure Networks
Unified Computing Systems
Jabber Inc
PostPath Inc
DiviTech A/S

CONTACTS: *Note: Officers with more than one job title may be intentionally listed here more than once.*

John T. Chambers, CEO
Frank Calderoni, CFO/Exec. VP
Susan Bostrom, Chief Mktg. Officer
Brian Schipper, Sr. VP-Human Resources
Rebecca J. Jacoby, CIO/Sr. VP
Padmasree Warrior, CTO
Mark Chandler, General Counsel/Sr. VP/Sec.
Richard J. Justice, Exec. VP-Worldwide Oper. & Bus. Dev.
Ned Hooper, Sr. VP-Corp. Dev. & Consumer Group
Jonathan Chadwick, Principal Acct. Officer/Corp. Controller/Sr. VP
Alan Baratz, Sr. VP-Network Software & Systems Tech. Group
Frank Calderoni, Sr. VP-Costumer Solutions Finance
David K. Holland, Treas./Sr. VP
Randy Pond, Exec. VP-Oper., Processes & Systems
John T. Chambers, Chmn.
Chris Dedicoat, Pres., European Markets
Angel L. Mendez, Exec. VP-Global Supply Chain Mgmt.

Phone: 408-526-4000	**Fax:**
Toll-Free: 800-553-6387	
Address: 170 W. Tasman Dr., San Jose, CA 95134 US	

GROWTH PLANS/SPECIAL FEATURES:

Cisco Systems, Inc. designs, manufactures and sells Internet protocol (IP)-based networking and other products related to the communications and information technology industry; and provides services associated with these products. The company provides a broad line of products for transporting data, voice and video. The firm's products, which include routers, switches and advanced technologies, are installed at large enterprises, public institutions, telecommunications companies, commercial businesses and personal residences. Advanced technologies operations involve emerging technologies such as application networking services, home networking, security storage area networking, unified communications, video systems and wireless technology. The application networking division helps IT departments integrate hardware and software. Home networking products connect different devices in the household, through wired or wireless connections, allowing users to share Internet access, printers, music, movies and games throughout the home. Security products include embedded security devices, firewalls and virtual private networks. Storage area networking products deliver connectivity between servers and storage systems. Unified communications integrate voice, video, data and mobile applications on fixed and mobile networks. The video systems segment consists of digital set-top boxes and digital media technology products. Wireless offerings provide a variety of in-building wireless LAN and outdoor wireless bridging products. In addition to its product offerings, Cisco provides a range of services, including technical support and training. The firm's business is divided into five segments based on region: the U.S. and Canada, European Markets, Emerging Markets, Asia Pacific and Japan. In 2008, Cisco acquired several companies including: Jabber Inc.; PostPath, Inc; Pure Networks; as well as acquiring the remaining 20% stock of Nuova Systems. Additionally, in June 2008, the firm entered into agreement to acquire DiviTech A/S, which will include DiviTech's digital-service management technology. Cisco's strategic push is now focused on Unified Computing Systems, which bundle server, storage and networking systems into one new product. Each of Cisco's new servers is capable of running hundreds of virtual servers by utilizing virtualization software.

FINANCIALS: **Sales and profits are in thousands of dollars—add 000 to get the full amount. 2008 Note: Financial information for 2008 was not available for all companies at press time.**

2008 Sales: $39,540,000	2008 Profits: $8,052,000	**U.S. Stock Ticker: CSCO**
2007 Sales: $34,922,000	2007 Profits: $7,333,000	**Int'l Ticker:** Int'l Exchange:
2006 Sales: $28,484,000	2006 Profits: $5,580,000	Employees: 67,318
2005 Sales: $24,801,000	2005 Profits: $5,741,000	Fiscal Year Ends: 7/31
2004 Sales: $22,045,000	2004 Profits: $4,401,000	Parent Company:

SALARIES/BENEFITS:

Pension Plan:	ESOP Stock Plan:	Profit Sharing:	Top Exec. Salary: $859,605	Bonus: $1,590,750
Savings Plan:	Stock Purch. Plan:		Second Exec. Salary: $750,000	Bonus: $1,484,700

OTHER THOUGHTS:

Apparent Women Officers or Directors: 8
Hot Spot for Advancement for Women/Minorities: Y

LOCATIONS: ("Y" = Yes)

West:	Southwest:	Midwest:	Southeast:	Northeast:	International:
Y	Y	Y	Y	Y	Y

Note: Financial information, benefits and other data can change quickly and may vary from those stated here.

CITIC PACIFIC LTD

www.citicpacific.com

Industry Group Code: 331000 **Ranks within this company's industry group:** Sales: 1 Profits: 1

Techology:		Medical/Drugs:		Engineering:		Transportation:		Chemicals/Petrochemicals:		Specialty:	
Computers:		Manufacturer:		Design:		Aerospace:		Oil/Gas Products:		Special Services:	
Software:		Contract Research:		Construction:	Y	Automotive:		Chemicals:		Consulting:	
Communications:	Y	Medical Services:		Eng. Services:		Shipping:		Oil/Chem. Svcs.:		Specialty Mgmt.:	
Electronics:		Labs:		Consulting:				Gases:		Products:	
Alternative Energy:		Bio. Services:						Other:		Other:	Y

TYPES OF BUSINESS:

Steel Manufacturing
Iron Ore Mining
Real Estate Development
Aviation Holdings
Environmental Services
Electricity Generation
Telecommunications

BRANDS/DIVISIONS/AFFILIATES:

CONTACTS:

Note: Officers with more than one job title may be intentionally listed here more than once.

Chang Zhenming, Managing Dir.
Paul Lo Kai Sing, Dir.-Human Resources
Paul Lo Kai Sing, Dir.-Admin.
Holly Chen Meng, Dir.-Investor Rel.
Kevin Kwan Kit Tong, Dir.-Financial Control
Aaron Wong Ha Hang, Dir.-Property Dev.
Cai Xinghai, Dir.-Industries
Wang Gongcheng, Dir.-Mineral Resources
Chang Zhenming, Chmn.

Phone: 85-2-2820-2111 **Fax:** 85-2-2877-2771
Toll-Free:
Address: 32nd Fl., CITIC Tower 1 Tim Mei Ave., Hong Kong, China

GROWTH PLANS/SPECIAL FEATURES:

Citic Pacific Ltd. is a holding company that, through its subsidiaries, is engaged in industries including steel manufacturing, iron ore mining, property and real estate administration, aviation, civil infrastructure, power generation and telecommunications, among others. The firm's steel manufacturing operations are carried out via Jiangyin Xingcheng Special Steel; Xin Yegang Special Steel; and Shijiazhuang Steel. CITIC Pacific's iron ore operations are carried out by Sino Iron Project. CITIC Pacific's Hong Kong properties consist of five commercial properties and three industrial properties. The firm's Shanghai properties include three commercial properties for lease. CITIC Pacific's aviation business segment comprises the firm's 10% interest in Hong Kong Air Cargo Terminals Ltd. and 17.5% stake in Cathay Pacific Airways Ltd. The firm's civil infrastructure division consists of holdings in toll roads and bridges, including a 70.8% interest in the Eastern Harbour Crossing and Western Harbour Tunnel of Hong Kong. The division's operations also include CITIC Pacific's environmental businesses, including, among others, its holdings in the Green Valley landfill; Envirospace Ltd., a company operating a chemical waste treatment plant; and Shanghai Laogang MSW Treatment Co. Ltd., a landfill and waste treatment facility. CITIC Pacific's power generation division builds, owns and operates power plants across China. The company's telecommunications business consist primarily of its 20% stake in Companhia de Telecomunicacoes de Macau S.A.R.L., a telecommunications provider in Macau.

FINANCIALS:

Sales and profits are in thousands of dollars—add 000 to get the full amount. 2008 Note: Financial information for 2008 was not available for all companies at press time.

2008 Sales: $5,989,180
2007 Sales: $5,797,420
2006 Sales: $6,070,440
2005 Sales: $
2004 Sales: $

2008 Profits: $-1,633,670
2007 Profits: $1,492,420
2006 Profits: $1,124,440
2005 Profits: $
2004 Profits: $

U.S. Stock Ticker:
Int'l Ticker: 0267 Int'l Exchange: Hong Kong-HKE
Employees:
Fiscal Year Ends:
Parent Company:

SALARIES/BENEFITS:

Pension Plan: ESOP Stock Plan: Profit Sharing: Top Exec. Salary: $ Bonus: $
Savings Plan: Stock Purch. Plan: Second Exec. Salary: $ Bonus: $

OTHER THOUGHTS:

Apparent Women Officers or Directors: 1
Hot Spot for Advancement for Women/Minorities:

LOCATIONS: ("Y" = Yes)

West:	Southwest:	Midwest:	Southeast:	Northeast:	International:
					Y

CITRIX SYSTEMS INC

www.citrix.com

Industry Group Code: 511207 **Ranks within this company's industry group:** Sales: 6 Profits: 5

Techology:		Medical/Drugs:		Engineering:		Transportation:		Chemicals/Petrochemicals:		Specialty:	
Computers:		Manufacturer:		Design:		Aerospace:		Oil/Gas Products:		Special Services:	Y
Software:	Y	Contract Research:		Construction:		Automotive:		Chemicals:		Consulting:	Y
Communications:		Medical Services:		Eng. Services:		Shipping:		Oil/Chem. Svcs.:		Specialty Mgmt.:	
Electronics:		Labs:		Consulting:				Gases:		Products:	
Alternative Energy:		Bio. Services:						Other:		Other:	

TYPES OF BUSINESS:

Computer Software-Application Server
Consulting Services
Training & Technical Support
Online Services

BRANDS/DIVISIONS/AFFILIATES:

XenApp
NetScaler Web
Access Gateway
WANScaler
XenDesktop
XenServer
Provisioning Server
EdgeSight

CONTACTS: *Note: Officers with more than one job title may be intentionally listed here more than once.*

Mark B. Templeton, CEO
Mark B. Templeton, Pres.
David J. Henshall, CFO/Sr. VP
Wes R. Wasson, Chief Mktg. Officer/Sr. VP
David R. Friedman, Sr. VP-Human Resources
David R. Friedman, General Counsel
Frank Artale, VP-Bus. Dev.
Brett Caine, Sr. VP/Gen. Mgr.-Online Svcs. Div.
Al J. Monserrat, Sr. VP-Sales & Svc.
Peter Levine, Sr. VP/Gen. Mgr.-Virtualization & Mgmt. Div.
Gordon Payne, Sr. VP/Gen. Mgr.-Delivery Systems Div.
Michael Cristinziano, VP-Strategic Dev., Mergers & Acquisitions
Thomas F. Bogan, Chmn.
James Stevenson, VP-U.K., Ireland & South Africa

Phone: 954-267-3000 **Fax:** 954-267-9319
Toll-Free: 800-424-8749
Address: 851 W. Cypress Creek Rd., Fort Lauderdale, FL 33309 US

GROWTH PLANS/SPECIAL FEATURES:

Citrix Systems, Inc. designs, develops and markets technology solutions that allow applications to be delivered, supported and shared on-demand with high performance, enhanced security and improved total cost of ownership. Citrix offers application delivery systems in three product groupings: application virtualization, application networking and desktop virtualization. Application virtualization products include Citrix XenApp (formerly Presentation Server), which runs the business logic of applications on a central server, transmitting only screen pixels, keystrokes and mouse movements through an encrypted channel to users' computers. The company's application networking products include NetScaler Web application delivery solutions, which accelerate application performances up to five times while reducing datacenter costs; Access Gateway, an SSL VPN (secure socket layer virtual private network) that securely delivers applications with policy-based SmartAccess control; and WANScaler solutions, which provide high-performance application delivery to branch office users. The firm's XenDesktop, announced in October 2007, is a fully integrated desktop delivery system. Virtualization and management systems offered by Citrix include XenServer, an enterprise-class platform for managing server virtualization in the datacenter as a flexible aggregated pool of computing and storage resources; Provisioning Server, which enables IT organizations to stream datacenter and desktop operating systems and workloads to both virtual and physical machines from a central location; and its EdgeSight application performance monitoring systems. The company's online services include GoToMyPC, GoToMeeting, GoToAssist and GoToWebinar. In addition, the company offers consulting, technical support and product training and certification services. In October 2007, Citrix acquired XenSource, Inc., a private provider of enterprise-grade virtual infrastructure solutions, for approximately $500 million. In October 2008, Citrix expanded its office in Beijing, China.

Citrix offers its employees educational assistance; onsite fitness centers; work life balance programs; an employee assistance plan; a company car allowance; ongoing professional development; and medical, dental, vision and life insurance.

FINANCIALS: **Sales and profits are in thousands of dollars—add 000 to get the full amount. 2008 Note: Financial information for 2008 was not available for all companies at press time.**

2008 Sales: $1,583,354	2008 Profits: $178,276	**U.S. Stock Ticker: CTXS**
2007 Sales: $1,391,942	2007 Profits: $214,483	**Int'l Ticker:** Int'l Exchange:
2006 Sales: $1,134,319	2006 Profits: $182,997	Employees: 4,620
2005 Sales: $908,722	2005 Profits: $165,609	Fiscal Year Ends: 12/31
2004 Sales: $741,157	2004 Profits: $131,546	Parent Company:

SALARIES/BENEFITS:

Pension Plan: Y	ESOP Stock Plan:	Profit Sharing:	Top Exec. Salary: $675,000	Bonus: $758,134
Savings Plan: Y	Stock Purch. Plan: Y		Second Exec. Salary: $383,750	Bonus: $233,720

OTHER THOUGHTS:

Apparent Women Officers or Directors: 1
Hot Spot for Advancement for Women/Minorities:

LOCATIONS: ("Y" = Yes)

West:	Southwest:	Midwest:	Southeast:	Northeast:	International:
Y	Y	Y	Y	Y	Y

CLARIANT INTERNATIONAL LTD

www.clariant.com

Industry Group Code: 325000 **Ranks within this company's industry group:** Sales: 19 Profits: 23

Techology:		Medical/Drugs:		Engineering:		Transportation:		Chemicals/Petrochemicals:		Specialty:	
Computers:		Manufacturer:		Design:		Aerospace:		Oil/Gas Products:		Special Services:	
Software:		Contract Research:		Construction:		Automotive:		Chemicals:	Y	Consulting:	
Communications:		Medical Services:		Eng. Services:		Shipping:		Oil/Chem. Svcs.:		Specialty Mgmt.:	
Electronics:		Labs:		Consulting:				Gases:		Products:	
Alternative Energy:		Bio. Services:						Other:		Other:	

TYPES OF BUSINESS:

Performance & Specialty Chemicals
Chemical Additives
Pigments & Dyes
Color & Additive Concentrates
Textile, Leather & Paper Chemicals

BRANDS/DIVISIONS/AFFILIATES:

Cartasol
Foron
Drimarene
Custom Manufacturing Business
International Chemical Investors Group
Sioen-EMB
Ricon Colors, Inc.
Rite Systems, Inc.

CONTACTS: *Note: Officers with more than one job title may be intentionally listed here more than once.*

Hariolf Kottmann, CEO
Patrick Jany, CFO
Johann Steiner, Head-Group Human Resources
Holger Schimanke, Head-Investor Rel.
Siegfried Fischer, Head-Functional Chemicals Div.
Peter Brandenberg, Head-Textile, Leather & Paper Chemicals Div.
Okke Koo, Head-Pigments & Additives Div.
Dominik von Bertrab, Head-Masterbatches Div.
Roland Losser, Chmn.

Phone: 41-61-469-6137	**Fax:** 41-61-469-6999
Toll-Free:	
Address: Rathausstrasse 61, Muttenz, CH-4132 Switzerland	

GROWTH PLANS/SPECIAL FEATURES:

Clariant International, Ltd. is a leading developer, producer and marketer of specialty chemicals, with over 100 group companies on five continents. The firm's businesses are organized into four divisions: textile, leather and paper chemicals; pigments and additives; masterbatches; and functional chemicals. The company's textile, leather and paper division includes products for dyeing, tanning, fatiguing and finishing leathers; products for pre-treating, dyeing, printing and finishing textiles; and paper colorants, chemicals and optical brighteners. Brands include the Cartasol brand paper dyes, Foron brand disperse dyes and Drimarene brand reactive dyes. Clariant's pigments and additives division develops and produces pigments for paints, laquers, plastics and special applications; additives to improve heat, light and weather resistance; high quality waxes; and halogen free flame retardants used in protective coatings, resins, thermoplastics and polyester fibers. Its pigment products are used in such applications as coatings, plastics, printing inks, cosmetics and polishes. The masterbatches division offers color and additive concentrates and performance solutions for application in such products as thermoplastic processors, packaging, electronics, carpet, textile and upholstery. The functional chemicals division makes component chemicals, founded on surfactants and polymers, for products and industries including biocides, crop protection, detergents, functional fluids (such as de-icers, brake fluids, car coolants and heat exchange fluids), metalworking, mining, oil services and personal care. Clariant is currently undertaking a transformation program to focus its efforts on its most lucrative product lines, predominantly within the surface and color technology fields. In July 2008, the company acquired Rite Systems, Inc. and Ricon Colors, Inc. In November 2008, Clariant sold its Dick Peters B.V. to German specialty chemicals group ALTANA AG.

FINANCIALS: **Sales and profits are in thousands of dollars—add 000 to get the full amount. 2008 Note: Financial information for 2008 was not available for all companies at press time.**

2008 Sales: $6,987,390	2008 Profits: $-32,030	**U.S. Stock Ticker:**
2007 Sales: $7,387,370	2007 Profits: $4,330	**Int'l Ticker: CLN** Int'l Exchange: Zurich-SWX
2006 Sales: $6,640,400	2006 Profits: $-63,900	Employees: 23,383
2005 Sales: $6,216,700	2005 Profits: $145,900	Fiscal Year Ends: 12/31
2004 Sales: $7,536,300	2004 Profits: $132,500	Parent Company:

SALARIES/BENEFITS:

Pension Plan:	ESOP Stock Plan:	Profit Sharing:	Top Exec. Salary: $	Bonus: $
Savings Plan:	Stock Purch. Plan:		Second Exec. Salary: $	Bonus: $

OTHER THOUGHTS:

Apparent Women Officers or Directors:
Hot Spot for Advancement for Women/Minorities:

LOCATIONS: ("Y" = Yes)

West:	Southwest:	Midwest:	Southeast:	Northeast:	International:
Y	Y	Y	Y	Y	Y

COGNOS INC

www.cognos.com

Industry Group Code: 511207 **Ranks within this company's industry group:** Sales: Profits:

Techology:		Medical/Drugs:		Engineering:		Transportation:		Chemicals/Petrochemicals:		Specialty:	
Computers:		Manufacturer:		Design:		Aerospace:		Oil/Gas Products:		Special Services:	
Software:	Y	Contract Research:		Construction:		Automotive:		Chemicals:		Consulting:	Y
Communications:		Medical Services:		Eng. Services:		Shipping:		Oil/Chem. Svcs.:		Specialty Mgmt.:	
Electronics:		Labs:		Consulting:				Gases:		Products:	
Alternative Energy:		Bio. Services:						Other:		Other:	

TYPES OF BUSINESS:

Business Intelligence Software
Consulting Services
Performance Management Software

BRANDS/DIVISIONS/AFFILIATES:

Cognos ReportNet
Cognos PowerPlay
Cognos Visualize
Cognos DecisionStream
Cognos NoticeCast
Cognos Performance Applications

CONTACTS: *Note: Officers with more than one job title may be intentionally listed here more than once.*

Robert G. Ashe, CEO
Les Rechan, COO
Robert G. Ashe, Pres.
Tom Manley, CFO
Dave Laverty, Chief Mktg. Officer/Sr. VP-Global Mktg.
Claudio Silvestri, CIO
Don Campbell, CTO
Peter Griffiths, Sr. VP-Prod.
Jane Campbell, VP-Prod. Eng.
Tom Manley, Sr. VP-Admin.
John Jussup, Chief Legal Officer/Corp. Sec./Sr. VP
Rob Rose, Chief Strategy Officer
John Lawlor, VP-Corp. Rel.
Tom Manley, Sr. VP-Finance
Rick Gilbody, Pres., Cognos Americas
Ad Voogt, Pres., Cognos Europe
David Pratt, VP-Global Professional Svcs.
Phillip Beniac, Pres., Cognos Asia Pacific
Renato Zambonini, Chmn.
Mel Zeldon, Sr. VP-Global Alliances

Phone: 613-738-1440 **Fax:** 613-738-0002
Toll-Free: 866-601-1934
Address: 3755 Riverside Dr., P.O. Box 9707, Station T, Ottawa, ON K1G 4K9 Canada

GROWTH PLANS/SPECIAL FEATURES:

Cognos, Inc. is a leading global provider of business intelligence (BI) and performance management (PM) software. The company develops, markets and supports an integrated BI platform that allows its clients to improve business performance by enabling effective decision-making at all levels of the organization through the consistent analysis and reporting of data from multiple perspectives. Cognos' software is designed to provide customers with the ability to effectively use data to make faster, more informed decisions in order to improve operational effectiveness, increase customer satisfaction, accelerate corporate response times and ultimately increase revenues and profits. The firm offers BI and analytic application components, application development tools, support and service, as well as education and consulting services. The firm's PM software allows users to effectively direct the full management cycle with planning, budgeting, consolidation, reporting, analysis and scorecarding capabilities. Cognos' brand names include Cognos ReportNet for business and production reporting; Cognos PowerPlay for online analytical processing; Cognos Visualize for data visualization; Cognos DecisionStream for data integration; Cognos NoticeCast for business activity monitoring; and Cognos Performance Applications for pre-built reports and metrics. The company serves more than 23,000 customers in more than 135 countries. Cognos solutions and services are also available from resellers, original equipment manufacturers (OEMs) and distributors worldwide.

FINANCIALS: **Sales and profits are in thousands of dollars—add 000 to get the full amount. 2008 Note: Financial information for 2008 was not available for all companies at press time.**

2008 Sales: $	2008 Profits: $	**U.S. Stock Ticker: COGN**
2007 Sales: $979,264	2007 Profits: $115,697	**Int'l Ticker: CSN** Int'l Exchange: Toronto-TSX
2006 Sales: $877,500	2006 Profits: $108,576	Employees: 3,507
2005 Sales: $825,531	2005 Profits: $124,474	Fiscal Year Ends: 2/28
2004 Sales: $683,531	2004 Profits: $100,897	Parent Company:

SALARIES/BENEFITS:

Pension Plan:	ESOP Stock Plan:	Profit Sharing:	Top Exec. Salary: $519,696	Bonus: $
Savings Plan:	Stock Purch. Plan: Y		Second Exec. Salary: $430,115	Bonus: $2,059

OTHER THOUGHTS:

Apparent Women Officers or Directors: 3
Hot Spot for Advancement for Women/Minorities: Y

LOCATIONS: ("Y" = Yes)

West:	Southwest:	Midwest:	Southeast:	Northeast:	International:
Y	Y	Y	Y	Y	Y

Note: Financial information, benefits and other data can change quickly and may vary from those stated here.

COMPAL ELECTRONICS INC

www.compal.com

Industry Group Code: 334419 **Ranks within this company's industry group:** Sales: 4 Profits: 3

Techology:		**Medical/Drugs:**		**Engineering:**		**Transportation:**		**Chemicals/Petrochemicals:**		**Specialty:**	
Computers:	Y	Manufacturer:		Design:		Aerospace:		Oil/Gas Products:		Special Services:	
Software:		Contract Research:		Construction:		Automotive:		Chemicals:		Consulting:	
Communications:	Y	Medical Services:		Eng. Services:		Shipping:		Oil/Chem. Svcs.:		Specialty Mgmt.:	
Electronics:		Labs:		Consulting:				Gases:		Products:	
Alternative Energy:		Bio. Services:						Other:		Other:	

TYPES OF BUSINESS:

Contract Manufacturing-Computers
Mobile Phones
PDAs
Notebook Computers
Monitors
Personal Music Players

BRANDS/DIVISIONS/AFFILIATES:

GROWTH PLANS/SPECIAL FEATURES:

Compal Electronics, Inc., headquartered in Taiwan, is one of the world's leading contract manufacturers of notebook computers, monitors, mobile phones and PDAs (personal digital assistants). Compal specializes in manufacturing high quality electronics marketed under its clients' brands. The company has established branches in China, the U.K. and the U.S. Compal's in-house research and development groups enable it to produce innovative and high-quality products at a rapid pace. The firm's manufacturing facilities, the Ping-Cheng Factory in Taiwan and the Kunshan Factory in China, are state-of-the-art and are certified for ISO-9001 international quality standards and ISO-14001 international environmental standards. Compal makes a wide variety of products including notebook computers, PDAs, PDAs with cellular phones incorporated, LCD monitors, televisions and portable music players.

Compal offers its employees company trips, an onsite fitness center, shuttle services, training programs and health insurance.

CONTACTS: *Note: Officers with more than one job title may be intentionally listed here more than once.*

Ruicong Chen, Gen. Mgr.
Wenbin Xu, Managing Dir.
Wenzhong Shen, Exec. Deputy Gen. Mgr.
Shaozu Gong, Sr. Deputy Gen. Mgr./Gen. Mgr.-Bus. Group
Zongbin Weng, Sr. Deputy Gen. Mgr./Gen. Mgr.-Bus. Group
Shengxiong Xu, Chmn.

Phone: 886-2-8797-8588 **Fax:** 886-2-2659-1566
Toll-Free:
Address: 581 Juikuang Rd., Neihu, Taipei, 11492 Taiwan

FINANCIALS: **Sales and profits are in thousands of dollars—add 000 to get the full amount. 2008 Note: Financial information for 2008 was not available for all companies at press time.**

2008 Sales: $11,937,700 | 2008 Profits: $372,550
2007 Sales: $11,730,000 | 2007 Profits: $270,000
2006 Sales: $11,472,000 | 2006 Profits: $262,500
2005 Sales: $7,963,900 | 2005 Profits: $252,600
2004 Sales: $6,320,000 | 2004 Profits: $

U.S. Stock Ticker:
Int'l Ticker: 2324 Int'l Exchange: Taipei-TPE
Employees: 30,000
Fiscal Year Ends: 12/31
Parent Company:

SALARIES/BENEFITS:

Pension Plan: Y | ESOP Stock Plan: | Profit Sharing: Y | Top Exec. Salary: $ | Bonus: $
Savings Plan: | Stock Purch. Plan: | Second Exec. Salary: $ | Bonus: $

OTHER THOUGHTS:

Apparent Women Officers or Directors:
Hot Spot for Advancement for Women/Minorities:

LOCATIONS: ("Y" = Yes)

West:	Southwest:	Midwest:	Southeast:	Northeast:	International:
					Y

COMPUTER SCIENCES CORPORATION (CSC)

www.csc.com

Industry Group Code: 541512 **Ranks within this company's industry group:** Sales: 4 Profits: 5

Techology:		Medical/Drugs:		Engineering:		Transportation:		Chemicals/Petrochemicals:		Specialty:	
Computers:		Manufacturer:		Design:		Aerospace:		Oil/Gas Products:		Special Services:	Y
Software:	Y	Contract Research:		Construction:		Automotive:		Chemicals:		Consulting:	Y
Communications:		Medical Services:		Eng. Services:		Shipping:		Oil/Chem. Svcs.:		Specialty Mgmt.:	Y
Electronics:		Labs:		Consulting:				Gases:		Products:	
Alternative Energy:		Bio. Services:						Other:		Other:	

TYPES OF BUSINESS:

IT Consulting
Credit Services
Customer Relationship Management
Business Process Reengineering
Management Consulting
Outsourcing
Supply Chain Management

BRANDS/DIVISIONS/AFFILIATES:

North American Public Sector
Dallas Technology Center
Computer Systems Advisers Sdn Bhd
Log.Sec Corp.
Object Builder Software

CONTACTS:

Note: Officers with more than one job title may be intentionally listed here more than once.

Michael W. Laphen, CEO
Michael W. Laphen, Pres.
Michael J. Mancuso, CFO/VP
Nathan (Gus) Siekierka, VP-Human Resources
William L. Deckelman, Jr., General Counsel/VP/Corp. Sec.
Randy E. Phillips, VP-Corp. Dev.
Bryan Brady, VP-Investor Rel.
Thomas R. Irvin, Treas./VP
Donald G. DeBuck, VP/Controller
Gawie M. Nienaber, VP/Associate General Counsel
M. Louise Turilli, VP/Deputy General Counsel/Asst. Sec.
Michael W. Laphen, Chmn.

Phone: 703-876-1000	**Fax:**
Toll-Free:	
Address: 3170 Fairview Park Dr., Falls Church, VA 22042 US	

GROWTH PLANS/SPECIAL FEATURES:

Computer Sciences Corporation (CSC) is a leading global provider of information technology and business process outsourcing, consulting and systems integration services and other professional services, specializing in the application of complex information technology (IT). The company delivers its services within three broad service lines: North American Public Sector (NPS), Global Outsourcing Services (GOS) and Business Services and Solutions (BS&S). The firm's consulting and professional services include advising clients on the strategic acquisition and utilization of IT, and on business strategy, security, modeling, simulation, engineering, operations, change management and business process reengineering. Its systems integration services encompass designing, developing, implementing and integrating complete information systems. CSC's outsourcing solutions involve operating all or a portion of a customer's technology infrastructure, including systems analysis, applications development, network operations, desktop computing and data center management. The company also provides business process outsourcing services such as procurement and supply chain, call centers and customer relationship management, credit services, claims processing and logistics. CSC licenses software systems for the financial services markets and provides end-to-end e-business solutions for large commercial and government clients. The company has major operations throughout North America, Europe and the Asia-Pacific region, including India. In January 2008, the company acquired First Consulting Group for $365 million. In February 2008, CSC opened its new Dallas Technology Center, a global customer service desk and client meeting facility. In August 2008, the company acquired the remaining 49% stake in Computer Systems Advisers Sdn Bhd (CSAM), a Malaysian IT service provider, making CSAM a wholly owned subsidiary. In December 2008, CSC acquired Log.Sec Corporation, a privately owned IT and logistics engineering firm, and Object Builder Software, a Bulgarian IT services firm.

CSC offers its employees educational assistance; credit union membership; an employee assistance program; flexible spending accounts; and medical, dental, vision, life and disability insurance.

FINANCIALS:

Sales and profits are in thousands of dollars—add 000 to get the full amount. 2008 Note: Financial information for 2008 was not available for all companies at press time.

2008 Sales: $16,499,500	2008 Profits: $544,600	**U.S. Stock Ticker: CSC**
2007 Sales: $14,854,900	2007 Profits: $397,300	**Int'l Ticker:** Int'l Exchange:
2006 Sales: $14,644,800	2006 Profits: $495,600	Employees: 89,000
2005 Sales: $14,080,000	2005 Profits: $758,100	Fiscal Year Ends: 3/31
2004 Sales: $14,767,600	2004 Profits: $519,400	Parent Company:

SALARIES/BENEFITS:

Pension Plan: Y	ESOP Stock Plan:	Profit Sharing:	Top Exec. Salary: $962,348	Bonus: $1,966,100
Savings Plan: Y	Stock Purch. Plan:		Second Exec. Salary: $540,500	Bonus: $537,700

OTHER THOUGHTS:

Apparent Women Officers or Directors: 2
Hot Spot for Advancement for Women/Minorities:

LOCATIONS: ("Y" = Yes)

West:	Southwest:	Midwest:	Southeast:	Northeast:	International:
Y	Y	Y	Y	Y	Y

Note: Financial information, benefits and other data can change quickly and may vary from those stated here.

COMPUWARE CORP

www.compuware.com

Industry Group Code: 511207 **Ranks within this company's industry group:** Sales: 7 Profits: 7

Techology:		Medical/Drugs:		Engineering:		Transportation:		Chemicals/Petrochemicals:		Specialty:	
Computers:		Manufacturer:		Design:		Aerospace:		Oil/Gas Products:		Special Services:	
Software:	Y	Contract Research:		Construction:		Automotive:		Chemicals:		Consulting:	
Communications:		Medical Services:		Eng. Services:		Shipping:		Oil/Chem. Svcs.:		Specialty Mgmt.:	
Electronics:		Labs:		Consulting:				Gases:		Products:	
Alternative Energy:		Bio. Services:						Other:		Other:	

TYPES OF BUSINESS:

Computer Software-Mainframes
Distributed Systems Products
Client/Server Systems Consulting
File & Data Management
Product Application Management & Development
Software for UNIX Systems
IT Staffing Services

BRANDS/DIVISIONS/AFFILIATES:

Abend-AID
XPEDITER
QACenter
STROBE
Covisint
Hilgraeve Inc.

CONTACTS: *Note: Officers with more than one job title may be intentionally listed here more than once.*

Peter Karmanos, Jr., CEO
Bob Paul, COO
Bob Paul, Pres.
Laura Fournier, CFO/Exec. VP
Chris Bockhausen, CTO/Sr. VP
Denise Starr, Chief Admin. Officer
Daniel S. Follis, Jr., General Counsel/VP/Sec.
Laura Fournier, Treas.
Peter Karmanos, Jr., Chmn.

Phone: 313-227-7300 **Fax:** 313-227-7555
Toll-Free: 800-521-9353
Address: 1 Campus Martius, Detroit, MI 48226 US

GROWTH PLANS/SPECIAL FEATURES:

Compuware Corp. provides software products and professional services for the information technology departments of businesses. The company offers products and services in application development, integration, testing and performance management. Compuware's mainframe products focus on improving the productivity of developers and analysts in analysis, unit testing, functional testing, performance testing, defect removal, fault management, file and data management and application performance management in the OS/390 and z/OS series environments. Generally, the company's strategy involves the purchase and marketing of external technologies alongside internal research and development efforts. The firm's products are grouped into the following product lines: File-AID, Abend-AID, XPEDITER, QACenter and STROBE, among others. Compuware's distributed products focus on improving the productivity of the entire development team, including architects, developers, testers and operating analysts. These products support requirements management, application development, unit and functional testing, and application performance analysis. Compuware's distributed products also help development teams in application profiling and rapid new application rollout, as well as in managing server and network application availability on multiple platforms including IBM z/Series (mainframe), Java, MicrosoftWindows and .NET, UNIX, Linux, Oracle and SAP. Subsidiary Covisint specifically addresses business-to-business and supply chain strategies. The company offers a broad range of IT staff supplementation services for distributed systems and mainframe environments, in which more than 4,000 professionals service 7,000 customers at six global centers. In February 2008, Covisint acquired Hilgraeve, Inc.

Employees are offered medical, vision and dental insurance; life and disability insurance; group legal coverage; a global employee stock purchase plan; a 401(k) plan; an employee assistance program; long-term care insurance; and veterinary pet insurance.

FINANCIALS: **Sales and profits are in thousands of dollars—add 000 to get the full amount. 2008 Note: Financial information for 2008 was not available for all companies at press time.**

2008 Sales: $1,229,611 | 2008 Profits: $134,394
2007 Sales: $1,213,002 | 2007 Profits: $158,092
2006 Sales: $1,205,361 | 2006 Profits: $142,960
2005 Sales: $1,231,839 | 2005 Profits: $76,482
2004 Sales: $1,264,647 | 2004 Profits: $49,832

U.S. Stock Ticker: CPWR
Int'l Ticker: Int'l Exchange:
Employees: 6,344
Fiscal Year Ends: 3/31
Parent Company:

SALARIES/BENEFITS:

Pension Plan:	ESOP Stock Plan:	Profit Sharing:	Top Exec. Salary: $1,050,000	Bonus: $3,420,750
Savings Plan: Y	Stock Purch. Plan: Y		Second Exec. Salary: $450,000	Bonus: $1,551,750

OTHER THOUGHTS:

Apparent Women Officers or Directors: 4
Hot Spot for Advancement for Women/Minorities: Y

LOCATIONS: ("Y" = Yes)

West:	Southwest:	Midwest:	Southeast:	Northeast:	International:
Y	Y	Y	Y	Y	Y

COMVERSE TECHNOLOGY INC

www.cmvt.com

Industry Group Code: 511213 **Ranks within this company's industry group:** Sales: Profits:

Techology:		Medical/Drugs:		Engineering:		Transportation:		Chemicals/Petrochemicals:		Specialty:	
Computers:		Manufacturer:		Design:		Aerospace:		Oil/Gas Products:		Special Services:	
Software:	Y	Contract Research:		Construction:		Automotive:		Chemicals:		Consulting:	
Communications:		Medical Services:		Eng. Services:		Shipping:		Oil/Chem. Svcs.:		Specialty Mgmt.:	
Electronics:		Labs:		Consulting:				Gases:		Products:	
Alternative Energy:		Bio. Services:						Other:		Other:	

TYPES OF BUSINESS:

Computer Software-Telecommunications
Voice Messaging Systems
Call Management Systems
Signaling Software
Security & Business Intelligence Software
Mobile Roaming Technology & Services

BRANDS/DIVISIONS/AFFILIATES:

Comverse, Inc.
Total Communications
Verint Systems, Inc.
Ulticom, Inc.
Signalware
Starhome
Application Store

CONTACTS: *Note: Officers with more than one job title may be intentionally listed here more than once.*

Andre Dahan, CEO
Andre Dahan, Pres.
Joseph Chinnici, CFO
John Bunyan, Chief Mktg. Officer
Lance Miyamoto, Exec. VP-Global Human Resources
John Spirtos, Corp. Dev. & Strategy
Joel Legon, Chief Acct. Officer
Dan Bodner, CEO/Pres., Verint Systems
Shawn Osborne, CEO/Pres., Uticom, Inc.
Charles Burdick, Chmn.

Phone: 212-739-1000 **Fax:**
Toll-Free:
Address: 810 7th Ave., New York, NY 10019 US

GROWTH PLANS/SPECIAL FEATURES:

Comverse Technology, Inc. (CTI), together with its subsidiaries, designs, develops, manufactures, markets and supports software, systems and related services for multimedia communication and information processing applications. The firm's products are used in a range of applications by wireless and wireline telecommunications network operators and service providers, call centers and other government, public and commercial organizations worldwide. Subsidiary Comverse, Inc. provides software, systems and services that enable network-based multimedia enhanced communication and converged billing services to over 500 communications service providers in 130 countries. These products, which make up the Total Communication portfolio, address advanced messaging solutions, personalized data and content-based solutions, and billing and account management. Comverse's services are compatible with a variety of deployment models, including in-network, hosted and managed services, and can also run in Voice over Internet Protocol (VoIP), circuit-switched and converged network systems. Through Verint Systems, Inc. CTI provides analytic software-based solutions for communications interception, networked video security and business intelligence. Subsidiary Ulticom, Inc. provides service-enabling signaling software for wireline, wireless and Internet communications. Its Signalware family of products is used by equipment manufacturers, application developers and service providers to deploy infrastructure and enhanced services within the mobility, messaging, payment and location segments. Starhome develops, integrates and manages value-added services for mobile operators, especially advanced roaming services. In February 2009, the company launched the Application Store, which allows telecom carriers more efficient and cost-effective ways to provide new services to their subscribers.

FINANCIALS: **Sales and profits are in thousands of dollars—add 000 to get the full amount. 2008 Note: Financial information for 2008 was not available for all companies at press time.**

2008 Sales: $	2008 Profits: $	**U.S. Stock Ticker: CMVT.PK**
2007 Sales: $	2007 Profits: $	**Int'l Ticker:** Int'l Exchange:
2006 Sales: $1,588,554	2006 Profits: $-39,870	Employees: 5,050
2005 Sales: $1,193,673	2005 Profits: $89,427	Fiscal Year Ends: 1/31
2004 Sales: $765,892	2004 Profits: $-5,386	Parent Company:

SALARIES/BENEFITS:

Pension Plan:	ESOP Stock Plan:	Profit Sharing:	Top Exec. Salary: $671,951	Bonus: $898,218
Savings Plan:	Stock Purch. Plan:		Second Exec. Salary: $400,000	Bonus: $334,882

OTHER THOUGHTS:

Apparent Women Officers or Directors: 1
Hot Spot for Advancement for Women/Minorities:

LOCATIONS: ("Y" = Yes)

West:	Southwest:	Midwest:	Southeast:	Northeast:	International:
Y	Y	Y	Y	Y	Y

CONOCOPHILLIPS COMPANY

www.conocophillips.com

Industry Group Code: 211111 **Ranks within this company's industry group:** Sales: 6 Profits: 13

Techology:		Medical/Drugs:		Engineering:		Transportation:		Chemicals/Petrochemicals:		Specialty:	
Computers:		Manufacturer:		Design:		Aerospace:		Oil/Gas Products:	Y	Special Services:	
Software:		Contract Research:		Construction:		Automotive:		Chemicals:	Y	Consulting:	
Communications:		Medical Services:		Eng. Services:		Shipping:		Oil/Chem. Svcs.:	Y	Specialty Mgmt.:	
Electronics:		Labs:		Consulting:				Gases:	Y	Products:	Y
Alternative Energy:		Bio. Services:						Other:	Y	Other:	

TYPES OF BUSINESS:

Oil & Gas Exploration & Production
Natural Gas Distribution
Refining
Pipelines
Oil Sands Operations
Chemical Production
Technology Investment
Gasoline Retail

BRANDS/DIVISIONS/AFFILIATES:

LUKOIL (OAO)
Conoco
Phillips 66
DCP Midstream LLC
Chevron Phillips Chemical Company LLC
Alaska Gas Pipe
Origin Energy
JET

CONTACTS: *Note: Officers with more than one job title may be intentionally listed here more than once.*

James J. Mulva, CEO
John A. Carrig, COO
John A. Carrig, Pres.
Sigmund L. Cornelius, CFO
W.C.W Chiang, Sr. VP-Mktg.
Carin S. Knickel, VP-Human Resources
Gene L. Batchelder, CIO/Sr. VP-Svcs.
Stephen R. Brand, Sr. VP-Tech.
Luc J. Messier, Sr. VP-Project Dev.
Janet Langford Kelly, General Counsel/Corp. Sec./Sr. VP-Legal
Jeff Sheets, Sr. VP-Planning & Strategy
Red Cavaney, Sr. VP-Public Affairs
Sigmund L. Cornelius, Sr. VP-Finance
Robert A. Ridge, VP-Health, Safety & Environment
James L. Gallogly, Exec. VP-Exploration & Prod.
W.C.W Chiang, Sr. VP-Refining/Transportation
Gregory Goff, Sr. VP-Commercial
James J. Mulva, Chmn.
Ryan M. Lance, Pres., Exploration & Prod., EMEA/Asia

Phone: 281-293-1000	**Fax:**
Toll-Free:	
Address: 600 N. Dairy Ashford Rd., Houston, TX 77079-1175 US	

GROWTH PLANS/SPECIAL FEATURES:

ConocoPhillips is an integrated global energy company. Its six business segments are exploration and production, midstream, refining and marketing, LUKOIL Investment, chemicals and emerging businesses. The exploration and production segment explores for, produces, transports and markets crude oil, natural gas and natural gas liquids worldwide. It also mines oil sands to extract bitumen, which it upgrades into synthetic crude oil. The midstream division gathers, processes and markets natural gas produced by the company and others, and also fractionates and markets natural gas liquids. This segment includes the firm's 50% equity investment in DCP Midstream, LLC. The refining and marketing segment purchases, refines, markets and transports crude oil and petroleum products, mainly in the U.S., Europe and Asia. The LUKOIL Investment segment consists of ConocoPhillips' 20% equity interest in OAO LUKOIL, an integrated oil and gas company headquartered in Russia. The chemicals group, including the company's 50% equity investment in Chevron Phillips Chemical Company LLC, manufactures and markets petrochemicals and plastics worldwide. The emerging businesses segment oversees businesses such as technologies related to hydrocarbon recovery (including heavy oil), refining, alternative energy, biofuels and the environment. In 2008, the company acquired 50% ownership interest in Transcanada's Keystone Oil Pipeline, a project capable of producing 590,000 barrels of crude oil per day, scheduled to begin deliveries in 2009. In April 2008, the company combined resources with BP to begin the Alaska Gas Pipe, a pipeline with the capacity to move 4 billion cubic feet of natural gas per day to markets in Canada and the U.S. In September 2008, ConocoPhillips and Origin Energy announced plans to create a long-term Australasian natural gas business focused on coal bed methane production and liquefied natural gas.

ConocoPhillips' employees receive benefits including spending accounts, insurance, a retirement plan, paid time off, scholarships and tuition reimbursement.

FINANCIALS: **Sales and profits are in thousands of dollars—add 000 to get the full amount. 2008 Note: Financial information for 2008 was not available for all companies at press time.**

2008 Sales: $240,842,000	2008 Profits: $-16,998,000	**U.S. Stock Ticker: COP**
2007 Sales: $187,437,000	2007 Profits: $11,891,000	**Int'l Ticker:** Int'l Exchange:
2006 Sales: $183,650,000	2006 Profits: $15,550,000	Employees: 32,600
2005 Sales: $179,442,000	2005 Profits: $13,529,000	Fiscal Year Ends: 12/31
2004 Sales: $135,076,000	2004 Profits: $8,129,000	Parent Company:

SALARIES/BENEFITS:

Pension Plan: Y	ESOP Stock Plan: Y	Profit Sharing:	Top Exec. Salary: $1,500,000	Bonus: $3,442,500
Savings Plan: Y	Stock Purch. Plan:		Second Exec. Salary: $817,500	Bonus: $1,186,291

OTHER THOUGHTS:

Apparent Women Officers or Directors: 5
Hot Spot for Advancement for Women/Minorities: Y

LOCATIONS: ("Y" = Yes)

West:	Southwest:	Midwest:	Southeast:	Northeast:	International:
Y	Y	Y	Y	Y	Y

CORNING INC

www.corning.com

Industry Group Code: 335921 **Ranks within this company's industry group:** Sales: 1 Profits: 1

Techology:		Medical/Drugs:		Engineering:		Transportation:		Chemicals/Petrochemicals:		Specialty:	
Computers:		Manufacturer:		Design:		Aerospace:		Oil/Gas Products:		Special Services:	
Software:		Contract Research:		Construction:		Automotive:		Chemicals:		Consulting:	
Communications:	Y	Medical Services:		Eng. Services:		Shipping:		Oil/Chem. Svcs.:		Specialty Mgmt.:	
Electronics:		Labs:		Consulting:				Gases:		Products:	
Alternative Energy:		Bio. Services:						Other:		Other:	

TYPES OF BUSINESS:

Glass & Optical Fiber Manufacturing
Electronic Displays
Optical Switching Products
Photonic Modules & Components
Networking Devices
Semiconductor Materials
Laboratory Supplies
Emissions Control Products

BRANDS/DIVISIONS/AFFILIATES:

Samsung Corning Precision Glass
InfiniCor
NexCor
LEAF
Vascade
MetroCor
Corning Cable Systems, LLC

CONTACTS: *Note: Officers with more than one job title may be intentionally listed here more than once.*

Wendell P. Weeks, CEO
Peter F. Volanakis, COO
Peter F. Volanakis, Pres.
James B. Flaws, CFO
Pamela C. Schneider, Chief of Staff/Sr. VP
Joseph A. Miller, Jr., CTO/Exec. VP
Kirk P. Gregg, Chief Admin. Officer/Exec. VP
Lawrence D. McRae, Sr. VP-Strategy & Corp. Dev.
Wendell P. Weeks, Chmn.

Phone: 607-974-9000	**Fax:** 607-974-5927
Toll-Free:	
Address: 1 Riverfront Plz., Corning, NY 14831 US	

GROWTH PLANS/SPECIAL FEATURES:

Corning, Inc. is a global corporation that operates in five business segments: display technologies, telecommunications, environmental technologies, life sciences and specialty materials. The display technologies segment manufactures glass substrates for active matrix liquid crystal displays (LCDs), used in notebook computers, flat panel desktop monitor and LCD televisions. Corning owns 50% of Samsung Corning Precision Glass, which produces glass substrates using a proprietary fusion process. The telecommunications segment produces optical fiber and cable, optical hardware and equipment, photonic modules and components, and optical networking devices for the telecommunications industry. Corning makes and sells InfiniCor fibers for local area networks, data centers and central offices; NexCor fibers for converged services networks; SMF-28e single mode optical fiber for additional transmission wavelengths in metropolitan and access networks; MetroCor fiber products for metropolitan networks; LEAF optical fiber for long-haul, regional and metropolitan networks; and Vascade submarine optical fibers for use in submarine networks. A large part of the firm's optical fiber is sold to subsidiaries such as Corning Cable Systems, LLC. In its environmental technologies segment, Corning produces ceramic products for emissions and pollution control, such as gasoline and diesel substrate and filter products. The company's life sciences segment manufactures laboratory products including microplates, coated slides, filter plates for genomics sample preparation, plastic cell culture dishes, flasks, cryogenic vials, roller bottles and other equipment. The specialty materials segment addresses unique customer needs, such as glass windows for space shuttles and optical components for high-tech industries. Manufacturing and development takes place at more than 48 plants in 15 countries. In August 2008, Corning completed the sale of its Steuben Glass division to Steuben Glass LLC, an affiliate of Schottenstein Stores Corporation. In January 2009, the company announced that it would be laying off approximately 3,500 employees.

FINANCIALS: **Sales and profits are in thousands of dollars—add 000 to get the full amount. 2008 Note: Financial information for 2008 was not available for all companies at press time.**

2008 Sales: $5,948,000	2008 Profits: $5,257,000	**U.S. Stock Ticker: GLW**
2007 Sales: $5,860,000	2007 Profits: $2,150,000	**Int'l Ticker:** Int'l Exchange:
2006 Sales: $5,174,000	2006 Profits: $1,855,000	Employees: 24,800
2005 Sales: $4,579,000	2005 Profits: $585,000	Fiscal Year Ends: 12/31
2004 Sales: $3,854,000	2004 Profits: $-2,165,000	Parent Company:

SALARIES/BENEFITS:

Pension Plan:	ESOP Stock Plan:	Profit Sharing:	Top Exec. Salary: $990,000	Bonus: $2,049,498
Savings Plan:	Stock Purch. Plan:		Second Exec. Salary: $811,000	Bonus: $1,435,632

OTHER THOUGHTS:

Apparent Women Officers or Directors: 2
Hot Spot for Advancement for Women/Minorities: Y

LOCATIONS: ("Y" = Yes)

West:	Southwest:	Midwest:	Southeast:	Northeast:	International:
	Y	Y		Y	Y

COVANCE INC

www.covance.com

Industry Group Code: 541710 **Ranks within this company's industry group:** Sales: 1 Profits: 1

Techology:		Medical/Drugs:		Engineering:		Transportation:		Chemicals/Petrochemicals:		Specialty:	
Computers:		Manufacturer:		Design:		Aerospace:		Oil/Gas Products:		Special Services:	Y
Software:	Y	Contract Research:	Y	Construction:		Automotive:		Chemicals:		Consulting:	Y
Communications:		Medical Services:	Y	Eng. Services:		Shipping:		Oil/Chem. Svcs.:		Specialty Mgmt.:	
Electronics:		Labs:	Y	Consulting:				Gases:		Products:	
Alternative Energy:		Bio. Services:						Other:		Other:	

TYPES OF BUSINESS:

Pharmaceutical Research & Development
Drug Preclinical/Clinical Trials
Laboratory Testing & Analysis
Approval Assistance
Health Economics & Outcomes Services
Online Tools

BRANDS/DIVISIONS/AFFILIATES:

LabLink
Study Tracker
Trial Tracker

CONTACTS: *Note: Officers with more than one job title may be intentionally listed here more than once.*

Joseph L. Herring, CEO
Wendel Barr, COO/Exec. VP
William Klitgaard, CFO/Sr. VP
James W. Lovett, General Counsel/Sr. VP
Richard F. Cimino, Pres., Late Stage Dev.
Joseph L. Herring, Chmn.
Anthony Cork, Pres., Early Dev. Europe

Phone: 609-452-4440 **Fax:**
Toll-Free: 888-268-2623
Address: 210 Carnegie Ctr., Princeton, NJ 08540 US

GROWTH PLANS/SPECIAL FEATURES:

Covance, Inc. is a leading drug development services company and contract research organization. It provides a wide range of product development services to pharmaceutical, biotechnology and medical device industries across the globe. The company also provides laboratory testing services for clients in the chemical, agrochemical and food businesses. The firm operates two business segments: early development services and late-stage development services. Covance's early development services include preclinical services (such as toxicology, pharmaceutical development, research products and a bioanalytical testing service) and Phase I clinical services. Its late-stage development services cover clinical development and support; clinical trials; periapproval and market access; and central laboratory operations. Covance has also introduced several Internet-based products: Study Tracker, an Internet-based client access product, which permits customers of toxicology services to review study data and schedules on a near real-time basis; LabLink, a client access program that allows customers of central laboratory services to review and query lab data; and Trial Tracker, a web-enabled clinical trial project management and tracking tool intended to allow both employees and customers of its late-stage clinical business to review and manage all aspects of clinical-trial projects. In October 2008, Covance purchased an early drug development facility in Greenfield, Indiana from Eli Lilly and Company. In addition, Covance upgraded several research facilities and in June 2008 opened a 50,000 square foot research clinic in Evansville, Indiana. In September 2008 , the firm announced plans to build a preclinical facility in China, and announced in 2009 that it plans to open clinical development offices in Ukraine, Slovakia and Israel. In December 2008, Covance purchased a minority stake in Caprion Proteomics, a provider of proteomics based services to the pharmaceutical industry.

Covance offers its employees benefits such as medical, dental and vision plans; a range of insurance benefits; employee assistance; financial planning services; and tuition reimbursement.

FINANCIALS: **Sales and profits are in thousands of dollars—add 000 to get the full amount. 2008 Note: Financial information for 2008 was not available for all companies at press time.**

2008 Sales: $1,827,067 | 2008 Profits: $196,760
2007 Sales: $1,631,516 | 2007 Profits: $175,929
2006 Sales: $1,406,058 | 2006 Profits: $144,998
2005 Sales: $1,250,400 | 2005 Profits: $119,600
2004 Sales: $1,056,397 | 2004 Profits: $97,947

U.S. Stock Ticker: CVD
Int'l Ticker: Int'l Exchange:
Employees: 9,600
Fiscal Year Ends: 12/31
Parent Company:

SALARIES/BENEFITS:

Pension Plan: | ESOP Stock Plan: | Profit Sharing: | Top Exec. Salary: $684,167 | Bonus: $955,000
Savings Plan: Y | Stock Purch. Plan: Y | | Second Exec. Salary: $355,833 | Bonus: $250,919

OTHER THOUGHTS:

Apparent Women Officers or Directors: 2
Hot Spot for Advancement for Women/Minorities: Y

LOCATIONS: ("Y" = Yes)

West:	Southwest:	Midwest:	Southeast:	Northeast:	International:
Y	Y	Y	Y	Y	Y

CRAY INC

www.cray.com

Industry Group Code: 334111 **Ranks within this company's industry group:** Sales: 17 Profits: 14

Techology:		Medical/Drugs:		Engineering:		Transportation:		Chemicals/Petrochemicals:		Specialty:	
Computers:	Y	Manufacturer:		Design:		Aerospace:		Oil/Gas Products:		Special Services:	
Software:	Y	Contract Research:		Construction:		Automotive:		Chemicals:		Consulting:	
Communications:		Medical Services:		Eng. Services:		Shipping:		Oil/Chem. Svcs.:		Specialty Mgmt.:	Y
Electronics:		Labs:		Consulting:				Gases:		Products:	
Alternative Energy:		Bio. Services:						Other:		Other:	

TYPES OF BUSINESS:

Computer Hardware-Supercomputers
Custom Computers
Software Design

BRANDS/DIVISIONS/AFFILIATES:

Cray XT3
Cray XT4
Cray XT5
Cray XMT

CONTACTS: *Note: Officers with more than one job title may be intentionally listed here more than once.*

Peter J. Ungaro, CEO
Peter J. Ungaro, Pres.
Brian C. Henry, CFO/Exec. VP
Ian W. Miller, Sr. VP-Sales & Mktg.
Linda J. Howitson, VP-Human Resources
Margaret A. (Peg) Williams, VP-R&D
Steve Scott, CTO/Sr. VP
Kenneth W. Johnson, General Counsel/Corp. Sec./Sr. VP
Wayne J. Kugel, VP-Oper.
Erin McGhee, Dir.-Public Rel.
Vic Chynoweth, Dir.-Investor Rel.
Jill Y. Hopper, VP-Gov't Programs
Charles A. Morreale, VP-Customer Support
Stephen C. Kiely, Chmn.

Phone: 206-701-2000 **Fax:** 206-701-2500
Toll-Free: 800-284-2729
Address: 411 1st Ave. S., Ste. 600, Seattle, WA 98104-2860 US

GROWTH PLANS/SPECIAL FEATURES:

Cray, Inc. is a global leader in the design, development, marketing and servicing of high-performance computer (HPC) systems, more commonly known as supercomputers, for government, industry and academic institutions. The company manufactures a standard supercomputer product line, as well as designing and manufacturing customized computers. Its key product lines include the XT5, XT4, XT3 and XMT supercomputers, all sold under the Cray brand name. The XT5 and XMT utilize the Linux operating system. The Cray XT5 system is a massively parallel processing (MPP) system that combines scalability with manageability, lower cost of ownership with reduced power and cooling requirements, and broader application support. The Cray XT5h Hybrid Supercomputer is an integrated hybrid supercomputer that consists of processing capabilities and vector processing with reconfigurable field programmable gate array hardware acceleration, allowing a single system to provide a variety of processing technologies for diverse workflows. The firm sells its products primarily through a direct sales force that operates throughout the U.S. and Canada, Europe, Japan and Asia-Pacific. The super computer systems are installed at more than 100 sites in over 20 countries. In September 2008, the company announced that it would introduce a low-end machine designed to handle tasks too large for a personal computer but not large enough to warrant a supercomputer. The firm expects to introduce the new product starting at $25,000.

Employees are offered medical and dental insurance; short- and long-term disability insurance; life insurance; a 401(k) plan; educational assistance; and an employee stock purchase plan.

FINANCIALS: **Sales and profits are in thousands of dollars—add 000 to get the full amount. 2008 Note: Financial information for 2008 was not available for all companies at press time.**

2008 Sales: $282,853	2008 Profits: $-31,346	**U.S. Stock Ticker: CRAY**
2007 Sales: $186,153	2007 Profits: $-5,719	**Int'l Ticker:** Int'l Exchange:
2006 Sales: $221,017	2006 Profits: $-12,070	Employees: 829
2005 Sales: $201,051	2005 Profits: $-64,308	Fiscal Year Ends: 12/31
2004 Sales: $145,849	2004 Profits: $-207,358	Parent Company:

SALARIES/BENEFITS:

Pension Plan:	ESOP Stock Plan:	Profit Sharing:	Top Exec. Salary: $350,000	Bonus: $437,500
Savings Plan: Y	Stock Purch. Plan: Y		Second Exec. Salary: $325,000	Bonus: $260,000

OTHER THOUGHTS:

Apparent Women Officers or Directors: 4
Hot Spot for Advancement for Women/Minorities: Y

LOCATIONS: ("Y" = Yes)

West:	Southwest:	Midwest:	Southeast:	Northeast:	International:
Y	Y	Y			Y

CSK HOLDINGS CORP

www.csk.co.jp

Industry Group Code: 541512 **Ranks within this company's industry group:** Sales: 17 Profits: 14

Techology:		Medical/Drugs:		Engineering:		Transportation:		Chemicals/Petrochemicals:		Specialty:	
Computers:		Manufacturer:		Design:		Aerospace:		Oil/Gas Products:		Special Services:	Y
Software:		Contract Research:		Construction:		Automotive:		Chemicals:		Consulting:	Y
Communications:		Medical Services:		Eng. Services:		Shipping:		Oil/Chem. Svcs.:		Specialty Mgmt.:	Y
Electronics:		Labs:		Consulting:				Gases:		Products:	
Alternative Energy:		Bio. Services:						Other:		Other:	

TYPES OF BUSINESS:

IT Services
Financial Services
Business Services

BRANDS/DIVISIONS/AFFILIATES:

CSK Group
CSK Institue for Sustainability, Ltd.
Business Extension Corp.
CSK Systems Corp.
Shimane CSK Corp.
CSK Prescendo Corp
CSK Network Systems Corp.
Cosmo Securities Co., Ltd.

CONTACTS: *Note: Officers with more than one job title may be intentionally listed here more than once.*

Yoshito Fukuyama, CEO
Yoshito Fukuyama, Pres.
Takahiro Suzuki, CFO
Taku Tamura, Exec. Officer
Tatsuyasu Kumazaki, Exec. Officer
Yoshiyuki Shinbori, Exec. Officer
Hiroshi Karakasa, Exec. Officer
Masahiro Aozono, Chmn.

Phone: 81-3-6438-3901 **Fax:** 03-6438-3507
Toll-Free:
Address: CSK Ayoma Bldg., 2-26-1 Minami-Aoyama, Minato-ku, Tokyo, 107-0062 Japan

GROWTH PLANS/SPECIAL FEATURES:

CSK Holdings Corporation, formerly CSK Corporation, is an umbrella company that offers information technology (IT) services through more than 30 subsidiaries. The companies within the CSK Group include CSK Systems Corp.; JIEC Co. Ltd.; CSI Solutions Corp.; ISAO Corp.; CSK System Management Corp.; Fukuoka CSK Corp.; Super Software Company Ltd., Hokkaido CSK Corp., CSK Systems (Shanghai) Co. Ltd., ServiceWare Corp.; and CSK Communications Corp., among many others. These companies generally focus on systems integration, systems management and business process outsourcing and operate via three business segments: securities-related services, technology services and financial services. Securities-related services include business process analysis/design; back office BPO; data analysis/management; and contact centers. Technology services include consulting; systems integration; data center services; systems management services; IT infrastructure development; and network monitoring. The financial services division operates in two main areas: real estate securitization and prepaid card business. In February 2007, the company established CSK-RB Securities Corp., a wholly-owned subsidiary that will provide securities services. In March 2007, the firm agreed to start a joint e-commerce platform business in partnership with Xavel, Inc. The proposed company will provide e-commerce systems and fulfillment services, and is to be called CSK Prescendo Corp. CSK Holdings Corp. will own 65% of the business. In August 2008, the firm acquired Cosmo Securities Co., Ltd.

FINANCIALS: Sales and profits are in thousands of dollars—add 000 to get the full amount. 2008 Note: Financial information for 2008 was not available for all companies at press time.

2008 Sales: $2,397,000	2008 Profits: $12,700	**U.S. Stock Ticker:**
2007 Sales: $2,459,800	2007 Profits: $86,800	**Int'l Ticker: 9737** Int'l Exchange: Tokyo-TSE
2006 Sales: $2,411,500	2006 Profits: $308,700	Employees: 9,878
2005 Sales: $3,199,900	2005 Profits: $333,400	Fiscal Year Ends: 3/31
2004 Sales: $3,581,000	2004 Profits: $202,700	Parent Company:

SALARIES/BENEFITS:

Pension Plan:	ESOP Stock Plan:	Profit Sharing:	Top Exec. Salary: $	Bonus: $
Savings Plan:	Stock Purch. Plan:		Second Exec. Salary: $	Bonus: $

OTHER THOUGHTS:

Apparent Women Officers or Directors:
Hot Spot for Advancement for Women/Minorities:

LOCATIONS: ("Y" = Yes)

West:	Southwest:	Midwest:	Southeast:	Northeast:	International:
					Y

CSL LIMITED

www.csl.com.au

Industry Group Code: 325414 **Ranks within this company's industry group:** Sales: 2 Profits: 1

Techology:		Medical/Drugs:		Engineering:		Transportation:		Chemicals/Petrochemicals:		Specialty:	
Computers:		Manufacturer:	Y	Design:		Aerospace:		Oil/Gas Products:		Special Services:	
Software:		Contract Research:		Construction:		Automotive:		Chemicals:		Consulting:	
Communications:		Medical Services:		Eng. Services:		Shipping:		Oil/Chem. Svcs.:		Specialty Mgmt.:	
Electronics:		Labs:	Y	Consulting:				Gases:		Products:	
Alternative Energy:		Bio. Services:	Y					Other:		Other:	

TYPES OF BUSINESS:

- Human Blood-Plasma Collection
- Plasma Products
- Immunohematology Products
- Vaccines
- Pharmaceutical Marketing
- Antivenom
- Drugs-Cancer

BRANDS/DIVISIONS/AFFILIATES:

ZLB Behring
CSL Bioplasma
CSL Behring LLC
CSL Pharmaceutical
CSL Biotherapies
Zenyth Therapeutics
CytoGam
ZLB Plasma Services

CONTACTS: *Note: Officers with more than one job title may be intentionally listed here more than once.*

Brian McNamee, CEO/Managing Dir.
Tony M. Cipa, Exec. Dir.-Finance
Kenneth J. Roberts, Dir.-Mktg.
Kenneth J. Roberts, Gen. Mgr.-Human Resources
Andrew Cuthbertson, Chief Scientific Officer
John Akehurst, Dir.-Eng.
Greg Boss, General Counsel/Sr. VP
Paul Walton, Sr. VP-Corp. Dev.
Rachel David, Dir.-Public Affairs
Elizabeth A. Alexander, Mgr.-Finance & Risk
Peter Turner, Pres., CSL Behring
Colin Armit, Pres., CSL Biotherapies
Mary Sontrop, Gen Mgr.-CSL Biotherapies, Australia & New Zealand
Edward Bailey, Australian General Counsel/Corp. Sec.
Elizabeth A. Alexander, Chmn.
Jeff Davies, Pres., Bioplasma Asia Pacific

Phone: 61-3-9389-1911 **Fax:** 61-3-9389-1434
Toll-Free:
Address: 45 Poplar Rd., Parkville, VIC 3052 Australia

GROWTH PLANS/SPECIAL FEATURES:

CSL Limited develops, manufactures and markets pharmaceutical products of biological origin in 27 countries worldwide. The company operates through several subsidiaries that manufacture and distribute pharmaceuticals, vaccines and diagnostics derived from human plasma. The firm's subsidiaries include CSL Behring, CSL Limited, CSL Bioplasma, CSL Biotherapies, CSL Research & Development, ZLB Behring and Zenyth Therapeutics. CSL Behring is a world leader in the manufacture of plasma products such as hemophilia treatments, immunoglobulins and wound healing agents. CSL Limited operates one of the largest plasma collection networks in the world, named ZLB Plasma Services, which includes 65 collection centers in the U.S. and eight in Germany. CSL Bioplasma is one of the largest manufacturers of plasma products in the southern hemisphere and works with the Red Cross and government entities to supply such products in Australia, New Zealand, Singapore, Malaysia and Hong Kong. It also provides contract plasma fractionation services. CSL Biotherapies, formerly CSL Pharmaceutical, manufactures and markets vaccines for human use, including children's vaccines, travel vaccines, respiratory vaccines and antivenom. Currently, its primary focus is the manufacturing of flu vaccines. The company's research and development portfolio includes treatments for stroke, acute coronary syndromes, cervical cancer, melanoma, genital warts, papilloma viruses and hepatitis C, in addition to a method of topical delivery of drugs to the eye. ZLB Behring holds the rights to CytoGam, an intravenous drug for the prevention of antibodies against cytomegalovirus in transplant patients. Zenyth Therapeutics develops and commercializes therapeutic antibodies for cancer and inflammation. In August 2008, the company agreed to acquire Talecris Biotherapeutics, a U.S.-based biotherapeutic and biotechnology company, for $3.1 billion.

CSL Limited provides flexible work arrangements, a Global Employee Share Plan for stock purchase, ongoing training programs and study assistance.

FINANCIALS: **Sales and profits are in thousands of dollars—add 000 to get the full amount. 2008 Note: Financial information for 2008 was not available for all companies at press time.**

2008 Sales: $2,698,750	2008 Profits: $499,350	**U.S. Stock Ticker:**
2007 Sales: $2,354,470	2007 Profits: $383,400	**Int'l Ticker: CSL** Int'l Exchange: Sydney-ASX
2006 Sales: $2,146,111	2006 Profits: $88,406	Employees: 7,000
2005 Sales: $1,965,359	2005 Profits: $176,824	Fiscal Year Ends: 6/30
2004 Sales: $1,650,196	2004 Profits: $219,625	Parent Company:

SALARIES/BENEFITS:

Pension Plan:	ESOP Stock Plan:	Profit Sharing:	Top Exec. Salary: $782,154	Bonus: $273,292
Savings Plan:	Stock Purch. Plan: Y		Second Exec. Salary: $409,753	Bonus: $273,292

OTHER THOUGHTS:

Apparent Women Officers or Directors: 3
Hot Spot for Advancement for Women/Minorities: Y

LOCATIONS: ("Y" = Yes)

West:	Southwest:	Midwest:	Southeast:	Northeast:	International:
		Y	Y	Y	Y

CTS CORP

www.ctscorp.com

Industry Group Code: 334419 **Ranks within this company's industry group:** Sales: 10 Profits: 6

Techology:		Medical/Drugs:		Engineering:		Transportation:		Chemicals/Petrochemicals:		Specialty:	
Computers:		Manufacturer:		Design:		Aerospace:		Oil/Gas Products:		Special Services:	Y
Software:		Contract Research:		Construction:		Automotive:		Chemicals:		Consulting:	
Communications:		Medical Services:		Eng. Services:		Shipping:		Oil/Chem. Svcs.:		Specialty Mgmt.:	Y
Electronics:	Y	Labs:		Consulting:				Gases:		Products:	
Alternative Energy:		Bio. Services:						Other:		Other:	

TYPES OF BUSINESS:

Electronic Components
Components & Sensors
Manufacturing & Assembly Services
Interconnect Systems
Supply Chain Services
Electronics Manufacturing Services

BRANDS/DIVISIONS/AFFILIATES:

CTS Electronics Manufacturing Solutions
Alpha Ceramics Inc
Tusonix Inc
Orion Manufacturing Inc

CONTACTS: *Note: Officers with more than one job title may be intentionally listed here more than once.*

Vinod M. Khilnani, CEO
Vinod M. Khilnani, Pres.
Matthew W. Long, Interim CFO/Treas.
Tony Corscadden, Sr. VP-Global Oper.
Matthew Long, Treas.
Donald R. Schroeder, Exec. VP/Pres., CTS Electronics Mfg. Solutions
H. Tyler Buchanan, Sr. VP
Roger R. Hemminghaus, Chmn.

Phone: 574-293-7511	**Fax:** 574-293-6146
Toll-Free:	
Address: 905 W. Blvd. N., Elkhart, IN 46514 US	

GROWTH PLANS/SPECIAL FEATURES:

CTS Corp. designs, manufactures and sells electronic components and custom electronic assemblies for the automotive, computer, communications, medical, industrial defense and aerospace markets. The company operates manufacturing facilities throughout North America, Asia and Europe. Its product lines serve major markets worldwide focused primarily on the needs of original equipment manufacturers. The company operates through two business segments: Components and Sensors; and Electronics Manufacturing Services (EMS). Components and sensors division consists of products which perform specific electronic functions for a given product family and are intended for use in customer assemblies. Components and sensors consist principally of automotive sensors and actuators used in commercial or consumer vehicles; electronic components used in communications infrastructure and computer markets; components used in computer and other high-speed applications, switches, resistor networks, and potentiometers used to serve multiple markets and fabricated piezoelectric materials and substrates used primarily in medical, industrial and defense and aerospace markets. Products from the Components and Sensors segment are principally sold in three major original equipment manufacturer (OEM) markets: automotive; communications; and computer. EMS includes the higher level assembly of electronic and mechanical components into a finished subassembly or assembly performed under a contract manufacturing agreement with an OEM or other contract manufacturer. Additionally, for some customers, the firm provides full turnkey manufacturing and completion including design, bill-of-material management, logistics and repair. Products from the EMS segment are principally sold in the communications, computer, medical, industrial, and defense and aerospace OEM markets. In January 2008, the company acquired Tusonix, Inc. for approximately $15 million. In March 2008, the firm acquired Orion Manufacturing, Inc. for $10 million.

Employees are offered medical and dental coverage; life insurance; a 401(k) plan; health and dependent care reimbursement accounts; and tuition reimbursement.

FINANCIALS: Sales and profits are in thousands of dollars—add 000 to get the full amount. 2008 Note: Financial information for 2008 was not available for all companies at press time.

2008 Sales: $691,707	2008 Profits: $29,886	**U.S. Stock Ticker: CTS**
2007 Sales: $685,945	2007 Profits: $25,412	**Int'l Ticker:** Int'l Exchange:
2006 Sales: $655,614	2006 Profits: $24,197	Employees: 5,044
2005 Sales: $617,484	2005 Profits: $20,756	Fiscal Year Ends: 12/31
2004 Sales: $531,316	2004 Profits: $19,956	Parent Company:

SALARIES/BENEFITS:

Pension Plan:	ESOP Stock Plan:	Profit Sharing:	Top Exec. Salary: $791,945	Bonus: $704,438
Savings Plan: Y	Stock Purch. Plan:		Second Exec. Salary: $432,000	Bonus: $351,055

OTHER THOUGHTS:

Apparent Women Officers or Directors:
Hot Spot for Advancement for Women/Minorities:

LOCATIONS: ("Y" = Yes)

West:	Southwest:	Midwest:	Southeast:	Northeast:	International:
Y	Y	Y		Y	Y

CUMMINS INC

www.cummins.com

Industry Group Code: 336300 **Ranks within this company's industry group:** Sales: 9 Profits: 6

Techology:		Medical/Drugs:		Engineering:		Transportation:		Chemicals/Petrochemicals:		Specialty:	
Computers:		Manufacturer:		Design:		Aerospace:		Oil/Gas Products:		Special Services:	
Software:		Contract Research:		Construction:		Automotive:	Y	Chemicals:		Consulting:	
Communications:		Medical Services:		Eng. Services:		Shipping:	Y	Oil/Chem. Svcs.:		Specialty Mgmt.:	
Electronics:		Labs:		Consulting:				Gases:		Products:	
Alternative Energy:	Y	Bio. Services:						Other:		Other:	

TYPES OF BUSINESS:

Automotive Products, Motors & Parts Manufacturing
Engines
Filtration Systems
Power Generation Systems
Alternators
Air Handling Systems
Filtration & Emissions Solutions
Fuel Systems

BRANDS/DIVISIONS/AFFILIATES:

Cummins Power Generation
Onan

CONTACTS: *Note: Officers with more than one job title may be intentionally listed here more than once.*

Theodore M. Solso, CEO
Tom Linebarger, COO
Tom Linebarger, Pres.
Pat Ward, CFO/VP
John C. Wall, CTO/VP
Mark Gerstle, Chief Admin. Officer/ VP-Corp. Quality
Marya M. Rose, General Counsel/VP/Sec.
Richard J. Freeland
Tony Satterthwaite, VP/Pres., Components Group
J. D. Kelly, VP/Pres., Engine Bus.
Steven M. Chapman, VP-Emerging Markets & Bus.
Theodore M. Solso, Chmn.

Phone: 812-377-5000 **Fax:** 812-377-3334
Toll-Free:
Address: 500 Jackson St., Columbus, IN 47202 US

GROWTH PLANS/SPECIAL FEATURES:

Cummins, Inc. designs, manufactures, distributes and services diesel and natural gas engines; electric power generation systems; and engine-related component products, including filtration and emissions solutions, fuel systems, controls and air handling systems. The engine segment, which generated 52% of 2007 sales, manufactures and markets diesel and natural gas-powered engines, parts, and services under the Cummins brand name for the heavy- and medium-duty truck, bus, recreational vehicle, light-duty automotive, agricultural, construction, mining, marine, oil and gas, rail and governmental equipment markets. The power generation segment generated 19% of 2007 revenue, and designs and manufactures components of power generation systems, including engines, controls, alternators, transfer switches and switchgear. Products are marketed principally under the Cummins Power Generation and Onan brands and include diesel and alternative-fuel electrical generator sets for commercial, institutional and consumer applications, such as office buildings, hospitals, factories, municipalities, utilities, universities, boats and homes. The components segment, which accounted for 19% of 2007 net sales, produces filters, silencers and intake and exhaust systems and commercial turbochargers. The distribution segment, producing 10% of revenue, consists of 17 company-owned and 15 joint ventures that distribute the company's products and services in over 70 countries and territories. Cummins serves customers through a network of more than 500 company-owned and independent distributor locations and roughly 5,200 dealer locations in more than 190 countries and territories. In 2007, the firm's North American heavy-duty truck engine market declined 50% due to new emissions regulations; over half of 2007 sales came from countries outside the U.S. In January 2008, Cummins entered into an agreement with Elmarco s.ro., a Czech nanotechnology designer, to develop nanofiber filtration technologies. In July 2008, the company concluded joint ventures with CNH Global N.V. and Iveco N.V.; Cummins will make Consolidated Diesel Company a subsidiary, and sell its interest in European Engine Alliance.

FINANCIALS: **Sales and profits are in thousands of dollars—add 000 to get the full amount. 2008 Note: Financial information for 2008 was not available for all companies at press time.**

2008 Sales: $14,342,000 — 2008 Profits: $755,000
2007 Sales: $13,048,000 — 2007 Profits: $739,000
2006 Sales: $11,362,000 — 2006 Profits: $715,000
2005 Sales: $9,918,000 — 2005 Profits: $550,000
2004 Sales: $8,438,000 — 2004 Profits: $350,000

U.S. Stock Ticker: CMI
Int'l Ticker: Int'l Exchange:
Employees: 39,800
Fiscal Year Ends: 12/31
Parent Company:

SALARIES/BENEFITS:

Pension Plan: | ESOP Stock Plan: | Profit Sharing: Y | Top Exec. Salary: $1,110,000 | Bonus: $6,274,000
Savings Plan: Y | Stock Purch. Plan: Y | Second Exec. Salary: $812,500 | Bonus: $2,840,750

OTHER THOUGHTS:

Apparent Women Officers or Directors: 3
Hot Spot for Advancement for Women/Minorities: Y

LOCATIONS: ("Y" = Yes)

West:	Southwest:	Midwest:	Southeast:	Northeast:	International:
Y	Y	Y	Y	Y	Y

DAELIM INDUSTRIAL CO LTD

www.daelim.co.kr

Industry Group Code: 234000 **Ranks within this company's industry group:** Sales: Profits:

Techology:		Medical/Drugs:		Engineering:		Transportation:		Chemicals/Petrochemicals:		Specialty:	
Computers:		Manufacturer:		Design:		Aerospace:		Oil/Gas Products:		Special Services:	
Software:		Contract Research:		Construction:	Y	Automotive:		Chemicals:		Consulting:	
Communications:		Medical Services:		Eng. Services:	Y	Shipping:		Oil/Chem. Svcs.:		Specialty Mgmt.:	
Electronics:		Labs:		Consulting:				Gases:		Products:	
Alternative Energy:		Bio. Services:						Other:	Y	Other:	

TYPES OF BUSINESS:

Construction
Petrochemicals Distribution

BRANDS/DIVISIONS/AFFILIATES:

CONTACTS:

Note: Officers with more than one job title may be intentionally listed here more than once.

Young Koo Lee, CEO
Jong In Kim, Pres./CEO-Eng. & Construction Div.
Jong Kook Park, Sr. VP-Admin.
Jong Kook Park, Sr. VP-Finance
Joo Hee Han, Pres./CEO-Petrochemical Div.
Young Koo Lee, Chmn.

Phone: 82-2-2011-7114 **Fax:** 82-2-2011-8000
Toll-Free:
Address: 146-12 Susong-Dong, Jongno-Gu, Seoul, 110-732 Korea

GROWTH PLANS/SPECIAL FEATURES:

Daelim Industrial Co., Ltd. is a construction and engineering firm operating in four primary divisions: building, housing, civil works and plants. The building division is engaged in the construction of offices; cultural and assembly facilities; commercial buildings, such as markets and department stores; educational facilities, such as university buildings; medical and sports facilities, such as the King Abdul Aziz University Hospital; and others, such as the Seoul Court House Complex and the U.S. Embassy in Bangladesh. Some of the division's projects include constructing the main stadium for the 1988 Seoul Olympics, the Sejong Performing Arts Center and the main campus of the Arabian Gulf University in Bahrain. The housing division has three main activities: constructing apartments and stores; redevelopment and reconstruction, primarily in residential areas of Korea; and remodeling, primarily of commercial and cultural facilities, such as Meyongdong Cathedral, the Daelim Contemporary Art Museum and the main building of the Bank of Korea. The civil works division has three broad categories of projects. The first combines expressways, airports, airfields and bridges. The second encompasses railroads, subways and tunnels. The third is engaged in the construction of dams; irrigation infrastructure; and harbors and marine facilities. Some of the division's projects include constructing the King Fahad International Airport in Saudi Arabia, the Ayer Rajah Expressway in Singapore, the Hwacheon Dam and the Dintulu Deepwater Port in Malaysia. Finally, the firm's plants division constructs chemical plants, such as oil refineries and petrochemical processing facilities, including plants in India, the Middle East, Africa, the U.S., Southeast Asia and Korea; and power plants, which Daelim has constructed both in Korea and abroad. In August 2008, the firm liquidated two of its construction subsidiaries. Also in August 2008, Daelim established a new wholly-owned construction subsidiary, headquartered in China.

FINANCIALS:

Sales and profits are in thousands of dollars—add 000 to get the full amount. 2008 Note: Financial information for 2008 was not available for all companies at press time.

2008 Sales: $	2008 Profits: $
2007 Sales: $3,641,270	2007 Profits: $339,070
2006 Sales: $3,412,040	2006 Profits: $188,700
2005 Sales: $6,138,686	2005 Profits: $355,780
2004 Sales: $5,655,905	2004 Profits: $434,751

U.S. Stock Ticker:
Int'l Ticker: 000210 Int'l Exchange: Seoul-KRX
Employees:
Fiscal Year Ends: 12/31
Parent Company:

SALARIES/BENEFITS:

Pension Plan:	ESOP Stock Plan:	Profit Sharing:	Top Exec. Salary: $	Bonus: $
Savings Plan:	Stock Purch. Plan:		Second Exec. Salary: $	Bonus: $

OTHER THOUGHTS:

Apparent Women Officers or Directors:
Hot Spot for Advancement for Women/Minorities:

LOCATIONS: ("Y" = Yes)

West:	Southwest:	Midwest:	Southeast:	Northeast:	International:
	Y				Y

DAESUNG INDUSTRIAL CO LTD

www.daesung.co.kr/eng

Industry Group Code: 447110 **Ranks within this company's industry group:** Sales: Profits:

Techology:		Medical/Drugs:		Engineering:		Transportation:		Chemicals/Petrochemicals:		Specialty:	
Computers:	Y	Manufacturer:		Design:	Y	Aerospace:		Oil/Gas Products:		Special Services:	
Software:		Contract Research:		Construction:		Automotive:		Chemicals:		Consulting:	
Communications:		Medical Services:		Eng. Services:		Shipping:		Oil/Chem. Svcs.:		Specialty Mgmt.:	
Electronics:	Y	Labs:		Consulting:				Gases:		Products:	
Alternative Energy:		Bio. Services:						Other:		Other:	

TYPES OF BUSINESS:

Basic Materials Manufacturing
Manufacturing Components for Electronics & Machinery
Construction
Energy Services
Telecommunications Services
Food Distribution Services
Tourism

BRANDS/DIVISIONS/AFFILIATES:

Daesung Industrial Gasses Co., Ltd.
Cambridge Filter Korea Co., Ltd.
Daesung Measuring Co., Ltd.
Daesung Nachi Co., Ltd.
Daesung Celtic Co., Ltd.
KahaTS Inc.
Munkyung Saejae Tourist Co., Ltd.

CONTACTS: *Note: Officers with more than one job title may be intentionally listed here more than once.*

Young Tae Kim, CEO

Phone: 82-2-21-70-2100 **Fax:** 82-2-72-39-339
Toll-Free:
Address: Gwanhung-dong 155-2, Jongro-gu, Seoul, 110-300 Korea

GROWTH PLANS/SPECIAL FEATURES:

Daesung Industrial Co., Ltd. is a Korean company providing energy services, materials manufacturing, machinery and electronics, construction services, leisure and food packages and telecommunications products. The company's energy service operations include the petroleum and gas division, which operates 40 petroleum stations and 15 LP gas filling stations; and its heat absorption and redistribution operations are handled by its Co-Gen. division. Daesung Industrial Co., Ltd. manufactures basic materials and components for electronics and machinery, as well as providing construction, energy, telecommunications and food distribution services. Some of the basic materials produced are industrial gases, manufactured by Daesung Industrial Gasses Co., Ltd., which manufactures nitrogen, oxygen and specialty gases. Cambridge Filter Korea Co., Ltd. manufactures several different types of filter used in the semiconductor, electronic appliance and biotechnology industries, such as HEPA (High Efficiency Particulate Air) filters and UV photon electron filters. The last basic material the company makes is detergent, for both industrial and home use. It has several divisions dedicated to machinery and electronics components manufacturing. The machinery business division manufactures hydraulic and pneumatic pressure tools; geared motors; industrial bearings; and even industrial robots. Daesung Measuring Co., Ltd. produces gas meters and other sensors. Its computer system integration division produces computer equipment, CAD/CAM (Computer-Aided Deslgn/Computer-Alded Manufacturing) software and high speed scanners. Daesung Nachi Co., Ltd. produces hydraulic valves; and Daesung Celtic Co., Ltd. produces home gas boilers. Its construction division has built numerous high-rise apartment complexes, as well as engaging in several environmental conservation projects such as waste treatment. The company offers leisure activities through Munkyung Saejae Tourist Co., Ltd. Its food business imports olive oil from Greece, honey from New Zealand and other products from around the world. KahaTS, Inc. handles the firm's telecommunications activities, including updating the company's website, as well as offering a payroll outsourcing system.

FINANCIALS: **Sales and profits are in thousands of dollars—add 000 to get the full amount. 2008 Note: Financial information for 2008 was not available for all companies at press time.**

2008 Sales: $	2008 Profits: $	**U.S. Stock Ticker:**
2007 Sales: $	2007 Profits: $	**Int'l Ticker: 005620** Int'l Exchange: Seoul-KRX
2006 Sales: $	2006 Profits: $	Employees:
2005 Sales: $6,690	2005 Profits: $	Fiscal Year Ends: 12/31
2004 Sales: $	2004 Profits: $	Parent Company:

SALARIES/BENEFITS:

Pension Plan:	ESOP Stock Plan:	Profit Sharing:	Top Exec. Salary: $	Bonus: $
Savings Plan:	Stock Purch. Plan:		Second Exec. Salary: $	Bonus: $

OTHER THOUGHTS:

Apparent Women Officers or Directors:
Hot Spot for Advancement for Women/Minorities:

LOCATIONS: ("Y" = Yes)

West:	Southwest:	Midwest:	Southeast:	Northeast:	International:
					Y

DAEWOO SHIPBUILDING & MARINE ENGINEERING CO LTD

www.dsme.co.kr

Industry Group Code: 336600 **Ranks within this company's industry group:** Sales: Profits:

Techology:		Medical/Drugs:		Engineering:		Transportation:		Chemicals/Petrochemicals:		Specialty:	
Computers:		Manufacturer:		Design:	Y	Aerospace:		Oil/Gas Products:		Special Services:	
Software:		Contract Research:		Construction:	Y	Automotive:		Chemicals:		Consulting:	
Communications:		Medical Services:		Eng. Services:	Y	Shipping:	Y	Oil/Chem. Svcs.:		Specialty Mgmt.:	
Electronics:		Labs:		Consulting:				Gases:		Products:	
Alternative Energy:		Bio. Services:						Other:		Other:	

TYPES OF BUSINESS:

Ship Building
Robotics R&D
Offshore Oil Rig Construction
Submarine Building

BRANDS/DIVISIONS/AFFILIATES:

Daewoo Mangalia Heavy Industries
DSME Shandong Co Ltd
DSEC
WELLIV
DSME E&R
DSME Construction
Shinhan Machinery

CONTACTS: *Note: Officers with more than one job title may be intentionally listed here more than once.*

Sang-Tae Nam, CEO
Dong-Gack Kim, COO/Sr. Exec. VP
Sang-Tae Nam, Pres.
Dong-Gack Kim, CFO/Sr. Exec. VP
Young-Man Lee, CTO/Sr. VP

Phone: 82-2-2129-0144	**Fax:** 82-2-756-4390
Toll-Free:	
Address: 85, Da-dong, Jung-gu, Seoul, 100-714 Korea	

GROWTH PLANS/SPECIAL FEATURES:

Daewoo Shipbuilding and Marine Engineering (DSME) Co., Ltd. builds vessels, drilling rigs, offshore platforms, floating oil production units, destroyers and submarines. Its subsidiaries include Daewoo Mangalia Heavy Industries (DMHI), in Romania; DSME Shandong Co., Ltd., in China; and five Korean subsidiaries: DSEC, WELLIV, DSME E&R, DSME Construction and Shinhan Machinery. In terms of production capacity, DSME can manufacture approximately 70 commercial vessels, 10 specialty vessels and 30 to 40 offshore and onshore plants annually. The firm can also repair and refurbish up to 200 vessels a year. Its commercial vessels include tankers; liquefied natural gas (LNG) and liquefied petroleum gas (LPG) carriers; passenger ferries, container ships; roll-on roll-off (RORO) carriers; chemical carriers; product tankers; and others. Specialty vessels include submarines; battle ships; destroyers; submarine rescue vehicles; and AUVs (Autonomous Underwater Vehicles) such as the Okpo 6000, which can operate up to 6,000 meters below the surface. DSME is one of the only companies in Korea which builds submarines. Offshore plants include fixed platforms, rigs and offshore oil and gas exploration and production plants. The firm is actively engaged in robotics R&D, including developing security, cleaning and personal humanoid robots; developing technology for sensory perception covering all five senses; and developing applied technology for painting and welding robots. It also engages in ship and ocean R&D, such as researching special and multipurpose propellers; developing noise and vibration reduction systems and software; and developing automation systems for offshore platforms and ships. The firm maintains shipyards in Korea and Romania and overseas branch offices in Japan, Greece, the U.K., Norway, Angola, the United Arab Emirates, Canada and Australia, as well as U.S. offices in New York and Houston. It employs approximately 1,500 design and R&D personnel.

FINANCIALS: **Sales and profits are in thousands of dollars—add 000 to get the full amount. 2008 Note: Financial information for 2008 was not available for all companies at press time.**

2008 Sales: $	2008 Profits: $	**U.S. Stock Ticker:**
2007 Sales: $6,170,000	2007 Profits: $60,000	**Int'l Ticker: 042660** Int'l Exchange: Seoul-KRX
2006 Sales: $6,132,159	2006 Profits: $63,039	Employees:
2005 Sales: $5,352,134	2005 Profits: $5,120	Fiscal Year Ends: 12/31
2004 Sales: $	2004 Profits: $	Parent Company:

SALARIES/BENEFITS:

Pension Plan:	ESOP Stock Plan:	Profit Sharing:	Top Exec. Salary: $	Bonus: $
Savings Plan:	Stock Purch. Plan:		Second Exec. Salary: $	Bonus: $

OTHER THOUGHTS:

Apparent Women Officers or Directors:
Hot Spot for Advancement for Women/Minorities:

LOCATIONS: ("Y" = Yes)

West:	Southwest:	Midwest:	Southeast:	Northeast:	International:
	Y			Y	Y

DAIHATSU MOTOR CO LTD

www.daihatsu.com

Industry Group Code: 336111 **Ranks within this company's industry group:** Sales: 17 Profits: 16

Techology:		Medical/Drugs:		Engineering:		Transportation:		Chemicals/Petrochemicals:		Specialty:	
Computers:		Manufacturer:		Design:		Aerospace:		Oil/Gas Products:		Special Services:	
Software:		Contract Research:		Construction:		Automotive:	Y	Chemicals:		Consulting:	
Communications:		Medical Services:		Eng. Services:		Shipping:		Oil/Chem. Svcs.:		Specialty Mgmt.:	
Electronics:		Labs:		Consulting:				Gases:		Products:	
Alternative Energy:		Bio. Services:						Other:		Other:	

TYPES OF BUSINESS:

Automobile Manufacturing
Industrial Engines
Electric Vehicles

BRANDS/DIVISIONS/AFFILIATES:

Daihatsu Motor Kyushu Co., Ltd.
Cuore
Sirion
Terios
Copen
Materia
Xenia

CONTACTS: *Note: Officers with more than one job title may be intentionally listed here more than once.*

Teruyuki Minoura, Pres.
Katsuyuki Kamio, Exec. VP-Product Mktg.
Hiroaki Iwabe, Dir.-Global Human Resources
Hiroshi Okano, Sr. Exec.-R&D
Kiyokazu Seo, Exec. VP-Eng.
Kiyokazu Seo, Exec. VP-Mfg.
Katsuhiko Okumura, Exec. VP-Gen. Admin.
Katsuyuki Kamio, Exec. VP-Global Oper.
Katsuhiko Okumura, Exec. VP-Corp. Planning
Katsuhiro Ikoma, Sr. Exec. Officer-Quality Group
Yasunori Nakawaki, Sr. Exec. Officer-Power Train Dev. Center
Tadafumi Aisaka, Sr. Exec. Officer-K-Car Dev. Center
Kousuke Shiramizu, Chmn.
Katsuyuki Kamio, Exec. VP-Overseas Oper.
Katsuhiko Okumura, Exec. VP-Purchasing

Phone: 81-072-751-8811 **Fax:** 81-072-753-6880
Toll-Free:
Address: 1-1 Daihatsu-cho, Ikeda-city, 563-8651 Japan

GROWTH PLANS/SPECIAL FEATURES:

Daihatsu Motor Co., Ltd., headquartered in Osaka, Japan, manufactures small, economy-priced passenger cars. Additionally, the company is engaged in the manufacture and sale of automobile parts, generators, machine tools and the repair and sale of industrial vehicles. Its models include the Materia, the Trevis, the Terios, the Coper, the Sirion, and the Cuore/Charade. The company specializes in compact wagons and SUVs. With five factories in Japan, Daihatsu produces approximately 909,000 vehicles annually, including the 187,000 Toyota cars it assembles on a contract basis. Toyota, Japan's largest automotive company, owns 51% of Daihatsu. The firm exports its models to over 140 countries. Daihatsu also manufactures electric vehicles and industrial engines. Subsidiaries of Daihatsu include Daihatsu Diesel Mfg. Co., Daihatsu Motor Kyushu Co., Aoi Machine Industry Co., Akashikikai Industry Co., Asano Gear Co., Ogino Corporation, Kanbishi Corporation, Daihatsu Car Net, Daihatsu Metal Co., Daihatsu Money Lending and Daihatsu Life Net. In November 2007, Daihatsu launched the Gran Max in Indonesia, a light weight commercial vehicle which offers two models: a pick up truck or a minibus. The minibus is the only vehicle in its class to feature sliding doors on both sides. In December 2007, Daihatsu launched the re-designed Tanto model. The Tanto was first introduced in 2003; the updated Tanto includes Tanto Custom, and offers enhanced safety, driving and environmental performance.

FINANCIALS: **Sales and profits are in thousands of dollars—add 000 to get the full amount. 2008 Note: Financial information for 2008 was not available for all companies at press time.**

2008 Sales: $16,993,738	2008 Profits: $348,742	**U.S. Stock Ticker:**
2007 Sales: $14,897,800	2007 Profits: $316,000	**Int'l Ticker: 7262** Int'l Exchange: Tokyo-TSE
2006 Sales: $12,266,500	2006 Profits: $305,100	Employees: 13,198
2005 Sales: $10,703,800	2005 Profits: $235,400	Fiscal Year Ends: 3/31
2004 Sales: $9,405,500	2004 Profits: $163,600	Parent Company:

SALARIES/BENEFITS:

Pension Plan: Y	ESOP Stock Plan:	Profit Sharing:	Top Exec. Salary: $	Bonus: $
Savings Plan:	Stock Purch. Plan:		Second Exec. Salary: $	Bonus: $

OTHER THOUGHTS:

Apparent Women Officers or Directors:
Hot Spot for Advancement for Women/Minorities:

LOCATIONS: ("Y" = Yes)

West:	Southwest:	Midwest:	Southeast:	Northeast:	International:
					Y

DAIMLER AG

www.daimler.com

Industry Group Code: 336111 **Ranks within this company's industry group:** Sales: 5 Profits: 8

Techology:		Medical/Drugs:		Engineering:		Transportation:		Chemicals/Petrochemicals:		Specialty:	
Computers:		Manufacturer:		Design:		Aerospace:	Y	Oil/Gas Products:		Special Services:	Y
Software:		Contract Research:		Construction:		Automotive:	Y	Chemicals:		Consulting:	
Communications:		Medical Services:		Eng. Services:		Shipping:		Oil/Chem. Svcs.:		Specialty Mgmt.:	
Electronics:		Labs:		Consulting:				Gases:		Products:	
Alternative Energy:		Bio. Services:						Other:		Other:	

TYPES OF BUSINESS:

Automobile Manufacturer
Financial Services
Commercial Vehicles, Trucks & Buses
Aerospace, Marine & Military Equipment
Financial Services & Insurance

BRANDS/DIVISIONS/AFFILIATES:

Mercedes-Benz
Chrysler Holding LLC
European Aeronautic Defense and Space Co EADS)
Automotive Fuel Cell Cooperation
Daimler Hero Motor Corporation Ltd.
Daimler Luft- und Raumfahrt Holding AG
Daimler North America Corporation LLC
Daimler Financial Services AG

CONTACTS: *Note: Officers with more than one job title may be intentionally listed here more than once.*

Dieter Zetsche, CEO
Bodo Uebber, Dir.-Finance
Gunther Fleig, Dir.-Human Resources & Labor Rel.
Thomas Weber, Dir.-Group Research & MCG Dev.
Rudiger Grube, Dir.-Corp. Dev.
Jorg Howe, Head-Global Comm.
Michael Muhlbayer, Sr. VP-Investor Rel./Treas.
Bodo Uebber, Dir.-Controlling & Financial Svcs.
Dieter Zetsche, Dir.-Mercedes Car Group
Andreas Renschler, Dir.-Truck Group & Buses
Dr. Manfred Bischoff, Chmn.
Ulrich Walker, CEO/Chmn., Daimler North East Asia Div.
Bodo Uebber, Dir.-Corporate Procurement Svcs.

Phone: 011-49-711-17-0 **Fax:** 011-49-711-17-94116
Toll-Free:
Address: Epplestrasse 225, Stuttgart, 70546 Germany

GROWTH PLANS/SPECIAL FEATURES:

Daimler AG, formerly DaimlerChrysler AG, develops, manufactures, distributes and sells a wide range of automotive products, mainly passenger cars, trucks, vans and buses. It also provides financial and other services relating to its automotive businesses. The company reports four business segments: The Mercedes-Benz Cars; Daimler Trucks; Daimler Financial Services; and Vans, Buses and Other. The Mercedes segment designs, produces and sells Mercedes-Benz passenger cars, Maybach luxury sedans and smart cars. The truck business manufactures and sells commercial vehicles under the brand names Mercedes-Benz, Freightliner, Sterling, Western Star Trucks, Thomas Built Buses and Mitsubishi Fuso. The Vans, Buses and Other segment operates four businesses: Mercedes-Benz Vans; Daimler Buses; Chrysler Holding LLC; and the EADS Group. Mercedes-Benz Vans and Daimler Buses offer Daimler's line of vans, city buses, coaches, intercity buses, midi buses and bus chassis. Chrysler Holding LLC, 19.9%-owned by Daimler, controls the Chrysler automobile activities and the EADS Group, 22.5%-owned, is a global supplier of aerospace and defense technologies. The Daimler Financial Services business provides auto financing, banking, insurance and related services. Daimler offers products and financial services primarily in Western Europe and in the NAFTA region. Approximately 50% of the 2007 revenue derived from sales in Western Europe and 20% from sales in the U.S. Almost half of the company's Western European sales came from Germany. Daimler also owns a 50.1% stake in Automotive Fuel Cell Cooperation. In August 2007, the company sold an 80.1% interest in Chrysler Holdings to Cerberus Capital Management L.P. In September 2007, Daimler Financial Services established a bank in Russia. In April 2008, Daimler signed an agreement to acquire an approximately 22.3% interest in Tognum AG from private equity firm EQT and, along with The Indian Hero Group, established an Indian joint venture, the Daimler Hero Motor Corporation Ltd.

FINANCIALS: **Sales and profits are in thousands of dollars—add 000 to get the full amount. 2008 Note: Financial information for 2008 was not available for all companies at press time.**

2008 Sales: $129,244,000
2007 Sales: $133,998,000
2006 Sales: $198,638,000
2005 Sales: $177,260,000
2004 Sales: $192,433,000

2008 Profits: $1,906,190
2007 Profits: $5,372,100
2006 Profits: $4,228,560
2005 Profits: $3,368,000
2004 Profits: $3,340,000

U.S. Stock Ticker: DCX
Int'l Ticker: DCX Int'l Exchange: Frankfurt-Euronext
Employees: 273,216
Fiscal Year Ends: 12/31
Parent Company:

SALARIES/BENEFITS:

Pension Plan: Y ESOP Stock Plan: Profit Sharing: Top Exec. Salary: $ Bonus: $
Savings Plan: Stock Purch. Plan: Second Exec. Salary: $ Bonus: $

OTHER THOUGHTS:

Apparent Women Officers or Directors: 1
Hot Spot for Advancement for Women/Minorities:

LOCATIONS: ("Y" = Yes)

West:	Southwest:	Midwest:	Southeast:	Northeast:	International:
Y	Y	Y	Y	Y	Y

Note: Financial information, benefits and other data can change quickly and may vary from those stated here.

DAIMLER TRUCKS NORTH AMERICA LLC www.daimler-trucksnorthamerica.com

Industry Group Code: 336120 **Ranks within this company's industry group:** Sales: Profits:

Techology:		Medical/Drugs:		Engineering:		Transportation:		Chemicals/Petrochemicals:		Specialty:	
Computers:		Manufacturer:		Design:		Aerospace:		Oil/Gas Products:		Special Services:	
Software:		Contract Research:		Construction:		Automotive:	Y	Chemicals:		Consulting:	
Communications:		Medical Services:		Eng. Services:		Shipping:		Oil/Chem. Svcs.:		Specialty Mgmt.:	
Electronics:		Labs:		Consulting:				Gases:		Products:	
Alternative Energy:		Bio. Services:						Other:		Other:	

TYPES OF BUSINESS:

Truck Manufacturing
Custom-Built Chassis
Van & Bus Manufacturing
Automobile Parts Manufacturing
Specialty Vehicle Manufacturing
Military Vehicle Manufacturing
Used Truck Dealerships
Truck Stops

BRANDS/DIVISIONS/AFFILIATES:

Chrysler LLC
Sterling Trucks
Western Star Trucks
Freightliner Custom Chassis
Thomas Built Buses
SelecTrucks
Detroit Diesel Corporation
TravelCenters of America

CONTACTS: *Note: Officers with more than one job title may be intentionally listed here more than once.*

Chris Patterson, CEO
Roger M. Nielsen, COO
Chris Patterson, Pres.
Juergen Kritschgau, CFO
Michael Delaney, Sr. VP-Mktg.
Elmar Boeckenhoff, Sr. VP-Tech.
Elmar Boeckenhoff, Sr. VP-Eng.
Juergen Kritschgau, VP-Finance/Controller
Jack Conlan, Sr. VP-Customer Support
Mark Lampert, Sr. VP-Sales

Phone: 503-745-8000	**Fax:** 503-745-8921
Toll-Free:	
Address: 4747 N. Channel Ave., Portland, OR 97217 US	

GROWTH PLANS/SPECIAL FEATURES:

Daimler Trucks North America LLC (formerly Freightliner LLC), a wholly-owned subsidiary of Daimler AG, is one of the largest manufacturers of medium- and heavy-duty trucks and specialized commercial vehicles in North America. The company sells and services several brands, including Freightliner, its line of medium- and heavy-duty trucks; Sterling, trucks used for vocational applications and local and regional distribution; Western Star, heavy-duty over-the-road and vocational trucks; Freightliner Custom Chassis, for motor homes, school and shuttle buses; and Thomas Built Buses, the company's line of school buses. Daimler Trucks operates a network of over 800 dealers and service centers in North America, including over 40 used truck sales centers (SelecTrucks). The company is also one of the largest exporters of heavy-duty trucks from North America, marketing vehicles in over 35 countries. Daimler Trucks offers a selection of high quality proprietary components, including Mercedes-Benz engines and Alliance parts. The firm is affiliated with Detroit Diesel Corporation, a leading manufacturer of diesel engines for the commercial truck market, and with Axle Alliance Company. The firm is also a partial owner of TravelCenters of America, the largest network of full-service truck stops in the U.S. The company is making efforts to bring diesel hybrid electric engines to market as an alternative for applications such as delivery vans and utility vehicles. Recently, the company began cutting its workforce. Layoffs included 800 from the closure of its Portland, OR manufacturing plant; 478 at its Mount Holly, NC truck-making plant; 260 at its Gastonia, NC parts plant; and 1,180 at its Cleveland truck plant in Rowan County, NC. By the time this contraction is complete, the company expects to have cut its workforce by roughly 4,000.

FINANCIALS: **Sales and profits are in thousands of dollars—add 000 to get the full amount. 2008 Note: Financial information for 2008 was not available for all companies at press time.**

2008 Sales: $	2008 Profits: $	**U.S. Stock Ticker: Subsidiary**
2007 Sales: $	2007 Profits: $	**Int'l Ticker:** Int'l Exchange:
2006 Sales: $	2006 Profits: $	Employees: 20,000
2005 Sales: $13,000,000	2005 Profits: $	Fiscal Year Ends: 12/31
2004 Sales: $	2004 Profits: $	Parent Company: DAIMLER AG

SALARIES/BENEFITS:

Pension Plan:	ESOP Stock Plan:	Profit Sharing:	Top Exec. Salary: $	Bonus: $
Savings Plan: Y	Stock Purch. Plan:		Second Exec. Salary: $	Bonus: $

OTHER THOUGHTS:

Apparent Women Officers or Directors:
Hot Spot for Advancement for Women/Minorities:

LOCATIONS: ("Y" = Yes)

West:	Southwest:	Midwest:	Southeast:	Northeast:	International:
Y		Y	Y	Y	Y

DANA HOLDINGS CORPORATION

www.dana.com

Industry Group Code: 336300 **Ranks within this company's industry group:** Sales: 13 Profits: 12

Techology:		Medical/Drugs:		Engineering:		Transportation:		Chemicals/Petrochemicals:		Specialty:	
Computers:		Manufacturer:		Design:		Aerospace:		Oil/Gas Products:		Special Services:	
Software:		Contract Research:		Construction:		Automotive:	Y	Chemicals:		Consulting:	
Communications:		Medical Services:		Eng. Services:		Shipping:		Oil/Chem. Svcs.:		Specialty Mgmt.:	
Electronics:		Labs:		Consulting:				Gases:		Products:	
Alternative Energy:		Bio. Services:						Other:		Other:	

TYPES OF BUSINESS:

Automotive Products, Motors & Parts Manufacturing
Engine Systems
Fluid Systems
Heavy Vehicle Technologies
Brake Components
Chassis & Drive Train Components
Filtration Products
Financial Services

BRANDS/DIVISIONS/AFFILIATES:

Spicer
Victor Reinz
Parish
Long
Dongfeng Dana Axle
Dongfeng Motor Co. Ltd.

CONTACTS: *Note: Officers with more than one job title may be intentionally listed here more than once.*

Gary L. Convis, CEO
James A. Yost, CFO/Exec. VP
Robert H. Marcin, Chief Admin. Officer
Marc S. Levin, General Counsel/VP/Sec.
Robert A. Fesenmyer, Pres., Global Bus. Dev.
Gilberto Ceratti, Pres., Structural Prod. Group, Driveshaft Prod.
Nick L. Stanage, Pres., Heavy Vehicle Prod.
Thomas R. Stone, Pres., Light Axel Prod. Group, Automotive Systems
John M. Devine, Chmn.
Paul E. Miller, VP-Purchasing

Phone: 419-535-4500 **Fax:** 419-535-4756
Toll-Free: 800-537-8823
Address: 4500 Dorr St., Toledo, OH 43615 US

GROWTH PLANS/SPECIAL FEATURES:

Dana Holdings Corporation (formerly Dana Corp.) supplies axle, driveshaft, structural, sealing and thermal management products for global vehicle manufacturers. With 113 facilities in 26 countries, Dana serves three primary markets: Light vehicles, commercial vehicles and off-highway vehicles. Dana's Automotive Systems Group (ASG) business unit sells products mostly into the light vehicle market, while its Heavy Vehicle Technologies and Systems Group (HVTSG) sells products to the commercial vehicle and off-highway markets. The ASG business unit has five operating segments: The axle segment, responsible for front and rear axles, differentials, torque couplings and modular assemblies; the driveshaft segment, responsible for driveshafts; the sealing segment, responsible for gaskets, cover modules, heat shields, and engine sealing systems; the thermal segment, responsible for cooling and heat transfer products; and the structures segment, responsible for frames, cradles and side rails. The HVTSG business unit has two operating segments. The commercial vehicle segment is responsible for axles, driveshafts, steering shafts, brakes, suspensions and tire management systems and the off-highway segment is responsible for axles, transaxles, driveshafts, end-fittings, transmissions, torque converters, electronic controls and brakes. The company's trademarks include Spicer, Victor Reinz, Parish and Long. In March 2007, Dana sold its engine hard parts business to MAHLE GmbH for approximately $97 million, and in July 2007 Dana sold its non-core fluid products hose and tubing business to Orphan Holding, A.S., for approximately $66.9 million. Also in July 2007, Dana and Dongfeng Motor Co. Ltd. announced the completion of a joint venture, Dongfeng Dana Axle, headquartered in China. In January 2008, Dana successfully emerged from Chapter 11 bankruptcy.

FINANCIALS: **Sales and profits are in thousands of dollars—add 000 to get the full amount. 2008 Note: Financial information for 2008 was not available for all companies at press time.**

2008 Sales: $8,095,000	2008 Profits: $18,000	**U.S. Stock Ticker: DAN**
2007 Sales: $8,721,000	2007 Profits: $-551,000	**Int'l Ticker:** Int'l Exchange:
2006 Sales: $8,504,000	2006 Profits: $-739,000	Employees: 45,000
2005 Sales: $8,611,000	2005 Profits: $-1,605,000	Fiscal Year Ends: 12/31
2004 Sales: $7,775,000	2004 Profits: $62,000	Parent Company:

SALARIES/BENEFITS:

Pension Plan:	ESOP Stock Plan:	Profit Sharing:	Top Exec. Salary: $1,035,000	Bonus: $5,500,000
Savings Plan:	Stock Purch. Plan:		Second Exec. Salary: $445,446	Bonus: $1,333,127

OTHER THOUGHTS:

Apparent Women Officers or Directors:
Hot Spot for Advancement for Women/Minorities:

LOCATIONS: ("Y" = Yes)

West:	Southwest:	Midwest:	Southeast:	Northeast:	International:
		Y	Y	Y	Y

DASSAULT AVIATION SA

www.dassault-aviation.com

Industry Group Code: 336410 **Ranks within this company's industry group:** Sales: 19 Profits: 13

Techology:		Medical/Drugs:		Engineering:		Transportation:		Chemicals/Petrochemicals:		Specialty:	
Computers:		Manufacturer:		Design:		Aerospace:	Y	Oil/Gas Products:		Special Services:	
Software:		Contract Research:		Construction:		Automotive:		Chemicals:		Consulting:	
Communications:		Medical Services:		Eng. Services:		Shipping:		Oil/Chem. Svcs.:		Specialty Mgmt.:	
Electronics:		Labs:		Consulting:				Gases:		Products:	
Alternative Energy:		Bio. Services:						Other:		Other:	

TYPES OF BUSINESS:

Aircraft Manufacturer
Business Jets
Military Aircraft
Unmanned Combat Aircraft
Aerospace Technology

BRANDS/DIVISIONS/AFFILIATES:

Falcon
Rafale
Mirage
nEUROn
Falcon 7X
Falcon 900EX
Falcon 900DX
Falcon 2000DX

CONTACTS:

Note: Officers with more than one job title may be intentionally listed here more than once.

Charles Edelstenne, CEO
Pierre Vivien, Sr. VP-Social Rel. & Human Resources
Didier Gondoin, Sr. VP-R&D
Didier Gondoin, Sr. VP-Eng.
Jacques Pellas, Corp. Sec.
Guy Piras, Exec. VP-Industrial Oper.
Yves Robins, Sr. VP-Institutional Rel. & Corp. Comm.
Loik Segalen, VP-Economic & Financial Affairs
Alain Bonny, Sr. VP-Military Customer Support
Olivier Villa, Sr. VP-Civil Aircraft
Jacques Miannay, Sr. VP-Total Quality
Claude Defawe, VP-Nat'l & Cooperative Military Sale
Charles Edelstenne, Chmn.
Eric Trappier, Exec. VP-Int'l
Guy Piras, Exec. VP-Procurement & Purchasing

Phone: 33-1-53-76-93-00 **Fax:** 33-1-53-76-93-20
Toll-Free:
Address: 9 Rond-Point des Champs-Elysees, Marcel Dassault, Paris, 75008 France

GROWTH PLANS/SPECIAL FEATURES:

Dassault Aviation S.A. engineers and produces civil and military aircraft. The company has three operating divisions: Dassault Falcon; Defense; and Space. The company's Falcon family of luxury business jets accounts for the majority of total sales, making Dassault one of the largest producers of business jets in the world. This line of aircraft includes the Falcon 50EX, a mid-size craft with three jets; the Falcon 2000DX, a widebody twinjet; the Falcon 2000EX, a widebody craft with two jets; the Falcon 900DX, a widebody trijet; the Falcon 900EX, a widebody craft with three jets; and the Falcon 7X, a widebody trijet. The firm's defense activities include producing the Rafale and Mirage 2000 lines of aircraft as well as acting as the primary contractor for the European nEUROn Uninhabited Combat Aircraft Vehicle (UCAV) project. Dassault's space division develops pyrotechnics equipment for space and military aircraft, aerospace telemetry systems and manned and unmanned vehicles for space travel. Dassault offers its services through a number of subsidiaries, including Dassault Falcon Jet, which is responsible for Falcon production in the U.S.; Dassaul Aircraft Services; Dassault Falcon Jet Wilmington, which is responsible for customizing Falcon interiors in the U.S.; Falcon Training center, offering service in France; Dassault Procurement services; and Sogitec Industries, which offers simulation training and documentation systems. Dassault's subsidiaries have operations across France, as well as in the U.S., the U.K., South America, the Middle East and Asla.

FINANCIALS:

Sales and profits are in thousands of dollars—add 000 to get the full amount. 2008 Note: Financial information for 2008 was not available for all companies at press time.

2008 Sales: $4,684,520	2008 Profits: $466,420	**U.S. Stock Ticker:**
2007 Sales: $4,770,380	2007 Profits: $428,030	**Int'l Ticker: AM** Int'l Exchange: Paris-Euronext
2006 Sales: $4,356,700	2006 Profits: $371,000	Employees: 8,452
2005 Sales: $4,175,720	2005 Profits: $371,500	Fiscal Year Ends: 12/31
2004 Sales: $4,213,480	2004 Profits: $381,700	Parent Company:

SALARIES/BENEFITS:

Pension Plan:	ESOP Stock Plan:	Profit Sharing:	Top Exec. Salary: $	Bonus: $
Savings Plan:	Stock Purch. Plan:		Second Exec. Salary: $	Bonus: $

OTHER THOUGHTS:

Apparent Women Officers or Directors:
Hot Spot for Advancement for Women/Minorities:

LOCATIONS: ("Y" = Yes)

West:	Southwest:	Midwest:	Southeast:	Northeast:	International:
				Y	Y

DASSAULT SYSTEMES SA

www.3ds.com

Industry Group Code: 511215 **Ranks within this company's industry group:** Sales: 2 Profits: 2

Techology:		Medical/Drugs:		Engineering:		Transportation:		Chemicals/Petrochemicals:		Specialty:	
Computers:		Manufacturer:		Design:		Aerospace:		Oil/Gas Products:		Special Services:	
Software:	Y	Contract Research:		Construction:		Automotive:		Chemicals:		Consulting:	
Communications:		Medical Services:		Eng. Services:		Shipping:		Oil/Chem. Svcs.:		Specialty Mgmt.:	
Electronics:		Labs:		Consulting:				Gases:		Products:	
Alternative Energy:		Bio. Services:						Other:		Other:	

TYPES OF BUSINESS:

Computer Software-Product Lifecycle Management
3D Imaging Software

BRANDS/DIVISIONS/AFFILIATES:

Enovia Matrixone Inc
CATIA
DELMIA
SIMULIA
ENOVIA
SolidWorks
3DVIA
Priware Limited

CONTACTS: *Note: Officers with more than one job title may be intentionally listed here more than once.*

Bernard Charles, CEO
Bernard Charles, Pres.
Thibault de Tersant, CFO/Exec. VP
Pascal Daloz, Exec. VP-Mktg.
Dominique Florack, Exec. VP-R&D
Laurence Barthes, CIO
Pascal Daloz, Exec. VP-Strategy
Thibault de Tersant, Exec. VP-Finance
Laurence Dors, Sr. Exec. VP-Global Dev. & Resources
Etienne Droit, Exec. VP-PLM Value Channel
Bruno Latchague, Exec. VP-PLM Bus. Transformation
Philippe Forestier, Exec. VP-Network Selling
Charles Edelstenne, Chmn.
Philippe Forestier, Pres., Americas

Phone: 33-1-61-62-61-62 **Fax:**
Toll-Free:
Address: 10 rue Marcel Dassault, Velizy-Villacoublay, 78140 France

GROWTH PLANS/SPECIAL FEATURES:

Dassault Systemes S.A. is a leading provider of product lifecycle management (PLM) software and 3D software solutions. The company's software applications and services enable businesses in a variety of industries around the world to digitally define and simulate products. Its products facilitate the design, simulation and production of complex systems, such as cars and aircraft, as well as the manufacturing facilities and systems used to produce them. Its applications are also employed to design and manufacture products for everyday life, from tableware and household appliances to jewelry. The company's services support industrial processes and provide a 3D vision of the entire lifecycle of products, from conception to maintenance. Its software brands include CATIA, which creates and simulates the digital product; DELMIA, which simulates manufacturing processes; SIMULIA for virtual testing; ENOVIA (including ENOVIA SmarTeam) for global collaborative lifecycle management; and SolidWorks, a set of modeling tools that create 3D designs. Dassault Systemes provides PLM software to an array of industries, including automotive, aerospace, shipbuilding, industrial equipment, high-tech, consumer goods, life sciences, construction and business services. Clients include Boeing, Chrysler, Goodyear, Lockheed Martin, Nikon, Toyota Motor, Adidas, LG Electronics, Hitachi, Guess, Nokia, Coca Cola and Procter & Gamble. PLM software offers these companies a competitive advantage in the market by reducing product introduction costs, managing supplier networks, extending design expertise globally and accelerating time to market. In 2007, Dassault launched the 3DVIA platform, dedicated to extending 3D content creation to new businesses and consumers by making 3D technology more accessible and user-friendly. In March 2008, the company's SolidWorks Corporation acquired U.K.-based software developer Priware Limited. In July 2008, the company announced that it had spun off Dassault Systemes Solutions France, its PLM sales division focused on smaller businesses in France, Belgium and Luxembourg, to Keonys.

FINANCIALS: **Sales and profits are in thousands of dollars—add 000 to get the full amount. 2008 Note: Financial information for 2008 was not available for all companies at press time.**

2008 Sales: $1,778,360 | 2008 Profits: $263,800
2007 Sales: $1,677,100 | 2007 Profits: $237,820
2006 Sales: $1,528,300 | 2006 Profits: $237,200
2005 Sales: $1,129,437 | 2005 Profits: $212,123
2004 Sales: $1,079,100 | 2004 Profits: $211,900

U.S. Stock Ticker: DASTY
Int'l Ticker: DSY Int'l Exchange: Paris-Euronext
Employees: 7,459
Fiscal Year Ends: 12/31
Parent Company:

SALARIES/BENEFITS:

Pension Plan: | ESOP Stock Plan: | Profit Sharing: | Top Exec. Salary: $881,282 | Bonus: $
Savings Plan: | Stock Purch. Plan: | | Second Exec. Salary: $818,219 | Bonus: $818,219

OTHER THOUGHTS:

Apparent Women Officers or Directors: 3
Hot Spot for Advancement for Women/Minorities: Y

LOCATIONS: ("Y" = Yes)

West:	Southwest:	Midwest:	Southeast:	Northeast:	International:
Y		Y		Y	Y

DEERE & CO

www.deere.com

Industry Group Code: 333000 **Ranks within this company's industry group:** Sales: 3 Profits: 3

Techology:		Medical/Drugs:		Engineering:		Transportation:		Chemicals/Petrochemicals:		Specialty:	
Computers:		Manufacturer:		Design:		Aerospace:		Oil/Gas Products:		Special Services:	Y
Software:		Contract Research:		Construction:		Automotive:	Y	Chemicals:		Consulting:	
Communications:		Medical Services:		Eng. Services:		Shipping:		Oil/Chem. Svcs.:		Specialty Mgmt.:	
Electronics:		Labs:		Consulting:				Gases:		Products:	
Alternative Energy:		Bio. Services:						Other:		Other:	

TYPES OF BUSINESS:

Construction & Agricultural Equipment
Commercial & Consumer Equipment
Forestry Equipment
Financing
Health Care Plans-HMO

BRANDS/DIVISIONS/AFFILIATES:

John Deere
John Deere Health Plan, Inc.
John Deere Construction & Forestry Company
John Deere Credit Company
John Deere Agricultural Holdings, Inc.
John Deere Construction Holdings, Inc.
John Deere Lawn & Grounds Care Holdings, Inc.
John Deere Commercial Worksite Products, Inc.

CONTACTS: *Note: Officers with more than one job title may be intentionally listed here more than once.*

Robert W. Lane, CEO
Michael J. Mack, Jr., CFO/Sr. VP
Metroe B. Hornbuckle, VP-Human Resources
James R. Jabanoski, VP-IT
Klaus G. Hoehn, VP-Advanced Tech.
Klaus G. Hoehn, VP-Eng.
James R. Jenkins, General Counsel/Sr. VP
Ganesh Jayaram, VP-Corp. Bus. Dev.
H.J. Markley, VP-Corp. Comm.
Marie Z. Ziegler, VP-Investor Rel.
James A. Davlin, VP/Treas.
Kenneth C. Huhn, VP-Industrial Rel.
Thomas K. Jarrett, VP-Taxes
Dennis R. Schwartz, VP-Pension Fund & Investments
Linda E. Newborn, VP/Chief Compliance Officer
Robert W. Lane, Chmn.
Markwart von Pentz, Pres., Agriculture-Europe, Africa & South America
H.J. Markley, Exec. VP-Global Supply Mgmt. & Logistics

Phone: 309-765-8000 **Fax:** 309-765-5671
Toll-Free:
Address: 1 John Deere Pl., Moline, IL 61265-8098 US

GROWTH PLANS/SPECIAL FEATURES:

Deere & Co., better known by its John Deere brand name, conduct business in four divisions: Agricultural equipment; commercial and consumer equipment; construction and forestry; and credit. The agricultural equipment segment manufactures and distributes farm equipment and service parts including tractors; combines and harvesters; tillage, seeding and soil preparation machinery; sprayers; hay and forage equipment; material handling equipment; integrated agricultural management systems technology; and precision agricultural irrigation equipment. The commercial and consumer equipment segment manufactures and distributes equipment and service parts, including small tractors for lawn, garden, commercial and utility purposes; riding and walk-behind mowers; golf course equipment; utility vehicles; landscape and irrigation equipment; and other outdoor power products. The construction and forestry segment manufactures and distributes machines and service parts used in construction, earthmoving, material handling and timber harvesting, including backhoe loaders; crawler dozers and loaders; four-wheel-drive loaders; excavators; motor graders; articulated dump trucks; landscape loaders; skid-steer loaders; and log skidders, loaders, forwarders and harvesters. The credit segment finances sales and leases by John Deere dealers of agricultural, commercial and consumer, and construction and forestry equipment. In addition, it provides wholesale financing to dealers of the foregoing equipment, provides operating loans and finances retail revolving charge accounts. In 2007, Deere & Co. acquired Ningbo Benye Tractor & Automobile Manufacture Co. Ltd. of China. Deere entered into a joint-venture agreement with Xuzhou Bohui Science and Technology Development CO. Ltd., to expand its construction equipment presence in China. In April 2008, the company announced plans for a new facility in Russia. In May 2008, the firm acquired T-Systems International, Inc., a Californian drip irrigation company, followed by the acquisition of the Israel-based Plastro Irrigation Systems, Ltd. in June 2008.

Deere & Co. offers its employees tuition reimbursement, fitness centers, flexible work arrangements, parent resources, day care services, company discounts and membership in a credit union.

FINANCIALS: **Sales and profits are in thousands of dollars—add 000 to get the full amount. 2008 Note: Financial information for 2008 was not available for all companies at press time.**

2008 Sales: $28,438,000	2008 Profits: $2,053,000	**U.S. Stock Ticker: DE**
2007 Sales: $24,082,200	2007 Profits: $1,821,700	**Int'l Ticker:** Int'l Exchange:
2006 Sales: $22,147,800	2006 Profits: $1,693,800	Employees: 56,700
2005 Sales: $21,190,800	2005 Profits: $1,446,800	Fiscal Year Ends: 10/31
2004 Sales: $19,204,200	2004 Profits: $1,406,100	Parent Company:

SALARIES/BENEFITS:

Pension Plan: Y	ESOP Stock Plan:	Profit Sharing:	Top Exec. Salary: $1,306,280	Bonus: $6,393,070
Savings Plan: Y	Stock Purch. Plan: Y		Second Exec. Salary: $551,465	Bonus: $1,898,567

OTHER THOUGHTS:

Apparent Women Officers or Directors: 7
Hot Spot for Advancement for Women/Minorities: Y

LOCATIONS: ("Y" = Yes)

West:	Southwest:	Midwest:	Southeast:	Northeast:	International:
Y	Y	Y	Y	Y	Y

DELL INC

www.dell.com

Industry Group Code: 334111 **Ranks within this company's industry group:** Sales: 4 Profits: 3

Techology:		Medical/Drugs:		Engineering:		Transportation:		Chemicals/Petrochemicals:		Specialty:	
Computers:	Y	Manufacturer:		Design:		Aerospace:		Oil/Gas Products:		Special Services:	Y
Software:		Contract Research:		Construction:		Automotive:		Chemicals:		Consulting:	
Communications:		Medical Services:		Eng. Services:		Shipping:		Oil/Chem. Svcs.:		Specialty Mgmt.:	
Electronics:		Labs:		Consulting:				Gases:		Products:	
Alternative Energy:		Bio. Services:						Other:		Other:	

TYPES OF BUSINESS:

Computer Hardware-PCs, Manufacturing
Direct Sales
Technical & Support Services
Online Music Service
Web Hosting Services
Printers & Accessories
Personal Music Players
Storage Devices

BRANDS/DIVISIONS/AFFILIATES:

OptiPlex
Dell Financial Servies L.P.
Inspiron
PowerApp
ZING Systems, Inc.
ASAP Software
EqualLogic, Inc.,
Alienware

CONTACTS: *Note: Officers with more than one job title may be intentionally listed here more than once.*

Michael S.Dell, CEO
Brian T. Gladden, CFO/Sr. VP
Mark Jarvis, Chief Mktg. Officer
Andrew Esparza, Sr. VP-Human Resources
Stephen F. Schuckenbrock, CIO
Jeffrey W. Clarke, Sr. VP-Bus. Product Group
Lawrence P. Tu, General Counsel/Sr. VP
Michael R. Cannon, Pres., Global Oper.
Timothy W. Mattox, VP-Strategy
Stephen F. Schuckenbrock, Sr. VP/Pres., Global Svcs.
Paul D. Bell, Sr. VP/Pres., Americas
Stephen Felice, Sr. VP/Pres., Asia-Pacific & Japan
Ronald G. Garriques, Pres., Global Consumer Group
Michael S. Dell, Chmn.
David A. Marmonti, Sr. VP/Pres., EMEA

Phone: 512-338-4400	**Fax:** 512-728-3653
Toll-Free: 800-289-3355	
Address: 1 Dell Way, Round Rock, TX 78682 US	

GROWTH PLANS/SPECIAL FEATURES:

Dell, Inc. designs, develops, manufactures, markets, sells, and supports a wide range of computing products that in many cases are customized to individual customer requirements. The company's product categories include desktop PCs, servers and networking products, storage, mobility products, and software and peripherals. A few of Dell's products include Dimension and OptiPlex desktop computers, Alienware, Latitude and Inspiron notebook computers, PowerEdge servers, PowerApp server appliances, Dell Precision workstation products and PowerVault storage products. The company utilizes a direct selling strategy to bypass retailers and middlemen by selling products online directly to end users, and also operates Dell Direct Stores in certain states, as well as in non-U.S. locations. The firm's technology service segment provides customized computer systems, system installation and management, guided technology transitions, online and telephone technical support and next-day on-site product service. Through Dell Financial Services L.P., a wholly-owned subsidiary of Dell, the company is able to offer or arrange various financial services for its business and consumer customers in the U.S. Through the company's ongoing research and development activities, it is able to stay competitive in the technology market. In August 2007, Dell acquired ZING Systems, Inc., a consumer technology and services company. In November 2007, Dell acquired ASAP Software, a software solutions and licensing services provider. In January 2008, the firm acquired EqualLogic, Inc., a storage provider, for $1.4 billion.

Dell sponsors a number of diversity events and donates computer equipment to schools in under-privileged neighborhoods. Dell employees enjoy a wide range of benefits including flexible spending accounts; full medical, dental and vision coverage; adoption assistance; product discounts; and an on-site fitness center.

FINANCIALS: **Sales and profits are in thousands of dollars—add 000 to get the full amount. 2008 Note: Financial information for 2008 was not available for all companies at press time.**

2008 Sales: $61,133,000	2008 Profits: $2,947,000	**U.S. Stock Ticker: DELL**
2007 Sales: $57,420,000	2007 Profits: $2,583,000	**Int'l Ticker:** Int'l Exchange:
2006 Sales: $55,788,000	2006 Profits: $3,602,000	Employees: 88,200
2005 Sales: $49,121,000	2005 Profits: $3,018,000	Fiscal Year Ends: 1/31
2004 Sales: $41,444,000	2004 Profits: $2,645,000	Parent Company:

SALARIES/BENEFITS:

Pension Plan:	ESOP Stock Plan:	Profit Sharing:	Top Exec. Salary: $950,000	Bonus: $
Savings Plan:	Stock Purch. Plan:		Second Exec. Salary: $766,346	Bonus: $934,176

OTHER THOUGHTS:

Apparent Women Officers or Directors: 3
Hot Spot for Advancement for Women/Minorities: Y

LOCATIONS: ("Y" = Yes)

West:	Southwest:	Midwest:	Southeast:	Northeast:	International:
Y	Y	Y	Y	Y	Y

DELPHI CORP

www.delphi.com

Industry Group Code: 336300 **Ranks within this company's industry group:** Sales: 5 Profits: 1

Techology:		Medical/Drugs:		Engineering:		Transportation:		Chemicals/Petrochemicals:		Specialty:	
Computers:		Manufacturer:		Design:		Aerospace:		Oil/Gas Products:		Special Services:	
Software:		Contract Research:		Construction:		Automotive:	Y	Chemicals:		Consulting:	
Communications:	Y	Medical Services:		Eng. Services:		Shipping:		Oil/Chem. Svcs.:		Specialty Mgmt.:	
Electronics:	Y	Labs:		Consulting:				Gases:		Products:	Y
Alternative Energy:		Bio. Services:						Other:		Other:	Y

TYPES OF BUSINESS:

Automobile Parts Manufacturing
Industrial Components
Dynamics & Propulsion
Safety Systems
Electronics & Mobile Communications
Ride & Handling Systems
Medical Technologies
Fuel Cell & Hybrid Technologies

BRANDS/DIVISIONS/AFFILIATES:

Delphi Calsonic Hungary Ltd.,

CONTACTS:

Note: Officers with more than one job title may be intentionally listed here more than once.

Rodney O'Neal, CEO
Rodney O'Neal, Pres.
John D. Sheehan, CFO/VP
Karen L. Healy, VP-Mktg.
Kevin M. Butler, VP-Human Resources Mgmt.
Bette M. Walker, CIO/VP
David M. Sherbin, General Counsel/VP/Chief Compliance Officer
John D. Sheehan, Chief Restructuring Officer/VP
Karen L. Healy, VP-Corp. Affairs & Oper. Support Group
Thomas S. Timko, Chief Acct. Officer/Controller
Mark R. Weber, Exec. VP-Global Bus. Svcs.
John P. Arle, Treas./VP
Marjorie Harris Loeb, Corp. Sec.
Robert S. Miller, Chmn.
Ronald M. Pirtle, Pres., Delphi EMEA
Sidney Johnson, VP-Global Supply Mgmt.

Phone: 248-813-2000 **Fax:** 248-813-2673
Toll-Free:
Address: 5725 Delphi Dr., Troy, MI 48098 US

GROWTH PLANS/SPECIAL FEATURES:

Delphi Corp. is a supplier of vehicle electronics, transportation components, integrated systems and other electronic technology. Delphi technologies are now found in more than 75 million vehicles, as well as communications, computer, energy and medical systems and consumer electronics. The company has six operating divisions: electronics and safety, which includes audio, entertainment and communications, safety systems, body controls and security systems, and power electronics, as well as advanced development of software and silicon; thermal systems, which includes heating, ventilating and air conditioning systems, components for multiple transportation markets and powertrain cooling and related technologies; powertrain systems, which includes systems integration in gasoline, diesel and fuel handling and full end-to-end systems including fuel injection, combustion, electronics controls, exhaust handling, and test and validation capabilities; electrical/electronic architecture, which includes complete electrical architecture and components products; automotive holdings group, which includes non-core product lines and plant sites that are slated for sale or spinoff; and corporate and other, which includes the product and service solutions business comprised of independent aftermarket, diesel aftermarket, original equipment service, consumer electronics and medical systems, in addition to the expenses of corporate administration, other expenses and income of a non-operating or strategic nature, and the elimination of inter-segment transactions. Delphi filed for Chapter 11 bankruptcy in October 2005. Meanwhile, former parent firm GM is on the hook for a massive amount of Delphi's pension obligations. In March 2008, the company dissolved two joint ventures: it bought out Calsonic Kansei Europe PLC. to take control of Delphi Calsonic Hungary Ltd., and sold its shares of Calsonic Harrison Co., Ltd. to Calsonic Kansei. In September 2008, Delphi and GM began restructuring agreements to bring Delphi out of Chapter 11.

FINANCIALS:

Sales and profits are in thousands of dollars—add 000 to get the full amount. 2008 Note: Financial information for 2008 was not available for all companies at press time.

2008 Sales: $18,060,000	2008 Profits: $3,037,000	**U.S. Stock Ticker: DPHIQ**
2007 Sales: $22,283,000	2007 Profits: $-3,065,000	**Int'l Ticker:** Int'l Exchange:
2006 Sales: $22,737,000	2006 Profits: $-5,464,000	Employees: 146,600
2005 Sales: $26,947,000	2005 Profits: $-2,357,000	Fiscal Year Ends: 12/31
2004 Sales: $28,622,000	2004 Profits: $-4,818,000	Parent Company:

SALARIES/BENEFITS:

Pension Plan:	ESOP Stock Plan:	Profit Sharing:	Top Exec. Salary: $1,200,000	Bonus: $
Savings Plan:	Stock Purch. Plan:		Second Exec. Salary: $630,000	Bonus: $

OTHER THOUGHTS:

Apparent Women Officers or Directors: 3
Hot Spot for Advancement for Women/Minorities: Y

LOCATIONS: ("Y" = Yes)

West:	Southwest:	Midwest:	Southeast:	Northeast:	International:
Y	Y	Y	Y	Y	Y

DENSO CORPORATION

www.globaldenso.com/en/

Industry Group Code: 336300 **Ranks within this company's industry group:** Sales: 1 Profits: 2

Techology:		Medical/Drugs:		Engineering:		Transportation:		Chemicals/Petrochemicals:		Specialty:	
Computers:		Manufacturer:		Design:		Aerospace:		Oil/Gas Products:		Special Services:	
Software:		Contract Research:		Construction:		Automotive:	Y	Chemicals:		Consulting:	
Communications:		Medical Services:		Eng. Services:		Shipping:		Oil/Chem. Svcs.:		Specialty Mgmt.:	
Electronics:	Y	Labs:		Consulting:				Gases:		Products:	Y
Alternative Energy:		Bio. Services:						Other:		Other:	

TYPES OF BUSINESS:

Automobile Parts Manufacturer
Engine Components
Automotive Electrical Systems
Automotive Electronic Systems
Thermal Systems
Small Motors
Semiconductors
Industrial Robots

BRANDS/DIVISIONS/AFFILIATES:

Denso Wave, Inc.
DIAS
Denso (China) Investment Co. Ltd.
Denso East Japan Corporation

CONTACTS:

Note: Officers with more than one job title may be intentionally listed here more than once.

Nobuaki Katoh, CEO
Nobuaki Katoh, Pres.
Shigehiro Nishimura, Managing Officer
Hiromi Tokuda, Exec. VP
Shinji Shirasaki, Managing Officer
Shinro Iwatsuki, Exec. VP
Akihiko Saito, Chmn.
Haruya Maruyama, CEO/Pres., Denso Int'l America, Inc.

Phone: 81-566-25-5850	**Fax:** 81-566-25-4537
Toll-Free:	
Address: 1-1 Showa-cho, Kariya, 448-8661 Japan	

GROWTH PLANS/SPECIAL FEATURES:

Denso Corporation is a global automotive parts manufacturer. The firm operates in 32 countries and regions across North and South America, Europe, Asia and Oceania. Denso's products fall under two categories: its primary automotive components business and a smaller industrial systems division. The automotive division is subdivided into five business groups: Powertrain control systems, which develops and manufactures components and engine management systems for both gasoline and diesel engines; electric systems, which develops and manufactures starters and alternators as well as a line of components for hybrid vehicles; electronic systems, which develops and manufactures electronic control units for automotive control systems; thermal systems, which is responsible for radiators and air conditioners; and information and safety systems, which offers safety systems and body electronics designed to provide driver assistance. Denso's industrial systems output, operated by subsidiary Denso Wave, Inc., consists of automatic identification readers, industrial robots, logic controllers and more. In February 2008, the firm agreed to end its capital alliance with Doowon Climate Control Co., Ltd. In March 2008, the company announced the creation of a new car A/C system manufacturing company, Denso East Japan Corporation. In April 2008, the company consolidated two Singapore based subsidiaries, Denso International Asia Pte. Ltd., and DensoInternational Singapore Pte. Ltd., to form DIAS; the firm also opened its fourth Tennessee factory. In January 2009, the company released a remote touch controller for navigation, A/C and audio systems in the Lexus RX. In February 2009, Denso made two announcements: in April 2009, Denso (China) Investment Co. Ltd., will acquire Denso Create Shanghai Inc., forming Denso Software Shanghai Co., Ltd.; and in July 2009, Denso Airs Corporation will be merged with GAC Corporation's A/C hose business to form Denso Air Systems Corporation.

FINANCIALS:

Sales and profits are in thousands of dollars—add 000 to get the full amount. 2008 Note: Financial information for 2008 was not available for all companies at press time.

2008 Sales: $40,109,100	2008 Profits: $2,435,570	**U.S. Stock Ticker: DNZOY**
2007 Sales: $30,590,678	2007 Profits: $1,738,729	**Int'l Ticker: 6902** Int'l Exchange: Tokyo-TSE
2006 Sales: $27,250,684	2006 Profits: $1,449,983	Employees: 118,853
2005 Sales: $26,033,900	2005 Profits: $1,233,100	Fiscal Year Ends: 3/31
2004 Sales: $24,255,800	2004 Profits: $1,041,500	Parent Company:

SALARIES/BENEFITS:

Pension Plan:	ESOP Stock Plan:	Profit Sharing:	Top Exec. Salary: $	Bonus: $
Savings Plan:	Stock Purch. Plan:		Second Exec. Salary: $	Bonus: $

OTHER THOUGHTS:

Apparent Women Officers or Directors:
Hot Spot for Advancement for Women/Minorities:

LOCATIONS: ("Y" = Yes)

West:	Southwest:	Midwest:	Southeast:	Northeast:	International:
Y	Y	Y	Y	Y	Y

DIC CORPORATION

www.dic.co.jp

Industry Group Code: 325000 **Ranks within this company's industry group:** Sales: 13 Profits: 15

Techology:		Medical/Drugs:		Engineering:		Transportation:		Chemicals/Petrochemicals:		Specialty:	
Computers:		Manufacturer:		Design:		Aerospace:		Oil/Gas Products:	Y	Special Services:	
Software:		Contract Research:		Construction:		Automotive:		Chemicals:	Y	Consulting:	
Communications:		Medical Services:		Eng. Services:		Shipping:		Oil/Chem. Svcs.:		Specialty Mgmt.:	
Electronics:		Labs:		Consulting:				Gases:		Products:	Y
Alternative Energy:		Bio. Services:						Other:		Other:	

TYPES OF BUSINESS:

Inks, Pigments & Printing Supplies
Packaging Materials
Synthetic Resins
Building Materials
Plastic Additives
Coatings & Finishes
Health Foods

BRANDS/DIVISIONS/AFFILIATES:

Sun Chemicals Corporation
DIC Lifetec Co Ltd
Dainippon Ink and Chemicals, Inc.

CONTACTS: *Note: Officers with more than one job title may be intentionally listed here more than once.*

Koji Oe, CEO
Koji Oe, Pres.
Yurtaka Hashimoto, Gen. Mgr.-R&D
Kazuo Kudo, Exec. VP-Corp. Strategy
Masayuki Saito, Exec. VP-Finance & Acct.
Kazuo Sugie, Exec. VP
Shunji Ehara, Managing Dir.-Tech, & Prod. Mgmt. Div.
Masahiko Sagara, Pres., Electronics & Info. Materials Bus. Oper.
Yoshihisa Kawamura, Pres., Graphic Arts Materials Bus. Oper.
Yoshitada Kuraoka, Gen. Mgr.-Purchasing

Phone: 81-3-3272-4511	**Fax:** 81-3-3278-8558
Toll-Free:	
Address: DIC Bldg., 3- 7-20, Nihonbashi Chuo-ku, Tokyo, 103-8233 Japan	

GROWTH PLANS/SPECIAL FEATURES:

DIC Corporation, formerly Dainippon Ink and Chemicals, Inc., is a manufacturer of inks and pigments, printing supplies and other chemical products. The company operates through 213 subsidiaries in 60 countries, organized into five business divisions. The Graphic Arts Materials segment manufactures inks, organic pigments, pigment intermediates, presensitized plates, graphic arts films and prepress equipment. Through this segment, DIC is one of the world's largest manufacturers of printing inks. The company's Industrial Materials segment makes alkyd, acrylic, phenolic and polyurethane resins, emulsions, latex, plasticizers, molding compounds and building materials, such as decorative wooden boards, home interior components, bathtubs and synthetic marble. The Electronics and Information materials segment offers adhesives, epoxy resins, liquid crystal materials, toners, jet inks, magnetic foils, UV curable coatings and high-performance plastic compounds. The High Performance and Applied Products segment consists of plastic molded products, pressure-sensitive adhesive materials, and building materials. The division serves customers in the construction, food packaging and automobile markets. The Others segment, through subsidiary DIC Lifetec Co., Ltd., is involved in the health food and fitness club businesses. One of the prime subsidiaries of the company is the U.S.-based Sun Chemicals Corporation, one of the largest ink manufacturers in the world.

FINANCIALS: Sales and profits are in thousands of dollars—add 000 to get the full amount. 2008 Note: Financial information for 2008 was not available for all companies at press time.

2008 Sales: $10,778,970	2008 Profits: $310,330	**U.S. Stock Ticker:**
2007 Sales: $10,156,640	2007 Profits: $224,670	**Int'l Ticker: 4631** Int'l Exchange: Tokyo-TSE
2006 Sales: $10,048,400	2006 Profits: $52,880	Employees: 25,164
2005 Sales: $8,571,650	2005 Profits: $90,556	Fiscal Year Ends: 3/31
2004 Sales: $8,331,308	2004 Profits: $54,299	Parent Company:

SALARIES/BENEFITS:

Pension Plan:	ESOP Stock Plan:	Profit Sharing:	Top Exec. Salary: $	Bonus: $
Savings Plan:	Stock Purch. Plan:		Second Exec. Salary: $	Bonus: $

OTHER THOUGHTS:

Apparent Women Officers or Directors:
Hot Spot for Advancement for Women/Minorities:

LOCATIONS: ("Y" = Yes)

West:	Southwest:	Midwest:	Southeast:	Northeast:	International:
Y	Y	Y		Y	Y

DIEBOLD INC

www.diebold.com

Industry Group Code: 334111 **Ranks within this company's industry group:** Sales: 15 Profits: 13

Techology:		**Medical/Drugs:**		**Engineering:**		**Transportation:**		**Chemicals/Petrochemicals:**		**Specialty:**	
Computers:	Y	Manufacturer:		Design:		Aerospace:		Oil/Gas Products:		Special Services:	
Software:	Y	Contract Research:		Construction:		Automotive:		Chemicals:		Consulting:	
Communications:		Medical Services:		Eng. Services:		Shipping:		Oil/Chem. Svcs.:		Specialty Mgmt.:	
Electronics:		Labs:		Consulting:				Gases:		Products:	
Alternative Energy:		Bio. Services:						Other:		Other:	

TYPES OF BUSINESS:

Computer Hardware-Automated Teller Machines
Self-Service Terminals
Security Systems
Technical Services
Software
Electronic Voting Machines

BRANDS/DIVISIONS/AFFILIATES:

Diebold North America
Diebold International
Diebold Elections Systems, Inc.
Procomp Industria Electronica S.A.
Opteva
Diebold 450 ATM

CONTACTS: *Note: Officers with more than one job title may be intentionally listed here more than once.*

Thomas W. Swidarski, CEO
Thomas W. Swidarski, Pres.
Leslie A. Pierce, Interim CFO
Sheila M. Rutt, Chief Human Resources Officer/VP
Sean F. Forrester, CIO/VP
Warren W. Dettinger, General Counsel/VP
George S. Mayes, Jr., Exec. VP-Global Oper.
Robert J. Warren, VP-Corp. Dev. & Finance
John D. Kristoff, Chief Comm. Officer/VP
Timothy J. McDannold, VP/Treas.
David Bucci, Sr. VP-Customer Solutions Group
M. Scott Hunter, Chief Tax Officer/VP
Dennis M. Moriarty, Sr. VP-Global Security Div.
Leslie A. Pierce, VP/Controller
John N. Lauer, Chmn.
James L.M. Chen, Sr. VP-EMEA & Asia Pacific Divisions
George S. Mayes, Jr., Sr. VP-Global Mfg. & Supply Chain

Phone: 330-490-4000 **Fax:** 330-490-3794
Toll-Free: 800-999-3600
Address: 5995 Mayfair Rd., North Canton, OH 44720-8077 US

GROWTH PLANS/SPECIAL FEATURES:

Diebold, Inc., incorporated in 1876, develops, manufactures, sells and services self-service transaction systems; electronic and physical security systems; software; and various products used to equip bank facilities and electronic voting terminals. The company's primary customers include banks and financial institutions, as well as public libraries, government agencies, utilities and various retail outlets. The company is comprised of three segments, Diebold North America (DNA), Diebold International (DI) and Diebold Elections Systems, Inc. (DESI). DNA sells financial and retail systems and also services them in the U.S. and Canada. The DI segment sells and services financial and retail systems in 90 countries worldwide. DESI manufactures and supplies electronic voting terminals and solutions, and is a producer of touch-screen-voting systems. Diebold's self-service product division provides self-service banking products and is a global supplier of ATMs. The firm's physical security and facility products division designs and manufactures several financial service solutions, including the proprietary remote teller system (RTS), vaults, safes, safe deposit boxes and drive-up banking equipment. The election systems division, supplied by both DESI and Procomp Industrial Electronica S.A., is one of the largest electronic voting system providers in the world. The integrated security solutions division provides global sales, service, installation, project management and monitoring of electronic security products. The software solutions and services division offers solutions consisting of multiple applications that process events and transactions. In August 2008, Diebold announced the closure of the 100-employee manufacturing plant in Newark, Ohio in early 2009. In August 2008, Diebold also stated its plan to leave the German market and close its subsidiary there, Diebold Germany GmbH.

Diebold offers its employees educational assistance, long term disability plan, employee assistance program, adoption assistance, flexible spending accounts and a college scholarship program.

FINANCIALS: **Sales and profits are in thousands of dollars—add 000 to get the full amount. 2008 Note: Financial information for 2008 was not available for all companies at press time.**

2008 Sales: $3,170,080	2008 Profits: $88,583	**U.S. Stock Ticker: DBD**
2007 Sales: $2,947,481	2007 Profits: $39,541	**Int'l Ticker:** Int'l Exchange:
2006 Sales: $2,920,974	2006 Profits: $104,552	Employees: 16,658
2005 Sales: $2,587,049	2005 Profits: $96,746	Fiscal Year Ends: 12/31
2004 Sales: $2,357,108	2004 Profits: $183,797	Parent Company:

SALARIES/BENEFITS:

Pension Plan:	ESOP Stock Plan:	Profit Sharing:	Top Exec. Salary: $550,000	Bonus: $392,500
Savings Plan: Y	Stock Purch. Plan: Y		Second Exec. Salary: $320,000	Bonus: $171,273

OTHER THOUGHTS:

Apparent Women Officers or Directors: 3
Hot Spot for Advancement for Women/Minorities: Y

LOCATIONS: ("Y" = Yes)

West:	Southwest:	Midwest:	Southeast:	Northeast:	International:
Y	Y	Y	Y	Y	Y

Note: Financial information, benefits and other data can change quickly and may vary from those stated here.

D-LINK CORPORATION

www.dlink.com

ndustry Group Code: 334110 **Ranks within this company's industry group:** Sales: 4 Profits: 3

Techology:		Medical/Drugs:		Engineering:		Transportation:		Chemicals/Petrochemicals:		Specialty:	
Computers:	Y	Manufacturer:		Design:		Aerospace:		Oil/Gas Products:		Special Services:	
Software:	Y	Contract Research:		Construction:		Automotive:		Chemicals:		Consulting:	
Communications:	Y	Medical Services:		Eng. Services:		Shipping:		Oil/Chem. Svcs.:		Specialty Mgmt.:	
Electronics:		Labs:		Consulting:				Gases:		Products:	
Alternative Energy:		Bio. Services:						Other:		Other:	

TYPES OF BUSINESS:

Networking Equipment Manufacturing & Distribution
Broadband Products
Modems
Telephony Products
Security Products
Software
Switches & Routers
Media Converters

BRANDS/DIVISIONS/AFFILIATES:

Bell Microproducts
V-Click

CONTACTS:

Note: Officers with more than one job title may be intentionally listed here more than once.

John Lee, CEO
I. C. Liao, Pres.
A.P. Chen, CFO
Tom Paterniti, VP-Bus. Dev.
John DiFrenna, VP-Channel Oper., U.S. & Mexico
Keith A. Karlsen, Exec. VP-D-Link Systems, Inc.
John Lee, Chmn.
Steven Joe, CEO-D-Link North America
Tom Paterniti, VP-Dist.

Phone: 886-2-6600-0123	**Fax:** 886-2-2790-0977
Toll-Free:	
Address: 1F, No. 289 Sinhu 3rd Rd., Neihu District, Taipei, 114 Taiwan	

GROWTH PLANS/SPECIAL FEATURES:

D-Link Corporation is a leading global designer, developer, manufacturer and distributor of networking, broadband, digital, voice and data communications products for mass consumer and small- to medium-sized business market segments. The company is one of the largest networking hardware vendors in the distribution channel, including value-added resellers, online retailers, retail chains, service providers and direct market resellers. D-Link, which is based in Taiwan, serves more than 100 countries from 90 offices located in 39 countries. Its products are sold through independent distributors worldwide, with North America and Europe as its largest markets. The firm manufactures ADSL and VDSL broadband products; cable modems; wireless LAN; IP telephony products (VOIP); remote router and security products; network attached storage; LAN switches; print servers; LAN hubs; network management software; LAN cards and network kits; media converters; transceivers; KVM switches; home phone line networks; analog modems; USB devices; audio/video converters; broadband Internet video phones; and home plug power lines. D-Link holds the patents and copyrights on a number of technological platforms, including Application Specific Integrated Circuit (ASIC) computer chips, hardware technology designs and software applications. The company is also a key contributor to the Digital Living Network Alliance (DLNA), a group that works to maintain industry standards in consumer electronics. The company's client list includes Microsoft, T-Moblle, Honeywell, Weston Group, Quakecon, Yahoo and Pavlov Media, among several other corporate and government customers.

FINANCIALS:

Sales and profits are in thousands of dollars—add 000 to get the full amount. 2008 Note: Financial information for 2008 was not available for all companies at press time.

2008 Sales: $1,087,000	2008 Profits: $100,200	**U.S. Stock Ticker:**
2007 Sales: $1,249,800	2007 Profits: $75,600	**Int'l Ticker: 2332** Int'l Exchange: Taipei-TPE
2006 Sales: $1,091,400	2006 Profits: $49,100	Employees: 2,087
2005 Sales: $967,400	2005 Profits: $78,000	Fiscal Year Ends: 12/31
2004 Sales: $966,584	2004 Profits: $77,966	Parent Company:

SALARIES/BENEFITS:

Pension Plan:	ESOP Stock Plan:	Profit Sharing:	Top Exec. Salary: $	Bonus: $
Savings Plan:	Stock Purch. Plan:		Second Exec. Salary: $	Bonus: $

OTHER THOUGHTS:

Apparent Women Officers or Directors:
Hot Spot for Advancement for Women/Minorities:

LOCATIONS: ("Y" = Yes)

West:	Southwest:	Midwest:	Southeast:	Northeast:	International:
Y					Y

DONGFENG MOTOR CORPORATION

www.dfmc.com.cn

Industry Group Code: 336111 **Ranks within this company's industry group:** Sales: Profits:

Techology:		Medical/Drugs:		Engineering:		Transportation:		Chemicals/Petrochemicals:		Specialty:	
Computers:		Manufacturer:		Design:		Aerospace:		Oil/Gas Products:		Special Services:	
Software:		Contract Research:		Construction:		Automotive:	Y	Chemicals:		Consulting:	
Communications:		Medical Services:		Eng. Services:		Shipping:		Oil/Chem. Svcs.:		Specialty Mgmt.:	
Electronics:		Labs:		Consulting:				Gases:		Products:	
Alternative Energy:		Bio. Services:						Other:		Other:	

TYPES OF BUSINESS:

Automobile Manufacturing
Truck & Bus Manufacturing
Auto Parts & Components Manufacturing
Vehicle Manufacturing Equipment

BRANDS/DIVISIONS/AFFILIATES:

Dongfeng Peugeot Citroen Automobiles Limited
Dongfeng-Yueda Kia Co., Ltd.
Dongfeng Honda Automobile (Wuhan) Co., Ltd.
Dongfeng Motor Co., Ltd.
Dongfeng Electric Vehicle Co., Ltd.

CONTACTS:

Note: Officers with more than one job title may be intentionally listed here more than once.

Xu Ping, CEO
Liu Zhangmin, Vice Gen. Mgr.
Li Shaozhu, Vice Gen. Mgr.
Tong Dongcheng, Vice Gen. Mgr.
Ouyang Jie, Vice Gen. Mgr.
Xu Ping, Chmn.

Phone: 86-719-8226-962 **Fax:** 86-719-8226-845
Toll-Free:
Address: 29 Baiye Rd., Wuhan, 430015 China

GROWTH PLANS/SPECIAL FEATURES:

Dongfeng Motor Corporation (DFM) is one of China's leading automakers and also one of the most heavily vested in foreign partnerships among Chinese automotive companies. It has production facilities in Wuhan and Guangzhou for passenger vehicles; in Shiyan, manufacturing medium and heavy duty commercial vehicles; and in Xiangfan for light commercial and passenger vehicles. The company's main business is manufacturing passenger vehicles, whole serial commercial vehicles, vehicle manufacturing equipment and auto parts and components. Established as a state-owned company in 1969, DFM was restructured in the 1990s and has sought out numerous joint ventures and integrated development with international automotive companies. DFM partnered with Citroen to establish Dongfeng Peugeot Citroen Automobiles Limited. Dongfeng's other joint-venture partners and affiliates include Nissan Motor Co., Ltd.; Kia Motors Corporation, with which it formed Dongfeng-Yueda Kia Co., Ltd.; and Honda Motor Co., Ltd., with which it formed Dongfeng Honda Automobile (Wuhan) Co., Ltd. Its other main subsidiaries are Dongfeng Motor Co., Ltd.; and Dongfeng Electric Vehicle Co., Ltd. Its commercial products include semi trailers and trucks and buses, both whole and incomplete; while its passenger vehicles include cars, multi-purpose vehicles (MPVs) and SUVs (Sport Utility Vehicles). Five of its passenger vehicles carry the Dongfeng brand, five carry the Peugeot Citroen brand, and Nissan and Honda both have one model apiece; while all of its commercial vehicles carry the Dongfeng brand. The company's headquarters is located in a designated economic development zone in Wuhan, the capital of Hubei Province.

FINANCIALS:

Sales and profits are in thousands of dollars—add 000 to get the full amount. 2008 Note: Financial information for 2008 was not available for all companies at press time.

2008 Sales: $
2007 Sales: $
2006 Sales: $
2005 Sales: $
2004 Sales: $

2008 Profits: $
2007 Profits: $
2006 Profits: $
2005 Profits: $
2004 Profits: $

U.S. Stock Ticker: Government-Owned
Int'l Ticker: Int'l Exchange:
Employees:
Fiscal Year Ends:
Parent Company:

SALARIES/BENEFITS:

Pension Plan: ESOP Stock Plan: Profit Sharing: Top Exec. Salary: $ Bonus: $
Savings Plan: Stock Purch. Plan: Second Exec. Salary: $ Bonus: $

OTHER THOUGHTS:

Apparent Women Officers or Directors:
Hot Spot for Advancement for Women/Minorities:

LOCATIONS: ("Y" = Yes)

West:	Southwest:	Midwest:	Southeast:	Northeast:	International:
					Y

Note: Financial information, benefits and other data can change quickly and may vary from those stated here.

DOW CHEMICAL COMPANY (THE)

www.dow.com

Industry Group Code: 325000 **Ranks within this company's industry group:** Sales: 2 Profits: 11

Techology:		Medical/Drugs:		Engineering:		Transportation:		Chemicals/Petrochemicals:		Specialty:	
Computers:		Manufacturer:		Design:		Aerospace:		Oil/Gas Products:	Y	Special Services:	
Software:		Contract Research:		Construction:		Automotive:		Chemicals:	Y	Consulting:	
Communications:		Medical Services:		Eng. Services:		Shipping:		Oil/Chem. Svcs.:	Y	Specialty Mgmt.:	
Electronics:		Labs:		Consulting:				Gases:		Products:	
Alternative Energy:	Y	Bio. Services:						Other:	Y	Other:	

TYPES OF BUSINESS:

Chemicals Manufacturer
Basic Chemicals
Plastics
Performance Chemicals
Agrochemicals
Hydrocarbons & Fuels

BRANDS/DIVISIONS/AFFILIATES:

Dow AgroSciences LLC
Dow Automotive
Dow Building Solutions
Dow Epoxy
Union Carbide Corporation
OAO Gazprom
Dow Portfolio Optimization
Rohm and Haas

CONTACTS: *Note: Officers with more than one job title may be intentionally listed here more than once.*

Andrew N. Liveris, CEO
Geoffery E. Merszei, CFO/Exec. VP
David E. Kepler, CIO/Chief Sustainability Officer/Exec. VP
William F. Banholzer, CTO/Exec. VP
Michael R. Gambrell, Exec. VP-Eng.
Michael R. Gambrell, Exec. VP-Mfg.
Charles J. Kalil, General Counsel/Corp. Sec./Exec. VP-Law
Heinz Haller, Exec. VP-Health, Agriculture & Infrastructure
Charles J. Kalil, Exec. VP-Gov't Affairs
Dave Kepler, Exec. VP-Business Svcs.
Juan Luciano, Sr. VP-Hydrocarbons & Basic Plastics Div.
Andrew N. Liveris, Chmn.

Phone: 989-636-1000 **Fax:** 989-832-1556
Toll-Free: 800-258-2436
Address: 2030 Dow Ctr., Midland, MI 48674 US

GROWTH PLANS/SPECIAL FEATURES:

The Dow Chemical Co. is a global chemical and plastics company. It delivers a broad range of products and services to customers in about 160 countries, has 150 manufacturing sites in 35 countries and produces roughly 3,300 products. The company operates in six segments: performance plastics; performance chemicals; agricultural sciences; basic plastics; basic chemicals; and hydrocarbons and energy. The performance plastics segment manufactures specialty plastics including polyurethanes. Business units belonging to this segment are Dow automotive, Dow building solutions and Dow epoxy. The performance chemicals segment manufactures specialty chemicals, designed polymers and latex/acrylic monomers. Dow latex, a part of this division, is a supplier of latexes for a wide range of industries and applications. The agricultural sciences segment encompasses the business unit Dow AgroSciences, LLC, a provider of pest management services and agricultural products. The basic plastics segment manufactures polyethylene, polypropylene and polystyrene. The basic chemicals segment produces core chemicals, ethylene oxide and ethylene glycol, which are sold to industries worldwide and serve as raw materials in Dow's products. The hydrocarbons and energy segment encompasses the procurement of fuels, natural gas liquids and crude oil-based raw materials, and also supplies monomers, power and steam for use in Dow's operations. In 2008 Dow created Dow Portfolio Optimization, which will evaluate Dow's various businesses and plan for a shifting focus to higher-growth operations. In late 2008, the firm announced that it will cut 5,000 jobs and cut 6,000 contract workers. In addition, it planned to close 20 plants. Long-term, Dow hopes to move away from commodity chemicals, which do not earn large profit margins, and focus more on specialty chemicals. It will reorganize along three separate divisions to help facilitate this strategy. In April 2009, the firm acquired chemicals giant Rohm & Haas for $15 billion.

FINANCIALS: **Sales and profits are in thousands of dollars—add 000 to get the full amount. 2008 Note: Financial information for 2008 was not available for all companies at press time.**

2008 Sales: $57,514,000	2008 Profits: $579,000	**U.S. Stock Ticker: DOW**
2007 Sales: $53,513,000	2007 Profits: $2,887,000	**Int'l Ticker:** Int'l Exchange:
2006 Sales: $49,124,000	2006 Profits: $3,724,000	Employees: 46,102
2005 Sales: $46,307,000	2005 Profits: $4,515,000	Fiscal Year Ends: 12/31
2004 Sales: $40,161,000	2004 Profits: $2,797,000	Parent Company:

SALARIES/BENEFITS:

Pension Plan:	ESOP Stock Plan:	Profit Sharing:	Top Exec. Salary: $1,583,333	Bonus: $3,456,000
Savings Plan:	Stock Purch. Plan:		Second Exec. Salary: $812,360	Bonus: $1,683,237

OTHER THOUGHTS:

Apparent Women Officers or Directors: 4
Hot Spot for Advancement for Women/Minorities: Y

LOCATIONS: ("Y" = Yes)

West:	Southwest:	Midwest:	Southeast:	Northeast:	International:
	Y	Y	Y	Y	Y

DOW CORNING CORPORATION

www.dowcorning.com

Industry Group Code: 325000 **Ranks within this company's industry group:** Sales: 22 Profits: 7

Techology:		Medical/Drugs:		Engineering:		Transportation:		Chemicals/Petrochemicals:		Specialty:	
Computers:		Manufacturer:		Design:	Y	Aerospace:		Oil/Gas Products:		Special Services:	Y
Software:		Contract Research:		Construction:		Automotive:		Chemicals:	Y	Consulting:	Y
Communications:		Medical Services:		Eng. Services:	Y	Shipping:		Oil/Chem. Svcs.:		Specialty Mgmt.:	
Electronics:		Labs:		Consulting:				Gases:		Products:	Y
Alternative Energy:		Bio. Services:						Other:	Y	Other:	

TYPES OF BUSINESS:

Silicone Materials
Sealants, Coatings & Lubricants
Adhesives
Insulating Materials
Design, Engineering & Testing Services
Custom Manufacturing & Packaging
Consulting
Nanotechnology Research

BRANDS/DIVISIONS/AFFILIATES:

Dow Chemical Company
Corning, Inc.
Dow Corning
Xiameter
Silicon Biotechnology

CONTACTS: *Note: Officers with more than one job title may be intentionally listed here more than once.*

Stephanie A. Burns, CEO
Stephanie A. Burns, Pres.
Joseph D. Sheets, CFO/VP/Pres., Americas Area
Brian J. Chermside, Chief Mktg. Officer/Exec. Dir.-Mktg. & Sales
Alan E. Hubbard, Chief Human Resources Officer/VP
Abbe M. Mulders, CIO/Exec. Dir.
Gregg A. Zank, CTO/Exec. Dir.-Science & Tech./VP
Robert D. Hansen, VP/Gen. Mgr.-Core Products
James R. Whitlock, VP/Exec. Dir.-Eng.
James R. Whitlock, VP/Exec. Dir.-Mfg.
Marie N. Eckstein, Chief Admin. Officer/Corp. VP
Sue K. McDonnell, General Counsel/Sec./VP
James R. Whitlock, VP/Exec. Dir.-Global Oper.
John D. Lyon, Exec. Dir.-Geographic Dev.
Thomas Cook, Corp. VP/Pres., Greater China/VP-Asia Area
Klaus Hoffmann, Pres., European Area
Kevin B. Kendrick, Exec. Dir.-Global Security
Peter Cartwright, Exec. Dir.-Environment, Health & Safety
Stephanie A. Burns, Chmn.
Jean-Marc Gilson, Pres., Asia Area/VP/Gen. Mgr.-Specialty Chemicals
Klaus Hoffmann, Dir.-Global Supply Chain, Silicone Rubber

Phone: 989-496-4000 **Fax:** 989-496-4393
Toll-Free:
Address: 2200 W. Salzburg Rd., P.O. Box 994, Midland, MI 48686-0994 US

GROWTH PLANS/SPECIAL FEATURES:

Dow Corning Corporation, a joint venture between The Dow Chemical Company and Corning, Inc., has been studying and manufacturing silicone and silicone products since 1943. Currently, the firm serves over 24 industries, including the automotive, chemical manufacturing, beauty, oil/gas and plastics industries. The company researches and develops applications of silicone in forms ranging from greases, gels and fluids to rigid materials such as resins. Dow Corning's 7,000 products, sold under the Dow Corning and Xiameter brands, include adhesives, insulating materials, sealants, coatings and lubricants. These products are used in computer chips, cell phones and consumer electronics; automotive coatings, paints and lubricants; laundry detergents; tubing for dialysis, hydrocephalus shunts and pacemaker leads; roofing materials and pavement sealants; and for waterproofing clothing fabric. Dow Corning is researching additional silicon-based technologies including using nanotechnology to toughen silicone resins and to develop new liquid crystal materials; and using room-temperature atmospheric pressure plasma to apply different coatings to various substrates, such as consumer electronics, medical devices, pharmaceuticals, airbags and textiles. It has also formed alliances to develop future products, including an alliance with Genencor to create a proprietary Silicon Biotechnology platform. Besides its silicone-based chemical products, the company also offers services and solutions for various industries, including analytical testing, application training and education, contract and toll manufacturing, material application testing and custom material blending. It also provides package recycling, custom packaging of material, facilities design and engineering, product development and environmental consulting. Dow Corning maintains operations internationally, with locations in the Americas, Asia, Europe and Australia; it recently received approval from the Chinese government to build a siloxanes (silicon-oxygen-based organic chemicals) manufacturing facility in China. In February 2009, the company announced it intends to eliminate 800 positions worldwide, or approximately 8% of its workforce.

FINANCIALS: **Sales and profits are in thousands of dollars—add 000 to get the full amount. 2008 Note: Financial information for 2008 was not available for all companies at press time.**

2008 Sales: $5,450,000	2008 Profits: $738,700	**U.S. Stock Ticker: Joint Venture**
2007 Sales: $4,943,100	2007 Profits: $690,100	**Int'l Ticker:** Int'l Exchange:
2006 Sales: $4,391,600	2006 Profits: $668,400	Employees: 10,000
2005 Sales: $3,878,700	2005 Profits: $506,500	Fiscal Year Ends: 12/31
2004 Sales: $3,372,600	2004 Profits: $238,300	Parent Company:

SALARIES/BENEFITS:

Pension Plan:	ESOP Stock Plan:	Profit Sharing:	Top Exec. Salary: $	Bonus: $
Savings Plan:	Stock Purch. Plan:		Second Exec. Salary: $	Bonus: $

OTHER THOUGHTS:

Apparent Women Officers or Directors: 4
Hot Spot for Advancement for Women/Minorities: Y

LOCATIONS: ("Y" = Yes)

West:	Southwest:	Midwest:	Southeast:	Northeast:	International:
Y		Y		Y	Y

DRS TECHNOLOGIES INC

www.drs.com

Industry Group Code: 334111 **Ranks within this company's industry group:** Sales: 14 Profits: 12

Techology:		Medical/Drugs:		Engineering:		Transportation:		Chemicals/Petrochemicals:		Specialty:	
Computers:	Y	Manufacturer:		Design:	Y	Aerospace:	Y	Oil/Gas Products:		Special Services:	
Software:		Contract Research:		Construction:		Automotive:	Y	Chemicals:		Consulting:	
Communications:	Y	Medical Services:		Eng. Services:		Shipping:		Oil/Chem. Svcs.:		Specialty Mgmt.:	
Electronics:	Y	Labs:		Consulting:				Gases:		Products:	
Alternative Energy:		Bio. Services:						Other:		Other:	

TYPES OF BUSINESS:

Computer Hardware & Systems
Aerospace & Defense Technology
Combat Control Systems
Communications Systems
Electro-Optical Systems
Power Generation, Conversion & Propulsion Equipment
Unmanned Vehicles
Data Storage Products

BRANDS/DIVISIONS/AFFILIATES:

C4I
RSTA
Sustainment Systems
Technical Services

CONTACTS: *Note: Officers with more than one job title may be intentionally listed here more than once.*

Mark S. Newman, CEO
Robert F. Mehmel, COO
Robert F. Mehmel, Pres.
Richard A. Schneider, CFO/Exec. VP
Andrea J. Mandel, Sr. VP-Human Resources
Louis J. Belsito, CIO/Sr. VP
Michael W. Hansen, VP-Tech. & Strategy
Nina Laserson Dunn, General Counsel/Exec. VP/Sec.
Robert Russo, Sr. VP-Oper.
Richard Goldberg, VP-Public Affairs
Patricia M. Williamson, VP-Investor Rel.
Thomas P. Crimmins, Controller/Sr. VP
Phillip M. Balisle, Exec. VP-Washington Oper.
Mike Bowman, Exec. VP-Washington Oper.
R. Alan Gross, Sr. VP-Compliance
Jason W. Rinsky, Sr. VP-Corp. Taxation
Mark S. Newman, Chmn.
David W. Stapley, Sr. VP-Int'l Bus. Dev. & Gov't Rel.
Albert S. Moran, Jr., VP-Strategic Supply Chain Initiatives

Phone: 973-898-1500 **Fax:** 973-898-4730
Toll-Free:
Address: 5 Sylvan Way, Parsippany, NJ 07054 US

GROWTH PLANS/SPECIAL FEATURES:

DRS Technologies, Inc. is a leading supplier of electronic defense products and systems, and military support services. The company develops and manufactures a range of products, from rugged computers and peripherals to systems and components, in the areas of communications, combat systems, data storage, digital imaging, electro-optics, flight safety and space. DRS sells its defense electronics systems to all branches of the U.S. military, government intelligence agencies, aerospace and defense contractors and international military forces. The firm operates through four divisions: the command, control, communications, computers and intelligence (C4I) division; the reconnaissance, surveillance and target acquisition (RSTA) division; the sustainment systems division; and the technical services division. The C4I group is a leading provider of naval computer workstations used to process and display integrated combat information. It produces surveillance, radar and tracking systems, acoustic signal processing and display equipment and combat control systems for U.S. and international military organizations. It also produces naval and industrial power generation, conversion, propulsion, distribution and control systems. The RSTA group is a leader in electro-optical infrared sighting, targeting and weapons guidance systems, high-performance focal plane arrays and infrared uncooled sensors, assemblies and components, which are used primarily in the aerospace and defense industries. It also produces unmanned vehicles, air combat training, electronic warfare and network systems. These products are used in some of the U.S. military's most important battlefield platforms, including Aegis Destroyers, Abrams Main Battle Tanks, Bradley Infantry Fighting Vehicles and Apache Helicopters. The sustainment systems division offers products and services such as fuel and water distribution, mobile power conditioning systems and heavy equipment transporters. The technical service division offers engineering and logistical services and other services. In addition, DRS is a leading manufacturer of deployable flight incident recorders and emergency locator beacon systems. The majority of the firm's business comes from the U.S. Department of Defense.

FINANCIALS: **Sales and profits are in thousands of dollars—add 000 to get the full amount. 2008 Note: Financial information for 2008 was not available for all companies at press time.**

2008 Sales: $3,295,384	2008 Profits: $165,769	**U.S. Stock Ticker: DRS**
2007 Sales: $2,821,113	2007 Profits: $103,572	**Int'l Ticker:** Int'l Exchange:
2006 Sales: $1,735,532	2006 Profits: $81,494	Employees: 10,200
2005 Sales: $1,308,600	2005 Profits: $60,677	Fiscal Year Ends: 3/31
2004 Sales: $1,001,250	2004 Profits: $44,720	Parent Company:

SALARIES/BENEFITS:

Pension Plan: Y	ESOP Stock Plan:	Profit Sharing:	Top Exec. Salary: $936,250	Bonus: $1,258,300
Savings Plan: Y	Stock Purch. Plan:		Second Exec. Salary: $504,400	Bonus: $581,100

OTHER THOUGHTS:

Apparent Women Officers or Directors: 4
Hot Spot for Advancement for Women/Minorities: Y

LOCATIONS: ("Y" = Yes)

West:	Southwest:	Midwest:	Southeast:	Northeast:	International:
Y	Y	Y	Y	Y	Y

DUPONT CENTRAL RESEARCH & DEVELOPMENT

www2.dupont.com/Science/en_US/rd/index.html

Industry Group Code: 541710 **Ranks within this company's industry group:** Sales: Profits:

Techology:		Medical/Drugs:		Engineering:		Transportation:		Chemicals/Petrochemicals:		Specialty:	
Computers:		Manufacturer:		Design:		Aerospace:		Oil/Gas Products:		Special Services:	
Software:		Contract Research:		Construction:		Automotive:		Chemicals:	Y	Consulting:	
Communications:		Medical Services:		Eng. Services:	Y	Shipping:		Oil/Chem. Svcs.:		Specialty Mgmt.:	
Electronics:		Labs:	Y	Consulting:				Gases:		Products:	Y
Alternative Energy:		Bio. Services:						Other:	Y	Other:	

TYPES OF BUSINESS:

Polymers & Materials Science
Biochemical Science & Engineering
Materials Science & Engineering
Chemical Science & Catalysis
Polymer Development & Fabrication
Molecular Biotechnology
Nanotechnology Research

BRANDS/DIVISIONS/AFFILIATES:

Neoprene
Tyvek
Kevlar
Mylar
Corian
Butacite
Suva
Nomex

CONTACTS: *Note: Officers with more than one job title may be intentionally listed here more than once.*

Uma Chowdhry, Chief Science Officer/Sr. VP
Uma Chowdhry, CTO
Mathieu Vrijsen, Sr. VP-DuPont Oper. & Eng.
David B. Miller, VP-DuPont Electronic & Comm. Tech.
Diane H. Gulyas, VP-DuPont Performance Materials
Terry Caloghiris, VP-DuPont Coatings & Color Tech.
Nicholas C. Fanandakis, VP-DuPont Applied Biosciences

Phone: 302-774-1000	**Fax:** 302-773-2631
Toll-Free: 800-441-7515	
Address: 1007 Market St., Wilmington, DE 19898 US	

GROWTH PLANS/SPECIAL FEATURES:

DuPont Central Research and Development (CR&D) group is DuPont's main research division and has been responsible for most of its major product breakthroughs, including Neoprene (the first synthetic rubber), Tyvek, Kevlar fiber, Mylar (polyester film), Corian solid surfaces, Butacite polyvinyl butyral, Suva refrigerants and Nomex fiber. Although DuPont has over 75 research and development facilities across the world, its primary science exploration has been undertaken at the Experimental Station, located in Wilmington, Delaware, since 1903. In addition to more general research and technologies, CR&D provides leveraged scientific services for existing businesses within DuPont. Organizations within this leveraged aspect include: CorporateCenter for Analytical Science, CorporateCenter for Engineering Research and Leveraged Information Technology and Research Services. CR&D operates under the auspices of the Growth Council, a group of senior DuPont business leaders who evaluate research proposals and manage a long-term portfolio of research projects. Council research is divided into three areas: biochemical science and engineering, material science and engineering and chemical science and engineering. DuPont directs roughly $1.5 billion annually towards research and development. Research and development currently under way at CR&D includes nanotechnology, emerging displays technologies, fuel cells energy sources and biomaterials produced from renewable resources such as corn. The company is hoping its developments will lead to foods that prevent diseases and brittle bones; smart materials that can adjust performance on their own; microorganisms that produce biodegradable products; and new materials for personal protection. CR&D is in the middle of a five-year, $35-million research and development alliance with the Massachusetts Institute of Technology (MIT) aimed at researching materials and biotechnology. As an example of their collaboration, CR&D and MIT, in conjunction with the U.S. Army Research Service, have opened the 28,000-square-foot Institute for Soldier Nanotechnologies at the MIT campus, devoted to research on nanotech fabrics for use by the military.

FINANCIALS: Sales and profits are in thousands of dollars—add 000 to get the full amount. 2008 Note: Financial information for 2008 was not available for all companies at press time.

2008 Sales: $	2008 Profits: $
2007 Sales: $	2007 Profits: $
2006 Sales: $	2006 Profits: $
2005 Sales: $	2005 Profits: $
2004 Sales: $	2004 Profits: $

U.S. Stock Ticker: Subsidiary
Int'l Ticker: Int'l Exchange:
Employees:
Fiscal Year Ends: 12/31
Parent Company: E I DU PONT DE NEMOURS & CO (DUPONT)

SALARIES/BENEFITS:

Pension Plan: Y	ESOP Stock Plan:	Profit Sharing:	Top Exec. Salary: $	Bonus: $
Savings Plan: Y	Stock Purch. Plan:		Second Exec. Salary: $	Bonus: $

OTHER THOUGHTS:

Apparent Women Officers or Directors: 2
Hot Spot for Advancement for Women/Minorities: Y

LOCATIONS: ("Y" = Yes)

West:	Southwest:	Midwest:	Southeast:	Northeast:	International:
				Y	

Note: Financial information, benefits and other data can change quickly and may vary from those stated here.

E I DU PONT DE NEMOURS & CO (DUPONT)

www2.dupont.com

Industry Group Code: 325000 **Ranks within this company's industry group:** Sales: 4 Profits: 4

Techology:		Medical/Drugs:		Engineering:		Transportation:		Chemicals/Petrochemicals:		Specialty:	
Computers:		Manufacturer:	Y	Design:		Aerospace:		Oil/Gas Products:		Special Services:	
Software:		Contract Research:		Construction:		Automotive:		Chemicals:	Y	Consulting:	
Communications:		Medical Services:		Eng. Services:		Shipping:		Oil/Chem. Svcs.:		Specialty Mgmt.:	
Electronics:		Labs:	Y	Consulting:				Gases:		Products:	Y
Alternative Energy:	Y	Bio. Services:						Other:		Other:	

TYPES OF BUSINESS:

Chemicals Manufacturing
Polymers
Performance Coatings
Nutrition & Health Products
Electronics Materials
Agricultural Seeds
Fuel-Cell, Biofuels & Solar Panel Technology
Contract Research & Development

BRANDS/DIVISIONS/AFFILIATES:

Pioneer
Teflon
Corian
Kevlar
Tyvek
Coastal Training Technologies Corporation
MapShots, Inc.

CONTACTS: *Note: Officers with more than one job title may be intentionally listed here more than once.*

Ellen J. Kullman, CEO
Richard R. Goodmanson, COO/Exec. VP
Jeffrey L. Keefer, CFO/Exec. VP
David G. Bills, Chief Mktg. & Sales Officer
W. Donald Johnson, Sr. VP-DuPont Human Resources
John Bedbrook, VP-R&D, Agriculture & Nutrition
Phuong Tram, VP-DuPont IT/CIO
Uma Chowdhry, CTO/Chief Science Officer/Sr. VP
Thomas M. Connelly, Jr., Chief Innovation Officer/Exec. VP
Mathieu Vrijsen, Sr. VP-DuPont Eng.
Thomas L. Sager, General Counsel/Sr. VP-DuPont Legal
Mathieu Vrijsen, Sr. VP-DuPont Oper.
Peter C. Hemken, VP-Strategic Dir. & Bus. Dev., Pioneer Hi-Bred
Karen A. Fletcher, VP-DuPont Investor Rel.
Susan M. Stalnecker, VP-Finance/Treas.
Criag F. Binetti, Sr. VP-DuPont Nutrition & Health
Diane H. Gulyas, Group VP-DuPont Performance Materials
Terry Caloghiris, Group VP-DuPont Coatings & Color Tech.
Nicholas C. Fanandakis, Group VP-DuPont Applied BioSciences
Charles O. Holliday, Jr., Chmn.
Don Wirth, VP-Global Oper.
Jeffrey A. Coe, Sr. VP-DuPont Sourcing & Logistics

Phone: 302-774-1000 **Fax:** 302-773-2631
Toll-Free: 800-441-7515
Address: 1007 Market St., Wilmington, DE 19898 US

GROWTH PLANS/SPECIAL FEATURES:

E. I. du Pont de Nemours & Co. (DuPont), founded in 1802, develops and manufactures products in the biotechnology, electronics, materials science, synthetic fibers and safety and security sectors. DuPont operates in five segments: Agriculture and Nutrition (A&N); Coatings and Color Technologies (C&CT); Electronic and Communication Technologies (E&C); Performance Materials (PM); and Safety and Protection (S&P). A&N delivers Pioneer brand seed products, insecticides, fungicides, herbicides, soy-based food ingredients, food quality diagnostic testing equipment and liquid food packaging systems. The C&CT segment supplies automotive coatings, titanium dioxide white pigments and pigment and dye-based inks for ink-jet digital printing. E&C provides a range of advanced materials for the electronics industry, flexographic printing, color communication systems and a range of fluoropolymer and fluorochemical products. PM manufactures polymer-based materials, which include engineered polymers, specialized resins and films for use in food packaging, sealants, adhesives, sporting goods and laminated safety glass. The S&P segment provides protective materials and safety consulting services. Significant brands include Teflon fluoropolymers, films, fabric protectors, fibers and dispersions; Corian surfaces; Kevlar high strength material; and Tyvek protective material. Recent acquisitions include Chemtura Corporation's fluorine chemicals business in February 2008; the Industrial Apparel line of Cardinal Health's Scientific and Production Products business in April 2008; Coastal Training Technologies Corporation, a producer and marketer of training programs, in October 2008; and MapShots, Inc., an agricultural data management company, in December 2008. Recent divestitures include DuPont Super Boll and FreeFall brand cotton products in February 2008; and its 8th Continent soy milk joint venture with General Mills in February 2008. Also in 2008, DuPont opened new offices in Abu Dhabi, U.A.E. and Hyderabad, India.

DuPont offers its employees tuition assistance, ongoing training programs, flexible work practices, adoption assistance, an employee resource program, an emergency backup childcare resource and dependent care spending accounts.

FINANCIALS: **Sales and profits are in thousands of dollars—add 000 to get the full amount. 2008 Note: Financial information for 2008 was not available for all companies at press time.**

2008 Sales: $30,529,000	2008 Profits: $2,007,000	**U.S. Stock Ticker: DD**
2007 Sales: $29,378,000	2007 Profits: $2,988,000	**Int'l Ticker:** Int'l Exchange:
2006 Sales: $27,421,000	2006 Profits: $3,148,000	Employees: 60,000
2005 Sales: $26,639,000	2005 Profits: $2,053,000	Fiscal Year Ends: 12/31
2004 Sales: $27,340,000	2004 Profits: $1,780,000	Parent Company:

SALARIES/BENEFITS:

Pension Plan: Y	ESOP Stock Plan:	Profit Sharing:	Top Exec. Salary: $1,320,000	Bonus: $2,207,000
Savings Plan: Y	Stock Purch. Plan:		Second Exec. Salary: $835,384	Bonus: $918,000

OTHER THOUGHTS:

Apparent Women Officers or Directors: 17
Hot Spot for Advancement for Women/Minorities: Y

LOCATIONS: ("Y" = Yes)

West:	Southwest:	Midwest:	Southeast:	Northeast:	International:
Y	Y	Y	Y	Y	Y

EASTMAN CHEMICAL COMPANY

www.eastman.com

Industry Group Code: 325000 **Ranks within this company's industry group:** Sales: 21 Profits: 14

Techology:		Medical/Drugs:		Engineering:		Transportation:		Chemicals/Petrochemicals:		Specialty:	
Computers:		Manufacturer:		Design:		Aerospace:		Oil/Gas Products:		Special Services:	Y
Software:		Contract Research:		Construction:		Automotive:		Chemicals:	Y	Consulting:	
Communications:		Medical Services:		Eng. Services:		Shipping:		Oil/Chem. Svcs.:	Y	Specialty Mgmt.:	
Electronics:		Labs:		Consulting:				Gases:		Products:	
Alternative Energy:		Bio. Services:						Other:		Other:	

TYPES OF BUSINESS:

Chemicals, Fibers & Plastics
Coatings, Adhesives & Additives
Performance & Intermediate Chemicals
Acetate Fibers & Textiles
Gasification Services
Food Safety Diagnostics
Logistics Services
PET, Polyethylene & Polymers

BRANDS/DIVISIONS/AFFILIATES:

Estron
Estrobond
Chromspun
Tenite
Visualize
Eastman Fibers Korea Limited

CONTACTS:

Note: Officers with more than one job title may be intentionally listed here more than once.

J. Brian Ferguson, CEO
James P. Roger, Pres.
Curt E. Espeland, CFO/Sr. VP
Mark J. Costa, Chief Mktg. Officer
Greg W. Nelson, CTO/Sr. VP
Norris P. Sneed, Chief Admin. Officer/Sr. VP
Theresa K. Lee, Corp. Sec./Chief Legal Officer/Sr. VP
Ronald C. Lindsay, Sr. VP-Corp. Strategy & Regional Leadership
Norris P. Sneed, Sr. VP-Comm. & Public Affairs
Mark J. Costa, Exec. VP-Polymers Bus. Group.
James P. Rogers, Head-Chemicals & Fibers Bus. Group.
J. Brian Ferguson, Chmn.

Phone: 423-229-2000 **Fax:** 423-229-2145
Toll-Free: 800-327-8626
Address: 200 S. Wilcox Dr., Kingsport, TN 37660 US

GROWTH PLANS/SPECIAL FEATURES:

Eastman Chemical Company manufactures and sells a broad portfolio of chemicals, plastics and fibers through 11 manufacturing sites in seven countries. The firm has five operating segments: Coatings, Adhesives, Specialty Polymers and Inks (CASPI); Fibers; Performance Chemicals and Intermediates (PCI); Performance Polymers; and Specialty Plastics (SP). The CASPI segment manufactures raw materials, liquid vehicles, additives and specialty polymers used in paints and coatings, inks and adhesives for the durable goods, packaged goods, automobile and housing markets. The Fibers segment manufactures Estron acetate tow and Estrobond triacetin plasticizers for use in cigarette filters; Estron natural and Chromspun solution-dyed acetate yarns for the apparel, home furnishing and industrial fabrics industries; and cellulose acetate and acetyl raw materials for other acetate fiber producers. The PCI segment manufactures complex organic molecules such as diketene derivatives, specialty ketones and specialty anhydrides for fiber and food ingredients. It also manufactures various intermediate chemicals based on oxo and acetyl chemistries for a wide range of end-use markets from durables to food products and pharmaceuticals. The Performance Polymers segment is one of the world's largest makers of PET, which is used in beverage, food, personal care, cosmetics and industrial packaging; health care and pharmaceutical uses; and household products. Lastly, the SP segment makes highly specialized copolyesters used in specialty packaging materials, in-store displays, medical devices, photographic film, nonwovens and LCDs; and Tenite and Visualize cellulosic plastics used mainly in consumer products. In December 2008, the company signed a joint venture agreement with SK Chemicals Co., to form a cellulose acetate tow manufacturing facility located in Korea. The company will consequently be called Eastman Fibers Korea Limited, and Eastman will have 80% ownership.

Employees are offered health and dental insurance; life and dependent life insurance; dependent care and health care reimbursement accounts; a college savings plan; and short- and long-term disability coverage.

FINANCIALS:

Sales and profits are in thousands of dollars—add 000 to get the full amount. 2008 Note: Financial information for 2008 was not available for all companies at press time.

2008 Sales: $6,726,000
2007 Sales: $6,830,000
2006 Sales: $6,779,000
2005 Sales: $6,460,000
2004 Sales: $6,580,000

2008 Profits: $346,000
2007 Profits: $300,000
2006 Profits: $409,000
2005 Profits: $557,000
2004 Profits: $170,000

U.S. Stock Ticker: EMN
Int'l Ticker: Int'l Exchange:
Employees: 10,500
Fiscal Year Ends: 12/31
Parent Company:

SALARIES/BENEFITS:

Pension Plan: ESOP Stock Plan: Y Profit Sharing: Top Exec. Salary: $1,136,538 Bonus: $1,500,000
Savings Plan: Y Stock Purch. Plan: Y Second Exec. Salary: $575,962 Bonus: $600,000

OTHER THOUGHTS:

Apparent Women Officers or Directors: 2
Hot Spot for Advancement for Women/Minorities: Y

LOCATIONS: ("Y" = Yes)

West:	Southwest:	Midwest:	Southeast:	Northeast:	International:
	Y		Y	Y	Y

EASTMAN KODAK CO

www.kodak.com

Industry Group Code: 333314 **Ranks within this company's industry group:** Sales: 2 Profits: 4

Techology:		Medical/Drugs:		Engineering:		Transportation:		Chemicals/Petrochemicals:		Specialty:	
Computers:		Manufacturer:	Y	Design:		Aerospace:		Oil/Gas Products:		Special Services:	
Software:	Y	Contract Research:		Construction:		Automotive:		Chemicals:	Y	Consulting:	
Communications:		Medical Services:		Eng. Services:		Shipping:		Oil/Chem. Svcs.:		Specialty Mgmt.:	
Electronics:	Y	Labs:		Consulting:				Gases:		Products:	Y
Alternative Energy:		Bio. Services:						Other:		Other:	

TYPES OF BUSINESS:

Photography Equipment
Films & Photographic Papers
Photo Processing Services & Equipment
Digital Cameras & Accessories
Commercial Printing Technology
Printers & Inks

BRANDS/DIVISIONS/AFFILIATES:

Intermate A/S
Design2Launch

CONTACTS:

Note: Officers with more than one job title may be intentionally listed here more than once.

Antonio M. Perez, CEO
Philip J. Faraci, COO
Philip J. Faraci, Pres.
Frank S. Sklarsky, CFO/Exec. VP
Jeffrey W. Hayzlett, Chief Mktg. Officer/VP
Robert L. Berman, Chief Human Resources Officer/Sr. VP
Kim VanGelder, CIO/VP
Terry R. Taber, CTO/VP
John Blake, Gen. Mgr.-Digital Capture & Imaging Devices/VP
Joyce P. Haag, General Counsel/Sr. VP
Victor Cho, Gen. Mgr.-Internet & Software Svcs./VP
Essie L. Calhoun, Dir.-Comm. Affairs/Chief Diversity Officer
Antoinette P. McCorvey, VP/Dir.-Investor Rel.
Diane E. Wolfong, Controller
Nicoletta A. Zongrone, VP/Gen. Mgr.-Retail Systems Solutions
Ying Yeh, Pres., North Asia Region & Bus. Dev., Asia-Pacific
Mary Jane Hellyar, Pres., Film, Photofinishing & Entertainment Group
Isidre Rosello, Gen. Mgr.-Digital Printing Solutions/VP
Antonio M. Perez, Chmn.
John O'Grady, Regional Managing Dir.-EMEA/VP

Phone: 585-724-4000	**Fax:** 585-724-0663
Toll-Free:	
Address: 343 State St., Rochester, NY 14650 US	

GROWTH PLANS/SPECIAL FEATURES:

Eastman Kodak Co., founded in 1880, develops, manufactures and markets traditional and digital imaging products, services and solutions for consumers, professionals, the entertainment industry and other commercial customers. Kodak operates in three segments: the Consumer Digital Imaging Group; the Film, Photofinishing and Entertainment Group (FPEG); and the Graphic Communications Group. The Consumer Digital Imaging Group encompasses digital cameras, kiosks, home printing systems, inkjet systems, digital imaging services and imaging sensors. FPEG is composed of traditional photographic products and services used to create motion pictures and capture and print photographs. The company manufactures and markets films, including motion picture, consumer, professional, industrial and aerial; one-time-use and re-loadable film cameras; color photographic papers; photographic processing chemicals; wholesale photofinishing services; on-site event imaging solutions; and equipment service. The Graphic Communications Group serves a variety of customers in the creative, in-plant, data center, commercial printing, packaging, newspaper and digital service bureau markets. Products include digital and traditional prepress equipment and consumables, including plates, chemistry and media; workflow software and digital controller development; color and black-and-white electrophotographic equipment; high-speed, high-volume commercial inkjet printing systems; high-speed production and workgroup document scanners; and micrographic peripherals and media, including micrographic films. In April 2008, Kodak acquired Intermate A/S, a supplier of remote monitoring and print connectivity solutions for transactional printing, and Design2Launch, a developer of collaborative end-to-end digital workflow solutions. In December 2008, the firm acquired flexographic printing solutions from NuPro Technologies, Inc. In January 2009, Kodak agreed to acquire the scanner division of BOWE BELL + HOWELL.

Eastman Kodak offers its employees education resources, flexible work arrangements, fitness centers, wellness programs, parenting resources, an employee assistance program, adoption resources, flexible spending accounts, a health savings account and medical, dental, AD&D and disability insurance.

FINANCIALS:

Sales and profits are in thousands of dollars—add 000 to get the full amount. 2008 Note: Financial information for 2008 was not available for all companies at press time.

2008 Sales: $9,416,000	2008 Profits: $-442,000	**U.S. Stock Ticker: EK**
2007 Sales: $10,301,000	2007 Profits: $676,000	**Int'l Ticker:** Int'l Exchange:
2006 Sales: $10,568,000	2006 Profits: $-601,000	Employees: 24,400
2005 Sales: $11,395,000	2005 Profits: $-1,261,000	Fiscal Year Ends: 12/31
2004 Sales: $13,517,000	2004 Profits: $556,000	Parent Company:

SALARIES/BENEFITS:

Pension Plan: Y	ESOP Stock Plan:	Profit Sharing:	Top Exec. Salary: $1,786,693	Bonus: $
Savings Plan: Y	Stock Purch. Plan:		Second Exec. Salary: $648,760	Bonus: $

OTHER THOUGHTS:

Apparent Women Officers or Directors: 16
Hot Spot for Advancement for Women/Minorities: Y

LOCATIONS: ("Y" = Yes)

West:	Southwest:	Midwest:	Southeast:	Northeast:	International:
Y		Y	Y	Y	Y

Note: Financial information, benefits and other data can change quickly and may vary from those stated here.

EATON CORP

www.eaton.com

Industry Group Code: 336300 **Ranks within this company's industry group:** Sales: 7 Profits: 3

Techology:		Medical/Drugs:		Engineering:		Transportation:		Chemicals/Petrochemicals:		Specialty:	
Computers:		Manufacturer:		Design:		Aerospace:	Y	Oil/Gas Products:		Special Services:	
Software:	Y	Contract Research:		Construction:		Automotive:	Y	Chemicals:		Consulting:	
Communications:		Medical Services:		Eng. Services:		Shipping:		Oil/Chem. Svcs.:		Specialty Mgmt.:	
Electronics:		Labs:		Consulting:				Gases:		Products:	
Alternative Energy:	Y	Bio. Services:						Other:		Other:	

TYPES OF BUSINESS:

Hydraulic Products
Electrical Power Distribution & Control Equipment
Truck Transmissions & Axles
Engine Components
Aerospace & Military Components

BRANDS/DIVISIONS/AFFILIATES:

Senyuan International Holdings Limited
Catalytica Energy Systems, Inc.
Schreder-Hazemeyer
Ronningen-Petter
Marina Power Lighting
Synflex
Arrow Hose & Tubing, Inc.
Babco Electric Group

CONTACTS: *Note: Officers with more than one job title may be intentionally listed here more than once.*

Alexander M. Cutler, CEO
Alexander M. Cutler, Pres.
Richard H. Fearon, CFO
Jeffrey M. Krakowiak, Sr. VP-Mktg. & Sales
Susan J. Cook, Exec. VP-Human Resources
William W. Blausey, Jr., CIO/VP
Yannis P. Tsavalas, CTO/VP
Mark M. McGuire, General Counsel/VP
Richard H. Fearon, Chief Planning Officer/Exec. VP
William B. Doggett, Sr. VP-Comm. & Public Affairs
William C. Hartman, Sr. VP-Investor Rel.
Billie K. Rawot, Sr. VP/Controller
Joseph P. Palchak, CEO-Automotive
James E. Sweetnam, CEO-Truck
Craig Arnold, CEO-Fluid Power
Randy W. Carson, CEO-Electrical
Alexander M. Cutler, Chmn.
Jean-Pierre Lacombe, Pres., Europe

Phone: 216-523-5000	**Fax:** 216-523-4787
Toll-Free: 800-386-1911	
Address: 1111 Superior Ave., Cleveland, OH 44114-2584 US	

GROWTH PLANS/SPECIAL FEATURES:

Eaton Corporation designs, manufactures, markets and services electrical systems and components in four business segments: fluid power, electrical, automotive and truck. The fluid power segment, the firm's largest segment, develops and sells fluid power products to industrial, mobile equipment and aerospace customers worldwide. The segment also handles Eaton's aerospace business, which serves commercial and military aviation, space, military weapon systems, marine, off-road and other severe environment applications. The electrical segment distributes electrical power and control equipment for industrial, commercial and residential markets. The automotive segment focuses on the powertrain and specialized sensor and actuator areas of passenger cars and light trucks. Its primary products include mirror and engine management controls, as well as engine air management systems, including superchargers, cylinder head modules, engine valves and lifters. The truck segment features drivetrain systems and components for medium-duty and heavy-duty commercial vehicles. Its products include manual and automatic transmissions, clutches, driveshafts, steering, drive and trailer axles, brakes, chassis control systems, and collision warning systems. During 2007, the company acquired Arrow Hose & Tubing Inc.; MGE small systems UPS business from Schneider Electric; Babco Electric Group; Pulizzi Engineering; Technology and related assets of SMC Electrical Products, Inc.'s industrial medium-voltage adjustable frequency drive business; Fuel components division of Saturn Electronics & Engineering, Inc.; Aphel Technologies Limited; Argo-Tech Corporation; and Power Protection Business of Power Products Ltd. In the first half of 2008, the firm acquired the engine valves business of Kirloskar Oil Engines Ltd.; The Moeller Group; and Phoenixtec Power Company Ltd. In August 2008, Eaton agreed to a joint-venture with Nittan Valve Co. Ltd. for engine valve products in Japan and Korea.

Eaton offers employees benefits including flexible spending accounts, a personal investment plan, employee assistance, tuition reimbursements, adoption assistance and work/life programs.

FINANCIALS: **Sales and profits are in thousands of dollars—add 000 to get the full amount. 2008 Note: Financial information for 2008 was not available for all companies at press time.**

2008 Sales: $15,376,000	2008 Profits: $1,058,000	**U.S. Stock Ticker: ETN**
2007 Sales: $13,033,000	2007 Profits: $994,000	**Int'l Ticker:** Int'l Exchange:
2006 Sales: $12,232,000	2006 Profits: $950,000	Employees: 75,000
2005 Sales: $10,874,000	2005 Profits: $805,000	Fiscal Year Ends: 12/31
2004 Sales: $9,712,000	2004 Profits: $648,000	Parent Company:

SALARIES/BENEFITS:

Pension Plan: Y	ESOP Stock Plan:	Profit Sharing:	Top Exec. Salary: $1,069,305	Bonus: $9,520,197
Savings Plan: Y	Stock Purch. Plan:		Second Exec. Salary: $511,695	Bonus: $2,894,807

OTHER THOUGHTS:

Apparent Women Officers or Directors: 2
Hot Spot for Advancement for Women/Minorities:

LOCATIONS: ("Y" = Yes)

West:	Southwest:	Midwest:	Southeast:	Northeast:	International:
Y	Y	Y	Y	Y	Y

EISAI CO LTD

www.eisai.co.jp

Industry Group Code: 325414 **Ranks within this company's industry group:** Sales: 1 Profits: 3

Techology:		Medical/Drugs:		Engineering:		Transportation:		Chemicals/Petrochemicals:		Specialty:	
Computers:		Manufacturer:	Y	Design:		Aerospace:		Oil/Gas Products:		Special Services:	
Software:		Contract Research:		Construction:		Automotive:		Chemicals:		Consulting:	
Communications:		Medical Services:		Eng. Services:		Shipping:		Oil/Chem. Svcs.:		Specialty Mgmt.:	
Electronics:		Labs:		Consulting:				Gases:		Products:	Y
Alternative Energy:		Bio. Services:						Other:		Other:	

TYPES OF BUSINESS:

Pharmaceuticals Manufacturing
Over-the-Counter Pharmaceuticals
Pharmaceutical Production Equipment
Diagnostic Products
Food Additives
Personal Health Care Products
Vitamins & Nutritional Supplements

BRANDS/DIVISIONS/AFFILIATES:

Aricept
Aciphex/Pariet
Coretec
Myonal
Chocola
Travelmin
Juvelux
MGI Pharma Inc

CONTACTS: *Note: Officers with more than one job title may be intentionally listed here more than once.*

Haruo Naito, CEO
Haruo Naito, Pres.
Hideaki Matsui, CFO
Soichi Matsuno, Deputy Pres., Global Human Resources
Kentaro Yoshimatsu, Sr. VP-R&D/Pres., Eisai R&D Mgmt. Co., Ltd.
Kazuo Hirai, VP-Info. System & Corp. Mgmt. Planning
Takafumi Asano, VP-Prod.
Kenta Takahashi, General Counsel/VP/Sr. Dir.-Legal Dept.
Makoto Shiina, Exec. VP-Strategy
Akira Fujiyoshi, VP-Corp. Comm. Dept.
Nobuo Deguchi, Exec. VP-Internal Control & Intellectual Property
Hajime Shimizu, Chmn/CEO-Eisai Corp. N. America/Chmn/CEO-Eisai Inc
Yutaka Tsuchiya, Chmn./Pres., Eisai Europe Ltd.
Yukio Akada, Chmn./Pres., Eisai China, Inc.
Masanori Tsuno, Pres., Eisai Medical Research, Inc.
Norihiko Tanikawa, Chmn.
Soichi Matsuno, Deputy Pres., Global Pharmaceuticals Bus.
Takafumi Asano, VP-Logistics & Transformation

Phone: 81-3-3817-3700 **Fax:** 81-3-3811-3077
Toll-Free:
Address: 4-6-10 Koishikawa, Bunkyo-ku, Tokyo, 112-8088 Japan

GROWTH PLANS/SPECIAL FEATURES:

Eisai Co., Ltd. primarily develops, manufactures and distributes medical products, operating in two segments: prescription pharmaceuticals, which represented 96.9% of its 2008 net sales, and other. These other products include over-the-counter pharmaceuticals, consumer health care products, food additives, pharmaceutical production equipment and diagnostic products. Its two largest pharmaceuticals, Aricept, a treatment for Alzheimer's dementia, and proton pump inhibitor (PPI) AcipHex/Pariet, a treatment for gastroesophageal reflux disease and ulcers, accounted for 39.6% and 24% of 2008 net sales, respectively. The firm's research teams are currently investigating new indications for Aricept including dementia associated with Parkinson's disease. Other prescription pharmaceuticals include Coretec, an agent for acute heart failure; Glakay, an osteoporosis treatment; Azeptin, an antiallergic agent; and Myonal, a muscle relaxant. In the consumer health care field, the firm's products include Seabond denture adhesive (manufactured by U.S.-based Combe Laboratories, Inc.); motion sickness remedy Travelmin; Breathe Right nasal strips (manufactured by GlaxoSmithKline plc); and Juvelux natural vitamin E preparation. Eisai has a long-standing leading position in the Japanese vitamin and nutritional supplement market, focusing on synthetic and natural vitamin E products and derivatives; it also markets a full line of vitamin-enriched dietary supplements under the brand name Chocola. The firm also markets diagnostic products and manufactures pharmaceutical production systems including continuous sterilization devices, inspection systems and ampoule packing machines. Geographically, North America generated 46.2% of 2008 net sales; Japan, 42.6%; Europe, 7.4%; and Asia and other regions, 3.8%. The company maintains approximately 32 overseas subsidiaries, in Asia, Europe and North America; and 12 domestic subsidiaries. In January 2008, the firm acquired U.S.-based MGI Pharma, Inc. for $3.9 billion. Now a subsidiary of Eisai Corporation of North America, MGI is a biopharmaceutical company that focuses on oncology and acute care.

FINANCIALS: **Sales and profits are in thousands of dollars—add 000 to get the full amount. 2008 Note: Financial information for 2008 was not available for all companies at press time.**

2008 Sales: $7,304,620	2008 Profits: $-169,110	**U.S. Stock Ticker: ESALY**
2007 Sales: $6,705,770	2007 Profits: $702,310	**Int'l Ticker: 4523** Int'l Exchange: Tokyo-TSE
2006 Sales: $5,113,100	2006 Profits: $539,200	Employees: 9,649
2005 Sales: $4,530,600	2005 Profits: $471,760	Fiscal Year Ends: 3/31
2004 Sales: $4,734,600	2004 Profits: $474,700	Parent Company:

SALARIES/BENEFITS:

Pension Plan: Y	ESOP Stock Plan:	Profit Sharing:	Top Exec. Salary: $	Bonus: $
Savings Plan:	Stock Purch. Plan:		Second Exec. Salary: $	Bonus: $

OTHER THOUGHTS:

Apparent Women Officers or Directors:
Hot Spot for Advancement for Women/Minorities:

LOCATIONS: ("Y" = Yes)

West:	Southwest:	Midwest:	Southeast:	Northeast:	International:
		Y		Y	Y

Note: Financial information, benefits and other data can change quickly and may vary from those stated here.

ELECTRONIC ARTS INC

www.ea.com

Industry Group Code: 511208 **Ranks within this company's industry group:** Sales: 2 Profits: 5

Techology:		Medical/Drugs:		Engineering:		Transportation:		Chemicals/Petrochemicals:		Specialty:	
Computers:		Manufacturer:		Design:		Aerospace:		Oil/Gas Products:		Special Services:	
Software:	Y	Contract Research:		Construction:		Automotive:		Chemicals:		Consulting:	
Communications:		Medical Services:		Eng. Services:		Shipping:		Oil/Chem. Svcs.:		Specialty Mgmt.:	
Electronics:		Labs:		Consulting:				Gases:		Products:	
Alternative Energy:		Bio. Services:						Other:		Other:	

TYPES OF BUSINESS:

Computer Software-Video Games
Online Interactive Games
E-Commerce Sales
Mobile Games

BRANDS/DIVISIONS/AFFILIATES:

EA Games
EA Sports
EA Casual Entertainment
Sims (The)
Madden NFL
Pogo.com
ThreeSF Inc
J2MSoft Inc

CONTACTS: *Note: Officers with more than one job title may be intentionally listed here more than once.*

John S. Riccitiello, CEO
John Pleasants, COO/Pres., Global Publishing
Eric Brown, CFO/Exec. VP
Gabrielle Toledano, Exec. VP-Human Resources
Stephen G. Bene, General Counsel/Sec./Sr. VP
Joel Linzner, Exec. VP-Bus. & Legal Affairs
Tammy Schachter, Sr. Dir.-Public Rel.
Ken Barker, Chief Acct. Officer/Sr. VP
Peter Moore, Pres., EA Sports Label
Frank Gibeau, Pres., EA Games Label
Gerhard Florin, Exec. VP-Publishing
Lawrence F. Probst, III, Chmn.

Phone: 650-628-1500 **Fax:** 650-628-1415
Toll-Free:
Address: 209 Redwood Shores Pkwy., Redwood City, CA 94065-1175 US

GROWTH PLANS/SPECIAL FEATURES:

Electronic Arts, Inc. (EA) develops, markets, publishes and distributes video game software. The company designs products for a number of platforms, including video game consoles, such as the Sony PlayStation 3, Microsoft Xbox 360 and Nintendo Wii; handheld game systems, including PlayStation Portable (PSP), Nintendo DS and Apple iPod; personal computers (PCs); and mobile phones. The company operates in four segments, or labels: EA Games, EA Sports, The Sims and EA Casual Entertainment. The EA Games label encompasses the largest percentage of the company's studios and development staff, focused on producing a diverse portfolio of action-adventure, role playing, racing and combat games, as well as massively-multiplayer online role-playing games (MMORPG) such as Warhammer Online. The EA Sports label produces a variety of sports-based video games, including the Madden NFL, FIFA Soccer and Tiger Woods PGA TOUR franchises. EA's The Sims label develops life simulation games and online communities, such as The Sims 2, which offers an online community of over 4 million unique monthly users. The EA Casual Entertainment label develops games that are intended to be quick to learn and play, making them easily accessible for a wide audience. Pogo, an online service with over 1.6 million subscribers, offers a variety of card, puzzle and word games. Through EA Mobile, the firm publishes games and related content for mobile phones. The company distributes games in over 35 countries worldwide. In June 2008, EA acquired ThreeSF, Inc., a gaming-based social network. In December 2008, the company acquired J2MSoft Inc., a Korean-based developer of PC online games. Also in December 2008, Electronic Arts announced plans to cut its worldwide workforce by approximately 10% and to consolidate or close at least nine of its studio and publishing locations.

EA offers its employees discounts on game systems; education reimbursement; medical insurance; a bonus plan; and an employee assistance program.

FINANCIALS: **Sales and profits are in thousands of dollars—add 000 to get the full amount. 2008 Note: Financial information for 2008 was not available for all companies at press time.**

2008 Sales: $3,665,000	2008 Profits: $-454,000	**U.S. Stock Ticker: ERTS**
2007 Sales: $3,091,000	2007 Profits: $76,000	**Int'l Ticker:** Int'l Exchange:
2006 Sales: $2,951,000	2006 Profits: $236,000	Employees: 9,000
2005 Sales: $3,129,000	2005 Profits: $504,000	Fiscal Year Ends: 3/31
2004 Sales: $2,957,141	2004 Profits: $577,292	Parent Company:

SALARIES/BENEFITS:

Pension Plan:	ESOP Stock Plan:	Profit Sharing:	Top Exec. Salary: $752,599	Bonus: $349,358
Savings Plan: Y	Stock Purch. Plan: Y		Second Exec. Salary: $750,000	Bonus: $625,350

OTHER THOUGHTS:

Apparent Women Officers or Directors: 3
Hot Spot for Advancement for Women/Minorities: Y

LOCATIONS: ("Y" = Yes)

West:	Southwest:	Midwest:	Southeast:	Northeast:	International:
Y	Y	Y	Y	Y	Y

ELECTRONIC DATA SYSTEMS CORP (EDS)

www.eds.com

Industry Group Code: 541512 **Ranks within this company's industry group:** Sales: Profits:

Techology:		Medical/Drugs:		Engineering:		Transportation:		Chemicals/Petrochemicals:		Specialty:	
Computers:		Manufacturer:		Design:		Aerospace:		Oil/Gas Products:		Special Services:	Y
Software:		Contract Research:		Construction:		Automotive:		Chemicals:		Consulting:	Y
Communications:		Medical Services:		Eng. Services:		Shipping:		Oil/Chem. Svcs.:		Specialty Mgmt.:	
Electronics:		Labs:		Consulting:				Gases:		Products:	
Alternative Energy:		Bio. Services:						Other:		Other:	

TYPES OF BUSINESS:

Consulting-Computer & Internet
Systems Integration & Development
Information Solutions
Process Management
Business Process Outsourcing
Internet Services

BRANDS/DIVISIONS/AFFILIATES:

Hewlett-Packard Co (HP)
EDS Applications Services
Business Process Outsourcing
EDS Agile Enterprise Platform
RelQ Software Private Limited
Saber Corp.
Nexagent
Vistorm Holdings Limited

CONTACTS:

Note: Officers with more than one job title may be intentionally listed here more than once.

Joe Eazor, Gen. Mgr.
Bobby Grisham, Sr. VP-Global Sales
Jeff Kelly, Sr. VP-Americas
David Gee, VP-Worldwide Mktg.
Andy Mattes, Sr. VP-Applications Svcs.
Dennis Stolkey, Sr. VP-U.S. Public Sector
Bill Thomas, Sr. VP-EMEA

Phone: 972-604-6000	**Fax:** 972-605-6033
Toll-Free:	
Address: 5400 Legacy Dr., Plano, TX 75024 US	

GROWTH PLANS/SPECIAL FEATURES:

Electronic Data Systems Corporation (EDS) is a leading global technology services company focused on providing business solutions. The company operates through three segments: infrastructure services, application services and business process outsourcing (BPO) services. EDS Infrastructure Services delivers hosting, storage, desktop, communications and security and privacy services that enable clients to drive down their total cost of ownership and increase the productivity of their information technology environments. EDS Applications Services helps organizations plan, develop, integrate and manage custom applications, packaged software and industry-specific solutions. The company offers applications development and management services on an outsourced or project basis. Services range from the outsourcing of all application development and systems integration to the management and implementation of EDS-owned or third-party industry applications. The firm's BPO segment enables clients to drive operational and organizational efficiency, business process integration, application integration and cost savings. Its BPO services include billing and clearing; card processing; credit; customer relationship management; document processing; finance and accounting; human resources outsourcing; insurance; payment; and supply management services. EDS also provides industry-specific offerings and industry experts supporting the financial services, manufacturing, healthcare, transportation, communications, energy and consumer and retail industries. The EDS Agile Enterprise Platform is a network-based utility architecture that serves as the foundation for the delivery of a significant portion of its BPO services. In August 2008, the firm was acquired by Hewlett-Packard Co. for $13.9 billion.

FINANCIALS:

Sales and profits are in thousands of dollars—add 000 to get the full amount. 2008 Note: Financial information for 2008 was not available for all companies at press time.

2008 Sales: $	2008 Profits: $	**U.S. Stock Ticker: Subsidiary**
2007 Sales: $22,134,000	2007 Profits: $716,000	**Int'l Ticker:** Int'l Exchange:
2006 Sales: $21,268,000	2006 Profits: $470,000	Employees: 117,000
2005 Sales: $19,757,000	2005 Profits: $150,000	Fiscal Year Ends: 12/31
2004 Sales: $19,863,000	2004 Profits: $158,000	Parent Company: HEWLETT-PACKARD CO (HP)

SALARIES/BENEFITS:

Pension Plan:	ESOP Stock Plan:	Profit Sharing:	Top Exec. Salary: $1,300,000	Bonus: $2,025,000
Savings Plan:	Stock Purch. Plan:		Second Exec. Salary: $1,125,000	Bonus: $2,250,000

OTHER THOUGHTS:

Apparent Women Officers or Directors: 3
Hot Spot for Advancement for Women/Minorities: Y

LOCATIONS: ("Y" = Yes)

West:	Southwest:	Midwest:	Southeast:	Northeast:	International:
Y	Y	Y	Y	Y	Y

ELI LILLY & COMPANY

www.lilly.com

Industry Group Code: 325412 **Ranks within this company's industry group:** Sales: 12 Profits: 27

Techology:		Medical/Drugs:		Engineering:		Transportation:		Chemicals/Petrochemicals:		Specialty:	
Computers:		Manufacturer:	Y	Design:		Aerospace:		Oil/Gas Products:		Special Services:	
Software:		Contract Research:		Construction:		Automotive:		Chemicals:		Consulting:	
Communications:		Medical Services:		Eng. Services:		Shipping:		Oil/Chem. Svcs.:		Specialty Mgmt.:	
Electronics:		Labs:	Y	Consulting:				Gases:		Products:	
Alternative Energy:		Bio. Services:						Other:		Other:	

TYPES OF BUSINESS:

Pharmaceuticals Discovery & Development
Veterinary Products

BRANDS/DIVISIONS/AFFILIATES:

Zyprexa
Prozac
Humalog
Gemzar
Coban
Applied Molecular Evolution Inc
Icos Corporation
ImClone Systems Inc.

CONTACTS: *Note: Officers with more than one job title may be intentionally listed here more than once.*

John Lechleiter, CEO
John Lechleiter, Pres.
Derica Rice, CFO/Sr. VP
Bryce D. Carmine, Exec. VP-Global Mktg. & Sales
Steven M. Paul, Exec. VP-Science
Michael Heim, CIO/VP-IT
Steven M. Paul, Exec. VP-Tech.
Thomas Verhoeven, Pres., Global Prod. Dev.
W. Darin Moody, VP-Corp. Eng. & Continuous Improvement
Frank Deane, Pres., Mfg.
Robert A. Armitage, General Counsel/Sr. VP
Gino Santini, Exec. Dir.-Corp. Strategy & Policy
Alex M. Azar II, Sr. VP-Corp. Affairs & Comm.
Thomas W. Grein, Treas./VP
Enrique Conterno, Pres., Lilly USA
Alfonso Zulueta, Pres./Gen. Mgr.-Lilly Japan
Alecia A. DeCoudreaux, General Counsel/VP
Tim Garnett, Chief Medical Officer/VP-Medical
John Lechleiter, Chmn.
Karim Bitar, Pres., European Operations

Phone: 317-276-2000	**Fax:**
Toll-Free: 800-545-5979	
Address: Lilly Corporate Ctr., Indianapolis, IN 46285 US	

GROWTH PLANS/SPECIAL FEATURES:

Eli Lilly & Co. researches, develops, manufactures and sells pharmaceuticals designed to treat a variety of conditions. Most of Eli Lilly's products are developed by its in-house research staff, which primarily directs its research efforts towards the search for products to prevent and treat cancer and diseases of the central nervous, endocrine and cardiovascular systems. The firm's other research lies in anti-infectives and products to treat animal diseases. Major brands include neuroscience products Zyprexa, Strattera, Prozac, Cymbalta and Permax; endocrine products Humalog, Humulin and Actos; oncology products Gemzar and Alimta; animal health products Tylan, Rumensin and Coban; cardiovascular products ReoPro and Xigris; anti-infectives Ceclor and Vancocin; and Cialis, for erectile dysfunction. In the U.S., the company distributes pharmaceuticals primarily through independent wholesale distributors. The company manufactures and distributes its products through facilities in the U.S., Puerto Rico and 25 other countries, which are then sold to markets in 135 countries throughout the world. In 2008, the firm owned 15 production and distribution facilities in the U.S. and Puerto Rico. Major research and development facilities abroad are located in the U.K., Canada, Singapore and Spain. In April 2008, the firm acquired Hypnion, Inc., a neuroscience drug discovery company focused on sleep disorder research. In October 2008, the company agreed to acquire ImClone Systems, Inc. for $6.5 billion.

Eli Lilly offers its employees domestic partner benefits and an employee assistance program, as well as up to 10 weeks of paid maternity leave. The firm also offers an on-site fitness center, flexible hours or telecommuting, parenting and dependant care leaves, adoption assistance and tuition reimbursement.

FINANCIALS: **Sales and profits are in thousands of dollars—add 000 to get the full amount. 2008 Note: Financial information for 2008 was not available for all companies at press time.**

2008 Sales: $20,378,000	2008 Profits: $-2,071,900	**U.S. Stock Ticker: LLY**
2007 Sales: $18,633,500	2007 Profits: $2,953,000	**Int'l Ticker:** Int'l Exchange:
2006 Sales: $15,691,000	2006 Profits: $2,662,700	Employees: 40,500
2005 Sales: $14,645,300	2005 Profits: $1,979,600	Fiscal Year Ends: 12/31
2004 Sales: $13,857,900	2004 Profits: $1,810,100	Parent Company:

SALARIES/BENEFITS:

Pension Plan: Y	ESOP Stock Plan:	Profit Sharing:	Top Exec. Salary: $1,339,125	Bonus: $2,709,053
Savings Plan: Y	Stock Purch. Plan:		Second Exec. Salary: $1,000,250	Bonus: $1,309,327

OTHER THOUGHTS:

Apparent Women Officers or Directors: 4
Hot Spot for Advancement for Women/Minorities: Y

LOCATIONS: ("Y" = Yes)

West:	Southwest:	Midwest:	Southeast:	Northeast:	International:
Y	Y	Y	Y	Y	Y

Note: Financial information, benefits and other data can change quickly and may vary from those stated here.

EMBRAER BRASILIAN AVIATION COMPANY

www.embraer.com

Industry Group Code: 336410 **Ranks within this company's industry group:** Sales: 17 Profits: 14

Techology:		Medical/Drugs:		Engineering:		Transportation:		Chemicals/Petrochemicals:		Specialty:	
Computers:		Manufacturer:		Design:		Aerospace:	Y	Oil/Gas Products:		Special Services:	Y
Software:		Contract Research:		Construction:		Automotive:		Chemicals:		Consulting:	
Communications:		Medical Services:		Eng. Services:		Shipping:		Oil/Chem. Svcs.:		Specialty Mgmt.:	Y
Electronics:		Labs:		Consulting:				Gases:		Products:	
Alternative Energy:		Bio. Services:						Other:		Other:	

TYPES OF BUSINESS:

Aircraft Manufacturer
Commuter Aircraft
Business Jets
Aircraft Maintenance
Military Aircraft

BRANDS/DIVISIONS/AFFILIATES:

EMB
ERJ

CONTACTS: *Note: Officers with more than one job title may be intentionally listed here more than once.*

Frederico P. F. Curado, CEO
Frederico P. F. Curado, Pres.
Antonio L. P. Manso, CFO
Antonio J. Franco, Exec. VP-Personnel
Satoshi Yokota, Exec. VP-Tech. Dev.
Horacio A. Forjaz, Exec. VP-Admin.
Flavio Rimoli, Exec. VP/Legal Counsel
Artur A. V. Coutinho, Exec. VP-Industrial Oper.
Satoshi Yokota, Exec. VP-Strategic Planning
Horacio A. Forjaz, Exec. VP-Corp. Comm.
Antonio L. P. Manso, Exec. VP-Finance
Luiz C. S. Aguiar, Exec. VP-Defense Market & Gov't
Mauro Kern Junior, Exec. VP-Airline Market
Luis C. Affonso, Exec. VP-Exec. Aviation
Antonio J. Franco, Exec. VP-Organizational Dev.
Mauricio Novis Botelho, Chmn.
Artur A. V. Coutinho, Exec. VP-Procurement

Phone: 55-12-3927-4404 **Fax:**
Toll-Free:
Address: Ave. Brigadeiro Faria Lima, 2170, Sao Jose dos Campos, Sao Paulo, 12227-901 Brazil

GROWTH PLANS/SPECIAL FEATURES:

Embraer, originally a government-controlled company established to produce aircraft for the Brazilian Air Force, has become one of the world's leading manufacturers of commercial aircraft. Its commercial customers include the U.S. discount airline JetBlue, US Airways and the HNA Group. The firm's business is divided into four primarily categories: commercial jets, defense systems, executive jets and aviation services. The firm's commercial aviation business, accounting for 64.4% of sales, produces the ERJ family of jets, EMB jets, and Embraer jets. The ERJ 145 family is composed of four regionally designed jets, the ERJ 135, ERJ 140, ERJ 145 and ERJ 145 XR. Each jet is built specifically for use in regional networks and seats between 37 and 50 passengers. The jets themselves offer a 95% systems commonality, intended to reduce parts requirements and reduce training costs. The Embraer jets, include four models, 170, 175, 190 and 195, and are all designed to provide greater mission range than common in regional jets, short ground turnaround time, common crew type rating, high fuel efficiency and enhanced cabin configuration flexibility. The firm's EMB jet is a pressurized twin wing-mounted turboprop aircraft that accommodates up to 30 passengers. The company's defense business, which accounts for 6.6% of sales, primarily manufactures transport, training, light attack and surveillance aircraft, which it sells to the Brazilian Air Force and the military forces of 16 other countries. The executive jet segment, which generates 16% of sales, supplies executive jets to companies, including fractional ownership companies, charter companies, air-taxi companies and high net-worth individuals. Lastly, the aviation services segment provides after-sales customer support services and manufactures spare parts for the company's fleets. Support services include field support, technical support and training. In 2008, the firm announced plans to build two new plants in Portugal.

FINANCIALS: **Sales and profits are in thousands of dollars—add 000 to get the full amount. 2008 Note: Financial information for 2008 was not available for all companies at press time.**

2008 Sales: $6,335,000	2008 Profits: $388,700	**U.S. Stock Ticker: ERJ**
2007 Sales: $5,245,200	2007 Profits: $489,300	**Int'l Ticker:** Int'l Exchange:
2006 Sales: $3,807,403	2006 Profits: $390,140	Employees: 19,265
2005 Sales: $3,829,907	2005 Profits: $445,719	Fiscal Year Ends: 12/31
2004 Sales: $3,807,403	2004 Profits: $380,206	Parent Company:

SALARIES/BENEFITS:

Pension Plan: Y	ESOP Stock Plan:	Profit Sharing: Y	Top Exec. Salary: $	Bonus: $
Savings Plan:	Stock Purch. Plan:		Second Exec. Salary: $	Bonus: $

OTHER THOUGHTS:

Apparent Women Officers or Directors:
Hot Spot for Advancement for Women/Minorities:

LOCATIONS: ("Y" = Yes)

West:	Southwest:	Midwest:	Southeast:	Northeast:	International:
			Y		Y

EMC CORP

www.emc.com

Industry Group Code: 334112 **Ranks within this company's industry group:** Sales: 1 Profits: 1

Techology:		Medical/Drugs:		Engineering:		Transportation:		Chemicals/Petrochemicals:		Specialty:	
Computers:	Y	Manufacturer:		Design:		Aerospace:		Oil/Gas Products:		Special Services:	
Software:	Y	Contract Research:		Construction:		Automotive:		Chemicals:		Consulting:	
Communications:		Medical Services:		Eng. Services:		Shipping:		Oil/Chem. Svcs.:		Specialty Mgmt.:	
Electronics:		Labs:		Consulting:				Gases:		Products:	
Alternative Energy:		Bio. Services:						Other:		Other:	

TYPES OF BUSINESS:

Computer Storage Equipment-Mainframe Disk Memory
Network Storage Systems
Management Protection Software
Consulting Services
Storage Management Services

BRANDS/DIVISIONS/AFFILIATES:

Iomega Corp
RSA Security Inc
Captiva Software Corporation
Document Sciences Corporation
Infra Corporation Pty Limited
Decho Corporation
VMware, Inc.
Symmetrix

CONTACTS:

Note: Officers with more than one job title may be intentionally listed here more than once.

Joseph M. Tucci, CEO
Joseph M. Tucci, Pres.
David I. Goulden, CFO/Exec. VP
Frank M. Hauck, Exec. VP-Global Mktg. & Customer Quality
John T. (Jack) Mollen, Exec. VP-Human Resources
Jeffrey M. Nick, CTO/Sr. VP
Paul T. Dacier, General Counsel/Exec. VP
Irina Simmons, Treas./Sr. VP
William J. Teuber, Jr., Vice Chmn.
Arthur W. Coviello, Jr., Pres., RSA Security Div.
David A. Donatelli, Pres., Storage Div.
Mark S. Lewis, Pres., Content Mgmt. & Archiving
Joseph M. Tucci, Chmn.
Rainer Erlat, Pres., EMEA

Phone: 508-435-1000	**Fax:** 508-497-6912
Toll-Free:	
Address: 176 South St., Hopkinton, MA 01748-9103 US	

GROWTH PLANS/SPECIAL FEATURES:

EMC Corporation, along with its subsidiaries, develops, delivers and supports systems, software and services for the storage, management and protection of electronic information. EMC operates in four segments: information storage; content management and archiving; RSA information security; and VMware virtual infrastructure. The information storage segment is composed of networked information storage systems, multi-platform software and services to support information lifecycle management strategies. EMC's storage systems can be deployed in a storage area network, network attached storage, content addressed storage or direct attached storage environment. Product lines include the Symmetrix, CLARiiON, Celera, Centera and Connectrix systems. EMC's content management and archiving software includes the Documentum and Captiva families. The RSA information security segment includes Smart Application Discovery Manager software. Subsidiary VMware, Inc. provides virtual infrastructure solutions and services for server consolidation; disaster recovery and business continuity; capacity planning and development; enterprise desktop hosting; test optimization; and software distribution. VMware's products include Infrastructure 3, Virtual Desktop Infrastructure, VMware Lab Manager, VMware Converter 3, VMware Server and the Virtual Appliance Marketplace. In February 2008, EMC agreed to acquire Pi Corporation, a developer of personal information management software and services. In March 2008, the firm acquired Document Sciences Corporation, a provider of document output management and customer communications management software. Also in March 2008, EMC acquired Infra Corporation Pty Limited, a provider of IT service management software. In April 2008, the company agreed to acquire Conchango plc, a technology consulting firm. In June 2008, the firm acquired Iomega Corporation, a data storage and protection company. In November 2008, EMC established Decho Corporation, a combination of its Mozy, Inc. and Pi Corp. subsidiaries that is focused on personal information management.

EMC offers its employees tuition assistance; credit union membership; a group legal plan; behavioral health benefits; flexible spending accounts; and medical, dental, prescription and vision insurance.

FINANCIALS:

Sales and profits are in thousands of dollars—add 000 to get the full amount. 2008 Note: Financial information for 2008 was not available for all companies at press time.

2008 Sales: $14,880,000	2008 Profits: $2,160,000	**U.S. Stock Ticker: EMC**
2007 Sales: $13,230,205	2007 Profits: $1,665,668	**Int'l Ticker:** Int'l Exchange:
2006 Sales: $11,155,090	2006 Profits: $1,227,601	Employees: 37,700
2005 Sales: $9,663,955	2005 Profits: $1,133,165	Fiscal Year Ends: 12/31
2004 Sales: $8,229,488	2004 Profits: $871,189	Parent Company:

SALARIES/BENEFITS:

Pension Plan:	ESOP Stock Plan:	Profit Sharing:	Top Exec. Salary: $1,000,000	Bonus: $3,520,000
Savings Plan: Y	Stock Purch. Plan: Y		Second Exec. Salary: $650,000	Bonus: $1,150,000

OTHER THOUGHTS:

Apparent Women Officers or Directors: 1
Hot Spot for Advancement for Women/Minorities: Y

LOCATIONS: ("Y" = Yes)

West:	Southwest:	Midwest:	Southeast:	Northeast:	International:
Y				Y	Y

Note: Financial information, benefits and other data can change quickly and may vary from those stated here.

EMERSON ELECTRIC CO

www.gotoemerson.com

Industry Group Code: 334500 **Ranks within this company's industry group:** Sales: 1 Profits: 1

Techology:		Medical/Drugs:		Engineering:		Transportation:		Chemicals/Petrochemicals:		Specialty:	
Computers:		Manufacturer:		Design:	Y	Aerospace:		Oil/Gas Products:		Special Services:	
Software:		Contract Research:		Construction:		Automotive:		Chemicals:		Consulting:	
Communications:	Y	Medical Services:		Eng. Services:		Shipping:		Oil/Chem. Svcs.:		Specialty Mgmt.:	
Electronics:	Y	Labs:		Consulting:				Gases:		Products:	Y
Alternative Energy:		Bio. Services:						Other:		Other:	

TYPES OF BUSINESS:

Engineering & Technology Products & Services
Industrial Automation Products
Power Products
Air Conditioning & Refrigeration Products
Appliances & Tools

BRANDS/DIVISIONS/AFFILIATES:

PlantWeb Digital Plant Architecture
Process Management
Industrial Automation
Network Power
Climate Technologies
Appliances & Tools
Damcos Holding A/S
Lionville Systems, Inc.

CONTACTS: *Note: Officers with more than one job title may be intentionally listed here more than once.*

David N. Farr, CEO
Edward L. Monser, COO
David N. Farr, Pres.
Walter J. Galvin, CFO/Sr. Exec. VP
Frank L. Steeves, General Counsel/Sec.
Craig W. Ashmore, Sr. VP-Planning & Dev.
Charles A. Peters, Sr. Exec. VP
Steven A. Sonnenberg, Exec. VP-Emerson Process Mgmt.
Edgar M. Purvis, Jr., Exec. VP-Emerson Climate Tech.
Ed Feeney, Exec. VP-Emerson Network Power
David N. Farr, Chmn.

Phone: 314-553-2000 **Fax:** 314-553-3527
Toll-Free:
Address: 8000 W. Florissant Ave., P.O. Box 4100, St. Louis, MO 63136 US

GROWTH PLANS/SPECIAL FEATURES:

Emerson Electric Co. designs and supplies technology products and engineering services, serving a wide range of industrial, commercial and consumer markets worldwide. The company is organized into five business segments. The Process Management segment, accounting for 26% of sales, provides measurement, control and diagnostic capabilities for automated industrial processes producing items such as foods, medicines, power and fuels. As part of this segment, Emerson offers PlantWeb Digital Plant Architecture, a platform designed to open communication between industrial plant devices and, with its accompanying software, collect and analyze information concerning plant assets and processes. These capabilities give customers the ability to predict changes in equipment and process performance and the impact they can have on plant operations. The Industrial Automation segment, accounting for 19%, assists clients in automating production lines. Products for this group include motors, transmissions, alternators, fluid controls and materials joining equipment. The Network Power segment, accounting for 25%, provides power and environmental conditioning systems to help ensure telecommunication systems, data networks and critical business applications operate continuously. The Climate Technologies segment, accounting for 15%, primarily focuses on household and commercial air-conditioning and refrigeration technologies for comfort and food safety. The Appliances and Tools segment, accounting for 15%, provides motors for a broad range of applications, appliances and integrated appliance solutions; tools for homeowners and professionals; and home and commercial storage systems. Emerson operates approximately 265 manufacturing locations in the U.S. and 165 overseas, evenly divided between Europe, Asia and other locations. In January 2009, the company opened a new regional headquarters facility in Dubai.

Employees are offered medical and life insurance, as well as disability coverage.

FINANCIALS: **Sales and profits are in thousands of dollars—add 000 to get the full amount. 2008 Note: Financial information for 2008 was not available for all companies at press time.**

2008 Sales: $24,807,000	2008 Profits: $2,412,000	**U.S. Stock Ticker: EMR**
2007 Sales: $22,131,000	2007 Profits: $2,136,000	**Int'l Ticker:** Int'l Exchange:
2006 Sales: $19,734,000	2006 Profits: $1,845,000	Employees: 140,700
2005 Sales: $17,305,000	2005 Profits: $1,422,000	Fiscal Year Ends: 9/30
2004 Sales: $15,615,000	2004 Profits: $1,257,000	Parent Company:

SALARIES/BENEFITS:

Pension Plan: Y	ESOP Stock Plan:	Profit Sharing: Y	Top Exec. Salary: $1,200,000	Bonus: $3,000,000
Savings Plan: Y	Stock Purch. Plan:		Second Exec. Salary: $710,000	Bonus: $1,175,000

OTHER THOUGHTS:

Apparent Women Officers or Directors: 2
Hot Spot for Advancement for Women/Minorities:

LOCATIONS: ("Y" = Yes)

West:	Southwest:	Midwest:	Southeast:	Northeast:	International:
Y	Y	Y	Y	Y	Y

EMPRESAS ICA SA DE CV

www.ica.com.mx

Industry Group Code: 234000 **Ranks within this company's industry group:** Sales: 25 Profits: 21

Techology:		Medical/Drugs:		Engineering:		Transportation:		Chemicals/Petrochemicals:		Specialty:	
Computers:		Manufacturer:		Design:	Y	Aerospace:		Oil/Gas Products:		Special Services:	
Software:		Contract Research:		Construction:	Y	Automotive:		Chemicals:		Consulting:	
Communications:		Medical Services:		Eng. Services:	Y	Shipping:		Oil/Chem. Svcs.:		Specialty Mgmt.:	Y
Electronics:		Labs:		Consulting:				Gases:		Products:	
Alternative Energy:		Bio. Services:						Other:		Other:	

TYPES OF BUSINESS:

Heavy Construction
Civic Construction
Industrial Construction
Transportation Infrastructure Management
Residential Construction
Design & Engineering Services
Airport Operations

BRANDS/DIVISIONS/AFFILIATES:

CasaFlex
FRAMEX
Consorcio del Mayab S.A. de. C.V.
Kronsa
ICA Fluor Daniel
ICA Reichmann
ICA CPC Argentina
GACN-Grupo Aeroportuario del Centro Norte

CONTACTS: *Note: Officers with more than one job title may be intentionally listed here more than once.*

Jose Luis Guerrero, CEO
Bernardo Quintana Isaac, Pres.
Alonso Quintana Kawage, CFO
Alonso Quintana Kawage, Exec. VP-Finance
Juan Carlos Santos, Dir. Gen.-ICA Fluor
Luis Z. Rocha, VP-Housing
Bernardo Quintana Isaac, Chmn.

Phone: 52-55-5272-9991	**Fax:** 52-55-52771428
Toll-Free:	
Address: Mineria No. 145, Edificio Central, Mexico City, 11800 Mexico	

GROWTH PLANS/SPECIAL FEATURES:

Empresas ICA S.A. de C.V. (ICA) is one of Mexico's largest engineering, procurement and construction companies. Its operates three divisions: construction (divided into the civil construction and industrial construction segments), infrastructure and housing. The company's civil construction segment builds highways, dams, airports, bridges, tunnels, subways and port facilities primarily in Mexico, with occasional projects in Latin America, the Caribbean, Asia and the U.S. The industrial construction division, through majority owned subsidiary ICA Fluor, builds industrial factories such as refineries, petrochemical plants, cement factories, automotive factories and electrical generation plants. ICA's construction divisions accounted for nearly 93% of the firm's revenues. The infrastructure segment mainly operates airports in Mexico through subsidiary OMA, as well as operating three highway concessions. The housing segment has built over 40,000 homes across Mexico. The firm has entered partnerships with leading companies around the world to develop and carry out new projects. Some of its current permanent partnerships include ICA Fluor (with Fluor Corporation), a construction partnership in the U.S.; Radio (with Solentanche Bachy), specializing in foundations and geotechnical work in Portugal, Spain and Central America; and Los Portales (with Grupo Raffo), developing real estate in Peru. In March 2008, the company acquired Consorcio del Mayab S.A. de. C.V., which controls the Kantunil-Cancun tollroad. In January 2008, the company's subsidiary signed a joint venture agreement with Controladora Garciavelez to establish CasaFlex, a company that produces manufactured housing based on multifunctional reinforced concrete modules.

FINANCIALS: **Sales and profits are in thousands of dollars—add 000 to get the full amount. 2008 Note: Financial information for 2008 was not available for all companies at press time.**

2008 Sales: $2,020,700	2008 Profits: $58,300	**U.S. Stock Ticker: ICA**
2007 Sales: $2,060,000	2007 Profits: $-72,000	**Int'l Ticker: ICA** Int'l Exchange: Mexico City-BMV
2006 Sales: $1,982,000	2006 Profits: $92,000	Employees: 17,902
2005 Sales: $1,730,800	2005 Profits: $47,200	Fiscal Year Ends: 12/31
2004 Sales: $1,175,600	2004 Profits: $14,000	Parent Company:

SALARIES/BENEFITS:

Pension Plan:	ESOP Stock Plan:	Profit Sharing:	Top Exec. Salary: $	Bonus: $
Savings Plan:	Stock Purch. Plan:		Second Exec. Salary: $	Bonus: $

OTHER THOUGHTS:

Apparent Women Officers or Directors:
Hot Spot for Advancement for Women/Minorities:

LOCATIONS: ("Y" = Yes)

West:	Southwest:	Midwest:	Southeast:	Northeast:	International:
					Y

ENERCON GMBH

www.enercon.de

Industry Group Code: 333611 **Ranks within this company's industry group:** Sales: Profits:

Techology:		Medical/Drugs:		Engineering:		Transportation:		Chemicals/Petrochemicals:		Specialty:	
Computers:		Manufacturer:		Design:		Aerospace:		Oil/Gas Products:		Special Services:	
Software:		Contract Research:		Construction:		Automotive:		Chemicals:		Consulting:	
Communications:		Medical Services:		Eng. Services:		Shipping:		Oil/Chem. Svcs.:		Specialty Mgmt.:	
Electronics:		Labs:		Consulting:				Gases:		Products:	Y
Alternative Energy:	Y	Bio. Services:						Other:		Other:	

TYPES OF BUSINESS:

Wind Turbine Manufacturing
Desalination Systems

BRANDS/DIVISIONS/AFFILIATES:

E-33
E-44
E-48
E-53
E-70
E-82
ENERCON Storm Control
ENERCON SCADA

CONTACTS:

Note: Officers with more than one job title may be intentionally listed here more than once.

Hans-Dieter Kettwig, Managing Dir.
Aloys Wobben, Chmn./Managing Dir.

Phone: 49-49-41-927-0 **Fax:** 49-49-41-927-109
Toll-Free:
Address: Dreekamp 5, Zurich, D-26605 Germany

GROWTH PLANS/SPECIAL FEATURES:

ENERCON GmbH, founded in 1984, manufactures and designs wind turbines. To support turbine installation, the firm operates mobile cranes of up to 800 tons; special transporters for blades and towers; and hundreds of service vehicles. The firm's turbines have featured gearless systems since 1992, allowing the turbines to operate with fewer rotating parts, resulting in almost frictionless performance. ENERCON currently offers six different turbine configurations, the E-33, rated for 330 kilowatts (kW) of power output; E-44, 900 kW; E-48, 800 kW; E-53, 800 kW; E-70, 2,300 kW; and E-82, 2,000 kW. Generally, all of ENERCON's turbine systems feature independent pitch control for each of the three rotor blades, as well as integrated lighting protection; and typically operate at speeds around 12-20 revolutions per minute (rpm), with some capable of operating as slow as 6 rpm and some as fast as 34 rpm. In order to prevent the shut-downs caused by high winds that other turbines systems may suffer from, the firm has developed ENERCON Storm Control software, which causes the rotor blades to rotate slightly out of sync with the wind, thus preventing damage by reducing the rotation speed, rather than ceasing rotation altogether. In order to connect the turbines to a power grid, the firm offers ENERCON SCADA, an upgradable and adaptable monitoring and control interface. Each turbine also comes equipped with a modem to signal a central data transmission facility of any malfunction. The firm's service and support division operates 160 statlons worldwide. ENERCON has three production facilities in Germany, as well as facilities in Turkey, India, Brazil, Sweden and Portugal. Its more than 12,500 installed turbines collectively generate approximately 12 gigawatts of power. The firm also offers eight very low energy reverse osmosis desalination systems.

FINANCIALS:

Sales and profits are in thousands of dollars—add 000 to get the full amount. 2008 Note: Financial information for 2008 was not available for all companies at press time.

2008 Sales: $	2008 Profits: $	**U.S. Stock Ticker:**
2007 Sales: $	2007 Profits: $	**Int'l Ticker: EWEC** Int'l Exchange: Brussels
2006 Sales: $	2006 Profits: $	Employees:
2005 Sales: $	2005 Profits: $	Fiscal Year Ends: 12/31
2004 Sales: $	2004 Profits: $	Parent Company:

SALARIES/BENEFITS:

Pension Plan:	ESOP Stock Plan:	Profit Sharing:	Top Exec. Salary: $	Bonus: $
Savings Plan:	Stock Purch. Plan:		Second Exec. Salary: $	Bonus: $

OTHER THOUGHTS:

Apparent Women Officers or Directors:
Hot Spot for Advancement for Women/Minorities:

LOCATIONS: ("Y" = Yes)

West:	Southwest:	Midwest:	Southeast:	Northeast:	International:
					Y

Note: Financial information, benefits and other data can change quickly and may vary from those stated here.

ENGLOBAL CORP

www.englobal.com

Industry Group Code: 541330 **Ranks within this company's industry group:** Sales: 10 Profits: 10

Techology:		Medical/Drugs:		Engineering:		Transportation:		Chemicals/Petrochemicals:		Specialty:	
Computers:		Manufacturer:		Design:	Y	Aerospace:		Oil/Gas Products:		Special Services:	
Software:		Contract Research:		Construction:		Automotive:		Chemicals:		Consulting:	
Communications:		Medical Services:		Eng. Services:	Y	Shipping:		Oil/Chem. Svcs.:	Y	Specialty Mgmt.:	
Electronics:	Y	Labs:		Consulting:	Y			Gases:		Products:	Y
Alternative Energy:		Bio. Services:						Other:		Other:	

TYPES OF BUSINESS:

Engineering Services
Petrochemicals Industry Support Services
Control & Instrumentation Systems
Consulting & Inspection Services
Project Management

BRANDS/DIVISIONS/AFFILIATES:

CONTACTS:

Note: Officers with more than one job title may be intentionally listed here more than once.

William A. Coskey, CEO
William A. Coskey, Pres.
Robert W. Raiford, CFO
Robert J. Church, Corp. Mgr.-Human Resources
Alex Schroeder, Manager-Corp. IT
Natalie S. Hairston, Corp. Sec./Chief Governance Officer
Michael M. Patton, Sr. VP-Bus. Dev.
Natalie S. Hairston, VP-Investor Rel.
Robert W. Raiford, Treas.
R. David Kelley, Sr. VP-Corp. Svcs.
Don A. Johnson, Mgr.-Health, Safety & Environmental
Michael H. Lee, Pres./COO-ENGlobal Land, Inc.
David W. Smith, Pres., ENGlobal Engineering, Inc.
William A. Coskey, Chmn.

Phone: 281-878-1000 **Fax:** 281-878-1010
Toll-Free: 800-411-6040
Address: 654 N. Sam Houston Pkwy E., Ste. 400, Houston, TX 77060-5914 US

GROWTH PLANS/SPECIAL FEATURES:

ENGlobal Corp. is a leading international provider of engineering services and systems to the petroleum refining, petrochemical, pipeline, production and processing industries. The firm operates in four segments: Engineering, Construction, Automation and Land. The engineering segment provides consulting services relating to the development, management and execution of projects requiring professional engineering and related project services. Services provided by this segment include feasibility studies, engineering, design, procurement and construction management. The engineering segment provides these services to the upstream, midstream and downstream energy industries and branches of the U.S. military, and in some instances it delivers its services via in-plant personnel assigned throughout the U.S. and internationally. The construction segment provides construction management personnel and services in the areas of inspection, mechanical integrity, vendor and turnaround surveillance, field support, construction, quality assurance and plant asset management. Its customers include pipeline, refining, utility, chemical, petroleum, petrochemical, oil and gas, and power industries throughout the U.S. Construction segment personnel are typically assigned to client facilities throughout the U.S. The automation segment provides services related to the design, fabrication, and implementation of process distributed control and analyzer systems, advanced automation and information technology projects. This segment's customers include members of the domestic and foreign energy related industries. Automation segment personnel assist in on-site commissioning, start-up and training for the company's specialized systems. The land segment provides land management, right-of-way, environmental compliance and governmental regulatory compliance services primarily to the pipeline, utility and telecom companies and other owner/operators of infrastructure facilities throughout the U.S. and Canada. Major customers include Chevron Phillips, ExxonMobil, Frontier Refining, Enterprise Products and Honeywell, Inc.

ENGlobal provides its employees with educational reimbursement; health, dental, vision and life insurance; short- and long-term disability benefits; a 401(k) plan; and flexible spending accounts.

FINANCIALS:

Sales and profits are in thousands of dollars—add 000 to get the full amount. 2008 Note: Financial information for 2008 was not available for all companies at press time.

2008 Sales: $493,332	2008 Profits: $18,258	**U.S. Stock Ticker: ENG**
2007 Sales: $363,227	2007 Profits: $12,464	**Int'l Ticker:** Int'l Exchange:
2006 Sales: $303,090	2006 Profits: $-3,486	Employees: 2,300
2005 Sales: $233,585	2005 Profits: $4,782	Fiscal Year Ends: 12/31
2004 Sales: $148,888	2004 Profits: $2,364	Parent Company:

SALARIES/BENEFITS:

Pension Plan:	ESOP Stock Plan:	Profit Sharing:	Top Exec. Salary: $316,250	Bonus: $
Savings Plan: Y	Stock Purch. Plan:		Second Exec. Salary: $245,000	Bonus: $

OTHER THOUGHTS:

Apparent Women Officers or Directors: 2
Hot Spot for Advancement for Women/Minorities: Y

LOCATIONS: ("Y" = Yes)

West:	Southwest:	Midwest:	Southeast:	Northeast:	International:
Y	Y		Y		Y

Note: Financial information, benefits and other data can change quickly and may vary from those stated here.

ENI SPA

www.eni.it

Industry Group Code: 211111 **Ranks within this company's industry group:** Sales: 9 Profits: 8

Techology:		Medical/Drugs:		Engineering:		Transportation:		Chemicals/Petrochemicals:		Specialty:	
Computers:		Manufacturer:		Design:		Aerospace:		Oil/Gas Products:	Y	Special Services:	
Software:		Contract Research:		Construction:	Y	Automotive:		Chemicals:	Y	Consulting:	
Communications:		Medical Services:		Eng. Services:	Y	Shipping:		Oil/Chem. Svcs.:	Y	Specialty Mgmt.:	
Electronics:		Labs:		Consulting:				Gases:	Y	Products:	
Alternative Energy:		Bio. Services:						Other:	Y	Other:	

TYPES OF BUSINESS:

Oil & Gas-Exploration & Production
Engineering & Construction Services
Oilfield Services
Refining & Transportation
Petrochemicals
Petroleum & Energy Research
Electricity Generation
Gas Stations

BRANDS/DIVISIONS/AFFILIATES:

Snam Rete Gas SpA
Italgas
EniPower SpA
Saipem SpA
Snamprogetti SpA
Agip
Polimeri Europa SpA
First Calgary Petroleums Ltd.

CONTACTS: *Note: Officers with more than one job title may be intentionally listed here more than once.*

Paolo Scaroni, CEO
Alessandro Bernini, CFO/Sr. VP
Angelo Caridi, COO-Refining & Mktg. Div.
Massimo Mantovani, Sr. VP-Legal Affairs
Salvatore Sardo, Chief Corp. Oper. Officer
Stefano Lucchini, Sr. VP-Public Affairs & Comm. Group
Claudia Carloni, Head-Investor Rel.
Roberto Ulissi, Sr. VP-Corp. Affairs & Governance
Claudio Descalzi, COO-Exploration & Prod. Div.
Domenico Dispenza, COO-Gas & Power Div.
Roberto Poli, Chmn.

Phone: 39-065-982-1 **Fax:** 39-065-982-2141
Toll-Free:
Address: Piazzale Enrico Mattei, 1, Rome, 00144 Italy

GROWTH PLANS/SPECIAL FEATURES:

Eni SpA is a diversified energy company that is approximately 30% owned by the Italian government. It conducts business in more than 70 countries and produces almost 1.8 million Barrels of Oil Equivalent (BOE) daily. The firm has four major divisions. The Exploration & Production Division has oil and natural gas projects in Italy, North Africa, West Africa, the North Sea, the Gulf of Mexico, Australia, South America, the Caspian Sea, the Middle East, Asia, India and Alaska. The firm estimates its reserves at approximately 6.4 billion BOE. The Gas & Power division sells approximately 2.785 trillion cubic feet of gas annually. It holds transmission rights on over 3,800 miles of high pressure gas pipelines outside Italy. The division also owns 50% of Snam Rete Gas SpA, which owns and manages almost 30,000 miles of pipeline. Italgas SpA and other subsidiaries distribute low pressure natural gas to over 1,310 municipalities, while EniPower Spa owns and manages power stations in seven Italian cities, with an installed capacity around of 5 gigawatts and an average annual output of 24.8 terawatts. The Refining & Marketing Division, mainly active in Europe, has an average processing rate of 710,000 barrels a day. The division's Agip brand gasoline stations dominate the Italian market while branching out into neighboring European countries. Polimeri Europa SpA produces and markets petrochemical products. The Engineering & Construction division operates through 43%-owned subsidiary Saipem SpA and Saipem's subsidiary Snamprogetti SpA. This segment offers oilfield services, engineering and contracting, developing everything from pipelines to offshore rigs. Eni also maintains a financing division, Sofid SpA. In November 2008, the company acquired First Calgary Petroleums Ltd.

FINANCIALS: Sales and profits are in thousands of dollars—add 000 to get the full amount. 2008 Note: Financial information for 2008 was not available for all companies at press time.

2008 Sales: $145,792,000	2008 Profits: $12,884,900
2007 Sales: $137,027,000	2007 Profits: $15,721,300
2006 Sales: $114,743,000	2006 Profits: $13,090,000
2005 Sales: $89,846,000	2005 Profits: $10,704,800
2004 Sales: $79,084,000	2004 Profits: $9,854,000

U.S. Stock Ticker: E
Int'l Ticker: ENI Int'l Exchange: Milan-BI
Employees: 75,862
Fiscal Year Ends: 12/31
Parent Company:

SALARIES/BENEFITS:

Pension Plan:	ESOP Stock Plan:	Profit Sharing:	Top Exec. Salary: $1,106,857	Bonus: $53,278
Savings Plan:	Stock Purch. Plan:		Second Exec. Salary: $335,653	Bonus: $82,581

OTHER THOUGHTS:

Apparent Women Officers or Directors: 1
Hot Spot for Advancement for Women/Minorities:

LOCATIONS: ("Y" = Yes)

West:	Southwest:	Midwest:	Southeast:	Northeast:	International:
Y	Y			Y	Y

ESSILOR INTERNATIONAL SA

www.essilor.com

Industry Group Code: 339113 **Ranks within this company's industry group:** Sales: 9 Profits: 7

Techology:		Medical/Drugs:		Engineering:		Transportation:		Chemicals/Petrochemicals:		Specialty:	
Computers:		Manufacturer:	Y	Design:		Aerospace:		Oil/Gas Products:		Special Services:	
Software:		Contract Research:		Construction:		Automotive:		Chemicals:		Consulting:	
Communications:		Medical Services:	Y	Eng. Services:		Shipping:		Oil/Chem. Svcs.:		Specialty Mgmt.:	
Electronics:		Labs:		Consulting:				Gases:		Products:	
Alternative Energy:		Bio. Services:						Other:		Other:	

TYPES OF BUSINESS:

Supplies-Ophthalmic Products
Corrective Lenses
Lens Treatments
Ophthalmic Instruments
Technical Consulting

BRANDS/DIVISIONS/AFFILIATES:

Essilor Bulgaria Eood
Optymal Ood
Essilor Canada
Westlab Optical Inc.
Essilor of America
Rainbow Optical Labs Inc.
Interstate Optical Co.
Empire Optical of California

CONTACTS: *Note: Officers with more than one job title may be intentionally listed here more than once.*

Xavier Fontanet, CEO
Hubert Sagnieres, COO
Laurent Vacherot, CFO
Bertrand Roy, Corp. Sr. VP-Strategic Mktg.
Henri Vidal, Corp. Sr. VP-Human Resources
Jean-Luc Schuppiser, Corp. Sr. VP-R&D
Didier Lambert, Corp. Sr. VP-Info. Systems
Patrick Poncin, Corp. Sr. VP-Global Eng.
Carol Xueref, Corp. Sr. VP-Legal Affairs
Claude Brignon, Corp. Sr. VP-Oper.
Carol Xueref, Corp. Sr. VP-Group Dev.
Patrick Cherrier, Pres., Asia Region
Jean Carrier-Guillomet, Pres., Essilor of America
Thomas Bayer, Pres., Essilor European Network
Bertrand de Lime, Pres., Latin America & Instruments
Xavier Fontanet, Chmn.
Claude Brignon, Corp. Sr. VP-World Oper.

Phone: 33-1-49-77-42-24	**Fax:** 33-1-49-77-44-20
Toll-Free:	
Address: 147 Rue de Paris, Charenton-le-Pont, 94220 France	

GROWTH PLANS/SPECIAL FEATURES:

Essilor International S.A. is a global designer, manufacturer and distributor of ophthalmic and optical products and supplies. Its products treat common sight problems, including myopia (nearsightedness), hyperopia (farsightedness), astigmatism and presbyopia (an aging-related process affecting the crystalline lens). Additionally, the company manufactures and sells optical instruments. Some of Essilor's brands include Varilux, Crizal and Airwear. Through partnerships, the company also offers lenses through Nikon and Transitions. The firm supplies its products through a global network of 270 prescription laboratories and 15 manufacturing facilities, which produced 215 million lenses in 2007. Additionally, the company operates three research and development centers and 12 distribution centers. In January 2008, Essilor of America acquired Interstate Optical Co., one of the country's five largest independent laboratories. Also in January, through a distribution subsidiary, Essilor acquired Unilab in Brazil. In February 2008, Essilor made three acquisitions. The firm's subsidiary Essilor Bulgaria Eood acquired Optymal Ood, which currently distributes Essilor lenses and instruments in Bulgaria. Another of Essilor's subsidiaries, Essilor Canada, acquired a majority stake in Westlab Optical Inc in Montreal. Lastly, the firm acquired Rainbow Optical Labs Inc., a prescription laboratory. In April 2008, the company acquired Galileo, a recognized brand in the Italian market. During that same month, Essilor of America (the wholly-owned subsidiary of Essilor International) acquired the majority stake in Empire Optical of California, Inc. in addition to the acquisition of two prescription laboratories: Advance Optical Sales Co., Inc. and Future Optics Inc. In June 2008, Essilor acquired a stake in Satisloh Holding AG, a subsidiary of Schweiter Technologies AG.

FINANCIALS: **Sales and profits are in thousands of dollars—add 000 to get the full amount. 2008 Note: Financial information for 2008 was not available for all companies at press time.**

2008 Sales: $4,096,023	2008 Profits: $518,010	**U.S. Stock Ticker: ESLOY.PK**
2007 Sales: $3,874,480	2007 Profits: $494,110	**Int'l Ticker: EF** Int'l Exchange: Paris-Euronext
2006 Sales: $3,548,900	2006 Profits: $436,900	Employees: 25,900
2005 Sales: $2,886,653	2005 Profits: $	Fiscal Year Ends: 12/31
2004 Sales: $2,623,401	2004 Profits: $309,800	Parent Company:

SALARIES/BENEFITS:

Pension Plan:	ESOP Stock Plan:	Profit Sharing: Y	Top Exec. Salary: $	Bonus: $
Savings Plan:	Stock Purch. Plan:		Second Exec. Salary: $	Bonus: $

OTHER THOUGHTS:

Apparent Women Officers or Directors: 1
Hot Spot for Advancement for Women/Minorities: Y

LOCATIONS: ("Y" = Yes)

West:	Southwest:	Midwest:	Southeast:	Northeast:	International:
Y	Y	Y	Y	Y	Y

Note: Financial information, benefits and other data can change quickly and may vary from those stated here.

EUROPEAN AERONAUTIC DEFENSE AND SPACE CO (EADS)

www.eads.net

Industry Group Code: 336410 **Ranks within this company's industry group:** Sales: 3 Profits: 8

Techology:		Medical/Drugs:		Engineering:		Transportation:		Chemicals/Petrochemicals:		Specialty:	
Computers:		Manufacturer:		Design:	Y	Aerospace:	Y	Oil/Gas Products:		Special Services:	Y
Software:		Contract Research:		Construction:		Automotive:		Chemicals:		Consulting:	
Communications:	Y	Medical Services:		Eng. Services:	Y	Shipping:		Oil/Chem. Svcs.:		Specialty Mgmt.:	
Electronics:		Labs:		Consulting:				Gases:		Products:	
Alternative Energy:		Bio. Services:						Other:		Other:	

TYPES OF BUSINESS:

Aircraft Manufacturing
Helicopter Manufacturing
Transport Aircraft
Military Aircraft
Defense Communications Systems
Satellites
Space Systems
Maintenance Services

BRANDS/DIVISIONS/AFFILIATES:

Airbus
Airbus Military
Eurocopter
Colibri
Panther
MBDA
Eurofighter GmbH
EADS Astrium

CONTACTS: *Note: Officers with more than one job title may be intentionally listed here more than once.*

Louis Gallois, CEO
Hans Peter Ring, CFO
Marwan Lahoud, Chief Mktg. Officer
Jussi Itavuori, Head-Human Resources
Jean Botti, CTO
Fabrice Bregier, Head-Operational Performance
Marwan Lahoud, Chief Strategy Officer
Pierre Bayle, Head-Corp. Comm.
Thomas Enders, Head-Airbus
Stefan Zoller, Head-Defense & Security
Alexander Reinhardt, Head-Corp. Media Rel.
Pedro Montoya, Chief Compliance Officer
Rudiger Grube, Chmn.
Ralph Crosby, Head-EADS North America

Phone: 31-20-655-48-00 **Fax:** 31-20-655-48-01
Toll-Free:
Address: Le Carre, Beechavenue 130-132, Schiphol-Rijk, 1119 PR The Netherlands

GROWTH PLANS/SPECIAL FEATURES:

The European Aeronautic Defence and Space Co. (EADS) is a leading aerospace and defense company worldwide. It was formed from the combination of several European aerospace companies, including DaimlerChrysler Aerospace (Germany); Aerospatiale Matra (France); and Construcciones Aeronauticas SA (Spain). The company operates through five major divisions: Airbus, which generated 64.5% of 2007 revenue; Military Transport Aircraft (MTA), 2.9%; Eurocopter, 10.7%; Defence & Security (DS), 14%; and EADS Astrium, 9.1%. Airbus captures roughly half of all commercial airliner orders worldwide and manufactures heavy military transport aircraft through subsidiary Airbus Military. Airbus's latest project is the model A380 model, one of the largest commercial jets available, with space for 555 passengers divided between two levels of seating. MTA designs and manufactures light and medium transport aircraft, and some special mission aircraft. More than 700 of these transports have been sold to air forces around the world, including those of Spain, Poland and the U.A.E. Eurocopter supplies helicopters to both the military and civil markets and is a dominant force in both arenas. The company's helicopter models include Colibri, Fennec, Panther, Cougar and Tiger. DS designs and manufactures manned and unmanned reconnaissance aircraft, including training aircraft. The division also provides secure communications and electronic warfare systems, and is home to over 40 guided missile programs for uses including air-to-air, ground-based air defense, naval force protection and warhead systems, provided through 50%-owned MBDA. The division owns 46% of Eurofighter GmbH. Astrium provides contracting in satellite systems and space transportation. It manufactured the International Space Station's Columbus laboratory. The company is also involved in turboprop plane and aircraft seat manufacturing; freighter conversion; and other activities. In December 2008, the company signed a joint venture agreement with National Aviation Company of India Limited for the creation of an Aircraft, Maintenance, Repair and Overhaul Center at Indira Gandhi International Airport in Delhi.

FINANCIALS: Sales and profits are in thousands of dollars—add 000 to get the full amount. 2008 Note: Financial information for 2008 was not available for all companies at press time.

2008 Sales: $57,301,500 — 2008 Profits: $2,115,110
2007 Sales: $51,815,700 — 2007 Profits: $-578,780
2006 Sales: $62,900,400 — 2006 Profits: $157,910
2005 Sales: $43,568,835 — 2005 Profits: $2,177,786
2004 Sales: $40,450,365 — 2004 Profits: $1,555,016

U.S. Stock Ticker: EADSF
Int'l Ticker: EAD Int'l Exchange: Paris-Euronext
Employees: 116,000
Fiscal Year Ends: 12/31
Parent Company:

SALARIES/BENEFITS:

Pension Plan: ESOP Stock Plan: Profit Sharing: Top Exec. Salary: $ Bonus: $
Savings Plan: Stock Purch. Plan: Second Exec. Salary: $ Bonus: $

OTHER THOUGHTS:

Apparent Women Officers or Directors: 1
Hot Spot for Advancement for Women/Minorities:

LOCATIONS: ("Y" = Yes)

West:	Southwest:	Midwest:	Southeast:	Northeast:	International:
				Y	Y

EVONIK DEGUSSA

www.degussa.com

Industry Group Code: 325000 **Ranks within this company's industry group:** Sales: Profits:

Techology:		Medical/Drugs:		Engineering:		Transportation:		Chemicals/Petrochemicals:		Specialty:	
Computers:		Manufacturer:		Design:		Aerospace:		Oil/Gas Products:		Special Services:	
Software:		Contract Research:		Construction:		Automotive:		Chemicals:	Y	Consulting:	
Communications:		Medical Services:		Eng. Services:		Shipping:		Oil/Chem. Svcs.:		Specialty Mgmt.:	
Electronics:		Labs:		Consulting:				Gases:		Products:	
Alternative Energy:		Bio. Services:						Other:		Other:	

TYPES OF BUSINESS:

Specialty Chemical Manufacturer
Construction Chemicals
Specialty Polymers
Paints & Coatings
Adhesives
Pharmaceutical Services
Fine & Industrial Chemicals
Personal Care Products

BRANDS/DIVISIONS/AFFILIATES:

Plexiglas
Creavis
Dynasilan
Aerisil
Degussa Corporation USA

CONTACTS: *Note: Officers with more than one job title may be intentionally listed here more than once.*

Heinz-Joachim Wagner, CFO
Ulrich Weber, Human Resources Officer
Patrik Wohlhauser, Dir.-Chemicals
Hans-Peter Schaufler, Dir.-Coatings & Colorants
Klaus Engel, Chmn.

Phone: 49-201-177-01 **Fax:** 49-201-177-3475
Toll-Free:
Address: Rellinghauser Strasse 1-11, Essen, D-45128 Germany

GROWTH PLANS/SPECIAL FEATURES:

Evonik Degussa is a world leader in high-yield specialty chemicals. The company offers materials for use in the following industries: construction chemicals; fine and industrial chemicals; performance materials; coatings and advanced fillers; and specialty polymers. With operations in over 100 countries, Evonik Degussa provides a wide range of products and services for numerous industries and applications. The company supplies carmakers and auto suppliers worldwide with products that include adhesives, paint and rubber additives and green tires containing a special polymer blend that results in better fuel economy and driving safety. The firm offers a wide portfolio of engineered polymers and methyl acrylate monomers for use in aircraft, building and auto construction, medical technology and cell phones. Evonik Degussa serves the pharmaceutical and biopharmaceutical industries at every stage of the drug manufacturing chain, from active ingredients to dosage and controlled release. The company also provides products in the paint and coating industry, including paints and coatings, sealants and adhesives. As part of the recent trend toward renewable raw materials, Evonik Degussa has been researching and producing nature-identical amino acids for animal nutrition. It is the only manufacturer to offer the four most important essential amino acids for animal nutrition: D-methionine, L-lysine, L-threonine and L-tryptophan. In 2009, Tesla Motors, Inc., an electric car startup, announced its consideration of Evonik Degussa as the producer of its battery cells, to be used in battery packs and chargers built into Daimler's electric Smart minicar. The firm also plans to partner with Japanese-based, industrial gas producer Taiyo Nippon Sanso Corp. to build a solar cell materials plant. The $220 million facility will produce monosilane gas, used as an insulator in solar cells, and is slated to begin production in 2011.

Evonik Degussa offers chemistry, technology, economics, and IT apprenticeships for students.

FINANCIALS: **Sales and profits are in thousands of dollars—add 000 to get the full amount. 2008 Note: Financial information for 2008 was not available for all companies at press time.**

2008 Sales: $	2008 Profits: $	**U.S. Stock Ticker: Subsidiary**
2007 Sales: $	2007 Profits: $	**Int'l Ticker:** Int'l Exchange:
2006 Sales: $14,875,300	2006 Profits: $1,888,190	Employees:
2005 Sales: $14,818,600	2005 Profits: $-603,990	Fiscal Year Ends: 12/31
2004 Sales: $15,336,800	2004 Profits: $406,500	Parent Company: EVONIK INDUSTRIES AG

SALARIES/BENEFITS:

Pension Plan:	ESOP Stock Plan:	Profit Sharing:	Top Exec. Salary: $	Bonus: $
Savings Plan:	Stock Purch. Plan:		Second Exec. Salary: $	Bonus: $

OTHER THOUGHTS:

Apparent Women Officers or Directors:
Hot Spot for Advancement for Women/Minorities:

LOCATIONS: ("Y" = Yes)

West:	Southwest:	Midwest:	Southeast:	Northeast:	International:
				Y	Y

EVONIK INDUSTRIES AG

www.evonik.com

Industry Group Code: 325000 **Ranks within this company's industry group:** Sales: 5 Profits: 13

Techology:		Medical/Drugs:		Engineering:		Transportation:		Chemicals/Petrochemicals:		Specialty:	
Computers:		Manufacturer:		Design:		Aerospace:		Oil/Gas Products:		Special Services:	
Software:		Contract Research:		Construction:		Automotive:		Chemicals:	Y	Consulting:	
Communications:		Medical Services:		Eng. Services:		Shipping:		Oil/Chem. Svcs.:		Specialty Mgmt.:	
Electronics:		Labs:		Consulting:				Gases:		Products:	
Alternative Energy:	Y	Bio. Services:						Other:	Y	Other:	

TYPES OF BUSINESS:

Chemicals, Manufacturing
Industrial Engineering
Electricity Generation
Real Estate
Renewable Energy-Biomass

BRANDS/DIVISIONS/AFFILIATES:

Evonik Degussa
STEAG
RAG Immobilien

CONTACTS: *Note: Officers with more than one job title may be intentionally listed here more than once.*

Klaus Engel, CEO
Heinz-Joachim Wagner, CFO
Ulrich Weber, Chief Human Resources
Bernd Brinker, Head-Investor Rel.
Klaus Engel, Chmn.

Phone: 49-201-177-01	**Fax:** 49-201-177-3475
Toll-Free:	
Address: Rellinghauser Strasse 1-11, Essen, 45128 Germany	

GROWTH PLANS/SPECIAL FEATURES:

Evonik Industries is an international industrial group with activities in more than 100 countries worldwide. The firm operates through three primary business areas: chemicals, energy and real estate. The chemicals segment, operating under subsidiary Evonik Degussa, holds production facilities in roughly 30 countries. This segment serves the automobile, plastics and rubbers, pharmaceutical, biotechnology, cosmetics, paint and sealants and adhesives industries. This segment has a strong focus on research and development, generating 20% of sales from products under five years of age. The energy segment, operating under subsidiary STEAG, focuses on coal-fired power generation, with capabilities spanning project development, financing, plant construction and operation. This segment is Germany's fifth largest power generator, with eight domestic plants and over 7,900 megawatts of total international installed output. Internationally, this segment has power stations in Turkey, Columbia and the Phillipines. This segment also offers Clean Competitive Electricity from Coal (CCEC) technology with 45% increased efficiency that is safer and more environment-friendly than conventional power stations. This technology is currently being used to build a new power plant in Duisburg-Walsum, Germany. The energy segment is also engaged in renewable energy sources, including biomass, biogas, geothermal and mine gas, maintaing ten biomass power plants. The real estate segment, operating under subsidiary RAG Immobilien, maintains housing units in Germany, focusing on the Ruhr region, Aachen and the northern Rhine cities of Düsseldorf, Cologne and Bonn. In December 2008, the company initiated production of Plexiglass acrylic molding compounds in the Chemical Industry Park in Shanghai, China. Also in December 2008, the firm entered a strategic alliance with Daimler AG for the research, development and production of cells for lithium-ion batteries to be used in commercial vehicles, buses, and passenger vehicles.

FINANCIALS: **Sales and profits are in thousands of dollars—add 000 to get the full amount. 2008 Note: Financial information for 2008 was not available for all companies at press time.**

2008 Sales: $21,002,200	2008 Profits: $377,100	**U.S. Stock Ticker: Private**
2007 Sales: $19,603,000	2007 Profits: $1,190,040	**Int'l Ticker:** Int'l Exchange:
2006 Sales: $19,188,700	2006 Profits: $1,420,980	Employees: 43,000
2005 Sales: $	2005 Profits: $	Fiscal Year Ends: 12/31
2004 Sales: $	2004 Profits: $	Parent Company:

SALARIES/BENEFITS:

Pension Plan:	ESOP Stock Plan:	Profit Sharing:	Top Exec. Salary: $	Bonus: $
Savings Plan:	Stock Purch. Plan:		Second Exec. Salary: $	Bonus: $

OTHER THOUGHTS:

Apparent Women Officers or Directors:
Hot Spot for Advancement for Women/Minorities:

LOCATIONS: ("Y" = Yes)

West:	Southwest:	Midwest:	Southeast:	Northeast:	International:
					Y

EXXON MOBIL CORPORATION (EXXONMOBIL) www.exxonmobil.com

Industry Group Code: 211111 **Ranks within this company's industry group:** Sales: 1 Profits: 1

Techology:		Medical/Drugs:		Engineering:		Transportation:		Chemicals/Petrochemicals:		Specialty:	
Computers:		Manufacturer:		Design:		Aerospace:		Oil/Gas Products:	Y	Special Services:	
Software:		Contract Research:		Construction:		Automotive:		Chemicals:	Y	Consulting:	
Communications:		Medical Services:		Eng. Services:		Shipping:		Oil/Chem. Svcs.:	Y	Specialty Mgmt.:	
Electronics:		Labs:		Consulting:				Gases:		Products:	
Alternative Energy:		Bio. Services:						Other:	Y	Other:	

TYPES OF BUSINESS:

Oil & Gas Exploration & Production
Gas Refining & Supply
Fuel Marketing
Power Generation
Coal & Mineral Exploration
Chemicals
Fuel Cell Research
Convenience Stores

BRANDS/DIVISIONS/AFFILIATES:

ExxonMobil Chemical
Exxon Neftegas Limited

CONTACTS: *Note: Officers with more than one job title may be intentionally listed here more than once.*

Rex W. Tillerson, CEO
Lucille J. Cavanaugh, VP-Human Resources
C. W. Matthews, General Counsel/VP
W. M. Colton, VP-Strategic Planning
K.P. Cohen, VP-Public Affairs
D. S. Rosenthal, VP-Investor Rel./Sec.
Donald D. Humphreys, Treas./Sr. VP
P. T. Mulva, Controller/VP
S. R. LaSala, VP/General Tax Counsel
J. Stephen Simon, Sr. VP
A.Tim Cejka, Sr. VP
Rex W. Tillerson, Chmn.

Phone: 972-444-1000	**Fax:** 972-444-1350
Toll-Free:	
Address: 5959 Las Colinas Blvd., Irving, TX 75039 US	

GROWTH PLANS/SPECIAL FEATURES:

Exxon Mobil Corporation (ExxonMobil) is one of the largest global petroleum and natural gas exploration and production companies in the world. ExxonMobil's various divisions and affiliated companies operate and market products in the U.S. and about 200 other countries and territories. Its principal business is energy, involving exploration and production crude oil and natural gas; manufacture of petroleum products; and transportation and sale of crude oil, natural gas and petroleum products. The company has a resource base of exploration and production acreage in 36 countries and production operations in 24 countries, producing more than 4.2 million oil equivalent barrels of oil and gas each day. The firm is also a major manufacturer and marketer of commodity petrochemicals, including olefins, aromatics, polyethylene and polypropylene plastics and a wide variety of specialty products. In addition, Exxon Mobil has interests in electric power generation facilities. Moreover, the firm has a chemical company and a coal and minerals company. The company has several divisions and hundreds of affiliates, many with names that include ExxonMobil, Exxon or Mobil. Overall, the firm has 11 separate global business units. The five global upstream businesses undertake exploration, development, production, gas marketing and upstream research. The four global downstream businesses carry out refining and supply, fuels marketing, lubricants and petroleum technology operations. Exxon Mobil spends more than $700 million annually towards research in new technologies, including developments in synthetic lubricants, catalyst research, nanotechnology, biomedical services and hydro-carbon-based fuel cells.

FINANCIALS: Sales and profits are in thousands of dollars—add 000 to get the full amount. 2008 Note: Financial information for 2008 was not available for all companies at press time.

2008 Sales: $459,579,000	2008 Profits: $45,220,000	**U.S. Stock Ticker: XOM**
2007 Sales: $390,328,000	2007 Profits: $40,610,000	**Int'l Ticker:** Int'l Exchange:
2006 Sales: $365,467,000	2006 Profits: $39,500,000	Employees: 79,900
2005 Sales: $358,955,000	2005 Profits: $36,130,000	Fiscal Year Ends: 12/31
2004 Sales: $291,252,000	2004 Profits: $25,330,000	Parent Company:

SALARIES/BENEFITS:

Pension Plan: Y	ESOP Stock Plan:	Profit Sharing:	Top Exec. Salary: $1,500,000	Bonus: $2,800,000
Savings Plan:	Stock Purch. Plan:		Second Exec. Salary: $935,000	Bonus: $2,150,000

OTHER THOUGHTS:

Apparent Women Officers or Directors: 2
Hot Spot for Advancement for Women/Minorities: Y

LOCATIONS: ("Y" = Yes)

West:	Southwest:	Midwest:	Southeast:	Northeast:	International:
Y	Y	Y	Y	Y	Y

EXXONMOBIL CHEMICAL

www.exxonmobilchemical.com

Industry Group Code: 325110 **Ranks within this company's industry group:** Sales: Profits:

Techology:		Medical/Drugs:		Engineering:		Transportation:		Chemicals/Petrochemicals:		Specialty:	
Computers:		Manufacturer:		Design:		Aerospace:		Oil/Gas Products:		Special Services:	
Software:		Contract Research:		Construction:		Automotive:		Chemicals:	Y	Consulting:	
Communications:		Medical Services:		Eng. Services:		Shipping:		Oil/Chem. Svcs.:	Y	Specialty Mgmt.:	
Electronics:		Labs:		Consulting:				Gases:		Products:	
Alternative Energy:		Bio. Services:						Other:	Y	Other:	

TYPES OF BUSINESS:

Plastics & Rubber Manufacturing
Petrochemicals
Catalyst Technology
Polypropylene

BRANDS/DIVISIONS/AFFILIATES:

Univation Technologies, LLC
Label-Lyte
XyMax
PxMax
Exxon Mobil Corporation (ExxonMobil)
Dow Chemical Company (The)

CONTACTS:

Note: Officers with more than one job title may be intentionally listed here more than once.

Rex W. Tillerson, CEO
Donald D. Humphreys, Treas./Sr. VP
J. Stephen Simon, Sr. VP
Mark W. Albers, Sr. VP
Rex W. Tillerson, Chmn.

Phone: 281-870-6000 **Fax:** 281-870-6661
Toll-Free:
Address: 13501 Katy Freeway, Houston, TX 77079 US

GROWTH PLANS/SPECIAL FEATURES:

ExxonMobil Chemical, a division of ExxonMobil Corp., is one of the world's largest petrochemical companies, manufacturing and marketing olefins, aromatics, fluids, synthetic rubber, polyethylene, polypropylene, oriented polypropylene packaging films, plasticizers, synthetic lubricant base-stocks, additives for fuels and lubricants, zeolite catalysts and other petrochemical products. The division has manufacturing locations in more than 20 countries and markets products in more than 150 countries. ExxonMobil Chemical is the only major olefins producer with proprietary pyrolysis-reactor technology, which delivers the highest olefin yields in the industry. The unit's XyMax and PxMax aromatics utilize proprietary zeolite shape-selective catalyst technology. This technology increases conversion and reduces losses versus other technologies in the production of higher olefins. Univation Technologies, LLC, a joint venture company owned by ExxonMobil Chemical and Dow Chemical Co., has developed the Prodigy catalyst technology that allows the production of resins at substantially lower cost than traditional staged processes. This technology is used in a broad range of applications such as pipes, films and blow molding. In 2008, the firm completed and started a new compound facility to supply polymers to the automotive, appliance and specialty consumer products industries.

FINANCIALS:

Sales and profits are in thousands of dollars—add 000 to get the full amount. 2008 Note: Financial information for 2008 was not available for all companies at press time.

2008 Sales: $
2007 Sales: $27,480,000
2006 Sales: $27,350,000
2005 Sales: $26,777,000
2004 Sales: $27,788,000

2008 Profits: $
2007 Profits: $4,563,000
2006 Profits: $4,382,000
2005 Profits: $3,943,000
2004 Profits: $3,428,000

U.S. Stock Ticker: Subsidiary
Int'l Ticker: Int'l Exchange:
Employees:
Fiscal Year Ends: 12/31
Parent Company: EXXON MOBIL CORPORATION (EXXONMOBIL)

SALARIES/BENEFITS:

Pension Plan: ESOP Stock Plan: Profit Sharing: Top Exec. Salary: $ Bonus: $
Savings Plan: Stock Purch. Plan: Second Exec. Salary: $ Bonus: $

OTHER THOUGHTS:

Apparent Women Officers or Directors:
Hot Spot for Advancement for Women/Minorities:

LOCATIONS: ("Y" = Yes)

West:	Southwest:	Midwest:	Southeast:	Northeast:	International:
	Y				Y

FAURECIA SA

www.faurecia.com

Industry Group Code: 336300 **Ranks within this company's industry group:** Sales: 6 Profits: 20

Techology:		Medical/Drugs:		Engineering:		Transportation:		Chemicals/Petrochemicals:		Specialty:	
Computers:		Manufacturer:		Design:		Aerospace:		Oil/Gas Products:		Special Services:	
Software:		Contract Research:		Construction:		Automotive:	Y	Chemicals:		Consulting:	
Communications:		Medical Services:		Eng. Services:		Shipping:		Oil/Chem. Svcs.:		Specialty Mgmt.:	
Electronics:		Labs:		Consulting:				Gases:		Products:	
Alternative Energy:		Bio. Services:						Other:		Other:	

TYPES OF BUSINESS:

Automobile Part Manufacturing
Vehicle Component Modules
Vehicle Seats
Vehicle Doors
Exhaust Systems
Front End Modules
Acoustic Engineering & Equipment

BRANDS/DIVISIONS/AFFILIATES:

CONTACTS: *Note: Officers with more than one job title may be intentionally listed here more than once.*

Yann Delabriere, CEO
Jean-Pierre Sounillac, Exec. VP-Group Human Resources
Bruno Montmerle, Exec. VP-Group Strategy
Thierry Lemane, Exec. VP-Group Comm.
Frank Imbert, Exec. VP-Group Financial
Jean-Marc Hannequin, Exec. VP-Exhaust Systems Prod. Group
Christophe Schmitt, Exec. VP-Interior Systems Prod. Group
Patrick Koller, Exec. VP-Seating Prod. Group
Arnaud de David-Beauregard, Exec. VP-Group Dev.
Yann Delabriere, Chmn.
Michael T. Heneka, Pres., Faurecia North America

Phone: 33-1-72-36-70-00	**Fax:** 33-1-72-36-70-07
Toll-Free:	
Address: 2 rue Hennape, Nanterre, 92735 France	

GROWTH PLANS/SPECIAL FEATURES:

Faurecia S.A., headquartered in France, is a global supplier of vehicle equipment, with 190 production facilities throughout Western Europe, Central Europe, North America, South America and Asia. It designs and assembles six major vehicle modules: seat, cockpit, acoustic package, door, front-end and exhaust system. Modules, which consist of a series of components, are mounted directly on vehicles during the assembly process, reducing time and production costs. The firm's door design activities focus on the development of hybrid parts (which utilize mixed materials), paint, high-quality finishes, foaming and slush. Faurecia equips 7 million vehicles with doors and door panels every year. The company also provides acoustic engineering and equipment such as floor coverings, carpets and insulators that effectively soundproof a vehicle's interior. In addition, the company is a lead supplier of front-end modules, which include front-end carriers, bumpers and fan cooling systems, and environmentally responsible exhaust systems. The company derives the majority of its sale from interior modules including seat modules. The firm supplies major automotive manufactures such as Peugeot domestically, while BMW, Ford, VW and Nissan are among the firm's international clients. In 2008, Faurecia divested control of its subsidiary Sieto, which Toyota Boshoku Corporation will now operate. Also in 2008, the firm announced plans to open an automotive seating trim cover production plant in Morocco.

Faurecia offers its employees professional training through its Faurecia University.

FINANCIALS: **Sales and profits are in thousands of dollars—add 000 to get the full amount. 2008 Note: Financial information for 2008 was not available for all companies at press time.**

2008 Sales: $16,001,860	2008 Profits: $-765,810	**U.S. Stock Ticker:**
2007 Sales: $16,867,850	2007 Profits: $-316,420	**Int'l Ticker: EO** Int'l Exchange: Paris-Euronext
2006 Sales: $15,519,560	2006 Profits: $-596,740	Employees: 61,357
2005 Sales: $14,927,470	2005 Profits: $-248,150	Fiscal Year Ends: 12/31
2004 Sales: $14,621,400	2004 Profits: $114,200	Parent Company:

SALARIES/BENEFITS:

Pension Plan:	ESOP Stock Plan:	Profit Sharing:	Top Exec. Salary: $	Bonus: $
Savings Plan:	Stock Purch. Plan:		Second Exec. Salary: $	Bonus: $

OTHER THOUGHTS:

Apparent Women Officers or Directors: 1
Hot Spot for Advancement for Women/Minorities:

LOCATIONS: ("Y" = Yes)

West:	Southwest:	Midwest:	Southeast:	Northeast:	International:
		Y	Y		Y

Note: Financial information, benefits and other data can change quickly and may vary from those stated here.

FEDERAL MOGUL CORP

www.federal-mogul.com

Industry Group Code: 336300 **Ranks within this company's industry group:** Sales: 15 Profits: 17

Techology:		Medical/Drugs:		Engineering:		Transportation:		Chemicals/Petrochemicals:		Specialty:	
Computers:		Manufacturer:		Design:		Aerospace:		Oil/Gas Products:		Special Services:	
Software:		Contract Research:		Construction:		Automotive:	Y	Chemicals:		Consulting:	
Communications:		Medical Services:		Eng. Services:		Shipping:		Oil/Chem. Svcs.:		Specialty Mgmt.:	
Electronics:		Labs:		Consulting:				Gases:		Products:	
Alternative Energy:		Bio. Services:						Other:		Other:	

TYPES OF BUSINESS:

Aftermarket Products & Services
Powertrain Products
Sealing Systems
Vehicle Safety & Performance Products

BRANDS/DIVISIONS/AFFILIATES:

AE
Glyco
Nüral
Goetze
Fel-Pro
FP Diesel
National
Payen

CONTACTS: *Note: Officers with more than one job title may be intentionally listed here more than once.*

Jose M. Alapont, CEO
Jose M. Alapont, Pres.
Jeff Kaminski, CFO/Sr. VP
William Bowers, Sr. VP-Sales & Mktg.
Pascal Goachet, Sr. VP-Global Human Resources & Organization
Mario Leone, Chief Info. Systems Officer/Sr. VP
Eric McAlexander, Sr. VP-Global Mfg. & Customer Satisfaction
Robert L. Katz, General Counsel/Sr. VP
Charles B. Grant, Sr. VP-Corp. Dev. & Strategic Planning
Steven K. Gaut, VP-Corp. Comm. & Gov't Rel.
Alan Haughie, Controller/VP/Chief Acct. Officer
James Burkhart, Sr. VP-Global Aftermarket
Rene Dalleur, Sr. VP-Vehicle Safety & Protection
Jean Brunol, Sr. VP-Bus. & Oper. Strategy
David Bozinksi, Treas./VP
Carl C. Icahn, Chmn.
Markus Wermers, Sr. VP-Global Purchasing

Phone: 248-354-7700	**Fax:** 248-354-8950
Toll-Free:	
Address: 26555 Northwestern Hwy., Southfield, MI 48033 US	

GROWTH PLANS/SPECIAL FEATURES:

Federal-Mogul Corp. supplies vehicular parts, components, modules and systems to global customers in the automotive, small engine, heavy-duty, marine, railroad, aerospace and industrial markets. The company operates in six business segments: Powertrain energy; powertrain sealings and bearings; vehicle safety and protection; automotive products; aftermarket products and services; and corporate. Top brands include Federal-Mogul, AE, Glyco, Goetze, Nural, Fel-Pro, FP Diesel, National, Payen, Abex, Beral, Ferodo, Thermo Quiet, Wagner, ANCO, Champion and MOOG. The powertrain energy segment, which accounted for 30% of revenue in 2007, offers products that include pistons; piston rings; piston pins; cylinder liners; valve seats and guides; and transmission components. The powertrain sealings and bearings segment, which accounted for 15%, offers engine bearings; bushings; and thrust washers for engine, transmission and driveline systems. The vehicle safety and protection segment, responsible for 11%, offers brake disc pads; brake shoes; brake linings and blocks; and element-resistant systems protection sleeving products. The automotive products segment, responsible for 5%, provides manufacturing operations for ignition, lighting, fuel, brake/steering and wiper products. The aftermarket products and services segment, which accounted for 39%, offers engines, gaskets, antifriction bearings and seals, chassis, wipers, fuel pumps, ignition and lighting. Customers include original equipment manufacturers (OEMs) of vehicles and industrial products and aftermarket retailers and wholesalers. Federal-Mogul has operations in 35 countries. In December 2007, Federal-Mogul emerged from Chapter 11 restructuring, undergone to deal with its outstanding asbestos liability. As part of restructuring, its workforce was reduced by about 10% and approximately 25 of its facilities were reorganized or closed. In July 2008, the firm began producing powertrain components at its new Brazilian facility. In August 2008, the firm announced plans for a new manufacturing facility in India.

Federal-Mogul offers its employees tuition assistance; medical, dental, prescription, vision and hearing insurance; and flexible spending accounts.

FINANCIALS: **Sales and profits are in thousands of dollars—add 000 to get the full amount. 2008 Note: Financial information for 2008 was not available for all companies at press time.**

2008 Sales: $6,865,600	2008 Profits: $-467,900	**U.S. Stock Ticker: FDML**
2007 Sales: $6,913,900	2007 Profits: $1,412,300	**Int'l Ticker:** Int'l Exchange:
2006 Sales: $6,326,400	2006 Profits: $-549,600	Employees: 43,400
2005 Sales: $6,286,000	2005 Profits: $-334,200	Fiscal Year Ends: 12/31
2004 Sales: $6,174,100	2004 Profits: $-334,000	Parent Company:

SALARIES/BENEFITS:

Pension Plan: Y	ESOP Stock Plan:	Profit Sharing:	Top Exec. Salary: $1,500,000	Bonus: $2,377,500
Savings Plan: Y	Stock Purch. Plan:		Second Exec. Salary: $548,360	Bonus: $608,405

OTHER THOUGHTS:

Apparent Women Officers or Directors:
Hot Spot for Advancement for Women/Minorities:

LOCATIONS: ("Y" = Yes)

West:	Southwest:	Midwest:	Southeast:	Northeast:	International:
Y	Y	Y	Y	Y	Y

FERRARI SPA

www.ferrariworld.com

Industry Group Code: 336111 **Ranks within this company's industry group:** Sales: Profits:

Techology:		Medical/Drugs:		Engineering:		Transportation:		Chemicals/Petrochemicals:		Specialty:	
Computers:		Manufacturer:		Design:		Aerospace:		Oil/Gas Products:		Special Services:	
Software:		Contract Research:		Construction:		Automotive:	Y	Chemicals:		Consulting:	
Communications:		Medical Services:		Eng. Services:		Shipping:		Oil/Chem. Svcs.:		Specialty Mgmt.:	
Electronics:		Labs:		Consulting:				Gases:		Products:	
Alternative Energy:		Bio. Services:						Other:		Other:	

TYPES OF BUSINESS:

Automobile Manufacturer
Sports Cars
Accessories

BRANDS/DIVISIONS/AFFILIATES:

Fiat S.p.A.
Maserati S.p.A.
F430
F430 Spider
Maranello
612 Scaglietti
599 GTB Fiorano
Scaglietti Programe

CONTACTS: *Note: Officers with more than one job title may be intentionally listed here more than once.*

Amedeo Felisa, CEO
Luca C. di Montezemolo, Pres.
Giancarlo Coppa, CFO
Mario Mairano, Human Resources
Giancarlo Coppa, Dir.-Admin.
Stefano Lai, Comm.
Giancarlo Coppa, Dir.-Finance & Controlling
Danny Bahar, Brand & Commercial
Luca C. di Montezemolo, Chmn.

Phone: 39-0-536-949-111 **Fax:** 39-0-536-949-714
Toll-Free:
Address: Via Abetone Inferiore 4, Maranello, Modena, 41053 Italy

GROWTH PLANS/SPECIAL FEATURES:

Ferrari S.p.A., based in Modena, Italy, is a leading manufacturer of high-performance sports cars, selling at prices from $140,000 and up. The firm has self-imposed a limit on its annual production, with approximately 5,600 cars manufactured annually, in order to maintain high levels of value and exclusivity. Current Ferrari vehicles include four 8 cylinder models, the F430, F430 Challenge, F430 Scuderia and F430 Spider; along with three 12 cylinder models, the Ferrari 612 Scaglietti, the FXX and the newest of the Maranello family, the Ferrari 599 GTB Fiorano. Named Fiorano after the circuit Ferrari uses to hone the performance of its road and track cars; GTB (or Gran Turismo Berlinetta) after the most famous Ferrari Berlinettas ever made; and 599 as the displacement of its 5999cc engine divided by 10, this supercar boasts 620-horsepower. The FXX is powered by a massive 6,262cc V12 engine that can turn out over 800 horsepower at 8,500 rpm. The company offers customers a line of pre-owned vehicles through its dealerships located all over the globe. Ferrari's Scaglietti Programe allows customers to have their Ferrari customized for a race or track set-up as long as the car remains street legal. Ferrari is a subsidiary of Fiat S.p.A., which owns a majority stake in the company (85%) after buying back the stake held by Mediobanca. Other investors include Mediobanca (an Italian bank), Mubadala Development Co. of the UAE (5%) and Piero Ferrari, son of the company's founder (10%). Fiat also owns Maserati S.p.A., another premier Italian manufacturer of sports cars, which was owned by Ferrari until 2005. In 2008, Ferrari announced it will create a company by late 2009 to oversee its vehicle imports to Russia. Ferrari sold 65 vehicles in Russia during 2007, which represented a 67% increase in sales from the previous year.

FINANCIALS: **Sales and profits are in thousands of dollars—add 000 to get the full amount. 2008 Note: Financial information for 2008 was not available for all companies at press time.**

2008 Sales: $	2008 Profits: $	**U.S. Stock Ticker: Private**
2007 Sales: $	2007 Profits: $	**Int'l Ticker:** Int'l Exchange:
2006 Sales: $	2006 Profits: $	Employees: 3,322
2005 Sales: $	2005 Profits: $	Fiscal Year Ends: 12/31
2004 Sales: $2,062,400	2004 Profits: $-36,800	Parent Company:

SALARIES/BENEFITS:

Pension Plan:	ESOP Stock Plan:	Profit Sharing:	Top Exec. Salary: $	Bonus: $
Savings Plan:	Stock Purch. Plan:		Second Exec. Salary: $	Bonus: $

OTHER THOUGHTS:

Apparent Women Officers or Directors:
Hot Spot for Advancement for Women/Minorities:

LOCATIONS: ("Y" = Yes)

West:	Southwest:	Midwest:	Southeast:	Northeast:	International:
Y	Y	Y	Y	Y	Y

FIAT SPA

www.fiatgroup.com

Industry Group Code: 336111 **Ranks within this company's industry group:** Sales: 8 Profits: 7

Techology:		Medical/Drugs:		Engineering:		Transportation:		Chemicals/Petrochemicals:		Specialty:	
Computers:		Manufacturer:		Design:		Aerospace:		Oil/Gas Products:		Special Services:	
Software:		Contract Research:		Construction:		Automotive:	Y	Chemicals:		Consulting:	
Communications:		Medical Services:		Eng. Services:		Shipping:		Oil/Chem. Svcs.:		Specialty Mgmt.:	
Electronics:		Labs:		Consulting:				Gases:		Products:	
Alternative Energy:		Bio. Services:						Other:		Other:	Y

TYPES OF BUSINESS:

Automobile Manufacturer
Agricultural & Construction Equipment
Commercial Vehicles
Automotive Retail
Automotive Components
Industrial Automation Systems
Publishing
Business Services

BRANDS/DIVISIONS/AFFILIATES:

Fiat Group Automobiles
Ferrari
Maserati
CNH Global
Iveco
Magneti Marelli
Teksid
Comau

CONTACTS:

Note: Officers with more than one job title may be intentionally listed here more than once.

Sergio Marchionne, CEO
Luigi Gubitosi, CFO
Roberto Pucci, Exec. VP-Human Resources
Harold Wester, CTO/Exec. VP
Harold Wester, Head-Eng.
Ferruccio Luppi, Exec. VP-Bus. Dev.
Simone Migliarino, Head-Comm.
Maurizio Francescatti, Head-Treasury
John P. Elkann, Vice Chmn.
Sergio Marchionne, CEO-Fiat Group
Paolo Rebaudengo, Head-Industrial Rel.
Alfredo Altavilla, CEO-Fiat Powertrain Technologies
Luca C. Di Montezemolo, Chmn.
Giorgio Frasca, Dir.-Int'l Rel.
Gianni Coda, CEO-Purchasing

Phone: 39-011-00-61111	**Fax:** 39-011-00-63798
Toll-Free:	
Address: 250 Via Nizza, Turin, 10126 Italy	

GROWTH PLANS/SPECIAL FEATURES:

Fiat SpA manufactures and sells automobiles, heavy machinery and components. The company is organized in 11 operating sectors: Fiat Group Automobiles; Ferrari; Maserati; agricultural and construction equipment; trucks and commercial vehicles; powertrain technologies; components; metallurgical products; production systems; publishing and communications; and corporate service companies. Fiat Group Automobiles sells Fiat, Lancia and Alfa Romeo cars, as well as light commercial vehicles. Ferrari and Maserati are both majority-owned by Fiat and world-renowned manufacturers of high-end sports cars. The company owns and operates several subsidiaries within the automotive industry. Agricultural and construction equipment is produced by CNH Global, which manufactures the Case IH and New Holland lines. Trucks and commercial vehicles are produced by Iveco, which manufactures light, medium and heavy trucks for on- or off-road uses, as well as buses; special-purpose military vehicles; and diesel, hybrid and hydrogen fuel cell engines. Fiat Powertrain Technologies (FPT) designs and builds engines for passenger and commercial vehicles and for industrial and marine applications. Fiat's components are designed, developed and manufactured by subsidiary Magneti Marelli, and include suspension systems and shock absorbers. Other subsidiaries include Teksid, which manufactures cast metal components and Comau, which designs and produces machine tools and production systems. In addition, Fiat owns Itedi, which publishes the Italian newspaper La Stampa and offers advertising services to more than 100,000 customers. In 2009, the firm plans to introduce two Magneti Marelli-owned joint ventures, one to further its automotive electronic systems operations and one to produce shock absorbers. In January 2009, Chrysler entered into a tentative alliance agreement with Fiat. The alliance would give Fiat a 35% stake in Chrysler while giving Chrysler access to Fiat small car engineering and technology. If the alliance is successful, Chrysler could quickly be building cars based on Fiat designs for sale in the U.S. and abroad.

FINANCIALS:

Sales and profits are in thousands of dollars—add 000 to get the full amount. 2008 Note: Financial information for 2008 was not available for all companies at press time.

2008 Sales: $80,147,000	2008 Profits: $2,322,890	**U.S. Stock Ticker: FIA**
2007 Sales: $78,998,300	2007 Profits: $2,772,350	**Int'l Ticker: F** Int'l Exchange: Milan-BI
2006 Sales: $81,376,200	2006 Profits: $1,672,100	Employees: 198,348
2005 Sales: $73,074,100	2005 Profits: $2,089,700	Fiscal Year Ends: 12/31
2004 Sales: $66,140,000	2004 Profits: $-2,148,000	Parent Company:

SALARIES/BENEFITS:

Pension Plan:	ESOP Stock Plan:	Profit Sharing:	Top Exec. Salary: $	Bonus: $
Savings Plan:	Stock Purch. Plan:		Second Exec. Salary: $	Bonus: $

OTHER THOUGHTS:

Apparent Women Officers or Directors:
Hot Spot for Advancement for Women/Minorities:

LOCATIONS: ("Y" = Yes)

West:	Southwest:	Midwest:	Southeast:	Northeast:	International:
					Y

Note: Financial information, benefits and other data can change quickly and may vary from those stated here.

FIRST AUTOMOTIVE GROUP CORPORATION

www.faw.com

Industry Group Code: 336111 **Ranks within this company's industry group:** Sales: Profits:

Techology:		Medical/Drugs:		Engineering:		Transportation:		Chemicals/Petrochemicals:		Specialty:	
Computers:		Manufacturer:		Design:		Aerospace:		Oil/Gas Products:		Special Services:	
Software:		Contract Research:		Construction:		Automotive:	Y	Chemicals:		Consulting:	
Communications:		Medical Services:		Eng. Services:		Shipping:		Oil/Chem. Svcs.:		Specialty Mgmt.:	
Electronics:		Labs:		Consulting:				Gases:		Products:	
Alternative Energy:		Bio. Services:						Other:		Other:	

TYPES OF BUSINESS:

Automobile Manufacturing
Parts Manufacturing
Truck Manufacturing

BRANDS/DIVISIONS/AFFILIATES:

First Automotive Works
Jiefang
Hongqi
Tianjin Automotive Xiali Co.
FAW-Volkswagen Automotive Company, Ltd.
ThyssenKrupp Presta Fawer (Changchun) Co. Ltd.
FAW Mazda Motor Sales Co. Ltd.
Deutz (Dalian) Engine Co. Ltd.

CONTACTS:

Note: Officers with more than one job title may be intentionally listed here more than once.

Zhu Yanfeng, Pres.

Phone: 86-431-85900715	**Fax:** 86-431-85730707
Toll-Free:	
Address: 2259 Dongfeng St., Changchun, 130011 China	

GROWTH PLANS/SPECIAL FEATURES:

First Automotive Group Corporation (FAW) is a state-owned Chinese automobile manufacturer. Founded in 1953 as First Automotive Works, it became one of the first vehicle producers in China starting with the 1956 rollout of Jiefang trucks and the 1958 launch of Hongqi cars. Through its own operating divisions and joint ventures, most notably with Volkswagen, FAW has since expanded its product line to include six categories: Commercial trucks; buses and coaches; passenger cars; mini vehicles; sport utility vehicles (SUVs) and pickups; and components and parts. Jiefang and Hongqi are still its two major brands. It sells over 7 million vehicles annually in more than 70 countries. Building on recent expansion, including the government-engineered takeover of state-owned small car manufacturer Tianjin Automotive Xiali Co., FAW companies are expected to benefit from nearly $2.5 billion in investment over the next five years. FAW wholly-owns 27 subsidiaries and maintains a controlling interest in 20 other subsidiaries. FAW's partnership with Volkswagen dates to 1991, when FAW-Volkswagen Automotive Company, Ltd. was established by FAW, Volkswagen and Audi. The joint venture produces the Jetta sedan, Bora IV, Caddy MVP, Golf IV, Magotan (European Passat), Sagitar (European Jetta), Audi A4 and Audi A6L. Other joint ventures include the Deutz (Dalian) Engine Co. Ltd. with Deutz AG; ThyssenKrupp Presta Fawer (Changchun) Co. Ltd. with ThyssenKrupp Presta AG; TRW Fawer Automobile Safety Systems Co. Ltd. with TRW Automotive; and Valeo Fawer Compressor (Changchun) Co. Ltd. with France's Valeo. FAW is also engaged in joint ventures with Toyota to produce the Dario branded Terios compact SUV, Corolla sedan, Vios sedan, Crown luxury sedan and Reiz (Mark X) performance sedan, as well as engines for Toyota Crown luxury sedans and large automotive stamping dies. FAW Mazda Motor Sales Co. Ltd., a joint venture between FAW and Mazda Motor Corporation, produces Mazda sports wagons, sports sedans and four door sedans.

FINANCIALS:

Sales and profits are in thousands of dollars—add 000 to get the full amount. 2008 Note: Financial information for 2008 was not available for all companies at press time.

2008 Sales: $	2008 Profits: $	**U.S. Stock Ticker: Government-Owned**
2007 Sales: $	2007 Profits: $	**Int'l Ticker:** Int'l Exchange:
2006 Sales: $	2006 Profits: $	Employees:
2005 Sales: $	2005 Profits: $	Fiscal Year Ends:
2004 Sales: $	2004 Profits: $	Parent Company:

SALARIES/BENEFITS:

Pension Plan:	ESOP Stock Plan:	Profit Sharing:	Top Exec. Salary: $	Bonus: $
Savings Plan:	Stock Purch. Plan:		Second Exec. Salary: $	Bonus: $

OTHER THOUGHTS:

Apparent Women Officers or Directors:
Hot Spot for Advancement for Women/Minorities:

LOCATIONS: ("Y" = Yes)

West:	Southwest:	Midwest:	Southeast:	Northeast:	International:
					Y

FLEXTRONICS INTERNATIONAL LTD

www.flextronics.com

Industry Group Code: 334419 **Ranks within this company's industry group:** Sales: 2 Profits: 11

Techology:		Medical/Drugs:		Engineering:		Transportation:		Chemicals/Petrochemicals:		Specialty:	
Computers:		Manufacturer:		Design:		Aerospace:		Oil/Gas Products:		Special Services:	Y
Software:	Y	Contract Research:		Construction:		Automotive:		Chemicals:		Consulting:	
Communications:		Medical Services:		Eng. Services:		Shipping:		Oil/Chem. Svcs.:		Specialty Mgmt.:	
Electronics:	Y	Labs:		Consulting:				Gases:		Products:	
Alternative Energy:		Bio. Services:						Other:		Other:	

TYPES OF BUSINESS:

Contract Manufacturing-Electronics
Telecommunications Equipment Manufacturing
Engineering, Design & Testing Services
Logistics Services
Camera Modules
Medical Devices
LCD Displays

BRANDS/DIVISIONS/AFFILIATES:

Solectron Corporation
Avail Medical Products Inc
Arima Computer Corporation
FRIWO Mobile Power

CONTACTS: *Note: Officers with more than one job title may be intentionally listed here more than once.*

Michael M. McNamara, CEO
Paul Read, CFO
Carrie L. Schiff, General Counsel/Sr. VP
Christopher Collier, Sr. VP-Finance
Werner Widmann, Pres., Multek
Michael J. Clarke, Pres., Infrastructure
Gernot Weiss, Pres., Mobile Market
Greg Westbrook, Pres., Consumer Digital
H. Raymond Bingham, Chmn.

Phone: 65-6543-2888	**Fax:** 65-5431-888
Toll-Free:	
Address: 2 Changi S. Ln., Singapore, 486123 Singapore	

GROWTH PLANS/SPECIAL FEATURES:

Flextronics International, Ltd. is a leading global provider of vertically-integrated advanced electronics manufacturing services (EMS) to original equipment manufacturers (OEMs). The services Flextronics offers across all the markets it serves include printed circuit board and flexible circuit fabrication; systems assembly and manufacturing; logistics; after-sales services; design and engineering services; original design manufacturer services; and components design and manufacturing. The company manufactures high-density, multilayer and flexible printed circuit board (PCB) as well as rigid-flex circuit board. It manufactures PCBs on a low-volume, quick-turn basis, as well as on a high-volume production basis. Flextronics' assembly and manufacturing operations, which generate the majority of its revenues, include PCB assembly and assembly of systems and subsystems that incorporate PCBs and complex electromechanical components. The company's design and engineering services include user interface and industrial design; mechanical engineering and tooling design; electronic system design; and PCB design. The firm's components solutions group designs and manufactures subsystem solutions for the electronics market, such as camera modules, power supplies, antennas, RF modules, MP3 players and digital cameras. Flextronics' global logistics services include freight forwarding, warehousing/inventory management and outbound/e-commerce solutions. The firm's after-sales services include product repair, re-manufacturing and maintenance. The firm's total manufacturing capacity is approximately 27 million square feet in over 25 countries across four continents. During 2008, the company's sales in Asia represented 56% of its total sales, while the Americas represented 28% and Europe represented 16%. In October 2007, Flextronics acquired Solectron Corporation for approximately $1.07 billion. In January 2008, the firm acquired Avail Medical Products Inc., a manufacturer of disposable medical devices. In March 2008, Flextronics acquired the design and services groups of Arima Computer Corporation as the first of a two phase acquisition of Arima's notebook and server businesses. In May 2008, the firm acquired CEAG AG's FRIWO Mobile Power business unit.

FINANCIALS: **Sales and profits are in thousands of dollars—add 000 to get the full amount. 2008 Note: Financial information for 2008 was not available for all companies at press time.**

2008 Sales: $27,558,135	2008 Profits: $-639,370	**U.S. Stock Ticker: FLEX**
2007 Sales: $18,853,688	2007 Profits: $508,638	**Int'l Ticker:** Int'l Exchange:
2006 Sales: $15,287,976	2006 Profits: $141,162	Employees: 162,000
2005 Sales: $15,760,717	2005 Profits: $339,871	Fiscal Year Ends: 3/31
2004 Sales: $14,479,262	2004 Profits: $-352,378	Parent Company:

SALARIES/BENEFITS:

Pension Plan:	ESOP Stock Plan:	Profit Sharing:	Top Exec. Salary: $1,250,000	Bonus: $4,750,000
Savings Plan: Y	Stock Purch. Plan:		Second Exec. Salary: $700,000	Bonus: $2,000,000

OTHER THOUGHTS:

Apparent Women Officers or Directors: 1
Hot Spot for Advancement for Women/Minorities:

LOCATIONS: ("Y" = Yes)

West:	Southwest:	Midwest:	Southeast:	Northeast:	International:
Y	Y	Y	Y	Y	Y

FLUOR CORP

www.fluor.com

Industry Group Code: 234000 **Ranks within this company's industry group:** Sales: 5 Profits: 4

Techology:		Medical/Drugs:		Engineering:		Transportation:		Chemicals/Petrochemicals:		Specialty:	
Computers:		Manufacturer:		Design:	Y	Aerospace:		Oil/Gas Products:		Special Services:	Y
Software:		Contract Research:		Construction:	Y	Automotive:		Chemicals:		Consulting:	
Communications:		Medical Services:		Eng. Services:	Y	Shipping:		Oil/Chem. Svcs.:		Specialty Mgmt.:	Y
Electronics:		Labs:		Consulting:	Y			Gases:		Products:	
Alternative Energy:		Bio. Services:						Other:		Other:	

TYPES OF BUSINESS:

Construction, Heavy & Civil Engineering
Power Plant Construction and Management
Facilities Management
Procurement Services
Consulting Services
Project Management
Asset Management
Staffing Services

BRANDS/DIVISIONS/AFFILIATES:

Fluor Construction Company
Department of Energy
Department of Homeland Security
Department of Defense
Kuwait Oil Company
LDK Solar Co
UNEC Engineering NV
Europea de Ingenieria Y Asesoramiento

CONTACTS: *Note: Officers with more than one job title may be intentionally listed here more than once.*

Alan L. Boeckmann, CEO
D. Michael Steuert, CFO/Sr. VP
Glenn Gilkey, Sr. VP-Human Resources
Ray F. Barnard, CIO/VP
Glenn Gilkey, Sr. VP-Admin.
Carlos M. Hernandez, Chief Legal Officer/Corp. Sec.
Lee Tashjian, VP-Corp. Comm.
Kenneth H. Lockwood, VP-Investor Rel. & Corp. Finance
Gary Smalley, Controller/VP
Dwayne Wilson, Pres., Industrial & Infrastructure
David T. Seaton, Pres., Energy & Chemicals
David E. Constable, Pres., Power
Richard P. Carter, Pres., Fluor Constructors International Inc
Alan L. Boeckmann, Chmn.
Kirk D. Grimes, Pres., Global Svcs.

Phone: 469-398-7000	**Fax:** 469-398-7255
Toll-Free:	
Address: 6700 Las Colinas Blvd., Irving, TX 75039 US	

GROWTH PLANS/SPECIAL FEATURES:

Fluor Corp., founded in 1912 as Fluor Construction Company, is a privately-held, global provider of engineering, procurement, construction and maintenance services. As well as being a primary service provider to the U.S. federal government, Fluor serves a diverse set of industries including oil and gas; chemical and petrochemicals; transportation; mining and metals; power; life sciences; and manufacturing. Fluor operates in five business segments: Oil and gas; industrial and infrastructure; government; global services; and power. The oil and gas segment offers design, engineering, procurement, construction and project management services to energy-related industries. The industrial and infrastructure segment provides design, engineering and construction services to the transportation, mining, life sciences, telecommunications, manufacturing, commercial, institutional, microelectronics and healthcare sectors. The government segment provides project management services, including environmental restoration, engineering, construction, site operations and maintenance, to the U.S. government, particularly to the Department of Energy, the Department of Homeland Security and the Department of Defense. The global services segment provides operations, maintenance and construction services, as well as industrial fleet outsourcing, plant turnaround services, temporary staffing, procurement services and construction-related support. The power segment provides such services as engineering, procurement, construction, program management, start-up, commissioning and maintenance to the gas fueled, solid fueled, renewable, nuclear and plant betterment marketplaces. In January 2008, the company was awarded a $334 million consultancy services contract to provide overall program management for the Kuwait Oil Company. In April 2008, Fluor was awarded an engineering, procurement and construction management contract by LDK Solar Co., Ltd. for a poly-silicon facility in China. In November 2008, the company acquired two private engineering firms in Europe: UNEC Engineering NV in Antwerp, Belgium, and Europea de Ingenieria Y Asesoramiento of Tarragona, Spain.

Fluor offers its employees a 401(k) plan; education assistance; an employee assistance program; and medical, dental, life and disability insurance.

FINANCIALS: **Sales and profits are in thousands of dollars—add 000 to get the full amount. 2008 Note: Financial information for 2008 was not available for all companies at press time.**

2008 Sales: $22,325,900	2008 Profits: $720,500	**U.S. Stock Ticker: FLR**
2007 Sales: $16,691,000	2007 Profits: $533,300	**Int'l Ticker:** Int'l Exchange:
2006 Sales: $14,078,500	2006 Profits: $263,500	Employees: 42,119
2005 Sales: $13,161,100	2005 Profits: $227,300	Fiscal Year Ends: 12/31
2004 Sales: $9,380,300	2004 Profits: $186,700	Parent Company:

SALARIES/BENEFITS:

Pension Plan: Y	ESOP Stock Plan:	Profit Sharing:	Top Exec. Salary: $1,153,335	Bonus: $5,220,000
Savings Plan: Y	Stock Purch. Plan:		Second Exec. Salary: $732,598	Bonus: $2,265,600

OTHER THOUGHTS:

Apparent Women Officers or Directors: 4
Hot Spot for Advancement for Women/Minorities: Y

LOCATIONS: ("Y" = Yes)

West:	Southwest:	Midwest:	Southeast:	Northeast:	International:
Y	Y	Y	Y	Y	Y

FMC TECHNOLOGIES INC

www.fmctechnologies.com

ndustry Group Code: 213111 **Ranks within this company's industry group:** Sales: 5 Profits: 5

Techology:		**Medical/Drugs:**		**Engineering:**		**Transportation:**		**Chemicals/Petrochemicals:**		**Specialty:**	
Computers:		Manufacturer:		Design:		Aerospace:		Oil/Gas Products:		Special Services:	
Software:		Contract Research:		Construction:		Automotive:		Chemicals:		Consulting:	
Communications:		Medical Services:		Eng. Services:		Shipping:		Oil/Chem. Svcs.:		Specialty Mgmt.:	
Electronics:		Labs:		Consulting:				Gases:		Products:	
Alternative Energy:	Y	Bio. Services:						Other:	Y	Other:	Y

TYPES OF BUSINESS:

Oil & Gas Production & Processing Equipment
Airport & Airline Equipment
Food Handling & Processing Systems

BRANDS/DIVISIONS/AFFILIATES:

Jetway
Technisys, Inc.
John Bean Technologies Corporation

CONTACTS: *Note: Officers with more than one job title may be intentionally listed here more than once.*

Peter D. Kinnear, CEO
Peter D. Kinnear, Pres.
William H. Schumann, III, CFO/Exec. VP
Randall S. Ellis, CIO/VP
Maryann T. Seaman, VP-Admin.
Jeffrey W. Carr, General Counsel/VP/Corp. Sec.
Jeffrey S. Beyersdorfer, Treas.
Jay A. Nutt, Controller
John T. Gremp, Exec. VP-Energy Systems
Tore Halvorsen, VP-Global Subsea Prod. Systems
Robert L. Potter, Sr. VP-Energy Processing & Global Surface Wellhead
Joseph H. Netherland, Chmn.

Phone: 281-591-4000	**Fax:** 281-591-4102
Toll-Free:	
Address: 1803 Gears Rd., Houston, TX 77067 US	

GROWTH PLANS/SPECIAL FEATURES:

FMC Technologies, Inc., formerly John Bean Manufacturing Co., designs, manufactures and services technologically sophisticated systems and products such as subsea production and processing systems, surface wellhead production systems, high pressure fluid control equipment, measurement solutions and marine loading equipment for the oil and gas industry. The company's business segments are: Energy Systems, FoodTech and Airport Systems. The Energy Systems business segment comprises Energy Production Systems and Energy Processing Systems. The Energy Production Systems division designs and manufactures systems and provides services used by the oil and gas companies involved in land and offshore, including deepwater, exploration and production of crude oil gas. The Energy Processing Systems division designs, manufactures and supplies technologically advanced high pressure valves and fittings for oilfield service customers, as well as manufacturing liquid and gas measurement and transportation equipment and systems to customers involved in the production, transportation and processing of crude oil, natural gas and petroleum-based refined products. The FoodTech division designs, manufactures and services technologically sophisticated food processing and handling systems used primarily for fruit juice production, frozen food production, shelf-stable food production and convenience food preparation for the food industry. The Airport Systems division is a global supplier of passenger boarding bridges, cargo loaders and other ground support products, as well as airport management services. The company's Jetway passenger boarding bridges provide passengers access from the aircraft to the terminal. In June 2007, FMC acquired Technisys, Inc., an electrical integration company. In August 2008, FMC completed the transition of its FoodTech and Airport Systems segment into an independent publicly-traded company, John Bean Technologies Corporation.

FMC Technologies offers its employees a benefits package that includes legal services, educational assistance, an employee assistance program, dependent care reimbursement and savings account plans, a Dollars for Doers volunteer program and a Matching Gift Plan.

FINANCIALS: **Sales and profits are in thousands of dollars—add 000 to get the full amount. 2008 Note: Financial information for 2008 was not available for all companies at press time.**

2008 Sales: $4,550,900	2008 Profits: $361,300	**U.S. Stock Ticker: FTI**
2007 Sales: $3,648,900	2007 Profits: $302,800	**Int'l Ticker:** Int'l Exchange:
2006 Sales: $2,915,400	2006 Profits: $276,300	Employees: 9,800
2005 Sales: $3,107,000	2005 Profits: $106,100	Fiscal Year Ends: 12/31
2004 Sales: $2,767,700	2004 Profits: $116,700	Parent Company:

SALARIES/BENEFITS:

Pension Plan: Y	ESOP Stock Plan:	Profit Sharing:	Top Exec. Salary: $781,430	Bonus: $1,218,570
Savings Plan: Y	Stock Purch. Plan:		Second Exec. Salary: $554,172	Bonus: $371,410

OTHER THOUGHTS:

Apparent Women Officers or Directors: 1
Hot Spot for Advancement for Women/Minorities:

LOCATIONS: ("Y" = Yes)

West:	Southwest:	Midwest:	Southeast:	Northeast:	International:
Y	Y	Y	Y	Y	Y

FOMENTO DE CONSTRUCCIONES Y CONTRATAS SA (FCC)

www.fcc.es

Industry Group Code: 234000 **Ranks within this company's industry group:** Sales: 8 Profits: 8

Techology:		Medical/Drugs:		Engineering:		Transportation:		Chemicals/Petrochemicals:		Specialty:	
Computers:		Manufacturer:		Design:	Y	Aerospace:		Oil/Gas Products:		Special Services:	Y
Software:		Contract Research:		Construction:	Y	Automotive:		Chemicals:		Consulting:	
Communications:		Medical Services:		Eng. Services:	Y	Shipping:	Y	Oil/Chem. Svcs.:		Specialty Mgmt.:	Y
Electronics:		Labs:		Consulting:	Y			Gases:		Products:	
Alternative Energy:		Bio. Services:						Other:		Other:	

TYPES OF BUSINESS:

Heavy Construction
Airport Operations
Urban Sanitation
Commuter Bus & Rail Lines
Logistics Services
Real Estate Development
Cement Manufacturing
Engineering Services

BRANDS/DIVISIONS/AFFILIATES:

Cementos Portland Valderrivas
FCC Medio Ambiente, S.A.
FCC Versia, S.A.
Aqualia, S.A.
Torre Picasso
Realia Business, S.A.

CONTACTS: *Note: Officers with more than one job title may be intentionally listed here more than once.*

Rafael Montes Sanchez, CEO
Jose E. Trueba Gutierrez, CFO
Antonio Perez Colmenero, Corp. Mgr.-Human & Other Resources
Juan Sanchez Espinosa de los Monteros, Manager-Info. Systems & Technologies Div.
Juan Sanchez Espinosa de los Monteros, Mgr.-Info. Systems & Technologies Div.
Jose E. Trueba Gutierrez, Manager-Corp. Admin.
Felipe Bernabe Garcia Perez, General Sec.
Raul Vazquez Perez, Corp. Manager-Corp. Dev.
Dieter Kiefer, CEO-Cementos Portland Valderrivas, Spain
Jose Mayor Oreja, Chmn.-FCC Construccion, S.A.
Jose Ignacio M.-Y. Y Canovas del Castillo, Chmn./Managing Dir.-Cement
Jose Luis de la Torre Sanchez, Chmn.-FCC Servicios
Baldomero Falcones Jaquotot, Chmn.

Phone: 34-93-496-49-00	**Fax:** 34-93-487-88-92
Toll-Free:	
Address: Balmes, 36, Barcelona, 08007 Spain	

GROWTH PLANS/SPECIAL FEATURES:

Fomento de Construcciones Y Contratas S.A. (FCC) is parent company to one of Spain's leading construction and service groups. It divides its business between construction, which generated approximately 46% of the firm's revenues; cement production, 15%; and other services, 39%. The firm's construction business consists of civil engineering, which accounted for 24.7% of this segment's revenues; non-residential building, 16%; and residential building, 35.5%. Construction projects have included oil and gas pipelines; highways; airports; and railways. The firm's cement business, with operations in the Eastern U.S. as well in Argentina, Uruguay and Tunisia, is conducted by Cementos Portland Valderrivas, a leading Spanish cement firm. Cement Sales accounted for 66.8% of sales; prepared concrete, 22%; dry mortar, 5.5%; and aggregates, 4.1%. FCC's services are conducted by its Environmental Services division, which generated 34% of FCC's total net revenue (excluding Versia); Versia (a part of Environmental Services), and Torre Picasso. The firm's environmental services are conducted by FCC itself, FCC Medio Ambiente, S.A.; FCC Versia, S.A.; and Aqualia, S.A. Services include sewer system maintenance; street cleaning; collecting, treating and eliminating solid urban waste; park and garden maintenance; full-service water management; and treating and eliminating industrial waste. Versia's services include logistics; parking; passenger transportation; urban furniture; handling; conservation and systems; and technical vehicle inspections. Torre Picasso provides real estate services, as does Realia Business, S.A., in which FCC owns a 25% interest. Realia is involved in real estate development, rental and other services. In September 2008, FCC acquired two photovoltaic plants in Cordoba, Spain and stakes in 5 infrastructure concessions of Acciona S.A.

FINANCIALS: **Sales and profits are in thousands of dollars—add 000 to get the full amount. 2008 Note: Financial information for 2008 was not available for all companies at press time.**

2008 Sales: $18,563,200	2008 Profits: $446,330	**U.S. Stock Ticker: FCC**
2007 Sales: $17,777,800	2007 Profits: $977,430	**Int'l Ticker: FCC** Int'l Exchange: Madrid-MCE
2006 Sales: $13,747,300	2006 Profits: $776,500	Employees: 67,562
2005 Sales: $9,640,270	2005 Profits: $572,430	Fiscal Year Ends: 12/31
2004 Sales: $8,632,740	2004 Profits: $493,570	Parent Company:

SALARIES/BENEFITS:

Pension Plan:	ESOP Stock Plan:	Profit Sharing:	Top Exec. Salary: $	Bonus: $
Savings Plan:	Stock Purch. Plan:		Second Exec. Salary: $	Bonus: $

OTHER THOUGHTS:

Apparent Women Officers or Directors:
Hot Spot for Advancement for Women/Minorities:

LOCATIONS: ("Y" = Yes)

West:	Southwest:	Midwest:	Southeast:	Northeast:	International:
			Y	Y	Y

FORD MOTOR CO

www.ford.com

Industry Group Code: 336111 **Ranks within this company's industry group:** Sales: 4 Profits: 23

Techology:		Medical/Drugs:		Engineering:		Transportation:		Chemicals/Petrochemicals:		Specialty:	
Computers:		Manufacturer:		Design:		Aerospace:		Oil/Gas Products:		Special Services:	Y
Software:		Contract Research:		Construction:		Automotive:	Y	Chemicals:		Consulting:	
Communications:		Medical Services:		Eng. Services:		Shipping:		Oil/Chem. Svcs.:		Specialty Mgmt.:	
Electronics:		Labs:		Consulting:				Gases:		Products:	
Alternative Energy:		Bio. Services:						Other:		Other:	

TYPES OF BUSINESS:

Automobile Manufacturer
Automobile Financing
Fuel-Cell & Hybrid Research

BRANDS/DIVISIONS/AFFILIATES:

Lincoln Mercury
Motorcraft
Volvo Car Corporation
Ford Sync
Taurus X
Mazda Motor Corporation
Ford Motor Credit Company (The)
F-Series Super Duty

CONTACTS:

Note: Officers with more than one job title may be intentionally listed here more than once.

Alan Mulally, CEO
Alan Mulally, Pres.
James D. Farley, VP-Mktg. & Comm.
Felicia J. Fields, VP-Human Resources & Corp. Svcs.
Gerhard Schmidt, VP-Research
Nicholas J. Smither, CIO/VP
Gerhard Schmidt, CTO/VP
Gerhard Schmidt, VP-Advanced Eng.
David G. Leitch, General Counsel/Sr. VP
Raymond F. Day, VP-Comm.
Neil M. Schloss, Treas./VP
Michael E. Banister, Exec. VP/CEO & Chmn.-Ford Motor Credit Co.
Mark Fields, Exec. VP/Pres., Americas
John Fleming, CEO/Pres., Ford Europe
J C. Mays, VP-Design/Chief Creative Officer
William C. Ford, Jr., Exec. Chmn.
John G. Parker, Exec. VP-APAC & Africa
Thomas K. Brown, Sr. VP-Global Purchasing

Phone: 313-322-3000	**Fax:** 313-845-6073
Toll-Free: 800-555-5259	
Address: 1 American Rd., Dearborn, MI 48126 US	

GROWTH PLANS/SPECIAL FEATURES:

Ford Motor Company operates in two segments: automotive and financial services. The automotive segment designs, manufactures, sells and services cars and trucks. Ford sold approximately 6.5 million vehicles worldwide in 2007 under the brands Ford, Mercury, Lincoln and Volvo. The firm provides after-sale vehicle services and products through approximately 16,700 franchised dealerships, such as maintenance and repair; vehicle accessories; and extended-service warranties. Ford markets these products and services under brands including: Genuine Ford; Lincoln-Mercury Parts and Service; Ford Extended Service Plan; and Motorcraft. Ford has a 33.4% stake in Mazda Motor Corporation. Ford's financial services segment, run through the Ford Motor Credit Company LLC, offers vehicle-related financing, leasing and insurance. New vehicles recently introduced include the Taurus X and Ford Flex, both full-size crossover vehicles; the F-Series Super Duty; and the Ford Escape Hybrid E85. Ford partnered with Microsoft to offer Ford Sync, the firm's first voice-activated in-car communications and entertainment system for mobile phones and music players. In March 2007, Ford agreed to sell its subsidiary Automotive Protection Corp. to an affiliate of Stone Point Capital LLC. In May 2007, Ford sold Aston Martin. In June 2008, the firm sold Jaguar Land Rover to Tata Motors. Also in June 2008, the company sold assembly plants in Georgia and Missouri. As of late 2008, Ford has placed its Volvo unit up for sale, part of a continuing downsizing and reorganization at Ford. The company hopes to quickly introduce fully electric vehicles to the U.S. market.

The company offers its employees medical, dental and prescription insurance; life and disability insurance; a savings plan; relocation packages; gift matching; dependent scholarships; recreation programs; tuition assistance; vehicle purchase programs; and group rates on auto, home, and life insurance.

FINANCIALS:

Sales and profits are in thousands of dollars—add 000 to get the full amount. 2008 Note: Financial information for 2008 was not available for all companies at press time.

2008 Sales: $146,277,000	2008 Profits: $-14,672,000	**U.S. Stock Ticker: F**
2007 Sales: $172,455,000	2007 Profits: $-2,723,000	**Int'l Ticker:** Int'l Exchange:
2006 Sales: $160,065,000	2006 Profits: $-12,613,000	Employees: 300,000
2005 Sales: $176,835,000	2005 Profits: $1,440,000	Fiscal Year Ends: 12/31
2004 Sales: $172,316,000	2004 Profits: $3,038,000	Parent Company:

SALARIES/BENEFITS:

Pension Plan:	ESOP Stock Plan:	Profit Sharing:	Top Exec. Salary: $2,000,000	Bonus: $7,000,000
Savings Plan: Y	Stock Purch. Plan:		Second Exec. Salary: $1,255,634	Bonus: $2,850,000

OTHER THOUGHTS:

Apparent Women Officers or Directors: 5
Hot Spot for Advancement for Women/Minorities: Y

LOCATIONS: ("Y" = Yes)

West:	Southwest:	Midwest:	Southeast:	Northeast:	International:
Y	Y	Y	Y	Y	Y

FOREST LABORATORIES INC

www.frx.com

Industry Group Code: 325412 **Ranks within this company's industry group:** Sales: 27 Profits: 20

Techology:		Medical/Drugs:		Engineering:		Transportation:		Chemicals/Petrochemicals:		Specialty:	
Computers:		Manufacturer:	Y	Design:		Aerospace:		Oil/Gas Products:		Special Services:	
Software:		Contract Research:		Construction:		Automotive:		Chemicals:		Consulting:	
Communications:		Medical Services:		Eng. Services:		Shipping:		Oil/Chem. Svcs.:		Specialty Mgmt.:	
Electronics:		Labs:	Y	Consulting:				Gases:		Products:	
Alternative Energy:		Bio. Services:						Other:		Other:	

TYPES OF BUSINESS:

Drugs, Manufacturing
Over-the-Counter Pharmaceuticals
Generic Pharmaceuticals
Antidepressants
Asthma Medications
Cardiovascular Products
OB/Gyn Products
Endocrinology

BRANDS/DIVISIONS/AFFILIATES:

Lexapro
Namenda
Benicar
Forest Research Institute
Forest Pharmaceuticals, Inc.
Forest Laboratories Europe
Inwood Laboratories
Cerexa, Inc.

CONTACTS: *Note: Officers with more than one job title may be intentionally listed here more than once.*

Howard Solomon, CEO
Lawrence S. Olanoff, COO
Lawrence S. Olanoff, Pres.
Francis I. Perier, Jr., CFO
Elaine Hochberg, Sr. VP-Mktg./Chief Commercial Officer
William J. Candee III, Sec.
Frank Murdolo, VP-Investor Rel.
Francis I. Perier, Jr., Sr. VP-Finance
Howard Solomon, Chmn.

Phone: 212-421-7850	**Fax:**
Toll-Free: 800-947-5227	
Address: 909 3rd Ave., New York, NY 10022 US	

GROWTH PLANS/SPECIAL FEATURES:

Forest Laboratories, Inc. develops, delivers and sells pharmaceutical products. It currently covers six therapeutic areas, developing treatments for respiratory, pain management, ob/gyn, endocrinology, central nervous system and cardiovascular conditions. Forest's four principal brands are Lexapro, an antidepressant; Benicar, a hypertension treatment; Namenda, a therapy for moderate or severe Alzheimer's disease; and Campral, which helps reduce withdrawals for those seeking to eliminate alcohol dependence. Other products include Aerobid, an asthma medication; AeroChamber Plus, an inhalant delivery system for asthma medications; Infasurf, used to prevent respiratory distress syndrome (RDS), a condition caused by a lack of surfactant, found mainly in premature infants; Armour Thyroid, Levothroid and Thyrolar, for treating hypothyroidism; Celexa, an antidepressant; Cervidil, used to prepare the cervix before inducing labor; and Combunox, a pain medication combining both opioids and non-steroidal anti-inflammatory drugs. Forest markets directly to physicians who have the most potential for growth and are agreeable to the introduction of new products, as well as to pharmacies, hospitals, managed care and other healthcare organizations. Forest Research Institute, Forest's scientific division, maintains labs on Long Island and in New Jersey. Subsidiary Forest Pharmaceuticals, Inc. manufactures and distributes Forest's branded prescription products in the U.S. Subsidiary Forest Laboratories Europe has two manufacturing sites in Dublin, Ireland and one in Bexley, Kent, and distributes prescription and over-the-counter drugs in Europe, the Middle East, Australia and Asia. Subsidiary Inwood Laboratories manufactures and supplies generic versions of Forest's medications. Cerexa, Inc., acquired in 2007, develops and commercializes treatments for life-threatening infections. In January 2009, the company's Savella, a selective serotonin and norepinephrine inhibitor, was approved by the FDA for the management of fibromyalgia, a chronic pain condition.

Employees at Forest receive financial assistance for adoption and fertility treatments; medical, dental and life insurance; flexible spending accounts; child-care resources; and a commuter benefit program.

FINANCIALS: **Sales and profits are in thousands of dollars—add 000 to get the full amount. 2008 Note: Financial information for 2008 was not available for all companies at press time.**

2008 Sales: $3,501,802	2008 Profits: $967,933	**U.S. Stock Ticker: FRX**
2007 Sales: $3,183,324	2007 Profits: $454,103	**Int'l Ticker:** Int'l Exchange:
2006 Sales: $2,793,934	2006 Profits: $708,514	Employees: 5,211
2005 Sales: $3,052,408	2005 Profits: $838,805	Fiscal Year Ends: 3/31
2004 Sales: $2,650,432	2004 Profits: $735,874	Parent Company:

SALARIES/BENEFITS:

Pension Plan:	ESOP Stock Plan:	Profit Sharing: Y	Top Exec. Salary: $1,162,500	Bonus: $635,000
Savings Plan: Y	Stock Purch. Plan:		Second Exec. Salary: $758,750	Bonus: $400,000

OTHER THOUGHTS:

Apparent Women Officers or Directors: 1
Hot Spot for Advancement for Women/Minorities: Y

LOCATIONS: ("Y" = Yes)

West:	Southwest:	Midwest:	Southeast:	Northeast:	International:
		Y		Y	Y

FOSTER WHEELER AG

www.fwc.com

Industry Group Code: 234000 **Ranks within this company's industry group:** Sales: 13 Profits: 6

Techology:		Medical/Drugs:		Engineering:		Transportation:		Chemicals/Petrochemicals:		Specialty:	
Computers:		Manufacturer:		Design:	Y	Aerospace:		Oil/Gas Products:		Special Services:	Y
Software:		Contract Research:		Construction:	Y	Automotive:		Chemicals:		Consulting:	
Communications:		Medical Services:		Eng. Services:	Y	Shipping:		Oil/Chem. Svcs.:	Y	Specialty Mgmt.:	
Electronics:		Labs:		Consulting:	Y			Gases:		Products:	
Alternative Energy:		Bio. Services:						Other:		Other:	

TYPES OF BUSINESS:

Engineering & Construction
Industrial Plant Design & Development
Energy Equipment
Power Systems Manufacturer
Steam Generation Equipment
Renewable Energy Technology

BRANDS/DIVISIONS/AFFILIATES:

Foster Wheeler, Ltd.
Foster Wheeler International Corp.
Foster Wheeler Energy, Ltd.
Foster Wheeler Constructors
Foster Wheeler Power Machinery Co., Ltd.
Foster Wheeler Power Systems, Inc.
Quotient Engineering, Inc.
Foster Wheeler USA Corp.

CONTACTS: *Note: Officers with more than one job title may be intentionally listed here more than once.*

Raymond J. Milchovich, CEO
Umberto della Sala, COO
Umberto della Sala, Pres.
Franco Baseotto, CFO/Exec. VP/Treas.
Peter J. Ganz, General Counsel/Exec. VP
Lisa Z. Wood, VP/Controller
Umberto della Sala, CEO-Global E&C Group
Gary Nedelka, Acting CEO-Global Power Group
Raymond J. Milchovich, Chmn.

Phone: 908-730-4000	**Fax:** 908-713-3245
Toll-Free:	
Address: Perryville Corp. Park, Clinton, NJ 08809-4000 US	

GROWTH PLANS/SPECIAL FEATURES:

Foster Wheeler AG, formerly Foster Wheeler, Ltd., provides services in the oil and gas, oil refining, chemical/petrochemical, pharmaceutical, environmental, power generation and power plant operation and maintenance industries through offices in more than 28 countries. The company operates through its numerous subsidiaries, including Foster Wheeler Power Machinery Co., Ltd.; Foster Wheeler International Corp.; Foster Wheeler Energy, Ltd.; Foster Wheeler Constructors; Foster Wheeler Power Systems, Inc.; and Foster Wheeler Facilities Management, Inc. The firm's engineering services include industrial plant construction, water treatment plant engineering, and petroleum, chemical and alternative fuel facilities construction. Foster Wheeler operates under two business groups: the Global Engineering and Construction (E&C) Group, which designs, engineers and constructs onshore and offshore upstream oil and gas processing facilities, natural gas liquefaction facilities and receiving terminals, gas-to-liquids facilities, oil refining, chemical and petrochemical, pharmaceutical and biotechnology facilities and related infrastructure; and the Global Power Group, which designs, manufactures and erects steam generating and auxiliary equipment for electric power generating stations and industrial facilities worldwide. Other services include the design, manufacture and installation of auxiliary equipment, which includes steam generators for solar thermal power plants, feedwater heaters, steam condensers and heat-recovery equipment. The company has engineered and built process, power and industrial facilities in over 125 countries. In February 2008, the company strengthened its foothold in the biotech and pharmaceutical markets with the acquisition of Biokinetics Inc., a leading U.S. biopharmaceutical process design company, from MPA Holdings LP. In July 2008, the company's operating unit Foster Wheeler USA Corporation acquired the assets of Quotient Engineering, Inc., a full-service engineering and design company. In February 2009, Foster Wheeler completed its redomestication to change the place of incorporation of its group holding company from Bermuda to Switzerland. The firm also reregistered its company as Foster Wheeler AG.

FINANCIALS: **Sales and profits are in thousands of dollars—add 000 to get the full amount. 2008 Note: Financial information for 2008 was not available for all companies at press time.**

2008 Sales: $6,854,290	2008 Profits: $526,620	**U.S. Stock Ticker: FWLT**
2007 Sales: $5,107,243	2007 Profits: $393,874	**Int'l Ticker:** Int'l Exchange:
2006 Sales: $3,495,048	2006 Profits: $261,984	Employees: 14,729
2005 Sales: $2,199,955	2005 Profits: $-109,749	Fiscal Year Ends: 12/31
2004 Sales: $2,661,324	2004 Profits: $-285,294	Parent Company:

SALARIES/BENEFITS:

Pension Plan:	ESOP Stock Plan:	Profit Sharing:	Top Exec. Salary: $992,250	Bonus: $2,484,500
Savings Plan:	Stock Purch. Plan:		Second Exec. Salary: $516,189	Bonus: $828,765

OTHER THOUGHTS:

Apparent Women Officers or Directors: 3
Hot Spot for Advancement for Women/Minorities: Y

LOCATIONS: ("Y" = Yes)

West:	Southwest:	Midwest:	Southeast:	Northeast:	International:
Y	Y	Y	Y	Y	Y

FREESCALE SEMICONDUCTOR INC

www.freescale.com

Industry Group Code: 334413 **Ranks within this company's industry group:** Sales: 9 Profits: 20

Techology:		Medical/Drugs:		Engineering:		Transportation:		Chemicals/Petrochemicals:		Specialty:	
Computers:	Y	Manufacturer:		Design:		Aerospace:		Oil/Gas Products:		Special Services:	
Software:		Contract Research:		Construction:		Automotive:		Chemicals:		Consulting:	
Communications:		Medical Services:		Eng. Services:		Shipping:		Oil/Chem. Svcs.:		Specialty Mgmt.:	
Electronics:		Labs:		Consulting:				Gases:		Products:	
Alternative Energy:		Bio. Services:						Other:		Other:	

TYPES OF BUSINESS:

Semiconductor Manufacturing
Control System Components
Networking & Wireless Equipment Components

BRANDS/DIVISIONS/AFFILIATES:

Blackstone Group LP (The)
Carlyle Group (The)
SigmaTel, Inc.
Intoto, Inc.

CONTACTS: *Note: Officers with more than one job title may be intentionally listed here more than once.*

Rich Beyer, CEO
Alan Campell, CFO/Sr. VP
Henri Richard, Chief Sales & Mktg. Officer
Michel Cadieux, Sr. VP-Human Resources & Security
Sandeep Chennakeshu, Chief Dev. Officer/Sr. VP
Sam Coursen, CIO/VP
Lisa T. Su, CTO/Sr. VP/Gen. Mgr.-Networking & Multimedia
John D. Torres, General Counsel/Sec./Sr. VP
Vivek Mohindra, Sr. VP-Strategy & Bus. Transformation
Rob Hatley, Global Comm.
Mitch Haws, VP-Investor Rel.
Denis Griot, Sr. VP/Chmn.-EMEA
Klaus Buehring, Sr. VP/Gen. Mgr.-RF, Analog & Sensor
Tom Deitrich, Sr. VP/Gen. Mgr.-Cellular Prod.
Rich Beyer, Chmn.
Joe Yiu, Sr. VP/Chmn.-Asia
Alex Pepe, Sr. VP-Supply Chain Organization

Phone: 512-895-2000 **Fax:** 512-895-2652
Toll-Free: 800-521-6274
Address: 6501 William Cannon Dr. W., Austin, TX 78735 US

GROWTH PLANS/SPECIAL FEATURES:

Freescale Semiconductor, Inc., a semiconductor manufacturer, specializes in embedded processors. It has four product lines: Microcontroller Solutions, which generated 32.8% of 2007 sales; Cellular Products, 21.3%; Networking and Multimedia, 19.6%; and Radio Frequency (RF), Analog and Sensors, 18.3%. Additionally, 8% was generated by other sources, including intellectual property. Microcontroller Solutions products comprise microcontrollers, embedded microprocessors and digital signal processors. These products are primarily utilized in automotive systems, such as airbags; consumer products, including alarm systems; industrial products, such as manufacturing equipment; and computer peripherals, including keyboards. Networking and Multimedia products serve the wireless networking, industrial and consumer markets, including systems that transmit and process data and voice signals. Specific products include wireless infrastructure equipment, such as cellular base stations; network access equipment, such as voice and data routers; pervasive computing equipment, including gaming, networked storage and imaging devices; industrial equipment, such as automated vehicles and robotics; and mobile consumer applications, including portable media players and personal navigation devices. Cellular Products are used in the manufacturing and design of handheld devices, such as cellular handsets. This portfolio of products includes power management solutions, RF integrated circuits (IC) and software protocol stacks. Lastly, RF, Analog and Sensors products comprise microcontrollers and microprocessors used to interface embedded systems with the outside world, such as in automotive, industrial, consumer, wireless and networking systems. The firm has 50 sales offices in 25 countries. Its largest business areas, geographically, include Singapore, which generated 31.5% of 2007 sales; the U.S., 26.1%; Hong Kong, 13%; and Germany, 11.2%. Freescale is owned by a consortium of private equity investors including The Blackstone Group and The Carlyle Group. In April 2008, Freescale acquired IC manufacturer SigmaTel, Inc. for $110 million. In October 2008, the firm acquired private software platform developer Intoto, Inc., which now operates under the Networking Systems Division.

FINANCIALS: **Sales and profits are in thousands of dollars—add 000 to get the full amount. 2008 Note: Financial information for 2008 was not available for all companies at press time.**

2008 Sales: $5,226,000	2008 Profits: $-7,939,000	**U.S. Stock Ticker: Private**
2007 Sales: $5,722,000	2007 Profits: $-1,613,000	**Int'l Ticker:** Int'l Exchange:
2006 Sales: $6,359,000	2006 Profits: $-1,994,000	Employees: 22,700
2005 Sales: $5,843,000	2005 Profits: $563,000	Fiscal Year Ends: 12/31
2004 Sales: $5,715,000	2004 Profits: $211,000	Parent Company:

SALARIES/BENEFITS:

Pension Plan:	ESOP Stock Plan:	Profit Sharing:	Top Exec. Salary: $887,500	Bonus: $1,462,500
Savings Plan:	Stock Purch. Plan:		Second Exec. Salary: $700,000	Bonus: $500,000

OTHER THOUGHTS:

Apparent Women Officers or Directors: 1
Hot Spot for Advancement for Women/Minorities: Y

LOCATIONS: ("Y" = Yes)

West:	Southwest:	Midwest:	Southeast:	Northeast:	International:
	Y				Y

Note: Financial information, benefits and other data can change quickly and may vary from those stated here.

FUELCELL ENERGY INC

www.fuelcellenergy.com

Industry Group Code: 333298 **Ranks within this company's industry group:** Sales: 1 Profits: 2

Techology:		Medical/Drugs:		Engineering:		Transportation:		Chemicals/Petrochemicals:		Specialty:	
Computers:		Manufacturer:		Design:		Aerospace:		Oil/Gas Products:		Special Services:	
Software:		Contract Research:		Construction:		Automotive:		Chemicals:		Consulting:	
Communications:		Medical Services:		Eng. Services:		Shipping:		Oil/Chem. Svcs.:		Specialty Mgmt.:	
Electronics:		Labs:		Consulting:				Gases:		Products:	
Alternative Energy:	Y	Bio. Services:						Other:		Other:	

TYPES OF BUSINESS:

Fuel Cell Technology

BRANDS/DIVISIONS/AFFILIATES:

Direct FuelCell
DFC300
DFC1500
DFC3000
DFC-ERG

CONTACTS:

Note: Officers with more than one job title may be intentionally listed here more than once.

R. Daniel Brdar, CEO
R. Daniel Brdar, Pres.
Joseph G. Mahler, CFO
Bruce A. Ludemann, Sr. VP-Mktg. & Sales
Christopher R. Bentley, Exec. VP-Gov't R&D Oper.
Christopher R. Bentley, Exec. VP-Strategic Mfg. Dev.
Joseph G. Mahler, Sec.
Joseph G. Mahler, Sr. VP-Corp. Strategy
Joseph G. Mahler, Treas.
R. Daniel Brdar, Chmn.

Phone: 203-825-6000 **Fax:** 203-825-6100
Toll-Free:
Address: 3 Great Pasture Rd., Danbury, CT 06813 US

GROWTH PLANS/SPECIAL FEATURES:

FuelCell Energy, Inc. develops and manufactures fuel cell power plants for ultra-clean, efficient and reliable electric power generation. To date, its products have generated over 200 million kWh of electricity and are operating at over 40 locations around the world. The firm has developed a proprietary patented carbonate fuel cell utilized for stationary power generation. Its patented fuel cell technology is known as the Direct FuelCell (DFC), because it introduces hydrocarbon fuel, such as pipeline natural gas or biogas from breweries, directly into the fuel cell without requiring external reforming for producing hydrogen. This one-step operation results in a more efficient, simpler and more cost-effective energy conversion system than other fuel cells which utilize complex external reforming equipment to convert fuel to hydrogen. It designs its products to meet the power requirements of a wide range of customers, including utilities, wastewater treatment plants, industrial facilities, hospitals, data centers, shopping centers and universities. The firm has three core power plants, the DFC300, DFC1500 and DFC3000, rated at 300 kilowatts (kW), 1.2 megawatts (MW) and 2.4 MW respectively, designed for applications up to 50 MW. Its latest product is the 2.2 MW DFC-ERG (Energy Recovery Generation) plant, which utilizes energy normally lost at pressure transformers in major natural gas lines to generate electricity. Significant funding for the organization comes from the U.S. Department of Energy, the Department of Defense and the Environmental Protection Agency, as well as other outside sources. In January 2008, FuelCell received approval from the Connecticut Department of Utility Control for 16.2 MW of projects and incorporates six of the firms DFC3000 fuel cells.

FINANCIALS:

Sales and profits are in thousands of dollars—add 000 to get the full amount. 2008 Note: Financial information for 2008 was not available for all companies at press time.

2008 Sales: $100,735	2008 Profits: $-93,357	**U.S. Stock Ticker: FCEL**
2007 Sales: $48,234	2007 Profits: $-68,674	**Int'l Ticker:** Int'l Exchange:
2006 Sales: $33,288	2006 Profits: $-76,105	Employees: 443
2005 Sales: $30,370	2005 Profits: $-68,186	Fiscal Year Ends: 10/31
2004 Sales: $31,386	2004 Profits: $-86,443	Parent Company:

SALARIES/BENEFITS:

Pension Plan: Y	ESOP Stock Plan:	Profit Sharing:	Top Exec. Salary: $364,130	Bonus: $87,500
Savings Plan: Y	Stock Purch. Plan:		Second Exec. Salary: $263,240	Bonus: $38,250

OTHER THOUGHTS:

Apparent Women Officers or Directors:
Hot Spot for Advancement for Women/Minorities:

LOCATIONS: ("Y" = Yes)

West:	Southwest:	Midwest:	Southeast:	Northeast:	International:
				Y	Y

Note: Financial information, benefits and other data can change quickly and may vary from those stated here.

FUJI HEAVY INDUSTRIES LTD (SUBARU)

www.fhi.co.jp

Industry Group Code: 336111 **Ranks within this company's industry group:** Sales: 18 Profits: 18

Techology:		Medical/Drugs:		Engineering:		Transportation:		Chemicals/Petrochemicals:		Specialty:	
Computers:		Manufacturer:		Design:		Aerospace:	Y	Oil/Gas Products:		Special Services:	
Software:		Contract Research:		Construction:		Automotive:	Y	Chemicals:		Consulting:	
Communications:		Medical Services:		Eng. Services:		Shipping:		Oil/Chem. Svcs.:		Specialty Mgmt.:	
Electronics:		Labs:		Consulting:				Gases:		Products:	
Alternative Energy:		Bio. Services:						Other:		Other:	

TYPES OF BUSINESS:

Automobile Manufacturing
Engines
Aircraft Manufacturing & Components
Buses
Railcars
Specialty Vehicles
Sanitation Vehicles
Waste Treatment & Recycling Technology

BRANDS/DIVISIONS/AFFILIATES:

Subaru
Subaru of America, Inc.
Robin
Outback
Forester
Subaru Research and Development, Inc.
Robin Europe Industrial Engine and Equipment
Robin Manufacturing U.S.A.

CONTACTS: *Note: Officers with more than one job title may be intentionally listed here more than once.*

Ikuo Mori, CEO
Ikuo Mori, Pres.
Kazushige Okuhara, Exec. VP-Subaru Global Mktg.
Kazushige Okuhara, Gen. Mgr.-Human Resources
Shunsuke Takagi, Exec. VP-Bus. Process & Info. Mgmt.
Shoichi Washizu, Exec. VP/Chief Gen. Mgr.-Subaru Eng. Div.
Hiroshi Komatsu, Sr. Exec. VP-Mfg. & Industrial Prod. Company
Shunsuke Takagi, Exec. VP-Gen. Admin.
Shunsuke Takagi, Exec. VP-Legal/Sec.
Shunsuke Takagi, Exec. VP-Strategy Dev.
Shunsuke Takagi, Exec. VP-Corp. Comm.
Shunsuke Takagi, Exec. VP-Finance, Acct. & Internal Audit
Hiroyuki Oikawa, Chmn.-Subaru of Indiana Automotive, Inc.
Norihisa Matsuo, Exec. VP-Eco Tech./Pres., Aerospace
Masatsugu Nagato, Exec VP/Chief Gen Mgr-Subaru Overseas Sales & Mktg
Hiroyuki Oikawa, Exec. VP-Subaru of America, Inc.
Hiroshi Komatsu, Sr. Exec. VP-Purchasing, Cost Planning & Mgmt.

Phone: 81-3-3347-2111 **Fax:** 81-3-3347-2338
Toll-Free:
Address: Subaru Bldg., 1-7-2 Nishishinjuku, Shinjuku-ku, Tokyo, 160-8316 Japan

GROWTH PLANS/SPECIAL FEATURES:

Fuji Heavy Industries Ltd. (FHI), perhaps best known for its Subaru cars, is a transportation conglomerate that also manufactures buses, railcars, engines, aircraft components and specialty vehicles. It operates four segments: Automotive, which generated 89.6% of 2007 sales; aerospace, 6.3%; industrial products, 3.3%; and other, mainly eco technologies, 0.8%. The automotive division does business as Subaru, the Japanese name for the Pleiades star-cluster, which also inspired Subaru's star-cluster logo. The division's cars include all-wheel-drive vehicles such as the Outback and Forester models, which are unique in that they are built on small-car platforms but have a sport utility vehicle (SUV) look and feel. Other models built by Subaru include Baja, Impreza, Legacy, Justy and the B9 Tribeca. The Subaru engine incorporates an unusual design, called the Horizontally-Opposed Boxer Engine, which the firm claims reduces vibration and is generally more compact than other designs. The firm's aerospace operations include the design and manufacture of fixed wing aircraft and parts. In addition to its own branded offerings including the T-1, T-3 and T-5 defense trainer jets, this division is responsible for the design and building of the center wing section of the Boeing 767 and 777. FHI's industrial products division manufactures Robin brand engines, which are mostly used in applications such as rammers, compressors and generators. Finally, the company's eco technologies division focuses on the manufacture of sanitation and recycling vehicles, as well as joining with partner companies to develop waste treatment and recycling technologies. FHI has operations throughout Asia as well as in the U.S., Canada and Europe, through subsidiaries including Subaru of America, Subaru Research and Development, Fuji Heavy Industries U.S.A, Robin Europe Industrial Engine and Equipment and Robin Manufacturing U.S.A. In all, the firm has 109 subsidiaries and nine affiliates.

FINANCIALS: **Sales and profits are in thousands of dollars—add 000 to get the full amount. 2008 Note: Financial information for 2008 was not available for all companies at press time.**

2008 Sales: $15,867,800
2007 Sales: $14,948,200
2006 Sales: $14,763,700
2005 Sales: $14,464,900
2004 Sales: $13,625,800

2008 Profits: $186,510
2007 Profits: $319,000
2006 Profits: $156,100
2005 Profits: $182,400
2004 Profits: $365,900

U.S. Stock Ticker:
Int'l Ticker: 7270 Int'l Exchange: Tokyo-TSE
Employees: 26,115
Fiscal Year Ends: 3/31
Parent Company:

SALARIES/BENEFITS:

Pension Plan: ESOP Stock Plan: Profit Sharing: Top Exec. Salary: $ Bonus: $
Savings Plan: Stock Purch. Plan: Second Exec. Salary: $ Bonus: $

OTHER THOUGHTS:

Apparent Women Officers or Directors:
Hot Spot for Advancement for Women/Minorities:

LOCATIONS: ("Y" = Yes)

West:	Southwest:	Midwest:	Southeast:	Northeast:	International:
Y		Y		Y	Y

FUJIFILM HOLDINGS CORP

www.fujifilm.com

Industry Group Code: 333314 **Ranks within this company's industry group:** Sales: 1 Profits: 1

Techology:		Medical/Drugs:		Engineering:		Transportation:		Chemicals/Petrochemicals:		Specialty:	
Computers:		Manufacturer:	Y	Design:		Aerospace:		Oil/Gas Products:		Special Services:	
Software:		Contract Research:		Construction:		Automotive:		Chemicals:		Consulting:	
Communications:		Medical Services:	Y	Eng. Services:		Shipping:		Oil/Chem. Svcs.:		Specialty Mgmt.:	
Electronics:	Y	Labs:		Consulting:				Gases:		Products:	Y
Alternative Energy:		Bio. Services:	Y					Other:		Other:	

TYPES OF BUSINESS:

Photographic Film & Paper
Cameras
Photographic Equipment
Medical Imaging

BRANDS/DIVISIONS/AFFILIATES:

FUJIFILM Europe B.V.
Fuji Xerox Co., Ltd.
FUJIFILM-RU
Perseus Proteomics, Inc.
FUJIFILM RI Pharma Co., Ltd.
FUJIFILM Medical Systems USA
IP Labs GmbH
Toyama Chemical

CONTACTS: *Note: Officers with more than one job title may be intentionally listed here more than once.*

Shigetaka Komori, CEO
Shigetaka Komori, Pres.
Toshio Takahashi, CFO
Shinpei Ikenoue, Sr. VP
Masahiro Asami, Corp. VP
Makio Watanabe, Corp. VP
Toshio Arima, Pres., Fuji Xerox

Phone: 81-3-3406-2111 **Fax:** 81-3-3406-2173
Toll-Free:
Address: 7-3 Akasaka 9-chome, Minato-ku, Tokyo, 107-0052 Japan

GROWTH PLANS/SPECIAL FEATURES:

FUJIFILM Holdings Corporation is a manufacturer of photographic film and paper. Its operations are conducted through 227 subsidiary companies. The firm provides strategic management of the entire Fujifilm Group, including its two major operating companies, Fujifilm Corporation and Fuji Xerox Co., Ltd. Fujifilm Holdings divides itself along the lines of its three major product groups: document solutions, imaging solutions and information solutions. The document solutions segment, produces copying machines, printers, fax machines and consumables for document service applications in offices. The information solutions segment handles materials and equipment for graphic arts, medical imaging and information systems; LCD materials; and recording media. The imaging solutions segment includes businesses related to color film, digital cameras, lab equipment, color paper, chemicals and services for photofinishing. The company maintains a presence in the pharmaceutical market through its subsidiary FUJIFILM RI Pharma Co., Ltd. and recent acquisition Toyama Chemical. In January 2008, the firm acquired IP Labs GmbH, a German photo service software provider, through subsidiary FUJIFILM Europe B.V. In February 2008, FUJIFILM announced plans to launch a new subsidiary, FUJIFILM India Private Limited. In April 2008, the firm opened a new WV Film factory through subsidiary FUJIFILM Opto Materials Co., Ltd. In July 2008, FUJIFILM agreed to merge its endoscope business operations into its medical systems business division. In November 2008, the company became part-owner of Tianjian Medi Tech Co., Ltd., a Chinese medical IT system firm. In December 2008, FUJIFILM acquired Empiric Systems, LLC, a U.S. radiology information systems manufacturer, through subsidiary FUJIFILM Medical Systems USA, Inc. In January 2009, the firm acquired its Russian medical/imaging products distributor, FUJIFILM-RU, from Marubeni Corporation. In February 2009, FUJIFILM acquired biopharmaceutical company Perseus Proteomics, Inc.

FINANCIALS: **Sales and profits are in thousands of dollars—add 000 to get the full amount. 2008 Note: Financial information for 2008 was not available for all companies at press time.**

2008 Sales: $24,484,400	2008 Profits: $1,043,540	**U.S. Stock Ticker: FUJIY**
2007 Sales: $23,580,729	2007 Profits: $291,915	**Int'l Ticker: 4901** Int'l Exchange: Tokyo-TSE
2006 Sales: $22,799,103	2006 Profits: $316,376	Employees: 76,358
2005 Sales: $23,620,300	2005 Profits: $789,700	Fiscal Year Ends: 3/31
2004 Sales: $24,154,600	2004 Profits: $776,600	Parent Company:

SALARIES/BENEFITS:

Pension Plan:	ESOP Stock Plan:	Profit Sharing:	Top Exec. Salary: $	Bonus: $
Savings Plan:	Stock Purch. Plan:		Second Exec. Salary: $	Bonus: $

OTHER THOUGHTS:

Apparent Women Officers or Directors:
Hot Spot for Advancement for Women/Minorities:

LOCATIONS: ("Y" = Yes)

West:	Southwest:	Midwest:	Southeast:	Northeast:	International:
Y		Y	Y	Y	Y

FUJITSU LABORATORIES LTD

jp.fujitsu.com/group/labs/en

Industry Group Code: 541710 **Ranks within this company's industry group:** Sales: Profits:

Techology:		Medical/Drugs:		Engineering:		Transportation:		Chemicals/Petrochemicals:		Specialty:	
Computers:	Y	Manufacturer:		Design:		Aerospace:		Oil/Gas Products:		Special Services:	
Software:	Y	Contract Research:		Construction:		Automotive:		Chemicals:		Consulting:	
Communications:	Y	Medical Services:		Eng. Services:		Shipping:		Oil/Chem. Svcs.:		Specialty Mgmt.:	
Electronics:	Y	Labs:		Consulting:				Gases:		Products:	Y
Alternative Energy:	Y	Bio. Services:						Other:		Other:	

TYPES OF BUSINESS:

Research & Development
Computing Research
RFID Technology
Semiconductors
Security & Encryption Technology
Robotics Research
Nanotechnology Research

BRANDS/DIVISIONS/AFFILIATES:

Fujitsu Limited

CONTACTS:

Note: Officers with more than one job title may be intentionally listed here more than once.

Kazuo Murano, Pres.

Phone: 81-44-754-2613	Fax:
Toll-Free:	
Address: 4-1-1, Kamikodanaka, Nakahara-ku, Kawasaki-shi, 211-8588 Japan	

GROWTH PLANS/SPECIAL FEATURES:

Fujitsu Laboratories Ltd. is Fujitsu Limited's central research and development unit. The firm has four locations in Japan, as well as two locations in China, one in the U.K., and three in the U.S. Fujitsu Lab's stated goal is to make ubiquitous networking a reality, meaning that communication would be possible anytime, anywhere and with anyone. To this end, the firm divides its research into four target areas. The Enabling a More Comfortable Society area is developing organic computer systems that can link multiple drives, servers and storage systems autonomously, allowing fast access to large quantities of data and perhaps someday repairing themselves. Other research in this area includes grid computing; utility computing; semiconductor technology; high-density data storage; advanced CAD (Computer-Aided Design) systems for product development; and System on a Chip (SoC) technologies. The Communicating Anytime, Anywhere area is developing wireless data exchange technology and services, such as wireless IC RFID (Radio Frequency Identification) tags, which could display product information while shopping and make payments automatically; new wireless signal amplifiers; web services that would mine Internet blogs for information about a particular store; and nanotechnology to enhance chip designs and encryption capabilities. The Supporting Safe and Secure Lifestyles area is researching encryption and biometric authentication technology; digital watermarking and steganography (hidden messages) to help prevent information leakage; environmentally friendly materials, including fuel cells; and bioinformatics, or computer technologies used in health-related fields, such as gene analysis software or microinjection technology. Lastly, the Making Interfaces Effortless area is researching bipedal robots featuring neural networks for domestic chores or security details; natural language processors to allow computers or robots to understand voice commands; and advanced I/O (input/output) devices, such as reprogrammable electronic paper displays that require minimal power, and an ultrasonic handwriting pen that requires no special pad.

FINANCIALS:

Sales and profits are in thousands of dollars—add 000 to get the full amount. 2008 Note: Financial information for 2008 was not available for all companies at press time.

2008 Sales: $	2008 Profits: $	**U.S. Stock Ticker: Subsidiary**
2007 Sales: $	2007 Profits: $	**Int'l Ticker:** Int'l Exchange:
2006 Sales: $	2006 Profits: $	Employees:
2005 Sales: $	2005 Profits: $	Fiscal Year Ends: 3/31
2004 Sales: $	2004 Profits: $	Parent Company: FUJITSU LIMITED

SALARIES/BENEFITS:

Pension Plan:	ESOP Stock Plan:	Profit Sharing:	Top Exec. Salary: $	Bonus: $
Savings Plan:	Stock Purch. Plan:		Second Exec. Salary: $	Bonus: $

OTHER THOUGHTS:

Apparent Women Officers or Directors:
Hot Spot for Advancement for Women/Minorities:

LOCATIONS: ("Y" = Yes)

West:	Southwest:	Midwest:	Southeast:	Northeast:	International:
Y	Y			Y	Y

Note: Financial information, benefits and other data can change quickly and may vary from those stated here.

FUJITSU LIMITED

www.fujitsu.com

Industry Group Code: 334111 **Ranks within this company's industry group:** Sales: 5 Profits: 7

Techology:		Medical/Drugs:		Engineering:		Transportation:		Chemicals/Petrochemicals:		Specialty:	
Computers:	Y	Manufacturer:		Design:		Aerospace:		Oil/Gas Products:		Special Services:	
Software:		Contract Research:		Construction:		Automotive:		Chemicals:		Consulting:	
Communications:		Medical Services:		Eng. Services:		Shipping:		Oil/Chem. Svcs.:		Specialty Mgmt.:	
Electronics:	Y	Labs:		Consulting:				Gases:		Products:	
Alternative Energy:		Bio. Services:						Other:		Other:	

TYPES OF BUSINESS:

Computer Hardware Manufacturing
Telecommunications Equipment
IT Outsourcing & Consulting Services
Microelectronics
Appliances & Consumer Electronics
Nanotechnology Research
Software Products
Flash Memory Products

BRANDS/DIVISIONS/AFFILIATES:

Fujitsu Laboratories, Ltd.
Fujitsu Services, Inc.
Nifty
FASL, LLC
Mandator AB
Promaintech Novaxa
Fujitsu Mobile-Phone Products Limited
Fujitsu Microelectronics America, Inc.

CONTACTS: *Note: Officers with more than one job title may be intentionally listed here more than once.*

Hiroaki Kurokawa, CEO
Kuniaki Nozoe, Pres.
Masamichi Ogura, CFO
Richard McCormack, Sr. VP-Mktg.
Tatsuo Tomita, Pres., Ubiquitous Products Bus. Group
Koichi Hironishi, Pres., Industries & Dist. Solutions Bus.
Hideaki Yumiba, Corp. First Sr. VP
Takashi Igarashi, Corp. First Sr. VP
Michiyoshi Mazuka, Chmn.

Phone: 81-03-6252-2175 **Fax:** 81-03-6252-2783
Toll-Free:
Address: Shiodome City Center, 1-5-2 Higashi-Shimbashi, Tokyo, 105-7123 Japan

GROWTH PLANS/SPECIAL FEATURES:

Fujitsu Limited is a provider of customer-focused information and communications products and services for the global marketplace. The company has three business segments: Technology Solutions; Ubiquitous Product Solutions; and Device Solutions. The Technology Solutions group, which accounts for 56.6% of 2007 revenue, incorporates two branches: Systems Platforms and Services. The Systems Platforms branch encompasses the development, manufacture and sales of server related systems, network equipment and other products. This segment includes products and services for mainframes, open standard servers, PC servers and optical transmission systems. The Services branch handles the firm's broad range of IT services, including IT consulting, systems integration, IT infrastructure management, managed services and outsourcing, enabling the company to offer cost-effective solutions tailored to specific customer objectives. The Ubiquitous Product Solutions group, which accounts for 20.6% of 2007 revenue, handles products and services including PCs, wireless devices and hard disc drives. The Device Solutions group, which accounts for 13.8% of 2007 revenue, provides devices through Fujitsu's subsidiary LSI Technology as well as various electronic components manufactured and sold under the Fujitsu name. The company's products include computing products, such as PCs, and software including middleware, ERP, e-commerce, storage management and system and network management products. The firm's telecommunications platforms, including IP switching and fiber-optic transmission systems, provide the communications backbone for many broadband networks. The company's other products include air conditioners, plasma screens, LCD projectors and car audio/video systems. Furthermore, the company is involved in research in fields from networking to nanotechnology. The company's nanotechnology research focuses on quantum computing and communications, nanomaterials and biotechnology. In December 2008, Fujitsu agreed to transfer its shares of Eudyna Devices, Inc. to Sunitomo Electric Industries. The transfer is expected to be complete in 2009. In November 2008, Fujitsu announced it will acquire a 50% share of Fujitsu Siemens Computers.

FINANCIALS: **Sales and profits are in thousands of dollars—add 000 to get the full amount. 2008 Note: Financial information for 2008 was not available for all companies at press time.**

2008 Sales: $53,308,650	2008 Profits: $481,070	**U.S. Stock Ticker: FJTSY**
2007 Sales: $43,249,400	2007 Profits: $868,500	**Int'l Ticker: 6702** Int'l Exchange: Tokyo-TSE
2006 Sales: $40,746,200	2006 Profits: $582,900	Employees: 160,977
2005 Sales: $44,511,766	2005 Profits: $298,196	Fiscal Year Ends: 3/31
2004 Sales: $45,123,400	2004 Profits: $470,500	Parent Company:

SALARIES/BENEFITS:

Pension Plan:	ESOP Stock Plan:	Profit Sharing:	Top Exec. Salary: $	Bonus: $
Savings Plan:	Stock Purch. Plan:		Second Exec. Salary: $	Bonus: $

OTHER THOUGHTS:

Apparent Women Officers or Directors:
Hot Spot for Advancement for Women/Minorities:

LOCATIONS: ("Y" = Yes)

West:	Southwest:	Midwest:	Southeast:	Northeast:	International:
Y	Y	Y		Y	Y

FUJITSU-SIEMENS COMPUTER HOLDING COMPANY www.fujitsu-siemens.com

Industry Group Code: 334111 **Ranks within this company's industry group:** Sales: Profits:

Techology:		Medical/Drugs:		Engineering:		Transportation:		Chemicals/Petrochemicals:		Specialty:	
Computers:	Y	Manufacturer:		Design:		Aerospace:		Oil/Gas Products:		Special Services:	Y
Software:	Y	Contract Research:		Construction:		Automotive:		Chemicals:		Consulting:	Y
Communications:		Medical Services:		Eng. Services:		Shipping:		Oil/Chem. Svcs.:		Specialty Mgmt.:	
Electronics:		Labs:		Consulting:				Gases:		Products:	
Alternative Energy:		Bio. Services:						Other:		Other:	

TYPES OF BUSINESS:

Computer Hardware-PCs & Laptops
Personal Digital Assistants
LCD TVs
Monitors & Peripherals
Servers
Storage Devices
Software Distribution
Support Services

BRANDS/DIVISIONS/AFFILIATES:

Fujitsu Limited
Dynamic Data Center
SCALEO
MYRICA
LOOX
AMILO
Fujitsu Siemens Computers IT Product Services

CONTACTS: *Note: Officers with more than one job title may be intentionally listed here more than once.*

Kai Flore, CEO
Kai Flore, Pres.
Barbara Schadler, Chief Mktg. Officer
Axel Varnbuler, Chief People Officer
Joseph Reger, CTO
Dieter Herzog, Exec. VP-Infrastructure Products
Richard Schlauri, Exec. VP-Infrastructure Svcs.
Herbert Schonebeck, Sr. VP-Consumer Products & Devices
Thomas Sieber, Exec. VP-Sales
Satoru Hayashi, Chmn.
Heribert Goggerle, Sr. VP-Supply Oper.

Phone: 31-346-59-8111	**Fax:** 31-346-56-1298
Toll-Free:	
Address: Het Kwadrant 1, Maarssen, 3606 AZ The Netherlands	

GROWTH PLANS/SPECIAL FEATURES:

Fujitsu-Siemens Computer Holding Company, founded as a 50/50 joint venture between Fujitsu Limited and Siemens AG, manufactures and distributes electronics. The company also supplies home and office desktop and laptop computers. The company offers products in three divisions: Home and home office, business and Fujitsu Siemens Computers IT Product Services. The home and home office division offers Microsoft and Adobe software, the SCALEO series of desktops, MYRICA liquid crystal display (LCD) TVs, LOOX personal digital assistants (PDAs), AMILO laptops, MYRICA and SCALEO monitors and peripherals and CONNECT2AIR wireless devices. The business division offers AMILO laptops; LOOX PDAs; SCENIC and CELSIUS desktops; STYLISTIC and LIFEBOOK tablet PCs; FUTRO thin client devices; Intel and Unix servers; entry, mid-level and enterprise storage devices; SCENICVIEW displays and projectors; peripherals; wireless devices; and software and licensing for Microsoft, Adobe, Novell, Oracle, IBM, Citrix, SAP and Symantec software. Fujitsu Siemens Computers IT Product Services, operating as a separate subsidiary, offers products and solutions to the international market for all leading server platforms. The company also offers financing, technical support and installation services for its products. It has production facilities in Germany and Japan. In November 2008, Fujitsu Limited agreed to buy out Siemens, giving Fujitsu 100% ownership after an expected April 1, 2009 closing.

FINANCIALS: **Sales and profits are in thousands of dollars—add 000 to get the full amount. 2008 Note: Financial information for 2008 was not available for all companies at press time.**

2008 Sales: $	2008 Profits: $	**U.S. Stock Ticker: Subsidiary**
2007 Sales: $8,600,000	2007 Profits: $	**Int'l Ticker:** Int'l Exchange:
2006 Sales: $7,000,000	2006 Profits: $	Employees: 10,500
2005 Sales: $7,276,400	2005 Profits: $84,980	Fiscal Year Ends: 3/31
2004 Sales: $6,437,600	2004 Profits: $46,600	Parent Company: FUJITSU LIMITED

SALARIES/BENEFITS:

Pension Plan:	ESOP Stock Plan:	Profit Sharing:	Top Exec. Salary: $	Bonus: $
Savings Plan:	Stock Purch. Plan:		Second Exec. Salary: $	Bonus: $

OTHER THOUGHTS:

Apparent Women Officers or Directors:
Hot Spot for Advancement for Women/Minorities:

LOCATIONS: ("Y" = Yes)

West:	Southwest:	Midwest:	Southeast:	Northeast:	International:
Y					Y

GAMESA CORPORACION TECNOLOGICA SA

www.gamesa.es

Industry Group Code: 333611 **Ranks within this company's industry group:** Sales: 2 Profits: 2

Techology:		Medical/Drugs:		Engineering:		Transportation:		Chemicals/Petrochemicals:		Specialty:	
Computers:		Manufacturer:		Design:		Aerospace:		Oil/Gas Products:		Special Services:	
Software:		Contract Research:		Construction:		Automotive:		Chemicals:		Consulting:	
Communications:		Medical Services:		Eng. Services:		Shipping:		Oil/Chem. Svcs.:		Specialty Mgmt.:	
Electronics:		Labs:		Consulting:				Gases:		Products:	
Alternative Energy:	Y	Bio. Services:						Other:		Other:	

TYPES OF BUSINESS:

Wind Turbine Manufacturing
Aeronautical Parts & Assemblies
Wind Farms
Technical Services
Solar Facilities, Development & Maintenance
Thermal Generation Plants, Development & Maintenance

BRANDS/DIVISIONS/AFFILIATES:

Gamesa Aeronautica
Gamesa Industrial
Gamesa Energia
Gamesa Eolica
Gamesa Servicios Avanzados

CONTACTS: *Note: Officers with more than one job title may be intentionally listed here more than once.*

Guillermo Ulacia Arnaiz, CEO
Cesar Fernandez de Velasco Munoz, COO
Javier Perea Saenz de Buruaga, Mktg. & Sales
Juana Maria Fernandez Martin del Campo, Human Resources
Antonio Mulumbres Garcia, CTO
Carlos Rodriguez-Quiroga Menende, Sec.
Felix Zarza Yabar, Dir.-Internal Audit
Antxon Berreteaga Lejarza, Dir.-Solar
Guillermo Ulacia Arnaiz, Chmn.

Phone: 90-2-73-4949	**Fax:**
Toll-Free:	
Address: Ramon Y Cajal 7-9, Vitoria, 01007 Spain	

GROWTH PLANS/SPECIAL FEATURES:

Gamesa Corporacion Tecnologica, based in Spain, manufactures and supplies products, installations and services in the aeronautics and renewable energy sectors. More than 50% of installed wind power capacity in Spain is supplied by Gamesa wind generations. The company, with more than 3,000 megawatts in-site installations of wind generatiors worldwide (over 1,000 megawatts manufactured in China and the U.S.), focuses its activities in five of its large collection of subsidiaries. Gamesa Aeronautica designs and manufactures large structural assemblies or aircraft parts for assembly in aircraft and helicopters. Gamesa Energia is charged with the development, construction, operation and sale of wind farms. It has operations in 16 countries, including several in the U.S., with worldwide production capacity of over 20,000 megawatts. The subsidiary has facilities in China, Italy, France, Taiwan, the U.S., Ireland, Mexico, India, Germany, Morocco and Portugal. Gamesa Servicios Avanzados performs a variety of different services, including development and maintenance of wind, solar and combined cycle (thermal and gas) power facilities; installation and control services for the petrochemical industry; and electrical services. Gamesa Eolica, one of the top five wind turbine manufacturers in the world, is the segment from which Gamesa derives the bulk of its revenue. Gamesa Industrial manufactures components for the aeronautics market in carbon fiber, fiberglass and Kevlar. As of November 2007, the development of seven new production facilities was underway across the globe, with a total investment of $154 million. These include facilities in Spain, four in Pennsylvania and one in China.

FINANCIALS: **Sales and profits are in thousands of dollars—add 000 to get the full amount. 2008 Note: Financial information for 2008 was not available for all companies at press time.**

2008 Sales: $4,857,800	2008 Profits: $429,220	**U.S. Stock Ticker: GCTAF**
2007 Sales: $3,819,760	2007 Profits: $297,070	**Int'l Ticker: GAM** Int'l Exchange: Madrid-MCE
2006 Sales: $3,153,100	2006 Profits: $410,000	Employees: 6,493
2005 Sales: $2,238,630	2005 Profits: $248,880	Fiscal Year Ends: 12/31
2004 Sales: $2,053,800	2004 Profits: $259,800	Parent Company:

SALARIES/BENEFITS:

Pension Plan:	ESOP Stock Plan:	Profit Sharing:	Top Exec. Salary: $	Bonus: $
Savings Plan:	Stock Purch. Plan:		Second Exec. Salary: $	Bonus: $

OTHER THOUGHTS:

Apparent Women Officers or Directors: 1
Hot Spot for Advancement for Women/Minorities:

LOCATIONS: ("Y" = Yes)

West:	Southwest:	Midwest:	Southeast:	Northeast:	International:
				Y	Y

GE AVIATION

www.geae.com

Industry Group Code: 336410 **Ranks within this company's industry group:** Sales: 10 Profits: 2

Techology:		Medical/Drugs:		Engineering:		Transportation:		Chemicals/Petrochemicals:		Specialty:	
Computers:		Manufacturer:		Design:		Aerospace:	Y	Oil/Gas Products:		Special Services:	
Software:		Contract Research:		Construction:		Automotive:		Chemicals:		Consulting:	
Communications:		Medical Services:		Eng. Services:		Shipping:		Oil/Chem. Svcs.:		Specialty Mgmt.:	
Electronics:		Labs:		Consulting:				Gases:		Products:	
Alternative Energy:		Bio. Services:						Other:		Other:	

TYPES OF BUSINESS:

Aircraft Manufacturer, Engines
Gas Turbine Manufacturing
Marine Engines
Engine Maintenance & Parts
Engine Leasing

BRANDS/DIVISIONS/AFFILIATES:

General Electric Co (The)
CF6
F110
GE Engine Services
GE Engine Leasing
Unison Industries
Middle River Aircraft Systems
GE Inspection Technologies

CONTACTS: *Note: Officers with more than one job title may be intentionally listed here more than once.*

David Joyce, CEO
David Joyce, Pres.
Shane Wright, CFO/VP
Kevin McAllister, VP-Sales
Jack Ryan, VP-Human Resources
Tammy Keefer, CIO-Info. Mgmt.
Jeanne Rosario, VP/Gen. Manager-Eng.
Paul McElhinney, VP-Legal Oper.
Herb Depp, VP-Oper.
Sarah Hedger, Gen. Mgr.-Bus. Dev.
Lorraine Bolsinger, VP/Gen. Mgr.-Systems
Russell Sparks, VP/Gen. Mgr.-Military Systems Oper.
Charles Blankenship, VP/Gen. Mgr.-Commercial Engine Oper.
Tom Gentile, VP/Gen. Mgr.-Svcs.
Scott Ernest, VP/Gen. Mgr.-Supply Chain

Phone: 513-243-2000	**Fax:**
Toll-Free:	
Address: 1 Neumann Way, Cincinnati, OH 45215-5301 US	

GROWTH PLANS/SPECIAL FEATURES:

GE Aviation, a subsidiary of General Electric Co., produces large and small jet engines for commercial, corporate, marine and military applications. The company's premier engine, the CF6, has logged over 325 million flight hours and powers a number of aircraft models, including the Airbus A330, the Boeing 747, the MD-11 and the DC-10. The firm's CF34 engines are widely used in regional jets while the firm's F110 engine typically powers the F-16 fighter jet. The aforementioned engines are a small sample of the company's offerings, which encompass 37 engine types that power 91 aircraft systems and 42 marine and industrial applications (for which the firm also manufactures gas turbines). GE Aviation complements its manufacturing operations with engine maintenance, material and asset management services. Maintenance services, carried out by subsidiary GE Engine Services, include overhaul, technology upgrades and engine exchange (whereby an old engine is replaced by an overhauled engine). Material services, undertaken by subsidiary GE Aviation Materials LP, encompass new parts, used parts and engine repair. Asset management services include engine leasing through GE Engine Leasing (a joint venture between GE Capital Aviation Services and GE Engine Services) as well as diagnostic service provision. Additional subsidiaries include Unison Industries, which designs, manufactures and integrates electrical and mechanical components and systems for aircraft engines and airframes; Middle River Aircraft Systems, which is focused on the engineering and manufacture of specialized aircraft structures; and GE Inspection Technologies, which designs, manufactures and services radiography and ultrasound systems designed to test materials without deforming them.

FINANCIALS: Sales and profits are in thousands of dollars—add 000 to get the full amount. 2008 Note: Financial information for 2008 was not available for all companies at press time.

2008 Sales: $19,239,000	2008 Profits: $3,684,000	**U.S. Stock Ticker: Subsidiary**
2007 Sales: $16,819,000	2007 Profits: $3,222,000	**Int'l Ticker:** Int'l Exchange:
2006 Sales: $13,017,000	2006 Profits: $2,802,000	Employees: 26,500
2005 Sales: $	2005 Profits: $	Fiscal Year Ends: 12/31
2004 Sales: $11,400,000	2004 Profits: $	Parent Company: GENERAL ELECTRIC CO (GE)

SALARIES/BENEFITS:

Pension Plan:	ESOP Stock Plan:	Profit Sharing:	Top Exec. Salary: $	Bonus: $
Savings Plan:	Stock Purch. Plan:		Second Exec. Salary: $	Bonus: $

OTHER THOUGHTS:

Apparent Women Officers or Directors: 5
Hot Spot for Advancement for Women/Minorities: Y

LOCATIONS: ("Y" = Yes)

West:	Southwest:	Midwest:	Southeast:	Northeast:	International:
Y	Y	Y	Y	Y	Y

GE ENERGY

www.gepower.com

Industry Group Code: 335000 **Ranks within this company's industry group:** Sales: 3 Profits:

Techology:		Medical/Drugs:		Engineering:		Transportation:		Chemicals/Petrochemicals:		Specialty:	
Computers:		Manufacturer:		Design:		Aerospace:		Oil/Gas Products:		Special Services:	
Software:		Contract Research:		Construction:		Automotive:		Chemicals:		Consulting:	Y
Communications:		Medical Services:		Eng. Services:		Shipping:		Oil/Chem. Svcs.:		Specialty Mgmt.:	
Electronics:		Labs:		Consulting:				Gases:		Products:	
Alternative Energy:	Y	Bio. Services:						Other:		Other:	

TYPES OF BUSINESS:

Generation Equipment-Turbines & Generators
Fuel Cells
Generators-Wind, Hydro, Geothermal & Turbo
Nuclear Fuel Systems
Pumps & Pipelines
Metering & Control Systems
Energy Management Systems
Consulting-Energy

BRANDS/DIVISIONS/AFFILIATES:

General Electric Company
Sondex plc
PrimStar Solar, Inc.
MapFrame
Kelman Limited

CONTACTS: *Note: Officers with more than one job title may be intentionally listed here more than once.*

John Krenicki, Jr., CEO
John Krenicki, Jr., Pres.
Thomas Saddlemire, CFO/VP
James Suciu, VP-Global Sales & Mktg.
Steve Schneider, VP-Power Generation
Robert Gleitz, Mgr.-Wind Generation
Joseph Anis, Region Exec.-Middle East
Kishore Hayaraman, Region Exec.-India

Phone: 678 844 6000	**Fax:** 678 844 6690
Toll-Free:	
Address: 4200 Wildwood Pkwy., Atlanta, GA 30339 US	

GROWTH PLANS/SPECIAL FEATURES:

GE Energy, a subsidiary of the General Electric Company, designs and supplies energy technology, from turbines to control systems. The company has installed over 1 million megawatts (MW) of steam- and gas-driven capacity in over 120 countries. It has created technology for every facet of power generation, and secures about 250 patents annually. The engineering and installation units of the firm operate in various industries, including standard power generation, oil and gas, renewables and energy management technology. The power generation unit handles projects involving power turbines, fuel cells, mobile generation and nuclear fuel systems. GE Energy has received over $1.8 billion in contracts to supply 32 gas turbines and additional equipment for power plant projects in Kuwait and Qatar that will add more than five gigawatts of capacity For production and transport, the oil and gas unit offers pumps, pipelines and metering and control systems. The renewables unit handles wind and hydro turbines, geothermal steam and turbo generators, and offers a full range of support services. The energy technology management unit offers a full line of products for metering and controlling the flow of energy as well as handling environmental and safety measures. GE Energy offers 1.5, 2.5 and 3.6 MW wind turbine turbines. In 2007, the company acquired a minority equity interest in PrimStar Solar, Inc., an emerging solar thin-film technology and manufacturing company. GE Energy also completed its acquisition of Sondex plc, a directional drilling company based In the U.K. In June 2008, the firm agreed to acquire MapFrame, to enhance its smart grid portfolio. In August 2008, the firm acquired the Northern Ireland-based Kelman Limited, also for its smart grid portfolio.

The company offers its employees a comprehensive benefits package including educational assistance and discounts on GE products.

FINANCIALS: Sales and profits are in thousands of dollars—add 000 to get the full amount. 2008 Note: Financial information for 2008 was not available for all companies at press time.

2008 Sales: $38,570,000	2008 Profits: $	**U.S. Stock Ticker: Subsidiary**
2007 Sales: $21,825,000	2007 Profits: $	**Int'l Ticker:** Int'l Exchange:
2006 Sales: $18,793,000	2006 Profits: $	Employees: 40,000
2005 Sales: $16,501,000	2005 Profits: $	Fiscal Year Ends: 12/31
2004 Sales: $17,300,000	2004 Profits: $	Parent Company: GENERAL ELECTRIC CO (GE)

SALARIES/BENEFITS:

Pension Plan:	ESOP Stock Plan:	Profit Sharing:	Top Exec. Salary: $	Bonus: $
Savings Plan: Y	Stock Purch. Plan:		Second Exec. Salary: $	Bonus: $

OTHER THOUGHTS:

Apparent Women Officers or Directors:
Hot Spot for Advancement for Women/Minorities:

LOCATIONS: ("Y" = Yes)

West:	Southwest:	Midwest:	Southeast:	Northeast:	International:
Y	Y	Y	Y	Y	Y

GE GLOBAL RESEARCH

www.ge.com/research

Industry Group Code: 541710 **Ranks within this company's industry group:** Sales: Profits:

Techology:		Medical/Drugs:		Engineering:		Transportation:		Chemicals/Petrochemicals:		Specialty:	
Computers:		Manufacturer:	Y	Design:	Y	Aerospace:		Oil/Gas Products:		Special Services:	
Software:		Contract Research:		Construction:		Automotive:		Chemicals:		Consulting:	
Communications:		Medical Services:		Eng. Services:		Shipping:		Oil/Chem. Svcs.:		Specialty Mgmt.:	
Electronics:	Y	Labs:		Consulting:				Gases:		Products:	
Alternative Energy:	Y	Bio. Services:						Other:		Other:	Y

TYPES OF BUSINESS:

Research & Development
Nuclear & Fossil Fuel Energy Technology
Wind, Solar, Hydroelectric & Biomass Technology
Fuel Cell & Energy Storage Technology
Nanotechnology
Photonics & Optoelectronics
Engine Technology
Biotechnology

BRANDS/DIVISIONS/AFFILIATES:

General Electric Co (GE)

CONTACTS:

Note: Officers with more than one job title may be intentionally listed here more than once.

Mark M. Little, Sr. VP/Dir.
Todd Alhart, Dir.-Comm. & Public Rel.

Phone: 518-387-5000	**Fax:** 518-387-6696
Toll-Free:	
Address: 1 Research Circle, Niskayuna, NY 12309 US	

GROWTH PLANS/SPECIAL FEATURES:

GE Global Research (GEGR) is the research and development arm of the General Electric Company. GEGR employs over 2,500 researchers at four multi-disciplinary facilities in the U.S., India, China and Germany. The company has advanced technology programs in energy, nanotechnology, photonics, advanced propulsion, materials and biotechnology. Energy research is devoted to both nuclear and fossil-fueled power and a large variety of alternative generation techniques. Renewable energies currently being investigated include photovoltaic, wind, biomass gasification, hydroelectric and various hydrogen technologies that include fuel cells and storage systems. Core technologies within the nanotechnology division include nanotubes, nanowires, nanocomposites, nano-structured optoelectronics and biomimetics. In photonics, GE researchers are developing optoelectronic materials, photonic devices, optoelectronic integration and signal management and architecture. The light energy conversion division strives to revolutionize the plastics and lighting business through the development of light-emitting polymers, photovoltaic polymers, flexible electronics and low-cost processing. GEGR's advanced propulsion division is working to design engines with superior power and speed through pulsed detonation phenomenon, pulsed detonation engine configurations, fuel preparation and delivery, performance and flight mission analysis and proof-of-concept engines. The firm also has materials research centers on ceramic composites, thermal barriers, superalloys and optical and luminescent materials, which are the company's trademark. In the biotechnology division, GEGR is focused on molecular medicine, clinical diagnostics and therapeutics, pharmaceutical development and bioinformatics. Lastly, the firm is researching solutions for port and cargo security using a wireless container security device. GEGR won the 2008 INFORMS Prize, from the Institute for Operations Research and the Management Sciences, for its operations research.

Employees at GE Global Research receive medical benefits, dental care, vision care, disability programs, product purchase discounts, educational assistance, adoption assistance, legal and financial information services, childcare assistance and more. The company also offers employee development and a variety of opportunities for student job-exposure and internship.

FINANCIALS:

Sales and profits are in thousands of dollars—add 000 to get the full amount. 2008 Note: Financial information for 2008 was not available for all companies at press time.

2008 Sales: $	2008 Profits: $	**U.S. Stock Ticker: Subsidiary**
2007 Sales: $	2007 Profits: $	**Int'l Ticker:** Int'l Exchange:
2006 Sales: $	2006 Profits: $	Employees: 3,100
2005 Sales: $	2005 Profits: $	Fiscal Year Ends: 12/31
2004 Sales: $	2004 Profits: $	Parent Company: GENERAL ELECTRIC CO (GE)

SALARIES/BENEFITS:

Pension Plan: Y	ESOP Stock Plan:	Profit Sharing:	Top Exec. Salary: $	Bonus: $
Savings Plan: Y	Stock Purch. Plan:		Second Exec. Salary: $	Bonus: $

OTHER THOUGHTS:

Apparent Women Officers or Directors:
Hot Spot for Advancement for Women/Minorities:

LOCATIONS: ("Y" = Yes)

West:	Southwest:	Midwest:	Southeast:	Northeast:	International:
				Y	Y

GE HEALTHCARE

www.gehealthcare.com

Industry Group Code: 339113 **Ranks within this company's industry group:** Sales: 2 Profits: 2

Techology:		Medical/Drugs:		Engineering:		Transportation:		Chemicals/Petrochemicals:		Specialty:	
Computers:		Manufacturer:	Y	Design:		Aerospace:		Oil/Gas Products:		Special Services:	
Software:	Y	Contract Research:		Construction:		Automotive:		Chemicals:		Consulting:	
Communications:		Medical Services:		Eng. Services:		Shipping:		Oil/Chem. Svcs.:		Specialty Mgmt.:	
Electronics:		Labs:		Consulting:				Gases:		Products:	
Alternative Energy:		Bio. Services:						Other:		Other:	

TYPES OF BUSINESS:

Medical Imaging & Information Technology
Magnetic Resonance Imaging Systems
Patient Monitoring Systems
Clinical Information Systems
Nuclear Medicine
Surgery & Vascular Imaging
X-Ray & Ultrasound Bone Densitometers
Clinical & Business Services

BRANDS/DIVISIONS/AFFILIATES:

GE Electric Co (GE)
GE Healthcare Bio-Sciences
GE Healthcare Technologies
GE Healthcare Information Technologies
Giraffe
Innova
Vital Signs
Whatman plc

CONTACTS: *Note: Officers with more than one job title may be intentionally listed here more than once.*

John Dineen, CEO
John Dineen, Pres.
Frank Schulkes, CFO/Exec. VP
Jean-Michel Cossery, Chief Mktg. Officer
Mike Hanley, VP-Human Resources
Russel P. Meyer, CIO
Michael J. Barber, CTO
Peter Y. Solmssen, General Counsel/Exec. VP
Ralph Strosin, General Mgr.-Oper.
Michael A. Jones, Exec. VP-Bus. Dev.
Lynne Gailey, Exec. VP-Global Comm.
Pete McCabe, CEO-Surgery
Peter Ehrenheim, CEO/Pres., Life Sciences
Vishal Wanchoo, CEO/Pres., Integrated IT Solutions
Reinaldo Garcia, CEO/Pres., Int'l

Phone: 414-721-2407 **Fax:**
Toll-Free:
Address: 3000 N. Grandview Blvd., Waukesha, WI 53188 US

GROWTH PLANS/SPECIAL FEATURES:

GE Healthcare, a subsidiary of GE, is a global leader in medical imaging and information technologies, patient monitoring systems and health care services. The company operates through seven divisions, including diagnostic imaging; global services; clinical systems; life systems; medical diagnostics; integrated information technology solutions; and interventional, cardiology and surgery. The diagnostic imaging business provides X-ray, digital mammography, computed tomography, magnetic resonance and molecular imaging technologies. GE Healthcare's global services business provides maintenance of a wide range of medical systems and devices. The clinical systems business provides technologies and services for clinicians and healthcare administrators. GE Healthcare's life sciences segment offers drug discovery, biopharmaceutical manufacturing and cellular technologies, enabling scientists and specialists around the world to discover new ways to predict, diagnose and treat disease earlier. The segment also makes systems and equipment for the purification of biopharmaceuticals. The firm's medical diagnostics business researches, manufactures and markets agents used during medical scanning procedures to highlight organs, tissue and functions inside the human body. The integrated information technology (IT) solutions business provides clinical and financial information technology solutions including enterprise and departmental IT products, revenue cycle management and practice applications, to help customers streamline healthcare costs and improve the quality of care. GE Healthcare's interventional, cardiology and surgery (ICS) business provides tools and technologies for fully integrated cardiac, surgical and interventional care. Some of the company's major products include Innova 3100, a digital imaging system for the heart and fine vessels, and Giraffe OmniBed and Incubators for critically ill and premature infants. Recent acquisitions include Vital Signs, a global provider of medical products; Whatman plc, a supplier of filtration products and technologies; VersaMed Corporation, a provider of portable critical care ventilators; and Image Diagnost International GmbH, a developer or innovative products optimized for the needs of diagnostic and screening mammography.

FINANCIALS: **Sales and profits are in thousands of dollars—add 000 to get the full amount. 2008 Note: Financial information for 2008 was not available for all companies at press time.**

2008 Sales: $17,392,000 | 2008 Profits: $2,851,000
2007 Sales: $16,997,000 | 2007 Profits: $3,056,000
2006 Sales: $16,560,000 | 2006 Profits: $3,142,000
2005 Sales: $15,016,000 | 2005 Profits: $2,601,000
2004 Sales: $13,411,000 | 2004 Profits: $2,263,000

U.S. Stock Ticker: Subsidiary
Int'l Ticker: Int'l Exchange:
Employees: 47,000
Fiscal Year Ends: 12/31
Parent Company: GENERAL ELECTRIC CO (GE)

SALARIES/BENEFITS:

Pension Plan: Y	ESOP Stock Plan:	Profit Sharing:	Top Exec. Salary: $	Bonus: $
Savings Plan: Y	Stock Purch. Plan:		Second Exec. Salary: $	Bonus: $

OTHER THOUGHTS:

Apparent Women Officers or Directors: 3
Hot Spot for Advancement for Women/Minorities: Y

LOCATIONS: ("Y" = Yes)

West:	Southwest:	Midwest:	Southeast:	Northeast:	International:
		Y			Y

GEMALTO NV

www.gemalto.com

Industry Group Code: 334413 **Ranks within this company's industry group:** Sales: 16 Profits: 11

Techology:		Medical/Drugs:		Engineering:		Transportation:		Chemicals/Petrochemicals:		Specialty:	
Computers:		Manufacturer:		Design:		Aerospace:		Oil/Gas Products:		Special Services:	Y
Software:		Contract Research:		Construction:		Automotive:		Chemicals:		Consulting:	
Communications:		Medical Services:		Eng. Services:		Shipping:		Oil/Chem. Svcs.:		Specialty Mgmt.:	
Electronics:	Y	Labs:		Consulting:				Gases:		Products:	
Alternative Energy:		Bio. Services:						Other:		Other:	

TYPES OF BUSINESS:

Computer Storage Equipment-Smart Cards
Smart Card Interfaces, Readers & Chipsets
Smart Card Software & Development Tools
Consulting, Training & Support Services
Online Security Programs

BRANDS/DIVISIONS/AFFILIATES:

Gemplus International SA
Axalto

CONTACTS:

Note: Officers with more than one job title may be intentionally listed here more than once.

Olivier Piou, CEO
Jacques Tierny, CFO
Paul Beverly, Exec. VP-Mktg./Pres., North America
Philippe Cabanettes, Exec. VP-Human Resources
Jean-Pierre Charlet, General Counsel/Exec. VP/Corp. Sec.
Claude Dahan, Exec. VP-Oper.
Martin McCourt, Exec. VP-Strategy, Mergers & Acquisitions
Jacques Seneca, Exec. VP-Security Bus. Unit
Philippe Vallee, Exec. VP-Telecomm. Bus. Unit
Philippe Cambriel, Exec. VP-Secure Transactions
Christophe Pagezy, Exec. VP-Corp. Projects
Alex Mandl, Exec. Chmn.

Phone: 31-20-562-06-80 **Fax:**
Toll-Free:
Address: Joop Geesinkweg 541-542, Amsterdam, 1096 AX The Netherlands

GROWTH PLANS/SPECIAL FEATURES:

Gemalto N.V., formed by the 2006 merger of Gemplus International S.A. and Axalto, is a leading global provider of digital security systems such as smart cards, payment terminals, card readers, online security programs, e-passports and subscriber identity module (SIM) cards. Gemalto serves the mobile telecommunications, public telephony, banking, retail, health care, transportation, identity, WLAN, pay-TV, e-government and access control markets. Smart cards are plastic cards approximately the size of credit cards that contain embedded microchips used to store and process information. The company's products conform to certification standards in every domain, including banking, JAVA GSM and telephony. Its products include memory and microprocessor-based smart cards, identification and financial smart cards, cards with radio-frequency chips (RFID), electronic tags, traditional magnetic strip cards and smart card interfaces, readers and chipsets, as well as smart card software and development tools. The firm also offers consulting, training and support services. Gemalto maintains 19 production sites, 31 personalization centers, 10 R&D centers and 85sales and marketing offices around the world. In September 2008, the company acquired the MULTOS business from Keycorp. In December of the same year, the firm agreed to acquire the NamITech South Africa business from Allied Technologies Limited.

FINANCIALS:

Sales and profits are in thousands of dollars—add 000 to get the full amount. 2008 Note: Financial information for 2008 was not available for all companies at press time.

2008 Sales: $2,238,260	2008 Profits: $203,840	**U.S. Stock Ticker:**
2007 Sales: $2,172,980	2007 Profits: $118,580	**Int'l Ticker: AXL** Int'l Exchange: Paris-Euronext
2006 Sales: $2,367,900	2006 Profits: $249,890	Employees: 10,000
2005 Sales: $2,200,000	2005 Profits: $	Fiscal Year Ends: 12/31
2004 Sales: $	2004 Profits: $	Parent Company:

SALARIES/BENEFITS:

Pension Plan:	ESOP Stock Plan:	Profit Sharing:	Top Exec. Salary: $	Bonus: $
Savings Plan:	Stock Purch. Plan:		Second Exec. Salary: $	Bonus: $

OTHER THOUGHTS:

Apparent Women Officers or Directors:
Hot Spot for Advancement for Women/Minorities:

LOCATIONS: ("Y" = Yes)

West:	Southwest:	Midwest:	Southeast:	Northeast:	International:
	Y			Y	Y

GENENTECH INC

www.gene.com

Industry Group Code: 325412 **Ranks within this company's industry group:** Sales: 17 Profits: 14

Techology:		Medical/Drugs:		Engineering:		Transportation:		Chemicals/Petrochemicals:		Specialty:	
Computers:		Manufacturer:	Y	Design:		Aerospace:		Oil/Gas Products:		Special Services:	
Software:		Contract Research:		Construction:		Automotive:		Chemicals:		Consulting:	
Communications:		Medical Services:		Eng. Services:		Shipping:		Oil/Chem. Svcs.:		Specialty Mgmt.:	
Electronics:		Labs:	Y	Consulting:				Gases:		Products:	
Alternative Energy:		Bio. Services:						Other:		Other:	

TYPES OF BUSINESS:

Drug Development & Manufacturing
Genetically Engineered Drugs

BRANDS/DIVISIONS/AFFILIATES:

Avastin
TNKase
Herceptin
Rituxan
Activase
Pulmozyme
Nutropin

CONTACTS:

Note: Officers with more than one job title may be intentionally listed here more than once.

Arthur D. Levinson, CEO
David A. Ebersman, CFO/Exec. VP
Richard H. Scheller, Exec. VP-Research
Susan Desmond-Hellmann, Pres., Prod. Dev.
Stephen G. Juelsgaard, Exec. VP/Corp. Sec.
Ian T. Clark, Exec. VP-Comm. Oper.
Robert E. Andreatta, Chief Acct. Officer/Controller
Stephen G. Juelsgaard, Chief Compliance Officer
Patrick Y. Yang, Exec. VP-Product Oper.
Arthur D. Levinson, Chmn.

Phone: 650-225-1000 **Fax:** 650-225-6000
Toll-Free:
Address: 1 DNA Way, South San Francisco, CA 94080 US

GROWTH PLANS/SPECIAL FEATURES:

Genentech, Inc. makes medicines by splicing genes into fast-growing bacteria that then produce therapeutic proteins and combat diseases on a molecular level. Genentech uses cutting-edge technologies such as computer visualization of molecules, micro arrays and sensitive assaying techniques to develop, manufacture and market pharmaceuticals for unmet medical needs. Genentech's research is directed toward the oncology, immunology and vascular biology fields. The company's products consist of a variety of cardio-centric medications, as well as cancer, growth hormone deficiency (GHD) and cystic fibrosis treatments. Biotechnology products offered by Genentech include Herceptin, used to treat metastatic breast cancers; Avastin, used to inhibit angiogenesis of solid-tumor cancers; Nutropin, a growth hormone for the treatment of GHD in children and adults; TNKase, for the treatment of acute myocardial infarction; and Pulmozyme, for the treatment of cystic fibrosis. The company also produces the Rituxan antibody, used for the treatment of patients with non-Hodgkin's lymphoma. Through its long-standing Genentech Access to Care Foundation, Genentech assists those without sufficient health insurance to receive its medicines. In 2008, sales to Genentech's three major distributors, AmerisourceBergen, McKesson and Cardinal Health, represented 86% of its total U.S. net product sales. There are three manufacturing sites in California, with an additional facility planned for 2010 licensure in Hillsboro, Oregon. In addition, it expects FDA licensure of a bulk drug substance manufacturing site in Singapore in 2010. The firm recently completed the acquisition of Tanox, a firm that focuses on monoclonal antibody technology and development partner for its Xolair asthma product. Roche Holdings, Ltd. owns 55.8% of Genentech. Roche hopes to acquire all of Genentech's outstanding stock.

For the last ten years, the company has been named to Fortune Magazine's 100 Best Companies to Work For. Every Friday evening, Genentech hosts socials called Ho-Hos, providing free food, beverages and a chance to socialize with co-workers.

FINANCIALS:

Sales and profits are in thousands of dollars—add 000 to get the full amount. 2008 Note: Financial information for 2008 was not available for all companies at press time.

2008 Sales: $13,418,000 | 2008 Profits: $3,427,000
2007 Sales: $11,724,000 | 2007 Profits: $2,769,000
2006 Sales: $9,284,000 | 2006 Profits: $2,113,000
2005 Sales: $6,633,372 | 2005 Profits: $1,278,991
2004 Sales: $4,621,157 | 2004 Profits: $784,816

U.S. Stock Ticker: DNA
Int'l Ticker: Int'l Exchange:
Employees: 11,186
Fiscal Year Ends: 12/31
Parent Company:

SALARIES/BENEFITS:

Pension Plan: | ESOP Stock Plan: | Profit Sharing: | Top Exec. Salary: $995,000 | Bonus: $2,725,000
Savings Plan: Y | Stock Purch. Plan: Y | | Second Exec. Salary: $503,833 | Bonus: $920,000

OTHER THOUGHTS:

Apparent Women Officers or Directors: 2
Hot Spot for Advancement for Women/Minorities: Y

LOCATIONS: ("Y" = Yes)

West:	Southwest:	Midwest:	Southeast:	Northeast:	International:
Y					Y

GENERAL DYNAMICS CORP

www.generaldynamics.com

Industry Group Code: 336410 **Ranks within this company's industry group:** Sales: 7 Profits: 7

Techology:		Medical/Drugs:		Engineering:		Transportation:		Chemicals/Petrochemicals:		Specialty:	
Computers:	Y	Manufacturer:		Design:	Y	Aerospace:	Y	Oil/Gas Products:		Special Services:	Y
Software:	Y	Contract Research:		Construction:	Y	Automotive:	Y	Chemicals:		Consulting:	Y
Communications:	Y	Medical Services:		Eng. Services:	Y	Shipping:	Y	Oil/Chem. Svcs.:		Specialty Mgmt.:	
Electronics:	Y	Labs:		Consulting:	Y			Gases:		Products:	Y
Alternative Energy:		Bio. Services:						Other:		Other:	

TYPES OF BUSINESS:

Aerospace Products & Services
Combat Vehicles & Systems
Telecommunications Systems
Naval Vessels & Submarines
Ship Management Services
Information Systems & Technology
Defense Systems & Services
Business Jets

BRANDS/DIVISIONS/AFFILIATES:

Gulfstream Aerospace
General Dynamics Advanced Information Systems
M1A1 Abrams Tank
Abrams Integrated Management
SNC Technologies, Inc.
ViPS Inc
Jet Aviation
AxleTech International

CONTACTS: *Note: Officers with more than one job title may be intentionally listed here more than once.*

Nicholas D. Chabraja, CEO
L. Hugh Redd, CFO/Sr. VP
Walter M. Oliver, Sr. VP-Human Resources
Tommy R. Augustsson, VP-IT
Gerard J. DeMuro, Exec. VP-Info. Systems & Tech.
Walter M. Oliver, Sr. VP-Admin.
David A. Savner, General Counsel/Sec./Sr. VP
Phebe N. Novakovic, Sr. VP-Planning & Dev.
Kendell Pease, VP-Gov't Rel. & Comm.
John W. Schwartz, Controller/VP
Jeffrey Kudlac, VP-Real Estate
John P. Casey, VP/Pres., Electric Boat
Lewis F. von Thaer, VP/Pres., Advanced Info. Systems
Charles M. Hall, Exec. VP-Combat Systems
Nicholas D. Chabraja, Chmn.
William O. Schmieder, VP-Int'l

Phone: 703-876-3000 **Fax:** 703-876-3125
Toll-Free:
Address: 2941 Fairview Park Dr., Ste. 100, Falls Church, VA 22042-4513 US

GROWTH PLANS/SPECIAL FEATURES:

General Dynamics Corp. (GDC) is one of the world's largest aerospace and defense contractors. Its customers include the U.S. military, other government organizations, the armed forces of allied nations and a diverse base of corporate and industrial buyers. The firm's operations are divided into four segments: Information systems and technology (IST), marine systems, combat systems and aerospace. The IST group provides defense and commercial customers with infrastructure and systems integration skills required to process, communicate and manage information effectively. The group has market-leading positions in the design, deployment and maintenance of wireline and wireless voice and data networks, telecommunications system security, encryption and fiber optics. The marine systems division provides the U.S. Navy with combat vessels, including nuclear submarines, surface combatants and auxiliary ships. The segment also provides ship management services for the U.S. government and builds commercial ships. The combat systems group provides systems integration, design, development, production and support for armored vehicles, armaments, munitions and components, with product lines including unmanned systems, medium-caliber guns, space propulsion systems, reactive armor and suspensions, engines and transmissions. It is the leading builder of armored vehicles and makes products such as the M1A1 Abrams Tank. The aerospace group designs, develops, manufactures and provides services for technologically advanced business jet aircraft under the Gulfstream name. Recent acquisitions include ViPS, Inc, a healthcare technology solutions provider; Jet Aviation; a Switzerland-based aviation services company; and AxleTech International, a private equity firm based in Washington, D.C.

FINANCIALS: Sales and profits are in thousands of dollars—add 000 to get the full amount. 2008 Note: Financial information for 2008 was not available for all companies at press time.

2008 Sales: $29,300,000	2008 Profits: $2,459,000	**U.S. Stock Ticker: GD**
2007 Sales: $27,240,000	2007 Profits: $2,072,000	**Int'l Ticker:** Int'l Exchange:
2006 Sales: $24,063,000	2006 Profits: $1,856,000	Employees: 92,300
2005 Sales: $20,975,000	2005 Profits: $1,461,000	Fiscal Year Ends: 12/31
2004 Sales: $18,868,000	2004 Profits: $1,227,000	Parent Company:

SALARIES/BENEFITS:

Pension Plan:	ESOP Stock Plan:	Profit Sharing:	Top Exec. Salary: $1,300,000	Bonus: $3,500,000
Savings Plan:	Stock Purch. Plan:		Second Exec. Salary: $572,500	Bonus: $900,000

OTHER THOUGHTS:

Apparent Women Officers or Directors: 3
Hot Spot for Advancement for Women/Minorities: Y

LOCATIONS: ("Y" = Yes)

West:	Southwest:	Midwest:	Southeast:	Northeast:	International:
Y	Y	Y	Y	Y	Y

GENERAL ELECTRIC CO (GE)

www.ge.com

Industry Group Code: 522220A **Ranks within this company's industry group:** Sales: 1 Profits: 1

Techology:		Medical/Drugs:		Engineering:		Transportation:		Chemicals/Petrochemicals:		Specialty:	
Computers:		Manufacturer:	Y	Design:		Aerospace:	Y	Oil/Gas Products:		Special Services:	
Software:		Contract Research:		Construction:		Automotive:		Chemicals:		Consulting:	
Communications:		Medical Services:		Eng. Services:		Shipping:		Oil/Chem. Svcs.:		Specialty Mgmt.:	
Electronics:		Labs:		Consulting:				Gases:		Products:	Y
Alternative Energy:	Y	Bio. Services:						Other:	Y	Other:	Y

TYPES OF BUSINESS:

Business Leasing & Finance
Energy Systems & Consulting
Insurance & Financial Services
Industrial & Electrical Equipment & Consumer Products
Television & Film Production & Distribution
Real Estate Investments & Finance
Medical Equipment
Transportation, Aircraft Engines, Rail Systems & Truck Fleet Management

BRANDS/DIVISIONS/AFFILIATES:

GE Commercial Finance
GE Infrastructure
GE Healthcare
NBC Universal
GE Money
GE Equipment Services
GE Industrial
GE Aviation

CONTACTS: *Note: Officers with more than one job title may be intentionally listed here more than once.*

Jeffrey R. Immelt, CEO
Keith S. Sherin, CFO
Beth Comstock, Chief Mktg. Officer/Sr. VP
John Lynch, Sr. VP-Corp. Human Resources
Mark M. Little, Sr. VP/Dir.-Global Research
Gary M. Reiner, CIO/Sr. VP
Brackett B. Denniston, III, General Counsel/Sr. VP
Wayne Hewett, VP-Oper.
Pamela Daley, Sr. VP-Corp. Bus. Dev.
Trevor Schauenberg, Corp. Investor Comm.
Kathryn A. Cassidy, Treas./VP
Michael A. Neal, CEO/Pres., GE Capital Finance
John G. Rice, CEO/Pres., GE Infrastructure
James Campbell, CEO/Pres., GE Industrial
Susan P. Peters, VP-Exec. Dev.
Jeffrey R. Immelt, Chmn.
Ferdinando Beccalli-Falco, CEO/Pres., Int'l
Wayne Hewett, VP-Supply Chain

Phone: 203-373-2211 **Fax:** 203-373-3131
Toll-Free:
Address: 3135 Easton Turnpike, Fairfield, CT 06828-0001 US

GROWTH PLANS/SPECIAL FEATURES:

General Electric Co. (GE) is one of the world's largest and most diversified corporations, with six operating divisions: Infrastructure, commercial finance, GE Money (formerly consumer finance), healthcare, NBC Universal and industrial. GE's infrastructure division, its largest industrial segment, produces, sells, finances and services equipment for the air and rail transportation, water treatment and energy generation industries. GE's commercial finance segment offers financial services mainly to manufacturers, distributors and end-users, including loans and leases. GE Money offers credit and deposit products to consumers, retailers, banks and auto dealers in over 50 countries. All of the lending and financial services units are managed by a unit known as GE Capital. The healthcare segment develops diagnostic and therapy equipment including MRI and CT scanners, x-ray, nuclear imaging and ultrasound equipment. NBC Universal, the company's network television affiliate, broadcasts to affiliated television stations within the U.S., produces live and recorded television programs, operates television broadcasting stations and produces and distributes films. GE's industrial segment produces and sells products including consumer appliances, industrial equipment and plastics and also provides asset management services for the transportation industry. In 2007, the firm made a number of acquisitions, the most significant of which were Trustreet Properties, Inc.; Diskont und Kredit AG and Disko Leasing GmbH (DISKO) and ASL Auto Service-Leasing GmbH (ASL), the leasing businesses of KG Allgemeine Leasing GmbH & Co.; and Sanyo Electric Credit Co., Ltd. Recent acquisitions include Kelman Limited of Northern Ireland; CitiCapital, Citigroup's North American commercial leasing and commercial equipment finance business; and Bank BPH of Poland.

GE provides its employees with tuition, adoption, parenting and child care assistance; education and career counseling; and legal and financial information services.

FINANCIALS: **Sales and profits are in thousands of dollars—add 000 to get the full amount. 2008 Note: Financial information for 2008 was not available for all companies at press time.**

2008 Sales: $182,515,000 | 2008 Profits: $17,410,000
2007 Sales: $172,488,000 | 2007 Profits: $22,208,000
2006 Sales: $151,568,000 | 2006 Profits: $20,742,000
2005 Sales: $136,580,000 | 2005 Profits: $16,720,000
2004 Sales: $134,481,000 | 2004 Profits: $16,285,000

U.S. Stock Ticker: GE
Int'l Ticker: Int'l Exchange:
Employees: 323,000
Fiscal Year Ends: 12/31
Parent Company:

SALARIES/BENEFITS:

Pension Plan: | ESOP Stock Plan: | Profit Sharing: | Top Exec. Salary: $3,300,000 | Bonus: $5,800,000
Savings Plan: Y | Stock Purch. Plan: | | Second Exec. Salary: $2,750,000 | Bonus: $7,590,000

OTHER THOUGHTS:

Apparent Women Officers or Directors: 10
Hot Spot for Advancement for Women/Minorities: Y

LOCATIONS: ("Y" = Yes)

West:	Southwest:	Midwest:	Southeast:	Northeast:	International:
Y	Y	Y	Y	Y	Y

Note: Financial information, benefits and other data can change quickly and may vary from those stated here.

GENERAL MOTORS CORP (GM)

www.gm.com

Industry Group Code: 336111 **Ranks within this company's industry group:** Sales: 3 Profits: 24

Techology:		Medical/Drugs:		Engineering:		Transportation:		Chemicals/Petrochemicals:		Specialty:	
Computers:		Manufacturer:		Design:		Aerospace:		Oil/Gas Products:		Special Services:	Y
Software:		Contract Research:		Construction:		Automotive:	Y	Chemicals:		Consulting:	
Communications:		Medical Services:		Eng. Services:		Shipping:		Oil/Chem. Svcs.:		Specialty Mgmt.:	
Electronics:		Labs:		Consulting:				Gases:		Products:	Y
Alternative Energy:		Bio. Services:						Other:		Other:	

TYPES OF BUSINESS:

Automobile, Truck & Engine Manufacturing
Locomotives
Automotive Electronics
Security & Information Services
Financing & Insurance
Parts & Service
Transmissions
Engines

BRANDS/DIVISIONS/AFFILIATES:

GM Daewoo Auto and Technology Co
Adam Opel AG
Vauxhall Motors Ltd
Saab Automobile AB
OnStar Corporation
GM Holden Ltd
Saturn Corp
Volt

CONTACTS: *Note: Officers with more than one job title may be intentionally listed here more than once.*

Frederick A. Henderson, CEO
Frederick A. Henderson, COO
Frederick A. Henderson, Pres.
Ray G. Young, CFO/Exec. VP
Jonathan Browning, VP-Global Sales, Service & Mktg. Oper.
Kathleen S. Barclay, VP-Global Human Resources
Lawrence D. Burns, VP-R&D
Ralph J. Szygenda, CIO/VP
Robert A. Lutz, Vice Chmn.-Global Prod. Dev.
James E. Queen, VP-Global Eng.
Gary L. Cowger, VP-Global Mfg. & Labor Rel.
Robert S. Osborne, General Counsel/VP
Lawrence S. Barclay, VP-Strategic Planning
Steven J. Harris, VP-Global Comm.
Nicholas S. Cyprus, Chief Acct. Officer/Controller
Thomas G. Stephens, Exec. VP-Global Powertrain & Global Quality
Troy A. Clarke, VP/Pres., GM North America
Nancy E. Polis, Corp. Sec.
Walter G. Borst, Treas.
G. Richard Wagoner, Jr., Interim Chmn.
Kent Kresa, VP/Pres., GM Europe
Bo I. Andersson, VP-Global Purchasing & Supply Chain

Phone: 313-556-5000	**Fax:** 313-556-5108
Toll-Free:	
Address: 300 Renaissance Ctr., Detroit, MI 48265 US	

GROWTH PLANS/SPECIAL FEATURES:

General Motors Corp. (GM) is engaged in the worldwide development, production and marketing of cars, trucks, automotive systems and locomotives. The firm sells eight brands of automobiles in the U.S.: Chevrolet, Pontiac, Buick, Cadillac, GMC, Saturn, Hummer and Saab. International brands include Opel, Vauxhall, Daewoo, Isuzu and Holden. GM parts and accessories are marketed under the GM, GM Goodwrench and ACDelco brands through GM's service and parts division, while its engines are marketed through GM Powertrain. The company's 49%-owned subsidiary, General Motors Acceptance Corporation (GMAC), provides financing, residential mortgage services, automobile service contracts and insurance coverage. GM's OnStar subsidiary is an industry leader in vehicle safety, security and information services and serves more than 2 million subscribers. The firm also has equity ownership stakes directly or indirectly through various regional subsidiaries, including GM Daewoo Auto & Technology Company, New United Motor Manufacturing, Inc., Shanghai General Motors Co., Ltd., SAIC-GM-Wuling Automobile Company Ltd. and CAMI Automotive Inc. In November 2008, the company sold its remaining stake in Suzuki Motor Corp. After a disastrous 2008 and huge financial losses, GM accepted $13.4 billion in bailout funds from the U.S. government, and it hopes to receive an additional $16.6 billion. Further, the company seeks $7.7 billion from the U.S. Department of Energy for the development of efficient cars. GM plans to sell or close Saab, Hummer and Saturn. Saab filed for bankruptcy in February 2009. GM will also scale back Pontiac, greatly downsize the dealer network, close several factories and slash tens of thousands of jobs. The firm expects large labor concessions from its unions. Despite these efforts, bankruptcy remains a possibility. To some extent, GM is pinning its future hopes on a yet-to-be-launched electric car concept named Volt.

FINANCIALS: **Sales and profits are in thousands of dollars—add 000 to get the full amount. 2008 Note: Financial information for 2008 was not available for all companies at press time.**

2008 Sales: $148,979,000	2008 Profits: $-30,860,000	**U.S. Stock Ticker: GM**
2007 Sales: $179,984,000	2007 Profits: $-38,732,000	**Int'l Ticker:** Int'l Exchange:
2006 Sales: $204,467,000	2006 Profits: $-1,978,000	Employees: 243,000
2005 Sales: $193,050,000	2005 Profits: $-10,417,000	Fiscal Year Ends: 12/31
2004 Sales: $195,351,000	2004 Profits: $2,701	Parent Company:

SALARIES/BENEFITS:

Pension Plan: Y	ESOP Stock Plan:	Profit Sharing:	Top Exec. Salary: $1,283,333	Bonus: $
Savings Plan: Y	Stock Purch. Plan:		Second Exec. Salary: $1,162,500	Bonus: $

OTHER THOUGHTS:

Apparent Women Officers or Directors: 9
Hot Spot for Advancement for Women/Minorities: Y

LOCATIONS: ("Y" = Yes)

West:	Southwest:	Midwest:	Southeast:	Northeast:	International:
Y	Y	Y	Y	Y	Y

Note: Financial information, benefits and other data can change quickly and may vary from those stated here.

GENZYME CORP

www.genzyme.com

Industry Group Code: 325412 **Ranks within this company's industry group:** Sales: 24 Profits: 24

Techology:		Medical/Drugs:		Engineering:		Transportation:		Chemicals/Petrochemicals:		Specialty:	
Computers:		Manufacturer:	Y	Design:		Aerospace:		Oil/Gas Products:		Special Services:	
Software:		Contract Research:		Construction:		Automotive:		Chemicals:		Consulting:	
Communications:		Medical Services:	Y	Eng. Services:		Shipping:		Oil/Chem. Svcs.:		Specialty Mgmt.:	
Electronics:		Labs:	Y	Consulting:				Gases:		Products:	
Alternative Energy:		Bio. Services:	Y					Other:		Other:	

TYPES OF BUSINESS:

Pharmaceuticals Discovery & Development
Genetic Disease Treatments
Surgical Products
Diagnostic Products
Genetic Testing Services
Oncology Products
Biomaterials
Medical Devices

BRANDS/DIVISIONS/AFFILIATES:

Renagel
Cerezyme
Fabrazyme
Mozobil
Thyrogen
MACI
Clolar
Synvisc-One

CONTACTS:

Note: Officers with more than one job title may be intentionally listed here more than once.

Henri A. Termeer, CEO
Henri A. Termeer, Pres.
Michael S. Wyzga, CFO
Zoltan Csimma, Chief Human Resources Officer/Sr. VP
Alan E. Smith, Chief Scientific Officer/Sr. VP-Research
Thomas J. DesRosier, Chief Legal Officer/General Counsel/Sr. VP
Mark R. Bamforth, Sr. VP-Corp. Oper. & Pharmaceuticals
Richard H. Douglas, Sr. VP-Corp. Dev.
Mary McGrane, Sr. VP-Gov't Rel.
Michael S. Wyzga, Exec. VP-Finance
Mark J. Enyedy, Sr. VP/Pres., Oncology & Multiple Sclerosis
John Butler, Sr. VP/Pres., Cardiometabolic & Renal
C. Ann Merrifield, Sr. VP/Pres., Genzyme & Biosurgery
Donald E. Pogorzelski, VP/Pres., Diagnostic Prod.
Henri A. Termeer, Chmn.
Sandford D. Smith, Pres., Int'l Group

Phone: 617-252-7500	**Fax:** 617-252-7600
Toll-Free:	
Address: 500 Kendall St., Cambridge, MA 02142 US	

GROWTH PLANS/SPECIAL FEATURES:

Genzyme Corporation is a major biotech drug manufacturer operating through four major units: Genetic Diseases; Cardiometabolic and Renal; Biosurgery; and Hematologic Oncology. The Genetic Diseases segment develops therapeutic products to treat patients suffering from genetic and other chronic debilitating diseases including lysosomal disorders (LSDs). Products include Cerezyme, an enzyme replacement treatment for Type 1 Gaucher disease and Fabrazyme for Fabry disease. The Cardiometabolic and Renal unit produces products for patients suffering from renal disease, including chronic renal failure, and endocrine and cardiovascular diseases. Products include Renagel, a calcium-free, metal-free phosphate binder for patients with Chronic Kidney disease on hemodialysis; and Thyrogen, an injection used as a diagnostic in follow-up screenings of cancer patients with thyroid cancer. The Biosurgery division develops biotherapeutics and biomaterial-based products for the orthopaedics sector and broader surgical areas. Its main products are Synvisc, a lubricant and pain reducer for the knee joint in patients with osteoarthritic knees; and the MACI implant, which uses the patient's own culture cartilage cells to repair a damaged knee joint. The Hematologic Oncology segment focuses on the treatment of cancer. Its main products consists of Mozobil, an injection used to mobilize stem cells in the blood stream for collection and for transplantation in patients with non-Hodgkin's lymphoma and multiple myeloma; and Clolar, a treatment for children with acute lymphoblastic leukemia. In February 2009, the FDA approved Synvisc-One, an injection designed for pain relief in osteoarthritic knees.

Employees are offered medical and dental insurance; life and dependent life insurance; business travel accident insurance; flexible spending accounts; short-and long-term disability coverage; a 401(k) plan; a stock purchase plan; financial education programs; tuition reimbursement; a college savings plan; and an employee discount program.

FINANCIALS:

Sales and profits are in thousands of dollars—add 000 to get the full amount. 2008 Note: Financial information for 2008 was not available for all companies at press time.

2008 Sales: $4,605,039	2008 Profits: $421,081	**U.S. Stock Ticker: GENZ**
2007 Sales: $3,813,519	2007 Profits: $480,193	**Int'l Ticker:** Int'l Exchange:
2006 Sales: $3,187,013	2006 Profits: $-16,797	Employees: 11,000
2005 Sales: $2,734,842	2005 Profits: $441,489	Fiscal Year Ends: 12/31
2004 Sales: $2,201,145	2004 Profits: $86,527	Parent Company:

SALARIES/BENEFITS:

Pension Plan:	ESOP Stock Plan:	Profit Sharing:	Top Exec. Salary: $1,503,620	Bonus: $2,142,000
Savings Plan: Y	Stock Purch. Plan: Y		Second Exec. Salary: $705,423	Bonus: $560,000

OTHER THOUGHTS:

Apparent Women Officers or Directors: 6
Hot Spot for Advancement for Women/Minorities: Y

LOCATIONS: ("Y" = Yes)

West:	Southwest:	Midwest:	Southeast:	Northeast:	International:
Y	Y	Y	Y	Y	Y

GEORG FISCHER LTD

www.georgfischer.com

Industry Group Code: 336300 **Ranks within this company's industry group:** Sales: 21 Profits: 11

Techology:		Medical/Drugs:		Engineering:		Transportation:		Chemicals/Petrochemicals:		Specialty:	
Computers:		Manufacturer:		Design:	Y	Aerospace:		Oil/Gas Products:		Special Services:	
Software:		Contract Research:		Construction:		Automotive:	Y	Chemicals:		Consulting:	
Communications:		Medical Services:		Eng. Services:	Y	Shipping:		Oil/Chem. Svcs.:		Specialty Mgmt.:	
Electronics:		Labs:		Consulting:				Gases:		Products:	Y
Alternative Energy:		Bio. Services:						Other:		Other:	

TYPES OF BUSINESS:

Automotive Components
Iron Casting
Manufacturing Technology
Machine Tools
Piping Systems
Design
Control systems

BRANDS/DIVISIONS/AFFILIATES:

Agie Charmilles Group
Actspark
Engemaq
Mikron
Step-Tec
Central Plastics
Alfa Plastics Inc
JRG Gunzenhauser AG

CONTACTS: *Note: Officers with more than one job title may be intentionally listed here more than once.*

Yves Serra, CEO
Yves Serra, Pres.
Stephan Wittmann, Dir.-Human Resources
Roland Groebil, Sec.
Ernst Willi, Dir.-Corp. Dev.
Bettina Schmidt, Head.-Comm.
Daniel Boesiger, Head-Investor Rel.
Roland Abt, Dir.-Finance & Controlling
Josef Edbauer, Dir.-GF Automotive
Pietro Lori, Dir.-GF Piping Systems
Michael Hauser, Dir.-GF AgieCharmilles
Barbara Senn, Head-Corp. Compliance
Martin Huber, Chmn.

Phone: 41-52-631-1111 **Fax:** 41-52-631-2837
Toll-Free:
Address: Amsler-Laffon-Strasse 9, Schaffhausen, CH-8201 Switzerland

GROWTH PLANS/SPECIAL FEATURES:

Georg Fischer Ltd. is a design and manufacturing firm with 150 subsidiaries operating through three divisions: automotive, piping systems and machine tools. The automotive division designs and manufactures cast components and systems for auto chassis, powertrains and bodies. The firm performs large-scale iron casting, sand and die casting and pressure die casting of iron and light metals. In addition, the firm sells automotive products such as mounting plates, mounting kits and the TRILEX Wheel System. The piping systems division supplies plastic and metal piping systems for industrial applications, gas and water utilities and construction projects. Products include industrial piping systems; piping system control and regulation products; distribution systems for gas and water; drinking water installation systems; and machines and tools for jointing plastic and metal piping systems. The division has a sales presence in over 100 countries to ensure round-the-clock customer support. The machine tools segment, also know as AgieCharmilles Group, designs and manufactures precision machinery for tool and mold making. The firm's wire-cut and die sinking electric discharge machines (EDM) and high-speed milling (HSM) technologies create forms down to the micro and nano ranges. Molds are produced for the mass production of consumer goods such as phone handsets, as well as for complex, customized precision components. The segment produces products under a number of brand names, including Agie, Charmilles, Actspark, Engemaq, Mikron, Step-Tec, System 3R and Intech EDM. In 2008, the company acquired Central Plastics, a supplier of piping systems to gas and water utilities, as well as Alfa Plastics Inc. and JRG Gunzenhauser AG.

FINANCIALS: **Sales and profits are in thousands of dollars—add 000 to get the full amount. 2008 Note: Financial information for 2008 was not available for all companies at press time.**

2008 Sales: $3,949,130	2008 Profits: $61,030	**U.S. Stock Ticker:**
2007 Sales: $3,977,430	2007 Profits: $216,690	**Int'l Ticker: FI-N** Int'l Exchange: Zurich-SWX
2006 Sales: $4,007,500	2006 Profits: $226,700	Employees: 14,326
2005 Sales: $3,655,100	2005 Profits: $153,500	Fiscal Year Ends: 12/31
2004 Sales: $2,713,100	2004 Profits: $80,470	Parent Company:

SALARIES/BENEFITS:

Pension Plan:	ESOP Stock Plan:	Profit Sharing:	Top Exec. Salary: $	Bonus: $
Savings Plan:	Stock Purch. Plan:		Second Exec. Salary: $	Bonus: $

OTHER THOUGHTS:

Apparent Women Officers or Directors: 3
Hot Spot for Advancement for Women/Minorities: Y

LOCATIONS: ("Y" = Yes)

West:	Southwest:	Midwest:	Southeast:	Northeast:	International:
Y		Y	Y	Y	Y

GETRONICS NV

www.getronics.com

Industry Group Code: 541512 **Ranks within this company's industry group:** Sales: Profits:

Techology:		Medical/Drugs:		Engineering:		Transportation:		Chemicals/Petrochemicals:		Specialty:	
Computers:		Manufacturer:		Design:		Aerospace:		Oil/Gas Products:		Special Services:	Y
Software:		Contract Research:		Construction:		Automotive:		Chemicals:		Consulting:	Y
Communications:		Medical Services:		Eng. Services:		Shipping:		Oil/Chem. Svcs.:		Specialty Mgmt.:	
Electronics:		Labs:		Consulting:				Gases:		Products:	
Alternative Energy:		Bio. Services:						Other:		Other:	

TYPES OF BUSINESS:

IT Consulting
Systems Integration
e-Commerce Support & Systems Development
Communication Technology Services
Technology Product Distribution

BRANDS/DIVISIONS/AFFILIATES:

Getronics Virtual University
Getronics PinkRoccade
Royal KPN NV

CONTACTS: *Note: Officers with more than one job title may be intentionally listed here more than once.*

Erik van der Meijden, CEO
Steven van Schilfgaarde, CFO
Peter Enneking, VP-Legal
Jos Schoemaker, Head-Global Service Delivery
Dave Baldwin, Gen. Manager-U.K. & Ireland

Phone: 31 88-661-0079	**Fax:**
Toll-Free:	
Address: Rontgenlaan 75, Zoetermeer, 2719 DX The Netherlands	

GROWTH PLANS/SPECIAL FEATURES:

Getronics NV, a subsidiary of Royal KPN NV, provides information and communication technology services to businesses. The company offers consulting in customer relations, applications integration, network management, security, telecommunications, technology integration, deployment and outsourcing to help clients increase productivity and reduce costs. Getronics organizes its services into the following categories: applications, workspace management, technology transformation, communication and security. The firm also distributes third-party computer and networking products. Getronics has strategic global alliances with Cisco, Microsoft and Dell as well as alliances and partnerships with the leaders in both applications and infrastructure technologies such as Documentum, Oracle, IBM, Nortel, Nokia and Compaq, among many others. Getronics has customers in the financial services, manufacturing, media, retail, telecommunications and government industries, with a presence in over 25 countries. In February 2008, the company sold Getronics Australia to UXC Ltd. In March 2008, Getronics released Future-Ready Workspace_ 2.0, allowing workspace tools to be used securely and in collaboration within a large organization. In June 2008, the company formed a partnership with CompuCom, a subsidiary of Court Square Capital Partners, to mutually enhance their IT platforms and boost their international clientele. In July 2008, Getronics sold its subsidiary, Everest, to Total Specific Solutions for an undisclosed amount. In September 2008, the company formed a global delivery alliance with Wipro Technologies, subsidiary of Wipro Limited; as part of the partnership, Getronic's onsite field support will be matched with Wipro's Deskside Managed Services. In December 2008, Getronics sold its Business Applications Services to Capgemini for an undisclosed amount.

Getronics provides unique training and development to its employees, including an online learning platform through the company's intranet called the Getronics Virtual University.

FINANCIALS: Sales and profits are in thousands of dollars—add 000 to get the full amount. 2008 Note: Financial information for 2008 was not available for all companies at press time.

2008 Sales: $	2008 Profits: $	**U.S. Stock Ticker: Subsidiary**
2007 Sales: $3,888,000	2007 Profits: $-214,600	**Int'l Ticker:** Int'l Exchange:
2006 Sales: $3,737,000	2006 Profits: $5,900	Employees: 24,780
2005 Sales: $3,138,362	2005 Profits: $5,460	Fiscal Year Ends: 12/31
2004 Sales: $3,112,090	2004 Profits: $67,766	Parent Company: ROYAL KPN NV

SALARIES/BENEFITS:

Pension Plan:	ESOP Stock Plan: Y	Profit Sharing: Y	Top Exec. Salary: $	Bonus: $
Savings Plan:	Stock Purch. Plan:		Second Exec. Salary: $	Bonus: $

OTHER THOUGHTS:

Apparent Women Officers or Directors:
Hot Spot for Advancement for Women/Minorities:

LOCATIONS: ("Y" = Yes)

West:	Southwest:	Midwest:	Southeast:	Northeast:	International:
				Y	Y

GILEAD SCIENCES INC

www.gilead.com

Industry Group Code: 325412 **Ranks within this company's industry group:** Sales: 22 Profits: 16

Techology:		Medical/Drugs:		Engineering:		Transportation:		Chemicals/Petrochemicals:		Specialty:	
Computers:		Manufacturer:	Y	Design:		Aerospace:		Oil/Gas Products:		Special Services:	
Software:		Contract Research:		Construction:		Automotive:		Chemicals:		Consulting:	
Communications:		Medical Services:		Eng. Services:		Shipping:		Oil/Chem. Svcs.:		Specialty Mgmt.:	
Electronics:		Labs:	Y	Consulting:				Gases:		Products:	
Alternative Energy:		Bio. Services:						Other:		Other:	

TYPES OF BUSINESS:

Viral & Bacterial Infections Drugs
Respiratory & Cardiopulmonary Diseases Drugs

BRANDS/DIVISIONS/AFFILIATES:

Vistide
Truvada
Emtriva
Atripla
Elvitegravir
Viread
Navitas Assets, LLC
Parion Sciences, Inc.

CONTACTS: *Note: Officers with more than one job title may be intentionally listed here more than once.*

John C. Martin, CEO
John F. Milligan, COO
John F. Milligan, Pres.
Robin Washington, CFO/Sr. VP
Kristen M. Metza, Sr. VP-Human Resources
Norbert W. Bischofberger, Exec. VP-R&D/Chief Scientific Officer
Anthony D. Caracciolo, Sr. VP-Mfg.
Gregg H. Alton, General Counsel/Sr. VP
Anthony D. Caracciolo, Sr. VP-Oper.
John Toole, Sr. VP-Corp. Dev.
Kevin Young, Exec. VP-Commercial Oper.
A. Bruce Montgomery, Sr. VP/Head-Respiratory Therapeutics
Richard J. Gorczynski, Sr. VP-Cardiovascular Research
William A. Lee, Sr. VP-Research
John C. Martin, Chmn.
Paul Carter, Sr. VP-Int'l Commercial Oper.

Phone: 650-574-3000	**Fax:** 650-578-9264
Toll-Free: 800-445-3235	
Address: 333 Lakeside Dr., Foster City, CA 94404 US	

GROWTH PLANS/SPECIAL FEATURES:

Gilead Sciences, Inc. is a biopharmaceutical company that discovers, develops and commercializes therapeutics for the treatment of life-threatening diseases such as viral and bacterial infections. The company expanded its efforts to include respiratory and cardiopulmonary diseases. The firm maintains research, development, manufacturing, sales and marketing facilities in the U.S., Europe and Australia and operates marketing subsidiaries in another 12 countries. Gilead currently has nine products on the market: Viread, Truvada and Emtriva, which are oral medicines used as part of a combination therapy to treat HIV; Atripla, an oral formulation for treatment of HIV; Hespera, an oral medication used for treatment of Hepatitis B; AmBisome, an antifungal agent to treat serious invasive fungal infections; Vistide, an antiviral medication for the treatment of cytomegalovirus retinitis in patients with AIDS; Letairis, for the treatment of pulmonary arterial hypertension; and Flolan, an injected medication for the long-term intravenous treatment of primary pulmonary hypertension. The company also derives revenues from licensing agreements for Macugen, a macular degeneration treatment developed by OSI Pharmaceuticals, Inc.; and Tamiflu, an influenza medication sold by F. Hoffman-LaRoche. In June 2007, FDA approved Letairis, the company's treatment of pulmonary arterial hypertension. In August 2007, the company entered an exclusive licensing and co-development agreement with Parion Sciences, Inc. to develop its P-680, a sodium channel inhibitor intended for treatment of pulmonary diseases, such as cystic fibrosis. In May 2008, Gilead acquired all of the assets related to Navitas Assets, LLC's cicletanine business. In May 2008, the firm received the first of four patents relating to its drug Viread. In July 2008, Gilead initiated a Phase III clinical trial for Elvitegravir, an integrase inhibitor being evaluated for use in treating HIV. In March 2009, Gilead agreed to acquire CV Therapeutics.

The company offers its employees a 401(k) plan, a stock purchase plan, an employee assistance plan, health benefits and tuition reimbursement.

FINANCIALS: **Sales and profits are in thousands of dollars—add 000 to get the full amount. 2008 Note: Financial information for 2008 was not available for all companies at press time.**

2008 Sales: $5,335,750	2008 Profits: $2,011,154	**U.S. Stock Ticker: GILD**
2007 Sales: $4,230,045	2007 Profits: $1,615,298	**Int'l Ticker:** Int'l Exchange:
2006 Sales: $3,026,139	2006 Profits: $-1,189,957	Employees: 3,441
2005 Sales: $2,028,400	2005 Profits: $813,914	Fiscal Year Ends: 12/31
2004 Sales: $1,324,621	2004 Profits: $449,371	Parent Company:

SALARIES/BENEFITS:

Pension Plan:	ESOP Stock Plan:	Profit Sharing:	Top Exec. Salary: $1,045,833	Bonus: $1,617,000
Savings Plan: Y	Stock Purch. Plan: Y		Second Exec. Salary: $637,958	Bonus: $523,609

OTHER THOUGHTS:

Apparent Women Officers or Directors: 1
Hot Spot for Advancement for Women/Minorities: Y

LOCATIONS: ("Y" = Yes)

West:	Southwest:	Midwest:	Southeast:	Northeast:	International:
Y				Y	Y

Note: Financial information, benefits and other data can change quickly and may vary from those stated here.

GKN PLC

www.gknplc.com

Industry Group Code: 336300 **Ranks within this company's industry group:** Sales: 17 Profits: 14

Techology:		Medical/Drugs:		Engineering:		Transportation:		Chemicals/Petrochemicals:		Specialty:	
Computers:		Manufacturer:		Design:		Aerospace:	Y	Oil/Gas Products:		Special Services:	
Software:		Contract Research:		Construction:		Automotive:	Y	Chemicals:		Consulting:	
Communications:		Medical Services:		Eng. Services:		Shipping:		Oil/Chem. Svcs.:		Specialty Mgmt.:	
Electronics:		Labs:		Consulting:				Gases:		Products:	
Alternative Energy:		Bio. Services:						Other:		Other:	

TYPES OF BUSINESS:

Automobile Parts-Manufacturing & Engineering
Aerospace Engineering
Driveshaft System Products
Powder Metallurgy
Off Highway Components
Engineering Support Services
Helicopters & Military Vehicles
Propulsion System Components

BRANDS/DIVISIONS/AFFILIATES:

Teleflex Aerospace Manufacturing Group
AutoStructures
Torque Technology
Cylinder Liners
Emitec
GKN Sinter Metals
Hoeganaes

CONTACTS: *Note: Officers with more than one job title may be intentionally listed here more than once.*

Kevin Smith, CEO
Maureen Constantine, Group Dir.-Human Resources
Grey Denham, Group Sec.
William Seeger, Dir.-Finance
Nigel Stein, CEO-Automotive
Marcus Bryson, CEO-Aerospace
Arthur Connelly, CEO-Driveline Driveshafts
Andrew R. Smith, CEO-Sinter Metals
Roy Brown, Chmn.

Phone: 44-1527-517-715 **Fax:** 44-1527-517-700
Toll-Free:
Address: Ipsley House, Ipsley Church Ln., P.O. Box 55, Redditch, Worcestershire B98 OTL UK

GROWTH PLANS/SPECIAL FEATURES:

GKN PLC is a world leader in automotive and aerospace engineering. GKN has a global presence in more than 30 different countries. The firm's businesses are divided into three groupings: automotive, powder metallurgy and aerospace. Its automotive business includes five divisions: Driveshafts, AutoStructures, Torque Technology, Cylinder Liners and Emitec, a joint venture. The driveshaft division designs and manufactures constant velocity jointed (CVJ) sideshafts and propeller shafts for passenger cars and light commercial vehicles. The torque technology division develops products to improve vehicle traction and stability. AutoStructures is a U.K.-based business that manufactures, develops and designs automobile chassis systems, modules and other structural assemblies. The company owns 59% of the Chinese based cylinder liner division, which produces truck engine cylinder liners mainly for the Chinese market. Emitec, 50% owned by Siemens AG and 50% by the company, designs and manufactures catalyst support materials for automotive exhaust systems. The powder metallurgy group includes GKN Sinter Metals, Hoeganaes, OffHighway and Industrial Distribution Services divisions. Sinter Metals produces high-performance automotive parts such as lubricated bearings and steering mechanisms. Hoeganaes supplies raw powdered metal materials in the U.S., Germany and Romania. The OffHighway division supplies components and systems to the mining, forestry, construction and agriculture industries. GKN's industrial and distribution services division offers repair and replacement services as well as operating warehouses and manufacturing facilities. The company's aerospace group has three divisions: Propulsion Systems and Special Products; Aerostructures North America; and Aerostructures Europe. GKN Aerospace manufactures and designs canopy systems, de-icing systems and complex metal alloy structures for both civilian and military aircraft. In July 2008, KGN Areospace signed a lifetime contract with Honeywell Engines for the design, manufacture and integration of nacelle systems for its HTF7000 series business jet turbofan engine. In September 2008, the company agreed to acquire the wing component manufacturing business of Airbus.

FINANCIALS: Sales and profits are in thousands of dollars—add 000 to get the full amount. 2008 Note: Financial information for 2008 was not available for all companies at press time.

2008 Sales: $6,491,970
2007 Sales: $5,739,820
2006 Sales: $7,147,710
2005 Sales: $6,366,780
2004 Sales: $6,075,300

2008 Profits: $-158,740
2007 Profits: $293,740
2006 Profits: $357,980
2005 Profits: $102,970
2004 Profits: $-200,700

U.S. Stock Ticker: GKNLY
Int'l Ticker: GKN Int'l Exchange: London-LSE
Employees: 38,147
Fiscal Year Ends: 12/31
Parent Company:

SALARIES/BENEFITS:

Pension Plan: ESOP Stock Plan: Profit Sharing: Top Exec. Salary: $ Bonus: $
Savings Plan: Stock Purch. Plan: Second Exec. Salary: $ Bonus: $

OTHER THOUGHTS:

Apparent Women Officers or Directors: 1
Hot Spot for Advancement for Women/Minorities:

LOCATIONS: ("Y" = Yes)

West:	Southwest:	Midwest:	Southeast:	Northeast:	International:
Y	Y	Y	Y	Y	Y

Note: Financial information, benefits and other data can change quickly and may vary from those stated here.

GLAXOSMITHKLINE PLC

www.gsk.com

Industry Group Code: 325412 **Ranks within this company's industry group:** Sales: 6 Profits: 2

Techology:		Medical/Drugs:		Engineering:		Transportation:		Chemicals/Petrochemicals:		Specialty:	
Computers:		Manufacturer:	Y	Design:		Aerospace:		Oil/Gas Products:		Special Services:	
Software:		Contract Research:		Construction:		Automotive:		Chemicals:		Consulting:	
Communications:		Medical Services:		Eng. Services:		Shipping:		Oil/Chem. Svcs.:		Specialty Mgmt.:	
Electronics:		Labs:	Y	Consulting:				Gases:		Products:	
Alternative Energy:		Bio. Services:						Other:		Other:	

TYPES OF BUSINESS:

Prescription Medications
Asthma Drugs
Respiratory Drugs
Antibiotics
Antivirals
Dermatological Drugs
Over-the-Counter & Nutritional Products

BRANDS/DIVISIONS/AFFILIATES:

Lanoxin
Lamictal
Adoair
Alvedon
Zantac
Nicorette
Ceravix
Genelabs Technologies

CONTACTS: *Note: Officers with more than one job title may be intentionally listed here more than once.*

Andrew Witty, CEO
Julian Heslop, CFO
Daniel Phelan, Chief of Staff
Moncef Slaoui, Chmn.-R&D
Bill Louv, CIO
David Pulman, Pres., Global Mfg. & Supply
Simon Bicknell, Company Sec./Compliance Officer/Sr. VP
David Redfern, Chief Strategy Officer
Duncan Learmouth, Sr. VP-Corp. Comm. & Comm. Partnerships
Marc Dunoyer, Pres., Asia Pacific & Japan
Deirdre Connelly, Pres., North American Pharmaceuticals
Eddie Gray, Pres., Pharmaceuticals Europe
John Clarke, Pres., Consumer Healthcare
Christopher Gent, Chmn.

Phone: 44-20-8047-5000 **Fax:** 44-20-8047-7807
Toll-Free: 888-825-5249
Address: 980 Great West Rd., Brentford, Middlesex, TW8 9GS UK

GROWTH PLANS/SPECIAL FEATURES:

GlaxoSmithKline (GSK) is a leading research-based pharmaceutical company formed from the merger of Glaxo Wellcome and SmithKline Beecham. Its subsidiaries consist of global drug and health companies engaged in the creation, discovery, development, manufacturing and marketing of pharmaceuticals and other consumer health products. GSK operates in two segments: pharmaceuticals, and consumer health care. The pharmaceuticals segment includes prescription medications and vaccines. GSK designs prescription medications for the treatment many conditions including heart and circulatory conditions, cancer, and malaria. Major prescription medication approvals in 2008 included Lamictal and Adoair for use in Japan. GSK's vaccines are designed to treat life-threatening illnesses such as hepatitis A, diphtheria, influenza and bacterial meningitis. GSK received several drug approvals by the Food and Drug Administration in 2008 including Ceravix, a cervical cancer vaccine. The consumer health care division is divided into three segments: over-the-counter, oral healthcare and nutritional healthcare. Products from the consumer health care segment include over-the-counter medications such as Citrucel and Nicorette; oral care products such as Aquafresh; and nutritional products such as Boost. Research and development operations take place at 17 sites in four countries. Its research areas include neuroscience, oncology, infectious diseases, cardiovascular/metabolic respiratory, musculoskeletal/inflammation and gastrointestinal/urology. In 2008, GSK agreed to divest four products, Eltroxin, Lanoxin, Imuran and Zyloric, to Aspen Global Incorporated. GSK announced in October 2008 that it agreed to acquire the Egyptian products business of Bristol Myers Squibb and the U.S. company Genelabs Technologies. In November 2008, it entered into an agreement with AstraZeneca to acquire a number of leading over-the-counter (OTC) medicines predominantly sold in Sweden, including Alvedon.

FINANCIALS: **Sales and profits are in thousands of dollars—add 000 to get the full amount. 2008 Note: Financial information for 2008 was not available for all companies at press time.**

2008 Sales: $36,127,200
2007 Sales: $33,700,100
2006 Sales: $45,595,800
2005 Sales: $37,783,631
2004 Sales: $34,863,347

2008 Profits: $10,594,000
2007 Profits: $11,264,500
2006 Profits: $10,793,000
2005 Profits: $8,400,952
2004 Profits: $7,015,930

U.S. Stock Ticker: GSK
Int'l Ticker: GSK Int'l Exchange: London-LSE
Employees: 110,000
Fiscal Year Ends: 12/31
Parent Company:

SALARIES/BENEFITS:

Pension Plan: Y ESOP Stock Plan: Y Profit Sharing: Top Exec. Salary: $1,523,000 Bonus: $2,250,000
Savings Plan: Y Stock Purch. Plan: Second Exec. Salary: $949,136 Bonus: $

OTHER THOUGHTS:

Apparent Women Officers or Directors: 3
Hot Spot for Advancement for Women/Minorities: Y

LOCATIONS: ("Y" = Yes)

West:	Southwest:	Midwest:	Southeast:	Northeast:	International:
Y	Y	Y	Y	Y	Y

GLOBAL VIA INFRASTRUCTURES SA (GLOBALVIA)

www.globalvia.com

Industry Group Code: 488490 **Ranks within this company's industry group:** Sales: Profits:

Techology:		Medical/Drugs:		Engineering:		Transportation:		Chemicals/Petrochemicals:		Specialty:	
Computers:		Manufacturer:		Design:		Aerospace:	Y	Oil/Gas Products:		Special Services:	
Software:		Contract Research:		Construction:		Automotive:	Y	Chemicals:		Consulting:	
Communications:		Medical Services:		Eng. Services:		Shipping:	Y	Oil/Chem. Svcs.:		Specialty Mgmt.:	
Electronics:		Labs:		Consulting:				Gases:		Products:	
Alternative Energy:		Bio. Services:						Other:		Other:	

TYPES OF BUSINESS:

Transportation Infrastructure Ownership & Operation
Highway Operations
Port Operations
Airport Operations
Railway Operations
Public Building Operations

BRANDS/DIVISIONS/AFFILIATES:

Corporacion Caja Madrid
FCC Construccion
Fomento de Construcciones Y Contratas SA (FCC)

GROWTH PLANS/SPECIAL FEATURES:

Global Via Infrastructuras S.A. (Global Via), an infrastructure development and management firm, was formed by Caja Madrid, a savings bank, and Fomento de Construcciones Y Contratas SA (FCC), via Corporacion Caja Madrid and FCC Construccion, both holding 50% shares in the joint venture. Global Via has a portfolio comprised of a wide range of products and a large number of infrastructure projects, of which approximately 75% are in Spain. The company's asset portfolio encompasses 40 infrastructure projects including motorways, metropolitan railways, ports, airports and public buildings. The Global Via project currently encompasses a total of 21 motorways (nine of which are non user tolled and the rest user toll), six railways, two airports, two hospitals, three commercial ports and four leisure ports. The company aims to participate in the financing of new greenfield projects as well as the acquisition of brownfield project assets currently in operation. The firm has operations in Spain, Andorra, Portugal, Ireland, Mexico, Costa Rica, Chile and the U.S. Global Via's U.S. offices are located in New York, Miami and Houston. During 2008, the firm acquired two Chilean toll roads for approximately $553 million. The first toll road, at approximately 218 kilometers in length, connects Santiago with Los Vilos and carries an average of 35,414 vehicles per day. The second toll road, at approximately 89 kilometers in length, connects Concepcion and Chillan, with an average of 7,280 vehicles per day.

CONTACTS: *Note: Officers with more than one job title may be intentionally listed here more than once.*

Jesus D. F. De Rivero, CEO
Francisco Javier Falces Valle, COO
Carmen Rubio, CFO
Luis Matallana, CTO
Jose Felipe Gomez, General Counsel
Miguel Garcia, Chief Officer-Bus. Networking
Rafael Nevado, Dir.-Bidding Department
Maria Luisa Castro, Chief Officer-O&M
Michael Lapola, Dir.-U.S.
Jesus D. F. De Rivero, Chmn.
Fernando Del Campo, Dir.-Int'l Dev.

Phone: 34-914-565-850 **Fax:** 34-916-625-607
Toll-Free:
Address: Paseo Castellana, 141-5 Planta, Edificio Cuzco IV, Madrid, 28046 Spain

FINANCIALS: **Sales and profits are in thousands of dollars—add 000 to get the full amount. 2008 Note: Financial information for 2008 was not available for all companies at press time.**

2008 Sales: $	2008 Profits: $
2007 Sales: $	2007 Profits: $
2006 Sales: $	2006 Profits: $
2005 Sales: $	2005 Profits: $
2004 Sales: $	2004 Profits: $

U.S. Stock Ticker: Joint Venture
Int'l Ticker: Int'l Exchange:
Employees:
Fiscal Year Ends:
Parent Company: FOMENTO DE CONSTRUCCIONES Y CONTRATAS SA (FCC)

SALARIES/BENEFITS:

Pension Plan:	ESOP Stock Plan:	Profit Sharing:	Top Exec. Salary: $	Bonus: $
Savings Plan:	Stock Purch. Plan:		Second Exec. Salary: $	Bonus: $

OTHER THOUGHTS:

Apparent Women Officers or Directors: 2
Hot Spot for Advancement for Women/Minorities:

LOCATIONS: ("Y" = Yes)

West:	Southwest:	Midwest:	Southeast:	Northeast:	International:
	Y		Y	Y	Y

Note: Financial information, benefits and other data can change quickly and may vary from those stated here.

GM DAEWOO AUTO AND TECHNOLOGY CO www.gmdaewoo.co.kr

Industry Group Code: 336111 **Ranks within this company's industry group:** Sales: Profits:

Techology:		Medical/Drugs:		Engineering:		Transportation:		Chemicals/Petrochemicals:		Specialty:	
Computers:		Manufacturer:		Design:		Aerospace:		Oil/Gas Products:		Special Services:	
Software:		Contract Research:		Construction:		Automotive:	Y	Chemicals:		Consulting:	
Communications:		Medical Services:		Eng. Services:		Shipping:		Oil/Chem. Svcs.:		Specialty Mgmt.:	
Electronics:		Labs:		Consulting:				Gases:		Products:	
Alternative Energy:		Bio. Services:						Other:		Other:	

TYPES OF BUSINESS:

Automobiles, Manufacturing
Marketing

BRANDS/DIVISIONS/AFFILIATES:

Daewoo Group
Daewoo Motor Co.
General Motors Corp (GM)
Suzuki Motor Corp
Shanghai Automotive Industry Corp
Matiz
Lacetti
Winstorm

CONTACTS: *Note: Officers with more than one job title may be intentionally listed here more than once.*

Michael Grimaldi, CEO
Michael Grimaldi, Pres.
Mark James, CFO
Dong-Woo Jang, VP-Personnel Department
Steve Clarke, VP-Technical Center
Tae-Wan Kim, VP-Design Ctr.
Ki-Joon Yu, Sr. VP-Mfg. Oper.
Mark James, VP-Admin.
Rick LaBelle, VP-Commercial Oper.
Sergio Rocha, VP-Planning
Jay Cooney, VP-Comm. & Public Policy
Mark James, VP-Finance
Dong-ho Lee, Pres., Daewoo Motor Sales
James Deluca, VP-Quality
Ronald D. Yuille, VP-Powertrain
Josef Edlinger, VP-Global Purchasing & Supply Chain

Phone: 82-32-520-2114	**Fax:** 82-32-520-4610
Toll-Free:	
Address: 199 Chongchon-dong, Pupyong-ku, Incheon, Korea	

GROWTH PLANS/SPECIAL FEATURES:

GM Daewoo Auto and Technology Co. primarily manufactures vehicles in the Asia-Pacific region. Formerly a member of the South Korean industrial conglomerate Daewoo Group operating under the name Daewoo Motor Company, the firm has been controlled by General Motors Corp. (GM) since 2002. The largest shareholders of the firm are GM, which currently owns 51% of the company; Suzuki Motor Corp., 11%; and Shanghai Automotive Industry Corp., 10%. Creditors own the remainder of the firm. GM Daewoo's models include the Matiz, Lacetti and Gentra mini-cars, as well as the Tosca sedan, G2X sports car, Winstorm sport utility vehicle (SUV), Damas van and Labo medium truck. Former models offered by the firm include the Rezzo, Statesman, Caravan, Gemini and Saemaeul Pickup. It also manufactures and sells vehicles under other brand names, including Chevrolet, Buick, Pontiac and Suzuki. GM Daewoo sold almost 1.9 million vehicles during 2007, 90% of which were exported to over 150 markets. Besides manufacturing vehicles, the firm does marketing work to advance GM and Saab products in Korea; and produces various GM branded vehicle components, including Holden engines, Allison transmissions and ACDelco service parts. GM Daewoo has vehicle manufacturing facilities in Bupyeong, Gunsan and Changwon, Korea; and a power train plant in Boryung, Korea that manufactures aluminum heads and blocks as well as transmissions. Additionally, the firm assembles cars and buses in its VIDAMCO facility in Hanoi, Vietnam. Research and development takes place at the Daewoo Design Center and GM Daewoo Technical Center. Current research projects include hybrid vehicles, concept cars and hydrogen fuel cells.

FINANCIALS: Sales and profits are in thousands of dollars—add 000 to get the full amount. 2008 Note: Financial information for 2008 was not available for all companies at press time.

2008 Sales: $	2008 Profits: $	**U.S. Stock Ticker: Subsidiary**
2007 Sales: $	2007 Profits: $	**Int'l Ticker:** Int'l Exchange:
2006 Sales: $	2006 Profits: $	Employees: 900
2005 Sales: $	2005 Profits: $	Fiscal Year Ends: 12/31
2004 Sales: $	2004 Profits: $	Parent Company: GENERAL MOTORS CORP (GM)

SALARIES/BENEFITS:

Pension Plan:	ESOP Stock Plan:	Profit Sharing:	Top Exec. Salary: $	Bonus: $
Savings Plan:	Stock Purch. Plan:		Second Exec. Salary: $	Bonus: $

OTHER THOUGHTS:

Apparent Women Officers or Directors:
Hot Spot for Advancement for Women/Minorities:

LOCATIONS: ("Y" = Yes)

West:	Southwest:	Midwest:	Southeast:	Northeast:	International:
					Y

GOODRICH CORPORATION

www.goodrich.com

Industry Group Code: 336410 **Ranks within this company's industry group:** Sales: 16 Profits: 11

Techology:		Medical/Drugs:		Engineering:		Transportation:		Chemicals/Petrochemicals:		Specialty:	
Computers:		Manufacturer:		Design:		Aerospace:	Y	Oil/Gas Products:		Special Services:	Y
Software:		Contract Research:		Construction:		Automotive:		Chemicals:		Consulting:	
Communications:		Medical Services:		Eng. Services:		Shipping:		Oil/Chem. Svcs.:		Specialty Mgmt.:	
Electronics:		Labs:		Consulting:				Gases:		Products:	Y
Alternative Energy:		Bio. Services:						Other:		Other:	

TYPES OF BUSINESS:

Aerospace Systems Manufacturer
Engine Systems
Electronic Systems
Technical Services
Aircraft Maintenance & Modification

BRANDS/DIVISIONS/AFFILIATES:

TEAC Aerospace Holdings Inc
Rolls-Royce Goodrich Engine Control Systems Ltd

CONTACTS: *Note: Officers with more than one job title may be intentionally listed here more than once.*

Marshall O. Larsen, CEO
Marshall O. Larsen, Pres.
Scott E. Kuechle, CFO/Exec. VP
Jennifer Pollino, Sr. VP-Human Resources
Jerry Witowski, Exec. VP-Tech. & Oper. Excellence
Terrence G. Linnert, Exec. VP-Admin.
Terrence G. Linnert, General Counsel
Joseph F. Andolino, VP-Bus. Dev. & Tax
Lisa Bottle, VP-Comm.
Paul S. Gifford, VP-Investor Rel.
Scott Cottrill, VP/Controller
John J. Carmola, Pres., Actuation & Landing Systems
Cynthia M. Egnotovich, Pres., Nacelles & Interior Systems
Curtis Reusser, Pres., Electronic Systems
Sally L. Geib, Associate General Counsel/VP/Corp. Sec.
Marshall O. Larsen, Chmn.

Phone: 704-423-7000 **Fax:** 704-423-5540
Toll-Free:
Address: 4 Coliseum Ctr., 2730 W. Tyvola Rd., Charlotte, NC 28217-4578 US

GROWTH PLANS/SPECIAL FEATURES:

Goodrich Corporation is one of the largest worldwide suppliers of components, systems and services to the commercial and general aviation markets. The company is also a leading supplier of aircraft products and satellite systems to the global military and space markets. Goodrich operates through three business segments: actuation and landing systems, nacelles and interior systems and electronic systems. The actuation and landing segment includes systems, components and related services related to aircraft taxi, take-off, flight control, wheels and brakes, actuation systems, landing and stopping, as well as engine components, including fuel delivery systems and rotating assemblies. The firm's nacelles and interior systems unit produces products and provides maintenance, repair and overhaul services associated with aircraft engines, including thrust reversers, cowlings, nozzles and their components, as well as aircraft interior products, including slides, seats, cargo and lighting systems, engineered polymer products, crew seating and ejection seats. This segment is also responsible for evacuation and propulsion systems. The electronic systems division includes a wide array of systems and components that provide flight performance measurements, flight management and control and safety data. These include systems that manage aircraft fuel, electrical systems, reconnaissance and surveillance systems, missile actuation systems, ice detection and de-icing systems, test equipment and lighting systems. In 2008, the firm acquired TEAC Aerospace Holdings, Inc., a leading provider of surveillance and debriefing equipment for defense and commercial carriers. In January 2009, Goodrich and Rolls-Royce Group plc formed a joint venture, Rolls-Royce Goodrich Engine Control Systems Limited, operated as Aero Engine Controls. Both companies hold 50% stakes in the venture.

FINANCIALS: Sales and profits are in thousands of dollars—add 000 to get the full amount. 2008 Note: Financial information for 2008 was not available for all companies at press time.

2008 Sales: $7,062,000	2008 Profits: $681,000	**U.S. Stock Ticker: GR**
2007 Sales: $6,392,200	2007 Profits: $482,600	**Int'l Ticker:** Int'l Exchange:
2006 Sales: $5,719,100	2006 Profits: $482,100	Employees: 25,000
2005 Sales: $5,202,600	2005 Profits: $263,600	Fiscal Year Ends: 12/31
2004 Sales: $4,700,400	2004 Profits: $172,200	Parent Company:

SALARIES/BENEFITS:

Pension Plan: Y	ESOP Stock Plan:	Profit Sharing:	Top Exec. Salary: $1,030,000	Bonus: $1,782,415
Savings Plan:	Stock Purch. Plan:		Second Exec. Salary: $492,000	Bonus: $532,735

OTHER THOUGHTS:

Apparent Women Officers or Directors: 5
Hot Spot for Advancement for Women/Minorities: Y

LOCATIONS: ("Y" = Yes)

West:	Southwest:	Midwest:	Southeast:	Northeast:	International:
Y	Y	Y	Y	Y	Y

GOOGLE INC

www.google.com

Industry Group Code: 514199B **Ranks within this company's industry group:** Sales: 1 Profits: 1

Techology:		Medical/Drugs:		Engineering:		Transportation:		Chemicals/Petrochemicals:		Specialty:	
Computers:		Manufacturer:		Design:		Aerospace:		Oil/Gas Products:		Special Services:	Y
Software:		Contract Research:		Construction:		Automotive:		Chemicals:		Consulting:	
Communications:		Medical Services:		Eng. Services:		Shipping:		Oil/Chem. Svcs.:		Specialty Mgmt.:	
Electronics:		Labs:		Consulting:				Gases:		Products:	
Alternative Energy:		Bio. Services:						Other:		Other:	

TYPES OF BUSINESS:

Search Engine-Internet
Paid Search Listing Advertising Services
News Site Search Service
Catalog Search Service
Shopping Site
Web Log Tool
Search and Advertising on Cell Phones

BRANDS/DIVISIONS/AFFILIATES:

Google
Google AdWords
Google AdSense
MySpace
DoubleClick
Adscape Media, Inc.
YouTube
Android

CONTACTS: *Note: Officers with more than one job title may be intentionally listed here more than once.*

Eric Schmidt, CEO
Patrick Pichette, CFO/Sr. VP
Omid Kordestani, Sr. VP-Worldwide Sales & Bus. Dev.
Laszlo Bock, VP-People Oper.
Alan Eustace, Sr. VP-Research & Eng.
Ben Fried, CIO
Sergey Brin, Pres., Tech./Co-Founder
Larry Page, Pres., Products/Co-Founder
W.M. Coughran, Jr., Sr. VP-Eng.
David C. Drummond, Chief Legal Officer
Urs Holzle, Sr. VP-Oper./Google Fellow
David C. Drummond, VP-Corp. Dev.
Vinton G. Cerf., Chief Internet Evangelist/VP
Rachel Whetstone, VP-Global Comm. & Public Affairs
Mark Fuchs, VP-Finance/Chief Acct. Officer
Shona Brown, Sr. VP-Bus. Oper.
Jeff Huber, Sr. VP-Eng.
Jonathan Rosenberg, Sr. VP-Product Management
Penry Price, VP-Advertising Sales, North America
Eric Schmidt, Chmn.
Omid Kordestani, Sr. VP-Global Sales & Bus. Dev.

Phone: 650-623-4000 **Fax:** 650-253-0001
Toll-Free:
Address: 1600 Amphitheatre Pkwy., Mountain View, CA 94043 US

GROWTH PLANS/SPECIAL FEATURES:

Google, Inc. operates Google.com, one of the worlds largest and most used search engines, which indexes the content of over 8 billion Internet pages. While Google charges nothing for its search engine, it charges fees to other sites that use its search technology, and has a lucrative program that enables business clients to bid for ad space. Google provides its services in 116 different languages, with more than 50% of its searches coming from outside the U.S. The company's technology employs a unique, distributed-computing system utilizing thousands of low-end servers rather than a small number of high-powered computers. The company offers Google AdWords, a global advertising program which presents ads to customers precisely when they are looking for what the advertiser has to offer. Google AdSense allows web sites in the Google Network to serve targeted ads from the AdWords advertisers. In March 2008, Google acquired marketing firm DoubleClick Inc. for $3.1 billion. In July 2007, the firm agreed to acquire Postini, Inc., an e-mail security company, for $625 million. Google hopes to dominate search-generated advertising on cellphones. It was instrumental in developing Android, an open source platform for cellphone handsets. In July 2008, the company announced that it has signed an agreement with Rambler Media to acquire ZAO Begun, a Russian context advertising service. In August 2008, Google released a beta version of its Internet browser called Chrome.

Employee benefits include medical, dental and vision insurance; 401(k); 18 weeks maternity leave; flexible spending accounts; college savings plan; adoption assistance; tuition reimbursement; free on-site lunches and dinners; paid vacation that increases with years of service;. Google also provides recreation facilities, financial planning classes and on-site dry cleaning, oil change and car wash facilities.

FINANCIALS: Sales and profits are in thousands of dollars—add 000 to get the full amount. 2008 Note: Financial information for 2008 was not available for all companies at press time.

2008 Sales: $21,795,550	2008 Profits: $4,226,858	**U.S. Stock Ticker: GOOG**
2007 Sales: $16,593,986	2007 Profits: $4,203,720	**Int'l Ticker:** Int'l Exchange:
2006 Sales: $10,604,917	2006 Profits: $3,077,446	Employees: 20,222
2005 Sales: $6,138,560	2005 Profits: $1,465,397	Fiscal Year Ends: 12/31
2004 Sales: $3,189,223	2004 Profits: $399,119	Parent Company:

SALARIES/BENEFITS:

Pension Plan: Y	ESOP Stock Plan:	Profit Sharing:	Top Exec. Salary: $450,000	Bonus: $1,843
Savings Plan: Y	Stock Purch. Plan:		Second Exec. Salary: $450,000	Bonus: $1,843

OTHER THOUGHTS:

Apparent Women Officers or Directors: 9
Hot Spot for Advancement for Women/Minorities: Y

LOCATIONS: ("Y" = Yes)

West:	Southwest:	Midwest:	Southeast:	Northeast:	International:
Y	Y			Y	Y

Note: Financial information, benefits and other data can change quickly and may vary from those stated here.

GRANITE CONSTRUCTION INC

www.graniteconstruction.com

Industry Group Code: 234000 **Ranks within this company's industry group:** Sales: 23 Profits: 19

Techology:		Medical/Drugs:		Engineering:		Transportation:		Chemicals/Petrochemicals:		Specialty:	
Computers:		Manufacturer:		Design:		Aerospace:		Oil/Gas Products:		Special Services:	
Software:		Contract Research:		Construction:	Y	Automotive:		Chemicals:		Consulting:	
Communications:		Medical Services:		Eng. Services:		Shipping:	Y	Oil/Chem. Svcs.:		Specialty Mgmt.:	
Electronics:		Labs:		Consulting:				Gases:		Products:	
Alternative Energy:		Bio. Services:						Other:		Other:	

TYPES OF BUSINESS:

Construction, Heavy & Civil Engineering
Infrastructure Projects
Site Preparation Services
Construction Materials Processing
Heavy Construction Equipment

BRANDS/DIVISIONS/AFFILIATES:

Granite East
Granite West
Granite Land Company

CONTACTS: *Note: Officers with more than one job title may be intentionally listed here more than once.*

William G. Dorey, CEO
Mark Boitano, COO/Exec. VP
William G. Dorey, Pres.
LeAnne M. Stewart, CFO/Sr. VP
Peg Wynn, VP-Human Resources
Michael Flutch, General Counsel/VP
Laurel Krzeminski, Controller/VP
Michael F. Donnino, Sr. VP/Mgr.-Granite East Div.
James H. Roberts, Sr. VP/Mgr.-Granite West Div.
David H. Watts, Chmn.

Phone: 831-724-1011 **Fax:** 831-722-9657
Toll-Free: 800-482-1518
Address: 585 W. Beach St., Watsonville, CA 95076 US

GROWTH PLANS/SPECIAL FEATURES:

Granite Construction, Inc. is one of the largest heavy civil construction contractors in the U.S. The firm operates nationwide, serving both public and private sector clients. Within the public sector, the company primarily concentrates on infrastructure projects, including the construction of roads, highways, bridges, dams, tunnels, canals, mass transit facilities and airports. Within the private sector, it performs site preparation services for buildings, plants, subdivisions and other facilities. Granite owns and leases substantial aggregate reserves and owns 158 construction materials processing plants. In addition, the company has one of the largest contractor-owned heavy construction equipment fleets in the U.S., with over 7,000 units. Granite is organized geographically into two business segments: Granite West and Granite East. Granite West operates out of 14 branch offices that serve local markets, as well as major infrastructure projects in the western region of the U.S. Each of its branch locations is aligned under one of three operating groups: Northwest, Northern California and Southwest. Granite East focuses on the firm's larger projects, such as mass transit facilities, highways, dams, bridges and airports. Granite East operates out of three regional offices: the Central Region, based in Lewisville, Texas; the Southeast Region, based in Tampa, Florida; and the Northeast Region, based in Tarrytown, New York. Granite also produces concrete, gravel, ready-mix asphalt, sand, and other construction materials. Company subsidiary Granite Land Company purchases, develops, operates, sells and invests in real estate. In December 2008, Granite Construction sold its minority interest in TIC Holdings, Inc., a heavy industrial construction firm, to Kiewit Corporation for an undisclosed amount.

Employee benefits include medical, dental and vision coverage; employee assistance plan; 401(k); stock purchase plan; flexible spending accounts; education reimbursement; and domestic partner benefits.

FINANCIALS: **Sales and profits are in thousands of dollars—add 000 to get the full amount. 2008 Note: Financial information for 2008 was not available for all companies at press time.**

2008 Sales: $2,674,244	2008 Profits: $122,404	**U.S. Stock Ticker: GVA**
2007 Sales: $2,737,914	2007 Profits: $112,065	**Int'l Ticker:** Int'l Exchange:
2006 Sales: $2,969,604	2006 Profits: $80,509	Employees: 3,500
2005 Sales: $2,641,352	2005 Profits: $83,150	Fiscal Year Ends: 12/31
2004 Sales: $2,136,212	2004 Profits: $57,007	Parent Company:

SALARIES/BENEFITS:

Pension Plan:	ESOP Stock Plan:	Profit Sharing:	Top Exec. Salary: $450,000	Bonus: $1,350,000
Savings Plan: Y	Stock Purch. Plan: Y		Second Exec. Salary: $350,000	Bonus: $490,000

OTHER THOUGHTS:

Apparent Women Officers or Directors: 4
Hot Spot for Advancement for Women/Minorities: Y

LOCATIONS: ("Y" = Yes)

West:	Southwest:	Midwest:	Southeast:	Northeast:	International:
Y	Y	Y	Y	Y	

GROUP LOTUS PLC

www.grouplotus.com

Industry Group Code: 336111 **Ranks within this company's industry group:** Sales: Profits:

Techology:		Medical/Drugs:		Engineering:		Transportation:		Chemicals/Petrochemicals:		Specialty:	
Computers:		Manufacturer:		Design:	Y	Aerospace:		Oil/Gas Products:		Special Services:	
Software:		Contract Research:		Construction:		Automotive:	Y	Chemicals:		Consulting:	
Communications:		Medical Services:		Eng. Services:	Y	Shipping:		Oil/Chem. Svcs.:		Specialty Mgmt.:	
Electronics:		Labs:		Consulting:	Y			Gases:		Products:	
Alternative Energy:		Bio. Services:						Other:		Other:	

TYPES OF BUSINESS:

Automobile Manufacturing
Sports Car Design & Manufacturing
Design & Engineering Services
Consulting Services
Driving Instruction Facilities
New & Pre-owned Sports Car Sales
Automotive Accessories
Lightweight Aluminum Manufacturing

BRANDS/DIVISIONS/AFFILIATES:

Proton Holdings Berhad
Lotus Cars Ltd.
Lotus Cars USA, Inc.
Lotus Engineering, Inc.
Evora
Spyker Cars N.V.
Lotus Lightweight Structures
Holden Lightweight Structures, Ltd.

CONTACTS: *Note: Officers with more than one job title may be intentionally listed here more than once.*

Michael J. Kimberley, CEO
Trevor Houghton-Berry, Head-Commercial Oper.
James Stronach, Dir.-Finance
Geraint Castleton-White, Head-Powertrain, Lotus Engineering, Inc.
Russell Carr, Head-Lotus Design
Paul Newsome, Managing Dir.-Lotus Engineering, Inc.
Michael J. Kimberley, Pres./CEO-Lotus Cars USA

Phone: 44-1953-608-000	**Fax:** 44-1953-608-300
Toll-Free:	
Address: Potash Ln., Hethel, Norwich, Norfolk NR14 8EZ UK	

GROWTH PLANS/SPECIAL FEATURES:

Group Lotus plc, majority owned by Malaysian automobile manufacturer Proton Holdings Berhad, operates a group of automotive divisions. The company's two main lines of business are sports car manufacturing, through Lotus Cars Ltd., and engineering consulting, through Lotus Engineering, Inc. Lotus offers a broad range of sports cars, including the Elise series; the Europa S; the 2-Eleven; the Exige, inspired by racecar design; and the new Evora 2+2 coupe, introduced in July 2008. Lotus Engineering provides consulting services including design, development and testing, as well as manufacturing and sale of finished products, to other carmakers. Lotus Cars USA, Inc. is responsible for sales, distribution and servicing of Lotus cars in North America through its dealer network. In March 2007, the company released the Lotus 2-Eleven, a light-weight track car; and the Lotus Exige GT3 concept vehicle, built up to Gran Turismo (GT) racing specs. In June 2007, Lotus Cars began retailing Lotus automobiles in South Korea through business partner LKO, Ltd. In July 2007, the Lotus Academy of Excellence opened, giving new owners the opportunity to train on Lotus's test track with its test drivers. In January 2008, Lotus Engineering entered a joint cooperation program with the King Abdulaziz City for Science and Technology (KACST) to promote ecologically driven automotive technology in Saudi Arabia. In February 2008, Lotus Engineering created a new research and development group focused on hybrid and electric vehicles. In May 2008, Lotus Cars signed a cooperation agreement with Spyker Cars N.V. to provide parts, platform and design services for future Spyker vehicles. Also in May, Group Lotus created Lotus Lightweight Structures after the acquisition of Holden Lightweight Structures, Ltd. The new company, based at a former Holden Lightweight site, will continue manufacturing light weight aluminum and composite structures.

FINANCIALS: **Sales and profits are in thousands of dollars—add 000 to get the full amount. 2008 Note: Financial information for 2008 was not available for all companies at press time.**

2008 Sales: $	2008 Profits: $	**U.S. Stock Ticker: Subsidiary**
2007 Sales: $	2007 Profits: $	**Int'l Ticker:** Int'l Exchange:
2006 Sales: $	2006 Profits: $	Employees: 1,508
2005 Sales: $303,900	2005 Profits: $-14,000	Fiscal Year Ends: 3/31
2004 Sales: $263,500	2004 Profits: $ 400	Parent Company: PROTON HOLDINGS BERHAD

SALARIES/BENEFITS:

Pension Plan: Y	ESOP Stock Plan:	Profit Sharing:	Top Exec. Salary: $	Bonus: $
Savings Plan:	Stock Purch. Plan:		Second Exec. Salary: $	Bonus: $

OTHER THOUGHTS:

Apparent Women Officers or Directors:
Hot Spot for Advancement for Women/Minorities:

LOCATIONS: ("Y" = Yes)

West:	Southwest:	Midwest:	Southeast:	Northeast:	International:
Y	Y	Y	Y	Y	Y

GRUPO ACS

www.grupoacs.com

Industry Group Code: 234000 **Ranks within this company's industry group:** Sales: 6 Profits: 3

Techology:		Medical/Drugs:		Engineering:		Transportation:		Chemicals/Petrochemicals:		Specialty:	
Computers:		Manufacturer:		Design:	Y	Aerospace:		Oil/Gas Products:		Special Services:	Y
Software:		Contract Research:		Construction:	Y	Automotive:		Chemicals:		Consulting:	
Communications:		Medical Services:		Eng. Services:	Y	Shipping:		Oil/Chem. Svcs.:		Specialty Mgmt.:	Y
Electronics:		Labs:		Consulting:	Y			Gases:		Products:	
Alternative Energy:		Bio. Services:						Other:		Other:	

TYPES OF BUSINESS:

Heavy Construction
Engineering Services
Civic Construction & Infrastructure
Industrial Services
Facility Maintenance
Passenger Transportation
Transportation Concessions

BRANDS/DIVISIONS/AFFILIATES:

Grupo Dragados, S.A.
Vias
Drace
Geocisa
Grupo Cobra
Grupo Etra
CYMI
Urbaser

CONTACTS: *Note: Officers with more than one job title may be intentionally listed here more than once.*

Florentino P. Rodriguez, CEO
Angel G. Altozano, Corp. Gen. Mgr.
Jose L. V. Perez, Sec.
Antonio G. Ferrer, Exec. Vice Chmn.
Florentino P. Rodriguez, Chmn.

Phone: 34-91-343-92-00	**Fax:** 34-91-343-94-56
Toll-Free:	
Address: Avda. Pio XII, No. 102, Madrid, 28036 Spain	

GROWTH PLANS/SPECIAL FEATURES:

Grupo ACS is a leading Spanish construction and engineering firm that services a wide variety of sectors, including transportation infrastructure, real estate, offshore activities, energy, hydraulics, environment, industrial equipment, concessions and maintenance. The company is massively international and performs its operations through the many subsidiaries, the most significant being Grupo Dragados, S.A., the Spanish construction giant. Other ACS companies include Vias, Drace, Geocisa, Grupo Cobra, Grupo Etra, CYMI and Urbaser. The firm has worked in more than 60 countries and currently maintains this global presence through operations on five continents. ACS operates primarily in four major areas: construction, industrial services, other services and concessions. The construction business has completed a tremendous amount of civil works projects, as well as commercial and residential structures. The industrial services division largely serves the energy and communications sectors through its applied design, installation and maintenance of the industrial infrastructure. Other company services include environmental projects, port operations and logistics, facility management and passenger transportation. The firm also runs certain transportation concessions worldwide, mainly highways, railroads and airports. In recent news, the company acquired an additional 4.83% of Union Fenosa, raising its stake in the electricity utility to 45.3%, for $966 million. The firm's subsidiary, Dragados, also recently strengthened its foothold in North America with the acquisition of Schiavone Construction Co., which specializes in major civil work projects, for $50 million.

FINANCIALS: **Sales and profits are in thousands of dollars—add 000 to get the full amount. 2008 Note: Financial information for 2008 was not available for all companies at press time.**

2008 Sales: $19,320,500	2008 Profits: $1,769,040	**U.S. Stock Ticker:**
2007 Sales: $16,713,900	2007 Profits: $3,505,000	**Int'l Ticker: ACS** Int'l Exchange: Barcelona-BME
2006 Sales: $19,016,796	2006 Profits: $1,721,450	Employees: 144,919
2005 Sales: $16,376,220	2005 Profits: $855,723	Fiscal Year Ends: 12/31
2004 Sales: $14,625,218	2004 Profits: $635,911	Parent Company:

SALARIES/BENEFITS:

Pension Plan:	ESOP Stock Plan:	Profit Sharing:	Top Exec. Salary: $	Bonus: $
Savings Plan:	Stock Purch. Plan:		Second Exec. Salary: $	Bonus: $

OTHER THOUGHTS:

Apparent Women Officers or Directors:
Hot Spot for Advancement for Women/Minorities:

LOCATIONS: ("Y" = Yes)

West:	Southwest:	Midwest:	Southeast:	Northeast:	International:
					Y

GRUPO FERROVIAL SA

www.ferrovial.com

Industry Group Code: 234000 **Ranks within this company's industry group:** Sales: 7 Profits: 23

Techology:		Medical/Drugs:		Engineering:		Transportation:		Chemicals/Petrochemicals:		Specialty:	
Computers:		Manufacturer:		Design:		Aerospace:		Oil/Gas Products:		Special Services:	
Software:		Contract Research:		Construction:	Y	Automotive:		Chemicals:		Consulting:	
Communications:		Medical Services:		Eng. Services:		Shipping:		Oil/Chem. Svcs.:		Specialty Mgmt.:	Y
Electronics:		Labs:		Consulting:				Gases:		Products:	
Alternative Energy:		Bio. Services:						Other:		Other:	

TYPES OF BUSINESS:

Airport & Infrastructure Management
Construction
Infrastructure Services

BRANDS/DIVISIONS/AFFILIATES:

Swissport International Ltd
Webber
BAA PLC
Cespa
Cadagua
Budimex
Amey PLC
Cintra

CONTACTS: *Note: Officers with more than one job title may be intentionally listed here more than once.*

Joaquin Ayuso Garcia, CEO
Nicolas Villen Jimenez, CFO
Jaime Aguirre de Carcer, Gen. Mgr.-Human Resources
Jose Ma Perez, General Sec.
Jose Manuel Ruiz de Gopequi, CEO-Ferrovial Agroman (Construction Div.)
Inigo Meiras, CEO-Airports Div.
Santiago Olivares, CEO-Ferrovial Servicios
Enrique Diaz-Rato, CEO-Cintra (Toll Roads & Car Parks Div.)
Rafael del Pino Y Calvo Sotelo, Chmn.

Phone: 34-91-586-25-00	**Fax:** 34-91-586-26-77
Toll-Free:	
Address: Principe de Vergara, 135, Madrid, 28002 Spain	

GROWTH PLANS/SPECIAL FEATURES:

Grupo Ferrovial S.A. is a leading infrastructure and industrial group with operations in 43 countries worldwide. The company's investments target four business areas: construction; airports; services; and toll roads and car parks. The infrastructure operations (airports, toll roads and car parks) are capital intensive and offer long-run profit potential, while the industrial operations (construction and services) provide the firm's current net positive income. Construction, the firm's original business, covers all aspects of civil engineering and building, including roads, railways, hydraulic works, maritime works, hydroelectric and industrial works. This division includes several subsidiaries: Cadagua, a water and waste treatment plant engineering and construction company; Budimex, Poland's largest construction company; and Webber, a construction group in Texas. Ferrovial's airports segment is the leading private airport operator in the world, with 10 airports handling 158.6 million passengers annually. It serves 436 airlines that fly to 1,000 destinations. The largest company in the airport division, BAA, owns and manages seven airports in the U.K.: Heathrow, Gatwick, Stansted, Southampton, Glasgow, Edinburgh and Aberdeen. The firm's other three airports are the Belfast Airport in the U.K., the Cerro Moreno Airport in Chile and the Naples Airport. The company's services segment consists of Amey, a British infrastructure maintenance subsidiary; Cespa, a municipal and waste-water treatment subsidiary; Swissport, an airport handling services company; and various infrastructure and maintenance companies in Spain and Portugal. Lastly, Cintra is the firm's toll road and car parks division. It manages 2,841 miles of toll road in Spain, North America, Portugal, Ireland, Greece and Chile and 266,805 parking spaces in Spain, Andorra and Puerto Rico. In 2007, BAA sold its interests in six Australian airports. In 2008, BAA sold its subsidiary World Duty Free Europe Limited to Autogrill S.p.A and agreed to sell a portfolio of 33 assets to The Arora Family Trust.

FINANCIALS: **Sales and profits are in thousands of dollars—add 000 to get the full amount. 2008 Note: Financial information for 2008 was not available for all companies at press time.**

2008 Sales: $18,672,700	2008 Profits: $43,600	**U.S. Stock Ticker: GRFRF.PK**
2007 Sales: $21,360,000	2007 Profits: $1,070,000	**Int'l Ticker: FER** Int'l Exchange: Madrid-MCE
2006 Sales: $17,033,300	2006 Profits: $1,965,970	Employees: 88,902
2005 Sales: $11,470,500	2005 Profits: $530,580	Fiscal Year Ends: 12/31
2004 Sales: $9,256,540	2004 Profits: $674,520	Parent Company:

SALARIES/BENEFITS:

Pension Plan:	ESOP Stock Plan:	Profit Sharing:	Top Exec. Salary: $	Bonus: $
Savings Plan:	Stock Purch. Plan:		Second Exec. Salary: $	Bonus: $

OTHER THOUGHTS:

Apparent Women Officers or Directors: 2
Hot Spot for Advancement for Women/Minorities:

LOCATIONS: ("Y" = Yes)

West:	Southwest:	Midwest:	Southeast:	Northeast:	International:
	Y	Y			Y

Note: Financial information, benefits and other data can change quickly and may vary from those stated here.

GS ENGINEERING & CONSTRUCTION CORP www.gsconst.co.kr/english/

Industry Group Code: 234000 **Ranks within this company's industry group:** Sales: Profits:

Techology:		Medical/Drugs:		Engineering:		Transportation:		Chemicals/Petrochemicals:		Specialty:	
Computers:		Manufacturer:		Design:		Aerospace:		Oil/Gas Products:		Special Services:	
Software:		Contract Research:		Construction:	Y	Automotive:		Chemicals:		Consulting:	
Communications:		Medical Services:		Eng. Services:	Y	Shipping:		Oil/Chem. Svcs.:		Specialty Mgmt.:	
Electronics:		Labs:		Consulting:				Gases:		Products:	
Alternative Energy:		Bio. Services:						Other:	Y	Other:	Y

TYPES OF BUSINESS:

Construction

BRANDS/DIVISIONS/AFFILIATES:

Xi
Eclat

CONTACTS: *Note: Officers with more than one job title may be intentionally listed here more than once.*

Myung-Soo Huh, CEO
Myung-Soo Huh, Pres.
Si-Min Kim, CFO/Exec. VP
Jong-Gyu Kim, Sr. VP-Human Resources
Young-Nam Lee, CTO/Sr. Exec. VP
Hwi-Sung Lee, Sr. Exec. VP-Civil Eng.
Yong-Deug Ha, Chief Legal Officer
Chang-Deuk Do, Sr. VP-Strategic Planning
Yong-Deug Ha, Sr. Exec. VP-Public Rel.
Geon-Soo Jang, Sr. Exec. VP-Architecture
Chan-Ho Lee, Sr. Exec. VP-Housing
Jung-Jae Huh, Sr. Exec. VP-Power & Environment
Hwi-Sung Lee, Sr. Exec. VP-Domestic Bus.
Chang-Soo Huh, Chmn.
Kee-Ju Jang, Exec. VP-Procurement & Project Monitoring

Phone: 82-2-2005-1114 **Fax:**
Toll-Free:
Address: GS Yeokjeon Twr., 537 Namdaemun-ro 5-ga, Joong-gu, Seoul, Korea

GROWTH PLANS/SPECIAL FEATURES:

GS Engineering and Construction Corporation (GS E&C), established in 1969, has six main construction divisions: Civil Engineering, Plant, Environment, Architecture, Housing and Power. The civil engineering division focuses on roads, bridges and railroads; underground spaces; and harbors and dredging. Projects of note include the 4.54 mile West Sea Grand Bridge, the Hopo Subway Yard in Busan and an LPG (Liquefied Petroleum Gas) offloading terminal in Incheon. The plant division constructs oil refineries and gas processing plants; petrochemical plants; and power plants and other energy related facilities, such as pipelines and storage facilities. Some of its major projects include the Azerpetrochim refinery in Azerbaijan, the $700 million QP Refinery Expansion in Qatar, a VCM/PVC (Vinyl Chloride Monomer is used to make Polyvinyl Chloride) plant in Saudi Arabia, and the coal-fired Power Plant No. 5 and 6 in Taean. The environment division handles water and wastewater treatment facilities, as well as waste treatment and recycling facilities. Some of its projects include the China Sanghae Songjiang sewage treatment facilities and the Incheon Namdong-gu food waste recycling center. The architecture division constructs intelligent buildings; research, educational and medical health care facilities; and cultural and sports facilities. Major projects include the COEX Convention Center, the Buddhist Hospital for Dongkook University and the main stadium for Iman University in Saudi Arabia. GS E&C's housing division constructs residential complexes under the Xi brand and studio apartments under the Eclat brand. One of its major accomplishments was being selected as the contractor for the Korea National Housing Corp. project. The Power segment focuses on the construction of combined cycle power plant and thermal fired power plants; co-generation plants and district heating; and nuclear power plants. This division is currently constructing Nuclear Power Plant No.1 & 2 in the southeastern part of Korea.

FINANCIALS: Sales and profits are in thousands of dollars—add 000 to get the full amount. 2008 Note: Financial information for 2008 was not available for all companies at press time.

2008 Sales: $4,971,500	2008 Profits: $266,300	**U.S. Stock Ticker:**
2007 Sales: $4,431,100	2007 Profits: $294,850	**Int'l Ticker: 006360** Int'l Exchange: Seoul-KRX
2006 Sales: $4,234,760	2006 Profits: $285,220	Employees:
2005 Sales: $6,255,637	2005 Profits: $285,291	Fiscal Year Ends: 12/31
2004 Sales: $453,578	2004 Profits: $168,771	Parent Company:

SALARIES/BENEFITS:

Pension Plan:	ESOP Stock Plan:	Profit Sharing:	Top Exec. Salary: $	Bonus: $
Savings Plan:	Stock Purch. Plan:		Second Exec. Salary: $	Bonus: $

OTHER THOUGHTS:

Apparent Women Officers or Directors:
Hot Spot for Advancement for Women/Minorities:

LOCATIONS: ("Y" = Yes)

West:	Southwest:	Midwest:	Southeast:	Northeast:	International:
					Y

GULFSTREAM AEROSPACE CORP

www.gulfstream.com

Industry Group Code: 336410 **Ranks within this company's industry group:** Sales: 18 Profits:

Techology:		Medical/Drugs:		Engineering:		Transportation:		Chemicals/Petrochemicals:		Specialty:	
Computers:		Manufacturer:		Design:	Y	Aerospace:	Y	Oil/Gas Products:		Special Services:	Y
Software:		Contract Research:		Construction:		Automotive:		Chemicals:		Consulting:	
Communications:		Medical Services:		Eng. Services:		Shipping:		Oil/Chem. Svcs.:		Specialty Mgmt.:	
Electronics:		Labs:		Consulting:				Gases:		Products:	
Alternative Energy:		Bio. Services:						Other:		Other:	

TYPES OF BUSINESS:

Aircraft Manufacturer
Business Jets
Support Services
Leasing & Financing

BRANDS/DIVISIONS/AFFILIATES:

General Dynamics Corp
G150
G200
G350
G450
G500
G550
G650

CONTACTS:

Note: Officers with more than one job title may be intentionally listed here more than once.

Joseph T. Lombardo, Pres.
Larry Flynn, VP-Mktg. & Sales
Mark Burns, Pres., Prod. Support
Pres Henne, Sr. VP-Eng., Programs & Test
Ira Berman, Sr. VP-Admin.
Ira Berman, General Counsel
Dennis Stuligross, Sr. VP-Oper.
Dan Clare, Sr. VP-Planning
Dan Clare, Sr. VP-Finance
Buddy Sams, Sr. VP-Gov't Programs & Sales
Bill Williams, VP-Product Support Materials

Phone: 912-965-3000 **Fax:** 912-965-3084
Toll-Free:
Address: 500 Gulfstream Rd., Savannah, GA 31407 US

GROWTH PLANS/SPECIAL FEATURES:

Gulfstream Aerospace Corp., a subsidiary of General Dynamics Corp., develops, manufactures, markets and provides maintenance and support services for technologically-advanced business jet aircraft. The company is also a leading provider of aircraft for government special-mission applications, including executive transportation, aerial reconnaissance, maritime surveillance, weather research, and astronaut training. Gulfstream's product line includes six aircraft, offering a wide range of price and performance options to business-jet customers. The group's jets include the mid-size G150; the large-cabin, mid-range G200 and G350; the long range G450; and the ultra long range G500 and G550. The firm offers several marketing programs through its financial services unit, including aircraft leases and third-party financing. Gulfstream also routinely accepts aircraft trade-ins for the sale of new Gulfstream models, and resells the used planes on the pre-owned market. The group offers several product enhancements for its planes, including the ultra-high-speed broadband multi-link (BBML) system, which allows customers to access the Internet at altitudes up to 51,000 feet; and the Enhanced Vision System (EVS), a forward-looking infrared (FLIR) camera that projects an infrared real-world image on the pilot's heads-up display, which allows the flight crew to see in conditions of low light and reduced visibility. In March 2007, Gulfstream acquired WECO Aerospace Systems, a privately held aviation-component overhaul company. Also in March 2007, the group began a seven-year infrastructure renewal program that includes a new service center; a new sales and design center; expansion of the existing manufacturing facilities; a new engineering building; and new paint hangars. In March 2008, Gulfstream introduced the G650 business jet, an all-new, extra-large cabin jet designed for ultra-long range flights. The aircraft, which offers the largest cabin, longest range, fastest speed and most advanced cockpit in the Gulfstream fleet, is expected to reach customers by 2012.

FINANCIALS:

Sales and profits are in thousands of dollars—add 000 to get the full amount. 2008 Note: Financial information for 2008 was not available for all companies at press time.

2008 Sales: $5,512,000
2007 Sales: $4,828,000
2006 Sales: $4,116,000
2005 Sales: $3,433,000
2004 Sales: $

2008 Profits: $
2007 Profits: $810,000
2006 Profits: $644,000
2005 Profits: $495,000
2004 Profits: $

U.S. Stock Ticker: Subsidiary
Int'l Ticker: Int'l Exchange:
Employees: 6,800
Fiscal Year Ends: 12/31
Parent Company: GENERAL DYNAMICS CORP

SALARIES/BENEFITS:

Pension Plan: Y
Savings Plan: Y
ESOP Stock Plan:
Stock Purch. Plan:
Profit Sharing:
Top Exec. Salary: $ Bonus: $
Second Exec. Salary: $ Bonus: $

OTHER THOUGHTS:

Apparent Women Officers or Directors:
Hot Spot for Advancement for Women/Minorities:

LOCATIONS: ("Y" = Yes)

West:	Southwest:	Midwest:	Southeast:	Northeast:	International:
Y	Y	Y	Y		Y

HALLIBURTON COMPANY

www.halliburton.com

Industry Group Code: 213111 **Ranks within this company's industry group:** Sales: 2 Profits: 3

Techology:		Medical/Drugs:		Engineering:		Transportation:		Chemicals/Petrochemicals:		Specialty:	
Computers:		Manufacturer:		Design:	Y	Aerospace:		Oil/Gas Products:	Y	Special Services:	
Software:	Y	Contract Research:		Construction:	Y	Automotive:		Chemicals:	Y	Consulting:	Y
Communications:		Medical Services:		Eng. Services:	Y	Shipping:		Oil/Chem. Svcs.:	Y	Specialty Mgmt.:	Y
Electronics:		Labs:		Consulting:	Y			Gases:		Products:	
Alternative Energy:		Bio. Services:						Other:		Other:	

TYPES OF BUSINESS:

Oil & Gas Drilling Support Services
Software Information Systems

BRANDS/DIVISIONS/AFFILIATES:

Landmark
Security DBS Drill Bits
Sperry Drilling Services
Easywell
Ultraline Service Corp.
Halliburton Energy Services Group
WellDynamics
OOO Burservice

CONTACTS: *Note: Officers with more than one job title may be intentionally listed here more than once.*

David J. Lesar, CEO
Andrew Lane, COO/Exec. VP
David J. Lesar, Pres.
Mark A. McCollum, CFO/Exec. VP
Lawrence Pope, Chief Human Resources Officer
Lawrence Pope, VP-Admin.
Bert Cornelison, General Counsel/Exec. VP
Tim Probert, Exec. VP-Strategy & Corp. Dev.
Christian Garcia, VP-Investor Rel.
Craig Nunez, Treas./Sr. VP
Sherry Williams, Corp. Sec./VP
Christopher (Cris) Gaut, Pres., Halliburton's Drilling & Evaluation Div.
Evelyn Angelle, Corp. Controller/Principal Acct. Officer/VP
James S. Brown, Pres., Western Hemisphere
David J. Lesar, Chmn.
Ahmed H.M. Lotfy, Pres., Eastern Hemisphere

Phone: 713-759-2605 **Fax:** 713-759-2635
Toll-Free: 888-669-3920
Address: 5 Houston Center, 1401 McKinney, Ste. 2400, Houston, TX 77010 US

GROWTH PLANS/SPECIAL FEATURES:

Halliburton Company is a provider of products and services to the energy industry. The firm serves major, national, and independent oil and gas companies around the world. The company has two business segments through which it operates. These divisions are: Drilling and Evaluation; and Completion and Production. The Drilling and Evaluation segment provides field and reservoir modeling, drilling, evaluation, and precise well-bore placement solutions that enable customers to model, measure, and optimize their well construction activities. This segment consists of Baroid Fluid Services, Sperry Drilling Services, Security DBS Drill Bits, wireline and perforating services, Landmark, and project management. The Completion and Production segment delivers cementing, stimulation, intervention, and completion services. This segment consists of production enhancement services, completion tools and services, and cementing services. Production enhancement services include stimulation services, pipeline process services, sand control services, and well intervention services. Completion tools and services include subsurface safety valves and flow control equipment, surface safety systems, packers and specialty completion equipment, intelligent completion systems, expandable liner hanger systems, sand control systems, well servicing tools, and reservoir performance services. Cementing services involve bonding the well and well casing while isolating fluid zones and maximizing wellbore stability. Also, the cementing service line provides casing equipment. In November 2007, Halliburton acquired OOO Burservice, a Russian directional drilling services provider. In June 2008, the firm acquired all intellectual property and assets of Protech Centerform. Protech Centerform is the world's only provider of casing centralization that uses a carbon fiber and ceramic composite compound applied directly to the casing. In July 2008, Halliburton acquired WellDynamics, a provider of intelligent well completion technology. In August 2008, the firm agreed to acquire Pinnacle Technologies, Inc., including the Pinnacle brand. Pinnacle is a provider of microseismic fracture mapping services and tiltmeter mapping services.

FINANCIALS: Sales and profits are in thousands of dollars—add 000 to get the full amount. 2008 Note: Financial information for 2008 was not available for all companies at press time.

2008 Sales: $18,279,000 2008 Profits: $1,538,000
2007 Sales: $15,264,000 2007 Profits: $3,499,000
2006 Sales: $12,955,000 2006 Profits: $2,348,000
2005 Sales: $10,100,000 2005 Profits: $2,358,000
2004 Sales: $19,878,000 2004 Profits: $-979,000

U.S. Stock Ticker: HAL
Int'l Ticker: Int'l Exchange:
Employees: 57,000
Fiscal Year Ends: 12/31
Parent Company:

SALARIES/BENEFITS:

Pension Plan: ESOP Stock Plan: Profit Sharing: Top Exec. Salary: $1,300,000 Bonus: $7,433,860
Savings Plan: Y Stock Purch. Plan: Y Second Exec. Salary: $700,000 Bonus: $2,269,410

OTHER THOUGHTS:

Apparent Women Officers or Directors: 3
Hot Spot for Advancement for Women/Minorities: Y

LOCATIONS: ("Y" = Yes)

West:	Southwest:	Midwest:	Southeast:	Northeast:	International:
Y	Y		Y		Y

HARRIS CORPORATION

www.harris.com

Industry Group Code: 334200 **Ranks within this company's industry group:** Sales: 2 Profits: 2

Techology:		Medical/Drugs:		Engineering:		Transportation:		Chemicals/Petrochemicals:		Specialty:	
Computers:		Manufacturer:		Design:	Y	Aerospace:		Oil/Gas Products:		Special Services:	Y
Software:	Y	Contract Research:		Construction:		Automotive:		Chemicals:		Consulting:	Y
Communications:	Y	Medical Services:		Eng. Services:	Y	Shipping:		Oil/Chem. Svcs.:		Specialty Mgmt.:	
Electronics:	Y	Labs:		Consulting:	Y			Gases:		Products:	Y
Alternative Energy:		Bio. Services:						Other:		Other:	

TYPES OF BUSINESS:

Communications Equipment Manufacturing
Wireless Communications Equipment
Broadcasting Equipment
Microwave Equipment

BRANDS/DIVISIONS/AFFILIATES:

Zandar Technologies
DESKTOPBOX
Harris Stratex

CONTACTS:

Note: Officers with more than one job title may be intentionally listed here more than once.

Howard L. Lance, CEO
Robert K. Henry, COO/Exec. VP
Howard L. Lance, Pres.
Gary L. McArthur, CFO/Sr. VP
Jeffrey S. Shuman, VP-Human Resources & Corp. Rel.
William H. Miller, Jr., CIO/VP-Info. Svcs.
R. Kent Buchanan, CTO
R. Kent Buchanan, VP-Eng.
Eugene S. Cavallucci, General Counsel/VP
Leon V. Shivamber, VP-Oper.
Ricardo A. Navarro, VP-Corp. Dev.
Pamela Padgett, VP-Corp. Comm.
Pamela Padgett, VP-Investor Rel.
Lewis A. Schwartz, Principal Acct. Officer/VP
Daniel R. Pearson, Pres., Gov't Comm. Systems Div.
Wesley B. Covell, Pres., Defense Programs
Timothy Thorsteinson, Pres., Broadcast Comm.
Peter Challan, VP-Gov't Rel.
Howard L. Lance, Chmn.
Leon V. Shivamber, VP-Supply Chain Mgmt.

Phone: 321-727-9100 **Fax:**
Toll-Free: 800-442-7747
Address: 1025 W. NASA Blvd., Melbourne, FL 32919-0001 US

GROWTH PLANS/SPECIAL FEATURES:

Harris Corporation, along with its subsidiaries, is an international communications and information technology company that provides sales and services to government and commercial markets in more than 150 countries. Harris operates through four divisions: RF Communications, Government Communications Systems, Broadcast Communications and Harris Stratex Networks. The RF Communications segment is a global supplier of secure radio communications products and systems for defense and government operations; and also performs advanced research, primarily for the U.S. Department of Defense and for international customers in government, defense and peacekeeping organizations. The Government Communications Systems segment designs, develops and supplies communications and information networks and equipment; develops integrated intelligence, surveillance and reconnaissance solutions; develops, designs and supports information systems for image and other data collection, processing, analysis, interpretation, display, storage and retrieval; offers enterprise IT and communications engineering, operations and support services; and conducts advanced research studies, primarily for various agencies of the U.S. government and other aerospace and defense companies. The Broadcast Communications segment serves the global digital and analog media markets, providing infrastructure and networking products and solutions, media and workflow solutions, and television and radio transmission equipment and systems. The Harris Stratex Networks segment offers reliable, flexible, scalable and cost-efficient wireless transmission network solutions, including microwave radio systems and network management software, which are backed by comprehensive services and support, primarily to mobile and fixed telephone service providers, private network operators, government agencies, transportation and utility companies, public safety agencies and broadcast system operators. In 2008, Harris acquired Zandar Technologies, a privately held developer and provider of high-quality multi-image display processors for television broadcast and professional video markets; and the assets of DESKTOPBOX, a technology firm offering an Internet broadcasting platform that synchronizes a television or radio broadcast and an automatic web page broadcast.

FINANCIALS:

Sales and profits are in thousands of dollars—add 000 to get the full amount. 2008 Note: Financial information for 2008 was not available for all companies at press time.

2008 Sales: $5,311,000	2008 Profits: $444,200	**U.S. Stock Ticker: HRS**
2007 Sales: $4,243,000	2007 Profits: $480,400	**Int'l Ticker:** Int'l Exchange:
2006 Sales: $3,474,800	2006 Profits: $237,900	Employees: 16,500
2005 Sales: $3,000,600	2005 Profits: $202,200	Fiscal Year Ends: 6/30
2004 Sales: $2,518,600	2004 Profits: $132,800	Parent Company:

SALARIES/BENEFITS:

Pension Plan:	ESOP Stock Plan:	Profit Sharing:	Top Exec. Salary: $972,115	Bonus: $1,422,777
Savings Plan: Y	Stock Purch. Plan:		Second Exec. Salary: $549,989	Bonus: $247,417

OTHER THOUGHTS:

Apparent Women Officers or Directors: 4
Hot Spot for Advancement for Women/Minorities: Y

LOCATIONS: ("Y" = Yes)

West:	Southwest:	Midwest:	Southeast:	Northeast:	International:
Y	Y	Y	Y	Y	Y

HDR INC

www.hdrinc.com

Industry Group Code: 234000 **Ranks within this company's industry group:** Sales: Profits:

Techology:		Medical/Drugs:		Engineering:		Transportation:		Chemicals/Petrochemicals:		Specialty:	
Computers:		Manufacturer:		Design:	Y	Aerospace:		Oil/Gas Products:		Special Services:	
Software:		Contract Research:		Construction:		Automotive:		Chemicals:		Consulting:	
Communications:		Medical Services:		Eng. Services:	Y	Shipping:		Oil/Chem. Svcs.:		Specialty Mgmt.:	
Electronics:		Labs:		Consulting:	Y			Gases:		Products:	
Alternative Energy:		Bio. Services:						Other:		Other:	

TYPES OF BUSINESS:

Engineering Services
Architectural Services
Consulting Services

BRANDS/DIVISIONS/AFFILIATES:

Henningson Engineering Company
StratBENCOST
TransDec
RailDec
GradeDec
RAP
AirLib
Interactive Value Assessment (IVA)

CONTACTS: *Note: Officers with more than one job title may be intentionally listed here more than once.*

Richard R. Bell, CEO
Terrence C. Cox, CFO
George A. Little, Pres., HDR Eng., Inc./Vice Chmn.
Merle S. Bachman, Pres., HDR Architecture
Richard R. Bell, Chmn.

Phone: 402-399-1000 **Fax:** 402-399-1238
Toll-Free: 800-366-4411
Address: 8404 Indian Hills Dr., Omaha, NE 68114-4049 US

GROWTH PLANS/SPECIAL FEATURES:

HDR, Inc. is an architectural, engineering and consulting firm that specializes in managing complex projects and solving engineering and architectural challenges for its clients. The company has more than 165 locations globally, including operations in all 50 states and within 60 countries worldwide. The employee-owned firm offers design-build services and program management for a variety of markets, including community architecture; hospitals and other health care projects; science and technology construction; transportation; power; justice; and wastewater and water resources. HDR's economic tools include StratBENCOST, an investment analysis tool for state and local transportation agencies engaged in multi-year strategic planning and budgeting for highways; TransDec, a cost-benefit analysis tool for both large and small urban areas and projects; RailDec, a decision support tool for state and local transportation agencies engaged in strategic planning and budgeting for rail and rail-related intermodal projects; GradeDec, a highway-rail grade crossing investment analysis tool; RAP, a suite of risk analysis tools; AirLib, a model for investigating the costs and benefits associated with liberalizing international air travel agreements; Interactive Value Assessment (IVA), a tool for conducting real-time business case evaluations; and Sustainability Business Case Tool (SBC), a tool for assessing the costs and benefits related to sustainable design. Repeat clients account for roughly 80% of the company's business. In January 2009, the firm acquired Devine Tarbell & Associates, Inc., an architectural, engineering and consulting firm. In September 2008, the firm acquired E.T. Archer Corporation, an engineering and project management firm. In May 2008, the company acquired the architecture and engineering firm, Claunch & Miller, Inc. In February 2008, HDR acquired Doherty & Associates.

HDR offers employees medical, dental and vision coverage; tuition assistance; a 401(k) plan; a flexible spending accounts; life insurance; short and long term disability; part-time employee benefits (for employees who work a minimum of 30 hours per week).

FINANCIALS: **Sales and profits are in thousands of dollars—add 000 to get the full amount. 2008 Note: Financial information for 2008 was not available for all companies at press time.**

2008 Sales: $ | 2008 Profits: $
2007 Sales: $ | 2007 Profits: $
2006 Sales: $ | 2006 Profits: $
2005 Sales: $ | 2005 Profits: $
2004 Sales: $ | 2004 Profits: $

U.S. Stock Ticker: Private
Int'l Ticker: Int'l Exchange:
Employees: 3,700
Fiscal Year Ends: 12/31
Parent Company:

SALARIES/BENEFITS:

Pension Plan: ESOP Stock Plan: Y Profit Sharing: Top Exec. Salary: $ Bonus: $
Savings Plan: Y Stock Purch. Plan: Second Exec. Salary: $ Bonus: $

OTHER THOUGHTS:

Apparent Women Officers or Directors:
Hot Spot for Advancement for Women/Minorities:

LOCATIONS: ("Y" = Yes)

West:	Southwest:	Midwest:	Southeast:	Northeast:	International:
Y	Y	Y	Y	Y	Y

Note: Financial information, benefits and other data can change quickly and may vary from those stated here.

HEWLETT-PACKARD CO (HP)

www.hp.com

Industry Group Code: 334111 **Ranks within this company's industry group:** Sales: 1 Profits: 1

Techology:		Medical/Drugs:		Engineering:		Transportation:		Chemicals/Petrochemicals:		Specialty:	
Computers:	Y	Manufacturer:		Design:		Aerospace:		Oil/Gas Products:		Special Services:	Y
Software:	Y	Contract Research:		Construction:		Automotive:		Chemicals:		Consulting:	Y
Communications:		Medical Services:		Eng. Services:		Shipping:		Oil/Chem. Svcs.:		Specialty Mgmt.:	
Electronics:		Labs:		Consulting:				Gases:		Products:	Y
Alternative Energy:		Bio. Services:						Other:		Other:	

TYPES OF BUSINESS:

Computer Hardware-PCs
Computer Software
Printers & Supplies
Scanners
Outsourcing
Servers
Consulting
Managed Print Services

BRANDS/DIVISIONS/AFFILIATES:

HP StorageWorks
Business Technology Optimization
Hewlett-Packard Laboratories
Electronic Data Systems Corporation (EDS)

CONTACTS: *Note: Officers with more than one job title may be intentionally listed here more than once.*

Mark V. Hurd, CEO
Mark V. Hurd, Pres.
Cathie Lesjak, CFO/Exec. VP
Michael Mendenhall, Chief Mktg. Officer/Sr. VP
Marcela Perez de Alonso, Exec. VP-Human Resources
Prith Banerjee, Sr. VP-Research/Dir.-HP Labs
Randall D. (Randy) Mott, CIO/Exec. VP
Shane Robison, CTO/Exec. VP
Pete Bocian, Chief Admin. Officer/Exec. VP
Michael J. Holston, General Counsel/Sec./Exec. VP
Shane Robison, Chief Strategy Officer
Todd Bradley, Exec. VP-Personal Systems Group
Ann M. Livermore, Exec. VP-Tech. Solutions Group
Vyomesh Joshi, Exec. VP-Imaging & Printing Group
Ron Rittenmeyer, CEO/Pres., Electronic Data Systems Corp. (EDS)
Mark V. Hurd, Chmn.

Phone: 650-857-1501	**Fax:** 650-857-5518
Toll-Free:	
Address: 3000 Hanover St., Palo Alto, CA 94304-1185 US	

GROWTH PLANS/SPECIAL FEATURES:

Hewlett-Packard Co. (HP) is a global provider of products, technologies, software and services to customers ranging from individuals to large enterprises, including the public and education sectors. Offerings span personal computing and other access devices; imaging and printing-related products and services; enterprise IT infrastructure; and multi-vendor services. The company operates in seven segments: Enterprise Storage and Servers (ESS); HP Services (HPS); HP Software; the Personal Systems Group (PSG); the Imaging and Printing Group (IPG); HP Financial Services (HPFS); and Corporate Investments. The ESS segment provides a broad portfolio of storage and server solutions such as the HP StorageWorks, whose offerings include entry-level, mid-range and high-end arrays, storage area networks, network attached storage, storage management software and virtualization technologies, as well as tape drives, tape libraries and optical archival storage. The HPS segment provides of portfolio of multi-vendor IT services, including technology services; consulting and integration; and outsourcing services such as computer department outsourcing and managed print services. The HP Software segment provides a suite of business technology optimization software solutions, including support, that allow customers to manage and automate their IT infrastructure, operations, applications, IT services and business processes under the Business Technology Optimization (BTO) brand. The PSG segment provides PCs, consumer PCs, workstations, handheld computing devices, digital entertainment systems, calculators and related accessories, software and services for the commercial and consumer markets. The IPG segment provides consumer and commercial printer hardware, printing supplies, printing media and scanning devices. The HPFS segment provides a broad range of value-added financial lifecycle management services. Lastly, the Corporate Investments segment includes the Hewlett-Packard Laboratories and certain business incubation projects. This division sells certain network infrastructure products, including Ethernet switch products that enhance computing and enterprise solutions under the brand ProCurve Networking. In August 2008, the firm acquired Electronic Data Systems Corporation (EDS) for $13.9 billion. EDS now operates within the HPS segment.

FINANCIALS: Sales and profits are in thousands of dollars—add 000 to get the full amount. 2008 Note: Financial information for 2008 was not available for all companies at press time.

2008 Sales: $118,364,000	2008 Profits: $8,329,000	**U.S. Stock Ticker: HPQ**
2007 Sales: $104,286,000	2007 Profits: $7,264,000	**Int'l Ticker:** Int'l Exchange:
2006 Sales: $91,658,000	2006 Profits: $6,198,000	Employees: 321,000
2005 Sales: $86,696,000	2005 Profits: $2,398,000	Fiscal Year Ends: 10/31
2004 Sales: $79,905,000	2004 Profits: $3,497,000	Parent Company:

SALARIES/BENEFITS:

Pension Plan: Y	ESOP Stock Plan:	Profit Sharing:	Top Exec. Salary: $1,400,000	Bonus: $8,624,000
Savings Plan: Y	Stock Purch. Plan:		Second Exec. Salary: $975,000	Bonus: $4,095,000

OTHER THOUGHTS:

Apparent Women Officers or Directors: 5
Hot Spot for Advancement for Women/Minorities: Y

LOCATIONS: ("Y" = Yes)

West:	Southwest:	Midwest:	Southeast:	Northeast:	International:
Y	Y	Y	Y	Y	Y

HEWLETT-PACKARD QUANTUM SCIENCE RESEARCH

www.hpl.hp.com/research/qsr/

ndustry Group Code: 541710 **Ranks within this company's industry group:** Sales: Profits:

Techology:		Medical/Drugs:		Engineering:		Transportation:		Chemicals/Petrochemicals:		Specialty:	
Computers:		Manufacturer:		Design:		Aerospace:		Oil/Gas Products:		Special Services:	
Software:		Contract Research:		Construction:		Automotive:		Chemicals:		Consulting:	
Communications:		Medical Services:		Eng. Services:		Shipping:		Oil/Chem. Svcs.:		Specialty Mgmt.:	
Electronics:	Y	Labs:		Consulting:				Gases:		Products:	
Alternative Energy:		Bio. Services:						Other:		Other:	Y

TYPES OF BUSINESS:

Research & Development-Nanotechnology
Molecular-Scale Electronics Research

BRANDS/DIVISIONS/AFFILIATES:

Hewlett-Packard Co (HP)
Advanced Studies Program
Hewlett-Packard Laboratories
Quantum Key Distribution

CONTACTS: *Note: Officers with more than one job title may be intentionally listed here more than once.*

Stan Williams, Dir.-Quantum Science Research/Sr. HP Fellow
Prith Banerjee, Dir.-HP Labs/Sr. VP-Research, HP
Ted Kamins, Principal Scientist, Nano Electric Materials
Duncan Stewart, Electronics Tester
Ray Beausoleil, Principal Scientist, Nanoscale Optics

Phone: 650-857-1501	**Fax:**
Toll-Free:	
Address: 1501 Page Mill Rd., Palo Alto, CA 94304-1126 US	

GROWTH PLANS/SPECIAL FEATURES:

Hewlett-Packard Quantum Science Research (QRS), founded in 1995, conducts research in nanoscale science and the fundamental physics of switching, with an emphasis on molecular-scale electronics. It is a research unit of the Advanced Studies Program of Hewlett-Packard Laboratories, which is itself a subsidiary of Hewlett-Packard Co. (HP). QRS focuses on fabricating, measuring and understanding the properties of nanometer-scale structures. In recent years, QRS devised a method of growing and connecting semiconductor nanowires in place. Potential applications include more effective sensors for detecting toxic gases and other chemical or biological substances; interconnecting leads in nanometer-scale electronic circuits; and developing devices within nanowires such as transistors. More recently, the firm has been conducting basic research on a variety of nanoscale classical and quantum optics, including developing quantum key distribution (QKD) applications. QKD aims at using quantum principles for security, such as the fact that simply looking at a quantum system changes it, allowing the recipient of the message to know if it has been intercepted. The quantum key can be encoded into very weak pulses of light or even single photons. Currently, QKD can only be used for messages within 60 miles, which is the maximum the weak light beam may travel through a fiber-optic cable without being amplified or otherwise modified, thus corrupting the original key. However, work is being done to extend this range. Researchers also hope to modify QKD for other applications, such as installing devices into mobile phones that securely transmit a quantum key to an ATM without having to plug in or type anything. The firm is also researching nanoscale optics, including attempting to utilize optical connections within blade servers themselves, essentially replacing the copper wires in the blades' processors, and between different servers, with multispectral tunable laser lights. QRS has overseas research laboratories in Beijing, China and St. Petersburg, Russia.

FINANCIALS: **Sales and profits are in thousands of dollars—add 000 to get the full amount. 2008 Note: Financial information for 2008 was not available for all companies at press time.**

2008 Sales: $	2008 Profits: $	**U.S. Stock Ticker: Subsidiary**
2007 Sales: $	2007 Profits: $	**Int'l Ticker:** Int'l Exchange:
2006 Sales: $	2006 Profits: $	Employees:
2005 Sales: $	2005 Profits: $	Fiscal Year Ends: 10/31
2004 Sales: $	2004 Profits: $	Parent Company: HEWLETT-PACKARD CO (HP)

SALARIES/BENEFITS:

Pension Plan:	ESOP Stock Plan:	Profit Sharing: Y	Top Exec. Salary: $	Bonus: $
Savings Plan: Y	Stock Purch. Plan:		Second Exec. Salary: $	Bonus: $

OTHER THOUGHTS:

Apparent Women Officers or Directors:
Hot Spot for Advancement for Women/Minorities:

LOCATIONS: ("Y" = Yes)

West:	Southwest:	Midwest:	Southeast:	Northeast:	International:
Y					Y

HIGH TECH COMPUTER CORPORATION (HTC) www.htc.com/tw

Industry Group Code: 334419 **Ranks within this company's industry group:** Sales: 7 Profits: 2

Techology:		Medical/Drugs:		Engineering:		Transportation:		Chemicals/Petrochemicals:		Specialty:	
Computers:	Y	Manufacturer:		Design:	Y	Aerospace:		Oil/Gas Products:		Special Services:	
Software:		Contract Research:		Construction:		Automotive:		Chemicals:		Consulting:	
Communications:	Y	Medical Services:		Eng. Services:	Y	Shipping:		Oil/Chem. Svcs.:		Specialty Mgmt.:	
Electronics:		Labs:		Consulting:				Gases:		Products:	
Alternative Energy:		Bio. Services:						Other:		Other:	

TYPES OF BUSINESS:

Original Design Manufacturing
Mobile Computing & Communications Hardware
Cellular Phones & Smartphones
PDAs
Contract Manufacturing

BRANDS/DIVISIONS/AFFILIATES:

HTC USA Inc
HTC Advantage X7500
HTC FUZE
HTC S720
HTC P4000
T-Mobile G1
Touch Diamond

CONTACTS: *Note: Officers with more than one job title may be intentionally listed here more than once.*

Peter Chou, CEO
Fred Liu, COO
Horace Luke, Chief Innovation Officer
Jason Mackenzie, VP, HTC America
Cher Wang, Chmn.

Phone: 886-3-375-3252	**Fax:** 886-3-375-3251
Toll-Free:	
Address: 23 Xinghua Rd., Taoyuan, 330 Taiwan	

GROWTH PLANS/SPECIAL FEATURES:

High Tech Computer Corporation (HTC) specializes in designing and manufacturing mobile computing and communications hardware, including cell phones, smart phones and PDAs. The company operates as an original equipment manufacturer (OEM) by providing contract design as well as manufacturing services. The firm's customers include major mobile device brands and wireless service providers such as Cingular; T-Mobile; Sprint; Verizon; Orange, 02; Vodafone Telus; and NTT DoCoMo. The company is a hardware platform development partner with Microsoft for the Windows CE operating system and makes 80% of the mobile phones running off of the Windows OS. The firm also has partnerships with Intel, Texas Instruments, QUALCOMM, Sony and Citizen. Some of the company's products include the T-Mobile G1, which features the Google Android operating system; Touch Diamond; HTC FUZE; AT&T Tilt; HTC P4000 PDA phone; the T-Mobile Wing; the Dash; the HTC Advantage X7500 mobile office device, and the HTC S720 smartphone.

FINANCIALS: **Sales and profits are in thousands of dollars—add 000 to get the full amount. 2008 Note: Financial information for 2008 was not available for all companies at press time.**

2008 Sales: $4,528,650	2008 Profits: $851,180	**U.S. Stock Ticker:**
2007 Sales: $3,650,000	2007 Profits: $890,000	**Int'l Ticker: 2498** Int'l Exchange: Taipei-TPE
2006 Sales: $3,202,894	2006 Profits: $774,060	Employees: 3,400
2005 Sales: $2,199,850	2005 Profits: $354,346	Fiscal Year Ends: 12/31
2004 Sales: $1,200,000	2004 Profits: $116,000	Parent Company:

SALARIES/BENEFITS:

Pension Plan:	ESOP Stock Plan:	Profit Sharing:	Top Exec. Salary: $	Bonus: $
Savings Plan:	Stock Purch. Plan:		Second Exec. Salary: $	Bonus: $

OTHER THOUGHTS:

Apparent Women Officers or Directors: 1
Hot Spot for Advancement for Women/Minorities:

LOCATIONS: ("Y" = Yes)

West:	Southwest:	Midwest:	Southeast:	Northeast:	International:
					Y

HILL-ROM HOLDINGS INC

www.hill-rom.com

Industry Group Code: 339113 **Ranks within this company's industry group:** Sales: 13 Profits: 12

Techology:		Medical/Drugs:		Engineering:		Transportation:		Chemicals/Petrochemicals:		Specialty:	
Computers:		Manufacturer:	Y	Design:		Aerospace:		Oil/Gas Products:		Special Services:	Y
Software:		Contract Research:		Construction:		Automotive:		Chemicals:		Consulting:	
Communications:		Medical Services:		Eng. Services:		Shipping:		Oil/Chem. Svcs.:		Specialty Mgmt.:	
Electronics:		Labs:		Consulting:				Gases:		Products:	Y
Alternative Energy:		Bio. Services:						Other:		Other:	

TYPES OF BUSINESS:

Equipment-Hospital Beds & Related Products
Specialized Therapy Products
Rentals

BRANDS/DIVISIONS/AFFILIATES:

Hill-Rom At Home
Safe Skin Program
Clear Lungs Program
Centurty+ Bed
TotalCare Sp02RT
TranStar

CONTACTS: *Note: Officers with more than one job title may be intentionally listed here more than once.*

Peter H. Soderberg, CEO
Peter H. Soderberg, Pres.
Gregory N. Miller, CFO/Sr. VP
John H. Dickey, Sr. VP-Human Resources
Sheri H. Edison, Chief Admin. Officer/Sr. VP
Patrick D. de Maynadier, General Counsel/Sr. VP/Sec.
Michael J. Grippo, VP-Bus. Dev. & Strategy
Blair A. Reith, Jr., VP-Corp. Comm.
Blair A. Reith, Jr., VP-Investor Rel.
Richard G. Keller, Chief Acct. Officer/VP
Kimberly K. Dennis, Sr. VP-Post Acute North America
Lauren Green-Caldwell, Dir.-Corp. Comm. & Public Rel.
Kenneth A. Camp, Sr. VP-Hillenbrand Industries
Rolf A. Classon, Chmn.

Phone: 812-934-7777 **Fax:** 812-934-8189
Toll-Free: 800-445-3730
Address: 1069 State Route 46 East, Batesville, IN 47006-9167 US

GROWTH PLANS/SPECIAL FEATURES:

Hill-Rom Holdings, Inc., formerly Hillenbrand Industries, Inc., was formed in March 2008 when it spun off the Batesville Casket Company subsidiary. The firm sells, rents and services hospital products, including hospital beds; non-invasive therapeutic surfaces and devices; stretchers and other transport systems; furniture; communication and locating systems; and operating room accessories. The company provides therapy products for acute care, homecare and long-term care, as well as a full line of stretchers under the TranStar name and specialized mattresses. Other products include nurse call systems, fetal monitoring information systems, siderail communications, surgical table accessories, bedside cabinets, tables and mattresses. The company's architectural products include customized, prefabricated modules that are either wall-mounted or on freestanding columns and allow medical equipment such as gases, communication accessories and electrical services to be kept safely in patient rooms. The firm primarily focuses on a line of electrically adjustable hospital beds that can be adjusted to varied orthopedic and therapeutic contours and positions. Hospital bed models include the TotalCare Sp02RT bed, a pulmonary bed that delivers rotation, percussion and vibration; the TotalCare bed, a bed designed for acute patients with little to no mobility; and the Affinity 4 bed, designed for the maternity department. Hill-Rom provides therapy systems to hospitals, long-term care facilities and homes through service centers located in the U.S., Canada and Western Europe. The company's products are sold directly and through distributorships. Hill-Rom also rents beds, infusion pumps, monitors and other equipment to hospitals, long-term care facilities and private homes.

The company offers employees medical, dental and vision insurance; medical, dependent and adoption spending accounts; life insurance; 401K plan; and tuition reimbursement.

FINANCIALS: Sales and profits are in thousands of dollars—add 000 to get the full amount. 2008 Note: Financial information for 2008 was not available for all companies at press time.

2008 Sales: $1,507,700	2008 Profits: $115,800	**U.S. Stock Ticker: HRC**
2007 Sales: $1,356,500	2007 Profits: $190,600	**Int'l Ticker:** Int'l Exchange:
2006 Sales: $1,288,300	2006 Profits: $221,500	Employees: 6,800
2005 Sales: $1,938,100	2005 Profits: $-96,300	Fiscal Year Ends: 9/30
2004 Sales: $1,829,300	2004 Profits: $188,200	Parent Company:

SALARIES/BENEFITS:

Pension Plan: Y	ESOP Stock Plan:	Profit Sharing:	Top Exec. Salary: $830,575	Bonus: $711,245
Savings Plan: Y	Stock Purch. Plan:		Second Exec. Salary: $424,102	Bonus: $202,881

OTHER THOUGHTS:

Apparent Women Officers or Directors: 3
Hot Spot for Advancement for Women/Minorities: Y

LOCATIONS: ("Y" = Yes)

West:	Southwest:	Midwest:	Southeast:	Northeast:	International:
Y		Y		Y	Y

Note: Financial information, benefits and other data can change quickly and may vary from those stated here.

HITACHI GLOBAL STORAGE TECHNOLOGIES www.hitachigst.com

Industry Group Code: 334112 **Ranks within this company's industry group:** Sales: Profits:

Techology:		Medical/Drugs:		Engineering:		Transportation:		Chemicals/Petrochemicals:		Specialty:	
Computers:	Y	Manufacturer:		Design:		Aerospace:		Oil/Gas Products:		Special Services:	
Software:	Y	Contract Research:		Construction:		Automotive:		Chemicals:		Consulting:	
Communications:		Medical Services:		Eng. Services:		Shipping:		Oil/Chem. Svcs.:		Specialty Mgmt.:	
Electronics:		Labs:		Consulting:				Gases:		Products:	
Alternative Energy:		Bio. Services:						Other:		Other:	

TYPES OF BUSINESS:

Computer Storage Equipment
Hard Drives
Software

BRANDS/DIVISIONS/AFFILIATES:

Hitachi Ltd
Fabrik Inc
Travelstar
Deskstar
Ultrastar
Endurastar

CONTACTS: *Note: Officers with more than one job title may be intentionally listed here more than once.*

Hiroaki Nakanishi, CEO
Robert Holleran, COO
Steve Milligan, Pres.
Steve Milligan, CFO
George Silva, Sr. VP-Worldwide Sales
Steven Campbell, CTO
Phil Duncan, Chief Admin. Officer
Christopher Dewees, General Counsel
George Silva, Sr. VP-Worldwide Oper.
James McNicholas, Sr. VP-Finance
Currie Munce, VP-Enterprise Bus. Group
Shinjiro Iwata, Exec. VP
Ian Sanders, VP-Media Bus. Group
Masaya Watanabe, Chief Strategist-Data Storage
Hiroaki Nakanishi, Chmn.
Toshihiko Tamiya, Sr. VP-Japan Oper.
David Beaver, Sr. VP-Supply Chain & Procurement

Phone: 408-717-6000 **Fax:** 408-256-6770
Toll-Free: 800-801-4618
Address: 3403 Yerba Buena Rd., San Jose, CA 95135 US

GROWTH PLANS/SPECIAL FEATURES:

Hitachi Global Storage Technologies, Inc. (HGST) manufactures hard disk drives and components for PCs, servers and electronic devices such as handheld computers and digital cameras. The company was formed in 2003 when Hitachi acquired 70% of IBM's disk drive business. IBM still maintains 30% ownership of the joint venture. The firm is committed to providing customers with a wide array of digital storage capacity options. HGST manufactures Travelstar hard disk drives for on-the-go storage; Deskstar desktop hard drives; Ultrastar server drives for online transaction and data analysis; and Endurastar drives, for automotive applications such as global positioning systems and audio and video entertainment. The firm offers primarily four sizes of drives: the 3.5 inch commercial and consumer desktop hard drive unit, the 2.5 inch product family, 1.8 inch consumer and commercial mobile hard drive unit and the 1-inch product family, featuring the Microdrive 3K8. The 1-inch Microdrive digital media has capacity up to 8 gigabytes, and was designed for hand-held applications such as digital cameras, PDAs, MP3 players and other emerging consumer electronics products. The firm's drives serve applications including automotive, industrial, consumer electronics, desktop, mobile and retail products. In February 2009, the company acquired Fabrik, Inc., a storage technology company comprising brand names such as G-Technology and SimpleTech.

FINANCIALS: Sales and profits are in thousands of dollars—add 000 to get the full amount. 2008 Note: Financial information for 2008 was not available for all companies at press time.

2008 Sales: $	2008 Profits: $	**U.S. Stock Ticker: Joint Venture**
2007 Sales: $2,147,500	2007 Profits: $	**Int'l Ticker:** Int'l Exchange:
2006 Sales: $	2006 Profits: $	Employees: 21,000
2005 Sales: $	2005 Profits: $	Fiscal Year Ends: 12/31
2004 Sales: $	2004 Profits: $	Parent Company: HITACHI LTD

SALARIES/BENEFITS:

Pension Plan:	ESOP Stock Plan:	Profit Sharing:	Top Exec. Salary: $	Bonus: $
Savings Plan:	Stock Purch. Plan:		Second Exec. Salary: $	Bonus: $

OTHER THOUGHTS:

Apparent Women Officers or Directors:
Hot Spot for Advancement for Women/Minorities:

LOCATIONS: ("Y" = Yes)

West:	Southwest:	Midwest:	Southeast:	Northeast:	International:
Y		Y			Y

HITACHI HIGH TECHNOLOGIES AMERICA INC www.hitachi-hhta.com

Industry Group Code: 541710 **Ranks within this company's industry group:** Sales: Profits:

Techology:		Medical/Drugs:		Engineering:		Transportation:		Chemicals/Petrochemicals:		Specialty:	
Computers:		Manufacturer:		Design:		Aerospace:		Oil/Gas Products:		Special Services:	
Software:		Contract Research:		Construction:		Automotive:		Chemicals:		Consulting:	
Communications:		Medical Services:		Eng. Services:		Shipping:		Oil/Chem. Svcs.:		Specialty Mgmt.:	
Electronics:	Y	Labs:		Consulting:				Gases:		Products:	Y
Alternative Energy:		Bio. Services:						Other:		Other:	

TYPES OF BUSINESS:

Research & Development
Semiconductor Manufacturing Equipment
Biotechnology Products
Industrial Equipment
Electronic & Industrial Materials
Electronic Components & Systems
Nanotechnology Research
Chromatography Systems

BRANDS/DIVISIONS/AFFILIATES:

Hitachi Ltd
Maxell
Hitachi Heat Sink
CyberPro
NanoFrontier

CONTACTS: *Note: Officers with more than one job title may be intentionally listed here more than once.*

Yasukuni Koga, VP-Investor Rel.
Hideo Naito, VP-Semiconductor Equipment Div.

Phone: 847-273-4141	**Fax:**
Toll-Free:	
Address: 10 N. Martingale Rd., Ste. 500, Schaumburg, IL 60173 US	

GROWTH PLANS/SPECIAL FEATURES:

Hitachi High Technologies America, Inc. (HTA) is a subsidiary of Hitachi, Ltd. of Japan. The company was formed in 2002 from the combination of Nissei Sangyo America, Ltd., a subsidiary of Hitachi High-Technologies Corporation of Tokyo, Japan; the Semiconductor Equipment Group of Hitachi America, Ltd.; and Hitachi Instruments, Inc., a subsidiary of Hitachi America, Ltd. HTA offers imaging and analysis tools for nanotechnology, research, failure analysis and inspection. It manufactures and markets a full line of electron microscopes, X-ray analysis systems and accessories. HTA operates through several divisions including semiconductor equipment, electron microscopes, life sciences, electronic components, electronic products, electronic applied systems and advanced materials. The semiconductor equipment division manufactures dry plasma etch systems. The electron microscope division manufactures advanced microscope systems. The life sciences division provides instruments and analytical equipment, including industry-leading DNA sequencers and isolation equipment, to the biotechnology, chemical and pharmaceutical industries. The electric components division sells LCD TVs, LCD monitors, plasma TVs, plasma monitors, LCD mobile displays, automotive in-dash displays, navigation displays, and digital signage monitors to original equipment manufacturers (OEMs) and other industrial clients. The electronic products division controls sales of the company's electronic microscopes related technologies. The electronic applied systems division offers advanced manufacturing services to the firm's clients. The advanced materials division offers products from semiconductor wafers to digital media and television products.

HTA offers its employees health plans, retirement packages, saving plans, tuition reimbursement, bonus incentives and company paid holidays.

FINANCIALS: Sales and profits are in thousands of dollars—add 000 to get the full amount. 2008 Note: Financial information for 2008 was not available for all companies at press time.

2008 Sales: $	2008 Profits: $	**U.S. Stock Ticker: Subsidiary**
2007 Sales: $	2007 Profits: $	**Int'l Ticker:** Int'l Exchange:
2006 Sales: $7,561,868	2006 Profits: $163,864	Employees: 10,043
2005 Sales: $9,723,950	2005 Profits: $139,715	Fiscal Year Ends: 3/31
2004 Sales: $7,866,700	2004 Profits: $67,800	Parent Company: HITACHI LTD

SALARIES/BENEFITS:

Pension Plan: Y	ESOP Stock Plan:	Profit Sharing:	Top Exec. Salary: $	Bonus: $
Savings Plan: Y	Stock Purch. Plan:		Second Exec. Salary: $	Bonus: $

OTHER THOUGHTS:

Apparent Women Officers or Directors:
Hot Spot for Advancement for Women/Minorities:

LOCATIONS: ("Y" = Yes)

West:	Southwest:	Midwest:	Southeast:	Northeast:	International:
Y	Y	Y	Y	Y	Y

HITACHI LTD

www.hitachi.com

Industry Group Code: 334111 **Ranks within this company's industry group:** Sales: 2 Profits: 16

Techology:		Medical/Drugs:		Engineering:		Transportation:		Chemicals/Petrochemicals:		Specialty:	
Computers:	Y	Manufacturer:	Y	Design:		Aerospace:		Oil/Gas Products:		Special Services:	Y
Software:		Contract Research:		Construction:		Automotive:		Chemicals:		Consulting:	Y
Communications:		Medical Services:		Eng. Services:		Shipping:		Oil/Chem. Svcs.:		Specialty Mgmt.:	
Electronics:	Y	Labs:		Consulting:				Gases:		Products:	
Alternative Energy:	Y	Bio. Services:						Other:	Y	Other:	

TYPES OF BUSINESS:

Computer Hardware Manufacturing
Consumer Appliances & Electronics
Materials Manufacturing
Financial Services Products
Power & Industrial Systems
Medical & Scientific Equipment
Transportation Systems
Consulting Services

BRANDS/DIVISIONS/AFFILIATES:

Clarion Co Ltd
Hitachi Global Storage Technologies
Hitachi High Technologies America Inc
Hitachi Medical Corporation
Hitachi Medical Systems America
Hitachi Consulting
Hitachi Chemical Bupont Microsystems LLC

CONTACTS: *Note: Officers with more than one job title may be intentionally listed here more than once.*

Kazuo Furukawa, CEO
Kazuo Furukawa, Pres.
Kazuhiro Mori, Exec. VP
Kunihiko Ohnuma, Exec. VP
Junzo Kawakami, Exec. VP
Manabu Shinomoto, Exec. VP
Etsuhiko Shoyama, Chmn.

Phone: 81-3-3258-1111 **Fax:**
Toll-Free:
Address: 6-6, Marunouchi 1-chome, Chiyoda-ku, Tokyo, 100-8280 Japan

GROWTH PLANS/SPECIAL FEATURES:

Hitachi, Ltd. is a Japan-based electronics company. Hitachi divides its products and services into the following seven segments: Information and Telecommunications Systems; Electronic Devices; Power and Industrial Systems; Digital Media and Consumer Products; High Functional Materials and Components; Logistics and Services; and Financial Services. Its Information and Telecommunication Systems segment includes communications infrastructure hardware, hard drives and other storage products. This segment accounts for 22% of revenues. The Electronic Devices segment creates a wide variety of digital devices and accounts for 10% of revenues. The Power and Industrial Systems segment, accounting for 28% of revenues, offers products and services in support of nuclear, thermal and hydroelectric power systems; railway systems; elevators and escalators. The main customers of this segment are power companies. Hitachi's growth strategy in recent years includes higher emphasis on environmental protection and alternative energy development. It is working to expand its nuclear power systems business, and has partial ownership of several U.S. and Canadian companies engaged in the construction and operation of nuclear power plants. The Digital Media and Consumer Products segment produces flat-panel TVs, digital consumer electronics and home appliances. This segment accounts for 12% of revenues. The High Functional Materials and Components segment develops such products as specialty steels, magnetic materials, semiconductor materials, and synthetic resin products. This segment accounts for 15% of revenues. The Logistics and Services segment, with 10% of revenues, conducts a range of operations such as freight transport and warehousing. The Financial Services segment works on both corporate and client needs and accounts for 3% of revenues. In mid-2007, the firm announced plans to stop making household computers, and also announced plans to cut 40% of the power consumption of products that will be shipped within the next five years.

FINANCIALS: **Sales and profits are in thousands of dollars—add 000 to get the full amount. 2008 Note: Financial information for 2008 was not available for all companies at press time.**

2008 Sales: $113,390,020
2007 Sales: $87,107,200
2006 Sales: $80,209,000
2005 Sales: $84,222,000
2004 Sales: $82,008,275

2008 Profits: $-587,060
2007 Profits: $-278,800
2006 Profits: $316,270
2005 Profits: $480,000
2004 Profits: $150,822

U.S. Stock Ticker: HIT
Int'l Ticker: 6501 Int'l Exchange: Tokyo-TSE
Employees: 347,810
Fiscal Year Ends: 3/31
Parent Company:

SALARIES/BENEFITS:

Pension Plan: ESOP Stock Plan: Profit Sharing: Top Exec. Salary: $ Bonus: $
Savings Plan: Stock Purch. Plan: Second Exec. Salary: $ Bonus: $

OTHER THOUGHTS:

Apparent Women Officers or Directors:
Hot Spot for Advancement for Women/Minorities:

LOCATIONS: ("Y" = Yes)

West:	Southwest:	Midwest:	Southeast:	Northeast:	International:
Y	Y	Y	Y	Y	Y

Note: Financial information, benefits and other data can change quickly and may vary from those stated here.

HOCHTIEF AG

www.hochtief.de

Industry Group Code: 234000 **Ranks within this company's industry group:** Sales: 4 Profits: 10

Techology:		Medical/Drugs:		Engineering:		Transportation:		Chemicals/Petrochemicals:		Specialty:	
Computers:		Manufacturer:		Design:	Y	Aerospace:		Oil/Gas Products:		Special Services:	
Software:		Contract Research:		Construction:	Y	Automotive:		Chemicals:		Consulting:	
Communications:		Medical Services:		Eng. Services:	Y	Shipping:		Oil/Chem. Svcs.:		Specialty Mgmt.:	
Electronics:		Labs:		Consulting:	Y			Gases:		Products:	
Alternative Energy:		Bio. Services:						Other:		Other:	

TYPES OF BUSINESS:

Heavy Construction
Airport Management & Consulting Services
Infrastructure Development
Geothermal Plant Construction

BRANDS/DIVISIONS/AFFILIATES:

HOCHTIEF AirPort
HOCHTIEF Projektentwicklung GmbH
HOCHTIEF PPP Solutions
HOCHTIEF Facility Management
Turner Company (The)
HOCHTIEF do Brasil
Lieghton Holdings, Ltd.
aurelis real estate GmbH & Co. Kg

CONTACTS: *Note: Officers with more than one job title may be intentionally listed here more than once.*

Herbert Lutkestratkotter, CEO
Burkhard Lohr, CFO
Albrecht Ehlers, Dir.-Svcs. & Labor Rel.
Herbert Lutkestratkotter, Dir.-Corp. Dev.
Herbert Lutkestratkotter, Dir.-Corp. Comm.
Burkhard Lohr, Dir.-Controlling, Auditing & Tax
Martin Rohr, Dir.-Real Estate
Herbert Lutkestratkotter, Dir.-HOCHTIEF Construction Svcs., Americas/Europe
Martin Kohlhaussen, Chmn.
Peter Noe, Dir.-HOTCHTIEF Construction Svcs., Asia Pacific
Martin Rohr, Dir.-Global Procurement

Phone: 49-201-824-0	**Fax:** 49-201-824-2777
Toll-Free:	
Address: Opernplatz 2, Essen, 45128 Germany	

GROWTH PLANS/SPECIAL FEATURES:

HOCHTIEF AG is a top international construction services provider that designs, builds, finances and operates large, technically demanding facilities worldwide. The company is organized through five divisions: HOCHTIEF AirPort; HOCHTIEF Development; and HOCHTIEF Construction Services divisions in the Americas, Asia Pacific and Europe. The AirPort division is an airport management and consulting company with stakes in the airports of Dusseldorf, Hamburg, Athens, Budapest, Sydney and Tirana, the capital of Albania. Development operates through three units: HOCHTIEF Projektentwicklung GmbH, a European inner-urban project development company; HOCHTIEF PPP Solutions, focusing on public infrastructure projects; HOCHTIEF Facility Management; and Deutsch Bau-und Siedlungs-Gesellschaft GmbH, an asset management company. The Americas division coordinates all of the activities in the region through subsidiaries in the U.S. and Brazil, including The Turner Company, a leading U.S. general construction contractor, and HOCHTIEF do Brasil, providing construction and facilities management services. The core of the Asia-Pacific division is affiliate company Leighton Holdings, Ltd., which operates the Australian subsidiaries Leighton Contractors Pty., Leighton Properties Pty., John Holland Group Pty., Thiess Pty.; and Leighton Asia (Northern), Ltd. and Leighton Asia (Southern), Ltd., in Hong Kong. It concentrates on infrastructure construction and project development, is expanding its mining operations and slowly increasing its Asian operations. The Europe division's leading company, HOCHTIEF Construction A.G., one of the world's largest construction firms, provides civil and structural engineering, as well as building construction. Recently, a joint venture called Suddeutsche Geothermie-Projekte GmbH & Co. KG, 40% owned by HOCHTIEF, was set up to operate, build, finance and plan a 5 megawatt geothermal plant in Germany. In December 2007, the company, along with its partner Redwood Grove International, acquired a 50% stake in aurelis real estate GmbH & Co. Kg, the real estate subsidiary of Deutsche Bann.

FINANCIALS: **Sales and profits are in thousands of dollars—add 000 to get the full amount. 2008 Note: Financial information for 2008 was not available for all companies at press time.**

2008 Sales: $25,783,870	2008 Profits: $419,100	**U.S. Stock Ticker: HOT**
2007 Sales: $22,205,420	2007 Profits: $165,870	**Int'l Ticker: HOT** Int'l Exchange: Frankfurt-Euronext
2006 Sales: $21,065,480	2006 Profits: $273,520	Employees: 41,469
2005 Sales: $18,545,954	2005 Profits: $212,208	Fiscal Year Ends: 12/31
2004 Sales: $14,459,711	2004 Profits: $98,207	Parent Company:

SALARIES/BENEFITS:

Pension Plan:	ESOP Stock Plan:	Profit Sharing:	Top Exec. Salary: $	Bonus: $
Savings Plan:	Stock Purch. Plan:		Second Exec. Salary: $	Bonus: $

OTHER THOUGHTS:

Apparent Women Officers or Directors:
Hot Spot for Advancement for Women/Minorities:

LOCATIONS: ("Y" = Yes)

West:	Southwest:	Midwest:	Southeast:	Northeast:	International:
Y	Y	Y	Y	Y	Y

HON HAI PRECISION INDUSTRY COMPANY LTD www.foxconn.com

Industry Group Code: 334419 **Ranks within this company's industry group:** Sales: 1 Profits: 1

Techology:		Medical/Drugs:		Engineering:		Transportation:		Chemicals/Petrochemicals:		Specialty:	
Computers:	Y	Manufacturer:		Design:	Y	Aerospace:		Oil/Gas Products:		Special Services:	Y
Software:		Contract Research:		Construction:		Automotive:		Chemicals:		Consulting:	
Communications:	Y	Medical Services:		Eng. Services:		Shipping:		Oil/Chem. Svcs.:		Specialty Mgmt.:	
Electronics:	Y	Labs:		Consulting:				Gases:		Products:	Y
Alternative Energy:		Bio. Services:						Other:		Other:	

TYPES OF BUSINESS:

Contract Electronics Manufacturing
Consumer Electronics & Components
Product Design Services
Cameras & Projectors
Optical Technology

BRANDS/DIVISIONS/AFFILIATES:

Foxconn Technology Group
eCMMS
Mac Mini
iPod
iPhone
Wii
Xbox 360
Motorola Inc

CONTACTS: *Note: Officers with more than one job title may be intentionally listed here more than once.*

Terry T.M. Gou, CEO
Terry T.M. Gou, Chmn.

Phone: 886-2-226-80970	**Fax:**
Toll-Free:	
Address: 2 Zihyou St., Tucheng City, Taipei Country, 236 Taiwan	

GROWTH PLANS/SPECIAL FEATURES:

Hon Hai Precision Industry Company Ltd., which does business under its registered trade name Foxconn Technology Group, is a technology manufacturer that focuses on joint-design and development, manufacturing, assembly and after-sales services for global communication, computer and customer-electronics firms. Foxconn is operated by a propriety business model called eCMMS (e-enabled Components, Modules, Moves and Services), and is one of the largest multinational electronics and computer components manufacturing service providers in the world. Its main areas of focus are nanotechnology, wireless connectivity, heat transfer, green manufacturing processes and material sciences. The firm holds more than 15,000 patents worldwide. Some of Foxconn's most notable contract design and manufacturing products include the Mac Mini, iPod and iPhone for Apple, Inc.; branded motherboards for Intel Corp.; the Wii for Nintendo; the Xbox 360 for Microsoft; Motorola cell phones; and a variety of computers for retailers such as Dell and Hewlett Packard. Other non-branded products include computer cases, motherboards, graphics cards and other computer components that are primarily sold to corporate users. The firm has locations in Brazil, Australia, China, the U.K., France, Hungary, the Czech Republic, Mexico, India and Canada.

FINANCIALS: **Sales and profits are in thousands of dollars—add 000 to get the full amount. 2008 Note: Financial information for 2008 was not available for all companies at press time.**

2008 Sales: $51,079,900	2008 Profits: $2,330,700	**U.S. Stock Ticker: Private**
2007 Sales: $40,510,000	2007 Profits: $1,840,000	**Int'l Ticker:** Int'l Exchange:
2006 Sales: $40,600,000	2006 Profits: $	Employees: 270,000
2005 Sales: $21,000,000	2005 Profits: $	Fiscal Year Ends: 12/31
2004 Sales: $16,935,700	2004 Profits: $930,500	Parent Company:

SALARIES/BENEFITS:

Pension Plan:	ESOP Stock Plan:	Profit Sharing:	Top Exec. Salary: $	Bonus: $
Savings Plan:	Stock Purch. Plan:		Second Exec. Salary: $	Bonus: $

OTHER THOUGHTS:

Apparent Women Officers or Directors:
Hot Spot for Advancement for Women/Minorities:

LOCATIONS: ("Y" = Yes)

West:	Southwest:	Midwest:	Southeast:	Northeast:	International:
Y	Y	Y		Y	Y

HONDA MOTOR CO LTD

www.honda.com

Industry Group Code: 336111 **Ranks within this company's industry group:** Sales: 6 Profits: 4

Techology:		Medical/Drugs:		Engineering:		Transportation:		Chemicals/Petrochemicals:		Specialty:	
Computers:		Manufacturer:		Design:		Aerospace:		Oil/Gas Products:		Special Services:	
Software:		Contract Research:		Construction:		Automotive:	Y	Chemicals:		Consulting:	
Communications:		Medical Services:		Eng. Services:		Shipping:		Oil/Chem. Svcs.:		Specialty Mgmt.:	
Electronics:		Labs:		Consulting:				Gases:		Products:	
Alternative Energy:		Bio. Services:						Other:		Other:	

TYPES OF BUSINESS:

Automobile Manufacturing
Motorcycles
ATVs & Personal Watercraft
Generators
Marine Engines
Lawn & Garden Equipment
Fuel Cell & Hybrid Vehicles
Airplanes

BRANDS/DIVISIONS/AFFILIATES:

Honda of America Manufacturing
Honda R&D Americas, Inc.
Honda Marine
Honda Engineering Co., Ltd.
Sundiro Honda Motorcycle Co., Ltd.
Honda Aircraft Company Inc
Accord
Civic

CONTACTS: *Note: Officers with more than one job title may be intentionally listed here more than once.*

Takeo Fukui, CEO
Takeo Fukui, Pres.
Koichi Kondo, COO-Regional Sales Oper./Exec. VP
Koki Hirashima, Gen. Supervisor-Info. Systems
Akio Hamada, COO-Prod. Oper.
Yoichi Hojo, COO-Bus. Mgmt. Oper.
Hiroshi Oshima, COO-Corp. Comm., Motor Sports
Takanobu Ito, COO-Automobile Oper.
Tatsuhiro Oyama, COO-Motorcycle Oper.
Takuji Yamada, COO-Power Prod. Oper.
Satoshi Aoki, Chmn.
Masaya Yamashita, COO-Purchasing

Phone: 81-3-3423-1111 **Fax:**
Toll-Free:
Address: 2-1-1 Minami-Aoyama, Minato-ku, Tokyo, 107-8556 Japan

GROWTH PLANS/SPECIAL FEATURES:

Honda Motor Co., Ltd., founded in 1948, develops, manufactures, distributes and provides financing for the sale of its motorcycles, automobiles and power products. With 32 factories around the world, Honda operates a network of approximately 454 subsidiaries and affiliates. Honda operates through four segments: motorcycles, automobiles, financial services and power products/other. Through its motorcycle unit, Honda produces sport, business and commuter model bikes, which utilize air- or water-cooled gasoline engines with 1-6 cylinders, manufactured by the company. This segment also includes the production of ATVs and personal watercraft. Within the automotive segment, the firm manufactures vehicles under the Acura and Honda trademarks. Honda models include the Civic, a sub-compact car; the Accord, an intermediate passenger car; the NSX, a specialty sports car; the Prelude, a compact car; the Integra, a compact passenger car; the Odyssey, a minivan; the Orthia, a sub-compact station wagon; the Partner, a sub-compact wagon for commercial utility; and the CR-V, an SUV, among others. Through its power products unit, Honda produces general purpose engines, water pumps, generators, outboard engines, tillers, electric four-wheel scooters, lawnmowers, snow throwers and compact household cogeneration units. In November 2007, Honda introduced the FCX Clarity, a next-generation fuel cell vehicle. The Clarity is currently available for lease only in Southern California. In 2008, the company's Honda Aircraft Company, Inc. subsidiary began offering sales and services of its HondaJet in the E.U., Mexico and Canada. In February 2008, Honda announced plans to retool its Marysville, Ohio motorcycle plant by mid-2009 to begin producing cars for the North American market. All motorcycle production from the Marysville motorcycle plant and the Hamamatsu factory in Japan will take place in a new plant located in Kumamoto, Japan.

FINANCIALS: **Sales and profits are in thousands of dollars—add 000 to get the full amount. 2008 Note: Financial information for 2008 was not available for all companies at press time.**

2008 Sales: $119,801,000	2008 Profits: $5,989,000	**U.S. Stock Ticker: HMC**
2007 Sales: $94,240,700	2007 Profits: $5,034,700	**Int'l Ticker: 7267** Int'l Exchange: Tokyo-TSE
2006 Sales: $84,218,000	2006 Profits: $5,074,800	Employees: 178,960
2005 Sales: $80,705,000	2005 Profits: $4,536,000	Fiscal Year Ends: 3/31
2004 Sales: $78,222,000	2004 Profits: $4,450,000	Parent Company:

SALARIES/BENEFITS:

Pension Plan:	ESOP Stock Plan:	Profit Sharing:	Top Exec. Salary: $	Bonus: $
Savings Plan:	Stock Purch. Plan:		Second Exec. Salary: $	Bonus: $

OTHER THOUGHTS:

Apparent Women Officers or Directors:
Hot Spot for Advancement for Women/Minorities:

LOCATIONS: ("Y" = Yes)

West:	Southwest:	Midwest:	Southeast:	Northeast:	International:
Y	Y	Y	Y	Y	Y

HONDA OF AMERICA MFG INC

www.hondamfg.com

Industry Group Code: 336111 **Ranks within this company's industry group:** Sales: Profits:

Techology:		Medical/Drugs:		Engineering:		Transportation:		Chemicals/Petrochemicals:		Specialty:	
Computers:		Manufacturer:		Design:		Aerospace:		Oil/Gas Products:		Special Services:	
Software:		Contract Research:		Construction:		Automotive:	Y	Chemicals:		Consulting:	
Communications:		Medical Services:		Eng. Services:		Shipping:	Y	Oil/Chem. Svcs.:		Specialty Mgmt.:	
Electronics:		Labs:		Consulting:				Gases:		Products:	
Alternative Energy:		Bio. Services:						Other:		Other:	

TYPES OF BUSINESS:

Automobile Manufacturing
Engine & Parts Manufacturing
Motorcycle & ATV Manufacturing
Personal Watercraft Manufacturing

BRANDS/DIVISIONS/AFFILIATES:

Honda Motor Co Ltd
Accord
Acura
Civic
CR-V
Gold Wing 1800
Honda of Canada Mfg., Inc.
Honda Transmission Mfg.

CONTACTS: *Note: Officers with more than one job title may be intentionally listed here more than once.*

Akio Hamada, COO
Tsuneo Tanai, Pres.

Phone: 937-642-5000	**Fax:** 937-644-6575
Toll-Free:	
Address: 24000 Honda Pkwy., Marysville, OH 43040-9251 US	

GROWTH PLANS/SPECIAL FEATURES:

Honda of America Manufacturing, Inc. (HAM), a subsidiary of Honda Motor Co., Ltd., manufactures produce automobiles, engines and motorcycles in four Ohio plants for the North American market, as well as export to more than 100 countries. The firm's plants are in Marysville, Anna and East Liberty. The Marysville auto plant builds approximately 440,000 vehicles per year. The Anna engine plant produces motorcycle and automobile engines, crankshafts, driveshafts, and suspension and brake components as well as testing engines, and it has an annual production capacity of 1.18 million units. The East Liberty auto plant is one of the most technologically advanced Honda manufacturing facilities in the world. The 1.9 million square foot plant produces 240,000 cars and light trucks annually, as well as exporting stamped parts to Honda of Canada Manufacturing, Inc., for its Civic models. The Ohio plants produce the Accord Coupe and Sedan; the Acura CL, TL and RDX; the Civic Sedan and natural-gas powered GX; the CR-V; and Element automobiles; and the Gold Wing 1800 and VTX 1800 V-Twin Cruiser motorcycles. Honda Motor Co. has other subsidiaries and operations based in Ohio including research and development and engineering facilities and a transmission manufacturing plant. In February 2008, Honda announced plans to discontinue motorcycle production in Marysville in 2009; production will be consolidated in Japan.

The company offers employees medical, dental, vision, basic life, accidental dismemberment, disability and prescription drug insurance; paid vacation and holidays; relocation assistance; a family festival; and an onsite wellness and fitness center.

FINANCIALS: **Sales and profits are in thousands of dollars—add 000 to get the full amount. 2008 Note: Financial information for 2008 was not available for all companies at press time.**

2008 Sales: $	2008 Profits: $	**U.S. Stock Ticker: Subsidiary**
2007 Sales: $1,889,200	2007 Profits: $	**Int'l Ticker:** Int'l Exchange:
2006 Sales: $	2006 Profits: $	Employees: 13,500
2005 Sales: $	2005 Profits: $	Fiscal Year Ends: 3/31
2004 Sales: $	2004 Profits: $	Parent Company: HONDA MOTOR CO LTD

SALARIES/BENEFITS:

Pension Plan: Y	ESOP Stock Plan:	Profit Sharing:	Top Exec. Salary: $	Bonus: $
Savings Plan: Y	Stock Purch. Plan: Y		Second Exec. Salary: $	Bonus: $

OTHER THOUGHTS:

Apparent Women Officers or Directors:
Hot Spot for Advancement for Women/Minorities:

LOCATIONS: ("Y" = Yes)

West:	Southwest:	Midwest:	Southeast:	Northeast:	International:
		Y			

Note: Financial information, benefits and other data can change quickly and may vary from those stated here.

HONEYWELL INTERNATIONAL INC

www.honeywell.com

Industry Group Code: 336410 **Ranks within this company's industry group:** Sales: 5 Profits: 4

Techology:		Medical/Drugs:		Engineering:		Transportation:		Chemicals/Petrochemicals:		Specialty:	
Computers:		Manufacturer:		Design:		Aerospace:	Y	Oil/Gas Products:		Special Services:	
Software:		Contract Research:		Construction:		Automotive:		Chemicals:	Y	Consulting:	
Communications:		Medical Services:		Eng. Services:		Shipping:		Oil/Chem. Svcs.:		Specialty Mgmt.:	
Electronics:	Y	Labs:		Consulting:				Gases:		Products:	Y
Alternative Energy:		Bio. Services:						Other:		Other:	

TYPES OF BUSINESS:

Aerospace & Defense Products
Automation & Control Systems
Turboprop Engines
Performance Polymers
Specialty Chemicals
Nuclear Services
Life Sciences
Nanotechnology & MEMS Research

BRANDS/DIVISIONS/AFFILIATES:

Honeywell Aerospace Solutions
Prestone
FRAM
Enraf Holdings B.V.
Hand Held Products, Inc.
Dimensions International
Maxon Corporation
Sentinel

CONTACTS: *Note: Officers with more than one job title may be intentionally listed here more than once.*

David M. Cote, CEO
David J. Anderson, CFO/Sr. VP
Mark James, Sr. VP-Human Resources
Larry E. Kittelberger, Sr. VP-Tech.
Peter M. Kreindler, General Counsel/Sr. VP
Larry E. Kittelberger, Sr. VP-Oper.
Rhonda Germany, VP-Strategy & Bus. Dev.
Mark James, Sr. VP-Comm.
Murray Grainger, VP-Investor Rel.
Rob Gillette, CEO/Pres., Aerospace
Andreas Kramvis, CEO/Pres., Specialty Materials
Roger Fradin, CEO/Pres., Automation & Control Solutions
Adriane M. Brown, CEO/Pres., Transportation Systems
David M. Cote, Chmn.

Phone: 973-455-2000 **Fax:** 973-455-4807
Toll-Free: 800-328-5111
Address: 101 Columbia Rd., Morristown, NJ 07962 US

GROWTH PLANS/SPECIAL FEATURES:

Honeywell International, Inc. is a leading producer of high-tech control systems, including turboprop engines for airplanes, specialty chemicals for heavy equipment, polymers for electronics, sensing and security technologies for buildings, homes and industry and process technology for refining and petrochemicals. The company is divided into four sectors: Aerospace solutions; automation and control solutions; specialty materials; transportation systems; and intellectual properties. The aerospace unit is associated with engines, electronic systems, integrated avionics systems and service solutions. It is Honeywell's largest segment, earning 35% of sales. The automation and control solutions division focuses on control products such as heating and air conditioning for homes and buildings, water controls and electronic systems for burners, broilers and furnaces, along with security and fire products and services. The specialty materials segment is involved in nylon products and services, fluorocarbons, specialty fibers, nuclear services and customized research chemicals for use in segments such as telecommunications, ballistic protection, pharmaceutical packaging and counterfeit avoidance. The transportation and power systems division includes charge air systems and thermal systems, as well as consumer car care products (under the Prestone, FRAM and Autolite brands). The firm is engaged in manufacturing, sales and research and development mainly in the U.S., Europe, Canada, Asia and Latin America. The Company recently acquired Maxon Corporation, an industrial combustion controls business. In February 2009, the company's Sentinel helicopter avionics system, which includes flight safety information, became available for use in the U.S.

Employees are offered medical, dental and life insurance; disability coverage; a pension plan; and a 401(k).

FINANCIALS: **Sales and profits are in thousands of dollars—add 000 to get the full amount. 2008 Note: Financial information for 2008 was not available for all companies at press time.**

2008 Sales: $36,556,000 | 2008 Profits: $2,792,000
2007 Sales: $34,589,000 | 2007 Profits: $2,444,000
2006 Sales: $31,367,000 | 2006 Profits: $2,083,000
2005 Sales: $27,652,000 | 2005 Profits: $1,638,000
2004 Sales: $25,593,000 | 2004 Profits: $1,246,000

U.S. Stock Ticker: HON
Int'l Ticker: Int'l Exchange:
Employees: 128,000
Fiscal Year Ends: 12/31
Parent Company:

SALARIES/BENEFITS:

Pension Plan: Y | ESOP Stock Plan: | Profit Sharing: | Top Exec. Salary: $1,618,269 | Bonus: $4,200,000
Savings Plan: Y | Stock Purch. Plan: | Second Exec. Salary: $775,962 | Bonus: $1,150,000

OTHER THOUGHTS:

Apparent Women Officers or Directors: 3
Hot Spot for Advancement for Women/Minorities: Y

LOCATIONS: ("Y" = Yes)

West:	Southwest:	Midwest:	Southeast:	Northeast:	International:
Y	Y	Y	Y	Y	Y

HOSPIRA INC

www.hospira.com

Industry Group Code: 339113 **Ranks within this company's industry group:** Sales: 11 Profits: 10

Techology:		Medical/Drugs:		Engineering:		Transportation:		Chemicals/Petrochemicals:		Specialty:	
Computers:		Manufacturer:	Y	Design:		Aerospace:		Oil/Gas Products:		Special Services:	Y
Software:		Contract Research:	Y	Construction:		Automotive:		Chemicals:		Consulting:	
Communications:		Medical Services:	Y	Eng. Services:		Shipping:		Oil/Chem. Svcs.:		Specialty Mgmt.:	
Electronics:		Labs:		Consulting:				Gases:		Products:	
Alternative Energy:		Bio. Services:						Other:		Other:	

TYPES OF BUSINESS:

Pharmaceutical Development
Generic Pharmaceuticals
Medication Delivery Systems
Anesthetics
Injectable Medications
Diagnostic Imaging Agents
Contract Manufacturing

BRANDS/DIVISIONS/AFFILIATES:

One 2 One
Sculptor Developmental Technologies
EndoTool

CONTACTS: *Note: Officers with more than one job title may be intentionally listed here more than once.*

Christopher B. Begley, CEO
Terrence C. Kearney, COO
Thomas E. Werner, CFO
Ron Squarer, Sr. VP-Global Mktg.
Ken Meyers, Sr. VP-People Dev.
Sumant Ramachandra, Sr. VP-R&D/Chief Science Officer
Brian J. Smith, General Counsel/Sec./Sr. VP
Ron Squarer, Sr. VP-Corp. Dev.
Thomas E. Werner, Sr. VP-Finance
Ken Meyers, Sr. VP-Organizational Transformation
Sumant Ramachandra, Sr. VP-Medical Affairs
Christopher B. Begley, Chmn.

Phone: 224-212-2000	**Fax:**
Toll-Free: 877-946-7747	
Address: 275 N. Field Dr., Lake Forest, IL 60045 US	

GROWTH PLANS/SPECIAL FEATURES:

Hospira, Inc. is a global specialty pharmaceutical and medication delivery company. The company's primary operations involve the research and development of generic pharmaceuticals, pharmaceuticals based on proprietary pharmaceuticals whose patents have expired. The company's activities include the development, manufacture and marketing of generic acute-care and oncology injectables, as well as integrated infusion therapy and medication management systems. Hospira divides its products into four categories: specialty injectable pharmaceuticals, other pharmaceuticals, medication management systems and other devices. The specialty injectable pharmaceuticals segment consists of approximately 200 injectable generic drugs; the proprietary sedation drug Precedex; and Retacrit, a biogeneric version of erythropoietin. The other pharmaceuticals segment consists primarily of large volume I.V. solutions and nutritional products. Through its One 2 One manufacturing services group, this segment also offers contract manufacturing services to proprietary pharmaceutical and biotechnology companies for formulation development, filling and finishing of injectable and oral drugs worldwide. The medication management systems segment's products include electronic drug delivery pumps, safety software, administration sets that are used to deliver I.V. fluids and medications and other related services. The other devices segment includes gravity administration sets; critical care devices; needlestick safety products; and other products. The firm operates under three reportable business segments: Americas; Europe, Middle East and Africa; and Asia Pacific. In February 2008, the company introduced an irinotecan hydrochloride injection for use with patients with colon or rectal cancer. In April 2008, Hospira acquired Sculptor Developmental Technologies, a software engineering company and subsidiary of St. Clair Health Corporation. In October 2008, the firm acquired the EndoTool glucose management system from MD Scientific LLC.

Hospira offers its employees medical, dental and vision plans, flexible spending accounts, tuition reimbursement, adoption assistance, an employee assistance program and a 401(k) plan.

FINANCIALS: **Sales and profits are in thousands of dollars—add 000 to get the full amount. 2008 Note: Financial information for 2008 was not available for all companies at press time.**

2008 Sales: $3,629,500	2008 Profits: $320,900	**U.S. Stock Ticker: HSP**
2007 Sales: $3,436,238	2007 Profits: $136,758	**Int'l Ticker:** Int'l Exchange:
2006 Sales: $2,688,505	2006 Profits: $237,679	Employees: 14,500
2005 Sales: $2,626,696	2005 Profits: $235,638	Fiscal Year Ends: 12/31
2004 Sales: $2,645,036	2004 Profits: $301,552	Parent Company:

SALARIES/BENEFITS:

Pension Plan: Y	ESOP Stock Plan:	Profit Sharing:	Top Exec. Salary: $925,358	Bonus: $1,225,209
Savings Plan: Y	Stock Purch. Plan:		Second Exec. Salary: $560,000	Bonus: $593,152

OTHER THOUGHTS:

Apparent Women Officers or Directors: 2
Hot Spot for Advancement for Women/Minorities:

LOCATIONS: ("Y" = Yes)

West:	Southwest:	Midwest:	Southeast:	Northeast:	International:
Y	Y	Y		Y	Y

Note: Financial information, benefits and other data can change quickly and may vary from those stated here.

HP LABS (HEWLETT-PACKARD LABORATORIES) www.hpl.hp.com

Industry Group Code: 541710 **Ranks within this company's industry group:** Sales: Profits:

Techology:		Medical/Drugs:		Engineering:		Transportation:		Chemicals/Petrochemicals:		Specialty:	
Computers:	Y	Manufacturer:		Design:		Aerospace:		Oil/Gas Products:		Special Services:	Y
Software:	Y	Contract Research:		Construction:		Automotive:		Chemicals:		Consulting:	
Communications:	Y	Medical Services:		Eng. Services:		Shipping:		Oil/Chem. Svcs.:		Specialty Mgmt.:	
Electronics:	Y	Labs:		Consulting:				Gases:		Products:	
Alternative Energy:		Bio. Services:						Other:		Other:	

TYPES OF BUSINESS:

Electronics Research
Printing & Imaging Technology
Internet & Computing Technology
Cloud Services
Sustainable Technologies

BRANDS/DIVISIONS/AFFILIATES:

Hewlett-Packard Co (HP)
HP IdeaLab
Bio-Info-Nano Research and Development Institute

CONTACTS: *Note: Officers with more than one job title may be intentionally listed here more than once.*

Prith Banerjee, Dir.-HP Labs/Sr. VP-Research, HP

Phone: 650-857-1501	**Fax:** 650-857-5518
Toll-Free:	
Address: 1501 Page Mill Rd., Palo Alto, CA 94304-1126 US	

GROWTH PLANS/SPECIAL FEATURES:

Hewlett-Packard Laboratories (HP Labs) is the research arm of parent Hewlett-Packard Co. (HP). HP Labs recently restructured, refocusing its efforts from some 150 projects down to a just a few with high payoff potential, organizing its research into 23 labs instead of the 12 it had before. These labs are located in Palo Alto, California; Bangalore, India; Beijing, China; Bristol, U.K.; Haifa, Israel; St. Petersburg, Russia; and Tokyo, Japan; with additional research teams in Princeton, New Jersey and in Barcelona, Spain. Following the restructuring, the firm now has five research areas; each of the 23 labs works in multiple research areas. Fourteen of the labs work in the information explosion area, focusing on acquiring, analyzing and delivering information for businesses and individuals. Twelve labs work in the dynamic cloud services area, developing personalized web platforms and cloud services (Internet- rather than desktop-based applications), usually based on a user's communities, calendar, location and preferences. Nine labs work in the content transformation area, working to transition data from analog to digital as well as from digital to physical products. Thirteen labs work in the intelligent infrastructure area, designing networks, devices and scalable architectures to securely connect business and individuals to content and services. Finally, six labs work in the sustainability area, seeking to lower the carbon footprint of technologies, business models and IT infrastructure. The firm recently launched HP IdeaLab on its web site, offering browsers an opportunity to try out and even possibly shape HP Labs' emerging technologies. HP Labs has an annual budget of approximately $150 million.

Following its restructuring efforts, HP Labs increased the number of internship opportunities for undergraduate and graduate students from around the world, and will begin hiring interns that show the greatest potential.

FINANCIALS: **Sales and profits are in thousands of dollars—add 000 to get the full amount. 2008 Note: Financial information for 2008 was not available for all companies at press time.**

2008 Sales: $	2008 Profits: $	**U.S. Stock Ticker: Subsidiary**
2007 Sales: $	2007 Profits: $	**Int'l Ticker:** Int'l Exchange:
2006 Sales: $	2006 Profits: $	Employees:
2005 Sales: $	2005 Profits: $	Fiscal Year Ends: 10/31
2004 Sales: $	2004 Profits: $	Parent Company: HEWLETT-PACKARD CO (HP)

SALARIES/BENEFITS:

Pension Plan:	ESOP Stock Plan:	Profit Sharing: Y	Top Exec. Salary: $	Bonus: $
Savings Plan: Y	Stock Purch. Plan:		Second Exec. Salary: $	Bonus: $

OTHER THOUGHTS:

Apparent Women Officers or Directors:
Hot Spot for Advancement for Women/Minorities:

LOCATIONS: ("Y" = Yes)

West:	Southwest:	Midwest:	Southeast:	Northeast:	International:
Y					Y

HUAWEI TECHNOLOGIES CO LTD

www.huawei.com

Industry Group Code: 334210 **Ranks within this company's industry group:** Sales: Profits:

Techology:		Medical/Drugs:		Engineering:		Transportation:		Chemicals/Petrochemicals:		Specialty:	
Computers:		Manufacturer:		Design:		Aerospace:		Oil/Gas Products:		Special Services:	
Software:	Y	Contract Research:		Construction:		Automotive:		Chemicals:		Consulting:	
Communications:	Y	Medical Services:		Eng. Services:		Shipping:		Oil/Chem. Svcs.:		Specialty Mgmt.:	
Electronics:		Labs:		Consulting:				Gases:		Products:	
Alternative Energy:		Bio. Services:						Other:		Other:	

TYPES OF BUSINESS:

Communications Equipment
Network Equipment
Software
Wireless Handsets

BRANDS/DIVISIONS/AFFILIATES:

SmartAX MA5600T
Huawei Marine Networks

CONTACTS: *Note: Officers with more than one job title may be intentionally listed here more than once.*

Ren Zhengfei, CEO
Ren Zhengfei, Pres.
Yang Zhirong, Pres., Huawei Access Network Prod. Line
Philip Jiang, Pres., Huawei Latin America
Sun Yafang, Chmn.
William Xu, Pres., Huawei Europe

Phone: 86-755-2878-0808 **Fax:** 86-755-2878-9251
Toll-Free:
Address: Bantian, Longgang District, Shenzhen, 518129 China

GROWTH PLANS/SPECIAL FEATURES:

Huawei Technologies Co., Ltd. specializes in the research, development, manufacture and marketing of communications equipment. It operates 100 branch offices worldwide, with its products deployed in over 100 countries, serving 1 billion users worldwide. Over 75% of 2008 sales were generated internationally. Huawei is working to become one of the world's leading suppliers of telecom equipment, providing competition to long-term leaders like Nortel and Alcatel. Its major customers include China Telecom, China Mobile, Telecom Egypt, Hutchison Telecom, Brasil Telecom and Bell Canada. Its products are divided into a number of categories, including data communications; digital medial entertainment; storage & network security; voice evolution solutions; data communications; terminals; mobile core networks; GSM; CDMA2000; UMTS; IP BSS; WiMAX; optical network; and broadband access. The firm's components, mainly based on its proprietary ASIC chips, are used in products such as switching; integrated access networks; DSL; optical transport; videoconferencing; intelligent networks; network support; GSM and GPRS applications; routers; and LAN switches. The company devotes a minimum of 10% of its sales revenue to research and development activities. It has 14 research and development sites in the U.S. India, Sweden and Russia; and maintains strategic partnerships with industry leaders such as Texas Instruments, Motorola, Microsoft, Intel and Sun Microsystems. In March 2008, China Network Communications Group (China Netcom), which provided fixed-line communications services for the 2008 Beijing Olympics, selected Huawei to supply 40% of its optical access solutions; the contract was filled with Huawei's SmartAX MA5600T ultra-broadband optical access equipment. In December 2008, the company launched a joint venture submarine cable subsidiary, Huawei Marine Networks, with partner firm Global Marine Systems Limited. Also in December 2008, Huawei established a new research and development center in Jakarta, Indonesia.

FINANCIALS: **Sales and profits are in thousands of dollars—add 000 to get the full amount. 2008 Note: Financial information for 2008 was not available for all companies at press time.**

2008 Sales: $
2007 Sales: $12,560,000
2006 Sales: $8,504,000
2005 Sales: $5,982,000
2004 Sales: $3,827,000

2008 Profits: $
2007 Profits: $674,000
2006 Profits: $512,000
2005 Profits: $708,000
2004 Profits: $624,000

U.S. Stock Ticker: Private
Int'l Ticker: Int'l Exchange:
Employees: 35,000
Fiscal Year Ends: 12/31
Parent Company:

SALARIES/BENEFITS:

Pension Plan: ESOP Stock Plan: Profit Sharing: Top Exec. Salary: $ Bonus: $
Savings Plan: Stock Purch. Plan: Second Exec. Salary: $ Bonus: $

OTHER THOUGHTS:

Apparent Women Officers or Directors: 1
Hot Spot for Advancement for Women/Minorities:

LOCATIONS: ("Y" = Yes)

West:	Southwest:	Midwest:	Southeast:	Northeast:	International:
Y	Y			Y	Y

HUNTSMAN CORPORATION

www.huntsman.com

Industry Group Code: 325000 **Ranks within this company's industry group:** Sales: 15 Profits: 10

Techology:		Medical/Drugs:		Engineering:		Transportation:		Chemicals/Petrochemicals:		Specialty:	
Computers:		Manufacturer:		Design:		Aerospace:		Oil/Gas Products:		Special Services:	
Software:		Contract Research:		Construction:		Automotive:		Chemicals:	Y	Consulting:	
Communications:		Medical Services:		Eng. Services:		Shipping:		Oil/Chem. Svcs.:		Specialty Mgmt.:	
Electronics:		Labs:		Consulting:				Gases:		Products:	
Alternative Energy:		Bio. Services:						Other:	Y	Other:	

TYPES OF BUSINESS:

Chemicals Manufacturing
Polyurethane Manufacturing
Advanced Materials & Surface Technologies
Performance Chemicals
Pigments

BRANDS/DIVISIONS/AFFILIATES:

Huntsman International

CONTACTS:

Note: Officers with more than one job title may be intentionally listed here more than once.

Peter R. Huntsman, CEO
Peter R. Huntsman, Pres.
J. Kimo Esplin, CFO/Exec. VP
R. Wade Rogers, VP-Global Human Resources
Maria Csiba-Womersly, CIO/VP
Samuel D. Scruggs, General Counsel/Exec. VP/Corp. Sec.
Martin Casey, VP-Strategic Planning
Russell R. (Russ) Stolle, Sr. VP-Global Public Affairs & Comm.
John R. Heskett, VP-Investor Rel. & Corp. Dev.
L. Russell Healy, VP/Controller
Anthony P. Hankins, Pres., Polyurethanes
Paul G. Hulme, Pres., Textile Effects
Donald J. Stanutz, Pres., Performance Prod.
Kevin J. Ninow, Pres., Base Chemicals & Polymers
Jon M. Huntsman, Chmn.
Brian V. Ridd, Sr. VP-Purchasing

Phone: 801-584-5700 **Fax:** 801-584-5781
Toll-Free:
Address: 500 Huntsman Way, Salt Lake City, UT 84108 US

GROWTH PLANS/SPECIAL FEATURES:

Huntsman Corporation (HC) is a global manufacturer of differentiated chemical products and inorganic chemical products. The company operates all of its businesses through wholly-owned subsidiary Huntsman International. HC's products are used in the adhesives, aerospace, automotive, construction products, durable and non-durable consumer products, electronics, medical, packaging, paints and coatings, power generation, refining, synthetic fiber, textile chemicals and dye industries. HC operates in four business segments: polyurethanes, materials and effects, performance products and pigments. The polyurethanes segment accounts for the production of including MDI products, PO (propylene oxide), polyols, PG (propylene glycol), TPU (thermoplastic urethane), aniline and MTBE (methyl tert-butyl ether) products. The materials and effects segment manufactures epoxy resin compounds and formulations; cross-linking, matting and curing agents; epoxy, acrylic and polyurethane-based adhesives; and textile chemicals and dyes. The firm's performance products segment is organized around three market groups: performance specialties, performance intermediates and maleic anhydride and licensing. In performance specialties, HC is a leading global producer of amines, carbonates and certain specialty surfactants. In performance intermediates, it consumes internally produced and third-party-sourced base petrochemicals in the manufacture of its surfactants, LAB and ethanolamines products. In maleic anhydride and licensing, HC licenses maleic anhydride manufacturing technology, mainly used in the production of fiberglass reinforced resins, and also supplies butane fixed bed catalyst used in the manufacture of maleic anhydride. This division also licenses technology on behalf of other Huntsman businesses. Finally, the pigments segment manufactures titanium dioxide, used in paints and coatings, plastics, paper, printing inks, fibers and ceramics. In January 2009, the company announced plans to close its pigments plant located in Grimsby, U.K.

FINANCIALS:

Sales and profits are in thousands of dollars—add 000 to get the full amount. 2008 Note: Financial information for 2008 was not available for all companies at press time.

2008 Sales: $10,215,000	2008 Profits: $609,000	**U.S. Stock Ticker: HUN**
2007 Sales: $9,650,800	2007 Profits: $-172,100	**Int'l Ticker:** Int'l Exchange:
2006 Sales: $8,730,900	2006 Profits: $229,800	Employees: 12,600
2005 Sales: $8,445,900	2005 Profits: $-34,600	Fiscal Year Ends: 12/31
2004 Sales: $9,562,500	2004 Profits: $-227,700	Parent Company:

SALARIES/BENEFITS:

Pension Plan: Y	ESOP Stock Plan:	Profit Sharing:	Top Exec. Salary: $1,464,500	Bonus: $750,000
Savings Plan: Y	Stock Purch. Plan:		Second Exec. Salary: $496,975	Bonus: $245,000

OTHER THOUGHTS:

Apparent Women Officers or Directors: 2
Hot Spot for Advancement for Women/Minorities:

LOCATIONS: ("Y" = Yes)

West:	Southwest:	Midwest:	Southeast:	Northeast:	International:
Y	Y	Y	Y	Y	Y

HYUNDAI ENGINEERING & CONSTRUCTION COMPANY LTD

www.hdec.co.kr

Industry Group Code: 234000 **Ranks within this company's industry group:** Sales: 16 Profits: 13

Techology:		Medical/Drugs:		Engineering:		Transportation:		Chemicals/Petrochemicals:		Specialty:	
Computers:		Manufacturer:		Design:	Y	Aerospace:		Oil/Gas Products:		Special Services:	
Software:		Contract Research:		Construction:	Y	Automotive:		Chemicals:		Consulting:	
Communications:		Medical Services:		Eng. Services:	Y	Shipping:		Oil/Chem. Svcs.:		Specialty Mgmt.:	
Electronics:		Labs:		Consulting:				Gases:		Products:	
Alternative Energy:		Bio. Services:						Other:		Other:	

TYPES OF BUSINESS:

Construction, Heavy & Civil Engineering
Power Plant Construction
Highway & Bridge Construction
Residential Construction
Commercial Construction

BRANDS/DIVISIONS/AFFILIATES:

Institute of Construction Technology
Hyundai Engineering Co., Ltd.
Hyundai Engineering & Steel Industries Co., Ltd.
Busan Jeongkwan Energy
Kyungin Canal Co., Ltd.
Hyundai Farm Land & Development Co., Ltd.
Hillstate

CONTACTS:

Note: Officers with more than one job title may be intentionally listed here more than once.

Jong-soo Lee, CEO
Jong-soo Lee, Pres.
Lee Ji-Song, Chmn.

Phone: 82-2-746-1114	**Fax:** 82-2-743-8963
Toll-Free:	
Address: 140-2, Kye-dong, Chongro-ku, Seoul, Korea	

GROWTH PLANS/SPECIAL FEATURES:

Hyundai Engineering & Construction Company Ltd. (also known as HDEC) is an international construction company based in South Korea. HDEC has expertise in a variety of structures, such as civil works, highways and bridges, housing, shipyards, dams, power plants (including nuclear power), airports, stadiums, hotels and retail complexes. The firm has offices in the Pacific Rim, the Middle East, Africa, the U.K. and the U.S. HDEC is organized into 12 divisions, which represent each of its service areas such as the Division of Civil Works and the Division of Housing, as well as the Institute of Construction Technology, which fulfills the firm's research and development needs. Subsidiaries of the company include Hyundai Engineering Co., Ltd.; Hyundai Engineering & Steel Industries Co., Ltd.; Busan Jeongkwan Energy; Kyungin Canal Co., Ltd.; and Hyundai Farm Land & Development Co., Ltd.

FINANCIALS:

Sales and profits are in thousands of dollars—add 000 to get the full amount. 2008 Note: Financial information for 2008 was not available for all companies at press time.

2008 Sales: $5,782,184	2008 Profits: $296,997	**U.S. Stock Ticker:**
2007 Sales: $4,492,324	2007 Profits: $220,584	**Int'l Ticker: 000720** Int'l Exchange: Seoul-KRX
2006 Sales: $5,410,300	2006 Profits: $	Employees:
2005 Sales: $4,152,000	2005 Profits: $	Fiscal Year Ends:
2004 Sales: $	2004 Profits: $	Parent Company:

SALARIES/BENEFITS:

Pension Plan:	ESOP Stock Plan:	Profit Sharing:	Top Exec. Salary: $	Bonus: $
Savings Plan:	Stock Purch. Plan:		Second Exec. Salary: $	Bonus: $

OTHER THOUGHTS:

Apparent Women Officers or Directors:
Hot Spot for Advancement for Women/Minorities:

LOCATIONS: ("Y" = Yes)

West:	Southwest:	Midwest:	Southeast:	Northeast:	International:
				Y	Y

HYUNDAI MOTOR COMPANY

www.hyundai-motor.com

Industry Group Code: 336111 **Ranks within this company's industry group:** Sales: 10 Profits: 13

Techology:		Medical/Drugs:		Engineering:		Transportation:		Chemicals/Petrochemicals:		Specialty:	
Computers:		Manufacturer:		Design:		Aerospace:		Oil/Gas Products:		Special Services:	
Software:		Contract Research:		Construction:		Automotive:	Y	Chemicals:		Consulting:	
Communications:		Medical Services:		Eng. Services:		Shipping:		Oil/Chem. Svcs.:		Specialty Mgmt.:	
Electronics:		Labs:		Consulting:				Gases:		Products:	
Alternative Energy:		Bio. Services:						Other:		Other:	

TYPES OF BUSINESS:

Automobile Manufacturing
Trucks
Buses
Light Commercial Vehicles
Machine Tools
Factory Automation Equipment
Material Handling Equipment
Specialty Vehicle Manufacturing

BRANDS/DIVISIONS/AFFILIATES:

Accent
Sonata
Elantra
Genesis Coupe
Hyundai Canada
Kia Motors Corp
Hyundai Motor America
Rotem Inc

CONTACTS: *Note: Officers with more than one job title may be intentionally listed here more than once.*

Mong-koo Chung, Co-CEO
Lee Jeong Dae, Pres.
Yang Seung Seok, Pres., Sales
Yeo Chul Youn, Co-CEO/Vice Chmn.
Jae Kook Choi, Vice Chmn.
Mong-koo Chung, Chmn.

Phone: 82-2-3464-1114	**Fax:** 82-2-3464-8719
Toll-Free:	
Address: 231 Yangjae-dong, Seocho-gu, Seoul, 137-938 Korea	

GROWTH PLANS/SPECIAL FEATURES:

Hyundai Motor Company is the number-one automobile manufacturer in South Korea and a leading automobile manufacturer worldwide. The firm designs and manufactures passenger cars; recreational vehicles; commercial vehicles, including trucks, buses and tractors; and specialty vehicles, including refrigerated vans and oil tankers. Popular export models include the Accent, a sub-compact; the Sonata, a mid-size sedan; the Elantra, a compact sedan; Tiburon, a sport coupe; the Santa Fe SUV; and the XG350 luxury sedan. Light commercial vehicles include the H-1 Truck, the H100 Truck and the H1 Mini Bus. Heavy commercial vehicles include small HD65/72 trucks, medium-sized HD120 trucks and busses, as well as cargo, dump, mixer and tractor trucks. Hyundai also makes machine tools for factory automation and material handling and owns approximately 39% of Kia Motors Corp. Subsidiary Hyundai Motor America has facilities throughout the U.S., including locations in New Jersey, Illinois, Georgia and California. The subsidiary distributes Hyundai vehicles in the U.S., which are sold and serviced by more than 600 dealerships. In addition to its U.S. operations, the firm has other overseas plants in Europe, India and China, as well as research and development centers in North America, Japan and Europe. During 2008, Hyundai began selling its new Sonata in the U.S. In the same year, the company acquired an approximate 30% stake in Shin Heung Securities Co., a second tier brokerage firm. In September 2008, Hyundai announced plans to build a $600 million factory in Brazil, with an annual capacity of 100,000 units. In October 2008, the firm launched its Genesis Coupe model, with plans for a U.S. release in 2009. In November 2008, the firm opened a new manufacturing plant in the Czech Republic. In February 2009, Hyundai established a new subsidiary, focused on business activities related to professional football.

FINANCIALS: **Sales and profits are in thousands of dollars—add 000 to get the full amount. 2008 Note: Financial information for 2008 was not available for all companies at press time.**

2008 Sales: $60,240,800	2008 Profits: $648,030	**U.S. Stock Ticker: HYMLF**
2007 Sales: $68,740,000	2007 Profits: $1,360,000	**Int'l Ticker: 005380** Int'l Exchange: Seoul-KRX
2006 Sales: $68,468,000	2006 Profits: $1,355,000	Employees: 51,471
2005 Sales: $46,358,200	2005 Profits: $1,472,600	Fiscal Year Ends: 12/31
2004 Sales: $32,351,620	2004 Profits: $62,188	Parent Company:

SALARIES/BENEFITS:

Pension Plan:	ESOP Stock Plan:	Profit Sharing:	Top Exec. Salary: $	Bonus: $
Savings Plan:	Stock Purch. Plan:		Second Exec. Salary: $	Bonus: $

OTHER THOUGHTS:

Apparent Women Officers or Directors:
Hot Spot for Advancement for Women/Minorities:

LOCATIONS: ("Y" = Yes)

West:	Southwest:	Midwest:	Southeast:	Northeast:	International:
Y		Y	Y	Y	Y

IBM GLOBAL SERVICES

www.ibm.com/services

Industry Group Code: 541512 **Ranks within this company's industry group:** Sales: 2 Profits:

Techology:		Medical/Drugs:		Engineering:		Transportation:		Chemicals/Petrochemicals:		Specialty:	
Computers:		Manufacturer:		Design:		Aerospace:		Oil/Gas Products:		Special Services:	
Software:		Contract Research:		Construction:		Automotive:		Chemicals:		Consulting:	Y
Communications:		Medical Services:		Eng. Services:		Shipping:		Oil/Chem. Svcs.:		Specialty Mgmt.:	
Electronics:		Labs:		Consulting:				Gases:		Products:	
Alternative Energy:		Bio. Services:						Other:		Other:	

TYPES OF BUSINESS:

Computer Services & Consulting
IT Services
Computer Operations Outsourcing
Customer Relationship Management
Supply Chain Management
Financial Management
Human Capital Management

BRANDS/DIVISIONS/AFFILIATES:

International Business Machines Corp (IBM)
Global Technology Services
Global Business Services

CONTACTS: *Note: Officers with more than one job title may be intentionally listed here more than once.*

Michael E. Daniels, Sr. VP-Global Tech. Svcs.
Virginia M. Rometty, Sr. VP-Enterprise Bus. Services
Robert W. Moffat, Jr., Sr. VP-Integrated Solutions
Bridget van Kralingen, Managing Partner-Global Bus. Services., NE Europe
Jim Bramante, Managing Partner-Global Bus. Services, Americas
Andrew Stevens, Managing Partner-Global Bus. Svcs., Asia Pacific

Phone: 914-499-1900	**Fax:** 914-765-7382
Toll-Free: 800-426-4968	
Address: New Orchard Rd., Armonk, NY 10504 US	

GROWTH PLANS/SPECIAL FEATURES:

IBM Global Services, a business segment of IBM Corp., provides consulting services to businesses of all sizes. The subsidiary as it operates today, which generates over half of parent company IBM's revenue, is largely the result of IBM's 2002 acquisition of PwC Consulting from Pricewaterhouse Coopers. The subsidiary operates in two segments: Global Technology Services (GTS) and Global Business Services (GBS). GTS offers strategic outsourcing services, business transformation outsourcing, integrated technology services and maintenance. GBS offers consulting and systems integration and application management services. In a nutshell, IBM Global Services provides clients with strategies on building e-commerce and supply chain management systems, as well as enterprise resource planning, and can then implement and manage those systems. Clients benefit from the company's long history of cutting-edge technology and continuing commitment to research and development. Information technology (IT) services offered include: business continuity and resiliency services; IT strategy and architecture services, integrated communications services, outsourcing, end user and middleware services; server, cabling and site facilities services; and storage and data storage services. While IBM Global Services tends to use IBM software and hardware, it often implements the products of other suppliers, such as Oracle, SAP and Siebel Systems. In November 2008, the firm announced its new program of bundled services, resilient cloud validation services, which utilizes cloud computing, or software as a service, and incorporates the internet to provide a resilient and uninterrupted flow of data and information for clients. These cloud-related validation services are offered in three segments: industry-specific business consulting services; technology consulting, design and implementation services; and cloud security. IBM plans to build a data center in North Carolina in order to deliver its cloud computing technologies to its clients. In addition, during 2008 the firm opened two new global delivery centers in Pune and Noida, India.

FINANCIALS: **Sales and profits are in thousands of dollars—add 000 to get the full amount. 2008 Note: Financial information for 2008 was not available for all companies at press time.**

2008 Sales: $58,892,000	2008 Profits: $	**U.S. Stock Ticker: Subsidiary**
2007 Sales: $54,100,000	2007 Profits: $	**Int'l Ticker:** Int'l Exchange:
2006 Sales: $48,300,000	2006 Profits: $	Employees: 190,000
2005 Sales: $47,357,000	2005 Profits: $	Fiscal Year Ends: 12/31
2004 Sales: $46,213,000	2004 Profits: $	Parent Company: INTERNATIONAL BUSINESS MACHINES CORP (IBM)

SALARIES/BENEFITS:

Pension Plan:	ESOP Stock Plan:	Profit Sharing:	Top Exec. Salary: $	Bonus: $
Savings Plan: Y	Stock Purch. Plan: Y		Second Exec. Salary: $	Bonus: $

OTHER THOUGHTS:

Apparent Women Officers or Directors: 2
Hot Spot for Advancement for Women/Minorities:

LOCATIONS: ("Y" = Yes)

West:	Southwest:	Midwest:	Southeast:	Northeast:	International:
				Y	Y

IBM RESEARCH

www.research.ibm.com

Industry Group Code: 541710 **Ranks within this company's industry group:** Sales: Profits:

Techology:		Medical/Drugs:		Engineering:		Transportation:		Chemicals/Petrochemicals:		Specialty:	
Computers:	Y	Manufacturer:		Design:		Aerospace:		Oil/Gas Products:		Special Services:	Y
Software:	Y	Contract Research:		Construction:		Automotive:		Chemicals:		Consulting:	
Communications:	Y	Medical Services:		Eng. Services:		Shipping:		Oil/Chem. Svcs.:		Specialty Mgmt.:	
Electronics:	Y	Labs:		Consulting:				Gases:		Products:	
Alternative Energy:		Bio. Services:						Other:		Other:	

TYPES OF BUSINESS:

Research & Development
Computing
Software
Networks, Servers & Embedded Systems
Materials Science
Nanomechanics
Display Technology
Semiconductor & Storage Technology

BRANDS/DIVISIONS/AFFILIATES:

Deep Blue
Blue Gene/L

CONTACTS:

Note: Officers with more than one job title may be intentionally listed here more than once.

Paul M. Horn, Managing Dir.-IBM Research/Sr. VP-IBM
Linda S. Sanford, Sr. VP-IT
Nicholas M. Donofrio, Exec. VP-Innovation & Tech., IBM
Linda S. Sanford, Sr. VP-Enterprise on Demand Transformation

Phone: 914-945-3000	**Fax:** 914-945-2141
Toll-Free:	
Address: 1101 Kitchawan Rd., Rte. 134, Yorktown Heights, NY 10598 US	

GROWTH PLANS/SPECIAL FEATURES:

IBM Research is the R&D arm of International Business Machines Corp. (IBM). It often works with private customers and academic and government research centers. The firm has eight principal research areas. Chemistry research covers optical materials, lubricants, lithography and display development. Computer Science & Engineering research covers artificial intelligence, mobile computing, data management, programming languages, user interface technologies, the Internet, computational biology and security and privacy. Electrical Engineering research covers design automation; nanotechnology and nanoscience; signal processing; and Very-Large-Scale Integration (VLSI) design. Materials Science research covers dielectric, electrically active organic, lithographic, magnetic and nanostructured materials; and superconductivity, measurement and analysis. Mathematical Sciences research covers algorithms and theory; knowledge discovery and data mining; and statistics. Physics research covers information systems, including quantum teleportation; information storage systems; magnetism; computational science; nanoscale phenomena, layered materials; and optical sciences. Services Science, Management & Engineering projects work to streamline engineering, computer science, social sciences, cognitive science, legal science and business strategy, addressing the skills gap in the modern workforce generated by the shift from labor-oriented to service-oriented work. Lastly, Systems projects focus on customizing personal systems of hardware, software and associated services, researching multimedia technologies, communications technology and deep (very complex) computing. IBM Research developed the Deep Blue chess-playing supercomputer, and, more recently, the Blue Gene/L supercomputer, capable of over 280 trillion floating-point calculations per second (flops), developed primarily to help understand how human proteins fold. In recent years, the company partnered with the Genome Institute of Singapore to research how cell processes are regulated; it announced it has improved the transistor, the building block of all microchips, developing chip circuitry that is smaller, faster and more power-efficient; and it announced numerous speech technology breakthroughs, including embedded speech recognition technology and in-vehicle satellite navigation systems.

FINANCIALS:

Sales and profits are in thousands of dollars—add 000 to get the full amount. 2008 Note: Financial information for 2008 was not available for all companies at press time.

2008 Sales: $	2008 Profits: $	**U.S. Stock Ticker: Subsidiary**
2007 Sales: $	2007 Profits: $	**Int'l Ticker:** Int'l Exchange:
2006 Sales: $	2006 Profits: $	Employees: 3,000
2005 Sales: $	2005 Profits: $	Fiscal Year Ends: 12/31
2004 Sales: $	2004 Profits: $	Parent Company: INTERNATIONAL BUSINESS MACHINES CORP (IBM)

SALARIES/BENEFITS:

Pension Plan:	ESOP Stock Plan:	Profit Sharing:	Top Exec. Salary: $	Bonus: $
Savings Plan:	Stock Purch. Plan:		Second Exec. Salary: $	Bonus: $

OTHER THOUGHTS:

Apparent Women Officers or Directors: 1
Hot Spot for Advancement for Women/Minorities:

LOCATIONS: ("Y" = Yes)

West:	Southwest:	Midwest:	Southeast:	Northeast:	International:
Y	Y			Y	Y

Note: Financial information, benefits and other data can change quickly and may vary from those stated here.

IKON OFFICE SOLUTIONS INC

www.ikon.com

Industry Group Code: 333313 **Ranks within this company's industry group:** Sales: Profits:

Techology:		Medical/Drugs:		Engineering:		Transportation:		Chemicals/Petrochemicals:		Specialty:	
Computers:	Y	Manufacturer:		Design:		Aerospace:		Oil/Gas Products:		Special Services:	Y
Software:	Y	Contract Research:		Construction:		Automotive:		Chemicals:		Consulting:	
Communications:		Medical Services:		Eng. Services:		Shipping:		Oil/Chem. Svcs.:		Specialty Mgmt.:	
Electronics:		Labs:		Consulting:				Gases:		Products:	
Alternative Energy:		Bio. Services:						Other:		Other:	

TYPES OF BUSINESS:

Business Machine Distributor
Document Management Services
Document Management Software
Business Equipment Leasing
Managed Print Services Outsourcing

BRANDS/DIVISIONS/AFFILIATES:

IKON Financial Services
Ricoh Company Ltd

CONTACTS:

Note: Officers with more than one job title may be intentionally listed here more than once.

Matthew J. Espe, CEO
Robert F. Woods, CFO/Sr. VP
Cathy L. Lewis, Sr. VP-Mktg.
Donna Venable, Sr. VP-Human Resources
Tracey Rothenberger, CIO/Sr. VP
Mark A. Hershey, General Counsel/Sec./Sr. VP
Dan Murphy, VP-Global Strategy
Dan Murphy, VP-Corp. Comm.
Jim Jacobson, Dir.-Investor Rel.
Richard Obetz, VP/Treas.
Jeffrey W. Hickling, Pres., IKON U.S.
Theodore E. Strand, VP/Controller
Wendy Pinckney, Dir.-Comm,
Henry Miller, Dir.-Corp. Finance
Matthew J. Espe, Chmn.

Phone: 610-296-8000 **Fax:** 610-408-7026
Toll-Free: 888-275-4566
Address: 70 Valley Stream Pkwy., Malvern, PA 19355-0989 US

GROWTH PLANS/SPECIAL FEATURES:

IKON Office Solutions, a wholly-owned subsidiary of Ricoh Americas Corporation, is an international document management service company and a distributor of equipment primarily made by Canon, Ricoh, Electronics for Imaging and Hewlett Packard. Its business service offerings include traditional copiers, printers, multi-functioning peripheral technologies and document management software, as well as other office equipment. The firm's document management software, primarily from companies such as Captaris, eCopy and Kofax, is designed to provide customized, document management solutions supported by the firm's enterprise services organization. IKON sells business machines and supplies through a large geographically-oriented sales force with 400 locations in North America and Europe. Other services include professional services; a blend of on-site and off-site managed document management services; customized workflow solutions; and an expansive customer service network. Professional services help companies assess the efficiency of information processes, meet regulatory compliance requirements and automate manual tasks, thereby reducing document costs. On-site services include document production management, mailroom services management, facsimile service management, imaging and records management and general office support services. IKON also offers legal document services for law firms and law departments that include the accessing, controlling and disseminating of information. Through IKON Financial Services, the company leases its business equipment, as well as non-IKON furniture. In May 2008, the firm expanded its printer line with three new IKON BusinessPro printers. In December 2008, the firm introduced the RICOH Pro C900 digital color printer. In 2008, the company was acquired by Ricoh Company Ltd.

IKON provides its employees with spouse and dependent life insurance; flexible spending accounts; an employee assistance program; a monthly investment program designed to encourage employee stock ownership; tuition reimbursement; a national merit scholarship program for children of employees; and discounted auto and homeowners insurance.

FINANCIALS:

Sales and profits are in thousands of dollars—add 000 to get the full amount. 2008 Note: Financial information for 2008 was not available for all companies at press time.

2008 Sales: $	2008 Profits: $	**U.S. Stock Ticker: Subsidiary**
2007 Sales: $4,168,300	2007 Profits: $114,500	**Int'l Ticker:** Int'l Exchange:
2006 Sales: $4,228,200	2006 Profits: $106,200	Employees: 25,000
2005 Sales: $4,377,305	2005 Profits: $60,666	Fiscal Year Ends: 9/30
2004 Sales: $4,613,551	2004 Profits: $83,694	Parent Company: RICOH COMPANY LTD

SALARIES/BENEFITS:

Pension Plan: Y	ESOP Stock Plan:	Profit Sharing:	Top Exec. Salary: $900,000	Bonus: $1,056,761
Savings Plan: Y	Stock Purch. Plan:		Second Exec. Salary: $550,000	Bonus: $381,325

OTHER THOUGHTS:

Apparent Women Officers or Directors: 4
Hot Spot for Advancement for Women/Minorities: Y

LOCATIONS: ("Y" = Yes)

West:	Southwest:	Midwest:	Southeast:	Northeast:	International:
Y	Y	Y	Y	Y	Y

ILLINOIS TOOL WORKS INC

www.itw.com

Industry Group Code: 333000 **Ranks within this company's industry group:** Sales: 5 Profits: 4

Techology:		Medical/Drugs:		Engineering:		Transportation:		Chemicals/Petrochemicals:		Specialty:	
Computers:		Manufacturer:		Design:	Y	Aerospace:		Oil/Gas Products:		Special Services:	
Software:	Y	Contract Research:		Construction:		Automotive:	Y	Chemicals:		Consulting:	
Communications:		Medical Services:		Eng. Services:		Shipping:		Oil/Chem. Svcs.:		Specialty Mgmt.:	
Electronics:		Labs:		Consulting:				Gases:		Products:	Y
Alternative Energy:		Bio. Services:						Other:		Other:	

TYPES OF BUSINESS:

Industrial Products & Equipment
Steel, Plastic & Paper Products
Power Systems & Electronics
Transportation-Related Components, Fasteners, Fluids & Polymers
Construction-Related Fasteners & Tools
Food Equipment & Adhesives
Decorative Surfacing Materials
Software

BRANDS/DIVISIONS/AFFILIATES:

Quasar International Inc.

CONTACTS: *Note: Officers with more than one job title may be intentionally listed here more than once.*

David B. Speer, CEO
Ronald D. Kropp, CFO/Sr. VP
James H. Wooten, Jr., General Counsel/Sr. VP/Corp. Sec.
John L. Brooklier, VP-Investor Rel.
David B. Speer, Chmn.

Phone: 847-724-7500	**Fax:** 847-657-4261
Toll-Free:	
Address: 3600 W. Lake Ave., Glenview, IL 60026 US	

GROWTH PLANS/SPECIAL FEATURES:

Illinois Tool Works, Inc. (ITW) is a multinational manufacturer of a diversified range of industrial products and equipment with approximately 875 operations in 54 countries. It operates in seven segments: industrial packaging, power systems & electronics, transportation, construction products, food equipment, polymers & fluids and other. The industrial packaging segment produces steel, plastic and paper products used for bundling, shipping and protecting transported goods. Products include steel and plastic strapping and related tools and equipment; and metal jacketing and other insulation products. The power systems & electronics segment produces equipment and consumables associated with specialty power conversion, metallurgy and electronics. Products include welding equipment and airport ground support equipment. The transportation division produces components, fasteners, fluids and polymers for transportation-related applications. Products include metal and plastic components and assemblies for automobiles and trucks; and polyester coatings and patch and repair products for the marine industry. The construction products segment produce tools, fasteners and other products for construction applications. Products include packaged hardware, fasteners, anchors and other products for retail. The food equipment division provides commercial food equipment and related service. Products include warewashing equipment; food processing equipment, including slicers, mixers and scales; and kitchen exhaust, ventilation and pollution control systems. The polymer & fluids segment offers adhesives, sealants, lubrication and cutting fluids, and janitorial and sanitation supplies. Products include hand wipes and cleaners for industrial applications; and adhesives for industrial, construction and consumer purposes. Products offered by the other segment include software and related services for industrial and health care applications; and static and contamination control equipment. The company owns approximately 3,900 unexpired U.S. patents and 1,700 applications for U.S. patents. In 2008, acquisitions included Avery Weigh-Tronix; Opto Diode Corp.; TRYMER; Stokvis Tape Group; VS Acquisition Holding, Inc.; Spray Nine Corporation; and Enodis plc.

FINANCIALS: **Sales and profits are in thousands of dollars—add 000 to get the full amount. 2008 Note: Financial information for 2008 was not available for all companies at press time.**

2008 Sales: $15,869,354	2008 Profits: $1,519,003	**U.S. Stock Ticker: ITW**
2007 Sales: $14,781,076	2007 Profits: $1,869,862	**Int'l Ticker:** Int'l Exchange:
2006 Sales: $12,784,342	2006 Profits: $1,717,746	Employees: 65,000
2005 Sales: $12,540,360	2005 Profits: $1,494,869	Fiscal Year Ends: 12/31
2004 Sales: $11,583,250	2004 Profits: $1,338,694	Parent Company:

SALARIES/BENEFITS:

Pension Plan:	ESOP Stock Plan:	Profit Sharing:	Top Exec. Salary: $948,077	Bonus: $1,781,000
Savings Plan:	Stock Purch. Plan:		Second Exec. Salary: $259,708	Bonus: $368,053

OTHER THOUGHTS:

Apparent Women Officers or Directors: 1
Hot Spot for Advancement for Women/Minorities:

LOCATIONS: ("Y" = Yes)

West:	Southwest:	Midwest:	Southeast:	Northeast:	International:
Y	Y	Y	Y	Y	Y

Note: Financial information, benefits and other data can change quickly and may vary from those stated here.

IMATION CORP

www.imation.com

Industry Group Code: 334112 **Ranks within this company's industry group:** Sales: 6 Profits: 6

Techology:		Medical/Drugs:		Engineering:		Transportation:		Chemicals/Petrochemicals:		Specialty:	
Computers:	Y	Manufacturer:		Design:		Aerospace:		Oil/Gas Products:		Special Services:	
Software:		Contract Research:		Construction:		Automotive:		Chemicals:		Consulting:	
Communications:		Medical Services:		Eng. Services:		Shipping:		Oil/Chem. Svcs.:		Specialty Mgmt.:	
Electronics:	Y	Labs:		Consulting:				Gases:		Products:	
Alternative Energy:		Bio. Services:						Other:		Other:	

TYPES OF BUSINESS:

Data Storage Products
Diskettes & Storage Tapes
Optical Storage Media
Imaging Systems
Hard Drives
Flash Memory Devices

BRANDS/DIVISIONS/AFFILIATES:

Imation
Memorex
TDK Life on Record
Disc Stakka
Global Data Media
Memcorp
Xtreme Accessories LLC

CONTACTS: *Note: Officers with more than one job title may be intentionally listed here more than once.*

Frank P. Russomanno, CEO
Frank P. Russomanno, Pres.
Paul R. Zellar, CFO/VP
Stephen F. Moss, Chief Mktg. Officer/VP
Jacqueline A. Chase, VP-Human Resources
Subodh Kulkarni, VP-R&D
Subodh Kulkarni, VP-Mfg.
John L. Sullivan, General Counsel/Sr. VP/Corp. Sec.
Peter A. Koehn, VP-Global Oper.
James C. Ellis, VP-Strategy & M&A
Bradley D. Allen, VP-Corp. Comm.
Bradley D. Allen, VP-Investor Rel.
Subodh Kulkarni, VP-Global Commercial Business
Linda W. Hart, Chmn.

Phone: 651-704-4000	**Fax:** 888-704-4200
Toll-Free: 888-466-3456	
Address: 1 Imation Pl., Oakdale, MN 55128-3421 US	

GROWTH PLANS/SPECIAL FEATURES:

Imation Corp. develops, manufactures, sources, markets and distributes removable data storage media products (both optical and magnetic) for users of a broad array of digital information technologies in approximately 100 countries worldwide. The primary brand names under which it sells its products are Imation, Memorex and TDK Life on Record. The firm offers a variety of products that capture, process, store, reproduce and distribute information and images for information-intensive markets, including enterprise computing, network servers, personal computing, graphic arts, medical imaging, photographic imaging, commercial and consumer markets. Products include 4mm and 8mm data cartridges, the Disc Stakka, USB flash devices, dictating cassettes, CD-R and CD-RW media discs, Tandberg VXA packet technology, storage accessories, Travan data cartridges, LTO/Ultrium data cartridges and the Odyssey removable HDD storage system. The company is a media supplier to the enterprise data center market, where organizations store, manage and protect mission-critical data. Imation also co-operates a global sales and marketing joint venture company, Global Data Media, with Moser Baer India, Ltd. to meet rising demand from consumers and businesses for high-capacity removable optical storage media. Through subsidiary Memcorp, the company also sells various consumer electronics products, such as flat panel displays and televisions, including LCD displays and digital picture frames; clock-radios; DVD players, karaoke systems; and MP3 players. Imation has recently been combining its global manufacturing and research & development functions into one operational unit to commercialize new products more rapidly. In June 2008, the company acquired substantially all of the assets of Xtreme Accessories, LLC (XtremeMac), a provider of consumer electronics products and accessories, for approximately $9 million.

The company offers a variety of benefits, including medical, dental and vision coverage; short-term and long-term disability coverage; life and AD&D insurance; legal services; pension and 401(k) plans; and tuition reimbursement.

FINANCIALS: **Sales and profits are in thousands of dollars—add 000 to get the full amount. 2008 Note: Financial information for 2008 was not available for all companies at press time.**

2008 Sales: $2,154,600	2008 Profits: $-33,300	**U.S. Stock Ticker: IMN**
2007 Sales: $2,062,000	2007 Profits: $-50,400	**Int'l Ticker:** Int'l Exchange:
2006 Sales: $1,584,700	2006 Profits: $76,400	Employees: 1,570
2005 Sales: $1,258,100	2005 Profits: $87,900	Fiscal Year Ends: 12/31
2004 Sales: $1,173,700	2004 Profits: $29,900	Parent Company:

SALARIES/BENEFITS:

Pension Plan: Y	ESOP Stock Plan:	Profit Sharing:	Top Exec. Salary: $625,012	Bonus: $
Savings Plan: Y	Stock Purch. Plan:		Second Exec. Salary: $365,238	Bonus: $

OTHER THOUGHTS:

Apparent Women Officers or Directors: 2
Hot Spot for Advancement for Women/Minorities: Y

LOCATIONS: ("Y" = Yes)

West:	Southwest:	Midwest:	Southeast:	Northeast:	International:
Y	Y	Y	Y		Y

IMI PLC

www.imiplc.com

Industry Group Code: 333000 **Ranks within this company's industry group:** Sales: 9 Profits: 8

Techology:		Medical/Drugs:		Engineering:		Transportation:		Chemicals/Petrochemicals:		Specialty:	
Computers:		Manufacturer:		Design:	Y	Aerospace:		Oil/Gas Products:		Special Services:	
Software:		Contract Research:		Construction:		Automotive:		Chemicals:		Consulting:	
Communications:		Medical Services:		Eng. Services:	Y	Shipping:		Oil/Chem. Svcs.:		Specialty Mgmt.:	
Electronics:		Labs:		Consulting:				Gases:		Products:	Y
Alternative Energy:		Bio. Services:						Other:		Other:	

TYPES OF BUSINESS:

Machinery Manufacturing
Fluid Controls
HVAC Components
Beverage Dispensers

BRANDS/DIVISIONS/AFFILIATES:

Norgren
Syron
Heimeier
Commtech
Cornelius
Bevcore
Northern Parts
DCI Marketing

CONTACTS: *Note: Officers with more than one job title may be intentionally listed here more than once.*

Martin Lamb, CEO
Douglas Hurt, Dir.-Finance
Matt Huckin, Dir.-Human Resources
John O'Shea, Corp. Sec.
Greg McDonald, Dir.-Bus. Dev.
Graham Truscott, Dir.-Comm.
Will Shaw, Dir.-Investor Rel.
Greg Croydon, Treas.
Peter Bissell, Dir.-Group Risk
Michelle Robinson, Dir.-Taxation
Huw Jenkins, Dir.-Mergers & Acquisitions
Norman Askew, Chmn.
Tony Finocchiaro, Gen. Mgr.-China
David Noble, Dir.-Supply Chain

Phone: 44-121-717-3700 **Fax:** 44-121-717-3701
Toll-Free:
Address: Lakeside, Solihull Parkway, Birmingham, B37 7XY UK

GROWTH PLANS/SPECIAL FEATURES:

IMI plc is an international engineering firm specializing in the areas of fluid controls and retail dispensation. The firm operates through five divisions, which include severe service, fluid power, indoor climate, beverage dispense and merchandising systems. The severe service segment includes engineering solutions in the areas of power generation, oil and gas production, petrochemicals and pulp and paper. The fluid power division, operating primarily through subsidiary Norgren, creates technologies related to the control of air and other fluids in precision engineering applications. The indoor climate division focuses on heating, ventilation and air conditioning systems, and operates under the TA, Heimeier, Commtech and FDI brands. The beverage dispense segment is geared toward beverage merchandising and dispensing, with major brands including Cornelius, Bevcore and Northern Parts. The merchandising systems division arranges for in-store merchandising programs. Key brands include Cannon, DCI Marketing, Artform and Display Technologies.

FINANCIALS: **Sales and profits are in thousands of dollars—add 000 to get the full amount. 2008 Note: Financial information for 2008 was not available for all companies at press time.**

2008 Sales: $2,788,790 | 2008 Profits: $170,170
2007 Sales: $2,345,750 | 2007 Profits: $175,890
2006 Sales: $2,814,400 | 2006 Profits: $135,900
2005 Sales: $2,686,980 | 2005 Profits: $32,460
2004 Sales: $3,164,540 | 2004 Profits: $316,454

U.S. Stock Ticker:
Int'l Ticker: IMI Int'l Exchange: London-LSE
Employees: 14,697
Fiscal Year Ends: 12/31
Parent Company:

SALARIES/BENEFITS:

Pension Plan: ESOP Stock Plan: Profit Sharing: Top Exec. Salary: $ Bonus: $
Savings Plan: Stock Purch. Plan: Second Exec. Salary: $ Bonus: $

OTHER THOUGHTS:

Apparent Women Officers or Directors: 3
Hot Spot for Advancement for Women/Minorities: Y

LOCATIONS: ("Y" = Yes)

West:	Southwest:	Midwest:	Southeast:	Northeast:	International:
					Y

IMPREGILO SPA

www.impregilo.it

Industry Group Code: 234000 **Ranks within this company's industry group:** Sales: 21 Profits: 16

Techology:		Medical/Drugs:		Engineering:		Transportation:		Chemicals/Petrochemicals:		Specialty:	
Computers:		Manufacturer:		Design:		Aerospace:		Oil/Gas Products:		Special Services:	
Software:		Contract Research:		Construction:	Y	Automotive:		Chemicals:		Consulting:	
Communications:		Medical Services:		Eng. Services:	Y	Shipping:		Oil/Chem. Svcs.:		Specialty Mgmt.:	Y
Electronics:		Labs:		Consulting:				Gases:		Products:	
Alternative Energy:		Bio. Services:						Other:		Other:	

TYPES OF BUSINESS:

Heavy Construction
Civil Engineering
Environmental Engineering
Infrastructure Management
Airport Operations

BRANDS/DIVISIONS/AFFILIATES:

Fisia Italimpianti
Fisia Babcock

CONTACTS: *Note: Officers with more than one job title may be intentionally listed here more than once.*

Alberto Rubegni, CEO
Massimo Ponzellini, Chmn.

Phone: 39-02-244-22111	**Fax:** 39-02-244-22293
Toll-Free:	
Address: Viale Italia 1, Sesto San Giovanni, Milan, 20099 Italy	

GROWTH PLANS/SPECIAL FEATURES:

Impregilo S.p.A., 29%-owned by IGLI S.p.A., is a leading Italian civil engineering and construction company with over a century of experience and operations in 21 countries, including the U.S. The Impregilo group is divided into three primary business segments: infrastructures, engineering and plant construction and concessions. The infrastructures unit is responsible for public-sector projects such as dams, hydroelectric plants, roads, bridges, airports, underground works and high-capacity rail projects. The engineering and plant construction segment supplies technical assistance for desalinization, water treatment, solid waste power plant facilities and remediation of contaminated areas on land and sea. It operates through Fisia Italimpianti and Fisia Babcock (Germany) and furnishes a laboratory and research center that provides backup for the segment's operations. The concessions unit manages motorways, airports, water distribution and treatment and renewable energy power production facilities Impregilo group is currently working on dam construction projects in Iceland (Karahnjukar), the Dominican Republic (Guaigui), Venezuela (Tocoma) and Ecuador (Mazar).

FINANCIALS: **Sales and profits are in thousands of dollars—add 000 to get the full amount. 2008 Note: Financial information for 2008 was not available for all companies at press time.**

2008 Sales: $3,991,960	2008 Profits: $226,220	**U.S. Stock Ticker: IPG**
2007 Sales: $3,770,300	2007 Profits: $60,700	**Int'l Ticker: IPG** Int'l Exchange: Milan-BI
2006 Sales: $3,734,700	2006 Profits: $210,800	Employees: 11,703
2005 Sales: $3,114,199	2005 Profits: $-456,544	Fiscal Year Ends: 12/31
2004 Sales: $3,822,957	2004 Profits: $-138,400	Parent Company:

SALARIES/BENEFITS:

Pension Plan:	ESOP Stock Plan:	Profit Sharing:	Top Exec. Salary: $	Bonus: $
Savings Plan:	Stock Purch. Plan:		Second Exec. Salary: $	Bonus: $

OTHER THOUGHTS:

Apparent Women Officers or Directors: 1
Hot Spot for Advancement for Women/Minorities:

LOCATIONS: ("Y" = Yes)

West:	Southwest:	Midwest:	Southeast:	Northeast:	International:
					Y

INDRAS SISTEMAS SA

www.indra.es

Industry Group Code: 541512A **Ranks within this company's industry group:** Sales: Profits:

Techology:		Medical/Drugs:		Engineering:		Transportation:		Chemicals/Petrochemicals:		Specialty:	
Computers:		Manufacturer:		Design:		Aerospace:		Oil/Gas Products:		Special Services:	Y
Software:	Y	Contract Research:		Construction:		Automotive:		Chemicals:		Consulting:	Y
Communications:		Medical Services:		Eng. Services:		Shipping:		Oil/Chem. Svcs.:		Specialty Mgmt.:	
Electronics:		Labs:		Consulting:				Gases:		Products:	
Alternative Energy:		Bio. Services:						Other:		Other:	

TYPES OF BUSINESS:

Data Management
IT Consulting

BRANDS/DIVISIONS/AFFILIATES:

Indra bmb
Europraxis
Indra Emac SA
Indra Espacio SA
Indra Sistemas de Seguriad SA

CONTACTS: *Note: Officers with more than one job title may be intentionally listed here more than once.*

Regino Moranchel, CEO
Rafael Gallego, Dir.-Oper.
Juan Carlos Baena, Dir. Corp Dev.
Juan Carlos Baena, Dir.-Finance
Emma Fernandez, Dir.-Innovation, Talent & Strategy
Angel Luccio, Dir.-Logistic Systems
Javier Piera, Dir.-Oper.
Santiago Roura, Dir.-Oper
Javier Monzon, Chmn.
Cristobal Morales, Dir.-Int'l
Javier de Andres, Dir.-Purchasing

Phone: 34-91-480-50-01	**Fax:** 34-91-480-50-58
Toll-Free:	
Address: Avenida de Bruselas 35, Madrid, 28108 Spain	

GROWTH PLANS/SPECIAL FEATURES:

Indra Sistemas SA is an IT company that provides products and services to a variety of industries. The firm is organized into two segments: services and solutions. The services division, accounting for 26% of total sales, involves the outsourcing of business processes and information systems carried out by subsidiary Indra bmb. The solutions unit, accounting for 74% of sales offers products that focus on obtaining, processing, transferring and managing data such as hospital management and banking facilities, air defense systems and electronic intelligence systems. Subsidiary Europraxis provides consulting on technological, operations and strategy issues. Other subsidiaries include Indra Emac SA, Indra Espacio SA and Indra Sistemas de Seguriad SA. The majority of sales are generated by the defense and security market, accounting for 29% of total sales; transport and traffic, 18%; energy and industry, 16%; public administration and healthcare, 14%; financial services, 13% and telecommunication and media, 10%. In May 2008, the company expanded its presence in Panama by opening two new offices.

FINANCIALS: **Sales and profits are in thousands of dollars—add 000 to get the full amount. 2008 Note: Financial information for 2008 was not available for all companies at press time.**

2008 Sales: $	2008 Profits: $	**U.S. Stock Ticker: ISMAF.PK**
2007 Sales: $	2007 Profits: $	**Int'l Ticker: IDR.MC** Int'l Exchange: Madrid-MCE
2006 Sales: $	2006 Profits: $	Employees:
2005 Sales: $	2005 Profits: $	Fiscal Year Ends: 12/31
2004 Sales: $	2004 Profits: $	Parent Company:

SALARIES/BENEFITS:

Pension Plan:	ESOP Stock Plan:	Profit Sharing:	Top Exec. Salary: $	Bonus: $
Savings Plan:	Stock Purch. Plan:		Second Exec. Salary: $	Bonus: $

OTHER THOUGHTS:

Apparent Women Officers or Directors: 4
Hot Spot for Advancement for Women/Minorities: Y

LOCATIONS: ("Y" = Yes)

West:	Southwest:	Midwest:	Southeast:	Northeast:	International:
			Y	Y	Y

Note: Financial information, benefits and other data can change quickly and may vary from those stated here.

INFINEON TECHNOLOGIES AG

www.infineon.com

Industry Group Code: 334413 **Ranks within this company's industry group:** Sales: 6 Profits: 19

Techology:		Medical/Drugs:		Engineering:		Transportation:		Chemicals/Petrochemicals:		Specialty:	
Computers:	Y	Manufacturer:		Design:		Aerospace:		Oil/Gas Products:		Special Services:	
Software:		Contract Research:		Construction:		Automotive:		Chemicals:		Consulting:	
Communications:		Medical Services:		Eng. Services:		Shipping:		Oil/Chem. Svcs.:		Specialty Mgmt.:	
Electronics:		Labs:		Consulting:				Gases:		Products:	
Alternative Energy:		Bio. Services:						Other:		Other:	

TYPES OF BUSINESS:

Semiconductor Manufacturing
Fiber-Optic Components
GPS Microchips
Embedded Memory Products
Broadband Components

BRANDS/DIVISIONS/AFFILIATES:

Qimonda
Inotera Memories, Inc.
SMARTi 3GE
S-GOLD3H
E-GOLDvoice
Danube
Hammerhead

CONTACTS: *Note: Officers with more than one job title may be intentionally listed here more than once.*

Peter Bauer, CEO
Wolfgang Ziebart, Pres.
Marco Schroter, CFO
Hermann Eul, Exec. VP-Mktg. & Sales
Marco Schroter, Dir.-Labor
Hermann Eul, Exec. VP-R&D
Hermann Eul, Exec. VP-Tech.
Reinhard Ploss, Exec. VP-Oper.
Michael Ruth, Corp. VP-Planning
Max Dietrich Kley, Chmn.

Phone: 49-89-234-28480	**Fax:**
Toll-Free:	
Address: Am Campeon 1-12, Neubiberg, 85579 Germany	

GROWTH PLANS/SPECIAL FEATURES:

Infineon Technologies AG designs, develops, manufactures and markets semiconductors and complete system solutions. The firm's products include standard commodity components, full-custom devices, semi-custom devices and application-specific components for memory, analog, digital and mixed-signal applications. Infineon's products are used in microelectronic applications, including computer systems, telecommunications systems, consumer goods, automotive products, industrial automation and control systems and chip card applications. The company's business is organized into three principal operating segments: communications; automotive, industrial and multimarket (AIM); and memory products. The firm's communications segment designs, develops, manufactures and markets semiconductors and fiber-optic components for communications access, wide area network, metropolitan area network, broadband and traditional carrier access markets, cellular, wireless and wired communications. Infineon's automotive and industrial segment makes semiconductors and complete systems for automotive and industrial uses. Qimonda, the company's memory products segment, makes semiconductor memory products with various packaging and configuration options and performance characteristics for standard, specialty and embedded memory needs. Recent innovations include: security chips for Patient Health Smart Cards; a 3.0 Gb/s Advanced Hard Disk Drive Read Channel, and a number of new processors and chips for mobile phones and ASDL. In 2007, Infineon spent $221 million on a DRAM module manufacturing facility in Malaysia. Additionally, the firm expanded its research and development operations in Singapore with an investment of $295 million and invested approximately $3 billion in a new front-end manufacturing facility in Singapore. Also in 2007, the company acquired DSL CPE (Customer Premises Equipment) from Texas Instruments and Mobility Products Group from LSI Corporation. The firm recently sold its POF (Plastic Optical Fiber) business to Avago Technologies and sold 50% of its shares in ALTIS Semiconductor S.N.C to Advanced Electric Systems (AES). It also sold 22.5% of its stake in its subsidiary Qimonda in 2007.

FINANCIALS: **Sales and profits are in thousands of dollars—add 000 to get the full amount. 2008 Note: Financial information for 2008 was not available for all companies at press time.**

2008 Sales: $6,084,000	2008 Profits: $-4,396,000	**U.S. Stock Ticker: IFX**
2007 Sales: $10,923,000	2007 Profits: $-523,000	**Int'l Ticker: IFX** Int'l Exchange: Frankfurt-Euronext
2006 Sales: $10,060,000	2006 Profits: $-340,000	Employees: 41,343
2005 Sales: $8,123,000	2005 Profits: $-375,000	Fiscal Year Ends: 9/30
2004 Sales: $8,946,000	2004 Profits: $76,000	Parent Company:

SALARIES/BENEFITS:

Pension Plan: Y	ESOP Stock Plan:	Profit Sharing:	Top Exec. Salary: $	Bonus: $
Savings Plan:	Stock Purch. Plan:		Second Exec. Salary: $	Bonus: $

OTHER THOUGHTS:

Apparent Women Officers or Directors: 1
Hot Spot for Advancement for Women/Minorities:

LOCATIONS: ("Y" = Yes)

West:	Southwest:	Midwest:	Southeast:	Northeast:	International:
Y		Y		Y	Y

INGERSOLL-RAND COMPANY LIMITED

company.ingersollrand.com

Industry Group Code: 333410 **Ranks within this company's industry group:** Sales: 1 Profits: 1

Techology:		Medical/Drugs:		Engineering:		Transportation:		Chemicals/Petrochemicals:		Specialty:	
Computers:		Manufacturer:		Design:		Aerospace:		Oil/Gas Products:		Special Services:	
Software:		Contract Research:		Construction:		Automotive:	Y	Chemicals:		Consulting:	
Communications:		Medical Services:		Eng. Services:		Shipping:		Oil/Chem. Svcs.:		Specialty Mgmt.:	
Electronics:	Y	Labs:		Consulting:				Gases:		Products:	
Alternative Energy:	Y	Bio. Services:						Other:		Other:	

TYPES OF BUSINESS:

Refrigeration and Controls
Industrial Equipment
Automotive Tools
Temperature-Controlled Semi-Trailers
Locks & Security Systems
Automotive Components
Specialty Industrial Vehicles
Golf Carts & Utility Vehicles

BRANDS/DIVISIONS/AFFILIATES:

Thermo King
Trane
Officine Meccaniche Industriali
Dor-O-Matic
Broadway
Kryptonite
Locknetics
Schlage

CONTACTS: *Note: Officers with more than one job title may be intentionally listed here more than once.*

Herbert L. Henkel, CEO
Herbert L. Henkel, Pres.
Steven R. Shawley, CFO/Sr. VP
Marcia J. Avedon, Sr. VP-Human Resources
Barry Libenson, CIO/VP
Patricia Nachtigal, General Counsel/Sr. VP
Mike Ryan, VP-Oper.
Patrick Shannon, VP-Strategy & Bus. Dev.
Marcia J. Avedon, Sr. VP-Comm.
David Kuhl, VP/Treas.
James R. Bolch, Sr. VP/Pres., Industrial Technologies Sector
Steven B. Hochhauser, Sr. VP/Pres., Security Technologies Sector
Mary Beth Gustaffson, VP/Deputy General Counsel
Richard W. Randall, VP/Controller
Herbert L. Henkel, Chmn.
Jeff Song, Pres., Ingersoll-Rand China

Phone: 441-295-2838	**Fax:** 201-573-3448
Toll-Free:	
Address: Clarendon House, 2 Church St., Hamilton, HM 11 Bermuda	

GROWTH PLANS/SPECIAL FEATURES:

Ingersoll-Rand Company Limited is a $17 billion global firm that handles business in three segments: manufacture of products and equipment for climate control; design, manufacture and sale of compressed air systems for industrial applications and mechanical and electronic security products through 100 plants worldwide. Ingersoll-Rand Climate Control produces Thermo King temperature-controlled semi-trailers and Hussman-brand stationary refrigeration equipment. Other products manufactured in this sector include HVAC systems, refrigerated displays, beverage coolers and walk-in freezers. Ingersoll-Rand Industrial products include Ingersoll-Rand air compressors, tools and assembly solutions; ARO pumps, valves, cylinders and air system components; GHH-Rand high-performance compressors; robotic adhesive dispensing equipment; ergonomic handling products and systems; micro turbines; automotive tools; engine starting systems; and fastener tightening systems. The segment consists of utility equipment and road development businesses. The firm's compact vehicle technologies group offers Club Car golf carts and utility vehicles and Bobcat compact loaders. Ingersoll-Rand Security and Safety products include Broadway architectural hardware; Dor-O-Matic door closures, exit devices and automatic door systems; Electronic Technologies Corporation's security systems integration services; and other brands such as Falcon, Glynn-Johnson, Kryptonite, Locknetics, Von Duprin and Schlage locks. In November 2007, Doosan Infracore purchased Ingersoll Rand's Bobcat, Utility Equipment and Attachments business units for approximately $4.9 billion. Ingersoll Rand signed an agreement in September 2007 to acquire privately owned Officine Meccaniche Industriali , which provides compressed-air treatment equipment. In June 2008, Ingersoll Rand acquired Trane and its heating, air conditioning and climate control systems services.

Ingersoll-Rand offers its employees various pension/retirement plans providing a fixed amount of retirement assistance based on employee tenure and age.

FINANCIALS: **Sales and profits are in thousands of dollars—add 000 to get the full amount. 2008 Note: Financial information for 2008 was not available for all companies at press time.**

2008 Sales: $13,227,400	2008 Profits: $-2,567,400	**U.S. Stock Ticker: IR**
2007 Sales: $8,763,100	2007 Profits: $733,100	**Int'l Ticker:** Int'l Exchange:
2006 Sales: $8,033,700	2006 Profits: $765,000	Employees: 60,000
2005 Sales: $7,263,700	2005 Profits: $1,054,200	Fiscal Year Ends: 12/31
2004 Sales: $9,393,600	2004 Profits: $1,218,700	Parent Company:

SALARIES/BENEFITS:

Pension Plan: Y	ESOP Stock Plan: Y	Profit Sharing:	Top Exec. Salary: $1,231,250	Bonus: $3,000,000
Savings Plan: Y	Stock Purch. Plan:		Second Exec. Salary: $508,333	Bonus: $540,000

OTHER THOUGHTS:

Apparent Women Officers or Directors: 6
Hot Spot for Advancement for Women/Minorities: Y

LOCATIONS: ("Y" = Yes)

West:	Southwest:	Midwest:	Southeast:	Northeast:	International:
Y	Y	Y	Y	Y	Y

INTEL CORP

www.intel.com

Industry Group Code: 334413 **Ranks within this company's industry group:** Sales: 1 Profits: 1

Techology:		Medical/Drugs:		Engineering:		Transportation:		Chemicals/Petrochemicals:		Specialty:	
Computers:	Y	Manufacturer:		Design:		Aerospace:		Oil/Gas Products:		Special Services:	
Software:	Y	Contract Research:		Construction:		Automotive:		Chemicals:		Consulting:	
Communications:	Y	Medical Services:		Eng. Services:		Shipping:		Oil/Chem. Svcs.:		Specialty Mgmt.:	
Electronics:		Labs:		Consulting:				Gases:		Products:	
Alternative Energy:		Bio. Services:						Other:		Other:	

TYPES OF BUSINESS:

Microprocessors
Semiconductors
Circuit Boards
Flash Memory Products
Software Development
Home Network Equipment
Digital Imaging Products
Demodulation & Tuner Applications Products

BRANDS/DIVISIONS/AFFILIATES:

Pentium
Dual Core
Havok
SpectraWatt Inc
Dual-Core Intel Itanium
Numonyx
NetEffect Inc
SpectraWatt Inc

CONTACTS:

Note: Officers with more than one job title may be intentionally listed here more than once.

Paul S. Otellini, CEO
Paul S. Otellini, Pres.
Stacy J. Smith, CFO/VP
Sean M. Maloney, Chief Sales & Mktg. Officer
Patricia Murray, Sr. VP/Dir.-Human Resources
Diane M. Bryant, CIO/VP
Justin R. Rattner, CTO/VP/Dir.-Corp. Tech. Group
Robert J. Baker, Sr. VP/Gen. Mgr.-Mfg. & Tech. Group
Andy D. Bryant, Chief Admin. Officer/Exec. VP
D. Bruce Sewell, General Counsel/Sr. VP
Andy D. Bryant, Exec. VP-Finance
Deborah S. Conrad, VP/Gen. Mgr.-Intel Corp. Mktg. Group
Arvind Sodhani, Exec. VP/Pres., Intel Capital
Cary I. Klafter, VP-Legal Affairs/Dir.-Corp. Legal/Sec.
Anand Chandrasekher, Sr. VP/Gen. Mgr.-Ultra Mobility Group
Craig R. Barrett, Chmn.

Phone: 408-765-8080	**Fax:**
Toll-Free: 800-628-8686	
Address: 2200 Mission College Blvd., Santa Clara, CA 95054 US	

GROWTH PLANS/SPECIAL FEATURES:

Intel Corp. is a major global semiconductor chip maker that develops advanced integrated digital technology platforms and components for the computing and communications industries. It operates in seven segments: Digital Enterprise, Mobility, NAND Products, Flash Memory, Digital Home, Digital Health and Software Solutions. The Digital Enterprise Group's products are incorporated into desktop computers, enterprise computing servers, workstations, a broad range of embedded applications, and other products that help make up the infrastructure for the Internet. This division produced 53% of the firm's 2007 revenues. The Mobility Group's products, which make up 28% of the firms revenue, include microprocessors and related chipsets designed for the notebook market segment and wireless connectivity products. The NAND Products Group produces memory products used in digital audio players, memory cards and solid-state drives. The Flash Memory Group provides NOR flash memory products for a variety of digital devices. Digital Home offers products for use in PCs and in-home consumer electronics devices. Digital Health offers technology products and explores global business opportunities in healthcare information technology, healthcare research productivity and personal healthcare. The Software and Solutions Group promotes Intel architecture as the platform of choice for software and services. In 2008, the firm spun off its solar energy technology business into a new company called SpectraWatt, Inc.; sold its RFID business to Impinj, Inc.; is in the process of divesting itself of its NOR flash memory assets to a new company called Numonyx (in a joint venture with STMicorelectronics); Intel acquired NetEffect Inc. for $8 million; and entered into agreement with EMCORE Corporation to sell the enterprise and storage assets of Intel's Optical Platform Division and the Intel Connects Cables business.

Employees are offered medical and dental coverage; an employee assistance program; a flexible spending account; child and back-up childcare; flexible work arrangements; employee discounts; tuition reimbursement.

FINANCIALS:

Sales and profits are in thousands of dollars—add 000 to get the full amount. 2008 Note: Financial information for 2008 was not available for all companies at press time.

2008 Sales: $37,586,000	2008 Profits: $5,292,000	**U.S. Stock Ticker: INTC**
2007 Sales: $38,334,000	2007 Profits: $6,976,000	**Int'l Ticker:** Int'l Exchange:
2006 Sales: $35,382,000	2006 Profits: $5,044,000	Employees: 83,900
2005 Sales: $38,826,000	2005 Profits: $8,664,000	Fiscal Year Ends: 12/31
2004 Sales: $34,209,000	2004 Profits: $7,516,000	Parent Company:

SALARIES/BENEFITS:

Pension Plan: Y	ESOP Stock Plan:	Profit Sharing: Y	Top Exec. Salary: $770,000	Bonus: $3,964,200
Savings Plan: Y	Stock Purch. Plan: Y		Second Exec. Salary: $455,000	Bonus: $1,673,400

OTHER THOUGHTS:

Apparent Women Officers or Directors: 6
Hot Spot for Advancement for Women/Minorities: Y

LOCATIONS: ("Y" = Yes)

West:	Southwest:	Midwest:	Southeast:	Northeast:	International:
Y	Y	Y	Y	Y	Y

INTERNATIONAL BUSINESS MACHINES CORP (IBM) www.ibm.com

Industry Group Code: 541512 **Ranks within this company's industry group:** Sales: 1 Profits: 1

Techology:		Medical/Drugs:		Engineering:		Transportation:		Chemicals/Petrochemicals:		Specialty:	
Computers:	Y	Manufacturer:		Design:		Aerospace:		Oil/Gas Products:		Special Services:	Y
Software:	Y	Contract Research:		Construction:		Automotive:		Chemicals:		Consulting:	Y
Communications:		Medical Services:		Eng. Services:		Shipping:		Oil/Chem. Svcs.:		Specialty Mgmt.:	
Electronics:	Y	Labs:		Consulting:				Gases:		Products:	
Alternative Energy:		Bio. Services:						Other:		Other:	

TYPES OF BUSINESS:

Computer Hardware
Supercomputers
Microelectronic Technology
Software Development
Networking Systems
IT Consulting & Outsourcing
Financial Services

BRANDS/DIVISIONS/AFFILIATES:

Rational Software Corp
MRO Software Inc
IBM Global Services
Filenet Corp
Internet Security Systems Inc
IBM Research
IBM Canada Ltd
IBM India Pvt Ltd

CONTACTS: *Note: Officers with more than one job title may be intentionally listed here more than once.*

Samuel J. Palmisano, CEO
Samuel J. Palmisano, Pres.
Mark Loughridge, CFO/Sr. VP
Jon C. Iwata, Sr. VP-Mktg.
J. Randall MacDonald, Sr. VP-Human Resources
John E. Kelly, III, Sr. VP-IBM Research
Linda S. Sanford, Sr. VP-IT & Enterprise On Demand Transformation
Robert W. Moffat, Jr., Sr. VP-Systems & Tech. Group
Robert C. Weber, General Counsel/Sr. VP-Legal & Regulatory Affairs
Jon C. Iwata, Sr. VP-Comm.
James J. Kavanaugh, Controller
Rodney C. Adkins, Sr. VP-Dev. & Mfg., IBM Systems & Tech. Group
Michael E. Daniels, Sr. VP-Global Tech. Svcs., BM Global Svcs.
Steven A. Mills, Sr. VP/Group Exec.-IBM Software Group
R. Frankin Kern, Sr. VP-IBM Global Business Svcs.
Samuel J. Palmisano, Chmn.
Virginia M Rometty, Sr. VP-IBM Global Sales & Distribution

Phone: 914-499-1900 **Fax:** 800-314-1092
Toll-Free: 800-426-4968
Address: 1 New Orchard Rd., Armonk, NY 10504 US

GROWTH PLANS/SPECIAL FEATURES:

International Business Machines Corp. (IBM) is a global producer of computer hardware and software, with one of the largest technology consulting businesses in the world. It operates in four primary segments: global technology services; global business services; software; systems and technology; and global financing. The global technology services segment primarily reflects IT infrastructure services and business process services. The global business services segment primarily reflects professional services and application outsourcing services. Capabilities include consulting and systems integration; and application management services. The systems and technology division provides IBM's clients with business solutions requiring advanced computing power and storage capabilities. Offerings include services; storage; microelectronics; engineering and technology services; and retail store solutions. The software segment consists primarily of middleware and operating systems software. Middleware software enables clients to integrate systems, processes and applications across a standard software platform. Offerings include information management software; operating systems; and Tivoli software for infrastructure management, including security and storage management. The global financing division's capabilities include commercial financing, client financing and remarketing. The company has manufacturing locations in Minnesota, New York and California in the U.S.; Mexico; Ireland; Hungary; France; China; and Singapore. Recent acquisitions include Encentuate in March 2008; and Telelogic AB, InfoDyne, FilesX and Diligent Technologies in April 2008. Also in 2008, the firm acquired Transitive, a developer of cross-platform virtualization. In 2009, IBM announced plans to acquire the e-mail service assets of Outblaze, Ltd., a provider of online messaging and collaboration services based in Hong Kong. Also in 2009, the company plans to open its first research facility in China.

The company offers its employees medical, dental and vision insurance; sickness and accident income plans; long-term disability and life insurance; and travel accident insurance. About 72% of IBM's workforce is outside the U.S.

FINANCIALS: Sales and profits are in thousands of dollars—add 000 to get the full amount. 2008 Note: Financial information for 2008 was not available for all companies at press time.

2008 Sales: $103,600,000	2008 Profits: $12,300,000	**U.S. Stock Ticker: IBM**
2007 Sales: $98,786,000	2007 Profits: $10,418,000	**Int'l Ticker:** Int'l Exchange:
2006 Sales: $91,424,000	2006 Profits: $9,492,000	Employees: 395,000
2005 Sales: $91,134,000	2005 Profits: $7,934,000	Fiscal Year Ends: 12/31
2004 Sales: $96,503,000	2004 Profits: $8,430,000	Parent Company:

SALARIES/BENEFITS:

Pension Plan:	ESOP Stock Plan:	Profit Sharing:	Top Exec. Salary: $1,800,000	Bonus: $5,800,000
Savings Plan: Y	Stock Purch. Plan: Y		Second Exec. Salary: $775,001	Bonus: $1,265,000

OTHER THOUGHTS:

Apparent Women Officers or Directors: 4
Hot Spot for Advancement for Women/Minorities: Y

LOCATIONS: ("Y" = Yes)

West:	Southwest:	Midwest:	Southeast:	Northeast:	International:
Y	Y	Y	Y	Y	Y

INTUIT INC

www.intuit.com

Industry Group Code: 511201 **Ranks within this company's industry group:** Sales: 1 Profits: 1

Techology:		Medical/Drugs:		Engineering:		Transportation:		Chemicals/Petrochemicals:		Specialty:	
Computers:		Manufacturer:		Design:		Aerospace:		Oil/Gas Products:		Special Services:	Y
Software:	Y	Contract Research:		Construction:		Automotive:		Chemicals:		Consulting:	
Communications:		Medical Services:		Eng. Services:		Shipping:		Oil/Chem. Svcs.:		Specialty Mgmt.:	
Electronics:		Labs:		Consulting:				Gases:		Products:	
Alternative Energy:		Bio. Services:						Other:		Other:	

TYPES OF BUSINESS:

Computer Software-Financial Management
Business Accounting Software
Consumer Finance Software
Tax Preparation Software
Online Financial Services

BRANDS/DIVISIONS/AFFILIATES:

QuickBooks
QuickBooks Payroll
Innovative Merchant Services
Quicken
Quicken.com
Intuit Real Estate Solutions
StepUp Commerce, Inc.
Digital Insight Corp.

CONTACTS: *Note: Officers with more than one job title may be intentionally listed here more than once.*

Brad D. Smith, CEO
Brad D. Smith, Pres.
Neil Williams, CFO/Sr. VP
Caroline Donahue, VP-Sales
Laura A. Fennell, General Counsel/VP/Corp. Sec.
Alexander Lintner, Sr. VP-Strategy & Corp. Dev.
Jeffrey Hank, Controller/VP
Scott D. Cook, Chmn.-Exec. Committee
Kiran Patel, Gen. Mgr./Sr. VP-Consumer Tax Unit
Peter Karpas, Sr. VP-Quicken Health Group
Sasan Goodarzi, Sr. VP
Bill Campbell, Chmn.

Phone: 650-944-6000	**Fax:** 650-944-3699
Toll-Free: 800-446-8848	
Address: 2632 Marine Way, Mountain View, CA 94043 US	

GROWTH PLANS/SPECIAL FEATURES:

Intuit, Inc. is a leading provider of software and web-based services designed to provide consumers, small businesses and accounting professionals with financial management and tax solutions. The company has six business segments: QuickBooks, Payroll and Payments, Consumer Tax, Professional Tax, Financial Institutions and Other Businesses. QuickBooks products include QuickBooks Simple Start, which provides accounting functionality suitable for very small, less complex businesses; QuickBooks Pro, which provides accounting functionality suitable for slightly larger businesses, including those with payroll needs; QuickBooks Pro for Mac; QuickBooks Premier; and QuickBooks Enterprise Solutions. The company also offers QuickBooks Online Edition, suitable for multiple users working in various locations. QuickBooks Payroll is a family of products sold on a subscription basis to small businesses that prepare their own payrolls. The Innovative Merchant Services business, part of the company's Payroll and Payments segment, offers credit card, debit card, electronic benefits, check guarantee and gift card processing services as well as web-based transaction processing services for online merchants. The Consumer and Professional Tax segments offer a variety of software and services for customers whose returns have varying levels of complexity and for accountants and tax preparers in public practice who serve multiple clients. The Financial Institutions segment was formed after the acquision of Digital Insight Corp. in February 2007, and primarily consists of outsourced online banking applications and services for banks and credit unions provided by our Digital Insight business. The Other Businesses segment includes the Quicken software, Quicken.com, Intuit Real Estate Solutions and its businesses in Canada and the U.K. In December 2007, Intuit acquired Homestead Technologies, Inc., which provides website and online store services for small businesses, for $170 million. In February 2008, the company acquired Electronic Clearing House, Inc., which provides electronic payment processing solutions, for $131 million.

Intuit's employees enjoy an employee assistance program, tuition assistance, adoption assistance and medical, vision and dental insurance.

FINANCIALS: **Sales and profits are in thousands of dollars—add 000 to get the full amount. 2008 Note: Financial information for 2008 was not available for all companies at press time.**

2008 Sales: $3,070,974	2008 Profits: $476,762	**U.S. Stock Ticker: INTU**
2007 Sales: $2,672,947	2007 Profits: $440,003	**Int'l Ticker:** Int'l Exchange:
2006 Sales: $2,293,010	2006 Profits: $416,963	Employees: 8,200
2005 Sales: $1,993,102	2005 Profits: $381,627	Fiscal Year Ends: 7/31
2004 Sales: $1,867,663	2004 Profits: $317,030	Parent Company:

SALARIES/BENEFITS:

Pension Plan:	ESOP Stock Plan:	Profit Sharing:	Top Exec. Salary: $1,100,000	Bonus: $3,250,000
Savings Plan: Y	Stock Purch. Plan: Y		Second Exec. Salary: $699,038	Bonus: $683,000

OTHER THOUGHTS:

Apparent Women Officers or Directors: 5
Hot Spot for Advancement for Women/Minorities: Y

LOCATIONS: ("Y" = Yes)

West:	Southwest:	Midwest:	Southeast:	Northeast:	International:
Y	Y	Y	Y	Y	Y

ISUZU MOTORS LTD

www.isuzu.co.jp

Industry Group Code: 336111 **Ranks within this company's industry group:** Sales: 16 Profits: 11

Techology:		Medical/Drugs:		Engineering:		Transportation:		Chemicals/Petrochemicals:		Specialty:	
Computers:		Manufacturer:		Design:		Aerospace:		Oil/Gas Products:		Special Services:	
Software:		Contract Research:		Construction:		Automotive:	Y	Chemicals:		Consulting:	
Communications:		Medical Services:		Eng. Services:		Shipping:		Oil/Chem. Svcs.:		Specialty Mgmt.:	
Electronics:		Labs:		Consulting:				Gases:		Products:	
Alternative Energy:		Bio. Services:						Other:		Other:	

TYPES OF BUSINESS:

Automobile Manufacturing
Trucks & Buses
Diesel Engines
Logistics Services

BRANDS/DIVISIONS/AFFILIATES:

Isuzu Motors America LLC
Isuzu Motors America Inc
Isuzu Automotive Europe
Isuzu Truck South Africa (Pty) Limited
Isuzu Ukraine
Isuzu-OAO Severstal-Auto

CONTACTS: *Note: Officers with more than one job title may be intentionally listed here more than once.*

Susumu Hosoi, Pres.
Hiroyoshi Sakai, Exec. Officer-Prod. Mktg.
Masashi Harada, Exec. Officer-Human Resources
Takashi Urata, Sr. Exec. Officer-Eng. Div.
Naotoshi Tsutsumi, Exec. VP-Mfg. Div.
Naoto Hakamata, Exec. Officer-Corp. Comm.
Goro Shintani, Exec. VP-Int'l Sales Headquarters
Yoshihiro Tadaki, Exec. VP-Japan Sales Headquarters
Tsutomu Yamada, Sr. Exec. Officer-Quality Assurance Div.
Yoshinori Ida, Chmn.
Hirokichi Nadachi, Sr. Exec. Officer-Europe Oper.

Phone: 81-3-5471-1141 **Fax:** 81-3-5471-1042
Toll-Free:
Address: 6-26-1 Minami-oi, Shinagawa-ku, Tokyo, 140-8722 Japan

GROWTH PLANS/SPECIAL FEATURES:

Isuzu Motors, Ltd., headquartered in Tokyo, Japan, manufactures and sells automobiles, sport-utility vehicles (SUVs), pickups, freight trucks, buses, automobile parts and diesel engines. Its SUV line includes the Ascender, the MU-7 in Thailand and the Panther in Indonesia. Chief pick-up trucks include the D-MAX, the i-350 and the i-280. Truck models come in heavy-, medium- and light-duty varieties, with featured models including (in descending size) the E-line (EXZ, EXR), the C-line (CXZ), the F-line (FVZ, FRR, FTR, FSR) and the light-duty N-line (NQR, NPR, NKR). Isuzu sells its buses under the Erga brand name, offering a normal version and a small version known as the Erga Mio. The company has focused on the development of fuel-efficient and low-emissions diesel engines for years and currently produces more than 60 diesel engine models sold to the automotive, industrial and maritime markets. The firm has more than 50 associated companies and approximately 95 subsidiaries, through which it also provides logistics services. Isuzu has a number of partnerships, including Isuzu Automotive Europe, a joint venture with Mitsubishi Corp. to expand sales in Europe; Isuzu Truck South Africa (Pty) Limited, a joint venture with GM South Africa; Isuzu Ukraine, which sells trucks and buses in the Ukraine; and Isuzu-OAO Severstal-Auto, which implements local production and sales of the ELF light-duty commercial trucks in Russia. Automotive customers include such industry giants as Saab, Renault and General Motors. Isuzu engines are manufactured in plants located on four continents, including four plants in the U.S. In early 2008, the company discontinued its SUV sales in North America. In February 2009, the company announced the merging of two U.S. subsidiaries, Isuzu Motors America LLC and Isuzu Motors America, Inc. The surviving company will be known as Isuzu Motors America LLC.

FINANCIALS: **Sales and profits are in thousands of dollars—add 000 to get the full amount. 2008 Note: Financial information for 2008 was not available for all companies at press time.**

2008 Sales: $19,180,300	2008 Profits: $757,330	**U.S. Stock Ticker:**
2007 Sales: $16,570,500	2007 Profits: $920,750	**Int'l Ticker: 7202** Int'l Exchange: Tokyo-TSE
2006 Sales: $13,452,100	2006 Profits: $	Employees: 7,571
2005 Sales: $13,425,818	2005 Profits: $539,250	Fiscal Year Ends: 3/31
2004 Sales: $13,539,600	2004 Profits: $517,900	Parent Company:

SALARIES/BENEFITS:

Pension Plan:	ESOP Stock Plan:	Profit Sharing:	Top Exec. Salary: $	Bonus: $
Savings Plan:	Stock Purch. Plan:		Second Exec. Salary: $	Bonus: $

OTHER THOUGHTS:

Apparent Women Officers or Directors:
Hot Spot for Advancement for Women/Minorities:

LOCATIONS: ("Y" = Yes)

West:	Southwest:	Midwest:	Southeast:	Northeast:	International:
Y		Y			Y

ITT CORPORATION

www.ittind.com

Industry Group Code: 336410 **Ranks within this company's industry group:** Sales: 15 Profits: 10

Techology:		Medical/Drugs:		Engineering:		Transportation:		Chemicals/Petrochemicals:		Specialty:	
Computers:		Manufacturer:		Design:		Aerospace:	Y	Oil/Gas Products:		Special Services:	
Software:	Y	Contract Research:		Construction:		Automotive:		Chemicals:		Consulting:	
Communications:		Medical Services:		Eng. Services:		Shipping:		Oil/Chem. Svcs.:		Specialty Mgmt.:	
Electronics:	Y	Labs:		Consulting:				Gases:		Products:	Y
Alternative Energy:		Bio. Services:						Other:		Other:	

TYPES OF BUSINESS:

Aerospace & Defense Electronics
Fluid Technology Products
Motion & Flow Control Products
Wastewater Treatment Systems
Military Tactical Software
Surveillance Systems
Meteorological Equipment

BRANDS/DIVISIONS/AFFILIATES:

Flygt
Sanitaire
Pure-Flo
Marlow Pumps
F.B. Leopold Company, Inc.
Dolphin Technology, Inc.

CONTACTS: *Note: Officers with more than one job title may be intentionally listed here more than once.*

Steven R. Loranger, CEO
Steven R. Loranger, Pres.
Denise L. Ramos, CFO/Sr. VP
Scott A. Crum, Sr. VP-Human Resources
Carol J. Zierhoffer, CIO/VP
Vincent A. Maffeo, General Counsel/Sr. VP
Aris C. Chicles, VP-Corp. Strategy & Dev.
Angela A. Buonocore, Chief Comm. Officer/Sr. VP
Robert Pagano, Jr., VP-Finance
Ann Davidson, Chief Ethics & Compliance Officer/VP
David F. Melcher, Sr. VP/Pres., Defense Electronics & Svcs.
Gretchen W. McClain, Sr. VP/Pres., Fluid & Motion Control
Donald E. Foley, Treas./Sr. VP
Steven R. Loranger, Chmn.

Phone: 914-641-2000 **Fax:** 914-696-2950
Toll-Free:
Address: 1133 Westchester Ave., White Plains, NY 10604 US

GROWTH PLANS/SPECIAL FEATURES:

ITT Corporation is a global, multi-industry engineering and manufacturing company, providing a wide range of equipment relating to three business segments: fluid technology; defense electronics and services; and motion and flow control. The fluid technology division is engaged in the design, development, production, sale and support of products, systems and services used to move, measure and manage fluids for the wastewater, residential and commercial water, industrial and biopharm, and advanced water treatment markets. It is a worldwide supplier of a range of pumps, mixers, heat exchangers, valves, controls and treatment systems for industrial, residential, agricultural and commercial applications. Its Flygt and Sanitaire brands are leaders in wastewater treatment. The defense electronics and services division develops, manufactures and supports high-tech electronic systems and components for worldwide defense and commercial markets, including tactical software, night vision equipment, aviation countermeasures, surveillance systems and meteorological equipment. Additionally, this segment provides communications systems and engineering and applied research. The aerospace/communications division of the defense electronics segment is the creator of the core technology used in the world's two largest tactical digitization programs: the U.S. Tactical Internet and the U.K. Bowman program. The motion and flow control division produces tubing systems for automotive brake and fuel supply systems; brake friction materials; marine pumps and related products; and switches, valves and controls for aerospace applications. ITT has operations in North America, Europe and the Middle East. In March 2009, the company was selected to supply high-end water pumps for two irrigation systems to the Andhra Pradesh irrigation projects in India.

FINANCIALS: **Sales and profits are in thousands of dollars—add 000 to get the full amount. 2008 Note: Financial information for 2008 was not available for all companies at press time.**

2008 Sales: $11,694,800	2008 Profits: $794,700	**U.S. Stock Ticker: ITT**
2007 Sales: $9,003,300	2007 Profits: $742,100	**Int'l Ticker:** Int'l Exchange:
2006 Sales: $7,807,900	2006 Profits: $581,100	Employees: 40,800
2005 Sales: $7,040,800	2005 Profits: $359,500	Fiscal Year Ends: 12/31
2004 Sales: $5,965,500	2004 Profits: $432,300	Parent Company:

SALARIES/BENEFITS:

Pension Plan: Y	ESOP Stock Plan:	Profit Sharing:	Top Exec. Salary: $1,056,539	Bonus: $2,250,000
Savings Plan:	Stock Purch. Plan:		Second Exec. Salary: $532,519	Bonus: $712,500

OTHER THOUGHTS:

Apparent Women Officers or Directors: 8
Hot Spot for Advancement for Women/Minorities: Y

LOCATIONS: ("Y" = Yes)

West:	Southwest:	Midwest:	Southeast:	Northeast:	International:
Y	Y	Y	Y	Y	Y

JABIL CIRCUIT INC

www.jabil.com

Industry Group Code: 334419 **Ranks within this company's industry group:** Sales: 3 Profits: 4

Techology:		Medical/Drugs:		Engineering:		Transportation:		Chemicals/Petrochemicals:		Specialty:	
Computers:		Manufacturer:		Design:	Y	Aerospace:		Oil/Gas Products:		Special Services:	Y
Software:		Contract Research:		Construction:		Automotive:		Chemicals:		Consulting:	
Communications:		Medical Services:		Eng. Services:		Shipping:		Oil/Chem. Svcs.:		Specialty Mgmt.:	
Electronics:	Y	Labs:		Consulting:				Gases:		Products:	Y
Alternative Energy:		Bio. Services:						Other:		Other:	

TYPES OF BUSINESS:

Electronic Manufacturing Services & Solutions
Maintenance & Support Services
Custom Design Services

BRANDS/DIVISIONS/AFFILIATES:

CONTACTS:

Note: Officers with more than one job title may be intentionally listed here more than once.

Timothy L. Main, CEO
Mark T. Mondello, COO
Timothy L. Main, Pres.
Forbes I. J. Alexander, CFO
William E. Peters, Sr. VP-Human Dev.
David Couch, CIO
Robert L. Paver, General Counsel/Corp. Sec.
Donald J. Myers, VP-Corp. Dev.
Beth A. Walters, VP-Comm.
Beth A. Walters, VP-Investor Rel.
Sergio A. Cadavrid, Treas.
John P. Lovato, CEO/Exec. VP-Consumer Div.
William D. Muir, Jr., CEO/Exec. VP-EMS Div.
Meheryar Dastoor, Controller
William D. Morean, Chmn.

Phone: 727-577-9749	**Fax:** 727-579-8529
Toll-Free:	
Address: 10560 Dr. Martin Luther King Jr. St. N., St. Petersburg, FL 33716 US	

GROWTH PLANS/SPECIAL FEATURES:

Jabil Circuit, Inc., with operations in 22 countries, is a provider of worldwide electronic manufacturing services and solutions. It provides electronics and mechanical design, production, product management and after-market services to companies in the aerospace, automotive, computing, consumer, defense, industrial, instrumentation, medical, networking, peripherals, storage and telecommunications industry. The company's business units are capable of providing customers with varying combinations of the following services: Integrated design and engineering; component selection, sourcing and procurement; automate assembly; design and implementation of product testing; parallel global production; enclosure service; systems assembly, direct-order fulfillment and configure-to-order; and after-market services. The firm conducts its operations in facilities located in Austria, Belgium, Brazil, China, England, France, Germany, Hungary, India, Ireland, Italy, Japan, Malaysia, Mexico, the Netherlands, Poland, Scotland, Singapore, Taiwan, Ukraine, Vietnam and the U.S. The largest customers include Cisco Systems, Inc.; EMC Corp.; Hewlett-Packard Co.; International Business Machines Corp. (IBM); Network Appliance; NEC Corp.; Nokia Corp.; Royal Philips Electronics; Tellabs, Inc.; and Valeo S.A.

FINANCIALS:

Sales and profits are in thousands of dollars—add 000 to get the full amount. 2008 Note: Financial information for 2008 was not available for all companies at press time.

2008 Sales: $12,779,703	2008 Profits: $133,892	**U.S. Stock Ticker: JBL**
2007 Sales: $12,290,592	2007 Profits: $73,236	**Int'l Ticker:** Int'l Exchange:
2006 Sales: $10,265,447	2006 Profits: $164,518	Employees: 61,000
2005 Sales: $7,524,386	2005 Profits: $203,875	Fiscal Year Ends: 8/31
2004 Sales: $6,252,897	2004 Profits: $166,900	Parent Company:

SALARIES/BENEFITS:

Pension Plan:	ESOP Stock Plan:	Profit Sharing:	Top Exec. Salary: $1,000,000	Bonus: $155,925
Savings Plan:	Stock Purch. Plan:		Second Exec. Salary: $675,000	Bonus: $77,963

OTHER THOUGHTS:

Apparent Women Officers or Directors: 2
Hot Spot for Advancement for Women/Minorities: Y

LOCATIONS: ("Y" = Yes)

West:	Southwest:	Midwest:	Southeast:	Northeast:	International:
Y		Y	Y	Y	Y

JACOBS ENGINEERING GROUP INC

www.jacobs.com

Industry Group Code: 234000 **Ranks within this company's industry group:** Sales: 11 Profits: 9

Techology:		Medical/Drugs:		Engineering:		Transportation:		Chemicals/Petrochemicals:		Specialty:	
Computers:		Manufacturer:		Design:	Y	Aerospace:		Oil/Gas Products:		Special Services:	Y
Software:		Contract Research:		Construction:	Y	Automotive:		Chemicals:		Consulting:	Y
Communications:		Medical Services:		Eng. Services:	Y	Shipping:		Oil/Chem. Svcs.:		Specialty Mgmt.:	
Electronics:		Labs:		Consulting:				Gases:		Products:	
Alternative Energy:		Bio. Services:						Other:		Other:	

TYPES OF BUSINESS:

Engineering & Design Services
Facility Management
Construction & Field Services
Technical Consulting Services
Environmental Services

BRANDS/DIVISIONS/AFFILIATES:

Edwards and Kelcey
Carter and Burgess
Neste Jacobs Oy of Kilpilahti
Rintekno
Jacobs Technology, Inc.

CONTACTS: *Note: Officers with more than one job title may be intentionally listed here more than once.*

Craig Martin, CEO
Craig Martin, Pres.
Andrew F. Kremer, Sr. VP-Global Sales
Patricia H. Summers, Sr. VP-Human Resources
Cora Carmody, Sr. VP-IT
John W. Prosser Jr., Exec. VP-Admin.
William C. Markley III, Sr. VP/General Counsel/Sec.
Thomas R. Hammond, Exec. VP-Oper.
John McLachlan, Sr. VP-Acquisitions & Strategy
John W. Prosser Jr., Exec. VP-Finance/Treas.
Thomas R. Hammond, Exec. VP
George A. Kunberger, Exec. VP-Oper.
Rogers F. Starr, Pres., Jacobs Technology, Inc.
Nazim Thawerbhoy, Sr. VP/Controller
Noel G. Watson, Chmn.

Phone: 626-578-3500	**Fax:** 626-568-7144
Toll-Free:	
Address: 1111 S. Arroyo Pkwy., Pasadena, CA 91109-7084 US	

GROWTH PLANS/SPECIAL FEATURES:

Jacobs Engineering Group, Inc. offers technical, professional, and construction services to industrial, commercial and governmental clients throughout North America, Europe, Asia, South America, India, the U.K. and Australia. The company's global network includes more than 160 offices in over 20 countries. The company provides project services, which include engineering, design and architecture; process, scientific, and systems consulting services; operations and maintenance services; and construction services, which include direct-hire construction and management services. Services are offered to selected industry groups such as oil and gas exploration, production, and refining; programs for various federal governments; pharmaceuticals and biotechnology; chemicals and polymers; buildings, which includes projects in the fields of health care and education as well as civic, governmental, and other buildings; infrastructure; technology and manufacturing; and pulp and paper, among others. Jacobs also provides pricing studies, project feasibility reports and automation and control system analysis for U.S. government agencies involved in defense and aerospace programs. In addition, the company is one of the leading providers of environmental engineering and consulting services in the U.S. and abroad, including hazardous and nuclear waste management and site cleanup and closure, providing support in such areas as underground storage tank removal, contaminated soil and water remediation, and long-term groundwater monitoring. Jacobs also designs, builds, installs, operates and maintains various types of soil and groundwater cleanup systems. In 2008, the company acquired a 60% stake in the Saudi Arabian firm, Zamel & Turbag Consulting Engineers. The same year, the company agreed to acquire L.E.S. Engineering Limited, a U.K.-based construction and service works contractor and a one-third stake in AWE Management Limited.

Employees are offered medical, dental and vision insurance; health and dependent care flexible spending accounts; an employee assistance program; disability coverage; life insurance; prepaid legal benefits; home and auto insurance; commuter assistance benefits; tuition reimbursements; and supplier discounts.

FINANCIALS: **Sales and profits are in thousands of dollars—add 000 to get the full amount. 2008 Note: Financial information for 2008 was not available for all companies at press time.**

2008 Sales: $11,252,159	2008 Profits: $420,742	**U.S. Stock Ticker: JEC**
2007 Sales: $8,473,970	2007 Profits: $287,130	**Int'l Ticker:** Int'l Exchange:
2006 Sales: $7,421,270	2006 Profits: $196,883	Employees: 42,700
2005 Sales: $5,635,001	2005 Profits: $131,608	Fiscal Year Ends: 9/30
2004 Sales: $4,594,235	2004 Profits: $115,574	Parent Company:

SALARIES/BENEFITS:

Pension Plan:	ESOP Stock Plan:	Profit Sharing:	Top Exec. Salary: $1,084,615	Bonus: $1,301,703
Savings Plan: Y	Stock Purch. Plan: Y		Second Exec. Salary: $850,000	Bonus: $1,020,129

OTHER THOUGHTS:

Apparent Women Officers or Directors: 3
Hot Spot for Advancement for Women/Minorities: Y

LOCATIONS: ("Y" = Yes)

West:	Southwest:	Midwest:	Southeast:	Northeast:	International:
Y	Y	Y	Y	Y	Y

Note: Financial information, benefits and other data can change quickly and may vary from those stated here.

JAGUAR CARS LTD

www.jaguar.com

Industry Group Code: 336111 **Ranks within this company's industry group:** Sales: Profits:

Techology:		**Medical/Drugs:**		**Engineering:**		**Transportation:**		**Chemicals/Petrochemicals:**		**Specialty:**	
Computers:		Manufacturer:		Design:		Aerospace:		Oil/Gas Products:		Special Services:	
Software:		Contract Research:		Construction:		Automotive:	Y	Chemicals:		Consulting:	
Communications:		Medical Services:		Eng. Services:		Shipping:		Oil/Chem. Svcs.:		Specialty Mgmt.:	
Electronics:		Labs:		Consulting:				Gases:		Products:	
Alternative Energy:		Bio. Services:						Other:		Other:	

TYPES OF BUSINESS:

Automobiles, Manufacturing
Racing

BRANDS/DIVISIONS/AFFILIATES:

Tata Motors Limited
Tata Group
X-Type
S-Type
XJ
XK
XKR
XF

CONTACTS: *Note: Officers with more than one job title may be intentionally listed here more than once.*

David Smith, CEO
Frank Lazzaro, CFO
Michael Ali, Dir.-IT

Phone: 44-24-7640-2121	**Fax:** 44-24-7620-2101
Toll-Free:	
Address: Browns Ln., Allesley, Coventry, West Midlands CVS 9DR UK	

GROWTH PLANS/SPECIAL FEATURES:

Jaguar Cars, Ltd., based in the U.K. and founded in 1922, manufactures a distinctive line of luxury sedans and sports cars. The company is a subsidiary of Tata Motors Limited, who acquired Jaguar from Ford Motor Co in 2008. Tata Motors, based in India, is part of the Tata Group conglomerate, which includes businesses ranging from steel production to retailing to inexpensive, compact car manufacturing. The company's current line includes four models: the S-Type, XJ, XK and the X-Type. The entry-level X-Type premium compact sedan, with a starting price around $35,000, is the company's first all-wheel drive model, designed to appeal to younger drivers. Launched in 2001, the expanded 2007 X-Type lineup includes the X-Type Sportwagon 3.0, with features like a 227 hp 3.0 liter V6 engine, and a new accessory audio connectivity module for iPod mp3 players. The 2009 Jaguar S-Type, starting at approximately $50,000, is a mid-size luxury sedan, available with either a 3.0-liter V6 or 4.2-liter V8 engine. The 2009 lineup also includes the S-Type R, with a supercharged 400 hp, 4.2 liter V8 engine, starting around $65,000. The company's flagship model, the XJ sedan, starts at $64,500. The car's monocoque alloy bodyshell boasts a 4.2 liter, 300 hp aluminumV8 engine, along with Bluetooth wireless technology. Jaguar's XK series includes XK and XKR coupes and convertibles, priced from $75,500. The company's concept cars include the R-D6, and the R-Coupe. The newly developed XF, a sports sedan, was introduced in late 2007. Jaguar Financial Services offers finance and payment packages for leasing or purchasing new and used Jaguars, in addition to car insurance. In August 2008, the company announced a collaboration with Lotus Engineering and Queen's University Belfast, to develop an engine which maximizes fuel efficiency when running on renewable fuels.

FINANCIALS: **Sales and profits are in thousands of dollars—add 000 to get the full amount. 2008 Note: Financial information for 2008 was not available for all companies at press time.**

2008 Sales: $	2008 Profits: $	**U.S. Stock Ticker: Subsidiary**
2007 Sales: $	2007 Profits: $	**Int'l Ticker:** Int'l Exchange:
2006 Sales: $	2006 Profits: $	Employees:
2005 Sales: $	2005 Profits: $	Fiscal Year Ends: 12/31
2004 Sales: $	2004 Profits: $	Parent Company: TATA MOTORS LIMITED

SALARIES/BENEFITS:

Pension Plan:	ESOP Stock Plan:	Profit Sharing:	Top Exec. Salary: $	Bonus: $
Savings Plan:	Stock Purch. Plan:		Second Exec. Salary: $	Bonus: $

OTHER THOUGHTS:

Apparent Women Officers or Directors:
Hot Spot for Advancement for Women/Minorities:

LOCATIONS: ("Y" = Yes)

West:	Southwest:	Midwest:	Southeast:	Northeast:	International:
Y	Y	Y	Y	Y	Y

JAIPRAKASH ASSOCIATES LIMITED

www.jilindia.com

Industry Group Code: 230000 **Ranks within this company's industry group:** Sales: Profits:

Techology:		Medical/Drugs:		Engineering:		Transportation:		Chemicals/Petrochemicals:		Specialty:	
Computers:		Manufacturer:		Design:		Aerospace:		Oil/Gas Products:		Special Services:	
Software:	Y	Contract Research:		Construction:	Y	Automotive:		Chemicals:		Consulting:	Y
Communications:		Medical Services:		Eng. Services:	Y	Shipping:		Oil/Chem. Svcs.:		Specialty Mgmt.:	
Electronics:		Labs:		Consulting:				Gases:		Products:	
Alternative Energy:		Bio. Services:						Other:		Other:	

TYPES OF BUSINESS:

Civil Engineering and Construction
Cement Manufacturing
Hydroelectric Power Plants
Real Estate Development
Information Technology Consulting
Software Development

BRANDS/DIVISIONS/AFFILIATES:

Jaypee Hotels Limited
Jaiprakash Hydro-Power Limited
Jaiprakash Power Ventures Limited
Jaypee Karcham Hydro Corporation Limited
Jaypee Cement Limited
Jaypee Infratech Limited
JPSK Sports Private Limited
Himalayan Expressway Ltd

CONTACTS: *Note: Officers with more than one job title may be intentionally listed here more than once.*

Manoj Gaur, CEO
S.D. Nailwal, CFO
H.K. Vaid, Company Sec.
H.K. Vaid, Pres., Corp. Affairs
Sunil Kumar Sharma, Exec. Vice Chmn.
S.K. Jain, Vice Chmn.
Sunny Gaur, Managing Dir.-Cement
Pankaj Gaur, Managing Dir.-Construction
Manoj Gaur, Chmn.

Phone: 91-120-460-9000 **Fax:** 91-120-460-9464
Toll-Free:
Address: 63, Basant Lok, Vasant Vihar, New Delhi, 110 057 India

GROWTH PLANS/SPECIAL FEATURES:

Jaiprakash Associates Limited (JAL) is an India-based industrial conglomerate. The company, along with its subsidiaries, operates in a number of business divisions, including Civil Engineering, Cement, Hydropower, Hospitality, Information Technology (IT) and Expressways. The firm offers a number of services, including surface and underground rock excavation, concrete manufacture and placement, hydro-mechanical equipment erection, steel structure construction, expressway construction, real estate development, IT infrastructure management and software development. Subsidiaries of the company include Jaypee Hotels Limited, which operates deluxe hotels in Delhi, Mussoorie and Arga; Jaiprakash Hydro-Power Limited, focused on the operations of a hydro-electric power plant in Himachal Pradesh; Jaiprakash Power Ventures Limited, which operates a hydro-electric plant in Uttaranchal; Jaypee Karcham Hydro Corporation Limited, focused on the development of a new plant slated to begin power generation in 2011; Jaypee Cement Limited, an operator of cement plants; Jaypee Power Grid Ltd., focused on developing power transmission infrastructure in Himachal Pradesh and Haryana; Jaypee Infratech Limited, focused on the construction of a controlled-access expressway; JPSK Sports Private Limited, focused on the construction of sporting complexes and racecar tracks; Himalayan Expressway Ltd.; and Madhya Pradesh Jaypee Minerals Limited, a joint venture between the firm and Madhya Pradesh State Mining Corporation Limited. In February 2008, the firm opened its sixth cement plant. In August 2008, JAL announced its intention to build a cement plant in Chhattisgarh, as well as two cement manufacturing units and an integrated aluminum complex in Madhya Pradesh. In December 2008, the company announced that it would be merging the operations of a number of its subsidiaries into the parent company's operations. Affected subsidiaries include Jaypee Hotels Ltd., Jaypee Cement Ltd. and Gujarat Anjan Cement. In January 2009, the company announced that it was considering merging its power-related subsidiaries into a single corporate entity sometime during the year.

FINANCIALS: **Sales and profits are in thousands of dollars—add 000 to get the full amount. 2008 Note: Financial information for 2008 was not available for all companies at press time.**

2008 Sales: $	2008 Profits: $	**U.S. Stock Ticker:**
2007 Sales: $821,880	2007 Profits: $112,950	**Int'l Ticker: 532532** Int'l Exchange: Bombay-BSE
2006 Sales: $687,100	2006 Profits: $141,960	Employees:
2005 Sales: $	2005 Profits: $	Fiscal Year Ends: 3/31
2004 Sales: $	2004 Profits: $	Parent Company:

SALARIES/BENEFITS:

Pension Plan:	ESOP Stock Plan:	Profit Sharing:	Top Exec. Salary: $	Bonus: $
Savings Plan:	Stock Purch. Plan:		Second Exec. Salary: $	Bonus: $

OTHER THOUGHTS:

Apparent Women Officers or Directors:
Hot Spot for Advancement for Women/Minorities:

LOCATIONS: ("Y" = Yes)

West:	Southwest:	Midwest:	Southeast:	Northeast:	International:
					Y

JDS UNIPHASE CORPORATION

www.jdsu.com

Industry Group Code: 334210 **Ranks within this company's industry group:** Sales: 8 Profits: 3

Techology:		Medical/Drugs:		Engineering:		Transportation:		Chemicals/Petrochemicals:		Specialty:	
Computers:		Manufacturer:		Design:		Aerospace:		Oil/Gas Products:		Special Services:	
Software:		Contract Research:		Construction:		Automotive:		Chemicals:		Consulting:	
Communications:	Y	Medical Services:		Eng. Services:		Shipping:		Oil/Chem. Svcs.:		Specialty Mgmt.:	
Electronics:	Y	Labs:		Consulting:				Gases:		Products:	
Alternative Energy:		Bio. Services:						Other:		Other:	

TYPES OF BUSINESS:

Telecommunications Equipment Manufacturing
Fiber Optic Products
Laser Products
Optical Test & Measurement Equipment

BRANDS/DIVISIONS/AFFILIATES:

Agility Communications Inc
Photonic Power Systems Inc
Test-Um Inc
Acterna Inc
Lightwave Electronics Corporation
Westover Scientific Inc
American Bank Note Holographics Inc
Circadiant

CONTACTS: *Note: Officers with more than one job title may be intentionally listed here more than once.*

Kevin Kennedy, CEO
Kevin Kennedy, Pres.
David Vellequette, CFO
Brett Hooper, VP-Human Resources
Marti Menacho, CIO
Matthew Fawcett, Head-Legal
Sharad Rastogi, VP-Corp. Dev.
Roy W. Bie, VP-Advanced Optical Tech. Group
Thomas Waechter, VP-Test & Measurement Group
Alan Lowe, VP-Comm., Optical Prod. Group
Martin A. Kaplan, Chmn.

Phone: 408-546-5000	**Fax:** 408-546-4300
Toll-Free:	
Address: 430 N. McCarthy Blvd., Milpitas, CA 95035 US	

GROWTH PLANS/SPECIAL FEATURES:

JDS Uniphase Corporation (JDSU) is a designer and manufacturer of products for fiber-optic communications. System manufacturers in the telecommunications, data communications and cable television industries, as well as original equipment manufacturers, deploy the company's fiber-optic components and modules to enable transmission of video, audio and text data. The company's fiber-optic components, modules and subsystems, alone and in combinations, are the building blocks for these systems. These products include transmitters, receivers, amplifiers, dispersion compensators, multiplexers and demultiplexers, add/drop modules, switches, optical performance monitors and couplers, splitters and circulators. Complementing its components, modules and subsystem products, JDSU's test and measurement equipment is used in manufacturing, research and development, system development and network maintenance environments for measuring performance of optical components. The firm sells its communications products to the world's leading and emerging telecommunications, data communications and cable television systems providers. In addition to fiber-optic communications, the company applies its optical technologies for use in the display, security, medical/environmental, instrumentation, aerospace and defense markets. Specific product applications include computer monitors and flat-panel displays, projection systems, photocopiers, facsimile machines, scanners, security products and decorative surface treatments. JDSU also supplies laser products for biotechnology, graphic arts and imaging, semiconductor processing, materials processing and a variety of other laser-based applications. In 2008 the company acquired the fiber division of Westover Scientific Inc., a provider of fiber optic inspection and cleaning solutions; American Bank Note Holographics, Inc., an originator, producer and marketer of holograms for security applications; and Circadiant, a firm that specializes in stressed signal test solutions.

Employees are offered medical, dental, vision and life insurance; short-and long-term disability coverage; an employee stock purchase plan; a 401(k) savings plan; educational reimbursement; an employee assistance program; and business travel accident insurance.

FINANCIALS: **Sales and profits are in thousands of dollars—add 000 to get the full amount. 2008 Note: Financial information for 2008 was not available for all companies at press time.**

2008 Sales: $1,530,100	2008 Profits: $-21,700	**U.S. Stock Ticker: JDSU**
2007 Sales: $1,396,800	2007 Profits: $-26,300	**Int'l Ticker:** Int'l Exchange:
2006 Sales: $1,204,300	2006 Profits: $-151,200	Employees: 7,100
2005 Sales: $712,200	2005 Profits: $-261,300	Fiscal Year Ends: 6/30
2004 Sales: $635,900	2004 Profits: $-118,100	Parent Company:

SALARIES/BENEFITS:

Pension Plan:	ESOP Stock Plan:	Profit Sharing:	Top Exec. Salary: $575,000	Bonus: $425,000
Savings Plan: Y	Stock Purch. Plan: Y		Second Exec. Salary: $444,231	Bonus: $473,200

OTHER THOUGHTS:

Apparent Women Officers or Directors: 4
Hot Spot for Advancement for Women/Minorities: Y

LOCATIONS: ("Y" = Yes)

West:	Southwest:	Midwest:	Southeast:	Northeast:	International:
Y	Y	Y	Y	Y	Y

JOHNSON & JOHNSON

www.jnj.com

Industry Group Code: 325412 **Ranks within this company's industry group:** Sales: 1 Profits: 1

Techology:		Medical/Drugs:		Engineering:		Transportation:		Chemicals/Petrochemicals:		Specialty:	
Computers:		Manufacturer:	Y	Design:		Aerospace:		Oil/Gas Products:		Special Services:	
Software:		Contract Research:		Construction:		Automotive:		Chemicals:		Consulting:	
Communications:		Medical Services:		Eng. Services:		Shipping:		Oil/Chem. Svcs.:		Specialty Mgmt.:	
Electronics:		Labs:	Y	Consulting:				Gases:		Products:	Y
Alternative Energy:		Bio. Services:						Other:		Other:	

TYPES OF BUSINESS:

Personal Health Care & Hygiene Products
Sterilization Products
Surgical Products
Pharmaceuticals
Skin Care Products
Baby Care Products
Contact Lenses
Medical Equipment

BRANDS/DIVISIONS/AFFILIATES:

Scios Inc
Centocor Inc
Alza Corp
Depuy Inc
Ethicon Inc
Cordis Corp
LifeScan Inc
Omrix Biopharmaceuticals Inc

CONTACTS: *Note: Officers with more than one job title may be intentionally listed here more than once.*

William C. Weldon, CEO
Dominic J. Caruso, CFO
Kaye Foster-Cheek, VP-Human Resources
Russell C. Deyo, General Counsel/VP/Chief Compliance Officer
Nicholas J. Valeriani, VP-Strategy & Growth
Dominic J. Caruso, VP-Finance
Colleen Goggins, Chmn., Consumer Group
Sheri McCoy, Chmn., Pharmaceutical Group
Alex Gorsky, Chmn.-Surgical Care Group
Donald M. Casey, Jr., Chmn.-Comprehensive Care Group
William C. Weldon, Chmn.

Phone: 732-524-0400 **Fax:** 732-214-0332
Toll-Free:
Address: 1 Johnson & Johnson Plz., New Brunswick, NJ 08933 US

GROWTH PLANS/SPECIAL FEATURES:

Johnson & Johnson, founded in 1886, is one of the world's most comprehensive and well-known manufacturers of health care products. The firm owns more than 250 companies in over 90 countries and markets its products in almost every country in the world. Johnson & Johnson's worldwide operations are divided into three segments consumer, pharmaceutical and medical devices and diagnostics. The company's principal consumer goods are personal care and hygiene products, including nonprescription drugs, adult skin and hair care, baby care oral care, first aid and sanitary protection products. Major consumer brands include Mylanta, Band-Aid, Tylenol Aveeno and Monistat. The pharmaceutical segment covers a wide spectrum of health fields, including antifungal, anti-infective, cardiovascular, dermatology, immunology, pain management, psychotropic and women's health. Among its pharmaceutical products are Risperdal, an antipsychotic used to treat schizophrenia, and Remicade for the treatment of Crohn's disease and rheumatoid arthritis. In the medical devices and diagnostics segment, Johnson & Johnson makes a number of products including suture and mechanical wound closure products, surgical instruments, disposable contact lenses, joint reconstruction products and intravenous catheters. Subsidiaries of the company include Cordis LLC, DePuy, Inc., Diabetes Diagnostics, Inc., Ethicon Endo-Surgery, Inc., LifeScan, Inc., McNeil Healthcare LLC, Neutrogena Corporation, SurgRx, Inc. and The Tylenol Company. In November 2008, Johnson & Johnson acquired HealthMedia, Inc. In December 2008, the company acquired Omrix Biopharmaceuticals, Inc. for $438 million. In January 2009, the firm completed its acquisition of Mentor Corporation, a producer of medical products for the aesthetic specialties market.

Johnson & Johnson offers its employees benefits that include medical coverage; an employee assistance program health assessments and health counseling; and on-site fitness centers and fitness classes at certain locations.

FINANCIALS: **Sales and profits are in thousands of dollars—add 000 to get the full amount. 2008 Note: Financial information for 2008 was not available for all companies at press time.**

2008 Sales: $63,747,000	2008 Profits: $12,949,000	**U.S. Stock Ticker: JNJ**
2007 Sales: $61,095,000	2007 Profits: $10,576,000	**Int'l Ticker:** Int'l Exchange:
2006 Sales: $53,324,000	2006 Profits: $11,053,000	Employees: 118,700
2005 Sales: $50,514,000	2005 Profits: $10,060,000	Fiscal Year Ends: 12/31
2004 Sales: $47,348,000	2004 Profits: $8,180,000	Parent Company:

SALARIES/BENEFITS:

Pension Plan:	ESOP Stock Plan:	Profit Sharing:	Top Exec. Salary: $1,725,000	Bonus: $9,188,120
Savings Plan: Y	Stock Purch. Plan:		Second Exec. Salary: $1,008,846	Bonus: $3,718,000

OTHER THOUGHTS:

Apparent Women Officers or Directors: 5
Hot Spot for Advancement for Women/Minorities: Y

LOCATIONS: ("Y" = Yes)

West:	Southwest:	Midwest:	Southeast:	Northeast:	International:
Y	Y	Y	Y	Y	Y

JOHNSON CONTROLS INC

www.johnsoncontrols.com

Industry Group Code: 336300 **Ranks within this company's industry group:** Sales: 2 Profits: 4

Techology:		Medical/Drugs:		Engineering:		Transportation:		Chemicals/Petrochemicals:		Specialty:	
Computers:		Manufacturer:		Design:	Y	Aerospace:		Oil/Gas Products:		Special Services:	Y
Software:		Contract Research:		Construction:	Y	Automotive:	Y	Chemicals:		Consulting:	
Communications:		Medical Services:		Eng. Services:		Shipping:		Oil/Chem. Svcs.:		Specialty Mgmt.:	
Electronics:		Labs:		Consulting:				Gases:		Products:	Y
Alternative Energy:	Y	Bio. Services:						Other:		Other:	

TYPES OF BUSINESS:

Automobile Parts & Controls
Automotive Batteries
Facilities Management
Automotive Interior Components
Energy Management Services
Building Security, Lighting & HVAC Systems

BRANDS/DIVISIONS/AFFILIATES:

Matasys Building Management System
Johnson Controls-Saft Advanced Power Solutions
Automotive Experience
Optima
Varta
Johnson Controls (Wuhu) Automotive Interiors
Metasys Sustainability Manager
Plastech Engineered Products

CONTACTS: *Note: Officers with more than one job title may be intentionally listed here more than once.*

Stephen A. Roell, CEO
Keith Wandell, COO
Keith Wandell, Pres.
R. Bruce McDonald, CFO/Exec. VP
Susan F. Davis, Exec. VP-Human Resources
Colin Boyd, CIO/VP-IT
Jerome D. Okarma, General Counsel/Sec./VP
Denise Zutz, VP-Strategy
Jacqueline F. Strayer, VP-Corp. Comm.
Jeffrey G. Augustin, VP-Finance
C. David Meyers, VP/Pres., Building Efficiency
Beda Bolzenius, VP/Pres., Automotive Experience
Alex A. Molinaroli, VP/Pres., Power Solutions
Charles A. Harvey, VP-Public Affairs & Diversity
Stephen A. Roell, Chmn.
Jeffrey S. Edwards, VP-Automotive Experience, Japan & Asia Pacific

Phone: 414-524-2363 **Fax:** 414-524-2070
Toll-Free: 800-524-6220
Address: 5757 N. Green Bay Ave. P.O. Box 591, Milwaukee, WI 53201 US

GROWTH PLANS/SPECIAL FEATURES:

Johnson Controls, Inc. is a leader in automotive interiors/batteries, building efficiency and facility management. The firm's Automotive Experience segment designs and manufactures concept cars; complete seat systems; seating components; electronics; instrument panels; overhead, door and cargo management systems; cockpits; and interior trim for manufacturers of cars and light trucks. The firm's Power Solutions division manufactures and replaces automotive batteries, focusing on innovations for hybrid electric vehicles. Its battery brands include Optima, Varta, Heliar (in South America), and LTH (in Mexico). Prominent clients include BMW; DaimlerChrysler; Ford; Toyota; Volkswagen; AutoZone; Interstate Battery System of America; and Wal-Mart. Johnson's Building Efficiency segment operates in 125 countries, supplying systems designed for heating; ventilation; air conditioning; lighting; security; and fire management. The U.S. Department of Defense utilizes Johnson Controls for the Pentagon's energy management and environmental control systems. Global WorkPlace Solutions, part of Building Efficiency, provides companies with a real-estate based approach to shareholder value. The Building Efficiency division also does facility management, using its patented Metasys Building Management System. It handles school districts, hospitals, factories, airports and government facilities. The company has a joint venture with Saft SA, a battery company, called Johnson Controls-Saft Advanced Power Solutions. In January 2008, the company acquired Metro Mechanical, Inc., a mechanical services company. In April 2008, Johnson and Chery Technology Co., Ltd., of Chery Automobile Co., Ltd., formed Johnson Controls (Wuhu) Automotive Interiors Co., Ltd. In July 2008, the firm agreed to acquire 70% interest in formerly bankrupt Plastech Engineered Products. Between July and October 2008 the firm acquired the following companies: PWI Energy, provider of greenhouse gas and energy management; Engineered Equipment and Systems Company, a representative of equipment manufacturers; and software company Gridlogix. In January 2009, Johnson Controls incorporated Gridlogix's technology into its Metasys building management system, launching the new Metasys Sustainability Manager.

FINANCIALS: **Sales and profits are in thousands of dollars—add 000 to get the full amount. 2008 Note: Financial information for 2008 was not available for all companies at press time.**

2008 Sales: $38,062,000	2008 Profits: $979,000	**U.S. Stock Ticker: JCI**
2007 Sales: $34,624,000	2007 Profits: $1,252,000	**Int'l Ticker:** Int'l Exchange:
2006 Sales: $32,235,000	2006 Profits: $1,028,000	Employees: 140,000
2005 Sales: $27,479,400	2005 Profits: $909,400	Fiscal Year Ends: 9/30
2004 Sales: $26,553,400	2004 Profits: $817,500	Parent Company:

SALARIES/BENEFITS:

Pension Plan: Y	ESOP Stock Plan:	Profit Sharing:	Top Exec. Salary: $1,325,000	Bonus: $5,408,000
Savings Plan: Y	Stock Purch. Plan:		Second Exec. Salary: $919,000	Bonus: $3,072,000

OTHER THOUGHTS:

Apparent Women Officers or Directors: 4
Hot Spot for Advancement for Women/Minorities: Y

LOCATIONS: ("Y" = Yes)

West:	Southwest:	Midwest:	Southeast:	Northeast:	International:
Y	Y	Y	Y	Y	Y

JUNIPER NETWORKS INC

www.juniper.net

Industry Group Code: 334110 **Ranks within this company's industry group:** Sales: 2 Profits: 2

Techology:		Medical/Drugs:		Engineering:		Transportation:		Chemicals/Petrochemicals:		Specialty:	
Computers:	Y	Manufacturer:		Design:		Aerospace:		Oil/Gas Products:		Special Services:	
Software:	Y	Contract Research:		Construction:		Automotive:		Chemicals:		Consulting:	
Communications:	Y	Medical Services:		Eng. Services:		Shipping:		Oil/Chem. Svcs.:		Specialty Mgmt.:	
Electronics:		Labs:		Consulting:				Gases:		Products:	
Alternative Energy:		Bio. Services:						Other:		Other:	

TYPES OF BUSINESS:

Networking Equipment
IP Networking Systems
Internet Routers
Network Security Products
Internet Software
Intrusion Prevention
Application Acceleration

BRANDS/DIVISIONS/AFFILIATES:

JUNOS
E-Series
J-Series
M-Series
T-Series
MX-Series
SDX Service Deployment System
SSL VPN

CONTACTS: *Note: Officers with more than one job title may be intentionally listed here more than once.*

Kevin Johnson, CEO
Robyn Denholm, CFO/Exec. VP
Lauren Patricia Flaherty, Chief Mktg. Officer/Exec. VP
Steven Rice, Exec. VP-Human Resources
Mitchell Gaynor, General Counsel
Michael Rose, Exec. VP-Service, Support & Oper.
Gene Zamiska, Chief Acct. Officer
Kim Perdikou, Exec. VP-Infrastructure Products Group
John Morris, Exec. VP-Worldwide Field Oper.
Mark Bauhaus, Exec. VP/Gen. Mgr.-Service Layer Tech. Bus. Group
Hitesh Sheth, Exec. VP/Gen. Mgr.-Ethernet Platforms Bus. Group
Scott Kriens, Chmn.

Phone: 408-745-2000	**Fax:** 408-745-2100
Toll-Free: 888-586-4737	
Address: 1194 N. Mathilda Ave., Sunnyvale, CA 94089-1206 US	

GROWTH PLANS/SPECIAL FEATURES:

Juniper Networks, Inc. is a provider of custom-designed Internet protocol (IP) networking platforms for Internet service providers, enterprises, governments and educational institutions. Operations are organized into two segments: infrastructure and service layer technologies (SLT). The infrastructure segment primarily offers scalable router products used to control and direct network traffic. Product families offered by the firm include the M-Series, T-Series and E-Series. The SLT segment offers services that protect networks as well as maximize existing bandwidth and acceleration of applications across a distributed network. The SLT product families include firewall services, virtual private network (VPN) systems, intrusion detection and prevention (IDP) and application acceleration platforms. The firm outsources manufacturing to companies such as IBM, Toshiba, Celestica and Plexus; these manufacturers create application-specific chips from Juniper's designs. Additionally, the company sells Internet backbone routers, which are offered through a direct sales force to Internet and telecommunication service providers around the world. The firm maintains several strategic alliances with prominent companies including Avaya, Ericsson, Lucent Technologies, Siemens, and more recently, Lockheed Martin, Microsoft and Oracle. Juniper's customers include wireline, wireless and cable ISPs; private enterprises; federal, state and local government agencies; and research and education institutions. The firm maintains international headquarters in the U.K., Hong Kong and Tokyo and sales offices in 40 countries worldwide. Juniper owns 500 technology patents, either issued or pending.

Employees are offered medical, dental and vision insurance; a 401(k) plan; and a stock purchase plan.

FINANCIALS: Sales and profits are in thousands of dollars—add 000 to get the full amount. 2008 Note: Financial information for 2008 was not available for all companies at press time.

2008 Sales: $3,572,376	2008 Profits: $511,749	**U.S. Stock Ticker: JNPR**
2007 Sales: $2,836,100	2007 Profits: $360,800	**Int'l Ticker:** Int'l Exchange:
2006 Sales: $2,303,580	2006 Profits: $-1,001,437	Employees: 5,879
2005 Sales: $2,063,957	2005 Profits: $350,701	Fiscal Year Ends: 12/31
2004 Sales: $1,336,019	2004 Profits: $128,228	Parent Company:

SALARIES/BENEFITS:

Pension Plan:	ESOP Stock Plan:	Profit Sharing:	Top Exec. Salary: $568,750	Bonus: $981,000
Savings Plan: Y	Stock Purch. Plan: Y		Second Exec. Salary: $529,772	Bonus: $506,414

OTHER THOUGHTS:

Apparent Women Officers or Directors: 4
Hot Spot for Advancement for Women/Minorities: Y

LOCATIONS: ("Y" = Yes)

West:	Southwest:	Midwest:	Southeast:	Northeast:	International:
Y	Y	Y	Y	Y	Y

KANEKA CORPORATION

www.kaneka.co.jp

Industry Group Code: 325000 **Ranks within this company's industry group:** Sales: 25 Profits: 20

Techology:		Medical/Drugs:		Engineering:		Transportation:		Chemicals/Petrochemicals:		Specialty:	
Computers:		Manufacturer:	Y	Design:		Aerospace:		Oil/Gas Products:	Y	Special Services:	
Software:		Contract Research:		Construction:		Automotive:		Chemicals:	Y	Consulting:	
Communications:		Medical Services:		Eng. Services:		Shipping:		Oil/Chem. Svcs.:		Specialty Mgmt.:	
Electronics:	Y	Labs:		Consulting:				Gases:		Products:	
Alternative Energy:		Bio. Services:						Other:		Other:	

TYPES OF BUSINESS:

Chemicals Manufacturing
Functional Plastics
PVC Piping
Caustic Soda
Specialty Fibers
Electronics Products
Expandable Plastic Products
Food Products

BRANDS/DIVISIONS/AFFILIATES:

Kanevinyl
Kanekalon
Protex
Hyperite
Belco
Apical
ULTIMA

CONTACTS: *Note: Officers with more than one job title may be intentionally listed here more than once.*

Kimikazu Sugawara, Pres.
Setsuo Shimazaki, Exec. Dir./Gen. Mgr.-Finance
Satomi Takahashi, Chief Dir.-R&D
Toshiji Kanou, Chief Dir.-Prod. Tech.
Setsuo Shimazaki, Exec. Dir./Gen. Mgr.-Acct.
Atsushi Ikenaga, Exec. VP
Hideyuki Matsui, Exec. VP
Kouji Sanpei, Exec. VP
Toshio Nakamura, Exec. VP
Masatoshi Takeda, Chmn.

Phone: 81-6-6226-5050	**Fax:** 81-6-6226-5037
Toll-Free:	
Address: 3-2-4, Nakanoshima, Kita-ku, Osaka, 530-8288 Japan	

GROWTH PLANS/SPECIAL FEATURES:

Kaneka Corporation is a leader in the manufacturing of a variety of finished and intermediate chemical products for commercial and industrial use. The company operates through seven business segments: chemicals, functional plastics, foodstuffs products, life science products, electronic products, expandable plastics and synthetic fibers. Kaneka's chemicals division manufactures caustic soda, hydrochloric acid, paste polyvinyl chloride (PVC) and rigid and flexible PVC compounds. The functional plastics division produces heat-resistant and self-extinguishing ABS resins, modified silicon polymer and allyl-terminated polyisobuthylenes. Kaneka's foodstuffs division produces margarine, shortening, yeast and confectionary fats. The life science products division manufactures pharmaceutical intermediates for antihypertensives and antibiotics, as well as a low-density lipoprotein (LDL) cholesterol absorption system. Its electronic products include photovoltaic systems, optical and heat-resistant polyimide films, magnet wire, bonded magnets and PVC pipes for underground cables. The expandable plastics division produces extruded polystyrene foam boards, insulating PVC sash windows, polyolefin foam and expandable polystyrene. The Kaneka line of synthetic fibers includes Kanekalon, a modacrylic fiber, and ULTIMA, a protein fiber made from collagen, both of which resemble human hair. Kaneka operates subsidiaries in the U.S., Belgium, Vietnam, Singapore, Malaysia, Australia and China. In April 2008, the company announced plans to expand its polyolefin foam manufacturing capabilities at its plant in Suzhou, China by 250%. In January 2009, the company announced plans to expand its solar cell production facilities from 80 megawatts (MW) to 150 MW.

FINANCIALS: **Sales and profits are in thousands of dollars—add 000 to get the full amount. 2008 Note: Financial information for 2008 was not available for all companies at press time.**

2008 Sales: $5,020,142	2008 Profits: $187,813	**U.S. Stock Ticker:**
2007 Sales: $4,008,225	2007 Profits: $155,559	**Int'l Ticker: 4118** Int'l Exchange: Tokyo-TSE
2006 Sales: $3,952,584	2006 Profits: $239,210	Employees: 7,430
2005 Sales: $3,957,333	2005 Profits: $223,573	Fiscal Year Ends: 3/31
2004 Sales: $3,788,800	2004 Profits: $147,900	Parent Company:

SALARIES/BENEFITS:

Pension Plan:	ESOP Stock Plan:	Profit Sharing:	Top Exec. Salary: $	Bonus: $
Savings Plan:	Stock Purch. Plan:		Second Exec. Salary: $	Bonus: $

OTHER THOUGHTS:

Apparent Women Officers or Directors:
Hot Spot for Advancement for Women/Minorities:

LOCATIONS: ("Y" = Yes)

West:	Southwest:	Midwest:	Southeast:	Northeast:	International:
	Y			Y	Y

KAWASAKI HEAVY INDUSTRIES LTD

www.khi.co.jp

Industry Group Code: 333000 **Ranks within this company's industry group:** Sales: 6 Profits: 7

Techology:		Medical/Drugs:		Engineering:		Transportation:		Chemicals/Petrochemicals:		Specialty:	
Computers:		Manufacturer:		Design:		Aerospace:	Y	Oil/Gas Products:		Special Services:	
Software:		Contract Research:		Construction:		Automotive:	Y	Chemicals:		Consulting:	
Communications:		Medical Services:		Eng. Services:		Shipping:	Y	Oil/Chem. Svcs.:		Specialty Mgmt.:	
Electronics:		Labs:		Consulting:				Gases:		Products:	
Alternative Energy:		Bio. Services:						Other:		Other:	

TYPES OF BUSINESS:

Recreational Vehicle & Machinery Manufacturing
Motorcycles, ATVs & Personal Watercraft
Helicopter & Aerospace Manufacturing
Industrial Machinery
Gas Turbines, Engines & Generators
Locomotives, Ships & Submarines
Plant & Infrastructure Manufacturing
Medical Equipment

BRANDS/DIVISIONS/AFFILIATES:

MULE
Jet Ski
HRP-3 Promet Mk-II
KHI Middle East FZE

CONTACTS:

Note: Officers with more than one job title may be intentionally listed here more than once.

Tadaharu Ohashi, Pres.
Yoshio Kawamura, Gen. Mgr.-Mktg. & Sales Div.
Sumihiro Ueda, Deputy Gen. Mgr.-Corp. Tech. Div.
Shuji Mihara, Sr. Mgr.-Corp. Planning
Mitsutoshi Takao, Sr. Mgr.-Finance & Acct.
Masatoshi Terasaki, Sr. Exec. VP
Akira Matsuzaki, Sr. Exec. VP
Chikashi Motoyama, Pres., Aerospace Company
Masashi Segawa, Pres., Rolling Stock Company
Masamoto Tazaki, Chmn.
Takeshi Sugawara, Deputy Gen. Mgr.-Supply Chain Div.

Phone: 81-78-371-9530 **Fax:** 81-78-371-9568
Toll-Free:
Address: Kobe Crystal Tower,1-3 Higashikawasaki-cho 1-chome, Chuo-ku, Kobe, 650-8680 Japan

GROWTH PLANS/SPECIAL FEATURES:

Kawasaki Heavy Industries, Ltd. (KHI), founded in 1878, manufactures a wide range of transportation equipment and industrial goods. KHI operates through seven business segments: shipbuilding; rolling stock and construction machinery; aerospace; gas turbines and machinery; plant and infrastructure engineering; consumer products and machinery; and other. The shipbuilding segment manufactures liquefied natural gas (LNG) and liquefied petroleum gas (LPG) carriers; container ships; VLCCs (Very Large Crude Carriers); bulk carriers; high-speed vessels; submarines; and maritime application equipment. The rolling stock business segment manufactures Shinkansen bullet electric train cars, electric and diesel locomotives, integrated transit systems, monorail cars, platform screen doors and wheel loaders. The aerospace business segment manufactures CH-47, CH-1 and BK117 helicopters; component parts for the Boeing 777 and 767 passenger airplanes; component parts for the Embraer 170 and 190 jet aircrafts; missiles; electronic equipment; and space equipment. The gas turbines and machinery business segment manufactures jet engines; small- and medium-size gas turbine generators; gas turbine cogeneration systems; gas turbines for naval vessels; steam turbines for marine and industrial applications; diesel engines; and aerodynamic machinery. The plant and infrastructure engineering segment manufactures cement, chemical and other industrial plants; power plants; municipal refuse incineration plants; LNG and LPG tanks; shield machines and tunnel boring machines; and wind power generation systems. The consumer products and machinery segment manufactures motorcycles, ATVs, MULE utility vehicles, Jet Ski personal watercraft and industrial robots. In addition, the company manufactures industrial hydraulic equipment. In July 2008, the company announced the creation of a new subsidiary, KHI Middle East FZE, located in Dubai, United Arab Emirates. The subsidiary will focus on KHI's expanding marketing and sales opportunities in the Middle East and North African regions. In August 2008, KHI launched its new bulk carrier Eria Colossus from its Tokyo shipyard, the 21st of its kind developed by KHI.

FINANCIALS:

Sales and profits are in thousands of dollars—add 000 to get the full amount. 2008 Note: Financial information for 2008 was not available for all companies at press time.

2008 Sales: $14,981,008	2008 Profits: $350,709	**U.S. Stock Ticker: KWHIY**
2007 Sales: $12,182,395	2007 Profits: $252,113	**Int'l Ticker: 7012** Int'l Exchange: Tokyo-TSE
2006 Sales: $11,258,083	2006 Profits: $140,180	Employees: 30,563
2005 Sales: $11,149,457	2005 Profits: $103,080	Fiscal Year Ends: 3/31
2004 Sales: $10,982,900	2004 Profits: $59,900	Parent Company:

SALARIES/BENEFITS:

Pension Plan:	ESOP Stock Plan:	Profit Sharing:	Top Exec. Salary: $	Bonus: $
Savings Plan:	Stock Purch. Plan:		Second Exec. Salary: $	Bonus: $

OTHER THOUGHTS:

Apparent Women Officers or Directors:
Hot Spot for Advancement for Women/Minorities:

LOCATIONS: ("Y" = Yes)

West:	Southwest:	Midwest:	Southeast:	Northeast:	International:
Y	Y	Y		Y	Y

Note: Financial information, benefits and other data can change quickly and may vary from those stated here.

KBR INC

www.kbr.com

Industry Group Code: 541330 **Ranks within this company's industry group:** Sales: 1 Profits: 3

Techology:		Medical/Drugs:		Engineering:		Transportation:		Chemicals/Petrochemicals:		Specialty:	
Computers:		Manufacturer:		Design:		Aerospace:		Oil/Gas Products:		Special Services:	Y
Software:		Contract Research:		Construction:	Y	Automotive:		Chemicals:		Consulting:	
Communications:		Medical Services:		Eng. Services:	Y	Shipping:		Oil/Chem. Svcs.:		Specialty Mgmt.:	
Electronics:		Labs:		Consulting:	Y			Gases:		Products:	
Alternative Energy:		Bio. Services:						Other:		Other:	

TYPES OF BUSINESS:

Engineering, Construction & Services
Energy & Petrochemical Projects
Program & Project Management
Consulting & Technology Services
Contingency Logistics
Operations & Maintenance

BRANDS/DIVISIONS/AFFILIATES:

KBR Nigeria, Ltd.
Turnaround Group of Texas, Inc.
Catalyst Interactive
BE&K Inc
Wabi Development

CONTACTS:

Note: Officers with more than one job title may be intentionally listed here more than once.

William P. Utt, CEO
William P. Utt, Pres.
T. Kevin DeNicola, CFO/Sr. VP
Timothy B. Challand, Pres., Tech.
Klaudia J. Brace, Sr. VP-Admin.
Andrew D. Farley, General Counsel/Sr. VP
Dennis Calton, Exec. VP-Oper.
Bruce A. Stanski, Pres., Gov't & Infrastructure Bus. Unit
David Zimmerman, Pres., Svcs.
John L. Rose, Pres., Upstream
John Quinn, Pres., Downstream
William P. Utt, Chmn.

Phone: 713-753-2000 **Fax:** 713-753-5353
Toll-Free:
Address: 601 Jefferson St., Houston, TX 77002 US

GROWTH PLANS/SPECIAL FEATURES:

KBR, Inc. is a global engineering, construction and services company supporting the energy, petrochemicals, government services and civil infrastructure sectors. It operates in six segments: government and infrastructure; upstream; services; downstream; technology; and ventures. The government and infrastructure segment provides program and project management, contingency logistics, operations and maintenance, construction management, engineering and other services to military and civilian branches of government and private clients worldwide. The upstream business provides services for large, complex upstream projects, including liquefied natural gas; gas-to-liquids; onshore oil and gas production facilities; offshore oil and gas production facilities, including platforms, floating production and subsea facilities; and onshore and offshore pipelines. The services division provides construction services, including major project reconstruction, construction management and module and pipe fabrication; and industrial services, including routine maintenance, small capital and turnaround services as well as high value services including startup commissioning, procurement support, facility services, supply chain solutions and electrical and instrumentation solutions. The downstream unit serves clients in the petrochemical, refining, coal gasification and syngas markets, executing projects throughout the world. The technology segment offers differentiated process technologies, including value-added technologies in the coal monetization, petrochemical, refining and syngas markets. It offers technology licenses and offers project management and engineering, procurement and construction for integrated solutions. The ventures business develops, provides assistance in arranging financing for, makes equity and/or debt investments and participates in managing entities owning assets generally from projects in which one of the firm's business units has a direct role in engineering, construction and/or operations and maintenance. In 2008, the company acquired Turnaround Group of Texas, Inc., a turnaround management and consulting company; Catalyst Interactive, an Australia-based provider of training and e-learning solutions; BE&K, Inc. an engineering, construction and maintenances services firm; and Wabi Development Corporation, a Canadian general contractor.

FINANCIALS:

Sales and profits are in thousands of dollars—add 000 to get the full amount. 2008 Note: Financial information for 2008 was not available for all companies at press time.

2008 Sales: $11,581,000	2008 Profits: $319,000	**U.S. Stock Ticker: KBR**
2007 Sales: $8,745,000	2007 Profits: $302,000	**Int'l Ticker:** Int'l Exchange:
2006 Sales: $8,805,000	2006 Profits: $168,000	Employees: 57,000
2005 Sales: $9,291,000	2005 Profits: $240,000	Fiscal Year Ends: 12/31
2004 Sales: $11,906,000	2004 Profits: $-303,000	Parent Company:

SALARIES/BENEFITS:

Pension Plan: Y	ESOP Stock Plan:	Profit Sharing:	Top Exec. Salary: $817,704	Bonus: $1,100,000
Savings Plan: Y	Stock Purch. Plan:		Second Exec. Salary: $375,006	Bonus: $419,400

OTHER THOUGHTS:

Apparent Women Officers or Directors: 1
Hot Spot for Advancement for Women/Minorities: Y

LOCATIONS: ("Y" = Yes)

West:	Southwest:	Midwest:	Southeast:	Northeast:	International:
	Y			Y	Y

KEY TRONIC CORP

www.keytronic.com

Industry Group Code: 334419 **Ranks within this company's industry group:** Sales: 12 Profits: 7

Techology:		Medical/Drugs:		Engineering:		Transportation:		Chemicals/Petrochemicals:		Specialty:	
Computers:	Y	Manufacturer:		Design:		Aerospace:		Oil/Gas Products:		Special Services:	
Software:		Contract Research:		Construction:		Automotive:		Chemicals:		Consulting:	
Communications:		Medical Services:		Eng. Services:		Shipping:		Oil/Chem. Svcs.:		Specialty Mgmt.:	
Electronics:	Y	Labs:		Consulting:				Gases:		Products:	
Alternative Energy:		Bio. Services:						Other:		Other:	

TYPES OF BUSINESS:

Contract Manufacturing-Electronics
Keyboard & Mouse Manufacturing

BRANDS/DIVISIONS/AFFILIATES:

KeyTronicEMS Co.

CONTACTS:

Note: Officers with more than one job title may be intentionally listed here more than once.

Jack W. Oehlke, CEO
Jack W. Oehlke, Pres.
Ronald F. Klawitter, CFO
Lawrence J. Bostwick, VP-Eng. & Quality
Ronald F. Klawitter, Exec. VP-Admin.
Kathleen L. Nemeth, Sec.
Douglas G. Burkhardt, VP-World Wide Oper.
Ronald F. Klawitter, Treas.
Craig D. Gates, Exec. VP/Gen. Mgr.
George R. Alford, VP-Materials
Dale F. Pilz, Chmn.

Phone: 509-928-8000	**Fax:** 509-927-5383
Toll-Free:	
Address: 4424 N. Sullivan Rd., Spokane, WA 99216 US	

GROWTH PLANS/SPECIAL FEATURES:

Key Tronic Corp., doing business as KeyTronicEMS Co., manufactures keyboards and mice for personal computers, terminals and workstations; and provides electronic manufacturing services (EMS) for distributors and resellers. Its manufacturing capabilities include tool making, product design, liquid injection molding, printed screened silver flexible circuit membranes, automated tape winding and box build, or pre-built products. The firm's automated manufacturing processes enable it to work closely with its customers during design and prototype stages of production for new custom products and to jointly increase productivity and reduce response time to the marketplace. It uses computer-aided design techniques and unique software to assist in preparation of the tool design layout and fabrications, reduce costs, improve component and product quality, and accelerate turnaround time during product development. Key Tronic's current customer production programs include consumer electronics and plastics; specialty printers and sub-assemblies; household products; gaming devices; telecommunication satellite units; multimedia touch panels; digital control panels; computer accessories; medical devices; exercise equipment; educational toys; industrial tools; networking equipment; scientific instruments; and security surveillance devices. The firm's largest customers include Zebra Technologies Corporation, which generated 18% of the company's 2008 revenue; Lexmark International, Inc., 15%; and International Gaming Technology, Inc. 18%. Other customers include Qualcomm, Clorox and Transaction Printer Group. Key Tronic operates facilities in the U.S., China and Mexico, engaged in production, testing, engineering and distribution.

Employees are offered medical, dental and vision insurance; life insurance; short-and long-term disability coverage; tuition reimbursement; and a 401(k) plan.

FINANCIALS:

Sales and profits are in thousands of dollars—add 000 to get the full amount. 2008 Note: Financial information for 2008 was not available for all companies at press time.

2008 Sales: $204,122	2008 Profits: $5,584	**U.S. Stock Ticker: KTCC**
2007 Sales: $201,712	2007 Profits: $5,230	**Int'l Ticker:** Int'l Exchange:
2006 Sales: $187,699	2006 Profits: $9,753	Employees: 2,502
2005 Sales: $202,877	2005 Profits: $4,376	Fiscal Year Ends: 6/30
2004 Sales: $148,901	2004 Profits: $ 110	Parent Company:

SALARIES/BENEFITS:

Pension Plan:	ESOP Stock Plan:	Profit Sharing:	Top Exec. Salary: $417,308	Bonus: $320,942
Savings Plan: Y	Stock Purch. Plan:		Second Exec. Salary: $290,230	Bonus: $189,471

OTHER THOUGHTS:

Apparent Women Officers or Directors: 1
Hot Spot for Advancement for Women/Minorities:

LOCATIONS: ("Y" = Yes)

West:	Southwest:	Midwest:	Southeast:	Northeast:	International:
Y	Y				Y

KIA MOTORS CORPORATION

www.kiamotors.com

Industry Group Code: 336111 **Ranks within this company's industry group:** Sales: 20 Profits: 19

Techology:		Medical/Drugs:		Engineering:		Transportation:		Chemicals/Petrochemicals:		Specialty:	
Computers:		Manufacturer:		Design:		Aerospace:		Oil/Gas Products:		Special Services:	
Software:		Contract Research:		Construction:		Automotive:	Y	Chemicals:		Consulting:	
Communications:		Medical Services:		Eng. Services:		Shipping:		Oil/Chem. Svcs.:		Specialty Mgmt.:	
Electronics:		Labs:		Consulting:				Gases:		Products:	
Alternative Energy:		Bio. Services:						Other:		Other:	

TYPES OF BUSINESS:

Automobiles, Manufacturing
Buses
Military Vehicles

BRANDS/DIVISIONS/AFFILIATES:

Hyundai Motor Company
Optima
Spectra
Sedona
Rio
Sorento
TianLiMa
Picanto

CONTACTS: *Note: Officers with more than one job title may be intentionally listed here more than once.*

Mong-Koo Chung, CEO
Ik Hwan Kim, Pres.
Chung Eui-sun, CEO/Pres.
Nam-Hong Cho, CEO/Pres.
Mong-Koo Chung, Chmn.

Phone: 82-2-3464-1114 **Fax:** 82-2-3464-6820
Toll-Free:
Address: 231 Yangjae-dong, Seocho-gu, Seoul, 137-938 Korea

GROWTH PLANS/SPECIAL FEATURES:

Kia Motors Corporation, one of the largest automobile manufacturers in Korea, is an affiliate of Hyundai Motor Company. Hyundai won approval to increase its ownership to a 51% controlling interest after Kia went bankrupt in 1997, though Hyundai now controls about 36%. Kia produces over 1.4 million vehicles a year in 14 manufacturing facilities in eight countries. Kia offers different models of cars which include: passenger cars including the Picanto, the Rio, the cee'd, the Cerato, the Magentis and the Opirus; SUV and MPV's, including the Carens, Carnival, Sportage, Sorento and Mohave; commercial vehicles, including trucks and passenger buses; and concept cars, which include the Koup, KED-5, Kee, ex_cee'd, Soul, Multi-S, Kia Sport, and KCD and KCV series. The company also produces buses and military vehicles. Kia has additional facilities located around the world, with its high-capacity plants in China, Iran, Indonesia, Egypt and Taiwan. Additionally, Kia is actively involved in sports marketing, acting as a major sponsor of the Australian Open, the Davis Cup and the FIFA World Cup. In May 2008, Kia signed an agreement with Microsoft Corp. to develop in-car infotainment systems. The systems will be based on Microsoft Auto software and applied to Hyundai-Kia automobiles. In June 2008, Kia celebrated the grand opening of its corporate center in Irvine, California, which will serve as the control center for U.S. operations.

FINANCIALS: **Sales and profits are in thousands of dollars—add 000 to get the full amount. 2008 Note: Financial information for 2008 was not available for all companies at press time.**

2008 Sales: $12,501,100 | 2008 Profits: $86,990
2007 Sales: $12,170,680 | 2007 Profits: $10,680
2006 Sales: $17,134,700 | 2006 Profits: $38,650
2005 Sales: $16,351,300 | 2005 Profits: $695,880
2004 Sales: $14,566,600 | 2004 Profits: $659,300

U.S. Stock Ticker:
Int'l Ticker: 000270 Int'l Exchange: Seoul-KRX
Employees: 32,745
Fiscal Year Ends: 12/31
Parent Company:

SALARIES/BENEFITS:

Pension Plan: ESOP Stock Plan: Profit Sharing: Top Exec. Salary: $ Bonus: $
Savings Plan: Stock Purch. Plan: Second Exec. Salary: $ Bonus: $

OTHER THOUGHTS:

Apparent Women Officers or Directors:
Hot Spot for Advancement for Women/Minorities:

LOCATIONS: ("Y" = Yes)

West:	Southwest:	Midwest:	Southeast:	Northeast:	International:
Y		Y	Y		Y

KIMBERLY-CLARK CORP

www.kimberly-clark.com

Industry Group Code: 322000 **Ranks within this company's industry group:** Sales: 1 Profits: 1

Techology:		Medical/Drugs:		Engineering:		Transportation:		Chemicals/Petrochemicals:		Specialty:	
Computers:		Manufacturer:	Y	Design:		Aerospace:		Oil/Gas Products:		Special Services:	
Software:		Contract Research:		Construction:		Automotive:		Chemicals:		Consulting:	
Communications:		Medical Services:		Eng. Services:		Shipping:		Oil/Chem. Svcs.:		Specialty Mgmt.:	
Electronics:		Labs:		Consulting:				Gases:		Products:	Y
Alternative Energy:		Bio. Services:						Other:		Other:	

TYPES OF BUSINESS:

Personal Care Products-Paper
Consumer Tissue Products
Safety Products
Healthcare Products

BRANDS/DIVISIONS/AFFILIATES:

Kleenex
Scott
Huggies
Kotex
Depend
Pull-Ups
Kimberly-Clark of South Africa
P.T. Kimberly-Lever Indonesia

CONTACTS: *Note: Officers with more than one job title may be intentionally listed here more than once.*

Thomas J. Falk, CEO
Thomas J. Falk, Pres.
Mark A. Buthman, CFO/Sr. VP
Anthony J. Palmer, Chief Mktg. Officer/Sr. VP
Lizanne C. Gottung, Sr. VP-Human Resources
Thomas J. Mielke, Sr. VP-Law
Christian Brickman, Chief Strategy Officer
Thomas J. Mielke, Chief Compliance Officer/Sr. VP Gov't Affairs
Robert W. Black, Pres., Developing & Emerging Markets
Joanne Bauer, Pres., Healthcare Bus.
Robert. E. Abernathy, Pres., North Atlantic Consumer Prod.
Jan B. Spencer, Pres., Kimberly-Clark Professional
Thomas J. Falk, Chmn.

Phone: 972-281-1200	**Fax:** 972-281-1490
Toll-Free:	
Address: 351 Phelps Dr., Irving, TX 75038 US	

GROWTH PLANS/SPECIAL FEATURES:

Kimberly-Clark Corp. (KC) is a global health and hygiene company that manufactures and markets a wide range of health and hygiene products around the world. KC operates in four segments: personal care; consumer tissue; KC professional and other; and healthcare. The personal care segment manufactures and markets disposable diapers, training and youth pants; swim pants; baby wipes; feminine and incontinence care products; and related products. Products in this segment are primarily for household use and are sold under brand names such as Huggies, Pull-Ups, Little Swimmer, GoodNites, Kotex, Lightdays, Depend and Poise. The consumer tissue segment manufactures and markets facial and bathroom tissue; paper towels; napkins; and related products for household use. Products in this division are sold under brands such as Kleenex, Scott, Cottonelle, Viva, Andrex, Scottex, Hakle and Page. The KC professional & other segment manufactures and markets facial and bathroom tissue; paper towels; napkins; wipers; and a range of safety products for the away-from-home marketplace. Brand names in this segment include Kimberly-Clark, Kleenex, Scott, WypAll, Kimtech, Kleenguard and Kimcare. The healthcare segment manufactures and markets surgical gowns; drapes; infection control products; sterilization wrap; disposable face masks and exam gloves; respiratory products; and other disposable medical products. Products in this division are sold under the Kimberly-Clark and Ballard brand names. In 2007, sales to Wal-Mart Stores, Inc. accounted for approximately 13% of the company's revenue. In May 2008, the company purchase the remaining stake in South African subsidiary Kimberly-Clark of South Africa from The Lion Match Company (Proprietary) Limited.

The company offers its employees medical and dental insurance; short- and long-term disability insurance; life insurance; an investment plan; and a retirement contribution plan.

FINANCIALS: **Sales and profits are in thousands of dollars—add 000 to get the full amount. 2008 Note: Financial information for 2008 was not available for all companies at press time.**

2008 Sales: $19,415,000	2008 Profits: $1,690,000	**U.S. Stock Ticker: KMB**
2007 Sales: $18,266,000	2007 Profits: $1,822,900	**Int'l Ticker:** Int'l Exchange:
2006 Sales: $16,746,900	2006 Profits: $1,499,500	Employees: 53,000
2005 Sales: $15,902,600	2005 Profits: $1,568,300	Fiscal Year Ends: 12/31
2004 Sales: $15,083,200	2004 Profits: $1,800,200	Parent Company:

SALARIES/BENEFITS:

Pension Plan: Y	ESOP Stock Plan:	Profit Sharing:	Top Exec. Salary: $1,212,497	Bonus: $2,498,992
Savings Plan:	Stock Purch. Plan:		Second Exec. Salary: $639,750	Bonus: $775,370

OTHER THOUGHTS:

Apparent Women Officers or Directors: 4
Hot Spot for Advancement for Women/Minorities: Y

LOCATIONS: ("Y" = Yes)

West:	Southwest:	Midwest:	Southeast:	Northeast:	International:
Y	Y	Y	Y	Y	Y

KIMLEY-HORN AND ASSOCIATES INC

www.kimley-horn.com

Industry Group Code: 541330 **Ranks within this company's industry group:** Sales: Profits:

Techology:		Medical/Drugs:		Engineering:		Transportation:		Chemicals/Petrochemicals:		Specialty:	
Computers:		Manufacturer:		Design:		Aerospace:	Y	Oil/Gas Products:		Special Services:	Y
Software:		Contract Research:		Construction:		Automotive:		Chemicals:		Consulting:	Y
Communications:		Medical Services:		Eng. Services:	Y	Shipping:		Oil/Chem. Svcs.:		Specialty Mgmt.:	
Electronics:		Labs:		Consulting:	Y			Gases:		Products:	
Alternative Energy:		Bio. Services:						Other:		Other:	Y

TYPES OF BUSINESS:

Engineering
Project Consulting

BRANDS/DIVISIONS/AFFILIATES:

CONTACTS: *Note: Officers with more than one job title may be intentionally listed here more than once.*

Mark S. Wilson, Pres.
Nicholas L. Ellis, CFO

Phone: 919-677-2000	**Fax:** 919-677-2050
Toll-Free:	
Address: 3001 Weston Pkwy., Cary, NC 27513-2301 US	

GROWTH PLANS/SPECIAL FEATURES:

Kimley-Horn and Associates, Inc. is an engineering and land planning firm. The firm operates approximately 65 offices throughout the U.S. The company offers a variety of services in a wide range of industries including the aviation industry; environmental services; forensic engineering; intelligent transportation systems; land development; transit; urban planning/landscape architecture; wireless communications; water resources; and transportation. The aviation division is able to plan, design and administer various construction projects. The environmental services division offers a variety of services such as planning and feasibility studies; environmental documentation; and environmental restoration. The forensic engineering segment offers sound engineering services to better understand a specific case. Intelligent transportation services provides a multitude of services including ITS architectures; systems engineering analyses; ITS master planning; deployment plans and feasibility studies. Land Development provides clients with several services such as planning, site engineering and surveying/mapping. The transit division includes services such as bus system planning, regional operations studies, modeling and simulation, as well as financial feasibility and cost studies. Urban planning/landscape segment is able to provide clients design, redevelopment, architecture and construction services. Wireless communications maintains contractors in approximately 41 states. In turn, the division is able to compile information on 3,950 towers. Water resources offers customers alternative supplies; flood control; stormwater management; wastewater collection; treatment and disposal; water resources permitting; and water supply, treatment and distribution. The transportation segment is able to provide a wide spectrum of services for mass transit and transportation system needs.

Employees of the firm are offered medical and dental coverage; a 401(k) plan; incentive based bonuses; a vision plan; short and long term disability; a prescription drug plan; an employee assistance program; a health care and dependant care flexible spending program; professional memberships; certifications and development programs; a quit smoking program; tuition reimbursement; worker's compensation; and a survivor income benefits plan

FINANCIALS: **Sales and profits are in thousands of dollars—add 000 to get the full amount. 2008 Note: Financial information for 2008 was not available for all companies at press time.**

2008 Sales: $	2008 Profits: $	**U.S. Stock Ticker: Private**
2007 Sales: $	2007 Profits: $	**Int'l Ticker:** Int'l Exchange:
2006 Sales: $	2006 Profits: $	Employees: 2,190
2005 Sales: $	2005 Profits: $	Fiscal Year Ends: 12/31
2004 Sales: $	2004 Profits: $	Parent Company:

SALARIES/BENEFITS:

Pension Plan:	ESOP Stock Plan:	Profit Sharing:	Top Exec. Salary: $	Bonus: $
Savings Plan:	Stock Purch. Plan:		Second Exec. Salary: $	Bonus: $

OTHER THOUGHTS:

Apparent Women Officers or Directors:
Hot Spot for Advancement for Women/Minorities:

LOCATIONS: ("Y" = Yes)

West:	Southwest:	Midwest:	Southeast:	Northeast:	International:
Y	Y	Y	Y	Y	

KODAK RESEARCH LABORATORIES

www.kodak.com/US/en/corp/ScienceTechnology

Industry Group Code: 541710 **Ranks within this company's industry group:** Sales: Profits:

Techology:		Medical/Drugs:		Engineering:		Transportation:		Chemicals/Petrochemicals:		Specialty:	
Computers:		Manufacturer:		Design:		Aerospace:		Oil/Gas Products:		Special Services:	
Software:	Y	Contract Research:		Construction:		Automotive:		Chemicals:	Y	Consulting:	
Communications:		Medical Services:		Eng. Services:		Shipping:		Oil/Chem. Svcs.:		Specialty Mgmt.:	
Electronics:	Y	Labs:		Consulting:				Gases:		Products:	Y
Alternative Energy:		Bio. Services:						Other:		Other:	

TYPES OF BUSINESS:

Photographic & Imaging R&D
Film & Digital Photo Technology
Electronic Sensors
Display Technologies
Chemistry
Electronic Imaging Products
Scanning Technologies
Inkjet Printing Technology

BRANDS/DIVISIONS/AFFILIATES:

Eastman Kodak Company
Kodachrome
Photoresist
Kodak Professional DCS Pro SLR
Picture Maker G3 Film Processing Station

CONTACTS: *Note: Officers with more than one job title may be intentionally listed here more than once.*

Terry R. Taber, CTO-Eastman Kodak Co.

Phone: 585-724-4000	**Fax:**
Toll-Free:	
Address: 1999 Lake Ave., Rochester, NY 14650 US	

GROWTH PLANS/SPECIAL FEATURES:

Kodak Research Laboratories, the research and development wing of the Eastman Kodak Company, conducts research in the fields of imaging (including color science; digital image processing and image understanding; and systems analysis, image modeling and image simulation) and technology (including chemistry; photographic media; electronic sensors; image communications; inkjet printing; display technologies; and wireless networks). Major innovations introduced by the Kodak R&D team have included Kodachrome film, the first electronic scanner, Photoresist (a photosensitive resin that loses its resistance to chemical etching when exposed to radiation, used in integrated circuit manufacture), organic light emitting diodes (OLEDS), the first practical megapixel CCD image sensor and the optics for the Chandra X-ray Space Telescope. Today, the firm is particularly interested in digital science and technologies such as OLEDs, image sensors and invisible watermarking. Kodak works closely with other companies and organizations, including MIT, Clarkson University and the Universities of Oxford, Cambridge and Manchester. Kodak's recent efforts include a project to better understand and improve longevity of inkjet printed photos; the Kodak Professional DCS Pro SLR, a professional quality, 14-megapixel digital camera system that accepts Nikon or Canon lenses; and the Picture Maker G3 Film Processing Station, a self-service kiosk that will process, preview, enhance and print 35mm film pictures and burn picture CDs in as little as seven minutes.

The firm offers employees medical, and dental coverage; flexible spending accounts; vacation buy; life insurance; retiree medical coverage; child care resource and referral; a 401(k) plan; a pension plan; relocation assistance; adoption assistance; an employee assistance program; health and wellness programs; flexible work arrangements; on-site fitness centers; a nursing mothers' program; and career development programs.

FINANCIALS: **Sales and profits are in thousands of dollars—add 000 to get the full amount. 2008 Note: Financial information for 2008 was not available for all companies at press time.**

2008 Sales: $	2008 Profits: $	**U.S. Stock Ticker: Subsidiary**
2007 Sales: $	2007 Profits: $	**Int'l Ticker:** Int'l Exchange:
2006 Sales: $	2006 Profits: $	Employees:
2005 Sales: $	2005 Profits: $	Fiscal Year Ends: 12/31
2004 Sales: $	2004 Profits: $	Parent Company: EASTMAN KODAK CO

SALARIES/BENEFITS:

Pension Plan: Y	ESOP Stock Plan:	Profit Sharing:	Top Exec. Salary: $	Bonus: $
Savings Plan: Y	Stock Purch. Plan:		Second Exec. Salary: $	Bonus: $

OTHER THOUGHTS:

Apparent Women Officers or Directors:
Hot Spot for Advancement for Women/Minorities:

LOCATIONS: ("Y" = Yes)

West:	Southwest:	Midwest:	Southeast:	Northeast:	International:
				Y	Y

KONAMI CORP

www.konami.co.jp

Industry Group Code: 511208 **Ranks within this company's industry group:** Sales: 4 Profits: 1

Techology:		Medical/Drugs:		Engineering:		Transportation:		Chemicals/Petrochemicals:		Specialty:	
Computers:		Manufacturer:		Design:		Aerospace:		Oil/Gas Products:		Special Services:	
Software:	Y	Contract Research:		Construction:		Automotive:		Chemicals:		Consulting:	
Communications:		Medical Services:		Eng. Services:		Shipping:		Oil/Chem. Svcs.:		Specialty Mgmt.:	
Electronics:		Labs:		Consulting:				Gases:		Products:	
Alternative Energy:		Bio. Services:						Other:		Other:	

TYPES OF BUSINESS:

Software-Games
Toys
Arcade Games
Mobile Phone Media Content
Sports Clubs
Health & Fitness Products
Casino Games
Casino Management Systems

BRANDS/DIVISIONS/AFFILIATES:

Metal Gear
Castlevania
Silent Hill
Yu-Gi-Oh! Official Card Game
Konami Casino Management System
Sportsplex Japan Co., Ltd.
Metal Gear Solid 4: Guns of the Patriots

CONTACTS: *Note: Officers with more than one job title may be intentionally listed here more than once.*

Kagemasa Kozuki, CEO
Kagemasa Kozuki, Pres.
Noriaki Yamaguchi, CFO/VP
Sadaharu Kitaya, Gen. Mgr.-Sales & Mktg. Div.
Mineaki Yoshiba, Corp. Officer-Human Resources
Akira Tamai, Corp. Finance & Acct. Officer
Fumiaki Tanaka, Corp. Officer-Digital Entertainment
Toshimitsu Oishi, Corp. Officer-Health & Fitness
Satoshi Sakamoto, Corp. Officer-Gaming & System
Kimihiko Higashio, VP
Kagemasa Kozuki, Chmn.
Kazumi Kitaue, Chmn.-Konami Digital Entertainment, Inc.

Phone: 81-3-5770-0573 **Fax:** 81-3-5412-3300
Toll-Free:
Address: 9-7-2, Akasaka, Minato-ku, Tokyo, 107-8323 Japan

GROWTH PLANS/SPECIAL FEATURES:

Konami Corp., founded in 1969, primarily produces entertainment products. It operates three segments: Digital Entertainment, which produced 60.2% of 2008 revenues; Health & Fitness, 29.1%; and Gaming & System, 6.2%. The Digital Entertainment business primarily produces video and computer games, as well as other entertainment products, including arcade games, game strategy guide books, action figures, animation, mobile content and trading card games. Some of its video game titles include the Metal Gear, Castlevania and Silent Hill franchises; it also markets the Yu-Gi-Oh! trading card game. It operates through four subsidiaries, located in Japan, the U.S., Hong Kong and Germany. The Health & Fitness segment operates health clubs as well as manufacturing and marketing various health-related products. During 2008, this segment operated 222 of its own health clubs, with 978,000 members, as well as managing 110 clubs for third parties. Its health-related products range from exercise machines to nutritional supplements. This division operates through a single subsidiary in Japan. Lastly, the Gaming & System business manufactures gaming equipment, primarily slot machines, and is licensed to sell these products to casinos in all Australian territories and states, eight Canadian provinces and 27 U.S. states. This division also sells the firm's Konami Casino Management System, which offers casinos real-time monitoring and management of its slot machines and other cash handling systems. Gaming & System operates through two subsidiaries in the U.S. and Australia. In March 2008, Konami acquired 86.5% of Sportsplex Japan Co., Ltd., which operates 13 fitness clubs in Tokyo, from Tokyo Electric Power Company, Inc. In June 2008, the firm launched the fourth installment of its Metal Gear franchise: Metal Gear Solid 4: Guns of the Patriots.

FINANCIALS: **Sales and profits are in thousands of dollars—add 000 to get the full amount. 2008 Note: Financial information for 2008 was not available for all companies at press time.**

2008 Sales: $2,968,380	2008 Profits: $183,102	**U.S. Stock Ticker: KNM**
2007 Sales: $2,374,240	2007 Profits: $137,323	**Int'l Ticker: 9766** Int'l Exchange: Tokyo-TSE
2006 Sales: $2,231,523	2006 Profits: $195,863	Employees: 12,991
2005 Sales: $2,427,500	2005 Profits: $97,600	Fiscal Year Ends: 3/31
2004 Sales: $2,586,924	2004 Profits: $190,217	Parent Company:

SALARIES/BENEFITS:

Pension Plan: Y	ESOP Stock Plan:	Profit Sharing:	Top Exec. Salary: $	Bonus: $
Savings Plan:	Stock Purch. Plan:		Second Exec. Salary: $	Bonus: $

OTHER THOUGHTS:

Apparent Women Officers or Directors:
Hot Spot for Advancement for Women/Minorities:

LOCATIONS: ("Y" = Yes)

West:	Southwest:	Midwest:	Southeast:	Northeast:	International:
Y					Y

KUMHO INDUSTRIAL CO LTD

www.kumhoenc.com/Eng/main.asp

Industry Group Code: 230000 **Ranks within this company's industry group:** Sales: Profits:

Techology:		Medical/Drugs:		Engineering:		Transportation:		Chemicals/Petrochemicals:		Specialty:	
Computers:		Manufacturer:		Design:	Y	Aerospace:		Oil/Gas Products:		Special Services:	
Software:		Contract Research:		Construction:	Y	Automotive:		Chemicals:		Consulting:	
Communications:		Medical Services:		Eng. Services:	Y	Shipping:		Oil/Chem. Svcs.:		Specialty Mgmt.:	
Electronics:		Labs:		Consulting:				Gases:		Products:	
Alternative Energy:		Bio. Services:						Other:	Y	Other:	Y

TYPES OF BUSINESS:

Engineering & Construction
Research & Development
Sewage Treatment

BRANDS/DIVISIONS/AFFILIATES:

Kumho E&C
[?]ullim
Kumho Asiana Group
ECOS
KIDEA

CONTACTS: *Note: Officers with more than one job title may be intentionally listed here more than once.*

Hoon Shin, Co-CEO
Wang-Hyun Moon, Mgr.-Investor Rel. Team
Won-Tae Lee, Co-CEO
Seong-San Kim, Co-CEO
Yon-Goo Lee, Co-CEO

Phone: 02-6303-0114	**Fax:**
Toll-Free:	
Address: Kumho Asiana Bldg. 1-ga, Sinmunno Jongno-gu, Seoul, 100-061 Korea	

GROWTH PLANS/SPECIAL FEATURES:

Kumho Industrial Co. Ltd., doing business as Kumho Engineering & Construction (Kumho E&C), offers a wide range of building services. It has worked on general architectural construction projects, building commercial centers, warehouses, leisure facilities and even whole cities. Kumho E&C's civil engineering projects have run the gamut from airports, railroads and highways to tunnels and bridges. The firm has built over 600,000 new homes, including state-of-the-art apartment complexes and high-rise residential buildings. The company's apartments are often branded [?]ullim, pronounced Uwoolim, which is a Korean word that translates Community in Harmony. Kumho E&C's plant engineering projects have included constructing petrochemical plants; installing factory automation equipment; building environmental facilities such as incinerators and water and sewage treatment plants; and energy-related facilities, including gasoline tanks, LNG (liquefied natural gas) pipelines and power plants. The firm operates a research and development institute near its office dedicated to finding environmentally friendly building materials; stronger and faster building techniques; and new architectural designs maximizing heating and cooling systems, water-proofing and structural integrity. The firm's Electrode Contract Oxydation System (ECOS) is a solution that facilitates the decomposition of sewage and is used in the removal of pollutants. Another sewage treatment is the KIDEA process, which was developed jointly by the company and the Korea Institute of Science & Technology, and removes 70-80% of nutrient salt from sewage. Kumho E&C is part of the Kumho Asiana Group.

FINANCIALS: **Sales and profits are in thousands of dollars—add 000 to get the full amount. 2008 Note: Financial information for 2008 was not available for all companies at press time.**

2008 Sales: $6,072,700	2008 Profits: $27,600	**U.S. Stock Ticker:**
2007 Sales: $5,339,000	2007 Profits: $135,000	**Int'l Ticker: 002990** Int'l Exchange: Seoul-KRX
2006 Sales: $6,207,400	2006 Profits: $56,900	Employees:
2005 Sales: $	2005 Profits: $	Fiscal Year Ends:
2004 Sales: $	2004 Profits: $	Parent Company:

SALARIES/BENEFITS:

Pension Plan:	ESOP Stock Plan:	Profit Sharing:	Top Exec. Salary: $	Bonus: $
Savings Plan:	Stock Purch. Plan:		Second Exec. Salary: $	Bonus: $

OTHER THOUGHTS:

Apparent Women Officers or Directors:
Hot Spot for Advancement for Women/Minorities:

LOCATIONS: ("Y" = Yes)

West:	Southwest:	Midwest:	Southeast:	Northeast:	International:
					Y

L-3 COMMUNICATIONS HOLDINGS INC

www.l-3com.com

Industry Group Code: 334200 **Ranks within this company's industry group:** Sales: 1 Profits: 1

Techology:		Medical/Drugs:		Engineering:		Transportation:		Chemicals/Petrochemicals:		Specialty:	
Computers:	Y	Manufacturer:		Design:		Aerospace:	Y	Oil/Gas Products:		Special Services:	
Software:	Y	Contract Research:		Construction:		Automotive:		Chemicals:		Consulting:	
Communications:	Y	Medical Services:		Eng. Services:		Shipping:		Oil/Chem. Svcs.:		Specialty Mgmt.:	
Electronics:		Labs:		Consulting:				Gases:		Products:	
Alternative Energy:		Bio. Services:						Other:		Other:	

TYPES OF BUSINESS:

Electronic Equipment-Specialized Communications
Intelligence, Surveillance & Reconnaissance Systems
Aviation & Aerospace Products
Telemetry Products
Instrumentation Products
Microwave Components
Security Systems
Airport Luggage Screening Systems

BRANDS/DIVISIONS/AFFILIATES:

L-3 Communications Corporation
Microdyne Outsourcing Inc
L-3 Titan Group
Geneva Aerospace Inc
Global Communications Solutions Inc
HAS Systems Pty Limited
International Resources Group Ltd

CONTACTS: *Note: Officers with more than one job title may be intentionally listed here more than once.*

Michael T. Strianese, CEO
Michael T. Strianese, Pres.
Ralph G. D'Ambrosio, CFO/VP
Kenneth W. Manne, VP-Human Resources
Paul De Lia, VP-Science, Tech. & R&D
Vincent T. Taylor, CIO/VP
A. Michael Andrews II, CTO/VP
Sheila M. Sheridan, VP-Admin.
Steven M. Post, General Counsel/Sr. VP/Corp. Sec.
David T. Butler III, Sr. VP-Bus. Oper.
Curtis Brunson, Sr. VP-Corp. Strategy & Dev.
Karen Tripp, VP-Corp. Comm.
Dan Azmon, Controller/Principal Acct. Officer
Jimmie V. Adams, Sr. VP-Washington Oper.
Robert W. RisCassi, Sr. VP
Lois Bailey, VP-Int'l Licensing
Christopher C. Cambria, Sr. VP/Sr. Counsel-M&A
Michael T. Strianese, Chmn.
Charles Wald, VP-Int'l
R.L. DeNino, VP-Procurement

Phone: 212-697-1111 **Fax:** 212-805-5477
Toll-Free:
Address: 600 3rd Ave., New York, NY 10016 US

GROWTH PLANS/SPECIAL FEATURES:

L-3 Communications Holdings, Inc., operating through its subsidiary L-3 Communications Corp., is a supplier of products and services used in various aerospace and defense platforms. The company operates through four business segments: Command, Control, Communications, Intelligence, Surveillance and Reconnaissance (C3ISR); Government Services; Aircraft Modernization and Maintenance (AM&M); and Specialized Products. The C3ISR segment specializes in signals intelligence and communications intelligence. The businesses in this segment provide equipment for U.S. and foreign government intelligence and reconnaissance applications. The Government Services division provides: training services; maintenance and logistics support; communications systems support; engineering services; and marksmanship training systems. Through the AM&M segment, the company offers specialized aircraft modernization and logistics support services. The Specialized Products segment provides naval warfare products, security systems, sensors and wireless communication products. L-3's systems and equipment are essential to many major communication, command and control, intelligence-gathering and space systems. The company's customers include the U.S. Department of Defense, the U.S. Department of Homeland Security, U.S. Government intelligence agencies, various aerospace and defense contractors, foreign governments and commercial customers. In 2007, the company acquired Geneva Aerospace, Inc., a provider of unmanned aerial vehicle technology, and Global Communications Solutions, Inc., a provider of portable satellite communications equipment and products. In March 2008, the company completed its acquisition of HAS Systems Pty Limited, an Australian provider of geospatial, marine and electronic systems for the defense and maritime industries. In April 2008, L-3 acquired Northrop Grumman's Electro-Optical Systems business. In December 2008, the company acquired International Resources Group Ltd., an international professional services firm.

L-3 Communications offers its employees medical, dental and vision plans; educational assistance; a 401(k) savings plan; and an employee stock purchase plan.

FINANCIALS: **Sales and profits are in thousands of dollars—add 000 to get the full amount. 2008 Note: Financial information for 2008 was not available for all companies at press time.**

2008 Sales: $14,901,000	2008 Profits: $949,000	**U.S. Stock Ticker: LLL**
2007 Sales: $13,960,500	2007 Profits: $756,100	**Int'l Ticker:** Int'l Exchange:
2006 Sales: $12,476,900	2006 Profits: $526,100	Employees: 65,000
2005 Sales: $9,444,700	2005 Profits: $508,500	Fiscal Year Ends: 12/31
2004 Sales: $6,897,000	2004 Profits: $381,900	Parent Company:

SALARIES/BENEFITS:

Pension Plan:	ESOP Stock Plan:	Profit Sharing:	Top Exec. Salary: $1,000,000	Bonus: $2,500,000
Savings Plan: Y	Stock Purch. Plan:		Second Exec. Salary: $650,000	Bonus: $550,000

OTHER THOUGHTS:

Apparent Women Officers or Directors: 6
Hot Spot for Advancement for Women/Minorities: Y

LOCATIONS: ("Y" = Yes)

West:	Southwest:	Midwest:	Southeast:	Northeast:	International:
Y	Y	Y	Y	Y	Y

L-3 TITAN GROUP

www.titan.com

Industry Group Code: 541512 **Ranks within this company's industry group:** Sales: Profits:

Techology:		Medical/Drugs:		Engineering:		Transportation:		Chemicals/Petrochemicals:		Specialty:	
Computers:		Manufacturer:		Design:		Aerospace:	Y	Oil/Gas Products:		Special Services:	Y
Software:		Contract Research:		Construction:		Automotive:		Chemicals:		Consulting:	
Communications:	Y	Medical Services:		Eng. Services:		Shipping:		Oil/Chem. Svcs.:		Specialty Mgmt.:	
Electronics:		Labs:		Consulting:				Gases:		Products:	
Alternative Energy:		Bio. Services:						Other:		Other:	

TYPES OF BUSINESS:

Consulting-Government InfoTech
Satellite Communication Systems
Intelligence & Surveillance Systems
Information Technology Systems
Homeland Security Consulting
Aerospace Engineering

BRANDS/DIVISIONS/AFFILIATES:

L-3 Communications Holdings Inc
Center for National Response

CONTACTS: *Note: Officers with more than one job title may be intentionally listed here more than once.*

A. Anton Frederickson, COO
A. Anton Frederickson, Pres.

Phone: 703-434-4000	**Fax:** 703-434-5075
Toll-Free:	
Address: 11955 Freedom Dr., Reston, VA 20190 US	

GROWTH PLANS/SPECIAL FEATURES:

L-3 Titan Group, a subsidiary of L-3 Communications, provides information and communications products and services to the Department of Defense, the Department of Homeland Security, intelligence agencies and other government customers. It works on over 2,000 contracts at a time, and more than 8,000 of its personnel have security clearances. It has over 300 locations in 24 countries, including Iraq and Afghanistan. Titan focuses on five business areas: Homeland Security and Homeland Defense; Enterprise Information Technology; Command, Control, Communications, Computer, Intelligence, Surveillance and Reconnaissance (C4ISR); Intelligence; and Aerospace. Titan provides the Department of Homeland Security with communication systems, such as APCO 25 compliant radio systems, that support first responders. Other services assist explosives detection, advanced physics research, US-VISIT (United States Visitor and Immigrant Status Indicator Technology Program) border security and U.S. Coast Guard training. The firm also runs the Center for National Response, a training facility that prepares first responders for potential terrorist threats. Titan's Enterprise Information Technology division provides end-to-end IT solutions that connect strategic and tactical levels of a customer's critical enterprise. C4ISR is the cornerstone of Titan's business and involves four distinct activities: gathering military information through intelligence, surveillance and reconnaissance; transmitting the information digitally through high-technology communications systems; processing the digitized information to facilitate command and control decision making; and disseminating commands electronically back to military and intelligence platforms for execution. The firm's Intelligence segment provides services for experts at all levels of security expertise. Finally, Titan's Aerospace division supports military aviation with systems engineering, advance systems design, aircraft modernization, systems integration, avionics technical support and life-cycle support services.

Employees of Titan receive medical, dental and vision coverage; life insurance; educational assistance; flexible spending accounts; and paid time off.

FINANCIALS: **Sales and profits are in thousands of dollars—add 000 to get the full amount. 2008 Note: Financial information for 2008 was not available for all companies at press time.**

2008 Sales: $	2008 Profits: $	**U.S. Stock Ticker: Subsidiary**
2007 Sales: $	2007 Profits: $	**Int'l Ticker:** Int'l Exchange:
2006 Sales: $	2006 Profits: $	Employees:
2005 Sales: $2,500,000	2005 Profits: $	Fiscal Year Ends: 12/31
2004 Sales: $2,046,525	2004 Profits: $-38,397	Parent Company: L-3 COMMUNICATIONS HOLDINGS INC

SALARIES/BENEFITS:

Pension Plan:	ESOP Stock Plan:	Profit Sharing:	Top Exec. Salary: $807,500	Bonus: $
Savings Plan: Y	Stock Purch. Plan: Y		Second Exec. Salary: $342,777	Bonus: $

OTHER THOUGHTS:

Apparent Women Officers or Directors:
Hot Spot for Advancement for Women/Minorities:

LOCATIONS: ("Y" = Yes)

West:	Southwest:	Midwest:	Southeast:	Northeast:	International:
Y	Y	Y	Y	Y	Y

LAND ROVER

www.landrover.com

Industry Group Code: 336111 **Ranks within this company's industry group:** Sales: Profits:

Techology:		**Medical/Drugs:**		**Engineering:**		**Transportation:**		**Chemicals/Petrochemicals:**		**Specialty:**	
Computers:		Manufacturer:		Design:		Aerospace:		Oil/Gas Products:		Special Services:	
Software:		Contract Research:		Construction:		Automotive:	Y	Chemicals:		Consulting:	
Communications:		Medical Services:		Eng. Services:		Shipping:		Oil/Chem. Svcs.:		Specialty Mgmt.:	
Electronics:		Labs:		Consulting:				Gases:		Products:	
Alternative Energy:		Bio. Services:						Other:		Other:	

TYPES OF BUSINESS:

Auto Manufacturing
Luxury Vehicles
Off-Road Vehicles

BRANDS/DIVISIONS/AFFILIATES:

Tata Motors Limited
Tata Group
Range Rover Sport
Freelander
Discovery
Range Rover
Defender
LR3

CONTACTS: *Note: Officers with more than one job title may be intentionally listed here more than once.*

David Smith, CEO-Jaguar & Land Rover
Frank Lazzaro, CFO-Jaguar & Land Rover
Des Thurlby, Dir.-Human Resources, Jaguar & Land Rover
Michael Ali, Dir.-IT, Jaguar & Land Rover

Phone: 44-1926-649-413 **Fax:**
Toll-Free:
Address: B523 Banbury Rd., Gaydon, Warwick, CV35 0RR UK

GROWTH PLANS/SPECIAL FEATURES:

Land Rover, acquired in 2008 by Tata Motors Limited from its former owner Ford, is a world leader in the design and production of 4x4 vehicles. New owner Tata Motors is based in India and is part of the Tata Group conglomerate, which includes businesses ranging from steel production to retailing to inexpensive, compact car manufacturing. Land Rover exports approximately 78% of vehicles to 169 countries. The U.S. is Land Rover's largest export market. The firm's vehicles are manufactured in Solihull, England. Currently, Land Rover markets four models in the U.S., including Range Rover, Range Rover Sport, LR3 and LR2. The firm also markets Discovery, Freelander and Defender in other areas of the world. The firm's newest Range Rover starts at about $77,950, and comes with a V8 engine, a six-speed automatic transmission, GPS navigation technology, a rear view camera and a DVD player. If customers choose to design their own vehicle, they can do so through the company's web site. Customers begin by choosing the vehicle, then the model, the color and the options. Land Rover models are designed for durability and off-road capability, and the company duly hosts a number of expeditions for adventurers and environmental researchers around the globe. The firm has dealerships available in nearly every state in the U.S. and most areas of U.K. Land Rover includes information on its website offering a range of technical information, special tools, diagnostic equipment and training materials. The biggest news at Land Rover is its LRX concept car, introduced at major auto shows in 2008. The LRX is smaller than other Land Rovers, lighter in weight and relatively low to the ground and will start production in mid-2009.

FINANCIALS: **Sales and profits are in thousands of dollars—add 000 to get the full amount. 2008 Note: Financial information for 2008 was not available for all companies at press time.**

2008 Sales: $	2008 Profits: $	**U.S. Stock Ticker: Subsidiary**
2007 Sales: $	2007 Profits: $	**Int'l Ticker:** Int'l Exchange:
2006 Sales: $	2006 Profits: $	Employees: 11,295
2005 Sales: $	2005 Profits: $	Fiscal Year Ends: 12/31
2004 Sales: $	2004 Profits: $	Parent Company: TATA MOTORS LIMITED

SALARIES/BENEFITS:

Pension Plan: Y	ESOP Stock Plan:	Profit Sharing:	Top Exec. Salary: $	Bonus: $
Savings Plan:	Stock Purch. Plan:		Second Exec. Salary: $	Bonus: $

OTHER THOUGHTS:

Apparent Women Officers or Directors:
Hot Spot for Advancement for Women/Minorities:

LOCATIONS: ("Y" = Yes)

West:	Southwest:	Midwest:	Southeast:	Northeast:	International:
Y	Y	Y	Y	Y	Y

LANXESS AG

www.lanxess.com

Industry Group Code: 325000 **Ranks within this company's industry group:** Sales: 16 Profits: 19

Techology:		Medical/Drugs:		Engineering:		Transportation:		Chemicals/Petrochemicals:		Specialty:	
Computers:		Manufacturer:		Design:		Aerospace:		Oil/Gas Products:		Special Services:	
Software:		Contract Research:		Construction:		Automotive:		Chemicals:	Y	Consulting:	
Communications:		Medical Services:		Eng. Services:		Shipping:		Oil/Chem. Svcs.:		Specialty Mgmt.:	
Electronics:		Labs:		Consulting:				Gases:		Products:	Y
Alternative Energy:		Bio. Services:						Other:		Other:	

TYPES OF BUSINESS:

Chemicals
Performance Chemicals
Chemical Intermediates
Engineering Plastics
Performance Rubber

BRANDS/DIVISIONS/AFFILIATES:

Bayer Chemical
Rhein Chemie
Petroflex SA

CONTACTS: *Note: Officers with more than one job title may be intentionally listed here more than once.*

Axel C. Heitmann, CEO
Matthias Zachert, CFO
Werner Breuers, Head-R&D
Werner Breuers, Dir.-Performance Polymers & Advanced Intermediates
Rainier van Roessel, Managing Dir.
Rolf Stomberg, Chmn.
Werner Breuers, Head-Procurement

Phone: 49-214-30-33333	**Fax:** 49-214-30-40944
Toll-Free:	
Address: Bldg. K10, Leverkusen, 51369 Germany	

GROWTH PLANS/SPECIAL FEATURES:

Lanxess AG, formerly Bayer Chemical, is an independent chemical manufacturing company. The firm has operations in over 18 countries, with major manufacturing sites in Germany, Belgium, the U.S., Canada, Argentina and China. Additional production facilities are located in Australia, Brazil, France, India, Italy, Japan, Mexico, the Netherlands, South Africa, Spain, Thailand and the U.K. The company has nearly 60 fully consolidated subsidiaries worldwide. Lanxess has a portfolio of approximately 5,000 chemical products, divided into three broad product segments: performance chemicals, advanced intermediates and performance polymers. Performance chemicals include material protection products, like disinfectants, industrial corrosion inhibitors, beverage preservatives; functional chemicals, plastic additives, phosphorus and specialty chemicals, organic and inorganic colorants; leather treatments; textile processing chemicals; paper processing chemicals, such as fluorescent whiteners, retention agents and colorants; rubber chemicals; and ion exchange resins. Subsidiary Rhein Chemie makes additives for the lubricant, rubber, polyurethanes and plastics industries. Advanced intermediates include basic chemicals (industrial chemicals and aromatic compounds); fine chemicals for the pharmaceutical and agrochemical industries; and inorganic pigments. The performance polymers segment encompasses the production of rubber and plastics, which have applications in the automotive and electrical/electronics industries. Products in this segment include styrenic resins, poly-butadiene rubber, technical rubber products and semi-crystalline products. About a quarter of the firm's sales are in Germany, with another third in the rest of Europe. The Americas collectively account for another quarter of sales, with Asia-Pacific representing most of the remainder. In May 2008, the company announced plans to close down the production facility of the Ion Exchange Resins business unit in Birmingham, New Jersey. In April 2008, Lanxess acquired approximately 70% of Brazil-based Petroflex S.A. for approximately $303.6 million and announced its hopes to acquire the remaining shares through a public takeover offer.

FINANCIALS: **Sales and profits are in thousands of dollars—add 000 to get the full amount. 2008 Note: Financial information for 2008 was not available for all companies at press time.**

2008 Sales: $8,864,970	2008 Profits: $230,520	**U.S. Stock Ticker:**
2007 Sales: $8,908,110	2007 Profits: $150,990	**Int'l Ticker: LXSG** Int'l Exchange: Frankfurt-Euronext
2006 Sales: $9,476,820	2006 Profits: $268,860	Employees: 14,797
2005 Sales: $9,757,960	2005 Profits: $-85,980	Fiscal Year Ends: 12/31
2004 Sales: $8,250,300	2004 Profits: $-14,600	Parent Company:

SALARIES/BENEFITS:

Pension Plan:	ESOP Stock Plan:	Profit Sharing:	Top Exec. Salary: $	Bonus: $
Savings Plan:	Stock Purch. Plan:		Second Exec. Salary: $	Bonus: $

OTHER THOUGHTS:

Apparent Women Officers or Directors:
Hot Spot for Advancement for Women/Minorities:

LOCATIONS: ("Y" = Yes)

West:	Southwest:	Midwest:	Southeast:	Northeast:	International:
	Y	Y	Y	Y	Y

LARSEN & TOUBRO LIMITED (L&T)

www.larsentoubro.com

Industry Group Code: 326199 **Ranks within this company's industry group:** Sales: Profits:

Techology:		Medical/Drugs:		Engineering:		Transportation:		Chemicals/Petrochemicals:		Specialty:	
Computers:		Manufacturer:		Design:	Y	Aerospace:		Oil/Gas Products:		Special Services:	Y
Software:		Contract Research:		Construction:	Y	Automotive:		Chemicals:		Consulting:	Y
Communications:		Medical Services:		Eng. Services:	Y	Shipping:	Y	Oil/Chem. Svcs.:		Specialty Mgmt.:	
Electronics:	Y	Labs:		Consulting:	Y			Gases:		Products:	Y
Alternative Energy:		Bio. Services:						Other:		Other:	Y

TYPES OF BUSINESS:

Construction & Engineering Services
Manufacturing Services
Shipbuilding
Contract Manufacturing
Electronic Engineering Services
Construction Equipment Manufacturing
Consulting
InfoTech Services

BRANDS/DIVISIONS/AFFILIATES:

L&T Infotech Ltd (Larsen & Toubro Infotech)

CONTACTS: *Note: Officers with more than one job title may be intentionally listed here more than once.*

A. M. Naik, Managing Dir.
K. Venkataramanan, CFO
K. Venkataramanan, Pres., Eng. & Construction
J. P. Nayak, Pres., Machinery & Industrial Prod.
K. V. Rangaswami, Pres., Construction
R. N. Mukhija, Pres., Electrical & Electronics
A. M. Naik, Chmn.

Phone: 91-22-22685656 **Fax:** 91-22-22685858
Toll-Free:
Address: L&T House, N. M. Marg, Ballard Estate, Mumbai, 400 011 India

GROWTH PLANS/SPECIAL FEATURES:

Larsen & Toubro Limited (L&T) is a technology, engineering, construction and manufacturing company based in India and with operations around the world. The company operates in six divisions: Engineering & Construction Projects (E&C); Heavy Engineering (HE); Engineering Construction & Contracts (ECC); Electrical & Electronics (EBG); Machinery & Industrial Products (MIPD); and Information Technology & Engineering Services (ID&ES). The E&C division offers process technology, basic and detailed engineering, modular fabrication, procurement, project management, construction and commissioning. It offers single-point-responsibility under stringent delivery schedules. The firm's modular fabrication facility in Hazira, India operates under this division. The HE division operates manufacturing facilities across India and supplies custom designed and engineered critical equipment and systems. L&T's shipbuilding business operates within this division. The shipyard primarily constructs niche vessels such as specialized heavy lift cargo vessels, CNG carriers, chemical tankers, defense and paramilitary vessels and other role specific vessels. The ECC division is one of India's largest engineering and construction services. The EBG division, operating through two manufacturing facilities in India and one in China, manufactures switchboards for different applications including marine, meters, automation systems, petroleum dispensing pumps, medical equipment and tooling solutions. The MIPD division produces a range of industrial machinery and products, including construction and mining equipment, hydraulic equipment, paper machinery, welding products, windmill components and cutting tools. The IT&ES division operates via subsidiary L&T Infotech and offers IT services and solutions around the world. In May 2008, the company sold its ready-mix concrete business to Lafarge India.

FINANCIALS: **Sales and profits are in thousands of dollars—add 000 to get the full amount. 2008 Note: Financial information for 2008 was not available for all companies at press time.**

2008 Sales: $	2008 Profits: $	**U.S. Stock Ticker:**
2007 Sales: $	2007 Profits: $	**Int'l Ticker: 500510** Int'l Exchange: Bombay-BSE
2006 Sales: $	2006 Profits: $	Employees:
2005 Sales: $	2005 Profits: $	Fiscal Year Ends:
2004 Sales: $	2004 Profits: $	Parent Company:

SALARIES/BENEFITS:

Pension Plan:	ESOP Stock Plan:	Profit Sharing:	Top Exec. Salary: $	Bonus: $
Savings Plan:	Stock Purch. Plan:		Second Exec. Salary: $	Bonus: $

OTHER THOUGHTS:

Apparent Women Officers or Directors:
Hot Spot for Advancement for Women/Minorities:

LOCATIONS: ("Y" = Yes)

West:	Southwest:	Midwest:	Southeast:	Northeast:	International:
					Y

LAYNE CHRISTENSEN COMPANY

www.laynechristensen.com

Industry Group Code: 234000 **Ranks within this company's industry group:** Sales: 27 Profits: 24

Techology:		Medical/Drugs:		Engineering:		Transportation:		Chemicals/Petrochemicals:		Specialty:	
Computers:		Manufacturer:		Design:		Aerospace:		Oil/Gas Products:		Special Services:	
Software:		Contract Research:		Construction:		Automotive:		Chemicals:		Consulting:	Y
Communications:		Medical Services:		Eng. Services:	Y	Shipping:		Oil/Chem. Svcs.:	Y	Specialty Mgmt.:	
Electronics:		Labs:		Consulting:	Y			Gases:		Products:	
Alternative Energy:		Bio. Services:						Other:		Other:	

TYPES OF BUSINESS:

Construction & Civil Engineering Services
Water Treatment Plant Development
Drilling Services
Oil & Gas Field Services
Unconventional Natural Gas Production

BRANDS/DIVISIONS/AFFILIATES:

SolmeteX
Tierdael Construction Co.
Wittman Hydro Planning Associates

CONTACTS: *Note: Officers with more than one job title may be intentionally listed here more than once.*

Andrew B. Schmitt, CEO
Andrew B. Schmitt, Pres.
Steven F. Crooke, General Counsel/VP/Sec.
Jerry W. Fanska, VP-Finance/Treas.
Gregory F. Aluce, Sr. VP/Pres., Water Resources Div.
Eric Despain, Sr. VP/Pres., Mineral Exploration
David A. B. Brown, Chmn.

Phone: 913-677-6800	**Fax:** 913-362-0133
Toll-Free:	
Address: 1900 Shawnee Mission Pkwy., Mission Woods, KS 66205 US	

GROWTH PLANS/SPECIAL FEATURES:

Layne Christensen Co. provides drilling and construction services and related products in two principal markets: water infrastructure and mineral exploration. In addition, the company is a producer of unconventional natural gas for the energy market. The firm operates in four segments: water infrastructure, mineral exploration and energy services. Through the water infrastructure division, Layne Christensen provides water systems services, such as test hole drilling, well construction, well development and testing, pump selection, equipment installation and pipeline construction; well and pump rehabilitation services; water and wastewater treatment and plant construction services; sewer rehabilitation; and environmental assessment drilling. The mineral exploration division conducts aboveground and underground drilling activities for the global mineral exploration industry. The energy services segment provides the exploration for, and acquisition, development, and production of, unconventional natural gas. The firm operates throughout North America, as well as Africa, Australia, Europe and, through our affiliates, in South America. Layne Christensen's customers include municipalities, investor-owned water utilities, industrial companies, global mining companies, consulting engineering firms, heavy civil construction contractors, oil and gas companies and agribusiness. In December 2007, the company acquired SolmeteX, a developer of specialized chemistries and processes for the removal of toxins from both drinking water and wastewater. In January 2008, Layne Christensen acquired Tierdael Construction Company, a heavy civil water infrastructure contractor. In May 2008, the company acquired Wittman Hydro Planning Associates, a water resource consulting and development firm.

FINANCIALS: **Sales and profits are in thousands of dollars—add 000 to get the full amount. 2008 Note: Financial information for 2008 was not available for all companies at press time.**

2008 Sales: $868,274	2008 Profits: $37,256	**U.S. Stock Ticker: LAYN**
2007 Sales: $722,768	2007 Profits: $26,252	**Int'l Ticker:** Int'l Exchange:
2006 Sales: $463,015	2006 Profits: $14,681	Employees: 3,600
2005 Sales: $343,462	2005 Profits: $9,754	Fiscal Year Ends: 1/31
2004 Sales: $272,053	2004 Profits: $2,651	Parent Company:

SALARIES/BENEFITS:

Pension Plan:	ESOP Stock Plan:	Profit Sharing:	Top Exec. Salary: $519,770	Bonus: $645,000
Savings Plan:	Stock Purch. Plan:		Second Exec. Salary: $249,885	Bonus: $250,000

OTHER THOUGHTS:

Apparent Women Officers or Directors:
Hot Spot for Advancement for Women/Minorities:

LOCATIONS: ("Y" = Yes)

West:	Southwest:	Midwest:	Southeast:	Northeast:	International:
Y	Y	Y	Y	Y	Y

LEAR CORP

www.lear.com

Industry Group Code: 336300 **Ranks within this company's industry group:** Sales: 10 Profits: 19

Techology:		Medical/Drugs:		Engineering:		Transportation:		Chemicals/Petrochemicals:		Specialty:	
Computers:		Manufacturer:		Design:		Aerospace:		Oil/Gas Products:		Special Services:	
Software:		Contract Research:		Construction:		Automotive:	Y	Chemicals:		Consulting:	
Communications:	Y	Medical Services:		Eng. Services:		Shipping:		Oil/Chem. Svcs.:		Specialty Mgmt.:	
Electronics:	Y	Labs:		Consulting:				Gases:		Products:	
Alternative Energy:		Bio. Services:						Other:		Other:	

TYPES OF BUSINESS:

Automobile Components
Automotive Interiors
Electrical Systems
Instrument Panels
Seat Systems
Flooring Systems
Entertainment & Wireless Systems
Keyless Entry Systems

BRANDS/DIVISIONS/AFFILIATES:

ProTec Plus Self-Aligning Head Restraint
OccuSense
Bombardier Recreational Products
Can-Am

CONTACTS:

Note: Officers with more than one job title may be intentionally listed here more than once.

Robert E. Rossiter, CEO
Robert E. Rossiter, Pres.
Matthew J. Simoncini, CFO/Sr. VP
Roger A. Jackson, Sr. VP-Human Resources
Daniel A. Ninivaggi, Chief Admin. Officer
Terrence B. Larkin, General Counsel/Corp. Sec./Sr. VP
Daniel A. Ninivaggi, Exec. VP-Strategic & Corp. Planning
Wendy L. Foss, Controller/VP/Chief Compliance Officer
Shari Burgess, VP/Treas.
Louis R. Salvatore, Sr. VP/Pres., Global Seating Systems
Raymond E. Scott, Sr. VP/Pres., Global Electrical Systems
Robert E. Rossiter, Chmn.
James M. Brackenbury, Sr. VP/Pres., European Oper.

Phone: 248-447-1500	**Fax:** 248-447-1722
Toll-Free:	
Address: 21557 Telegraph Rd., Southfield, MI 48033 US	

GROWTH PLANS/SPECIAL FEATURES:

Lear Corp. is one of the world's largest automotive interior systems suppliers, serving every major automotive manufacturer, including General Motors, Ford, DaimlerChrysler, BMW, Fiat, Volkswagen, Renault-Nissan, Toyota and Subaru. The firm currently operates 215 facilities in 35 countries. Its business is conducted through two segments: seating and electronic and electrical. The seating segment consists of the manufacture, assembly and supply of vehicle seating requirements. Products include the ProTec Plus Self-Aligning Head Restraint, which provides longer and earlier support for an occupant's head in a rear-impact collision; and OccuSense, a technology that detects the size and weight of an occupant to control airbag deployment. The electronic and electrical segment comprises four categories: electrical distribution systems; smart junction boxes and body control modules; wireless systems; and specialty electronics. New electronic technology allows the integration of wiring and electronic products within the overall electrical architecture of the vehicle. Lear has the ability to integrate engineering, research, design, development and validation testing of all automotive interior systems with its research and development studio, its six advanced technology centers and its product engineering centers worldwide. In June 2008, the company agreed to acquire a 75% stake in the automotive fabric business of New Trend Group Co., Ltd.

Employees are offered medical, dental and vision insurance; flexible spending accounts; an employee assistance program; life insurance; disability coverage; a stock purchase plan; a 401(k) plan; a pension plan; a financial planning program; and tuition reimbursement.

FINANCIALS:

Sales and profits are in thousands of dollars—add 000 to get the full amount. 2008 Note: Financial information for 2008 was not available for all companies at press time.

2008 Sales: $13,570,500	2008 Profits: $-689,900	**U.S. Stock Ticker: LEA**
2007 Sales: $15,995,000	2007 Profits: $241,500	**Int'l Ticker:** Int'l Exchange:
2006 Sales: $17,838,900	2006 Profits: $-707,500	Employees: 80,000
2005 Sales: $17,089,200	2005 Profits: $-1,381,500	Fiscal Year Ends: 12/31
2004 Sales: $16,960,000	2004 Profits: $422,200	Parent Company:

SALARIES/BENEFITS:

Pension Plan: Y	ESOP Stock Plan:	Profit Sharing:	Top Exec. Salary: $1,119,318	Bonus: $2,310,000
Savings Plan: Y	Stock Purch. Plan: Y		Second Exec. Salary: $925,000	Bonus: $1,295,000

OTHER THOUGHTS:

Apparent Women Officers or Directors: 2
Hot Spot for Advancement for Women/Minorities:

LOCATIONS: ("Y" = Yes)

West:	Southwest:	Midwest:	Southeast:	Northeast:	International:
Y	Y	Y	Y	Y	Y

LEARJET INC

www.bombardier.com

Industry Group Code: 336410 **Ranks within this company's industry group:** Sales: Profits:

Techology:		Medical/Drugs:		Engineering:		Transportation:		Chemicals/Petrochemicals:		Specialty:	
Computers:		Manufacturer:		Design:		Aerospace:	Y	Oil/Gas Products:		Special Services:	
Software:		Contract Research:		Construction:		Automotive:		Chemicals:		Consulting:	
Communications:		Medical Services:		Eng. Services:		Shipping:		Oil/Chem. Svcs.:		Specialty Mgmt.:	
Electronics:		Labs:		Consulting:				Gases:		Products:	
Alternative Energy:		Bio. Services:						Other:		Other:	

TYPES OF BUSINESS:

Aircraft Manufacturer
Business Jet Manufacturing

BRANDS/DIVISIONS/AFFILIATES:

Bombardier Inc
Learjet 45 XR
Learjet 40 XR
Learjet 60 XR
Learjet 85

CONTACTS: *Note: Officers with more than one job title may be intentionally listed here more than once.*

Laurent Beaudoin, CEO-Bombardier, Inc.
Pierre Beaudoin, Pres./COO-Bombardier Aerospace

Phone: 316-946-2000	**Fax:** 316-946-2220
Toll-Free:	
Address: 1 Learjet Way, Wichita, KS 67209 US	

GROWTH PLANS/SPECIAL FEATURES:

Learjet, a subsidiary of Bombardier, is a manufacturer of high-performance business jets and was a pioneer in the industry, producing its first jet in 1964. Based in Wichita, Kansas, the company has built over 2,000 aircraft to date. Models include the Learjet 40, a premium light aircraft; the Learjet 45, a super-light jet; and the Special Edition Learjet 60, a mid-size jet. In addition, the company offers enhanced performance versions of the Learjet 40 and 45: the Learjet 40 XR and the Learjet 45 XR. The 45 holds up to nine people and is the only jet in its weight class to be certified by both the U.S. FAA and the European Aviation Safety Agency. The Learjet 60 holds up to eight passengers, offers stand-up room, a day bed for longer trips, and is equipped with DVD/VCR video systems. The 45 XR offers a higher take-off weight, faster climbs, increased speeds and more cabin leg room than the standard version. The Learjet 40 is derived from the 45, but is less costly to buy and operate. All these Learjet models have a maximum cruising speed of Mach 0.81 (534 mph) and are certified to fly at up to 51,000 feet. The jets usually fly at an altitude higher than most air traffic, avoiding traffic and turbulent weather. In 2007, the 60 XR entered service with Cloud Nine Aviation of Los Angeles, California. The firm's newest plane, the Learjet 85, was released October 2007. It features a larger cabin and increased range, as well as having cruising speeds up to Mach 0.82. The company's planes, classified as light and medium jets, can carry between seven and nine passengers. The jets usually fly at an altitude higher than most air traffic, avoiding traffic and turbulent weather.

FINANCIALS: Sales and profits are in thousands of dollars—add 000 to get the full amount. 2008 Note: Financial information for 2008 was not available for all companies at press time.

2008 Sales: $	2008 Profits: $	**U.S. Stock Ticker: Subsidiary**
2007 Sales: $	2007 Profits: $	**Int'l Ticker:** Int'l Exchange:
2006 Sales: $	2006 Profits: $	Employees: 850
2005 Sales: $	2005 Profits: $	Fiscal Year Ends: 1/31
2004 Sales: $	2004 Profits: $	Parent Company: BOMBARDIER INC

SALARIES/BENEFITS:

Pension Plan:	ESOP Stock Plan:	Profit Sharing:	Top Exec. Salary: $	Bonus: $
Savings Plan:	Stock Purch. Plan:		Second Exec. Salary: $	Bonus: $

OTHER THOUGHTS:

Apparent Women Officers or Directors:
Hot Spot for Advancement for Women/Minorities:

LOCATIONS: ("Y" = Yes)

West:	Southwest:	Midwest:	Southeast:	Northeast:	International:
		Y			

LENOVO GROUP LIMITED

www.lenovo.com

Industry Group Code: 334111 **Ranks within this company's industry group:** Sales: 10 Profits: 5

Techology:		Medical/Drugs:		Engineering:		Transportation:		Chemicals/Petrochemicals:		Specialty:	
Computers:	Y	Manufacturer:		Design:		Aerospace:		Oil/Gas Products:		Special Services:	
Software:		Contract Research:		Construction:		Automotive:		Chemicals:		Consulting:	
Communications:	Y	Medical Services:		Eng. Services:		Shipping:		Oil/Chem. Svcs.:		Specialty Mgmt.:	
Electronics:		Labs:		Consulting:				Gases:		Products:	
Alternative Energy:		Bio. Services:						Other:		Other:	

TYPES OF BUSINESS:

Manufacturing-PCs
Servers
Notebook Computers
Handheld Computers
Peripherals
Cellular Phones

BRANDS/DIVISIONS/AFFILIATES:

Legend Group Limited
Legend Group Holdings
IBM
Thinkpad

CONTACTS: *Note: Officers with more than one job title may be intentionally listed here more than once.*

Yang Yuanqing, CEO
William J. Amelio, Pres.
Wong Wai Ming, CFO/Sr. VP
Deepak Advani, Chief Mktg. Officer/Sr. VP
Kenneth Dipietro, Sr. VP-Human Resources
He Zhiqiang, CTO/Sr. VP
Frances K. O'Sullivan, Sr. VP-Prod. Group
Michael O'Neill, General Counsel/Sr. VP
Rory Read, Sr. VP-Oper.
Cuong Viet Do, Sr. VP/Chief Strategy Officer
Deepak Advani, Sr. VP-e-commerce
Christopher J. Askew, Sr. VP-Svcs.
David D. Miller, Sr. VP/Pres., Asia Pacific
Liu Zhijun, Sr. VP-Mobile Bus. Unit
Yibing Wu, Chief Transformation Officer
Liu Chuanzhi, Chmn.
Mike Van Duijl, Sr. VP/Pres., Lenovo EMEA
Gerry P. Smith, Sr. VP-Global Supply Chain

Phone: 866-458-4465 **Fax:** 877-411-1329
Toll-Free: 866-458-4465
Address: 1009 Think Pl., Morrisville, NC 27560 US

GROWTH PLANS/SPECIAL FEATURES:

Lenovo Group Limited, formerly Legend Group Limited, is one of the largest PC manufacturers in China, with approximately 28% market share. The company markets and manufactures its own line of PCs, notebook computers, printers, servers, handheld computers and cellular phones in China. Lenovo has major research centers in Yamato, Japan; Beijing, Shanghai and Shenzhen, China, and Research Triangle Park, North Carolina, the United States, along with major operational hubs in Beijing, Paris, Research Triangle Park and Singapore. The company has geographical segments located in the Americas; Europe, Middle East and Africa (EMEA); Asia Pacific (excluding Greater China), and Greater China. IBM has a 7% interest in the firm. Lenovo is the third-largest PC manufacturer in the world, after Dell and Hewlett-Packard. Under an agreement with IBM, Lenovo is the preferred supplier of PCs to IBM and will be allowed to use the IBM brand, including the Think brand, through 2010. Lenovo continues to sell and manufacture its own line of PCs, as well as notebook computers, printers, servers, handheld computers and cellular phones in China. Legend Group Holdings, which is controlled by the Chinese government, owns a majority stake in the firm. Lenovo's most recent product releases include laptop and desktop computers with the Intel Core 2 Duo processor.

The firm offers its employees a benefits package that includes retirement savings options, an employee assistance program, flexible spending accounts, an educational assistance program and personal financial planning. Lenovo has a global partnership with the NBA and was the first Chinese company to join the Olympic Partner Program.

FINANCIALS: Sales and profits are in thousands of dollars—add 000 to get the full amount. 2008 Note: Financial information for 2008 was not available for all companies at press time.

2008 Sales: $16,352,000	2008 Profits: $2,450,000	**U.S. Stock Ticker: LNVGY**
2007 Sales: $13,978,000	2007 Profits: $1,887,000	**Int'l Ticker:** Int'l Exchange:
2006 Sales: $13,276,000	2006 Profits: $1,858,000	Employees: 19,000
2005 Sales: $2,906,677	2005 Profits: $144,330	Fiscal Year Ends: 3/31
2004 Sales: $2,971,200	2004 Profits: $135,700	Parent Company:

SALARIES/BENEFITS:

Pension Plan: Y	ESOP Stock Plan:	Profit Sharing:	Top Exec. Salary: $	Bonus: $
Savings Plan:	Stock Purch. Plan:		Second Exec. Salary: $	Bonus: $

OTHER THOUGHTS:

Apparent Women Officers or Directors: 1
Hot Spot for Advancement for Women/Minorities:

LOCATIONS: ("Y" = Yes)

West:	Southwest:	Midwest:	Southeast:	Northeast:	International:
				Y	Y

Note: Financial information, benefits and other data can change quickly and may vary from those stated here.

LEXMARK INTERNATIONAL INC

www.lexmark.com

Industry Group Code: 334119 **Ranks within this company's industry group:** Sales: 7 Profits: 6

Techology:		Medical/Drugs:		Engineering:		Transportation:		Chemicals/Petrochemicals:		Specialty:	
Computers:	Y	Manufacturer:		Design:		Aerospace:		Oil/Gas Products:		Special Services:	
Software:		Contract Research:		Construction:		Automotive:		Chemicals:		Consulting:	
Communications:		Medical Services:		Eng. Services:		Shipping:		Oil/Chem. Svcs.:		Specialty Mgmt.:	
Electronics:		Labs:		Consulting:				Gases:		Products:	
Alternative Energy:		Bio. Services:						Other:		Other:	

TYPES OF BUSINESS:

Computer Accessories-Printers
Laser & Inkjet Printers
Printer Consumables
Typewriters & Supplies
Connectivity Products
Document Software
Managed Print Services Outsourcing

BRANDS/DIVISIONS/AFFILIATES:

IBM

CONTACTS: *Note: Officers with more than one job title may be intentionally listed here more than once.*

Paul J. Curlander, CEO
John W. Gamble Jr., CFO/Exec. VP
Jeri Isbell, VP-Human Resources
Robert J. Patton, General Counsel/Sec./VP
Gary D. Stromquist, Corp. Controller/VP
Paul A. Rooke, Exec. VP/Pres., Consumer Printer Div.
Marty Canning, VP/Pres., Printing Solutions & Svcs. Div.
Paul J. Curlander, Chmn.
Ronaldo Foresti, VP-Asia Pacific & Latin America

Phone: 859-232-2000	**Fax:** 859-232-2403
Toll-Free: 800-539-6275	
Address: 740 W. New Circle Rd., Lexington, KY 40550 US	

GROWTH PLANS/SPECIAL FEATURES:

Lexmark International, Inc., a former subsidiary of International Business Machines Corp. (IBM), is a global developer, manufacturer and supplier of laser and inkjet printers and associated consumable supplies for the office and home markets. Its products are sold in over 150 countries across the Americas, Europe, the Middle East, Africa, Asia, the Pacific Rim and the Caribbean. The firm has six manufacturing sites and approximately 70 sales offices. The company's research and development activity for the past several years has focused on laser and inkjet printers, associated supplies and network connectivity products. In addition to its laser and inkjet printers, Lexmark sells dot matrix printers for printing single and multi-part forms by business users, as well as the consumable supplies used by its large installed base of printers. Because consumable supplies must be replaced on average one to three times a year, depending on type of printer and usage, demand for laser and inkjet print cartridges is increasing at a higher rate than their associated printer shipments. Besides its core printer business, the firm manufactures a broad line of other office imaging products, including supplies for IBM-branded printers; after-market supplies for original equipment manufacturer products; and typewriters and typewriter supplies that are sold under the IBM trademark. International sales, including exports from the U.S., accounted for approximately 57% of the firm's revenue, which was $5 billion at the end of fiscal 2007. Lexmark's offerings include outsourced "managed print services," a service where Lexmark takes over ownership and/or operation of a client's printers, copiers and fax machines with the goal of savings substantial operating costs for the client.

Employees are offered a 401(k) plan; a stock purchase plan; and health benefits.

FINANCIALS: **Sales and profits are in thousands of dollars—add 000 to get the full amount. 2008 Note: Financial information for 2008 was not available for all companies at press time.**

2008 Sales: $4,528,400	2008 Profits: $240,200	**U.S. Stock Ticker: LXK**
2007 Sales: $4,973,900	2007 Profits: $300,800	**Int'l Ticker:** Int'l Exchange:
2006 Sales: $5,108,100	2006 Profits: $338,400	Employees: 14,000
2005 Sales: $5,221,500	2005 Profits: $356,300	Fiscal Year Ends: 12/31
2004 Sales: $5,313,800	2004 Profits: $568,700	Parent Company:

SALARIES/BENEFITS:

Pension Plan:	ESOP Stock Plan:	Profit Sharing:	Top Exec. Salary: $1,003,846	Bonus: $590,625
Savings Plan: Y	Stock Purch. Plan: Y		Second Exec. Salary: $565,269	Bonus: $430,071

OTHER THOUGHTS:

Apparent Women Officers or Directors: 3
Hot Spot for Advancement for Women/Minorities: Y

LOCATIONS: ("Y" = Yes)

West:	Southwest:	Midwest:	Southeast:	Northeast:	International:
Y		Y			Y

LG DISPLAY CO LTD

www.lgphilips-lcd.com

Industry Group Code: 334119 **Ranks within this company's industry group:** Sales: 4 Profits: 3

Techology:		Medical/Drugs:		Engineering:		Transportation:		Chemicals/Petrochemicals:		Specialty:	
Computers:		Manufacturer:		Design:		Aerospace:		Oil/Gas Products:		Special Services:	
Software:		Contract Research:		Construction:		Automotive:		Chemicals:		Consulting:	
Communications:		Medical Services:		Eng. Services:		Shipping:		Oil/Chem. Svcs.:		Specialty Mgmt.:	
Electronics:	Y	Labs:		Consulting:				Gases:		Products:	
Alternative Energy:		Bio. Services:						Other:		Other:	

TYPES OF BUSINESS:

LCD Panel Manufacturing

BRANDS/DIVISIONS/AFFILIATES:

Philips Group
LG Electronics
Royal Philips Electronics
LG Display America, Inc.

CONTACTS:

Note: Officers with more than one job title may be intentionally listed here more than once.

Young Soo Kwon, CEO/Co-Pres.
Ron Wirahadiraksa, Co-Pres.
Ron Wirahadiraksa, CFO
Bock Kwon, Exec. VP-Overseas Mktg. Center
In-Jae Chung, CTO/Exec. VP
Sang Beom Han, Exec. VP-IT Bus.
Jong Sik Kim, Chief Prod. Officer/Exec. VP
Sang Deog Yeo, Exec. VP-TV Bus. Unit
Jae Geol Ju, Exec. VP-Japan Svc. Center
Rudy Provoost, Chmn.

Phone: 82-2-3777-0790 **Fax:**

Toll-Free:

Address: LG Twin Towers, W Tower, 17th Fl., 20 Yeouido-dong, Seoul, 150-721 Korea

GROWTH PLANS/SPECIAL FEATURES:

LG Display Co., Ltd., formerly LG Philips LCD, Inc., operates in the digital display business and is headquartered in Seoul, South Korea. The Korean company LG and the Dutch company Royal Philips combined business operations in 1999; LG Electronics owns 37.9% while Royal Philips Electronics owns 13.2% of the company. LG Display develops and manufactures TFT-LCD panels for televisions, monitors, notebook PCs and emerging mobile applications such as WebPad, e-Book, car navigation, fingerprint recognition systems and online stock trading. LG Display is a member of the Philips Group, which spans a wide range of industries including consumer products, lighting, medical systems and semiconductors. The firm's international sales network is directed through locations in Germany, Japan, Taiwan, Hong Kong and China as well as LG Display America, Inc., with representatives and distributors in California. Early in 2007, the company began full-scale mass production at its back-end LCD module plant in Wroclaw, Poland, the firm's eighth fabrication facility in Europe. Additionally, LG Display plans to maximize its capacity at its other existing production facilities to meet continued, rising demand and also plans to build a new generation 8 production facility, with mass production slated for 2009. In late 2007, the firm introduced its 52-inch multi-touch display, with a 90 Hz touch response time, 1920 x 1080 Full HD resolution and a light transmission rate of 95% to 100%. To date it's the world's largest multi-touch display, using infrared image sensors that recognize two separate touch points as well as gestures. In April 2008, the firm sold a minority stake in its Guangzhou plant to Skyworth Digital Holdings Limited, a Chinese television manufacturer. In September 2008, the firm announced a joint venture with AmTRAN, a Taiwanese OEM/ODM LCD television company, to create new LCD module and television technologies.

FINANCIALS:

Sales and profits are in thousands of dollars—add 000 to get the full amount. 2008 Note: Financial information for 2008 was not available for all companies at press time.

2008 Sales: $12,410,800	2008 Profits: $829,320	**U.S. Stock Ticker: LPL**
2007 Sales: $10,952,000	2007 Profits: $1,025,630	**Int'l Ticker: 034220** Int'l Exchange: Seoul-KRX
2006 Sales: $11,423,871	2006 Profits: $-744,923	Employees: 20,903
2005 Sales: $10,577,626	2005 Profits: $568,632	Fiscal Year Ends: 12/31
2004 Sales: $8,742,830	2004 Profits: $1,788,570	Parent Company:

SALARIES/BENEFITS:

Pension Plan: Y	ESOP Stock Plan: Y	Profit Sharing:	Top Exec. Salary: $	Bonus: $
Savings Plan:	Stock Purch. Plan:		Second Exec. Salary: $	Bonus: $

OTHER THOUGHTS:

Apparent Women Officers or Directors:
Hot Spot for Advancement for Women/Minorities:

LOCATIONS: ("Y" = Yes)

West:	Southwest:	Midwest:	Southeast:	Northeast:	International:
Y					Y

LG ELECTRONICS INC

www.lge.com

Industry Group Code: 334220 **Ranks within this company's industry group:** Sales: 2 Profits: 2

Techology:		Medical/Drugs:		Engineering:		Transportation:		Chemicals/Petrochemicals:		Specialty:	
Computers:		Manufacturer:		Design:		Aerospace:		Oil/Gas Products:		Special Services:	
Software:		Contract Research:		Construction:		Automotive:		Chemicals:		Consulting:	
Communications:		Medical Services:		Eng. Services:		Shipping:		Oil/Chem. Svcs.:		Specialty Mgmt.:	
Electronics:	Y	Labs:		Consulting:				Gases:		Products:	
Alternative Energy:		Bio. Services:						Other:		Other:	

TYPES OF BUSINESS:

Manufacturing-Electronics
Cellular Handsets
Telecommunications Equipment
Computer Products
Home Appliances & Electronics
Security Systems
Displays
Audio Systems

BRANDS/DIVISIONS/AFFILIATES:

LG Corporation
LG-Shaker Air-Conditioning Co.
H.G. Ibrahim Shaker Co.

CONTACTS: *Note: Officers with more than one job title may be intentionally listed here more than once.*

Yong Nam, CEO/Vice Chmn.
Yu-Sig Kang, COO/Vice Chmn.
Hee-Gook Lee, Pres.
James Jeong, CFO
Hee-Gook Lee, CTO
B.B. Hwang, CEO-LG Electronics Digital Media Co.
Simon Kang, CEO-LG Electronics Digital Display Co.
Skott Ahn, CEO-LG Electronics Mobile Comm. Co.
Michael Ahn, CEO-LG Electronics North America
Bon Moo Koo, Chmn.
James Kim, Pres./CEO-LG Electronics, Europe

Phone: 82-2-3777-3427 **Fax:** 82-2-3777-3428
Toll-Free:
Address: LG Twin Towers, 20 Yeouido-dong, Yeoungdeungpo-gu, Seoul, 150-721 Korea

GROWTH PLANS/SPECIAL FEATURES:

LG Electronics, Inc., owned by holding company LG Corporation, is a Korean manufacturer of telecommunications equipment, home appliances, televisions, audio equipment, security systems and computer products. The company has four lines of business: mobile communications, digital appliances, digital display and digital media. LG's mobile communications division produces UMTS (WCDMA), CDMA and GSM mobile handsets. The mobile communications division also manufactures wireline telephones, wireless telephone networking equipment, VoIP equipment and telecommunications mainframes. LG's digital appliance division manufactures home appliances for home ubiquitous networking including refrigerators, air conditioners, dish washers, washers and dryers, ovens and vacuum cleaners. In addition, the company is a leading global supplier of home appliance components such as washing machine motors. The digital display division includes plasma screen, liquid crystal display (LCD), high definition, flat panel and projection TVs. Finally, LG's digital media division manufactures VCRs, notebook computers, optical storage devices, monitors, video tape and DVDs. LG also manufactures security equipment, including cameras and iris access systems, and audio equipment, such as home and car stereos. The firm has offices throughout Asia, Europe, Africa, the Middle East, Latin America and North America. With 110 operating units worldwide, LG is a truly global firm. R&D is a focus here, with dozens of research centers worldwide, including the LG Electronics Institute of Technology in Seoul, Korea. The firm has partnered with Prada, GE, Siemens, Toyota, Google, Qualcomm, Hitachi, Nortel, Microsoft, Sun Microsystems, Dolby, and a variety of other companies. Recently, the company began construction of an air-conditioning production facility in Saudi Arabia, through its joint venture subsidiary LG-Shaker Air-Conditioning Company, partnered with H.G. Ibrahim Shaker Company.

The company offers its employees extensive training resources through three learning centers (two in South Korea and one in China), as well as the Learning Net, an online education system available to all employees.

FINANCIALS: **Sales and profits are in thousands of dollars—add 000 to get the full amount. 2008 Note: Financial information for 2008 was not available for all companies at press time.**

2008 Sales: $36,220,000	2008 Profits: $1,560,000	**U.S. Stock Ticker:**
2007 Sales: $25,298,000	2007 Profits: $1,315,000	**Int'l Ticker: 066570** Int'l Exchange: Seoul-KRX
2006 Sales: $24,263,000	2006 Profits: $223,000	Employees: 82,000
2005 Sales: $23,217,000	2005 Profits: $686,000	Fiscal Year Ends: 12/31
2004 Sales: $21,513,000	2004 Profits: $1,349,000	Parent Company:

SALARIES/BENEFITS:

Pension Plan:	ESOP Stock Plan:	Profit Sharing:	Top Exec. Salary: $	Bonus: $
Savings Plan:	Stock Purch. Plan:		Second Exec. Salary: $	Bonus: $

OTHER THOUGHTS:

Apparent Women Officers or Directors:
Hot Spot for Advancement for Women/Minorities:

LOCATIONS: ("Y" = Yes)

West:	Southwest:	Midwest:	Southeast:	Northeast:	International:
					Y

Note: Financial information, benefits and other data can change quickly and may vary from those stated here.

LINDE GROUP

www.linde.de

Industry Group Code: 333000 **Ranks within this company's industry group:** Sales: 4 Profits: 5

Techology:		Medical/Drugs:		Engineering:		Transportation:		Chemicals/Petrochemicals:		Specialty:	
Computers:		Manufacturer:		Design:	Y	Aerospace:		Oil/Gas Products:	Y	Special Services:	Y
Software:		Contract Research:		Construction:	Y	Automotive:		Chemicals:		Consulting:	
Communications:		Medical Services:		Eng. Services:	Y	Shipping:		Oil/Chem. Svcs.:		Specialty Mgmt.:	
Electronics:		Labs:		Consulting:				Gases:	Y	Products:	Y
Alternative Energy:		Bio. Services:						Other:		Other:	

TYPES OF BUSINESS:

Industrial & Medical Gases
Engineering & Construction-Gas & Chemical Plants
Plant Components Manufacturing
Microelectronics Manufacturing Equipment
Olefin Plants
Logistics & Supply Chain Solutions
Welding Products

BRANDS/DIVISIONS/AFFILIATES:

BOC Group PLC (The)
Linde Gas
Linde Engineering
Linde Gist
African Oxygen Ltd
Saudi Industrial Gas Co. Ltd
Elgas

CONTACTS: *Note: Officers with more than one job title may be intentionally listed here more than once.*

Wolfgang Reitzle, CEO
Wolfgang Reitzle, Pres.
Georg Denoke, CFO
J. Kent Masters, Dir.-Americas, South Pacific & Africa
Aldo Belloni, Head-Eng. Div. & Electronics Bus.
J. Kent Masters, Head-Healthcare & Packaged Gases
Manfred Schneider, Chmn.
Aldo Belloni, Dir.-Europe, Middle East, China, South & East Asia

Phone: 49-89-35757-01 **Fax:** 49-89-35757-1075
Toll-Free:
Address: Leopoldstrasse 252, Munich, 80807 Germany

GROWTH PLANS/SPECIAL FEATURES:

The Linde Group is a leading industrial gas and engineering company operating in approximately 100 countries worldwide. The company is a top global builder of hydrogen production facilities, equips virtually all existing liquid hydrogen filling stations and operates two hydrogen liquefaction plants in Germany. Linde is divided into two primary segments: Linde Gas and Linde Engineering. Linde Gas supplies industrial and medical gases, particularly targeting on-site and health care businesses. Linde Gas products include oxygen, nitrogen, argon, acetylene, carbon dioxide, hydrogen, carbon monoxide, inert gases, medical gases, purified gases, and testing gases. Linde Engineering constructs various types of processing facilities, including hydrogen, oxygen, olefin, chemical, petrochemical, synthesis gas, natural gas, air separation, thermal-oxidation exhaust air-cleaning, refinery furnaces and cryogenic plants. Linde Engineering also manufactures plant components, liquefied gas tanks, vacuum-brazed heat exchangers, coil-wound heat exchangers and reactors, and catalysts. Through subsidiary BOC Edwards, the company provides compressed and bulk gases, chemicals and equipment. Through Gist, the company offers logistic services and supply chain solutions to a range of commercial and industrial sectors, including grocery, retail, electronics and gas. Linde's South Africa-based African Oxygen Ltd. (Afrox) provides gases for the African continent as well as manufacturing welding equipment. Early in 2008, subsidiary LifeGas acquired the medical business of Sky Oxygen, Inc. In May 2008, the firm acquired a 51% share of Saudi Industrial Gas Co. Ltd. In October 2008, Linde acquired the remaining 50% of Australian liquefied petroleum gas (LPG) company Elgas for approximately $160 million. In December 2008, the company announced that it would partner with Samsung Engineering to build a $1.3 billion turnkey ethylene plant at Dahej, India, on behalf of a subsidiary of the Indian state-owned Oil and Natural Gas Corporation Ltd.

FINANCIALS: **Sales and profits are in thousands of dollars—add 000 to get the full amount. 2008 Note: Financial information for 2008 was not available for all companies at press time.**

2008 Sales: $17,070,700 | 2008 Profits: $1,046,110
2007 Sales: $16,589,500 | 2007 Profits: $1,342,690
2006 Sales: $12,737,400 | 2006 Profits: $2,885,700
2005 Sales: $9,237,900 | 2005 Profits: $807,000
2004 Sales: $11,136,600 | 2004 Profits: $477,800

U.S. Stock Ticker: LNAGF
Int'l Ticker: LIN Int'l Exchange: Frankfurt-Euronext
Employees: 52,000
Fiscal Year Ends: 12/31
Parent Company:

SALARIES/BENEFITS:

Pension Plan: ESOP Stock Plan: Profit Sharing: Top Exec. Salary: $ Bonus: $
Savings Plan: Stock Purch. Plan: Second Exec. Salary: $ Bonus: $

OTHER THOUGHTS:

Apparent Women Officers or Directors:
Hot Spot for Advancement for Women/Minorities:

LOCATIONS: ("Y" = Yes)

West:	Southwest:	Midwest:	Southeast:	Northeast:	International:
	Y	Y	Y	Y	Y

LITE-ON TECHNOLOGY CORP

www.liteon.com

Industry Group Code: 334119 **Ranks within this company's industry group:** Sales: Profits:

Techology:		Medical/Drugs:		Engineering:		Transportation:		Chemicals/Petrochemicals:		Specialty:	
Computers:	Y	Manufacturer:		Design:		Aerospace:		Oil/Gas Products:		Special Services:	
Software:		Contract Research:		Construction:		Automotive:		Chemicals:		Consulting:	
Communications:		Medical Services:		Eng. Services:		Shipping:		Oil/Chem. Svcs.:		Specialty Mgmt.:	
Electronics:	Y	Labs:		Consulting:				Gases:		Products:	
Alternative Energy:		Bio. Services:						Other:		Other:	

TYPES OF BUSINESS:

Electronics & Computer Components
Computer Hardware
Computer Accessories
Networking Products
LED Lamps
Personal Digital Assistants
Portable Navigation Devices

BRANDS/DIVISIONS/AFFILIATES:

Lite-On Corp.
Silitech Technology Corporation
Actron Technology
Li Shin International Enterprise Corporation
Diodes, Inc.
Logah Technology, Inc.
DragonJet Corporation
Maxi Switch, Inc.

CONTACTS: *Note: Officers with more than one job title may be intentionally listed here more than once.*

K. C. Terng, CEO
Paul Lo, CTO
Danny Liao, Chief Strategy Officer/CEO-Lite-On IT
Julia Wang, Dir.-Public Rel.
Julia Wang, Dir.-Investor Rel.
Brownson Chu, VP-Finance
David Lin, CEO-Lite-On Group/Vice Chmn.-Lite-On Tech.
Warren Chen, Deputy CEO-Lite-On Group/CEO-Core Investment
Raymond Soong, Chmn.-Lite-On Group
Paul Lo, CEO-Lite-On Automotive Int'l

Phone: 886-2-8798-2888	**Fax:** 886-2-8798-2866
Toll-Free:	
Address: 22F, 392 Ruey Kuang Rd., Neihu, Taipei, 114 Taiwan	

GROWTH PLANS/SPECIAL FEATURES:

Lite-On Technology Corp. is a world-leading manufacturer of electronics products. Its products and services are generally divided into three categories: Components; Module; and System. The Components category is subdivided into power supply, including power switches, AC adapters, various power supplies and solar energy products; and opto electronics, which mainly produces various sized LED lamps and some infrared lights. The Module category has three subdivisions: phone camera modules; network products, primarily internal and external modems; and desktop computer cases. Lastly, the System category produces monitors; various portable entertaining systems (PES), including Bluetooth wireless speakers and FM transmitters and receivers; inkjet and laser printers; input devices, including keyboards, mice and remote controls; network switches; wireless access points and Ethernet cards; personal digital assistants (PDAs); and portable navigation devices (PNDs). The firm has manufacturing facilities in most Southeast Asian countries, as well as Western Europe, Canada and the U.S. The company is the largest subsidiary of electronics company Lite-On Corp. The other 11 subsidiaries and affiliates that comprise the Lite-On Group are Silitech Technology Corporation; Actron Technology; Li Shin International Enterprise Corporation; Diodes, Inc.; Logah Technology, Inc.; DragonJet Corporation; Maxi Switch, Inc.; Lite-On Automotive Corp.; Lite-On Semiconductor Corp.; Lite-On IT Corp.; and Lite-On Japan. In April 2008, Wistron Corporation acquired the firm's digital display business for $279.7 million. The digital display business had accounted for 45% of 2007 sales, followed by power supply, 20%; imaging, which includes phone camera modules and PDAs, 10%; opto electronics, 6%; and others, 19%.

Employees of Lite-On offers receive benefits including life, medical and business travel insurance; some on-site fitness and recreational facilities; subsidized domestic and overseas travel plans; some staff cafeterias and stores; emergency assistance; subsidies for marriage, hospitalization, funerals and childbirth; holiday and birthday gift vouchers; and scholarships for employees and their children.

FINANCIALS: **Sales and profits are in thousands of dollars—add 000 to get the full amount. 2008 Note: Financial information for 2008 was not available for all companies at press time.**

2008 Sales: $	2008 Profits: $	**U.S. Stock Ticker:**
2007 Sales: $	2007 Profits: $	**Int'l Ticker: 2301** Int'l Exchange: Taipei-TPE
2006 Sales: $	2006 Profits: $	Employees: 3,841
2005 Sales: $6,800,000	2005 Profits: $240,000	Fiscal Year Ends: 12/31
2004 Sales: $4,872,300	2004 Profits: $236,300	Parent Company:

SALARIES/BENEFITS:

Pension Plan: Y	ESOP Stock Plan:	Profit Sharing: Y	Top Exec. Salary: $	Bonus: $
Savings Plan:	Stock Purch. Plan:		Second Exec. Salary: $	Bonus: $

OTHER THOUGHTS:

Apparent Women Officers or Directors: 1
Hot Spot for Advancement for Women/Minorities:

LOCATIONS: ("Y" = Yes)

West:	Southwest:	Midwest:	Southeast:	Northeast:	International:
Y	Y		Y		Y

Note: Financial information, benefits and other data can change quickly and may vary from those stated here.

LOCKHEED MARTIN CORP

www.lockheedmartin.com

Industry Group Code: 336410 **Ranks within this company's industry group:** Sales: 4 Profits: 3

Techology:		Medical/Drugs:		Engineering:		Transportation:		Chemicals/Petrochemicals:		Specialty:	
Computers:	Y	Manufacturer:		Design:	Y	Aerospace:	Y	Oil/Gas Products:		Special Services:	Y
Software:	Y	Contract Research:		Construction:	Y	Automotive:		Chemicals:		Consulting:	
Communications:	Y	Medical Services:		Eng. Services:	Y	Shipping:		Oil/Chem. Svcs.:		Specialty Mgmt.:	
Electronics:	Y	Labs:		Consulting:				Gases:		Products:	Y
Alternative Energy:		Bio. Services:						Other:		Other:	

TYPES OF BUSINESS:

Aerospace & Defense Technology
Military Aircraft
Defense Electronics
Systems Integration & Technology Services
Communications Satellites & Launch Services
Undersea, Shipboard, Land & Airborne Systems & Subsystems

BRANDS/DIVISIONS/AFFILIATES:

Orion
Skunk Works
Management Systens Designers, Inc.
RLM Systems, Ltd.
3Dsolve, Inc.
Aculight Corporation

CONTACTS: *Note: Officers with more than one job title may be intentionally listed here more than once.*

Robert J. Stevens, CEO
Robert J. Stevens, Pres.
Bruce L. Tanner, CFO/Exec. VP
Linda Gooden, Exec. VP-Info. Systems & Global Svcs.
Ralph D. Heath, Exec. VP-Aeronautics
Christopher E. Kubasik, Exec. VP-Electronic Systems
Joanne M. Maguire, Exec. VP-Space Systems
Robert J. Stevens, Chmn.

Phone: 301-897-6000	**Fax:** 301-897-6704
Toll-Free:	
Address: 6801 Rockledge Dr., Bethesda, MD 20817 US	

GROWTH PLANS/SPECIAL FEATURES:

Lockheed Martin Corp. specializes in developing and servicing advanced technological systems. It serves domestic and international customers with products and services that have defense, civil and commercial applications, with principal customers being agencies of the U.S. government. The company operates in four segments: aeronautics; electronic systems; information systems & global services (IS&GS); and space systems. The aeronautics segment is engaged in the design, research and development, systems integration, production, sustainment, support and upgrade of advanced military aircraft, air vehicles and related technologies. Major products and programs include design, development, production and sustainment of the F-35 stealth multi-role international coalition fighter; the F-16 international multi-role fighter and U-2 high-altitude reconnaissance aircraft. It also produces major components for Japan's F-2 fighter and is a co-developer of the T-50 advanced jet trainer. The Skunk Works advanced development organization provides system solutions using rapid prototyping and advanced technologies. The electronic systems segment designs, researches, develops, integrates, produces and sustains systems and subsystems for undersea, shipboard, land and airborne applications. Major products include tactical missiles and weapon fire control systems; ground combat vehicle integrations; and surveillance and reconnaissance systems. The IS&GS segment provides federal services, IT solutions and technology expertise across a broad spectrum of applications and customers. It provides full life cycle support and highly specialized talent in the areas of software and systems engineering, including capabilities in space, air and ground systems, and also provides logistics, mission operations support, peacekeeping and nation-building services for a wide variety of U.S. defense and civil government agencies in the U.S. and abroad. The space systems segment designs, researches, develops, engineers and produces satellites, strategic and defensive missile systems and space transportation systems. In September 2008, the company acquired Aculight Corporation, a provider of laser-based solutions.

Employees are offered healthcare coverage; a retirement plan; and a 401(k) plan.

FINANCIALS: **Sales and profits are in thousands of dollars—add 000 to get the full amount. 2008 Note: Financial information for 2008 was not available for all companies at press time.**

2008 Sales: $42,731,000	2008 Profits: $3,217,000	**U.S. Stock Ticker: LMT**
2007 Sales: $41,862,000	2007 Profits: $3,033,000	**Int'l Ticker:** Int'l Exchange:
2006 Sales: $39,620,000	2006 Profits: $2,529,000	Employees: 146,000
2005 Sales: $37,213,000	2005 Profits: $1,825,000	Fiscal Year Ends: 12/31
2004 Sales: $35,526,000	2004 Profits: $1,266,000	Parent Company:

SALARIES/BENEFITS:

Pension Plan: Y	ESOP Stock Plan:	Profit Sharing:	Top Exec. Salary: $1,627,500	Bonus: $12,400,000
Savings Plan: Y	Stock Purch. Plan:		Second Exec. Salary: $891,346	Bonus: $2,874,500

OTHER THOUGHTS:

Apparent Women Officers or Directors: 4
Hot Spot for Advancement for Women/Minorities: Y

LOCATIONS: ("Y" = Yes)

West:	Southwest:	Midwest:	Southeast:	Northeast:	International:
Y	Y	Y	Y	Y	Y

LOGICA PLC

www.logica.com

Industry Group Code: 541512 **Ranks within this company's industry group:** Sales: 10 Profits: 12

Techology:		**Medical/Drugs:**		**Engineering:**		**Transportation:**		**Chemicals/Petrochemicals:**		**Specialty:**	
Computers:		Manufacturer:		Design:		Aerospace:		Oil/Gas Products:		Special Services:	Y
Software:		Contract Research:		Construction:		Automotive:		Chemicals:		Consulting:	Y
Communications:		Medical Services:		Eng. Services:		Shipping:		Oil/Chem. Svcs.:		Specialty Mgmt.:	
Electronics:		Labs:		Consulting:				Gases:		Products:	
Alternative Energy:		Bio. Services:						Other:		Other:	

TYPES OF BUSINESS:

IT Consulting
Systems Integration
Outsourced Services
Management Consulting

BRANDS/DIVISIONS/AFFILIATES:

WM Data
Medici Data Oy
Edinfor

CONTACTS:

Note: Officers with more than one job title may be intentionally listed here more than once.

Andy Green, CEO
Jim McKenna, COO
Seamus Keating, CFO
Laurent Allard, CIO
Serge Dubrana, CEO-Tech.
Craig Boundy, CEO-Global Oper.
Crister Stjernfelt, Exec. VP-Nordic Region
Patrick Guimbal, CEO-France
Joe Hemming, CEO-U.K.
Jean-Marc Lazzari, CEO-Outsourcing Svcs.
David Tyler, Chmn.
Joao Baptista, CEO-Int'l

Phone: 44-20-7637-9111	**Fax:** 44-20-7468-7006
Toll-Free:	
Address: 250 Brook Dr., Green Park, Reading, RG2 6UA UK	

GROWTH PLANS/SPECIAL FEATURES:

Logica plc, formerly LogicaCMG plc, provides management and IT consulting services, systems development and integration, and outsourced management of specific business processes. The company also provides strategic consulting, project management and support services. The firm offers messaging, mobile Internet, mobile payment, device management, billing, customer care, operational support systems, training and support services and outsourcing capabilities to the IT segments of major companies internationally. Logica structures its business around five core vertical markets: energy and utilities; financial services; telecom and media; industry, distribution and transport; and the public sector. Logica maintains a partnership with SAP in which it delivers SAP's enterprise resource planning services to its customers. Clients include BMW, BT Group, Deutsche Bank, Time Warner, AT&T, Shell, Ford and France Telecom, as well as the U.K. National Codification Bureau and the banking systems of Hawaii, Ireland, Latvia, Montreal, Queensland, France, Slovenia, Berlin and Scotland, among many others. In November 2007, WM Data, a Logica company, purchased Medici Data Oy, which will be integrated into WM's health care business unit. Before the acquisition, WM held a 36% interest in Medici Data. The company recently introduced a new facility in Chennai and a new corporate payment service. In January 2008, the company created a new outsourcing services division to address unmet needs across Europe. In March 2008, the company acquired a 40% minority interest in Edinfor, an international outsourcing company.

The company offers its employees medical and dental insurance; an employee stock purchase plan; a 401(k) plan; flexible spending accounts; short- and long-term disability insurance; life and AD&D insurance; and an employee assistance program.

FINANCIALS:

Sales and profits are in thousands of dollars—add 000 to get the full amount. 2008 Note: Financial information for 2008 was not available for all companies at press time.

2008 Sales: $5,322,940	2008 Profits: $57,710	**U.S. Stock Ticker:**
2007 Sales: $4,559,210	2007 Profits: $249,380	**Int'l Ticker: LOG** Int'l Exchange: London-LSE
2006 Sales: $4,819,350	2006 Profits: $177,390	Employees: 40,000
2005 Sales: $2,503,090	2005 Profits: $93,890	Fiscal Year Ends: 12/31
2004 Sales: $3,216,400	2004 Profits: $44,818	Parent Company:

SALARIES/BENEFITS:

Pension Plan:	ESOP Stock Plan:	Profit Sharing:	Top Exec. Salary: $	Bonus: $
Savings Plan: Y	Stock Purch. Plan: Y		Second Exec. Salary: $	Bonus: $

OTHER THOUGHTS:

Apparent Women Officers or Directors: 2
Hot Spot for Advancement for Women/Minorities: Y

LOCATIONS: ("Y" = Yes)

West:	Southwest:	Midwest:	Southeast:	Northeast:	International:
Y	Y	Y	Y	Y	Y

LOGITECH INTERNATIONAL SA

www.logitech.com

Industry Group Code: 334119 **Ranks within this company's industry group:** Sales: 10 Profits: 7

Techology:		Medical/Drugs:		Engineering:		Transportation:		Chemicals/Petrochemicals:		Specialty:	
Computers:	Y	Manufacturer:		Design:		Aerospace:		Oil/Gas Products:		Special Services:	
Software:		Contract Research:		Construction:		Automotive:		Chemicals:		Consulting:	
Communications:		Medical Services:		Eng. Services:		Shipping:		Oil/Chem. Svcs.:		Specialty Mgmt.:	
Electronics:	Y	Labs:		Consulting:				Gases:		Products:	
Alternative Energy:		Bio. Services:						Other:		Other:	

TYPES OF BUSINESS:

Computer Accessories
Keyboards & Mice
Imaging Devices
Control Devices
Interface Devices
Cordless Technology

BRANDS/DIVISIONS/AFFILIATES:

3Dconnexion
Slim Devices, Inc.
WiLife, Inc.
Ultimate Ears
SightSpeed, Inc.
Logitech QuickCam

CONTACTS: *Note: Officers with more than one job title may be intentionally listed here more than once.*

Gerald P. Quindlen, CEO
Gerald P. Quindlen, Pres.
Mark J. Hawkins, CFO
David Henry, Chief Mktg. Officer
Mark J. Hawkins, Sr. VP-IT
Junien Labrousse, Exec. VP-Prod.
L. Joseph Sullivan, Sr. VP-Worldwide Oper.
Mark J. Hawkins, Sr. VP-Finance
David Henry, Sr. VP-Customer Experiences
Guerrino de Luca, Chmn.

Phone: 41-21-863-51-11 **Fax:** 41-21-863-53-11
Toll-Free:
Address: Moulin du Choc, Romanel-sur-Morges, CH-1122 Switzerland

GROWTH PLANS/SPECIAL FEATURES:

Logitech International S.A. is an industry leader in personal interface products for personal computers and other digital platforms. It operates in a single segment, encompassing the design, development, production, marketing and support of personal peripheral products. The firm's product family includes wired and wireless mice, trackballs and keyboards; speakers and headphones for PCs and iPods; gaming controllers and accessories; cordless and corded headsets for PCs and mobile phones; 3D control devices; universal remotes; and webcams. Logitech's game controls and accessories include joysticks, steering wheels, gamepads, mice, keyboards and headsets. It offers products for the PlayStation 2, PlayStation 3, PSP, Xbox 360, PC and Wii. Subsidiary 3Dconnexion offers 3D controllers such as the SpaceNavigator, for use with Google Earth and other 3D applications. Subsidiary Slim Devices, Inc. specializes in network-based audio systems for digital music. The firm's webcams feature one-button video instant messaging and software that enables access to public and private webcams directly from mobile phones. Logitech is the official webcam partner of YouTube Video Toolbox and its newest Logitech QuickCam software, version 11.5, features one-touch YouTube video uploading. In general, pointing devices, including mice, generated 27.9% of 2008 net sales; audio equipment, 20.2%; keyboards, 19.3%; video equipment, 10.1%; gaming products, 6.2%; remotes, 5.2%; and original equipment manufacturer (OEM) supplies, 12.8%. Jointly based in the U.S. and Switzerland, Logitech has manufacturing facilities in Asia, predominantly China, and offices in North America, Europe and Asia-Pacific. In November 2007, Logitech acquired PC-based video surveillance equipment provider WiLife, Inc. for $24 million. In August 2008, Logitech acquired Ultimate Ears for $34.3 million. Ultimate Ears manufactures various earphones, including custom-fit in-ear monitors for music professionals. In November 2008, the company acquired SightSpeed, Inc., a provider of Internet-based video communications services, such as video calling, for $30 million.

FINANCIALS: **Sales and profits are in thousands of dollars—add 000 to get the full amount. 2008 Note: Financial information for 2008 was not available for all companies at press time.**

2008 Sales: $2,370,496	2008 Profits: $231,026	**U.S. Stock Ticker: LOGI**
2007 Sales: $2,066,569	2007 Profits: $229,848	**Int'l Ticker: LOGN** Int'l Exchange: Zurich-SWX
2006 Sales: $1,796,715	2006 Profits: $181,105	Employees: 9,393
2005 Sales: $1,482,600	2005 Profits: $149,300	Fiscal Year Ends: 3/31
2004 Sales: $1,268,470	2004 Profits: $132,153	Parent Company:

SALARIES/BENEFITS:

Pension Plan:	ESOP Stock Plan:	Profit Sharing:	Top Exec. Salary: $719,231	Bonus: $754,074
Savings Plan: Y	Stock Purch. Plan: Y		Second Exec. Salary: $660,000	Bonus: $183,922

OTHER THOUGHTS:

Apparent Women Officers or Directors: 2
Hot Spot for Advancement for Women/Minorities: Y

LOCATIONS: ("Y" = Yes)

West:	Southwest:	Midwest:	Southeast:	Northeast:	International:
Y					Y

LORAL SPACE & COMMUNICATIONS LTD

www.loral.com

Industry Group Code: 334220 **Ranks within this company's industry group:** Sales: 6 Profits: 5

Techology:		Medical/Drugs:		Engineering:		Transportation:		Chemicals/Petrochemicals:		Specialty:	
Computers:		Manufacturer:		Design:		Aerospace:	Y	Oil/Gas Products:		Special Services:	Y
Software:		Contract Research:		Construction:		Automotive:		Chemicals:		Consulting:	
Communications:	Y	Medical Services:		Eng. Services:		Shipping:		Oil/Chem. Svcs.:		Specialty Mgmt.:	
Electronics:	Y	Labs:		Consulting:				Gases:		Products:	
Alternative Energy:		Bio. Services:						Other:		Other:	

TYPES OF BUSINESS:

Satellite Equipment
Communications & Weather Satellite Systems
Fixed Satellite & Network Services
Information Delivery Systems
Managed Communications Networks
Internet Services

BRANDS/DIVISIONS/AFFILIATES:

Loral Skynet
Space Systems/Loral Inc
SkyReach
SkyReachSM Cellular Backhaul
XTAR LLC

CONTACTS: *Note: Officers with more than one job title may be intentionally listed here more than once.*

Michael B. Targoff, CEO/Vice Chmn.
Michael B. Targoff, Pres.
Harvey B. Rein, CFO/Sr. VP
Avi Katz, General Counsel/Sec./Sr. VP
Russell R. Mack, VP-Bus. Ventures
Jeanette H. Clonan, VP-Comm.
Jeanette H. Clonan, VP-Investor Rel.
Richard P. Mastoloni, Sr. VP-Finance/Treas.
John Capogrossi, VP/Controller
Barry J. Sitler, VP-Tax
C. Patrick DeWitt, Sr. VP/CEO-Space Systems/Loral, Inc.
Arnold Friedman, Sr. VP-Worldwide Mktg. & Sales-Space Systems/Loral
Mark H. Rachesky, Chmn.

Phone: 212-697-1105	**Fax:** 212-338-5662
Toll-Free:	
Address: 600 3rd Ave., New York, NY 10016 US	

GROWTH PLANS/SPECIAL FEATURES:

Loral Space & Communications, Ltd. is a leader in satellite communications. Subsidiary Loral Skynet Corporation manages and operates the firm's Satellite Services business. It maintains satellites in geosynchronous orbits, approximately 22,000 miles above the equator, which provide high-bandwidth services and serve as the backbone for many forms of telecommunications. Customers lease transponder capacity for distribution of cable television programming, for direct-to-home (DTH) video transmission, live video feeds from breaking news and sporting events and broadband data distribution. Skynet Network Services' aspect, SkyReach, is a group of hub-based Internet protocol (IP) services that provides customers with secure private networks and high-speed Internet access using Skynet's established satellite/fiber structure. The SkyReachSM Cellular Backhaul for mobile and cell phone users replaces E1/T1 lines with satellite lines, allowing for better network and operator connectivity. Subsidiary Space Systems/Loral, Inc. designs and manufactures satellites and space system components for commercial and government broadcasting applications including fixed satellite services, direct to home broadcasting, broadband data distribution, wireless telephony, digital radio, military communications, weather monitoring and air traffic management. The company currently operates a fleet of four satellites and counts HBO, Disney, Global Crossing, BT North America and China Central TV as major customers. Loral also owns 56% of XTAR, LLC, a joint venture with Spanish telecommunications company HISDESAT. XTAR provides X-band services to government users in the U.S., Spain and other allied countries, including the U.S. Department of State, the Spanish Ministry of Defense and the Danish armed forces. In 2008, Space Systems/Loral was selected to provide space craft to Intelsat, an international provider of fixed satellite services.

Employees are offered health insurance; life insurance; and a pension plan.

FINANCIALS: **Sales and profits are in thousands of dollars—add 000 to get the full amount. 2008 Note: Financial information for 2008 was not available for all companies at press time.**

2008 Sales: $869,398	2008 Profits: $-692,916	**U.S. Stock Ticker: LORL**
2007 Sales: $882,454	2007 Profits: $29,659	**Int'l Ticker:** Int'l Exchange:
2006 Sales: $797,333	2006 Profits: $-22,720	Employees: 2,500
2005 Sales: $626,400	2005 Profits: $1,017,256	Fiscal Year Ends: 12/31
2004 Sales: $522,100	2004 Profits: $-176,700	Parent Company:

SALARIES/BENEFITS:

Pension Plan: Y	ESOP Stock Plan:	Profit Sharing:	Top Exec. Salary: $1,152,000	Bonus: $1,142,375
Savings Plan:	Stock Purch. Plan:		Second Exec. Salary: $953,654	Bonus: $441,508

OTHER THOUGHTS:

Apparent Women Officers or Directors: 1
Hot Spot for Advancement for Women/Minorities:

LOCATIONS: ("Y" = Yes)

West:	Southwest:	Midwest:	Southeast:	Northeast:	International:
Y				Y	Y

LOUIS BERGER GROUP INC (THE)

www.louisberger.com

Industry Group Code: 234000 **Ranks within this company's industry group:** Sales: Profits:

Techology:		Medical/Drugs:		Engineering:		Transportation:		Chemicals/Petrochemicals:		Specialty:	
Computers:		Manufacturer:		Design:	Y	Aerospace:		Oil/Gas Products:		Special Services:	
Software:		Contract Research:		Construction:	Y	Automotive:		Chemicals:		Consulting:	
Communications:		Medical Services:		Eng. Services:	Y	Shipping:		Oil/Chem. Svcs.:		Specialty Mgmt.:	Y
Electronics:		Labs:		Consulting:	Y			Gases:		Products:	
Alternative Energy:		Bio. Services:						Other:		Other:	Y

TYPES OF BUSINESS:

Architectural & Engineering Services
Civil Engineering
Environmental Engineering
Transportation Infrastructure
Project Management
Consulting Services
Hydrologic Engineering
Seismic & Geotechnical Services

BRANDS/DIVISIONS/AFFILIATES:

Louis Berger SAS
Ammann & Whitney Consulting Engineers Inc
Berger/ABAM Engineers Inc
Berger Devine Yaeger Inc
Klohn Crippen Berger Ltd
Berger, Lehman Associates PC
CHELBI Engineering Consultants Inc
RBA Group Inc (The)

CONTACTS: *Note: Officers with more than one job title may be intentionally listed here more than once.*

Nicolas J. (Nick) Masucci, CEO
Michel Jichlinski, COO/Exec. VP/Pres., Washington, D.C. Office
Larry Pesesky, Sr. VP-Environmental Sciences
Julius Haas, Chief Structural Engineer/VP
Jim Bach, VP-U.S. Oper.
Dennis Conklin, Chief Highway Engineer
Thomas Lewis, Sr. VP-Environmental Group
John Hotopp, Sr. VP-Cultural Resource Group
Robert J. Nardi, Sr. VP-Facilities Planning
Derish M. Wolff, Chmn.

Phone: 973-407-1000	**Fax:** 973-267-6468
Toll-Free:	
Address: 412 Mt. Kemble Ave., Morristown, NJ 07960-6654 US	

GROWTH PLANS/SPECIAL FEATURES:

The Louis Berger Group, Inc. (Berger) is an infrastructure engineering, environmental science and economic development company with more than 140 offices throughout the U.S. and in more than 60 countries worldwide. Berger offers services in such areas as civil, structural, mechanical, electrical and environmental engineering; program management; planning; environmental sciences; cultural resources; information science; finance; economics; and construction management. The group operates through a number of subsidiary companies. Louis Berger SAS, based in Paris, France, provides design and supervision services for transportation and privately financed infrastructure projects, water supply and urban sanitation systems. It also offers management and human resource development services. BergerAvart, Inc., offers architectural and engineering services within Florida. Ammann & Whitney Consulting Engineers, Inc. provides structural, civil, architectural, mechanical, electrical engineering and construction inspection services for such projects as bridges, highways, airports, transit stations, schools and government and military installations. Berger/ABAM Engineers, Inc. offers planning, environmental science, civil and structural engineering, project management and construction support consulting services. Berger Devine Yaeger, Inc. provides architectural, engineering, planning and surveying solutions. Klohn Crippen Berger Ltd. designs hydroelectric power plants, dams, tunnels and pumped storage schemes; serves mining clients internationally; and provides seismic and geotechnical services throughout Canada. Berger, Lehman Associates, P.C. is one of the largest engineering, economic and environmental planning organizations in the U.S., serving state, municipal and local agencies as well as corporate and industrial clients. CHELBI Engineering Consultants, Inc. provides project support services in China. The RBA Group, Inc. offers its clients engineering, planning and architectural services.

Berger offers employees medical and dental coverage; life and travel insurance; a new employee hiring referral award; tuition reimbursement; flexible spending accounts; a cafeteria plan; and registration fee payment for professional licenses.

FINANCIALS: **Sales and profits are in thousands of dollars—add 000 to get the full amount. 2008 Note: Financial information for 2008 was not available for all companies at press time.**

2008 Sales: $	2008 Profits: $	**U.S. Stock Ticker: Private**
2007 Sales: $	2007 Profits: $	**Int'l Ticker:** Int'l Exchange:
2006 Sales: $	2006 Profits: $	Employees: 4,000
2005 Sales: $	2005 Profits: $	Fiscal Year Ends: 6/30
2004 Sales: $541,000	2004 Profits: $	Parent Company:

SALARIES/BENEFITS:

Pension Plan:	ESOP Stock Plan:	Profit Sharing:	Top Exec. Salary: $	Bonus: $
Savings Plan: Y	Stock Purch. Plan:		Second Exec. Salary: $	Bonus: $

OTHER THOUGHTS:

Apparent Women Officers or Directors:
Hot Spot for Advancement for Women/Minorities:

LOCATIONS: ("Y" = Yes)

West:	Southwest:	Midwest:	Southeast:	Northeast:	International:
Y	Y	Y	Y	Y	Y

LSI CORPORATION

www.lsi.com

Industry Group Code: 334413 **Ranks within this company's industry group:** Sales: 14 Profits: 13

Techology:		Medical/Drugs:		Engineering:		Transportation:		Chemicals/Petrochemicals:		Specialty:	
Computers:	Y	Manufacturer:		Design:		Aerospace:		Oil/Gas Products:		Special Services:	
Software:		Contract Research:		Construction:		Automotive:		Chemicals:		Consulting:	
Communications:		Medical Services:		Eng. Services:		Shipping:		Oil/Chem. Svcs.:		Specialty Mgmt.:	
Electronics:		Labs:		Consulting:				Gases:		Products:	
Alternative Energy:		Bio. Services:						Other:		Other:	

TYPES OF BUSINESS:

Integrated Circuits
Application-Specific Integrated Circuits (ASICs)
System-on-a-Chip Products
Storage Area Network Solutions

BRANDS/DIVISIONS/AFFILIATES:

RapidChip
CoreWare
Metta Technology, Inc.
StoreAge Networking Technologies, Ltd.

CONTACTS:

Note: Officers with more than one job title may be intentionally listed here more than once.

Abhi Talwalkar, CEO
Abhi Talwalkar, Pres.
Bryon Look, CFO/Exec. VP
Phil Brace, Sr. VP-Mktg.
Jon Gibson, VP-Human Resources
Claudine Simson, CTO/Exec. VP
Andrew Micallef, Exec. VP-Worldwide Mfg. Oper.
Jean F. Rankin, General Counsel/Exec. VP/Sec.
Phil Brace, Sr. VP-Corp. Planning
Phil Bullinger, Sr. VP/Gen. Mgr.-Engenio Storage Group
Jeff Richardson, Exec. VP-Network & Storage Prod. Group
Ruediger Stroh, Exec. VP-Storage Peripherals Group
Flavio Santoni, Exec. VP/Gen. Mgr.-Engenio Storage Group
Gregorio Reyes, Chmn.

Phone: 408-433-8000	**Fax:** 408-954-3220
Toll-Free: 866-574-5741	
Address: 1621 Barber Ln., Milpitas, CA 95035 US	

GROWTH PLANS/SPECIAL FEATURES:

LSI Corporation designs, develops, manufactures and markets complex, high-performance semiconductors and storage systems. Its integrated circuits (ICs) are used in a wide range of communication devices, including devices used for wireless, broadband, data networking and set-top box applications. LSI provides IC products and board-level products for use in consumer applications, high-performance storage controllers and systems for storage area networks. The firm's semiconductor segment develops application-specific integrated circuits (ASICs) under the brand names RapidChip and CoreWare, as well as standard products, which include microprocessors for wireless handsets, Ethernet products for local area networks, silicon solutions for broadband infrastructures, and encoders and decoders for video games and digital television systems. In the storage systems segment, LSI offers a broad line of network storage that spans customer enterprises from workgroup to data center. The firm's product lines range from intelligent controller and drive modules to complete storage systems. These allow its products to be integrated on a component basis or configured into a complete storage solution, increasing manufacturer flexibility in creating differentiated products. Modular products also allow indirect channel partners to customize solutions, bundling LSI's products with value-added components, software and services. The firm's subsidiaries include StoneAge Networking Technologies Ltd. and Metta Technology. In April 2008, the company acquired the hard drive semiconductor business of Infineon Technologies AG.

Employees are offered flexible spending accounts; dependent care accounts; life insurance; business travel accident insurance; auto and home insurance; pre-paid legal services; identity theft insurance; a 401(k) plan; a profit sharing plan; a stock purchase plan; and credit union services.

FINANCIALS:

Sales and profits are in thousands of dollars—add 000 to get the full amount. 2008 Note: Financial information for 2008 was not available for all companies at press time.

2008 Sales: $2,677,077	2008 Profits: $-622,253	**U.S. Stock Ticker: LSI**
2007 Sales: $2,603,643	2007 Profits: $-2,486,819	**Int'l Ticker:** Int'l Exchange:
2006 Sales: $1,982,148	2006 Profits: $169,638	Employees: 5,488
2005 Sales: $1,919,250	2005 Profits: $-5,623	Fiscal Year Ends: 12/31
2004 Sales: $1,700,164	2004 Profits: $-463,531	Parent Company:

SALARIES/BENEFITS:

Pension Plan:	ESOP Stock Plan:	Profit Sharing: Y	Top Exec. Salary: $800,010	Bonus: $
Savings Plan: Y	Stock Purch. Plan: Y		Second Exec. Salary: $400,005	Bonus: $

OTHER THOUGHTS:

Apparent Women Officers or Directors: 3
Hot Spot for Advancement for Women/Minorities: Y

LOCATIONS: ("Y" = Yes)

West:	Southwest:	Midwest:	Southeast:	Northeast:	International:
Y		Y			Y

LUKOIL (OAO)

www.lukoil.com

Industry Group Code: 211111 **Ranks within this company's industry group:** Sales: 11 Profits: 9

Techology:		Medical/Drugs:		Engineering:		Transportation:		Chemicals/Petrochemicals:		Specialty:	
Computers:		Manufacturer:		Design:		Aerospace:		Oil/Gas Products:	Y	Special Services:	
Software:		Contract Research:		Construction:		Automotive:		Chemicals:	Y	Consulting:	
Communications:		Medical Services:		Eng. Services:		Shipping:		Oil/Chem. Svcs.:		Specialty Mgmt.:	
Electronics:		Labs:		Consulting:				Gases:		Products:	
Alternative Energy:		Bio. Services:						Other:		Other:	

TYPES OF BUSINESS:

Oil & Gas Exploration & Production
Petroleum Refining
Pipeline Operations
Gas Stations
Ocean Terminals & Oil Tankers
Natural Gas & Petrochemical Processing Plants

BRANDS/DIVISIONS/AFFILIATES:

OAO YuGK TGK-8
ZAO Rostovneft
EUROPA-MIL
Akpet Company (The)
Yuzhnaya-Khylchuya Field

CONTACTS: *Note: Officers with more than one job title may be intentionally listed here more than once.*

Vagit Alekperov, Pres.
Sergei Kukura, First VP-Finance & Economics
Vladimir Nekrasov, First VP-Refining, Mktg. & Distribution
Anatoly Moskalenko, Head-Human Resources
Dzhevan Cheloyants, Head-Tech.
Ivan Masliaev, Head-Legal Support
Leonid Fedun, Head-Strategic Dev. & Investment Analysis
Anatoly Barkov, Head-Corp. Security, Comm. & Gen. Affairs
Alexander Matytsyn, Head-Treasury & Corp. Financing
Ravil Maganov, First Exec. VP-Exploration & Prod.
Lyubov Khoba, Chief Accountant
Vladimir Mulyak, Head-Oil & Gas Prod. & Infrastructure
Valery Grayfer, Chmn.
Valery Subbotin, VP-Supplies & Sales

Phone: 7-495-627-44-44 **Fax:** 7-495-625-7016
Toll-Free:
Address: 11 Sretensky Blvd., Moscow, 101000 Russia

GROWTH PLANS/SPECIAL FEATURES:

Lukoil OAO, Russia's largest oil company, operates in oil and gas exploration and production and the production and sale of petroleum products. In terms of capacity, the company has 1.3% of global proven oil reserves; and it represents 18% of both Russia's total oil production and its refining capacity. The company has 15.7 billion barrels of proven oil reserves, making it a world leading private oil company by proven reserves. Lukoil has operations in 30 countries worldwide, which include oil reserves in six countries. The company utilizes Transneft's pipeline network, among others, to network from Siberia to Western Europe, along with the Caspian Pipeline Consortium, which stretches from the Black Sea to Kazakhstan. Lukoil's refining operations processed 52.2 million tons of oil in 2007 through nine refineries located in Russia and eastern Europe. The company also has four natural gas processing plants, which produced 579 billion cubic feet of gas in 2007, and petrochemical processing plants with a total capacity of 2.18 million cubic tons. Subsidiaries of Lukoil exported 42.2 million tons of crude oil in 2007, representing 16.7% of total Russian crude oil exports. The company's marketing network spans 24 countries including Russia, Azerbaijan, Belarus, Georgia, Moldova, Ukraine, Bulgaria, Hungary, Finland, Estonia, Latvia, Lithuania, Poland, Serbia, Montenegro, Romania, Macedonia, Cyprus, Turkey, Belgium, Luxemburg, Czech Republic, and Slovakia and the U.S. Lukoil also operates approximately 6,090 gas stations. ConocoPhillips holds a 20% stake in LUKOIL. Recent company acquisition include an 82.3% stake in OAO YuGK TGK-8 (TGK-8); the ZAO Rostovneft distribution network; two retail networks; EUROPA-MIL; and the Akpet Company. In June 2008, Lukoil started production at the Yuzhnaya-Khylchuya field, the biggest field in the Nenets autonomous district with proved oil reserves of more than 500 mln barrels. In September 2008, Lukoil increased its interest in TGK-8 to 95.4%.

FINANCIALS: **Sales and profits are in thousands of dollars—add 000 to get the full amount. 2008 Note: Financial information for 2008 was not available for all companies at press time.**

2008 Sales: $107,680,000
2007 Sales: $81,891,000
2006 Sales: $67,684,000
2005 Sales: $56,200,000
2004 Sales: $33,845,000

2008 Profits: $9,144,000
2007 Profits: $9,511,000
2006 Profits: $7,484,000
2005 Profits: $6,443,000
2004 Profits: $4,248,000

U.S. Stock Ticker: LUKOY
Int'l Ticker: LKOH Int'l Exchange: Moscow-MICEX
Employees: 151,400
Fiscal Year Ends: 12/31
Parent Company:

SALARIES/BENEFITS:

Pension Plan:	ESOP Stock Plan:	Profit Sharing:	Top Exec. Salary: $	Bonus: $
Savings Plan:	Stock Purch. Plan:		Second Exec. Salary: $	Bonus: $

OTHER THOUGHTS:

Apparent Women Officers or Directors: 1
Hot Spot for Advancement for Women/Minorities:

LOCATIONS: ("Y" = Yes)

West:	Southwest:	Midwest:	Southeast:	Northeast:	International:
				Y	Y

Note: Financial information, benefits and other data can change quickly and may vary from those stated here.

LUXOTTICA GROUP SPA

www.luxottica.it

Industry Group Code: 333314 **Ranks within this company's industry group:** Sales: 3 Profits: 2

Techology:		Medical/Drugs:		Engineering:		Transportation:		Chemicals/Petrochemicals:		Specialty:	
Computers:		Manufacturer:		Design:		Aerospace:		Oil/Gas Products:		Special Services:	
Software:		Contract Research:		Construction:		Automotive:		Chemicals:		Consulting:	
Communications:		Medical Services:		Eng. Services:		Shipping:		Oil/Chem. Svcs.:		Specialty Mgmt.:	
Electronics:		Labs:		Consulting:				Gases:		Products:	Y
Alternative Energy:		Bio. Services:						Other:		Other:	

TYPES OF BUSINESS:

Lens/Eyeglass Frame Manufacturing
Vision Plan Provider
Lens/Eyeglass Frame Retailer
Eye Care Services

BRANDS/DIVISIONS/AFFILIATES:

Ray Ban
Oakly, Inc.
Luxottica, S.r.l.
LensCrafters, Inc.
EyeMed Vision Care, LLC
FeatherWates SPF
D.O.C Optics
I.C. Optics, S.r.l.

CONTACTS: *Note: Officers with more than one job title may be intentionally listed here more than once.*

Andrea Guerra, CEO
Enrico Cavatorta, CFO
Fabio D'Angelantonio, Head-Group Mktg.
Nicola Pela, Head-Group Human Resources
Umberto Soccal, CTO
Marco Vendramini, Group Chief Admin. Officer
Mario Lugli, General Counsel
Sabina Grossi, Head-Investor Rel.
Enrico Mistron, Controller
Frank Baynham, Exec. VP-Stores, Retail North America
Tom Coleman, Exec. VP-Retail Asia-Pacific
Crhis Beer, COO-Retail, Asia-Pacifica, Australia & New Zealand
George Minakakis, COO-Greater China
Leonardo Del Vecchio, Exec. Chmn.
Kerry Bradley, COO-Retail, North America

Phone: 39-02-863341	**Fax:** 39-02-86334092
Toll-Free:	
Address: Via C. Cantu, 2, Milan, 20123 Italy	

GROWTH PLANS/SPECIAL FEATURES:

Luxottica Group S.p.A. is one of the world's largest manufacturers and retailers of prescription and fashion eyeglass frames and sunglasses. The company is the largest optical and sun glasses retailer in North America, operating three leading retail brands: LensCrafters, Pearle Vision and Sunglass Hut. Company-owned brands include Ray Ban, Vogue, Persol, Arnette, Killer Loop, Revo, Sferoflex and Luxottica. It licenses brands from Prada, Ungaro, Versace, Chanel, DKNY, Bvlgari, Moschino, Brooks Brothers, Miu Miu, Anne Klein and others. Some of the firm's subsidiaries include Luxottica, S.r.l.; Killer Loop Eyewear, S.r.l.; Tristar Optical Co., Ltd.; Collezione Rathschuler; Luxottica Leasing, SPA; Luxottica USA; LensCrafters, Inc.; Luxottica Luxembourg; and other retail and wholesale subsidiaries located worldwide. In 2007, Luxottica distributed sunglasses in more than 6,400 storefronts, through its wholesale and retail networks in 130 countries worldwide. Luxottica is involved in the U.S. health care market through subsidiary EyeMed Vision Care, LLC. EyeMed offers members a vision plan including a network of optometrists, ophthalmologists and opticians; and Luxottica eyeglass frames. Luxottica manufactures one of the only prescription sunglass lenses, called FeatherWates SPF, to receive the Skin Cancer Foundation's Seal of Recommendation. In 2007, Luxottica commenced a ten-year eyeglasses licensing agreement, worth over $1.75 billion, for the design, production and worldwide distribution of prescription frames and sunglasses under the Polo Ralph Lauren name. In February 2007, the Group acquired the retail optical business of D.O.C Optics, with 100 stores in the American Midwest, for approximately $110 million. In March 2007, the company acquired two sunglasses retail chains in South Africa with a total 65 stores, for approximately $13.96 million. In October 2007, Luxottica opened its first ILORI store, a high-end luxury eyewear brand, in SoHo, New York. In November 2007, the firm acquired Oakley, Inc. for $2.1 billion.

FINANCIALS: **Sales and profits are in thousands of dollars—add 000 to get the full amount. 2008 Note: Financial information for 2008 was not available for all companies at press time.**

2008 Sales: $6,881,300	2008 Profits: $522,550	**U.S. Stock Ticker: LUX**
2007 Sales: $7,251,929	2007 Profits: $718,766	**Int'l Ticker: LUX** Int'l Exchange: Milan-BI
2006 Sales: $5,175,835	2006 Profits: $405,345	Employees: 64,000
2005 Sales: $5,260,312	2005 Profits: $411,959	Fiscal Year Ends: 12/31
2004 Sales: $3,917,844	2004 Profits: $345,208	Parent Company:

SALARIES/BENEFITS:

Pension Plan:	ESOP Stock Plan:	Profit Sharing:	Top Exec. Salary: $1,152,808	Bonus: $780,042
Savings Plan:	Stock Purch. Plan:		Second Exec. Salary: $178,301	Bonus: $1,316,699

OTHER THOUGHTS:

Apparent Women Officers or Directors: 4
Hot Spot for Advancement for Women/Minorities: Y

LOCATIONS: ("Y" = Yes)

West:	Southwest:	Midwest:	Southeast:	Northeast:	International:
Y	Y	Y	Y	Y	Y

LYONDELLBASELL INDUSTRIES

www.lyondellbasell.com

Industry Group Code: 325110 **Ranks within this company's industry group:** Sales: Profits:

Techology:		Medical/Drugs:		Engineering:		Transportation:		Chemicals/Petrochemicals:		Specialty:	
Computers:		Manufacturer:		Design:		Aerospace:		Oil/Gas Products:	Y	Special Services:	
Software:		Contract Research:		Construction:		Automotive:		Chemicals:	Y	Consulting:	
Communications:		Medical Services:		Eng. Services:		Shipping:		Oil/Chem. Svcs.:	Y	Specialty Mgmt.:	
Electronics:		Labs:		Consulting:				Gases:		Products:	
Alternative Energy:		Bio. Services:						Other:		Other:	

TYPES OF BUSINESS:

Polymers & Petrochemicals
Intermediate & Performance Chemicals
Petroleum Products
Refining

BRANDS/DIVISIONS/AFFILIATES:

Lyondell Chemical Co.
Basell AF
Access Industries
Solvay Engineered Ploymers, Inc.

CONTACTS:

Note: Officers with more than one job title may be intentionally listed here more than once.

Volker Trautz, CEO
Alan Bigman, CFO/Exec. VP
Cees Los, General Counsel/Sr. VP

Phone: 31-10-275-5500	**Fax:**
Toll-Free:	
Address: P.O. Box 2416, Rotterdam, 3000 CK The Netherlands	

GROWTH PLANS/SPECIAL FEATURES:

LyondellBasell Industries AF S.C.A. is one of the world's largest producers and marketers of polymers, petrochemicals and fuels. It is owned by Access Industries, a private equity firm. The company was formed in 2007 through the merger between Basell AF S.C.A., a chemical manufacturing company and polypropylene producer, and Lyondell Chemical Co., a leading manufacturer of chemicals and plastics and a refiner of crude oil. Access Industries, the parent company of Basell AF, retained ownership of the merged companies. The firm operates in four segments: chemicals; polymers; fuels; and technology and R&D. The chemicals segment offers various services and applications such as insulation; home furnishings; adhesives and sealants; aircraft deicers; cosmetics; cleaners; films; optical resins; carpeting; foam cups and more. Also, the firm is one of the world's leading providers of propylene oxide and has manufacturing plants in Asia, Europe and North America. The polymers division produces and markets polyolefins and advanced polyolefins. Currently, the firm has 19 polymers joint ventures. Some client services offered include; clothing; medical tubing; pharmaceutical packaging; and toys. The fuels segment offers its clients automotive and industrial engine lube oils; heating oil; and automotive, aviation and diesel fuels. The firm operates two refineries. Both refineries have access to major pipelines and ports. The technology segment is responsible for process licensing, catalyst sales and technology services. Sales in the U.S. account for 55% of the firm's sales, with sales in Europe and the rest of the world accounting for 39% and 6% of sales, respectively. In February 2008, LyondellBasell acquired Solvay Engineered Polymers, Inc., supplier of polypropylene compounds. In April 2009, the firm purchased the Shell oil refinery and associated businesses in France. In January 2009, two of LyondellBasell's largest operating companies filed for bankruptcy protection. In February 2009, the U.S. Bankruptcy Court approved the firm's debtor-in-possession financing package.

FINANCIALS:

Sales and profits are in thousands of dollars—add 000 to get the full amount. 2008 Note: Financial information for 2008 was not available for all companies at press time.

2008 Sales: $	2008 Profits: $	**U.S. Stock Ticker: Subsidiary**
2007 Sales: $17,073,000	2007 Profits: $1,032,000	**Int'l Ticker:** Int'l Exchange:
2006 Sales: $44,735,000	2006 Profits: $168,000	Employees: 10,905
2005 Sales: $18,606,000	2005 Profits: $531,000	Fiscal Year Ends: 12/31
2004 Sales: $5,946,000	2004 Profits: $54,000	Parent Company: ACCESS INDUSTRIES

SALARIES/BENEFITS:

Pension Plan:	ESOP Stock Plan:	Profit Sharing:	Top Exec. Salary: $1,250,000	Bonus: $3,000,000
Savings Plan:	Stock Purch. Plan:		Second Exec. Salary: $752,544	Bonus: $1,204,070

OTHER THOUGHTS:

Apparent Women Officers or Directors:
Hot Spot for Advancement for Women/Minorities:

LOCATIONS: ("Y" = Yes)

West:	Southwest:	Midwest:	Southeast:	Northeast:	International:
	Y				Y

Note: Financial information, benefits and other data can change quickly and may vary from those stated here.

MAGNA INTERNATIONAL INC

www.magna.com

Industry Group Code: 336300 **Ranks within this company's industry group:** Sales: 4 Profits: 10

Techology:		Medical/Drugs:		Engineering:		Transportation:		Chemicals/Petrochemicals:		Specialty:	
Computers:		Manufacturer:		Design:	Y	Aerospace:		Oil/Gas Products:		Special Services:	Y
Software:		Contract Research:		Construction:	Y	Automotive:	Y	Chemicals:		Consulting:	
Communications:		Medical Services:		Eng. Services:		Shipping:		Oil/Chem. Svcs.:		Specialty Mgmt.:	
Electronics:		Labs:		Consulting:				Gases:		Products:	
Alternative Energy:		Bio. Services:						Other:		Other:	

TYPES OF BUSINESS:

Automobile Parts Manufacturer
Vehicle Assembly Services
Seating & Interior Products
Closure Systems
Body & Chassis Systems
Mirror, Lighting & Glass Systems
Exterior Decorative Systems
Drivetrain Components

BRANDS/DIVISIONS/AFFILIATES:

Intier Automotive Inc
Magna Donnelly
Decoma International Inc
Cosma International
Magna Powertrain
Magna Seating
Magna Car Top Systems
Magna Steyr

CONTACTS: *Note: Officers with more than one job title may be intentionally listed here more than once.*

Donald Walker, Co-CEO
Vincent J. Galifi, CFO/Exec. VP
Scott E. Paradise, VP-Mktg., Americas
Marc Neeb, Exec. VP-Global Human Resources
Jeffrey O. Palmer, Chief Legal Officer/Exec. VP
Peter Koob, Exec. VP-Corp. Dev.
Louis Tonelli, VP-Investor Rel.
Paul Brock, Treas.
Herbert Demel, COO-Vehicles & Powertrain
Tom Skudutis, COO-Exteriors & Interiors
Joachim Volker Hirsch, VP-Special Projects
Siegfried Wolf, Co-CEO
Frank Stronach, Chmn.
Manfred Eibeck, Exec. VP-Magna Europe

Phone: 905-726-2462	**Fax:** 905-726-7164
Toll-Free:	
Address: 337 Magna Dr., Aurora, ON L4G 7K1 Canada	

GROWTH PLANS/SPECIAL FEATURES:

Magna International, Inc. is a global supplier of high-tech automotive components, systems and complete modules. The firm designs, engineers and manufactures a full range of interior and exterior systems, in addition to providing complete vehicle assembly services to major automotive manufacturers. Some of the company's notable customers are Chrysler Group; Daimler AG; Porsche; Toyota; General Motors; BMW; Volkswagen; Nissan; Lexus; Mitsubishi; Tata Automotive; and Ford Motor Company. The firm employs tens of thousands of people worldwide at 240 manufacturing divisions and 86 product development, engineering and sales centers in 25 countries in North and South America, Africa, Europe and Asia. Through its divisions and subsidiaries, the company provides metallic body and chassis systems, hydro-formed components and assemblies, seating and interior systems, power train products, closure systems, mirror systems, roof systems, electronic systems and exterior body products, as well as engine, transmission and fueling systems and components. Magna's primary operating subsidiaries include Cosma International; Magna Powertrain; Decoma International; Magna Seating; Magna Mirrors; Magna Closures; Magna Car Top Systems; Magna Electronics; Magna Steyr; Magna Donnelly; and Intier Automotive, Inc. In February 2008, the firm made two acquisitions: Allied Transportation Technology, Inc., which will provide the company with new ultrasonic technology; and Zhangjiagang Suxing Electronics, which will deliver new technologies to the Chinese market. In July 2008, Magna acquired Technoplast, a producer of exterior and interior plastic components, located in Russia. In October 2008, Magna acquired BluWav Systems LLC, a Michigan-based supplier of electric and energy-management systems for the hybrid electric, plug-in hybrid and battery electric automotive markets. In December 2008, the company announced plans to close an auto parts plant in Nova Scotia and to open two new production facilities in Russia.

FINANCIALS: **Sales and profits are in thousands of dollars—add 000 to get the full amount. 2008 Note: Financial information for 2008 was not available for all companies at press time.**

2008 Sales: $23,704,000	2008 Profits: $71,000	**U.S. Stock Ticker: MGA**
2007 Sales: $26,067,000	2007 Profits: $663,000	**Int'l Ticker: MG.A** Int'l Exchange: Toronto-TSX
2006 Sales: $24,180,000	2006 Profits: $528,000	Employees: 74,350
2005 Sales: $22,811,000	2005 Profits: $639,000	Fiscal Year Ends: 12/31
2004 Sales: $20,653,000	2004 Profits: $692,000	Parent Company:

SALARIES/BENEFITS:

Pension Plan:	ESOP Stock Plan:	Profit Sharing:	Top Exec. Salary: $200,000	Bonus: $
Savings Plan:	Stock Purch. Plan:		Second Exec. Salary: $110,500	Bonus: $6,153,500

OTHER THOUGHTS:

Apparent Women Officers or Directors: 2
Hot Spot for Advancement for Women/Minorities:

LOCATIONS: ("Y" = Yes)

West:	Southwest:	Midwest:	Southeast:	Northeast:	International:
		Y	Y	Y	Y

Note: Financial information, benefits and other data can change quickly and may vary from those stated here.

MAGNETI MARELLI HOLDING SPA

www.magnetimarelli.com

Industry Group Code: 336300 **Ranks within this company's industry group:** Sales: Profits:

Techology:		Medical/Drugs:		Engineering:		Transportation:		Chemicals/Petrochemicals:		Specialty:	
Computers:		Manufacturer:		Design:		Aerospace:		Oil/Gas Products:		Special Services:	
Software:		Contract Research:		Construction:		Automotive:	Y	Chemicals:		Consulting:	
Communications:		Medical Services:		Eng. Services:		Shipping:		Oil/Chem. Svcs.:		Specialty Mgmt.:	
Electronics:		Labs:		Consulting:				Gases:		Products:	
Alternative Energy:		Bio. Services:						Other:		Other:	

TYPES OF BUSINESS:

Automotive Components
Power Train Systems
Motor Sport Components
Lighting
Automotive Performance Research Equipment

BRANDS/DIVISIONS/AFFILIATES:

Fiat SpA
Cofap
Jaeger
Seima
Descam
Automotive Lighting
Step9
Wintax

CONTACTS: *Note: Officers with more than one job title may be intentionally listed here more than once.*

Eugenio Razelli, CEO
Eugenio Razelli, Pres.
Donatella Penati, CFO
Sergio Garue, Dir.-Sales Coordination
Livio Milan, Dir.-Human Resources
Stefan Firenze, CIO
Gianpaolo Accossato, General Counsel
Sergio Garue, Dir.-Bus. Dev.
Andrea Anfossi, Dir.-Comm.
Donatella Penati, Dir.-Finance
Paolo Arrighi, Compliance Officer
Ferruccio Bondesan, Quality Coordination
Luigi Ippolito, Dir.-Innovation
Guiseppe Morchio, Chmn.
Roberto Minella, Purchasing Coordination

Phone: 39-02-9722-7111 **Fax:** 39-02-9722-7355
Toll-Free:
Address: Viale Aldo Borletti 61/63, Milano, 20011 Italy

GROWTH PLANS/SPECIAL FEATURES:

Magneti Marelli Holding S.p.A, a subsidiary of Fiat, designs and manufactures components and systems for lighting, suspension, exhaust and powertrain applications. Magneti Marelli supplies the world's major car manufacturers such as Renault, Citroen, Peugeot, the Fiat Group, Ford, Volkswagen, Audi, Seat, BMW, DaimlerChrysler, GM-Opel, Volvo, Saab, Nissan, Toyota and Daewoo. Its portfolio of brands includes Cofap, Jaeger, Seima, Siem, Descam and Automotive Lighting. Subsidiary Automotive Lighting is a global leader in exterior automotive lighting systems; where other subsidiaries specialize in electronic systems, exhaust systems and powertrain items. Magneti Marelli also maintains a motor sport division that offers a line of performance-enhancing products, including the Step9 engine and chassis control unit, capable of driving an engine at speeds of up to 20,000 rpm. The unit also has product lines in alternators, motors and voltage regulators; fuel systems and ignition; sensors; electronic control systems; data acquisition, display and lap trigger; and software. Magneti Marelli has industrial and research facilities in Italy, France, Spain, Great Britain, Germany, Poland, Czech Republic, Russia, Turkey, the U.S., Mexico, Brazil, Argentina, China, Malaysia and South Africa. The company has recently entered several joint venture agreements. In 2007, Magneti Marelli, Suzuki Motor Corporation and Maruti Suzuki India Limited created a joint venture in India aimed at the production of electronic control units for diesel engines. In 2008, Magneti Marelli and Endurance Technologies created a joint venture to manufacture shock absorbers for motor vehicles in India and Thailand. Also in 2008, the firm also created a joint venture with Sumi Motherson Group for engine control components and with Telecom Italia to create onboard infomobility services.

FINANCIALS: **Sales and profits are in thousands of dollars—add 000 to get the full amount. 2008 Note: Financial information for 2008 was not available for all companies at press time.**

2008 Sales: $
2007 Sales: $
2006 Sales: $6,069,200
2005 Sales: $5,183,660
2004 Sales: $4,647,400

2008 Profits: $
2007 Profits: $
2006 Profits: $
2005 Profits: $
2004 Profits: $

U.S. Stock Ticker: Subsidiary
Int'l Ticker: Int'l Exchange:
Employees: 25,195
Fiscal Year Ends: 12/31
Parent Company: FIAT SPA

SALARIES/BENEFITS:

Pension Plan: ESOP Stock Plan: Profit Sharing: Top Exec. Salary: $ Bonus: $
Savings Plan: Stock Purch. Plan: Second Exec. Salary: $ Bonus: $

OTHER THOUGHTS:

Apparent Women Officers or Directors: 1
Hot Spot for Advancement for Women/Minorities:

LOCATIONS: ("Y" = Yes)

West:	Southwest:	Midwest:	Southeast:	Northeast:	International:
		Y			Y

Note: Financial information, benefits and other data can change quickly and may vary from those stated here.

MARATHON OIL CORP

www.marathon.com

Industry Group Code: 211111 **Ranks within this company's industry group:** Sales: 14 Profits: 11

Techology:		Medical/Drugs:		Engineering:		Transportation:		Chemicals/Petrochemicals:		Specialty:	
Computers:		Manufacturer:		Design:		Aerospace:		Oil/Gas Products:	Y	Special Services:	
Software:		Contract Research:		Construction:		Automotive:		Chemicals:		Consulting:	
Communications:		Medical Services:		Eng. Services:		Shipping:		Oil/Chem. Svcs.:	Y	Specialty Mgmt.:	
Electronics:		Labs:		Consulting:				Gases:		Products:	
Alternative Energy:		Bio. Services:						Other:	Y	Other:	

TYPES OF BUSINESS:

Oil & Gas Exploration & Production
Petroleum Marketing, Refining & Transportation
Gas Stations
Energy Marketing

BRANDS/DIVISIONS/AFFILIATES:

Marathon Petroleum Company LLC
Pilot Travel Centers LLC
Speedway SuperAmerica LLC
Marathon Oil Ireland, Ltd.

CONTACTS: *Note: Officers with more than one job title may be intentionally listed here more than once.*

Clarence P. Cazalot, Jr., CEO
Clarence P. Cazalot, Jr., Pres.
Janet F. Clark, CFO/Exec. VP
Eileen M. Campbell, VP-Human Resources
Thomas K. Sneed, CIO
Steven B. Hinchman, Exec. VP-Tech. & Svcs.
William F. Schwind, Jr., General Counsel/VP/Sec.
Jerry Howard, VP-Corp. Affairs
Howard J. Thill, VP-Investor Rel. & Public Affairs
Paul C. Reinbolt, VP-Finance/Treas.
R. Douglas Rogers, VP-Health, Environment & Safety
Michael K. Stewart, VP-Acct./Controller
Daniel J. Sullenbarger, VP-Corp. Compliance & Ethics
Stephen J. Landry, VP-Tax
Thomas J. Usher, Chmn.

Phone: 713-629-6600	**Fax:**
Toll-Free:	
Address: 5555 San Felipe St., Houston, TX 77056-2723 US	

GROWTH PLANS/SPECIAL FEATURES:

Marathon Oil Corp. explores for crude oil and natural gas worldwide, operates refineries and maintains U.S. retail gas outlets. It operates in four segments: Exploration and products (E&P); oil sands mining (OSM); refining, marketing and transportation (RM&T); and integrated gas (IG). The E&P segment explores for, produces and markets liquid hydrocarbons and natural gas on a worldwide basis. It conducts its exploration, development and production activities in 10 countries. Principal exploration activities are in the U.S., Angola, Norway and Indonesia. Principal development and production activities are in the U.S., the U.K., Norway, Ireland, Equatorial Guinea, Libya and Gabon. In 2008, the division's net sales averaged 381,000 barrels of oil equivalent per day. The OSM segment mines, extracts and transports bitumen from oil sands deposits in Alberta, Canada, and upgrades the bitumen to produce and market synthetic crude oil and by-products. The RM&T segment refines, markets and transports crude oil and petroleum products, primarily in the Midwest, upper Great Plains, Gulf Coast and southeastern regions of the U.S. The IG segments markets and transports products manufactured from natural gas, such as liquefied natural gas and methanol, on a worldwide basis. This segment is also developing other projects to link stranded natural gas resources with key demand areas. Marathon-branded retail gas outlets, operated by third-party entrepreneurs, include more than 4,400 locations across 17 states, as well as 1,600 Speedway locations. In October 2008, the company completed the sale of its 50% ownership in Pilot Travel Centers LLC. Also in October 2008, the firm sold its non-operated interests in the Heimdal area offshore Norway. In December 2008, Marathon agreed to sell subsidiary Marathon Oil Ireland, Ltd., to Star Energy Group.

The company offers its employees medical and dental coverage; life and disability insurance; flexible spending accounts; tuition reimbursement; and an employee assistance program.

FINANCIALS: **Sales and profits are in thousands of dollars—add 000 to get the full amount. 2008 Note: Financial information for 2008 was not available for all companies at press time.**

2008 Sales: $77,193,000	2008 Profits: $3,528,000	**U.S. Stock Ticker: MRO**
2007 Sales: $64,552,000	2007 Profits: $3,956,000	**Int'l Ticker:** Int'l Exchange:
2006 Sales: $64,896,000	2006 Profits: $5,234,000	Employees: 19,794
2005 Sales: $62,986,000	2005 Profits: $3,032,000	Fiscal Year Ends: 10/31
2004 Sales: $49,465,000	2004 Profits: $1,261,000	Parent Company:

SALARIES/BENEFITS:

Pension Plan: Y	ESOP Stock Plan:	Profit Sharing:	Top Exec. Salary: $1,294,000	Bonus: $6,264,000
Savings Plan: Y	Stock Purch. Plan:		Second Exec. Salary: $706,000	Bonus: $1,745,400

OTHER THOUGHTS:

Apparent Women Officers or Directors: 3
Hot Spot for Advancement for Women/Minorities: Y

LOCATIONS: ("Y" = Yes)

West:	Southwest:	Midwest:	Southeast:	Northeast:	International:
Y	Y	Y	Y	Y	Y

MATRIX SERVICE COMPANY

www.matrixservice.com

Industry Group Code: 234000 **Ranks within this company's industry group:** Sales: 28 Profits: 25

Techology:		Medical/Drugs:		Engineering:		Transportation:		Chemicals/Petrochemicals:		Specialty:	
Computers:		Manufacturer:		Design:	Y	Aerospace:		Oil/Gas Products:		Special Services:	
Software:		Contract Research:		Construction:	Y	Automotive:		Chemicals:		Consulting:	
Communications:		Medical Services:		Eng. Services:	Y	Shipping:		Oil/Chem. Svcs.:	Y	Specialty Mgmt.:	
Electronics:		Labs:		Consulting:				Gases:		Products:	
Alternative Energy:		Bio. Services:						Other:		Other:	

TYPES OF BUSINESS:

Heavy Construction & Civil Engineering
Plant Maintenance Services
Storage Tank Services
Petrochemical Industry Services

BRANDS/DIVISIONS/AFFILIATES:

Plains All American Pipeline
BP plc
Sunoco Inc
Bechtel Group Inc
Enbridge Energy Partners LP
Chevron Corporation
Matrix Service Industrial Contractors, Inc.
Matrix Service, Inc.

CONTACTS: *Note: Officers with more than one job title may be intentionally listed here more than once.*

Michael J. Bradley, CEO
Joseph F. Montalbano, COO/VP
Michael J. Bradley, Pres.
Thomas E. Long, CFO/VP
Nancy E. Austin, VP-Human Resources
Lansing G. Smith, VP-Eng.
Albert D. Fosbenner, VP-Admin.
John S. Newmeister, VP-Corp. Dev.
Kevin Cavanah, VP-Financial Reporting
Kevin Cavanah, VP-Acct.
Vance R. Davis, VP-AST Svcs.
James P. Ryan, Pres., Matrix Service, Inc.
Matthew J. Petrizzo, Pres., Matrix Service Industrial Contractors, Inc.
Bradley J. Rinehart, VP-Midwestern Oper.
Michael J. Hall, Chmn.

Phone: 866-367-6879 **Fax:** 918-838-8810
Toll-Free:
Address: 5100 E. Skelly Dr., Ste. 700, Tulsa, OK 74135 US

GROWTH PLANS/SPECIAL FEATURES:

Matrix Service Company and its subsidiaries provide construction, repair and maintenance services, primarily to the liquefied natural gas, petroleum, petrochemical, power generation, power delivery, terminal, pipeline, utility, chemical, transportation, pulp and paper, food and beverage, heavy industrial and industrial gas industries throughout the U.S. and Canada. The company operates in two segments: construction services and repair and maintenance. Construction services include turnkey projects; renovations, upgrades and expansions for large and small projects, electrical and instrumentation; mechanical, piping and equipment installations; tank engineering, design, fabrication and erection; and steel, steel plate, vessel and pipe fabrication. Fabrication facilities are located in Washington, California, Oklahoma, Texas, Illinois, South Carolina, Delaware, Pennsylvania, Michigan and Ontario, Canada. The company's repair and maintenance services include plant maintenance, turnaround services, outages, industrial cleaning, hydroblasting and substation and above ground storage tank repair and maintenance. Matrix's major customers are Plains All American Pipeline, British Petroleum, Sunoco, Bechtel Group, Enbridge Energy and Chevron. In October 2007, subsidiary Matrix Service, Inc. received an increase of its existing contract with SemCrude, L.P. for the construction of 12 above ground storage tanks valued at $27 million, to 22 storage tanks, now valued at $51 million. In September 2008, the company announced an agreement to acquire the engineering and construction assets of CB&I, a firm specializing in large steel construction.

Matrix Service Company offers its employees a 401(k) plan, tuition reimbursement, a professional development program for project managers, advancement opportunities, a business casual dress environment, an employee assistance program, company-sponsored events and medical, prescription, vision and dental plan options.

FINANCIALS: **Sales and profits are in thousands of dollars—add 000 to get the full amount. 2008 Note: Financial information for 2008 was not available for all companies at press time.**

2008 Sales: $731,301	2008 Profits: $21,414	**U.S. Stock Ticker: MTRX**
2007 Sales: $639,846	2007 Profits: $19,171	**Int'l Ticker:** Int'l Exchange:
2006 Sales: $493,927	2006 Profits: $7,653	Employees: 3,202
2005 Sales: $439,138	2005 Profits: $-38,830	Fiscal Year Ends: 5/31
2004 Sales: $608,761	2004 Profits: $9,542	Parent Company:

SALARIES/BENEFITS:

Pension Plan:	ESOP Stock Plan:	Profit Sharing:	Top Exec. Salary: $516,667	Bonus: $371,700
Savings Plan: Y	Stock Purch. Plan:		Second Exec. Salary: $273,780	Bonus: $118,120

OTHER THOUGHTS:

Apparent Women Officers or Directors: 1
Hot Spot for Advancement for Women/Minorities:

LOCATIONS: ("Y" = Yes)

West:	Southwest:	Midwest:	Southeast:	Northeast:	International:
Y	Y	Y		Y	Y

MAXIM INTEGRATED PRODUCTS INC

www.maxim-ic.com

Industry Group Code: 334413 **Ranks within this company's industry group:** Sales: 17 Profits: 9

Techology:		Medical/Drugs:		Engineering:		Transportation:		Chemicals/Petrochemicals:		Specialty:	
Computers:		Manufacturer:		Design:		Aerospace:		Oil/Gas Products:		Special Services:	
Software:		Contract Research:		Construction:		Automotive:		Chemicals:		Consulting:	
Communications:		Medical Services:		Eng. Services:		Shipping:		Oil/Chem. Svcs.:		Specialty Mgmt.:	
Electronics:	Y	Labs:		Consulting:				Gases:		Products:	
Alternative Energy:		Bio. Services:						Other:		Other:	

TYPES OF BUSINESS:

Integrated Circuits-Analog & Mixed Signal
High-Frequency Design Processes
Manufacturing Capabilities
Power Conversion Chips

BRANDS/DIVISIONS/AFFILIATES:

Dallas Semiconductor Corp.
Vitesse Semiconductor Corp.

CONTACTS: *Note: Officers with more than one job title may be intentionally listed here more than once.*

Tunc Doluca, CEO
Tunc Doluca, Pres.
Bruce E. Kiddoo, CFO
Matthew J. Murphy, VP-Worldwide Sales
Charles G. Rigg, Sr. VP-Admin.
Charles G. Rigg, General Counsel
Paresh Maniar, Exec. Dir.-Investor Rel.
Vijay Ullal, Group Pres.
Pirooz Parvarandeh, Group Pres.
Richard Hood, VP
Christopher J. Neil, Div. VP
B. Kipling Hagopian, Chmn.

Phone: 408-737-7600 **Fax:** 408-737-7194
Toll-Free: 800-998-8800
Address: 120 San Gabriel Dr., Sunnyvale, CA 94086 US

GROWTH PLANS/SPECIAL FEATURES:

Maxim Integrated Products, Inc. designs, develops, manufactures and markets analog, mixed-signal, high frequency and digital circuits. Its products are primarily created by wholly-owned subsidiary Dallas Semiconductor Corporation. Maxim's circuits connect the analog and digital world by detecting, measuring, amplifying and converting real-world signals into the digital signals necessary for computer processing. It produces electronic interface products to interact with people, through audio, video, touchpad, key pad and security devices; the physical world, through motion, time, temperature and humidity sensors; power sources, via conversion, charging, supervision and regulation systems; and other digital systems, including wireless, storage and fiber optic systems. Maxim's products serve four major end-markets: industrial, which includes automotive products, automatic test equipment, and military and medical equipment and instruments; communications, including base stations, networking/data communications and telecommunications; consumer products, specifically cell phones, digital cameras, gps, handhelds and media players and home entertainment products; and computing, including notebook and desktop computers, peripherals, servers and workstations and storage. The company also offers the use of its manufacturing capabilities for custom designs. Some of Maxim's newest products include one of the industry's smallest DC/DC converters; one of the first fully integrated switch-mode/linear LED drivers; bidirectional video filters/buffers for portable consumer devices; high-voltage, low-power linear regulators for automotive and industrial applications; dual-band, dual-mode tuners for Japanese digital broadcasts; a programmable high-brightness LED driver for automotive and other lighting applications; and one of the first chips to convert an all-analog power supply to a fully programmable, digital power-management solution. In October 2008, the company agreed to acquire Mobilygen, a private, fables semiconductor company that specializes in H.264 video compression.

Employees are offered health insurance; health club subsidies; preventative wellness screenings; life and AD&D coverage; disability coverage; an educational assistance program; flexible spending accounts; an employee assistance program; and business travel accident insurance.

FINANCIALS: **Sales and profits are in thousands of dollars—add 000 to get the full amount. 2008 Note: Financial information for 2008 was not available for all companies at press time.**

2008 Sales: $2,052,783 | 2008 Profits: $317,725
2007 Sales: $2,009,124 | 2007 Profits: $286,227
2006 Sales: $1,856,945 | 2006 Profits: $387,701
2005 Sales: $1,617,734 | 2005 Profits: $462,277
2004 Sales: $1,439,263 | 2004 Profits: $419,752

U.S. Stock Ticker: MXIM.PK
Int'l Ticker: Int'l Exchange:
Employees: 9,810
Fiscal Year Ends: 8/31
Parent Company:

SALARIES/BENEFITS:

Pension Plan: | ESOP Stock Plan: | Profit Sharing: | Top Exec. Salary: $498,077 | Bonus: $2,334,209
Savings Plan: Y | Stock Purch. Plan: | | Second Exec. Salary: $400,000 | Bonus: $1,902,767

OTHER THOUGHTS:

Apparent Women Officers or Directors:
Hot Spot for Advancement for Women/Minorities:

LOCATIONS: ("Y" = Yes)

West:	Southwest:	Midwest:	Southeast:	Northeast:	International:
Y	Y	Y	Y	Y	Y

MAZDA MOTOR CORPORATION

www.mazda.com

Industry Group Code: 336111 **Ranks within this company's industry group:** Sales: 14 Profits: 10

Techology:		Medical/Drugs:		Engineering:		Transportation:		Chemicals/Petrochemicals:		Specialty:	
Computers:		Manufacturer:		Design:		Aerospace:		Oil/Gas Products:		Special Services:	
Software:		Contract Research:		Construction:		Automotive:	Y	Chemicals:		Consulting:	
Communications:		Medical Services:		Eng. Services:		Shipping:		Oil/Chem. Svcs.:		Specialty Mgmt.:	
Electronics:		Labs:		Consulting:				Gases:		Products:	
Alternative Energy:		Bio. Services:						Other:		Other:	

TYPES OF BUSINESS:

Automobiles, Manufacturing
Commercial Vans & Trucks
Hydrogen Engine Technology

BRANDS/DIVISIONS/AFFILIATES:

Mazda North American Operations
Mazda Canada
Ford Motor Company
MCM Energy Service Company
Miata
Bongo
Titan

CONTACTS: *Note: Officers with more than one job title may be intentionally listed here more than once.*

Hisakazu Imaki, CEO
Hisakazu Imaki, Pres.
David E. Friedman, CFO
Philip G. Spender, Exec. VP-Mktg. & Sales
Takashi Yamanouchi, Exec. VP-Human Resources
Philip G. Spender, Exec. VP-R&D
Philip G. Spender, Exec. VP-IT
Takashi Yamanouchi, Exec. VP-Admin.
David E. Friedman, Sr. Managing Exec. Officer-Corp. Planning
Yuji Harada, Managing Exec. Officer-Corp. Comm.
Daniel T. Morris, Sr. Managing Exec. Officer-Mktg. & Overseas Sales
Seita Kanai, Pres., Mazda Engineering & Technology Co., Ltd.
James J. O'Sullivan, Pres./CEO-Mazda Motor of America, Inc.
Keishi Egawa, Exec. VP/COO-Mazda Motor of America, Inc.
Hisakazu Imaki, Chmn.
James M. Muir, Pres./CEO-Mazda Motor Europe GmbH
Takashi Yamanouchi, Exec. VP-Purchasing

Phone: 81-82-282-1111 **Fax:** 81-82-287-5190
Toll-Free:
Address: 3-1 Shinchi, Fuchu-cho, Aki-gun, Hiroshima, 100-0011 Japan

GROWTH PLANS/SPECIAL FEATURES:

Mazda Motor Corporation, established in 1920, is one of Japan's largest automakers. Mazda operates three production facilities in Japan and 13 overseas facilities, including joint ventures in the U.S. (Missouri), China, Taiwan, Thailand, the Philippines and South Africa with Ford Motor Company, which holds a 13% share in the firm. The company has been exporting cars to the U.S. and Europe for almost 40 years, and with Mazda cars and trucks now being sold in nearly 130 countries, overseas sales account for over two-thirds of annual revenues. Working closely with Ford, the company has recently revamped much of its passenger car, truck, minivan and utility vehicle product line, rolling out new models including the Mazda 6, Mazda 3, Mazda 8 and the RX-8, a high-performance sports car. Other popular models include the Miata sports-convertible, the Tribute sport utility vehicle and the BT-50 pick-up. The company's line of commercial vehicles targets the light industrial sector with high-efficiency diesel vans and trucks. Marketed under brand names including Bongo, Titan, Mazda E-Series and Mazda T-Series, these vehicles are available in various configurations of cargo bed and cabin size. Many of these vehicles are produced on an outsourced basis, with Bongo vans and trucks being built by Nissan and Mitsubishi. Mazda markets passenger micro-mini vans and trucks under the model name Scrum, with vehicles being manufactured on a third-party OEM basis by Suzuki Motor Corporation. The firm operates a joint venture with Mitsubishi named MCM Energy Service Company, which provides electricity and steam to two of Mazda's Japanese production facilities. In June 2008, the company announced its intention to raise the average fuel efficiency of Mazda cars sold worldwide by 30% by 2015. In December 2008, the firm announced that it would cut production by at least 148,000 units in 2009, in response to slow sales globally.

FINANCIALS: **Sales and profits are in thousands of dollars—add 000 to get the full amount. 2008 Note: Financial information for 2008 was not available for all companies at press time.**

2008 Sales: $34,757,890	2008 Profits: $918,350	**U.S. Stock Ticker: MZDAF**
2007 Sales: $27,640,000	2007 Profits: $630,000	**Int'l Ticker: 7261** Int'l Exchange: Tokyo-TSE
2006 Sales: $24,830,200	2006 Profits: $	Employees: 366,626
2005 Sales: $24,212,280	2005 Profits: $413,118	Fiscal Year Ends: 3/31
2004 Sales: $27,604,100	2004 Profits: $320,900	Parent Company:

SALARIES/BENEFITS:

Pension Plan:	ESOP Stock Plan:	Profit Sharing:	Top Exec. Salary: $	Bonus: $
Savings Plan:	Stock Purch. Plan:		Second Exec. Salary: $	Bonus: $

OTHER THOUGHTS:

Apparent Women Officers or Directors:
Hot Spot for Advancement for Women/Minorities:

LOCATIONS: ("Y" = Yes)

West:	Southwest:	Midwest:	Southeast:	Northeast:	International:
Y	Y	Y	Y	Y	Y

MCAFEE INC

www.mcafee.com

Industry Group Code: 511211 **Ranks within this company's industry group:** Sales: 2 Profits: 2

Techology:		Medical/Drugs:		Engineering:		Transportation:		Chemicals/Petrochemicals:		Specialty:	
Computers:		Manufacturer:		Design:		Aerospace:		Oil/Gas Products:		Special Services:	
Software:	Y	Contract Research:		Construction:		Automotive:		Chemicals:		Consulting:	
Communications:		Medical Services:		Eng. Services:		Shipping:		Oil/Chem. Svcs.:		Specialty Mgmt.:	
Electronics:		Labs:		Consulting:				Gases:		Products:	
Alternative Energy:		Bio. Services:						Other:		Other:	

TYPES OF BUSINESS:

Software-Security
Virus Protection Software
Network Management Software

BRANDS/DIVISIONS/AFFILIATES:

McAfee Total Protection
LoJack for Laptops
Registry Power Cleaner
McAfee PCI Certifications Service
McAfee Network DPL Discovery
McAfee OK Mobile
Reconnex
Secure Computing Corporation

CONTACTS:

Note: Officers with more than one job title may be intentionally listed here more than once.

David DeWalt, CEO
Albert A. Pimentel, COO
David DeWalt, Pres.
Albert A. Pimentel, CFO
David Milam, Chief Mktg. Officer/Exec. VP
Joseph Gabbert, Exec. VP-Human Resources
Christopher Bolin, CTO/Exec. VP
Mark Cochran, General Counsel/Exec. VP
Gerhard Watzinger, Exec. VP-Corp. Strategy & Bus. Dev.
Keith Krzeminski, Chief Acct. Officer/Sr. VP-Finance
Michael DeCesare, Exec. VP-Worldwide Sales
Todd Gebhart, Exec. VP/Gen. Mgr.-Consumer, Mobile & Small Bus.
Dan Ryan, Exec. VP/Gen. Mgr.-Network Security Bus. Unit
George Kurtz, Sr. VP-Gen. Mgr-Risk & Compliance Bus. Unit
Charles J. Robel, Chmn.

Phone: 408-988-3832 **Fax:** 408-970-9727
Toll-Free:
Address: 3965 Freedom Cir., Santa Clara, CA 95054 US

GROWTH PLANS/SPECIAL FEATURES:

McAfee, Inc. is a developer and supplier of software-based computer security systems that prevent intrusions on networks and protect computer systems from attacks. It allows home users, businesses, government agencies, service providers and partners to block attacks, prevent disruptions and continuously track and improve their security. The company's products are categorized for Home and Home Office, Small Business, Medium Business and Large Enterprise. Home and Home Office products are geared toward users who work from home on one or multiple computers. Products consist of PC protection software such as McAfee Total Protection, which works as an anti-virus and maintains an enhanced firewall. LoJack for Laptops tracks and recovers lost or stolen computers and is supported by a professional theft recovery team. Registry Power Cleaner software repairs registry errors and protects data with automatic backups. Small Business products are designed for businesses with 10-50 computers. The McAfee PCI Certification Service offers analysis of compliance status, assisting companies in completing PCI DSS requirement. The McAfee Site Advisor reviews the security of websites and issues safety ratings before the user visits them. Medium Business products are targeted towards businesses with 100-1,000 computers and consist of data protection products such as the McAfee Network DPL Discovery, which protects sensitive data; compliance services, such as McAfee Email Security Service, which blocks viruses carried by e-mail; and network security products such as Total Protection for Secure Businesses. Enterprise products are geared toward companies with hundreds to tens of thousands computers. McAfee OK Mobile and Content Safety inspects content and certification for mobile devices. The McAfee Policy Auditor provides automated manual audit processes. In 2008, the company acquired Reconnex, a data loss prevention (DPL) company for $46 million and Secure Computing Corporation for $418 million.

FINANCIALS:

Sales and profits are in thousands of dollars—add 000 to get the full amount. 2008 Note: Financial information for 2008 was not available for all companies at press time.

2008 Sales: $1,600,065	2008 Profits: $172,209	**U.S. Stock Ticker: MFE**
2007 Sales: $1,308,220	2007 Profits: $166,980	**Int'l Ticker:** Int'l Exchange:
2006 Sales: $1,142,327	2006 Profits: $137,529	Employees: 5,600
2005 Sales: $987,299	2005 Profits: $138,828	Fiscal Year Ends: 12/31
2004 Sales: $910,542	2004 Profits: $225,065	Parent Company:

SALARIES/BENEFITS:

Pension Plan:	ESOP Stock Plan:	Profit Sharing:	Top Exec. Salary: $675,000	Bonus: $1,250,000
Savings Plan:	Stock Purch. Plan:		Second Exec. Salary: $550,000	Bonus: $655,278

OTHER THOUGHTS:

Apparent Women Officers or Directors:
Hot Spot for Advancement for Women/Minorities:

LOCATIONS: ("Y" = Yes)

West:	Southwest:	Midwest:	Southeast:	Northeast:	International:
Y	Y	Y	Y	Y	Y

MCDERMOTT INTERNATIONAL INC

www.mcdermott.com

Industry Group Code: 541330 **Ranks within this company's industry group:** Sales: 3 Profits: 2

Techology:		Medical/Drugs:		Engineering:		Transportation:		Chemicals/Petrochemicals:		Specialty:	
Computers:		Manufacturer:		Design:	Y	Aerospace:		Oil/Gas Products:		Special Services:	Y
Software:		Contract Research:		Construction:	Y	Automotive:		Chemicals:		Consulting:	
Communications:		Medical Services:		Eng. Services:	Y	Shipping:		Oil/Chem. Svcs.:		Specialty Mgmt.:	
Electronics:		Labs:		Consulting:				Gases:		Products:	
Alternative Energy:	Y	Bio. Services:						Other:		Other:	

TYPES OF BUSINESS:

Engineering Services
Power Generation Services
Nuclear Fuel Assemblies
Government Services
Marine Construction
Procurement Services
Project Management
Consulting

BRANDS/DIVISIONS/AFFILIATES:

J. Ray McDermott, S.A.
BWX Technologies, Inc.
Y-12 National Security Complex
Pantex Plant
Los Alamos National Laboratory
Babcock & Wilcox Company (The)
Babcock & Wilcox Companies (The)

CONTACTS: *Note: Officers with more than one job title may be intentionally listed here more than once.*

John A. Fees, CEO
John A. Fees, Pres.
Michael S. Taff, CFO/Sr. VP
Preston Johnson, Jr., Sr. VP-Human Resources
John C. Knowles, CIO/VP
John T. Nesser, III, Chief Admin. & Legal Officer/Exec. VP
Liane K. Hinrichs, General Counsel/VP/Corp. Sec.
John D. Krueger, VP-Corp. Dev. & Strategic Planning
John E. Roueche, III, VP-Corp. Comm.
John E. Roueche, III, VP-Investor Rel.
Dennis S. Baldwin, Chief Acct. Officer/VP
James C. Lewis, Treas./VP
J. Timothy Woodard, VP-Chief Risk Officer
Robert A. Deason, CEO/Pres., J. Ray McDermott, S.A.
Thomas A. Henzler, Corp. Compliance Officer
Bruce W. Wilkinson, Chmn.

Phone: 281-870-5901 **Fax:**
Toll-Free:
Address: 777 N. Eldridge Pkwy., Houston, TX 77079 US

GROWTH PLANS/SPECIAL FEATURES:

McDermott International, Inc. is a leading energy services company that operates three main business segments: Offshore oil and gas construction services; government operations; and power generation systems. The offshore construction services are provided through subsidiary J. Ray McDermott, S.A. (JRMSA) and its subsidiaries. JRMSA and its subsidiaries design, engineer, fabricate and install offshore drilling and production facilities, as well as install marine pipelines and subsea production systems. It operates in most major offshore oil and gas producing regions throughout the world, including Mexico, the Gulf of Mexico, the Middle East, the Caspian Sea, India and Asia Pacific. This segment owns, or operates through a joint-venture, one derrick vessel and six combination derrick-pipe laying vessels, equipped with various cranes, welding equipment, pile-driving hammers and other equipment; and tug boats, barges and utility boats to support its operations. The government operations segment, with services performed by subsidiary BWX Technologies, Inc. and its subsidiaries, supplies nuclear components to the U.S. government, as well as processing uranium; offering environmental site restoration services; and managing and operating U.S. government-owned facilities, primarily within the nuclear weapons complex of the U.S. Department of Energy. Facilities served by the segment include the Y-12 National Security Complex, the Pantex Plant and Los Alamos National Laboratory. The power generation systems segment, run by the Babcock & Wilcox Company (B&W) and its subsidiaries, provides a variety of services, equipment and systems to generate steam and electric power at energy facilities worldwide. In June 2008, JRMSA entered a joint venture with a subsidiary of state-owned China Shipbuilding Industry Corporation. In July 2008, the firm purchased the Intech group of companies. In August 2008, B&W entered into a definitive agreement to acquire Nuclear Fuel Services, Inc., a provider of specialty nuclear fuels and related services.

FINANCIALS: **Sales and profits are in thousands of dollars—add 000 to get the full amount. 2008 Note: Financial information for 2008 was not available for all companies at press time.**

2008 Sales: $6,572,423	2008 Profits: $429,302	**U.S. Stock Ticker: MDR**
2007 Sales: $5,631,610	2007 Profits: $607,828	**Int'l Ticker:** Int'l Exchange:
2006 Sales: $4,120,141	2006 Profits: $330,515	Employees: 26,400
2005 Sales: $1,856,311	2005 Profits: $205,687	Fiscal Year Ends: 12/31
2004 Sales: $1,923,019	2004 Profits: $61,639	Parent Company:

SALARIES/BENEFITS:

Pension Plan: Y	ESOP Stock Plan:	Profit Sharing:	Top Exec. Salary: $750,000	Bonus: $1,462,500
Savings Plan: Y	Stock Purch. Plan:		Second Exec. Salary: $500,000	Bonus: $650,000

OTHER THOUGHTS:

Apparent Women Officers or Directors: 2
Hot Spot for Advancement for Women/Minorities:

LOCATIONS: ("Y" = Yes)

West:	Southwest:	Midwest:	Southeast:	Northeast:	International:
Y	Y	Y	Y	Y	Y

MEADOW VALLEY CORPORATION

www.meadowvalley.com

Industry Group Code: 234000 **Ranks within this company's industry group:** Sales: Profits:

Techology:		Medical/Drugs:		Engineering:		Transportation:		Chemicals/Petrochemicals:		Specialty:	
Computers:		Manufacturer:		Design:	Y	Aerospace:		Oil/Gas Products:		Special Services:	
Software:		Contract Research:		Construction:	Y	Automotive:		Chemicals:		Consulting:	
Communications:		Medical Services:		Eng. Services:	Y	Shipping:		Oil/Chem. Svcs.:		Specialty Mgmt.:	
Electronics:		Labs:		Consulting:				Gases:		Products:	
Alternative Energy:		Bio. Services:						Other:		Other:	

TYPES OF BUSINESS:

Heavy Construction & Civil Engineering
Construction Materials-Concrete, Sand & Gravel
Design Services
Mining
Ready-Mix Concrete
Technical Services

BRANDS/DIVISIONS/AFFILIATES:

Meadow Valley Contractors, Inc.
Ready Mix, Inc.

CONTACTS: *Note: Officers with more than one job title may be intentionally listed here more than once.*

Bradley E. Larson, CEO
Kenneth D. Nelson, Chief Admin. Officer
David D. Doty, Corp. Sec.
David D. Doty, Principal Acct. Officer
Alan Terril, VP-Nevada

Phone: 602-437-5400	**Fax:** 602-437-1681
Toll-Free:	
Address: 4602 E. Thomas Rd., Phoenix, AZ 85018 US	

GROWTH PLANS/SPECIAL FEATURES:

Meadow Valley Corp., based in Phoenix, Arizona, is engaged in the construction industry as a provider of construction services and a supplier of construction materials. The construction services segment (CSS) specializes in structural concrete construction of highway bridges and overpasses and the paving of highways and airport runways. The construction materials segment (CMS) provides ready-mix concrete, sand and gravel products both to itself and other contractors. CSS operates throughout Nevada, Arizona and Utah, with principal operations in the Las Vegas, Nevada and Phoenix, Arizona metropolitan areas. Meadow Valley also owns Meadow Valley Contractors, Inc., a heavy construction contractor for both public and private infrastructure projects, including the construction of bridges and overpasses, channels, roadways, highways and airport runways. Another subsidiary, Apex Testing Corp., acquired in 2006, provides geotechnical, environmental and field and laboratory technical services. The company owns 53% of Ready Mix, Inc., which manufactures and distributes ready mix concrete, crushed landscaping rock and other miscellaneous rock and sand products. Meadow Valley owns or leases most of the equipment used in its business, including cranes, backhoes, graders, loaders, trucks, trailers, pavers, rollers, construction materials processing plants, batch plants and related equipment. The raw materials necessary for most operations are obtained from multiple sources. CMS does have one full-time mining operation in Nephi, Utah. In February 2009, the company was acquired by Dallas-based private equity firm Insight Equity Holdings LLC for approximately $61 million.

FINANCIALS: **Sales and profits are in thousands of dollars—add 000 to get the full amount. 2008 Note: Financial information for 2008 was not available for all companies at press time.**

2008 Sales: $
2007 Sales: $205,919
2006 Sales: $195,522
2005 Sales: $183,872
2004 Sales: $166,831

2008 Profits: $
2007 Profits: $4,061
2006 Profits: $4,166
2005 Profits: $4,203
2004 Profits: $ 573

U.S. Stock Ticker: Private
Int'l Ticker: Int'l Exchange:
Employees: 510
Fiscal Year Ends: 12/31
Parent Company:

SALARIES/BENEFITS:

Pension Plan: ESOP Stock Plan: Profit Sharing: Top Exec. Salary: $250,000 Bonus: $363,785
Savings Plan: Stock Purch. Plan: Second Exec. Salary: $150,000 Bonus: $230,400

OTHER THOUGHTS:

Apparent Women Officers or Directors:
Hot Spot for Advancement for Women/Minorities:

LOCATIONS: ("Y" = Yes)

West:	Southwest:	Midwest:	Southeast:	Northeast:	International:
Y	Y				

MEDTRONIC INC

www.medtronic.com

Industry Group Code: 339113 **Ranks within this company's industry group:** Sales: 3 Profits: 3

Techology:		Medical/Drugs:		Engineering:		Transportation:		Chemicals/Petrochemicals:		Specialty:	
Computers:		Manufacturer:	Y	Design:		Aerospace:		Oil/Gas Products:		Special Services:	
Software:		Contract Research:	Y	Construction:		Automotive:		Chemicals:		Consulting:	
Communications:		Medical Services:		Eng. Services:		Shipping:		Oil/Chem. Svcs.:		Specialty Mgmt.:	
Electronics:		Labs:	Y	Consulting:				Gases:		Products:	
Alternative Energy:		Bio. Services:						Other:		Other:	Y

TYPES OF BUSINESS:

Equipment-Defibrillators & Pacing Products
Neurological Devices
Diabetes Management Devices
Ear, Nose & Throat Surgical Equipment
Pain Management Devices
Catheters & Stents
Cardiac Surgery Equipment

BRANDS/DIVISIONS/AFFILIATES:

Talent Abdominal Stent Graft
Restore Medical Inc
CryroCath Technologies Inc
Ablation Frontiers Inc
Ventor Technologies Inc.
INFUSE Bone Graft
Continuous Glucose Monitoring
Integrated Power Console (IPC)

CONTACTS: *Note: Officers with more than one job title may be intentionally listed here more than once.*

William A. Hawkins, CEO
William A. Hawkins, Pres.
Gary Ellis, CFO/Sr. VP
Martha Goldberg Aronson, Chief Talent Officer/Sr. VP
Stephen N. Oesterle, Sr. VP-Medicine & Tech.
Terrance Carlson, General Counsel/Corp. Sec./Sr. VP
H. James Dallas, Sr. VP-Quality & Oper.
Catherine Szyman, Sr. VP-Strategy & Innovation
Susan Alpert, Chief Regulatory Officer/Sr. VP
Bob Blankenmeyer, Sr. VP/Pres., Surgical Tech.
Scott R. Ward, Sr. VP/Pres., Cardiovascular
Stephen Mahle, Exec. VP-Healthcare Policy & Regulatory
William A. Hawkins, Chmn.
Jean-Luc Butel, Sr. VP/Pres., Medtronic Int'l

Phone: 763-514-4000 **Fax:** 763-514-4879
Toll-Free: 800-328-2518
Address: 710 Medtronic Pkwy., Minneapolis, MN 55432 US

GROWTH PLANS/SPECIAL FEATURES:

Medtronic, Inc. is a global leader in medical technology, whose professed mission is alleviating pain, restoring health and extending life for millions of people around the world. The firm operates in seven business sectors: cardiac rhythm disease management; surgical technologies; neuromodulation; spinal; cardiovascular; physio-control; and diabetes. Medtronic is one of the world's largest suppliers of medical devices for cardiac rhythm management, including pacemakers and implantable cardiac defibrillators. The surgical technologies division develops products for the treatment of ear, nose and throat (ENT) and neurological diseases, as well as for cranial, spinal, sinus and orthopedic maladies. The neuromodulation division develops, manufactures and markets devices for the treatment of neurological, urological and gastroenterological disorders. The spinal division produces medical devices and implants used in the treatment of spinal conditions. The cardiovascular segment offers minimally invasive products and therapies to treat coronary artery disease, aortic and thoracic aneurysms, and peripheral vascular disease. The physio-control segment produces external defibrillators, including manual defibrillators used by hospitals and emergency response personnel, as well as automated external defibrillators used in public settings. The diabetes unit provides glucose monitors, insulin pumps and other products, as well as informational resources available on the firm's web site. In 2008, the FDA approved the firm's Talent Abdominal Stent Graft for repairing aortic aneurysms. Recent company acquisitions include Restore Medical, Inc; CryoCath Technologies Inc; the Repose product line from InfluENT Medical; Ablation Frontiers, Inc.; and Ventor Technologies Inc. In February 2009, the company agreed to acquire CoreValve, Inc. a developer of aortic valve replacement products. Also in 2009, Medtronic launched the Integrated Power Console (IPC) platform for the use in spinal cranial and ENT surgeries.

Employees are offered medical insurance; disability coverage; retirement plans; stock ownership; and adoption and eldercare assistance.

FINANCIALS: **Sales and profits are in thousands of dollars—add 000 to get the full amount. 2008 Note: Financial information for 2008 was not available for all companies at press time.**

2008 Sales: $13,515,000	2008 Profits: $2,231,000	**U.S. Stock Ticker: MDT**
2007 Sales: $12,299,000	2007 Profits: $2,802,000	**Int'l Ticker:** Int'l Exchange:
2006 Sales: $11,292,000	2006 Profits: $2,546,700	Employees: 40,351
2005 Sales: $10,054,600	2005 Profits: $1,803,900	Fiscal Year Ends: 4/30
2004 Sales: $9,087,200	2004 Profits: $1,959,300	Parent Company:

SALARIES/BENEFITS:

Pension Plan:	ESOP Stock Plan:	Profit Sharing:	Top Exec. Salary: $1,092,000	Bonus: $987,656
Savings Plan: Y	Stock Purch. Plan: Y		Second Exec. Salary: $996,000	Bonus: $971,749

OTHER THOUGHTS:

Apparent Women Officers or Directors: 6
Hot Spot for Advancement for Women/Minorities: Y

LOCATIONS: ("Y" = Yes)

West:	Southwest:	Midwest:	Southeast:	Northeast:	International:
Y	Y	Y	Y	Y	Y

MENTOR GRAPHICS CORP

www.mentor.com

Industry Group Code: 511215 **Ranks within this company's industry group:** Sales: 6 Profits: 6

Techology:		Medical/Drugs:		Engineering:		Transportation:		Chemicals/Petrochemicals:		Specialty:	
Computers:		Manufacturer:		Design:		Aerospace:		Oil/Gas Products:		Special Services:	
Software:	Y	Contract Research:		Construction:		Automotive:		Chemicals:		Consulting:	Y
Communications:		Medical Services:		Eng. Services:		Shipping:		Oil/Chem. Svcs.:		Specialty Mgmt.:	
Electronics:		Labs:		Consulting:				Gases:		Products:	
Alternative Energy:		Bio. Services:						Other:		Other:	

TYPES OF BUSINESS:

Software-Component Design, Simulation & Testing
Electronic Design Automation Tools
Consulting Services

BRANDS/DIVISIONS/AFFILIATES:

Ponte Solutions, Inc.
Flomerics Group plc
Questa
ModelSim
ADVance MS
Calibre
Seamless
Eldo

CONTACTS: *Note: Officers with more than one job title may be intentionally listed here more than once.*

Walden C. Rhines, CEO
Gregory K. Hinckley, Pres.
Maria Pope, CFO/VP
Brian Derrick, VP-Corp. Mktg.
Ananthan Thandri, CIO/VP
Dean Freed, General Counsel/VP
Ry Schwark, Dir.-Public Rel.
Ry Schwark, Dir.-Investor Rel.
Ethan Manuel, Corp. Treas.
L. Don Maulsby, Sr. VP-World Trade
Jue-Hsien Cherm, VP/Gen. Mgr.-Deep Submicron Div.
Henry Potts, VP/Gen. Mgr.-System Design Div.
Simon Bloch, VP/Gen. Mgr.-Design & Synthesis Div.
Walden C. Rhines, Chmn.
Hanns Windele, VP-Europe

Phone: 503-685-7000	**Fax:** 503-685-1204
Toll-Free: 800-592-2210	
Address: 8005 SW Boeckman Rd., Wilsonville, OR 97070 US	

GROWTH PLANS/SPECIAL FEATURES:

Mentor Graphics Corp., a leader in electronic design automation (EDA), provides software and hardware design tools for electronic products. The company manufactures, markets and supports advanced computer software and emulation hardware systems used to automate the design, analysis and testing of electronic hardware and embedded systems software in electronic systems and components. The products are primarily marketed to large companies in the military, aerospace, communications, computer, consumer electronics, semiconductor, networking, multimedia and transportation industries. The company's offerings include scalable verification, physical design and verification, integrated printed circuit board (PCB) and field-programmable gate array systems design, electronic system level (ESL) design, electrical and electronic system design and harness engineering, embedded systems design and platform-based design tools and products, as well as providing consulting and support services. Mentor's field programmable gate array products include the ModelSim and Precision series. The firm's scalable verification products include the Questa, ADVance MS and Seamless lines; its IC nanometer design products include the Calibre and Eldo series. Mentor's embedded systems products include the Nucleus and Edge lines. The firm's design-for-test products include ATPG and compression products, memory test products, boundary scanners, logic BIST and yield learning and diagnosis products. In addition, the company offers one C++ based design system, Catapult C Synthesis, and a system modeling program, SystemVision. In May 2008, the firm acquired the assets of Ponte Solutions, Inc., a developer of model-based design for manufacturing (DFM) solutions. In October 2008, Mentor acquired Flomerics Group plc, a U.K.-based supplier of computational fluid dynamics analysis products.

Employees of Mentor receive adoption assistance; employee assistance; medical, dental, vision and prescription drug coverage; life and AD&D insurance; child and elder care resources; credit union access; tuition reimbursement; and a prenatal care program.

FINANCIALS: **Sales and profits are in thousands of dollars—add 000 to get the full amount. 2008 Note: Financial information for 2008 was not available for all companies at press time.**

2008 Sales: $789,101	2008 Profits: $-88,802	**U.S. Stock Ticker: MENT**
2007 Sales: $879,732	2007 Profits: $28,771	**Int'l Ticker:** Int'l Exchange:
2006 Sales: $802,839	2006 Profits: $27,204	Employees: 4,500
2005 Sales: $705,249	2005 Profits: $5,807	Fiscal Year Ends: 1/31
2004 Sales: $710,956	2004 Profits: $-20,550	Parent Company:

SALARIES/BENEFITS:

Pension Plan:	ESOP Stock Plan:	Profit Sharing:	Top Exec. Salary: $640,884	Bonus: $762,845
Savings Plan: Y	Stock Purch. Plan: Y		Second Exec. Salary: $523,853	Bonus: $566,954

OTHER THOUGHTS:

Apparent Women Officers or Directors: 2
Hot Spot for Advancement for Women/Minorities:

LOCATIONS: ("Y" = Yes)

West:	Southwest:	Midwest:	Southeast:	Northeast:	International:
Y	Y	Y			Y

MERCK & CO INC

www.merck.com

Industry Group Code: 325412 **Ranks within this company's industry group:** Sales: 9 Profits: 5

Techology:		Medical/Drugs:		Engineering:		Transportation:		Chemicals/Petrochemicals:		Specialty:	
Computers:		Manufacturer:	Y	Design:		Aerospace:		Oil/Gas Products:		Special Services:	
Software:		Contract Research:		Construction:		Automotive:		Chemicals:		Consulting:	
Communications:		Medical Services:		Eng. Services:		Shipping:		Oil/Chem. Svcs.:		Specialty Mgmt.:	
Electronics:		Labs:	Y	Consulting:				Gases:		Products:	
Alternative Energy:		Bio. Services:						Other:		Other:	

TYPES OF BUSINESS:

Pharmaceuticals Development & Manufacturing
Cholesterol Drugs
Hypertension Drugs
Heart Failure Drugs
Allergy & Asthma Drugs
Animal Health Products
Vaccines
Preventative Drugs

BRANDS/DIVISIONS/AFFILIATES:

Merck Institute for Science Education
Sirna Therapeutics, Inc.
Singulair
Propecia
Merck BioVentures
Fosamax
Gardasil
EMEND

CONTACTS: *Note: Officers with more than one job title may be intentionally listed here more than once.*

Richard Clark, CEO
Peter N. Kellogg, CFO/Exec. VP
Wendy Yarno, Chief Mktg. Officer
Mirian Graddick-Weir, Exec. VP-Human Resources
Peter S. Kim, Pres., Research Laboratories
J. Chris Scalet, CIO/Exec. VP-Global Svcs.
Willie Deese, Pres., Mfg. Div.
Bruce N. Kuhlik, General Counsel/Exec. VP
Adele Ambrose, Chief Comm. Officer
John Canan, Controller/Sr. VP
Kenneth C. Frazier, Pres., Global Human Health
Margaret McGlynn, Pres., Merck Vaccines & Infectious Diseases
Celia Colbert, Sr. VP/Sec.
Mark McDonough, VP/Treas.
Richard Clark, Chmn.
Stefan Oschmann, Pres., EMEA & Canada

Phone: 908-423-1000	**Fax:** 908-735-1253
Toll-Free:	
Address: 1 Merck Dr., Whitehouse Station, NJ 08889-0100 US	

GROWTH PLANS/SPECIAL FEATURES:

Merck & Co., Inc. is a leading research-driven pharmaceutical company that manufactures a broad range of products sold in approximately 150 countries. These products include therapeutic and preventative drugs generally sold by prescription and medications used to control and alleviate disease. The company operates in two segments. The Pharmaceutical segment includes human health pharmaceutical products consisting of therapeutic and preventative agents, sold by prescription. Medications include Fosamax, for the prevention of osteoporosis; Zocor, for lowering cholesterol; and Singulair, a seasonal allergy and asthma medication. The Vaccines and Infectious Diseases segment includes preventative vaccines such as Rotateq, designed to prevent gastroenteritis in infants and children; and Gardasil, a vaccine for the prevention of HPV. The segment also produces therapeutic agents for the treatment of infections such as Invanz and Cancidas, an anti-fungal product. The company also manufactures Propecia, a popular treatment for male pattern baldness. Recent FDA approved products include EMEND, a drug that prevents chemotherapy-induced nausea and ISENTRESS (raltegravir) tablets, which treats patients with the HIV-1 infection. In late 2008, Merck established a new unit, Merck BioVentures. This new group will focus on biotech drugs, including generic biotech drugs know as follow-on biologics. Also, the company will continue to focus on growing sales in emerging markets, particularly China and India. In February 2009, Merck agreed to acquire the portfolio of follow-on biologic therapeutic candidates, as well as the commercial manufacturing facilities in Boulder Colorado, of Insmed Inc. In March 2009, Merck and Schering-Plough announced their agreement that Merck will acquire Schering-Plough for $41.1 billion.

Employees are offered medical, vision and dental insurance; health and dependent care accounts; a 401(k) plan; a pension plan; financial planning services; life insurance; business travel accident insurance; credit union membership; educational assistance and scholarship programs; and corporate discounts on cars, travel, entertainment and electronics.

FINANCIALS: **Sales and profits are in thousands of dollars—add 000 to get the full amount. 2008 Note: Financial information for 2008 was not available for all companies at press time.**

2008 Sales: $23,850,300	2008 Profits: $7,808,400	**U.S. Stock Ticker: MRK**
2007 Sales: $24,197,700	2007 Profits: $3,275,400	**Int'l Ticker:** Int'l Exchange:
2006 Sales: $22,636,000	2006 Profits: $4,433,800	Employees: 55,200
2005 Sales: $22,011,900	2005 Profits: $4,631,300	Fiscal Year Ends: 12/31
2004 Sales: $22,938,600	2004 Profits: $5,813,400	Parent Company:

SALARIES/BENEFITS:

Pension Plan: Y	ESOP Stock Plan:	Profit Sharing:	Top Exec. Salary: $1,616,670	Bonus: $4,311,059
Savings Plan: Y	Stock Purch. Plan:		Second Exec. Salary: $922,560	Bonus: $1,395,554

OTHER THOUGHTS:

Apparent Women Officers or Directors: 7
Hot Spot for Advancement for Women/Minorities: Y

LOCATIONS: ("Y" = Yes)

West:	Southwest:	Midwest:	Southeast:	Northeast:	International:
Y	Y	Y	Y	Y	Y

MERCK KGAA

www.merck.de

Industry Group Code: 325412 **Ranks within this company's industry group:** Sales: 18 Profits: 23

Techology:		Medical/Drugs:		Engineering:		Transportation:		Chemicals/Petrochemicals:		Specialty:	
Computers:	Y	Manufacturer:	Y	Design:		Aerospace:		Oil/Gas Products:		Special Services:	
Software:		Contract Research:		Construction:		Automotive:		Chemicals:	Y	Consulting:	
Communications:		Medical Services:		Eng. Services:		Shipping:		Oil/Chem. Svcs.:		Specialty Mgmt.:	
Electronics:	Y	Labs:		Consulting:				Gases:		Products:	Y
Alternative Energy:	Y	Bio. Services:						Other:		Other:	

TYPES OF BUSINESS:

Pharmaceuticals
Over-the-Counter Drugs & Vitamins
Generic Drugs
Chemicals
LCD Components
Reagents & Diagnostics
Nanotechnology Research

BRANDS/DIVISIONS/AFFILIATES:

Merck Serono S.A.
Erbitux
Nasivin
Merck4Biosciences
Merck4Cosmetics
Merck4Food
Merck4LCDs & Emerging Technologies
Nano Terra LLC

CONTACTS: *Note: Officers with more than one job title may be intentionally listed here more than once.*

Karl-Ludwig Kley, Chmn.-Exec. Board
Michael Becker, CFO
Karl-Ludwig Kley, Dir.-Human Resources
Bernd Reckmann, Dir.-Corp. Info. Svcs.
Bernd Reckmann, Dir.-Prod.
Bernd Reckmann, Dir.-Eng.
Karl-Ludwig Kley, Dir.-Legal
Karl-Ludwig Kley, Dir.-Strategic Planning
Karl-Ludwig Kley, Dir.-Corp. Comm.
Michael Becker, Dir.-Acct., Finance, Controlling & Tax
Bernd Reckmann, Mgr.-Darmstadt & Gernsheim Sites
Elmar Schnee, Dir.-Pharmaceuticals Bus. Sector
Bernd Reckmann, Dir.-Chemicals Bus. Sector
Wilhelm Simson, Chmn.-Supervisory Board

Phone: 49-6151-72-0	**Fax:** 49-6151-72-2000
Toll-Free:	
Address: Frankfurter St. 250, Darmstadt, 64293 Germany	

GROWTH PLANS/SPECIAL FEATURES:

Merck KGaA is a global pharmaceuticals and chemicals company with 192 companies in 61 countries. Outside Germany, Merck maintains research sites in France, Spain, the U.K., the U.S. and Japan. It has two main businesses: Pharmaceuticals and Chemicals. The Pharmaceuticals business manufactures prescription drugs and over-the-counter products through two divisions, Merck Serano and Consumer Health Care. Merck Serono's products target oncology, neuro-degenerative diseases, fertility, endocrinology, cardio metabolic care and new specialist therapies. Products include colorectal cancer drug Erbitux; multiple sclerosis treatment Rebif; Type 2 diabetes treatment Glucophage; and Raptiva, a new type of treatment for psoriasis. The Consumer Health Care division offers products such as cough and cold; naturals-plant sourced; naturals-marine sourced; vitamins and minerals; dermatology; and other products. Specific products include nasal decongestant Nasivin; Mediflor medicinal teas; Cebion multivitamins; and bioManan slimming aids. The Chemical business has six segments. The biosciences segment offers life sciences research products including proteins, enzymes, reagents, kits and other supplies. The cosmetics segment supplies insect repellent and basic supplies for cosmetics including active ingredients, pigments and UV filters. The food segment offers quality control products; monitoring products for cleaning, hygiene, process water and wastewater; packaging design pigments; and raw materials, including mineral salts. The liquid crystals and emerging technologies segment manufactures licristal, licrivue and lisicon brand liquid crystals for LCD TVs, optical films and organic semiconductors; isitag brand printable semiconducting polymers for RFID tags; and isishape brand photovoltaic materials. The pharmaceutical segment supplies chemicals for all areas of pharmaceuticals manufacturing. Lastly, the printing, plastics and coatings segment offers numerous pigments. In February 2009, the company agreed to acquire MediCult for $55 million.

FINANCIALS: **Sales and profits are in thousands of dollars—add 000 to get the full amount. 2008 Note: Financial information for 2008 was not available for all companies at press time.**

2008 Sales: $10,000,300	2008 Profits: $501,600	**U.S. Stock Ticker:**
2007 Sales: $9,337,530	2007 Profits: $4,657,720	**Int'l Ticker: MRK** Int'l Exchange: Frankfurt-Euronext
2006 Sales: $8,352,950	2006 Profits: $1,335,880	Employees:
2005 Sales: $7,697,680	2005 Profits: $898,150	Fiscal Year Ends: 12/31
2004 Sales: $	2004 Profits: $	Parent Company:

SALARIES/BENEFITS:

Pension Plan:	ESOP Stock Plan:	Profit Sharing:	Top Exec. Salary: $	Bonus: $
Savings Plan:	Stock Purch. Plan:		Second Exec. Salary: $	Bonus: $

OTHER THOUGHTS:

Apparent Women Officers or Directors: 2
Hot Spot for Advancement for Women/Minorities:

LOCATIONS: ("Y" = Yes)

West:	Southwest:	Midwest:	Southeast:	Northeast:	International:
Y		Y	Y	Y	Y

MERCK SERONO SA

www.merckserono.net

Industry Group Code: 325412 **Ranks within this company's industry group:** Sales: Profits:

Techology:		Medical/Drugs:		Engineering:		Transportation:		Chemicals/Petrochemicals:		Specialty:	
Computers:		Manufacturer:	Y	Design:		Aerospace:		Oil/Gas Products:		Special Services:	
Software:		Contract Research:		Construction:		Automotive:		Chemicals:		Consulting:	
Communications:		Medical Services:		Eng. Services:		Shipping:		Oil/Chem. Svcs.:		Specialty Mgmt.:	
Electronics:		Labs:	Y	Consulting:				Gases:		Products:	
Alternative Energy:		Bio. Services:						Other:		Other:	

TYPES OF BUSINESS:

Pharmaceuticals Development
Fertility Drugs
Neurology Drugs
Growth & Metabolism Drugs
Dermatology Drugs
Oncology Research

BRANDS/DIVISIONS/AFFILIATES:

GONAL-f
Ovidrel/Ovitrelle
Luveris
Crinone
Cetrotide
Rebif
Saizen
EMD Serono Inc

CONTACTS: *Note: Officers with more than one job title may be intentionally listed here more than once.*

Elmar Schnee, Pres.
Richard Douge, Head-Global Mktg.
Francois Naef, VP-Human Resources
Bernhard Kirschbaum, Exec. VP-Global R&D
Hanns-Eberhard Erle, Head-Tech. Oper.
Francois Naef, Chief Admin. Officer
Francois Naef, VP-Legal
Vincent Aurentz, Head-Portfolio Mgmt. & Bus. Dev.
Francois Naef, Head-Comm.
Dorothea Wenzel, Head-Controlling
Fereydoun Firouz, Head-Commercial U.S.
Roberto Gradnik, Head-Commercial Europe
Wolfgang Wein, Head-Oncology
Franck Latrille, Head-Commercial Int'l

Phone: 41-22-414-3000 **Fax:** 41-22-414-2179
Toll-Free:
Address: 9, chemin des Mines, Case postale 54, Geneva 20, CH-1211 Switzerland

GROWTH PLANS/SPECIAL FEATURES:

Merck Serono SA, formerly Serono SA, is a global biotechnology company that focuses on six therapeutic areas: oncology, neurodegenerative diseases, fertility, endocrinology, cardio-metabolic care and new specialist therapies. The company was formed in January 2007 when Merck KGaA acquired Serono in a $13 billion transaction. The company researches both traditional pharmaceutical drugs, consisting of small molecules treating the symptoms of a disease, and biopharmaceuticals, comprised of large molecules such as proteins that target the underlying mechanism of a disease. For colorectal cancer, Merck Serono has developed Erbitux, a monoclonal antibody also sold for the treatment of head and neck cancer, and UFT, an oral 5-FU (5-fluorouracil) therapy. Rebif is Merck Serono's disease modifying drug, used to treat relapsing forms of multiple sclerosis. Infertility treatments developed by the company include GONAL-f, Pergoveris, Luveris, Ovidrel/Ovitrelle, Crinone and Cetrotide. Merck Serono offers a range of specialized endocrinology products. For childhood and adult growth hormone deficiency, as well as for children born small for gestational age (SGA), or with chronic renal failure or Turner's syndrome, the company has developed Saizen. Serostim, meanwhile, is used to treat HIV-associated wasting, and Zorbtive has been developed for the treatment of short bowel syndrome. Cardio-metabolic care treatments developed by Merck Serono include Glucophage/GlucophageXR and Glucovance for diabetes; Concor/ConcorCor for cardiovascular disease; and Euthyrox for hypothyroidism, euthyroid goiter and suppressive therapy of differentiated thyroid cancer. As part of its effort to develop products in new specialist areas with unmet medical needs, the company partnered with Genentech to develop and commercialize the psoriasis drug Raptiva. Merck Serono also has a number of products in development for the treatment of such diseases as systemic lupus erythematosus, rheumatoid arthritis and Crohn's disease. In Canada and the U.S., the Merck Serono division operates as EMD Serono, Inc.

FINANCIALS: **Sales and profits are in thousands of dollars—add 000 to get the full amount. 2008 Note: Financial information for 2008 was not available for all companies at press time.**

2008 Sales: $	2008 Profits: $	**U.S. Stock Ticker: Subsidiary**
2007 Sales: $	2007 Profits: $	**Int'l Ticker:** Int'l Exchange:
2006 Sales: $2,804,900	2006 Profits: $735,400	Employees: 4,775
2005 Sales: $2,586,400	2005 Profits: $-105,300	Fiscal Year Ends: 12/31
2004 Sales: $2,177,900	2004 Profits: $494,200	Parent Company: MERCK KGAA

SALARIES/BENEFITS:

Pension Plan:	ESOP Stock Plan:	Profit Sharing:	Top Exec. Salary: $	Bonus: $
Savings Plan:	Stock Purch. Plan:		Second Exec. Salary: $	Bonus: $

OTHER THOUGHTS:

Apparent Women Officers or Directors: 1
Hot Spot for Advancement for Women/Minorities:

LOCATIONS: ("Y" = Yes)

West:	Southwest:	Midwest:	Southeast:	Northeast:	International:
				Y	Y

MICHAEL BAKER CORPORATION

www.mbakercorp.com

Industry Group Code: 230000 **Ranks within this company's industry group:** Sales: 1 Profits: 1

Techology:		Medical/Drugs:		Engineering:		Transportation:		Chemicals/Petrochemicals:		Specialty:	
Computers:		Manufacturer:		Design:	Y	Aerospace:		Oil/Gas Products:		Special Services:	Y
Software:	Y	Contract Research:		Construction:	Y	Automotive:		Chemicals:		Consulting:	
Communications:		Medical Services:		Eng. Services:	Y	Shipping:		Oil/Chem. Svcs.:	Y	Specialty Mgmt.:	Y
Electronics:		Labs:		Consulting:	Y			Gases:		Products:	
Alternative Energy:		Bio. Services:						Other:		Other:	

TYPES OF BUSINESS:

Engineering & Construction
Infrastructure Projects
Facilities Management
Oilfield Services
Offshore Services
Consulting Services

BRANDS/DIVISIONS/AFFILIATES:

CONTACTS:
Note: Officers with more than one job title may be intentionally listed here more than once.

Bradley L. Mallory, CEO
Bradley L. Mallory, Pres.
Craig O. Stuver, Interim CFO
David G. Greenwood, Exec. VP-Mktg.
Jeremy N. Gill, VP-IT
Edward L. Wiley, Exec. VP-Eng.
H. James McKnight, General Counsel/Corp. Sec./Exec. VP
Jospeh Beck, Dir.-Corp. Dev.
David G. Higie, VP-Corp. Comm.
David G. Higie, VP-Investor Rel.
Craig O. Stuver, Chief Acct. Officer/Treas./Sr. VP
James Kempton, VP-Controller
James Johnson, Sr. VP-Mktg., Energy Div.
John G. Kurgan, Exec. VP-Eng.
Michael Ziemianski, Chief Resources Officer/VP
Richard L. Shaw, Chmn.

Phone: 412-269-6300 **Fax:** 412-375-3980
Toll-Free: 800-642-2537
Address: Airside Business Park, 100 Airside Dr., Moon Township, PA 15108 US

GROWTH PLANS/SPECIAL FEATURES:

Michael Baker Corporation (Baker) provides engineering, energy consulting and management services for public- and private-sector clients worldwide. The firm's engineering segment provides a variety of design and related services, principally in the U.S., including program management; design-build; construction management; consulting; planning; surveying; mapping; geographic information systems; architectural and interior design; construction inspection; constructability reviews; site assessment and restoration; strategic regulatory analysis; and regulatory compliance. The engineering segment has designed a wide range of projects, such as highways, bridges, airports, busways, corporate headquarters, data centers, correctional facilities and educational facilities. It has also provided services in the water/wastewater, pipeline, emergency, consequence management, resource management and telecommunications markets. Baker's energy segment provides a range of services to operating energy production facilities, such as complete outsourcing solutions; training; personnel recruitment; pre-operations engineering; maintenance management systems; field operations and maintenance; procurement; and supply chain management. The energy segment serves both major and minor independent oil and gas producing companies worldwide. For onshore operations, Baker has full managerial and administrative responsibilities for clients' producing properties. Offshore, Baker operates a network of marine vessels; helicopters; shore bases; information technology; safety and compliance systems; specialists; and a leadership team that manages the sharing of resources. The company has managed services agreements with oil and gas producers in the Gulf of Mexico, Texas, Wyoming and Montana. Internationally, Baker operates offices in Thailand, Venezuela, the U.K., Mexico and Nigeria.

FINANCIALS:
Sales and profits are in thousands of dollars—add 000 to get the full amount. 2008 Note: Financial information for 2008 was not available for all companies at press time.

2008 Sales: $699,395 — 2008 Profits: $29,154
2007 Sales: $726,965 — 2007 Profits: $19,340
2006 Sales: $646,668 — 2006 Profits: $10,332
2005 Sales: $579,278 — 2005 Profits: $5,051
2004 Sales: $552,046 — 2004 Profits: $8,394

U.S. Stock Ticker: BKR
Int'l Ticker: Int'l Exchange:
Employees: 4,903
Fiscal Year Ends: 12/31
Parent Company:

SALARIES/BENEFITS:

Pension Plan: ESOP Stock Plan: Profit Sharing: Top Exec. Salary: $430,498 Bonus: $157,224
Savings Plan: Y Stock Purch. Plan: Second Exec. Salary: $266,800 Bonus: $58,864

OTHER THOUGHTS:

Apparent Women Officers or Directors: 1
Hot Spot for Advancement for Women/Minorities: Y

LOCATIONS: ("Y" = Yes)

West:	Southwest:	Midwest:	Southeast:	Northeast:	International:
Y	Y	Y	Y	Y	Y

MICRON TECHNOLOGY INC

www.micron.com

Industry Group Code: 334413 **Ranks within this company's industry group:** Sales: 7 Profits: 16

Techology:		Medical/Drugs:		Engineering:		Transportation:		Chemicals/Petrochemicals:		Specialty:	
Computers:	Y	Manufacturer:		Design:		Aerospace:		Oil/Gas Products:		Special Services:	
Software:		Contract Research:		Construction:		Automotive:		Chemicals:		Consulting:	
Communications:		Medical Services:		Eng. Services:		Shipping:		Oil/Chem. Svcs.:		Specialty Mgmt.:	
Electronics:		Labs:		Consulting:				Gases:		Products:	
Alternative Energy:		Bio. Services:						Other:		Other:	

TYPES OF BUSINESS:

Components-Semiconductor Memory
PCs & Peripherals
Flash Memory Devices
CMOS Image Sensors

BRANDS/DIVISIONS/AFFILIATES:

IM Flash Technologies, LLC
Intel Corp
Avago Technologies Ltd.
Aptina Imaging

CONTACTS:

Note: Officers with more than one job title may be intentionally listed here more than once.

Steven R. Appleton, CEO
D. Mark Durcan, COO
D. Mark Durcan, Pres.
Ronald C. Foster, CFO/VP-Finance
Mark W. Adams, VP-Worldwide Sales
Pat Otte, VP-Human Resources
James E. Mahoney, VP-Info. Systems
Brian J. Shields, VP-Worldwide Wafer Fabrication
Roderic W. Lewis, General Counsel/VP-Legal Affairs/Corp. Sec.
Jay L. Hawkins, VP-Oper.
Kipp A. Bedard, VP-Investor Rel.
Norman L. Schlachter, Treas.
John F. Schreck, DRAM Dev.
Brian M. Shirley, VP-Memory
Dean A. Klein, VP-Memory System Dev.
Frankie F. Roohparvar, VP-NAND Dev.
Steven R. Appleton, Chmn.
Paul C. Mullen, VP-Int'l OEM Sales
Steve Thorsen, VP-Worldwide Procurement

Phone: 208-368-4000	**Fax:** 208-368-4435
Toll-Free:	
Address: 8000 S. Federal Way, Boise, ID 83707-0006 US	

GROWTH PLANS/SPECIAL FEATURES:

Micron Technology, Inc. and its subsidiaries design, develop, manufacture and market semiconductor memory products and personal computer systems. Its products are used in a range of electronic devices, including personal computers, workstations, servers, cell phones, digital cameras and other consumer and industrial products. The products are sold to computing and consumer, networking, telecommunications and imaging markets. Micron has two segments: Memory, producing dynamic random access memory (DRAM), accounting for 54% of 2008 sales, and NAND flash memory, 35% of sales; and Imaging, producing complementary metal-oxide semiconductor (CMOS) image sensors, 11%. DRAMs are high-density, low-cost-per-bit RAM storage units. Micron offers double data rate (DDR) and DDR2 DRAM, primarily used for the main system memory in computers; and synchronous DRAM (SDRAM), used in networking devices, servers, consumer electronics, communications equipment, computer peripherals and as memory upgrades to older computers. NAND products are re-writable, non-volatile semiconductor devices, meaning they retain memory after power has been shut off. It is used in mobile devices such as digital cameras, MP3 players, USB Flash Drives and cellular phones. IM Flash Technologies, LLC, a joint venture with Intel Corp., produces Micron's NAND products. CMOS image sensors are semiconductor devices that capture and process images into pictures or video for consumer and industrial applications. They are used in digital cameras, automotive systems and other emerging applications. The firm has manufacturing facilities located in the U.S., Italy, Japan, Puerto Rico and Singapore. In March 2008, the company launched Aptina Imaging, a new independent division for the company's CMOS business. In April of the same year, the company agreed to form a DRAM joint venture with Nanya Technology Corporation to be named MeiYa Technology Corporation. In October 2008, the firm announced plans to reduce its global workforce by 15% over the next two years, as part of the restructuring of its memory operations.

Employees are offered medical, dental, vision and life insurance; short-and long-term disability coverage, business travel accident coverage; and educational assistance.

FINANCIALS:

Sales and profits are in thousands of dollars—add 000 to get the full amount. 2008 Note: Financial information for 2008 was not available for all companies at press time.

2008 Sales: $5,841,000	2008 Profits: $-1,619,000	**U.S. Stock Ticker: MU**
2007 Sales: $5,688,000	2007 Profits: $-320,000	**Int'l Ticker:** Int'l Exchange:
2006 Sales: $5,272,000	2006 Profits: $408,000	Employees: 22,800
2005 Sales: $4,880,200	2005 Profits: $188,000	Fiscal Year Ends: 8/31
2004 Sales: $4,404,200	2004 Profits: $157,200	Parent Company:

SALARIES/BENEFITS:

Pension Plan:	ESOP Stock Plan:	Profit Sharing:	Top Exec. Salary: $950,000	Bonus: $233,712
Savings Plan: Y	Stock Purch. Plan:		Second Exec. Salary: $600,000	Bonus: $127,080

OTHER THOUGHTS:

Apparent Women Officers or Directors: 1
Hot Spot for Advancement for Women/Minorities: Y

LOCATIONS: ("Y" = Yes)

West:	Southwest:	Midwest:	Southeast:	Northeast:	International:
Y	Y	Y	Y	Y	Y

MICROSOFT CORP

www.microsoft.com

Industry Group Code: 511204 **Ranks within this company's industry group:** Sales: 1 Profits: 1

Techology:		Medical/Drugs:		Engineering:		Transportation:		Chemicals/Petrochemicals:		Specialty:	
Computers:	Y	Manufacturer:		Design:		Aerospace:		Oil/Gas Products:		Special Services:	
Software:	Y	Contract Research:		Construction:		Automotive:		Chemicals:		Consulting:	
Communications:	Y	Medical Services:		Eng. Services:		Shipping:		Oil/Chem. Svcs.:		Specialty Mgmt.:	
Electronics:		Labs:		Consulting:				Gases:		Products:	Y
Alternative Energy:		Bio. Services:						Other:		Other:	

TYPES OF BUSINESS:

Computer Software
Personal Communications Services
Video Games Systems
Mobile Communications
Voice-Enabled Mobile Search
Internet Search Engine
E-Mail Services
Instant Messaging

BRANDS/DIVISIONS/AFFILIATES:

Windows Vista
Xbox
MSN
Danger, Inc.
Fast Search & Transfer ASA
Navic Networks
Greenfiled Online Inc
DATAllegro Inc.

CONTACTS: *Note: Officers with more than one job title may be intentionally listed here more than once.*

Steve Ballmer, CEO
Kevin Turner, COO
Christopher Liddell, CFO
Mich Mathews, Sr. VP-Central Mktg. Group
Lisa Brummel, Sr. VP-Human Resources
Rick Rashid, Sr. VP-Research
David Vaskevitch, CTO/Sr. VP
Brad Smith, General Counsel/Sr. VP-Legal & Corp. Affairs/Sec.
Eric Rudder, Sr. VP-Technical Strategy
Qi Lu, Pres., Online Svcs.
Robert J. Bach, Pres., Entertainment & Devices Div.
Stephen Elop, Pres., Microsoft Bus. Div.
Ray Ozzie, Chief Software Architect
Bob Muglia, Pres., Server & Tools Bus.
Bill Gates, Chmn.
Jean-Philippe Courtois, Pres., Microsoft Int'l

Phone: 425-882-8080 **Fax:** 425-936-7329
Toll-Free: 800-642-7676
Address: 1 Microsoft Way, Redmond, WA 98052-7329 US

GROWTH PLANS/SPECIAL FEATURES:

Microsoft Corp. develops, manufactures and supports software for businesses, government and consumers. Microsoft operates in five segments. The client segment produces technical architecture, engineering and product delivery of the Windows product family. Its Vista operating system includes advances in security, digital media, user interfaces, and other areas that enhance the user and developer experience. The company's latest operating system, introduced in 2009, is Windows 7. The server and tools segment develops and markets Windows server products and operating systems. The division's most recent products include Windows Server 2008, SQL Server 2008 and Visual Studio 2008. The online services business segment consists of an on-line advertising platform and provides personal services including MSN Video Service and Windows Live Search. The business division offers the Microsoft Dynamics business solutions and the Microsoft Office system. The entertainment and devices division is responsible for developing, producing and marketing the Xbox and Xbox 360 video game systems, including consoles and accessories, third-party games, games published under the Microsoft brand and Xbox Live operations, as well as research, sales and support of those products. In April 2008, Microsoft completed the acquisition of Danger, Inc., which was combined with the Mobile Communications Business of the Entertainment and Devices Division. That same month, Microsoft acquired Fast Search & Transfer ASA. In June 2008, it acquired Navic Networks, a provider of television advertising solutions. In addition, the firm agreed to acquire Greenfiled Online Inc, a European price comparison site. In September 2008, Microsoft acquired DATAllegro Inc., a provider of data warehouse appliances.

FINANCIALS: **Sales and profits are in thousands of dollars—add 000 to get the full amount. 2008 Note: Financial information for 2008 was not available for all companies at press time.**

2008 Sales: $60,420,000	2008 Profits: $17,681,000	**U.S. Stock Ticker: MSFT**
2007 Sales: $51,122,000	2007 Profits: $14,065,000	**Int'l Ticker:** Int'l Exchange:
2006 Sales: $44,282,000	2006 Profits: $12,599,000	Employees: 91,000
2005 Sales: $39,788,000	2005 Profits: $12,254,000	Fiscal Year Ends: 6/30
2004 Sales: $36,835,000	2004 Profits: $8,168,000	Parent Company:

SALARIES/BENEFITS:

Pension Plan:	ESOP Stock Plan:	Profit Sharing:	Top Exec. Salary: $640,833	Bonus: $700,000
Savings Plan: Y	Stock Purch. Plan: Y		Second Exec. Salary: $620,833	Bonus: $600,000

OTHER THOUGHTS:

Apparent Women Officers or Directors: 3
Hot Spot for Advancement for Women/Minorities: Y

LOCATIONS: ("Y" = Yes)

West:	Southwest:	Midwest:	Southeast:	Northeast:	International:
Y	Y	Y	Y	Y	Y

MITSUBISHI CORP

www.mitsubishicorp.com

Industry Group Code: 333000 **Ranks within this company's industry group:** Sales: 1 Profits: 1

Techology:		Medical/Drugs:		Engineering:		Transportation:		Chemicals/Petrochemicals:		Specialty:	
Computers:		Manufacturer:		Design:		Aerospace:	Y	Oil/Gas Products:	Y	Special Services:	
Software:	Y	Contract Research:		Construction:		Automotive:	Y	Chemicals:	Y	Consulting:	Y
Communications:		Medical Services:	Y	Eng. Services:		Shipping:		Oil/Chem. Svcs.:		Specialty Mgmt.:	
Electronics:	Y	Labs:		Consulting:				Gases:		Products:	Y
Alternative Energy:	Y	Bio. Services:						Other:		Other:	Y

TYPES OF BUSINESS:

Machinery & Automotive Manufacturing
Financial Services
Metals Mining & Production
Chemicals
Food Products & Commodities
Petroleum Exploration & Production
IT Services & Equipment
Solar Cells & Fuel-Cell Systems

BRANDS/DIVISIONS/AFFILIATES:

Mitsubishi Chemical
Frontier Carbon
Mitsubishi Motors
IT Frontier
Nikkei MC
Lithium Energy Japan
MC Global Voyager Fund Limted
Art Coffee

CONTACTS: *Note: Officers with more than one job title may be intentionally listed here more than once.*

Yorihiko Kojima, CEO
Yorihiko Kojima, Pres.
Ichiro Mizuno, CFO
Takeru Ishibashi, CIO
Tomohiko Fujiyama, Sr. VP.-Corp. Strategy
Ichiro Ando, Controller
Mutsumi Kotsuka, CEO-Metals Group
Koichi Komatsu, CEO-Bus. Innovation Group
Masaaki Seita, CEO-Chemicals Group
Seiji Kato, CEO-Energy Bus. Group
Mikio Sasaki, Chmn.

Phone: 81-3-3210-2121 **Fax:** 81-3-3210-8583
Toll-Free:
Address: 6-3 Marunouchi 2-chrome, Chiyoda-ku, Tokyo, 100-8086 Japan

GROWTH PLANS/SPECIAL FEATURES:

Mitsubishi Corporation is one of Japan's largest general trading companies, with customers around the world in virtually every industry, including energy, metals, machinery, chemicals, food and general merchandise. The company's approximately 500 consolidated subsidiaries and affiliates fall into six business groups. The new business group consists of the company's financial technology, information and communication technology (including fiber optic and wireless sytems) logistics technology and market technology. The segment's subsidiary, IT Frontier, provides information technology equipment and services. The new business segment operates medical facilities and leases medical equipment. The energy business group includes natural gas and petroleum exploration and production and carbon and propane businesses. The metals group is involved in the mining of coal and ferrous and non-ferrous metals, as well as the production of automotive components, steel and other metallic components. The machinery group manufactures power and electrical systems, power plants, defense systems, aeronautical and space systems, industrial and agricultural machinery and automotive parts and vehicles. The automotive group also produces parts for Isuzu and Honda cars and trucks. The chemicals group manufactures petrochemicals, methanol, ammonia, fertilizer, plastics and other substances. The living essentials group produces food products, food commodities, textiles and other consumer products including paper products, packaging material, building materials, cement, glass and tires. In 2008, the company dissolved 16 subsidiaries including: Benten Limited and MFLC Corporation. In March 2008, the company and Mitsubishi UFJ Securities Co. jointly established MC, The Bank of Tokyo–Mitsubishi UFJ, Ltd., a fund management company. In June 2008, the firm entered an agreement with CIMA Energy Ltd. to acquire a 34% partnership interest in the company. Also through the agreement, CIMA will sell and market liquefied natural gas imported by the firm through the Freeport LNG Terminal in Texas. In December 2008, the company established New Company, a nuclear fuel fabrication business.

FINANCIALS: **Sales and profits are in thousands of dollars—add 000 to get the full amount. 2008 Note: Financial information for 2008 was not available for all companies at press time.**

2008 Sales: $60,308,100 — 2008 Profits: $4,627,900
2007 Sales: $46,297,333 — 2007 Profits: $3,784,493
2006 Sales: $40,430,200 — 2006 Profits: $2,931,950
2005 Sales: $38,548,400 — 2005 Profits: $1,695,700
2004 Sales: $15,093,800 — 2004 Profits: $1,092,100

U.S. Stock Ticker: MSBHY.PK
Int'l Ticker: 8058 Int'l Exchange: Tokyo-TSE
Employees: 53,738
Fiscal Year Ends: 3/31
Parent Company:

SALARIES/BENEFITS:

Pension Plan: ESOP Stock Plan: Profit Sharing: Top Exec. Salary: $ Bonus: $
Savings Plan: Stock Purch. Plan: Second Exec. Salary: $ Bonus: $

OTHER THOUGHTS:

Apparent Women Officers or Directors:
Hot Spot for Advancement for Women/Minorities:

LOCATIONS: ("Y" = Yes)

West:	Southwest:	Midwest:	Southeast:	Northeast:	International:
					Y

Note: Financial information, benefits and other data can change quickly and may vary from those stated here.

MITSUBISHI ELECTRIC CORPORATION

global.mitsubishielectric.com

Industry Group Code: 335000 **Ranks within this company's industry group:** Sales: 2 Profits: 4

Techology:		Medical/Drugs:		Engineering:		Transportation:		Chemicals/Petrochemicals:		Specialty:	
Computers:	Y	Manufacturer:		Design:	Y	Aerospace:		Oil/Gas Products:	Y	Special Services:	
Software:		Contract Research:		Construction:		Automotive:	Y	Chemicals:	Y	Consulting:	
Communications:	Y	Medical Services:		Eng. Services:	Y	Shipping:		Oil/Chem. Svcs.:	Y	Specialty Mgmt.:	
Electronics:	Y	Labs:		Consulting:				Gases:		Products:	
Alternative Energy:		Bio. Services:						Other:		Other:	

TYPES OF BUSINESS:

Electronic Equipment Manufacturer
Power Plant Manufacturing, Nuclear & Fossil
Wind & Solar Generation Systems
Consumer Electronics
Telecommunications & Computer Equipment
Industrial Automation Systems
Chips & Memory Devices
Semiconductors

BRANDS/DIVISIONS/AFFILIATES:

Mitsubishi

CONTACTS:

Note: Officers with more than one job title may be intentionally listed here more than once.

Setsuhiro Shimomura, CEO
Setsuhiro Shimomura, Pres.
Takashi Sasakawa, Exec. Officer-Global Strategic Mktg.
Masanori Saito, Sr. VP-Human Resources
Kazuo Kyuma, Sr. Exec. Officer-R&D
Takahiko Kondo, Exec. VP-Info. Systems & Network Svcs.
Yasuji Nagayama, Sr. Exec. Officer-Oper.
Mitsuo Muneyuki, Sr. Exec. Officer-Strategy
Masanori Saito, Sr. VP-Public Rel.
Yukihiro Sato, Exec. VP-Acct. & Finance
Masanori Saito, Sr. VP-Advertising
Noboru Kurihara, Sr. Exec. Officer-Electronic Systems
Makoto Kondo, Sr. Exec. Officer-Bldg. Systems
Kenichiro Yamanishi, Sr. Exec. Officer-Semiconductor & Device
Tamotsu Nomakuchi, Chmn.

Phone: 81-3-3218-2111	**Fax:** 81-3-3218-2185
Toll-Free:	
Address: Tokyo Bldg. 2-7-3 Marunouchi, Chiyoda-ku, Tokyo, 100-8310 Japan	

GROWTH PLANS/SPECIAL FEATURES:

Mitsubishi Electric Corporation, part of the Mitsubishi group of companies, is a global manufacturer, distributor and marketer of electrical and electronic equipment used in information processing and communications; space development and satellite communications; consumer electronics; industrial technology; energy; transportation; and building equipment. The company has five primary business segments: Energy and Electric Systems; Home Appliances; Information and Communication Systems; Industrial Automation Systems; and Electronic Devices. The Energy and Electric Systems segment manufactures nuclear and fossil fuel power generation plants and monitoring systems, including wind turbines, solar panels and other electricity generators; turbine generators and hydraulic turbine generators; elevators; security systems; railway systems; and large scale display systems. This segment accounted for 23.1% of revenues in 2008. The Home Appliances segment manufactures home electronics such as air conditioners, flat-screen televisions, DVD players, computers and computer monitors accounting for 21.9% of revenues. The Industrial Automation Systems segment includes the manufacturing of logic controllers, circuit breakers and robotics; which are created and customized for multiple industrial uses. This segment accounts for 22.2 % of revenues. The Information and Communication Systems segment includes mobile phones, satellites, aerospace communication systems, GPS units, enterprise information technology networks and Internet servers and makes up 14.1% of the company's income. The Electronic Devices segment makes power modules, high-frequency devices, optical devices, LCD devices and microcomputers; it represents 4.2% of company revenues. Other business activities include procurement, logistics, real estate, advertising and finance. These account for 14.5% of revenues. Mitsubishi is among the largest solar power technology manufacturers in the world, making modules for residential and commercial use. The company recently announced that its solar modules will power one of the largest non-profit photovoltaic systems in California, providing 50% of the power needs for a San Francisco-area school.

FINANCIALS:

Sales and profits are in thousands of dollars—add 000 to get the full amount. 2008 Note: Financial information for 2008 was not available for all companies at press time.

2008 Sales: $40,498,200	2008 Profits: $1,579,800	**U.S. Stock Ticker: MIELY**
2007 Sales: $34,641,700	2007 Profits: $1,105,100	**Int'l Ticker: 6503** Int'l Exchange: Tokyo-TSE
2006 Sales: $30,805,000	2006 Profits: $817,880	Employees: 97,661
2005 Sales: $32,600,000	2005 Profits: $6,798,000	Fiscal Year Ends: 3/31
2004 Sales: $31,917,800	2004 Profits: $424,400	Parent Company:

SALARIES/BENEFITS:

Pension Plan:	ESOP Stock Plan:	Profit Sharing:	Top Exec. Salary: $	Bonus: $
Savings Plan:	Stock Purch. Plan:		Second Exec. Salary: $	Bonus: $

OTHER THOUGHTS:

Apparent Women Officers or Directors:
Hot Spot for Advancement for Women/Minorities:

LOCATIONS: ("Y" = Yes)

West:	Southwest:	Midwest:	Southeast:	Northeast:	International:
Y	Y	Y	Y	Y	Y

Note: Financial information, benefits and other data can change quickly and may vary from those stated here.

MITSUBISHI MOTORS CORP

www.mitsubishi-motors.com

Industry Group Code: 336111 **Ranks within this company's industry group:** Sales: 15 Profits: 17

Techology:		Medical/Drugs:		Engineering:		Transportation:		Chemicals/Petrochemicals:		Specialty:	
Computers:		Manufacturer:		Design:		Aerospace:		Oil/Gas Products:		Special Services:	
Software:		Contract Research:		Construction:		Automotive:	Y	Chemicals:		Consulting:	
Communications:		Medical Services:		Eng. Services:		Shipping:		Oil/Chem. Svcs.:		Specialty Mgmt.:	
Electronics:		Labs:		Consulting:				Gases:		Products:	
Alternative Energy:		Bio. Services:						Other:		Other:	

TYPES OF BUSINESS:

Automobiles, Manufacturing
Automobile Parts
Racing

BRANDS/DIVISIONS/AFFILIATES:

Lithium Energy Japan
Mitsubishi Motors North America, Inc.
Mitsubishi Motors Credit of America, Inc.
MMSK Corporation
Mitsubishi Corporation (Korea) Ltd.
Outlander
Eclipse
Galant

CONTACTS: *Note: Officers with more than one job title may be intentionally listed here more than once.*

Takashi Nishioka, CEO
Osamu Masuko, COO
Osamu Masuko, Pres.
Hiizu Ichikawa, CFO
Fujio Cho, Managing Dir.-Domestic Oper.
Heki Kasugai, Exec. VP-Corp. Planning
Hiizu Ichikawa, Managing Dir.-Finance Group
Makoto Maeda, Managing Dir.-Prod. Group
Hiroshi Harunari, Pres./CEO-Mitsubishi Motors North America
Osamu Masuko, Chief Bus. Ethics Officer
Mitsuo Hashimoto, Corp. Gen. Mgr.-Quality Affairs Office
Takashi Nishioka, Chmn.
Kazuyuki Kikuchi, Managing Dir.-Overseas Oper.

Phone: 81-3-6719-2111 **Fax:** 81-3-6719-0014
Toll-Free:
Address: 33-8, Shiba 5-chome, Minato-ku, Tokyo, 108-8410 Japan

GROWTH PLANS/SPECIAL FEATURES:

Mitsubishi Motors Corporation is a global manufacturer and distributor of automobiles, trucks, buses, parts and power trains. The company has 50 consolidated subsidiaries and its products are sold in more than 160 countries. Mitsubishi Motors has seven car manufacturing facilities in five countries; seven engine, transmission and parts manufacturing facilities in four countries; and five research and development centers, which are in four countries. Mitsubishi Motors North America, Inc. (MMNA) oversees all of the company's North American operations, including sales, manufacturing, finance and research and development. It manufactures and markets coupes, convertibles, sedans and sport utility vehicles through a network of almost 700 dealers in the U.S., Canada, Mexico and the Caribbean. The Mitsubishi brand includes the Montero, Eclipse sports coupe, the Outlander SUV, L200 Strada pickup and the Galant mid-size sedan. Mitsubishi Motors Credit of America, Inc. provides Mitsubishi retailers with a variety of wholesale financing and retail options to assist clients in purchasing or leasing Mitsubishi brand vehicles. Traditionally sales outside Japan have accounted for about 80% of total company sales. Recently, Mitsubishi's management has been focusing on new product development while trimming costs, which has meant job cuts. In 2008, Mitsubishi, in collaboration with GS Yuasa, broke ground on a factory for joint venture Lithium Energy Japan, a company that will produce lithium ion batteries for the electric vehicle (EV) market. In May 2008, Mitsubishi and PSA Peugeot Citroen signed a joint venture agreement to produce vehicles in a new plant in Russia. The company recently announced its entrance into the Korean market via MMSK Corporation, the sole distributor of Mitsubishi cars in Korea and a joint venture between Mitsubishi, Mitsubishi Corporation (Korea) Ltd. and Daewoo Motor Sales Corp.

FINANCIALS: **Sales and profits are in thousands of dollars—add 000 to get the full amount. 2008 Note: Financial information for 2008 was not available for all companies at press time.**

2008 Sales: $26,726,600	2008 Profits: $345,880	**U.S. Stock Ticker: MMTOF.PK**
2007 Sales: $21,951,200	2007 Profits: $87,140	**Int'l Ticker: 7211** Int'l Exchange: Tokyo-TSE
2006 Sales: $21,200,700	2006 Profits: $-921,700	Employees: 34,911
2005 Sales: $21,226,300	2005 Profits: $-4,747,800	Fiscal Year Ends: 3/31
2004 Sales: $23,849,100	2004 Profits: $-2,039,200	Parent Company:

SALARIES/BENEFITS:

Pension Plan:	ESOP Stock Plan:	Profit Sharing:	Top Exec. Salary: $	Bonus: $
Savings Plan:	Stock Purch. Plan:		Second Exec. Salary: $	Bonus: $

OTHER THOUGHTS:

Apparent Women Officers or Directors:
Hot Spot for Advancement for Women/Minorities:

LOCATIONS: ("Y" = Yes)

West:	Southwest:	Midwest:	Southeast:	Northeast:	International:
Y		Y			Y

MITSUI CHEMICALS INC

www.mitsui-chem.co.jp

Industry Group Code: 325000 **Ranks within this company's industry group:** Sales: 8 Profits: 18

Techology:		Medical/Drugs:		Engineering:		Transportation:		Chemicals/Petrochemicals:		Specialty:	
Computers:		Manufacturer:	Y	Design:		Aerospace:		Oil/Gas Products:	Y	Special Services:	
Software:		Contract Research:		Construction:		Automotive:		Chemicals:	Y	Consulting:	
Communications:		Medical Services:		Eng. Services:		Shipping:		Oil/Chem. Svcs.:		Specialty Mgmt.:	
Electronics:		Labs:		Consulting:				Gases:		Products:	Y
Alternative Energy:		Bio. Services:						Other:		Other:	

TYPES OF BUSINESS:

Petrochemical Producer
Agrochemicals
Industrial Products
Pharmaceuticals & Medical
Packaging
Dyes & Pigments
Phenols

BRANDS/DIVISIONS/AFFILIATES:

Mitsui Chemicals Crop Life, Inc.
Mitsui Takeda Chemicals
Mitsui Chemical Industrial Products Co., Ltd.
Mitsui Fine Chemicals Inc.
Sekisui Chemical Co., Ltd.
Silvue Technologies Group, Inc.
SDC Technologies, Inc.
Mitsui Chemicals India Pvt. Ltd.

CONTACTS: *Note: Officers with more than one job title may be intentionally listed here more than once.*

Kenji Fujiyoshi, CEO
Kenji Fujiyoshi, Pres.
Hiroshi Tokumaru, Managing Dir.-Human Resources
Akihiro Yamaguchi, Sr. Managing Dir.-R&D
Yoshiyuki Shinohara, Sr. Managing Dir.-IT Planning Div.
Yoshiyuki Shinohara, Sr. Managing Dir.-Prod. & Tech. Center
Hiroshi Tokumaru, Managing Dir.-Admin.
Hiroshi Tokumaru, Managing Dir.-Legal Div.
Toshikazu Tanaka, Exec. VP-Corp. Planning
Hiroshi Tokumaru, Managing Dir.-Corp. Comm.
Koichi Sano, Managing Dir.-Finance & Acct. Div.
Kiichi Suzuki, Pres., Advanced Chemicals Div.
Hirokazu Kajiura, Pres., Performance Chemicals Division
Keiichi Sano, Pres., Basic Chemicals Div.
Toshikazu Tanaka, Exec. VP-Mitsui Chemicals America, Inc.
Hiroyuki Nakanishi, Chmn.
Toshikazu Tanaka, Exec. VP-Mitsui Chemicals Europe GmbH
Yoshiyuki Shinohara, Sr. Managing Dir.-Purchasing Div.

Phone: 81-3-6253-2100 **Fax:** 81-3-6253-4245
Toll-Free:
Address: Shiodome, 5-2 Higashi-Shimbashi 1-chome, Minato-ku, Tokyo, 105-7117 Japan

GROWTH PLANS/SPECIAL FEATURES:

Mitsui Chemicals, Inc. (MCI) is a Japanese chemical manufacturer that specializes in petrochemicals, phenols and specialty polymers. The company has numerous subsidiaries, both in Japan and overseas, with manufacturing and sales sites in the U.S., Mexico, Germany, Scotland, Singapore, China, Indonesia, Thailand, Malaysia, India and South Korea. Mitsui operates five manufacturing sites and three sales offices throughout Japan. The company is organized into three segments: performance materials, advanced chemicals and basic chemicals. The performance materials business sector includes the automotive and industrial materials division; the packaging and engineering materials division; living and energy materials division; the information and electronics materials division; and Mitsui Chemicals Polyurethanes, Inc. As a whole, the segment produces plastics used for films, packaging materials, automotive parts and pipes, among others. The advanced chemicals business sector, which contains the fine and performance chemicals division and the agrochemicals division, manufactures chemicals used in optical lenses, medical materials, disinfectants, solvents, organic peroxides, insecticides and fungicides. The basic chemicals business sector includes the feedstocks division, the phenols division, the pure terephthalic acid (PTA) and polyethylene terephthalate (PET) division, the industrial chemicals division and Prime Polymer Co., Ltd. The division's products include petrochemical raw materials, phenols, synthetic fiber raw materials, PET resins, industrial chemicals, polyethylene and polypropylene. Additionally, the company produces biodegradable plastic for use in films, sheets, agricultural materials and composting materials. In June 2008, Mitsui Chemicals acquired SDC Technologies, Inc. In December 2008, the company acquired Tohcello Co., Ltd. In January 2009, MCI ceased aniline production and sales. In February 2009, the company announced plans to reorganize by merging several subsidiaries to streamline operations.

FINANCIALS: **Sales and profits are in thousands of dollars—add 000 to get the full amount. 2008 Note: Financial information for 2008 was not available for all companies at press time.**

2008 Sales: $17,832,917	2008 Profits: $247,840	**U.S. Stock Ticker:**
2007 Sales: $14,299,551	2007 Profits: $443,007	**Int'l Ticker: 4183** Int'l Exchange: Tokyo-TSE
2006 Sales: $12,521,600	2006 Profits: $375,200	Employees: 12,814
2005 Sales: $11,430,738	2005 Profits: $243,896	Fiscal Year Ends: 3/31
2004 Sales: $10,313,400	2004 Profits: $118,000	Parent Company:

SALARIES/BENEFITS:

Pension Plan:	ESOP Stock Plan:	Profit Sharing:	Top Exec. Salary: $	Bonus: $
Savings Plan:	Stock Purch. Plan:		Second Exec. Salary: $	Bonus: $

OTHER THOUGHTS:

Apparent Women Officers or Directors:
Hot Spot for Advancement for Women/Minorities:

LOCATIONS: ("Y" = Yes)

West:	Southwest:	Midwest:	Southeast:	Northeast:	International:
Y	Y	Y		Y	Y

Note: Financial information, benefits and other data can change quickly and may vary from those stated here.

MOLEX INC

www.molex.com

Industry Group Code: 334119 **Ranks within this company's industry group:** Sales: 9 Profits: 8

Techology:		Medical/Drugs:		Engineering:		Transportation:		Chemicals/Petrochemicals:		Specialty:	
Computers:	Y	Manufacturer:		Design:		Aerospace:		Oil/Gas Products:		Special Services:	
Software:		Contract Research:		Construction:		Automotive:		Chemicals:		Consulting:	
Communications:	Y	Medical Services:		Eng. Services:		Shipping:		Oil/Chem. Svcs.:		Specialty Mgmt.:	
Electronics:		Labs:		Consulting:				Gases:		Products:	
Alternative Energy:		Bio. Services:						Other:		Other:	

TYPES OF BUSINESS:

Electronic Components
Transportation Products
Commercial Products
Micro Products
Automation & Electrical Products
Integrated Products
Global Sales & Marketing Organization

BRANDS/DIVISIONS/AFFILIATES:

Woodhead Industries Inc
AFlrextech Inc

CONTACTS: *Note: Officers with more than one job title may be intentionally listed here more than once.*

Martin P. Slark, CEO
Liam McCarthy, COO
Liam McCarthy, Pres.
David D. Johnson, CFO/Exec. VP
Graham C. Brock, Exec. VP/Pres., Global Sales & Mktg. Div.
David D. Johnson, Treas.
James E. Fleischhacker, Exec. VP/Pres., Global Transportation Prod. Div.
John H. Krehbiel, Jr., Co-Chmn.
David B. Root, Exec. VP/Pres., Global Commercial Prod. Div.
Katsumi Hirokawa, Exec. VP/Pres., Global Micro Prod. Div.
Frederick A. Krehbiel, Co-Chmn.

Phone: 630-969-4550	**Fax:** 630-968-8356
Toll-Free: 800-786-6539	
Address: 2222 Wellington Ct., Lisle, IL 60532-1682 US	

GROWTH PLANS/SPECIAL FEATURES:

Molex, Inc. is a manufacturer of electronic components. It designs, manufactures and sells more than 100,000 products, including terminals, connectors, planar cables, cable assemblies, interconnection systems, backplanes, integrated products and mechanical and electronic switches. The company also provides manufacturing services to integrate specific components into a customer's product. The firm is organized into six divisions: transportation products; commercial products; micro products; automation and electrical products; integrated products; and global sales and marketing organization. The transportation products segment specializes in interconnection for cockpit, engine and infotainment functions in automobiles and other transportation equipment. The commercial products segment specializes in high-speed, high-signal-integrity, high-signal interconnect applications. The micro products segment focuses on portable digital product applications. The automation and electrical products segment focuses on harsh-environment technology for factory automation, temporary lighting, power and ergonomic products in construction, industrial and other applications. The integrated products segment produces higher-level assemblies using Molex interconnect technologies, usually in fiber optic, printed circuit board, flex circuit and other applications. The global sales and marketing organization segment comprises regional sales and industry marketing support teams, which provide customers with access to the Molex products. Molex operates 45 manufacturing facilities in 19 countries including France, Germany, Ireland, Italy, Poland, Japan, China, India and Thailand. Major customers include AT&T; AMD; Canon; Cisco; IBM; Lucent; Motorola; Sony; Toshiba; and Xerox. In July 2008, the company acquired Taiwan-based AFlrextech, Inc.

FINANCIALS: **Sales and profits are in thousands of dollars—add 000 to get the full amount. 2008 Note: Financial information for 2008 was not available for all companies at press time.**

2008 Sales: $3,328,347	2008 Profits: $215,437	**U.S. Stock Ticker: MOLX**
2007 Sales: $3,265,874	2007 Profits: $240,768	**Int'l Ticker:** Int'l Exchange:
2006 Sales: $2,861,289	2006 Profits: $236,091	Employees: 32,160
2005 Sales: $2,554,458	2005 Profits: $150,116	Fiscal Year Ends: 6/30
2004 Sales: $2,246,700	2004 Profits: $176,000	Parent Company:

SALARIES/BENEFITS:

Pension Plan:	ESOP Stock Plan:	Profit Sharing:	Top Exec. Salary: $878,333	Bonus: $
Savings Plan:	Stock Purch. Plan: Y		Second Exec. Salary: $568,332	Bonus: $

OTHER THOUGHTS:

Apparent Women Officers or Directors: 1
Hot Spot for Advancement for Women/Minorities:

LOCATIONS: ("Y" = Yes)

West:	Southwest:	Midwest:	Southeast:	Northeast:	International:
Y		Y	Y	Y	Y

MONSANTO CO

www.monsanto.com

Industry Group Code: 115112 **Ranks within this company's industry group:** Sales: 2 Profits: 1

Techology:		Medical/Drugs:		Engineering:		Transportation:		Chemicals/Petrochemicals:		Specialty:	
Computers:		Manufacturer:		Design:		Aerospace:		Oil/Gas Products:		Special Services:	
Software:		Contract Research:		Construction:		Automotive:		Chemicals:	Y	Consulting:	
Communications:		Medical Services:		Eng. Services:		Shipping:		Oil/Chem. Svcs.:		Specialty Mgmt.:	
Electronics:		Labs:		Consulting:				Gases:		Products:	
Alternative Energy:		Bio. Services:						Other:		Other:	

TYPES OF BUSINESS:

Agricultural Biotechnology Products & Chemicals Manufacturing
Herbicides
Seeds
Genetic Products
Lawn & Garden Products

BRANDS/DIVISIONS/AFFILIATES:

Asgrow
Roundup Ready
Agroeste Sementes
Delta and Pine Land Company
Seminis
De Ruiter Seeds Group BV
Marmot SA
Aly Participacoes Ltda

CONTACTS: *Note: Officers with more than one job title may be intentionally listed here more than once.*

Hugh Grant, CEO
Hugh Grant, Pres.
Terrell K. Crews, CFO/Exec. VP
Steven C. Mizell, Exec. VP-Human Resources
Robert T. Fraley, CTO/Exec. VP
Mark J. Leidy, Exec. VP-Mfg.
Janet M. Holloway, Chief of Staff/VP
David F. Snively, General Counsel/Sr. VP/Sec.
Carl M. Casale, Exec. VP-Oper. & Strategy
Cheryl Morley, Sr. VP-Corp. Strategy
Janet M. Holloway, Sr. VP-Comm. Rel.
Scarlett Lee Foster, VP-Investor Rel.
Richard B. Clark, VP/Controller
Robert A. Paley, VP/Treas.
Nicole M. Ringenberg, VP-Finance & Oper./Global Commercial
Terrell K. Crews, CEO-Seminis
Gerald A. Steiner, Exec. VP-Corp. Affairs & Sustainability
Hugh Grant, Chmn.
Kerry J. Preete, Exec. VP-Int'l Commercial

Phone: 314-694-1000	**Fax:** 314-694-8394
Toll-Free:	
Address: 800 N. Lindbergh Blvd., St. Louis, MO 63167 US	

GROWTH PLANS/SPECIAL FEATURES:

Monsanto Co. is a global provider of agricultural products for farmers. The company operates in two principal business segments: Seeds and Genomics; and Agricultural Productivity. The Seeds and Genomics segment is responsible for producing seed brands and patenting genetic traits that enable seeds to resist insects, disease, drought and weeds. Major seed brands produced by Monsanto include Agroceres, Asgrow, DEKALB, Stoneville, Vistive, Monsoy, Holden's Foundation Seeds, American Seeds, Inc., Seminis, Royal Sluis and Petoseed. The company's genetic trait products include Roundup Ready traits in soybeans, corn, canola and cotton; Bollgard and Bollgard II traits in cotton; and YieldGard Corn Borer and YieldGard Rootworm traits in corn. The Agricultural Productivity segment produces herbicide products. The firm's branded herbicides include Roundup, Harness, Degree, Machete, Maverick, Certainty, Outrider and Monitor. Monsanto market its seeds and commercial herbicides through a variety of channels and directly to farmers. Residential herbicides are marketed through the Scotts Miracle-Gro Company. Subsidiaries include Delta and Pine Land Company, a developer of cotton and soybean seeds; and Agroeste Sementes, a Brazilian corn seed company. In 2008, the company acquired the Dutch holding company, De Ruiter Seeds Group B.V. for $850 million; Marmot, S.A. which operates the private Guatemalan seed company Semillas Cristiani Burkhard; and Aly Participacoes Ltda., which operates sugarcane technology companies, CanaVialis S.A. and Alellyx S.A. Also in 2008, the company sold its POSILAC bovine somatotropin brand and related business to Eli Lilly and Company for $300 million.

Employees are offered medical, dental, and vision insurance; life insurance; disability coverage; a pension plan; a 401(k) plan; a stock purchase plan; long term care insurance; adoption assistance; group auto and home insurance; an employee assistance program; and relocation assistance.

FINANCIALS: Sales and profits are in thousands of dollars—add 000 to get the full amount. 2008 Note: Financial information for 2008 was not available for all companies at press time.

2008 Sales: $11,365,000	2008 Profits: $2,024,000	**U.S. Stock Ticker: MON**
2007 Sales: $8,563,000	2007 Profits: $993,000	**Int'l Ticker:** Int'l Exchange:
2006 Sales: $7,294,000	2006 Profits: $689,000	Employees: 21,700
2005 Sales: $6,275,000	2005 Profits: $255,000	Fiscal Year Ends: 8/31
2004 Sales: $5,457,000	2004 Profits: $267,000	Parent Company:

SALARIES/BENEFITS:

Pension Plan: Y	ESOP Stock Plan:	Profit Sharing:	Top Exec. Salary: $1,286,019	Bonus: $3,326,796
Savings Plan: Y	Stock Purch. Plan: Y		Second Exec. Salary: $566,827	Bonus: $840,000

OTHER THOUGHTS:

Apparent Women Officers or Directors: 5
Hot Spot for Advancement for Women/Minorities: Y

LOCATIONS: ("Y" = Yes)

West:	Southwest:	Midwest:	Southeast:	Northeast:	International:
Y	Y	Y	Y	Y	Y

MOTOROLA INC

www.motorola.com

Industry Group Code: 334220 **Ranks within this company's industry group:** Sales: 3 Profits: 6

Techology:		Medical/Drugs:		Engineering:		Transportation:		Chemicals/Petrochemicals:		Specialty:	
Computers:	Y	Manufacturer:		Design:		Aerospace:		Oil/Gas Products:		Special Services:	
Software:		Contract Research:		Construction:		Automotive:		Chemicals:		Consulting:	
Communications:	Y	Medical Services:		Eng. Services:		Shipping:		Oil/Chem. Svcs.:		Specialty Mgmt.:	
Electronics:		Labs:		Consulting:				Gases:		Products:	
Alternative Energy:		Bio. Services:						Other:		Other:	

TYPES OF BUSINESS:

Telecommunications Equipment-Cellular Telephones
Two-Way Radio Communication Products
Wireless Communication Systems
Electronic Systems
Broadband Products
Communications Software

BRANDS/DIVISIONS/AFFILIATES:

Motorola Good Technology Group
TUT Systems Inc
Motorola Labs
Symbol Technologies Inc

CONTACTS: *Note: Officers with more than one job title may be intentionally listed here more than once.*

Greg Brown, Co-CEO/CEO-Broadband Mobility Solutions
Greg Brown, Pres.
Paul Liska, CFO/Exec. VP
Greg A. Lee, Sr. VP-Human Resources
Leslie Jones, CIO/Sr. VP
A. Peter Lawson, General Counsel/Exec. VP/Sec.
Karen P. Tandy, Sr. VP-Public Affairs & Comm.
Sanjay K. Jha, Co-CEO/CEO-Mobile Devices
Kathy Paladino, Sr. VP/Pres., Enterprise Mobility
Daniel M. Moloney, Exec. VP/Pres., Home & Networks Mobility Bus.
Gene Delaney, Sr. VP/Pres., Gov't & Public Safety
David W. Dorman, Chmn.
Bob Perez, Sr. VP-Integrated Supply Chain

Phone: 847-576-5000 **Fax:** 847-576-5372
Toll-Free:
Address: 1303 E. Algonquin Rd., Schaumburg, IL 60196 US

GROWTH PLANS/SPECIAL FEATURES:

Motorola, Inc., a portable radio and cellular phone pioneer, provides a broad range of mobile technologies, products and services. The company operates in three business segments: Mobile Devices; Home and Networks Mobility; and Enterprise Mobility Solutions. The mobile devices segment, representing approximately 42% of sales, designs, manufactures, sells and services wireless handsets with integrated software and accessory products, and also licenses intellectual property. Products are marketed worldwide to carriers and consumers through direct sales, distributors, dealers, retailers and, in certain markets, through licensees. Customers include Sprint Nextel, AT&T, Verizon, China Mobile and America Movil. The home and networks mobility segment, representing approximately 32% of sales, designs, manufactures, sells, installs and services digital and Internet Protocol (IP) video and broadcast network interactive set-tops; end-to-end video delivery solutions; broadband access infrastructure systems; and associated data and voice customer premise equipment to cable television and telecom service providers. The segment also designs and supports wireless access systems, including cellular infrastructure systems and wireless broadband systems, for wireless service providers. Customers include Comcast, Verizon, KDDI in Japan, China Mobile and Sprint Nextel. The enterprise mobility solutions segment, representing approximately 26% of sales, designs, manufactures, sells, installs and services analog and digital two-way radio; voice and data communications products and systems for private networks; wireless broadband systems; and end-to-end enterprise mobility solutions to a wide range of enterprise markets, including government and public safety agencies, as well as retail, utility, transportation, manufacturing, healthcare and other commercial customers. Major customers include the U.S. Government, IBM, Ingram Micro and Wal-Mart. In September 2008, Motorola announced the acquisition of AirDefense, Inc., a wireless local area network service provider. In November 2008, Satyam Computer Services Ltd. took over Motorola's software development center in Malaysia.

FINANCIALS: **Sales and profits are in thousands of dollars—add 000 to get the full amount. 2008 Note: Financial information for 2008 was not available for all companies at press time.**

2008 Sales: $30,146,000	2008 Profits: $-4,244,000	**U.S. Stock Ticker: MOT**
2007 Sales: $36,622,000	2007 Profits: $-49,000	**Int'l Ticker:** Int'l Exchange:
2006 Sales: $42,847,000	2006 Profits: $3,661,000	Employees: 64,000
2005 Sales: $35,262,000	2005 Profits: $4,578,000	Fiscal Year Ends: 12/31
2004 Sales: $29,663,000	2004 Profits: $1,532,000	Parent Company:

SALARIES/BENEFITS:

Pension Plan:	ESOP Stock Plan:	Profit Sharing:	Top Exec. Salary: $1,500,000	Bonus: $1,493,000
Savings Plan:	Stock Purch. Plan:		Second Exec. Salary: $857,500	Bonus: $486,214

OTHER THOUGHTS:

Apparent Women Officers or Directors: 4
Hot Spot for Advancement for Women/Minorities: Y

LOCATIONS: ("Y" = Yes)

West:	Southwest:	Midwest:	Southeast:	Northeast:	International:
	Y	Y	Y	Y	Y

Note: Financial information, benefits and other data can change quickly and may vary from those stated here.

MOTOROLA LABS

www.motorola.com/content.jsp?globalObjectId=6584-11664

Industry Group Code: 541710 **Ranks within this company's industry group:** Sales: Profits:

Techology:		Medical/Drugs:		Engineering:		Transportation:		Chemicals/Petrochemicals:		Specialty:	
Computers:		Manufacturer:		Design:		Aerospace:		Oil/Gas Products:		Special Services:	
Software:	Y	Contract Research:		Construction:		Automotive:		Chemicals:		Consulting:	
Communications:	Y	Medical Services:		Eng. Services:		Shipping:		Oil/Chem. Svcs.:		Specialty Mgmt.:	
Electronics:	Y	Labs:		Consulting:				Gases:		Products:	
Alternative Energy:	Y	Bio. Services:						Other:		Other:	

TYPES OF BUSINESS:

Research & Development-Communications
Semiconductors
Software & Networking Products
Nanotubes
Display Technology
Imaging Systems
Advanced Materials

BRANDS/DIVISIONS/AFFILIATES:

Motorola Inc
Motorola Technology
Nano-emissive Display

CONTACTS:

Note: Officers with more than one job title may be intentionally listed here more than once.

Bill Olson, Dir-Int'l & Environmental R&D, Motorola Tech.
Padmasree Warrior, CTO-Motorola, Inc.
Dragan Boscovic, Dir.-Eng. & Tech., Motorola Technology
Ken Zdunek, VP-Networks Research
Fred Kitson, VP-Applications Research
Vida Ilderem, VP-Physical & Digital Realization Research
Gary Grube, Sr. Fellow-Wireless & Solutions Research

Phone: 847-576-5000	**Fax:** 847-576-5372
Toll-Free:	
Address: 1303 E. Algonquin Rd., Schaumburg, IL 60196 US	

GROWTH PLANS/SPECIAL FEATURES:

Motorola Labs, part of Motorola, Inc.'s Motorola Technology sector, conducts applied communications research. It is organized into four main research labs, each with sub-labs under them. The Networks Research Lab, which has four sub-labs, focuses on autonomic networks, converged services framework, mobile IP and all IP wireless networks research. Its goal is the seamless transition of products from one network type to another, such as from intranets to extranets, or from wired to wireless networks. The Applications Research Lab, which has six sub-labs, focuses on autonomics personalization, mobile gaming, social networking, 3D graphics and avatars and MPEG4 and other audio codecs research. Its goal is to develop technologies to allow content and services to seamless transition from one device to another, such as from a mobile to set-top device or a wireless network, striving for applications that can adapt to a user's changing interests. The Physical and Digital Realization Research Lab, which has 10 sub-labs, focuses on nanotechnology, nanomaterials, networked sensing, visual communications, environmental technology, printed electronics and cognitive small systems research. Its goals include developing new display technologies, accelerating data transfer rates, miniaturizing embedded devices and personalizing products. It recently developed a new low-temperature technique for growing carbon nanotubes on plastic to create what it calls a Nano-Emissive Display (NED), which is brighter than plasma displays and viewable from more angles than LCDs, while costing less to create and consuming 20-30% less power than either. It is also developing light-emitting inks and paper thin printed circuits. Lastly, the Wireless and Solutions Research Lab, which has 12 sub-labs, focuses on affordable wireless broadband, ad hoc networks, OFDM (Orthogonal Frequency Division Multiplexing), cognitive radio and software define radio research. Its main goal is developing affordable wireless networks and self-adapting systems. This segment has developed wind- and solar-powered wireless base stations.

FINANCIALS:

Sales and profits are in thousands of dollars—add 000 to get the full amount. 2008 Note: Financial information for 2008 was not available for all companies at press time.

2008 Sales: $	2008 Profits: $	**U.S. Stock Ticker: Subsidiary**
2007 Sales: $	2007 Profits: $	**Int'l Ticker:** Int'l Exchange:
2006 Sales: $	2006 Profits: $	Employees:
2005 Sales: $	2005 Profits: $	Fiscal Year Ends: 12/31
2004 Sales: $	2004 Profits: $	Parent Company: MOTOROLA INC

SALARIES/BENEFITS:

Pension Plan:	ESOP Stock Plan:	Profit Sharing:	Top Exec. Salary: $	Bonus: $
Savings Plan:	Stock Purch. Plan:		Second Exec. Salary: $	Bonus: $

OTHER THOUGHTS:

Apparent Women Officers or Directors: 1
Hot Spot for Advancement for Women/Minorities:

LOCATIONS: ("Y" = Yes)

West:	Southwest:	Midwest:	Southeast:	Northeast:	International:
	Y	Y	Y	Y	Y

MSCSOFTWARE CORP

www.mscsoftware.com

Industry Group Code: 511215 **Ranks within this company's industry group:** Sales: 7 Profits: 5

Techology:		Medical/Drugs:		Engineering:		Transportation:		Chemicals/Petrochemicals:		Specialty:	
Computers:		Manufacturer:		Design:		Aerospace:		Oil/Gas Products:		Special Services:	
Software:	Y	Contract Research:		Construction:		Automotive:		Chemicals:		Consulting:	
Communications:		Medical Services:		Eng. Services:		Shipping:		Oil/Chem. Svcs.:		Specialty Mgmt.:	
Electronics:		Labs:		Consulting:	Y			Gases:		Products:	
Alternative Energy:		Bio. Services:						Other:		Other:	

TYPES OF BUSINESS:

Software-Computer-Aided Engineering
Engineering Consulting
Custom Software Development
Simulation Software
Product Lifecycle Management Software

BRANDS/DIVISIONS/AFFILIATES:

SimOffice
MSC Nastran
SimManager
Adams
SimXpert
MacNeal Group LLC

CONTACTS: *Note: Officers with more than one job title may be intentionally listed here more than once.*

William Weyand, CEO
Glenn Wienkoop, COO
Glenn Wienkoop, Pres.
Sam M. Auriemma, CFO/Exec. VP
Amir A. Mobayen, Worldwide Sales & Svcs.
Randy Gorrell, Sr. VP-Human Resources
Reza S. Sadeghi, CTO
John Mongelluzzo, Exec. VP-Bus. Admin.
John Mongelluzzo, Exec. VP-Legal Affairs/Sec.
Frank Kovacs, VP-Strategic Alliances
Jennifer Brannon, Sr. Mgr.-Public Rel.
Joanne Keates, VP-Investor Rel.
William Weyand, Chmn.
Christopher St. John, Sr. VP-Asia Pacific Oper.

Phone: 714-540-8900	**Fax:** 714-784-4056
Toll-Free: 800-328-4672	
Address: 2 MacArthur Pl., Santa Ana, CA 92707 US	

GROWTH PLANS/SPECIAL FEATURES:

MSC.Software Corporation (MSC) is a leading global provider of virtual product development tools using simulation software. Operating in 22 countries, the company provides services and systems to optimize product design and quality and reduce costs and time-to-market as well as information systems and software integration systems through its product lifecycle management software. MSC's most popular software products include SimOffice, SimXpert, MSC Nastran and Adams. The firm's solutions are intended to equip engineers with greater freedom to innovate design concepts, optimize complex solutions and exploit materials as a design variable. MCAE analysis is used to simulate the performance of a design before its physical manufacture, reducing the costly physical testing of prototypes and permitting a substantial increase in the number of design trade-offs and design cycles. Engineers use MSC's simulation software worldwide in industries including aerospace, automotive, defense, shipbuilding, consumer products and electronics. Major clients in these fields include Boeing, Lockheed Martin and Ford. The company also provides strategic consulting services to customers to improve the integration and performance of its technologies. In June 2008, MSC acquired the MacNeal Group, LLC.

FINANCIALS: **Sales and profits are in thousands of dollars—add 000 to get the full amount. 2008 Note: Financial information for 2008 was not available for all companies at press time.**

2008 Sales: $254,386	2008 Profits: $-6,246	**U.S. Stock Ticker: MNSC.PK**
2007 Sales: $246,651	2007 Profits: $-10,320	**Int'l Ticker:** Int'l Exchange:
2006 Sales: $259,686	2006 Profits: $13,802	Employees: 1,116
2005 Sales: $295,637	2005 Profits: $11,818	Fiscal Year Ends: 12/31
2004 Sales: $267,285	2004 Profits: $10,879	Parent Company:

SALARIES/BENEFITS:

Pension Plan:	ESOP Stock Plan:	Profit Sharing:	Top Exec. Salary: $567,500	Bonus: $143,750
Savings Plan: Y	Stock Purch. Plan: Y		Second Exec. Salary: $373,300	Bonus: $67,340

OTHER THOUGHTS:

Apparent Women Officers or Directors: 2
Hot Spot for Advancement for Women/Minorities:

LOCATIONS: ("Y" = Yes)

West:	Southwest:	Midwest:	Southeast:	Northeast:	International:
Y	Y	Y	Y	Y	Y

MWH GLOBAL INC

www.mw.com

Industry Group Code: 234000 **Ranks within this company's industry group:** Sales: Profits:

Techology:		Medical/Drugs:		Engineering:		Transportation:		Chemicals/Petrochemicals:		Specialty:	
Computers:		Manufacturer:		Design:	Y	Aerospace:		Oil/Gas Products:		Special Services:	Y
Software:	Y	Contract Research:		Construction:	Y	Automotive:		Chemicals:		Consulting:	Y
Communications:		Medical Services:		Eng. Services:	Y	Shipping:		Oil/Chem. Svcs.:		Specialty Mgmt.:	Y
Electronics:		Labs:		Consulting:	Y			Gases:		Products:	
Alternative Energy:		Bio. Services:						Other:		Other:	

TYPES OF BUSINESS:

Engineering & Construction Services
Environmental Engineering
Water & Waste Treatment Analysis
Facilities Development
Infrastructure Asset Management
Consulting
Government Relations & Lobbying
Software & IT Services

BRANDS/DIVISIONS/AFFILIATES:

KnowledgeNet
MWH Laboratories
Asset Group (The)
Montgomery Group (The)
MWH Constructors
MWH Automation & Information Solutions
MWH Smart Systems
MWH Applied Research

CONTACTS:

Note: Officers with more than one job title may be intentionally listed here more than once.

Robert B. Uhler, CEO
Alan J. Krause, COO
Alan J. Krause, Pres.
David Barnes, CFO
Richard Parry, Legal Officer/ Chief Risk Officer
Don Smith, Chief-Strategy Implementation
Dan McConville, Pres., MWH Americas, Inc.
Joseph D. Adams, Jr., Pres., MWH Constructors, Inc.
Paul F. Boulos, Pres., MWH Soft, Inc.
Bruce K. Howard, Pres., MWH Bus. Solutions
Donald L. Smith, Chmn.
David Nickols, Pres., EMEA

Phone: 303-533-1900 **Fax:** 303-533-1901
Toll-Free:
Address: 370 Interlocken Crescent, Ste. 300, Broomfield, CO 80021 US

GROWTH PLANS/SPECIAL FEATURES:

MWH Global, Inc. is one of the world's leading providers of consulting, engineering, construction and management services to the water, natural resources and infrastructure industries. Through 197 global offices, MWH specializes in proprietary software and process automation packages in the areas of environmental engineering, power generation, facilities development, laboratory services, construction, asset management, financial services, IT consulting and government relations. One of these packages, KnowledgeNet, links the firm's worldwide employee base, allowing instant collaboration on projects and the elimination of redundancies in its system. MWH conducts its operations through several independent divisions: environmental engineering, power solutions, facilities, program management, laboratory services, asset management, financial consulting, construction, information technology, applied research and government relations. Subsidiaries include MWH Laboratories, providing water and wastewater analysis services; The Asset Group, providing infrastructure asset management services; The Montgomery Group, providing financial and management consulting services; MWH Constructors, providing construction services; MWH Automation & Information Solutions, providing process automation, SCADA and enterprise-wide software and hardware solutions; MWH Smart Systems, providing software and IT services throughout Europe; MWH Applied Research, conducting research on water and industrial waste treatment; and mCapitol Management, providing government relations and lobbying services. MWH Soft is the creator of H2ONET, an integrated water distribution analysis software package. In 2008, the firm expanded its footprint in Canada with the acquisition of Northern EnviroSearch Ltd., a Calgary-based environmental consulting firm. Later in the year, MWH acquired Ground Water International S.A., a large hydrogeological consulting firm in Lima, Peru. The acquisition furthers MWH's efforts to expand its South American presence and add to its water resources and mining services portfolio. Additionally, the firm recently signed two contracts, worth $220 million, with the city of Tallahassee, Florida to provide construction management-at-risk services to upgrade Tallahassee's wastewater treatment facilities.

FINANCIALS:

Sales and profits are in thousands of dollars—add 000 to get the full amount. 2008 Note: Financial information for 2008 was not available for all companies at press time.

2008 Sales: $ 2008 Profits: $
2007 Sales: $ 2007 Profits: $
2006 Sales: $ 2006 Profits: $
2005 Sales: $ 2005 Profits: $
2004 Sales: $ 2004 Profits: $

U.S. Stock Ticker: Private
Int'l Ticker: Int'l Exchange:
Employees:
Fiscal Year Ends: 9/30
Parent Company:

SALARIES/BENEFITS:

Pension Plan: ESOP Stock Plan: Profit Sharing: Top Exec. Salary: $ Bonus: $
Savings Plan: Stock Purch. Plan: Second Exec. Salary: $ Bonus: $

OTHER THOUGHTS:

Apparent Women Officers or Directors: 3
Hot Spot for Advancement for Women/Minorities: Y

LOCATIONS: ("Y" = Yes)

West:	Southwest:	Midwest:	Southeast:	Northeast:	International:
Y	Y	Y	Y	Y	Y

NATIONAL SEMICONDUCTOR CORP

www.national.com

Industry Group Code: 334413 **Ranks within this company's industry group:** Sales: 18 Profits: 7

Techology:		Medical/Drugs:		Engineering:		Transportation:		Chemicals/Petrochemicals:		Specialty:	
Computers:	Y	Manufacturer:		Design:		Aerospace:		Oil/Gas Products:		Special Services:	
Software:		Contract Research:		Construction:		Automotive:		Chemicals:		Consulting:	
Communications:		Medical Services:		Eng. Services:		Shipping:		Oil/Chem. Svcs.:		Specialty Mgmt.:	
Electronics:		Labs:		Consulting:				Gases:		Products:	
Alternative Energy:		Bio. Services:						Other:		Other:	

TYPES OF BUSINESS:

Chips-Analog
Mixed-Signal Integrated Circuits
Information Appliances
Enterprise Networking Products
Display Products

BRANDS/DIVISIONS/AFFILIATES:

Xignal Technologies AG

CONTACTS: *Note: Officers with more than one job title may be intentionally listed here more than once.*

Brian L. Halla, CEO
Donald Macleod, COO
Donald Macleod, Pres.
Lewis Chew, CFO/Sr. VP
Suneil Parulekar, Sr. VP-Worldwide Mktg. & Sales
Edward Sweeney, Sr. VP-Worldwide Human Resources
Ulrich J. Seif, CIO/Sr. VP
Ahmad Bahai, CTO-NS Labs
C.S. Liu, Sr. VP-Worldwide Mfg.
Todd DuChene, General Counsel/Sr. VP/Corp. Sec.
Mike Polacek, Sr. VP-Bus. Dev. & Key Market Segments
Dennis Monticelli, CTO-Analog
Detlev Kunz, Sr. VP/Gen. Mgr.-Prod. Group
Mohan Yegnashankaran, Sr. VP-Tech. Support
Brian L. Halla, Chmn.
Simon Yu, VP/Managing Dir.-Asia Pacific
Jennifer J. Bleakney, VP-Worldwide Dist. & Customer Support

Phone: 408-721-5000 **Fax:** 408-739-9803
Toll-Free: 800-272-9959
Address: 2900 Semiconductor Dr., Santa Clara, CA 95051 US

GROWTH PLANS/SPECIAL FEATURES:

National Semiconductor Corp. designs, develops, manufactures and markets semiconductor products, including analog, mixed-signal and other integrated circuits. These products are used in information appliances; personal systems; wireless communications; flat-panel and CRT displays; power management; local and wide area networks; and consumer applications. The company is divided into two operational groups: Power Management and Signal Path. The Power Management Group consists of four business units: Advanced Power, Infrastructure Power, Mobile Devices Power and Performance Power. These units design, develop and manufacture high-efficiency switching voltage regulators and controllers; high-performance low drop-out voltage regulators; LED drivers; precision voltage references; battery management integrated circuits; Mobile Pixel Link (MPL) serial bridges; and display drivers. The segment also contains the ASIC & Telecom business unit, which supplies user-designed application-specific products in the form of standard cells, gate arrays and full custom devices. The unit also supplies key telecommunications components for analog and digital line cards, as well as 8-bit and 16-bit microcontrollers. The Analog Signal Path Group is divided into business units by the devices they create and includes: Amplifiers; Audio; Data Conversion; Interface; and Hi-Rel which supplies integrated circuits and contract services to the high reliability market, which includes avionics, defense, space and the federal government. In addition to these two operating groups, National Semiconductor has a centralized Worldwide Sales and Marketing Group, a Technology Development Group and a Manufacturing Operations Group. The firm's major customers include Apple Computer, LG Electronics, Motorola, Nokia, Siemens and Sony.

Employees are offered medical and dental insurance; tuition reimbursement; an employee stock purchase plan; a profit sharing program; a 401(k) plan; life insurance; disability benefits; an employee assistance program; family assistance benefits; on-site dry cleaning, dental care, banking, postal services and fitness centers; commuter benefits; store discounts; a subsidized employee cafeteria; and credit union.

FINANCIALS: **Sales and profits are in thousands of dollars—add 000 to get the full amount. 2008 Note: Financial information for 2008 was not available for all companies at press time.**

2008 Sales: $1,885,900	2008 Profits: $332,300	**U.S. Stock Ticker: NSM**
2007 Sales: $1,929,900	2007 Profits: $375,300	**Int'l Ticker:** Int'l Exchange:
2006 Sales: $2,158,100	2006 Profits: $449,200	Employees: 7,300
2005 Sales: $1,913,100	2005 Profits: $415,300	Fiscal Year Ends: 5/31
2004 Sales: $1,983,100	2004 Profits: $282,800	Parent Company:

SALARIES/BENEFITS:

Pension Plan: Y	ESOP Stock Plan:	Profit Sharing: Y	Top Exec. Salary: $879,735	Bonus: $1,112,500
Savings Plan:	Stock Purch. Plan: Y		Second Exec. Salary: $593,077	Bonus: $600,000

OTHER THOUGHTS:

Apparent Women Officers or Directors:
Hot Spot for Advancement for Women/Minorities:

LOCATIONS: ("Y" = Yes)

West:	Southwest:	Midwest:	Southeast:	Northeast:	International:
Y	Y	Y	Y	Y	Y

NAVTEQ CORPORATION

www.navteq.com

Industry Group Code: 511215 **Ranks within this company's industry group:** Sales: Profits:

Techology:		Medical/Drugs:		Engineering:		Transportation:		Chemicals/Petrochemicals:		Specialty:	
Computers:		Manufacturer:		Design:		Aerospace:		Oil/Gas Products:		Special Services:	
Software:	Y	Contract Research:		Construction:		Automotive:		Chemicals:		Consulting:	
Communications:		Medical Services:		Eng. Services:		Shipping:		Oil/Chem. Svcs.:		Specialty Mgmt.:	
Electronics:		Labs:		Consulting:				Gases:		Products:	Y
Alternative Energy:		Bio. Services:						Other:		Other:	

TYPES OF BUSINESS:

Digital Map Information
Route Planning Technology
Vehicle Navigation
Internet-Based Mapping
Location-Based Services
Geographic Information Systems

BRANDS/DIVISIONS/AFFILIATES:

Picture Map International
Traffic.com, Inc.
The Map Network
Nokia Corporation

CONTACTS:

Note: Officers with more than one job title may be intentionally listed here more than once.

Judson Green, CEO
Judson Green, Pres.
Tiffany Treacy, VP-Prod. Mgmt.
Bob Richter, Public Rel.

Phone: 312-894-7000 **Fax:** 312-894-7050
Toll-Free: 866-462-8837
Address: 425 West Randolph St., Chicago, IL 60606 US

GROWTH PLANS/SPECIAL FEATURES:

Navteq Corporation is a provider of digital map information for automotive navigation systems, mobile navigation devices and Internet mapping applications. A number of its 3,600 employees are tasked solely with maintaining and continuously upgrading its geographical database, through 187 offices in 39 countries, covering 15 million points of interest on six continents. Navteq is most prominent in North America (covering close to 100% of population and road networks), Western Europe (100%) and Eastern Europe (29%). Products are offered to both businesses and individuals and consist of a broad range of navigation tools including databases of urban and rural transportation grids that are often incorporated into GPS products by systems manufactures (such as Harman Becker, Alpine and Siemens) and mobile navigation device manufacturers (such as Garmin, Dell and Thales). Other tools include route planning that allows for driving directions and route optimization via the Internet and is used by web sites including MapQuest, Microsoft/MSN, Google and Yahoo!. In addition, location-based services provide geographic information about specific locations tailored to the proximity of a specific user. It is primarily utilized by mobile directory assistance services, emergency response systems and geographic information systems, which render geographic representations of information for use by government and utility agencies. Recently, Navteq has expanded its market coverage to include Singapore, Malaysia, Mexico and Puerto Rico. In July 2008, Navteq was acquired by Nokia Corp. for $8.1 billion.

FINANCIALS:

Sales and profits are in thousands of dollars—add 000 to get the full amount. 2008 Note: Financial information for 2008 was not available for all companies at press time.

2008 Sales: $	2008 Profits: $	**U.S. Stock Ticker: Subsidiary**
2007 Sales: $853,387	2007 Profits: $172,950	**Int'l Ticker:** Int'l Exchange:
2006 Sales: $581,619	2006 Profits: $109,970	Employees: 3,349
2005 Sales: $496,512	2005 Profits: $170,830	Fiscal Year Ends: 12/31
2004 Sales: $392,858	2004 Profits: $54,066	Parent Company: NOKIA CORPORATION

SALARIES/BENEFITS:

Pension Plan:	ESOP Stock Plan:	Profit Sharing:	Top Exec. Salary: $630,000	Bonus: $567,000
Savings Plan: Y	Stock Purch. Plan:		Second Exec. Salary: $364,423	Bonus: $164,250

OTHER THOUGHTS:

Apparent Women Officers or Directors: 1
Hot Spot for Advancement for Women/Minorities: Y

LOCATIONS: ("Y" = Yes)

West:	Southwest:	Midwest:	Southeast:	Northeast:	International:
		Y			Y

Note: Financial information, benefits and other data can change quickly and may vary from those stated here.

NCR CORPORATION

www.ncr.com

Industry Group Code: 334111 **Ranks within this company's industry group:** Sales: 13 Profits: 10

Techology:		Medical/Drugs:		Engineering:		Transportation:		Chemicals/Petrochemicals:		Specialty:	
Computers:	Y	Manufacturer:		Design:		Aerospace:		Oil/Gas Products:		Special Services:	
Software:	Y	Contract Research:		Construction:		Automotive:		Chemicals:		Consulting:	Y
Communications:		Medical Services:		Eng. Services:		Shipping:		Oil/Chem. Svcs.:		Specialty Mgmt.:	
Electronics:		Labs:		Consulting:				Gases:		Products:	
Alternative Energy:		Bio. Services:						Other:		Other:	

TYPES OF BUSINESS:

Point-of-Sale Computer Systems
Barcode Scanning Equipment
Automatic Teller Machines (ATMs)
Transaction Processing Equipment
Point-of-Sale & Store Automation
Data Warehousing
Printer Consumables
Consulting Services

BRANDS/DIVISIONS/AFFILIATES:

Systemedia
Cisco Systems
NCI Ltd

CONTACTS:

Note: Officers with more than one job title may be intentionally listed here more than once.

Bill Nuti, CEO
Bill Nuti, Pres.
Tony Massetti, CFO
Peter Leav, Sr. VP-Global Sales
Andrea Ledford, Sr. VP-Human Resources
Peter Lieb, General Counsel/Sr. VP
Peter Dorsman, Sr. VP-Global Oper.
Dan Bogan, Sr. VP/Gen. Mgr.-NCR Consumables
Christine Wallace, Sr. VP-NCR Svcs.
Bill Nuti, Chmn.

Phone: 937-445-5000 **Fax:** 937-445-1682
Toll-Free: 800-225-5627
Address: 1700 S. Patterson Blvd., Dayton, OH 45479 US

GROWTH PLANS/SPECIAL FEATURES:

NCR Corporation provides information technology and related services to various industries, enabling client companies to interact more efficiently with customers. The company offers financial institutions, retailers and independent deployers financial-oriented self service technologies, such as ATMs, cash dispensers, software solutions and consulting services relating to ATM security, software and bank branch optimization. Financial self service solutions are designed to quickly and reliably process consumer transactions and incorporate advanced features such as automated check cashing/deposit, automated cash deposit, web-enablement, bill payment and the dispensing of non-cash items. NCR provides retail store automation solutions for the general merchandise, food, drug, travel, hospitality, health care, entertainment, gaming and public sector segments. The company has focused its investments and resources on self-service technologies with expanded offerings to include self-ticketing and self-check-in/out systems for the travel industry; self-service food ordering; and patient management check-in/out in the health care sector. The firm provides maintenance and support services for its products, including complete systems management and site assessment and site preparation, staging, installation and implementation. NCR is also involved in the resale and service of third-party computer hardware from select manufacturers, such as Cisco Systems. Subsidiary, Systemedia develops, produces and markets a line of printer consumables for various print technologies, including paper rolls for receipts in ATMs and point of sale (POS) solutions; inkjet and laser printer supplies; thermal transfer and ink ribbons; labels; laser documents; business forms; and specialty media items such as photo and presentation papers and two-sided thermal paper. In 2008, the firm reorganized its business segments into three geographical groups: Americas; Europe, Middle East and Africa (EMEA); and Asia Pacific and Japan (APJ). In August 2008, the company acquired NCI Ltd., a U.K. provider of teller connectivity software for the finance business.

FINANCIALS:

Sales and profits are in thousands of dollars—add 000 to get the full amount. 2008 Note: Financial information for 2008 was not available for all companies at press time.

2008 Sales: $5,315,000	2008 Profits: $228,000	**U.S. Stock Ticker: NCR**
2007 Sales: $4,970,000	2007 Profits: $274,000	**Int'l Ticker:** Int'l Exchange:
2006 Sales: $4,582,000	2006 Profits: $382,000	Employees: 23,200
2005 Sales: $6,029,000	2005 Profits: $529,000	Fiscal Year Ends: 12/31
2004 Sales: $5,984,000	2004 Profits: $285,000	Parent Company:

SALARIES/BENEFITS:

Pension Plan:	ESOP Stock Plan:	Profit Sharing:	Top Exec. Salary: $1,000,000	Bonus: $2,368,432
Savings Plan:	Stock Purch. Plan:		Second Exec. Salary: $522,832	Bonus: $575,489

OTHER THOUGHTS:

Apparent Women Officers or Directors: 3
Hot Spot for Advancement for Women/Minorities: Y

LOCATIONS: ("Y" = Yes)

West:	Southwest:	Midwest:	Southeast:	Northeast:	International:
Y		Y	Y	Y	Y

Note: Financial information, benefits and other data can change quickly and may vary from those stated here.

NEC CORPORATION

www.nec.com

Industry Group Code: 334111 **Ranks within this company's industry group:** Sales: 6 Profits: 11

Techology:		Medical/Drugs:		Engineering:		Transportation:		Chemicals/Petrochemicals:		Specialty:	
Computers:	Y	Manufacturer:		Design:		Aerospace:		Oil/Gas Products:		Special Services:	
Software:	Y	Contract Research:		Construction:		Automotive:		Chemicals:		Consulting:	
Communications:	Y	Medical Services:		Eng. Services:		Shipping:		Oil/Chem. Svcs.:		Specialty Mgmt.:	
Electronics:	Y	Labs:		Consulting:				Gases:		Products:	
Alternative Energy:		Bio. Services:						Other:		Other:	

TYPES OF BUSINESS:

Computer Hardware Manufacturing
Lithium-Ion Batteries
Servers & Supercomputers
Telecommunications & Wireless Equipment
Semiconductor Manufacturing Equipment
Broadband & Networking Equipment
Operating Systems & Application Software
Nanotube Research

BRANDS/DIVISIONS/AFFILIATES:

NEC Corporation of America
NEC Electronics Corp.
NEC Display Solutions, Ltd.
Tohuko Chemical Co., Ltd.
ESTEEMO Co., Ltd.
Adcore-Tech Co., Ltd.
Sony NEC Optiarc Inc.
Automotive Energy Supply Corporation

CONTACTS: *Note: Officers with more than one job title may be intentionally listed here more than once.*

Kaoru Yano, Pres.
Toshimitsu Iwanami, Sr. VP-Sales
Shigeki Satake, Gen. Mgr.-Human Resources
Fujio Okada, Gen. Mgr.-Legal
Takayuki Morita, Gen. Mgr.-Bus. Dev.
Takao Ono, Gen. Mgr.-Corp. Finance
Nik Kishinoue, Exec. VP-Carrier Network Solutions
Kazuhiko Kobayashi, Exec. VP-Enterprise Solutions
Yasuo Matoi, Exec. VP-Social Infrastructure Solutions
Hajime Sasaki, Chmn.
Makoto Imai, Sr. VP/CEO-NEC Corp. of America

Phone: 81-3-3454-1111 **Fax:** 81-3-3798-1510
Toll-Free: 800-268-3997
Address: 7-1, Shiba 5-Chome, Minato-ku, Tokyo, 108-8001 Japan

GROWTH PLANS/SPECIAL FEATURES:

NEC Corp. is a provider of advanced IT, networking support and semiconductor solutions to government entities, communication services and business enterprises. Accordingly, the firm is divided into three operating segments: IT Solutions, Network Solutions and Electronic Devices. The IT Solutions segment produces hardware and software, including operating systems and application software. In hardware, NEC's computers division competes against Fujitsu for the number-one position among Japanese PC makers. NEC manufactures high-end computers, servers and supercomputers, personal computers (PCs), monitors, optical drives, floppy disk drives, servers and storage systems; and provides customized hardware integration and technical services. This segment of the firm sells primarily to government agencies and enterprises. Through its Network Solutions division, the company sells broadband, enterprise and wireless network equipment; mobile phone base stations; satellite communications systems; telecommunications systems; and industrial and aerospace systems. The firm's Electronic Devices segment makes semiconductors, LCDs and electronic components. NEC also operates BIGLOBE, Japan's largest Internet service provider. In 2007, the company, in partnership with its subsidiary, NEC TOKIN Corporation and Nissan Motor Co., Ltd., established a joint venture, Automotive Energy Supply Corporation. The new company will focus on lithium-ion batteries for automotive applications. NEC invests more than $3 billion yearly in research and development at its 15 R&D centers throughout the world. In July 2008, the company and Sumitomo Electric Industries, Ltd. agreed to acquire OCC Holdings, a submarine fiber optic manufacturer. In October 2008, the firm acquired NetCracker Technology Corp., a provider of operation support systems.

FINANCIALS: **Sales and profits are in thousands of dollars—add 000 to get the full amount. 2008 Note: Financial information for 2008 was not available for all companies at press time.**

2008 Sales: $46,171,500	2008 Profits: $226,800	**U.S. Stock Ticker: NIPNY**
2007 Sales: $46,526,500	2007 Profits: $91,300	**Int'l Ticker: 6701** Int'l Exchange: Tokyo-TSE
2006 Sales: $49,299,700	2006 Profits: $-100,600	Employees: 154,786
2005 Sales: $48,017,200	2005 Profits: $772,200	Fiscal Year Ends: 3/31
2004 Sales: $47,022,000	2004 Profits: $394,000	Parent Company:

SALARIES/BENEFITS:

Pension Plan:	ESOP Stock Plan:	Profit Sharing:	Top Exec. Salary: $	Bonus: $
Savings Plan:	Stock Purch. Plan:		Second Exec. Salary: $	Bonus: $

OTHER THOUGHTS:

Apparent Women Officers or Directors:
Hot Spot for Advancement for Women/Minorities:

LOCATIONS: ("Y" = Yes)

West:	Southwest:	Midwest:	Southeast:	Northeast:	International:
Y	Y	Y		Y	Y

Note: Financial information, benefits and other data can change quickly and may vary from those stated here.

NEC LABORATORIES AMERICA INC

www.nec-labs.com

Industry Group Code: 541710 **Ranks within this company's industry group:** Sales: Profits:

Techology:		Medical/Drugs:		Engineering:		Transportation:		Chemicals/Petrochemicals:		Specialty:	
Computers:	Y	Manufacturer:		Design:		Aerospace:		Oil/Gas Products:		Special Services:	
Software:	Y	Contract Research:		Construction:		Automotive:		Chemicals:		Consulting:	
Communications:	Y	Medical Services:		Eng. Services:		Shipping:		Oil/Chem. Svcs.:		Specialty Mgmt.:	
Electronics:	Y	Labs:		Consulting:				Gases:		Products:	
Alternative Energy:		Bio. Services:						Other:		Other:	

TYPES OF BUSINESS:

Communications Technology
Electronics
Broadband & Mobile Networking
Computing
Software
Storage Technologies
Security Systems
Quantum Computing

BRANDS/DIVISIONS/AFFILIATES:

NEC Corporation
NEC Research Institute
NEC USA
Computer and Communications Research Laboratory

CONTACTS: *Note: Officers with more than one job title may be intentionally listed here more than once.*

Robert E. Millstein, CEO
Robert E. Millstein, Pres., NEC Labs
Hajime Sasaki, Chmn.-NEC Corp.
Kaoru Yano, Pres., NEC Corp.

Phone: 609-520-1555 **Fax:** 609-951-2481
Toll-Free:
Address: 4 Independence Way, Ste. 200, Princeton, NJ 08540 US

GROWTH PLANS/SPECIAL FEATURES:

NEC Laboratories America, Inc. (NEC Labs) is the U.S.-based research facility in NEC Corporation's global network of research laboratories. NEC Labs is responsible for the technology research and early market validation for NEC's core business. Operating through two laboratories, located in Princeton, NJ and Cupertino, CA, the company focuses on work in the areas of information analysis and management; broadband and mobile networking; robust and secure systems; machine learning; system architecture, analysis and verification; and quantum IT. NEC Labs' information analysis and management segment is currently developing sophisticated communications networks and databases that are intent-aware, or able to rapidly detect users' intentions and goals. Its broadband and mobile networking division is developing high-performance metropolitan optical networks; mobility management solutions; overlay networks; self-organizing, ad-hoc wireless networks; grid networking; and optical/wireless integration solutions. The company's robust and secure systems segment is developing survivable grid storage solutions, cognitive capabilities in survivable systems and fault detection in complex systems. NEC Labs' machine learning division develops computers with intelligent capabilities, specifically machines that can observe data, learn from data, change behavior and make decisions. Its system architecture, analysis and verification segment focuses on advanced systems architecture; low-power, tamper-resistant and secure embedded processing architectures to support mobile commerce, digital rights management and multimedia delivery; and practical software analysis and verification technologies. NEC Labs' quantum IT segment is researching new quantum algorithms, decoherence effects in physical systems, methods to protect quantum systems from noise, quantum communication and new applications of quantum computation. In 2008, the company announced its collaboration with the National Science Foundation Center for Autonomic Computing and its joint research efforts to further the efficiency and reduce the administration costs of autonomic computing systems.

NEC Labs offers employees tuition assistance; credit union membership; an employee assistance program; flexible spending accounts; and comprehensive insurance.

FINANCIALS: **Sales and profits are in thousands of dollars—add 000 to get the full amount. 2008 Note: Financial information for 2008 was not available for all companies at press time.**

2008 Sales: $	2008 Profits: $	**U.S. Stock Ticker: Subsidiary**
2007 Sales: $	2007 Profits: $	**Int'l Ticker:** Int'l Exchange:
2006 Sales: $	2006 Profits: $	Employees:
2005 Sales: $	2005 Profits: $	Fiscal Year Ends: 3/31
2004 Sales: $	2004 Profits: $	Parent Company: NEC CORPORATION

SALARIES/BENEFITS:

Pension Plan:	ESOP Stock Plan:	Profit Sharing:	Top Exec. Salary: $	Bonus: $
Savings Plan: Y	Stock Purch. Plan:		Second Exec. Salary: $	Bonus: $

OTHER THOUGHTS:

Apparent Women Officers or Directors:
Hot Spot for Advancement for Women/Minorities:

LOCATIONS: ("Y" = Yes)

West:	Southwest:	Midwest:	Southeast:	Northeast:	International:
Y				Y	

Note: Financial information, benefits and other data can change quickly and may vary from those stated here.

NETAPP INC

www.netapp.com

Industry Group Code: 334112 **Ranks within this company's industry group:** Sales: 5 Profits: 5

Techology:		Medical/Drugs:		Engineering:		Transportation:		Chemicals/Petrochemicals:		Specialty:	
Computers:	Y	Manufacturer:		Design:		Aerospace:		Oil/Gas Products:		Special Services:	
Software:	Y	Contract Research:		Construction:		Automotive:		Chemicals:		Consulting:	
Communications:		Medical Services:		Eng. Services:		Shipping:		Oil/Chem. Svcs.:		Specialty Mgmt.:	
Electronics:	Y	Labs:		Consulting:				Gases:		Products:	
Alternative Energy:		Bio. Services:						Other:		Other:	

TYPES OF BUSINESS:

Data Management Solutions
Storage Solutions
Data Protection Software Products
Data Protection Platform Products
Storage Security Products
Data Retention & Archive Software Products
Storage Management & Application Software
Management Tools

BRANDS/DIVISIONS/AFFILIATES:

Data ONTAP
Network Appliance
NetCache
NetStore
NearStore
Data ONTAP
FlexVol
Onaro Inc

CONTACTS: *Note: Officers with more than one job title may be intentionally listed here more than once.*

Dan Warmenhoven, CEO
Tom Georgens, COO
Tom Georgens, Pres.
Steve Gomo, CFO/Exec. VP
Jay Kidd, Chief Mktg. Officer
Gwen McDonald, Sr. VP-Human Resources
Steve Kleiman, Chief Scientist/Sr. VP
Marina Levinson, CIO/Sr. VP
Rob Salmon, Exec. VP-Field Oper.
James Lau, Chief Strategy Officer/Exec. VP
Steve Gomo, Exec. VP-Finance
Ed Deenihan, Exec. VP-NetApp Global Svcs.
Mark Jon Bluth, Sr. VP-Oper.
Rich Clifton, Gen. Mgr.-Virtualization & Grid Infrastructures
D. Patrick Linehan, Sr. VP-Worldwide Sales
Dan Warmenhoven, Chmn.

Phone: 408-822-6000	**Fax:** 408-822-4501
Toll-Free:	
Address: 495 E. Java Dr., Sunnyvale, CA 94089 US	

GROWTH PLANS/SPECIAL FEATURES:

NetApp, Inc. (formerly Network Appliance, Inc.) is a provider of data management solutions. The NetApp enterprise-class storage solutions are interoperable across all platforms. The storage solutions are all based on Data ONTAP, an optimized, scalable and flexible operating system that supports any mix of SAN, NAS and IP SAN environments concurrently. Data ONTAP software platform integrates seamlessly into UNIX, Linux, Windows and Web environments. The Data ONTAP operating system provides the foundation to build storage infrastructure and an enterprise-wide data fabric for business applications. It includes the patented NetApp WAFL (Write Anywhere File Layout) file management system and the RADI-DP (RAID Double Parity), a double-parity software RAID architecture. It supports all of the major industry-standard protocols' storage, as well as a suite of data management, data replication and data protection software products. The firm offers a variety of data management tools and software, including the FlexVol technology, which enables storage architectures to be more efficient and achieve higher utilization using flexible volumes that do not require repartitioning of physical storage space; FlexClone technology, which enables data cloning or the instant replication of data volumes and data sets; Deduplication technology, which provides the ability to eliminate duplicate data within primary and secondary disk storage environments; FlexShare technology, which directs how storage system resources are used to deliver an appropriate level of service for each application; FlexCache technology, which allows the creation of read-writeable replicas of volumes by creating caching volumes on multiple storage controllers; and MultiStore software, which allows for the creation of separate logical partitions in storage systems and network storage resources. In January 2008, NetApp acquired Onaro, a privately owned firm located in Massachusetts.

NetApp offers employees medical, dental and vision insurance; flexible spending account; mass transit/parking account; an employee assistance program; an employee stock purchase plan; paid volunteer days, adoption assistance; and educational assistance.

FINANCIALS: **Sales and profits are in thousands of dollars—add 000 to get the full amount. 2008 Note: Financial information for 2008 was not available for all companies at press time.**

2008 Sales: $3,303,167	2008 Profits: $309,738	**U.S. Stock Ticker: NTAP**
2007 Sales: $2,804,282	2007 Profits: $297,735	**Int'l Ticker:** Int'l Exchange:
2006 Sales: $2,066,456	2006 Profits: $266,452	Employees: 7,645
2005 Sales: $1,598,131	2005 Profits: $225,754	Fiscal Year Ends: 4/30
2004 Sales: $1,170,310	2004 Profits: $152,087	Parent Company:

SALARIES/BENEFITS:

Pension Plan:	ESOP Stock Plan:	Profit Sharing:	Top Exec. Salary: $786,538	Bonus: $507,160
Savings Plan: Y	Stock Purch. Plan: Y		Second Exec. Salary: $582,500	Bonus: $346,704

OTHER THOUGHTS:

Apparent Women Officers or Directors: 3
Hot Spot for Advancement for Women/Minorities: Y

LOCATIONS: ("Y" = Yes)

West:	Southwest:	Midwest:	Southeast:	Northeast:	International:
Y				Y	Y

Note: Financial information, benefits and other data can change quickly and may vary from those stated here.

NIDEC CORPORATION

www.nidec.co.jp

Industry Group Code: 334112 **Ranks within this company's industry group:** Sales: 4 Profits: 4

Techology:		Medical/Drugs:		Engineering:		Transportation:		Chemicals/Petrochemicals:		Specialty:	
Computers:		Manufacturer:		Design:		Aerospace:		Oil/Gas Products:		Special Services:	
Software:		Contract Research:		Construction:		Automotive:		Chemicals:		Consulting:	
Communications:		Medical Services:		Eng. Services:		Shipping:		Oil/Chem. Svcs.:		Specialty Mgmt.:	
Electronics:	Y	Labs:		Consulting:				Gases:		Products:	
Alternative Energy:		Bio. Services:						Other:		Other:	

TYPES OF BUSINESS:

Spindle Motor Manufacturing
Brushless DC Motors
Brushless DC Fans
Actuators
Hard Drive Base Plates & Top Covers
Measuring Instruments

BRANDS/DIVISIONS/AFFILIATES:

Nidec Copal Electronics Corporation
Nidec Brilliant Co Ltd
Nidec Machinery Corporation
Nidec Sankyo Corporation
Nidec Motors & Actuators
Nidec Pigeon Corporation
Nidec Servo Corporation

CONTACTS: *Note: Officers with more than one job title may be intentionally listed here more than once.*

Shigenobu Nagamori, CEO
Hiroshi Kobe, COO/Exec. VP
Shigenobu Nagamori, Pres.
Yasunobu Toriyama, CFO/Exec. VP
Kenji Sawamura, Exec. VP
Juntaro Fujii, Exec. VP
Yasuo Hamaguchi, First Sr. VP
Tadaaki Hamada, Sr. VP
Shigenobu Nagamori, Chmn.

Phone: 81-75-935-6140 **Fax:** 81-75-935-6141
Toll-Free:
Address: 338 Tonoshiro-cho, Kuze Minami-ku, Kyoto, 601-8205 Japan

GROWTH PLANS/SPECIAL FEATURES:

Nidec Corporation, through a number of subsidiaries, manufactures spindle motors for computer hard disk drives. Sales of its hard disk drive spindle motors accounted for approximately 30.1% of 2008 sales. The firm also produces a variety of other products, including small precision brushless DC motors used in high-speed, continuous-duty applications, such as CD-ROM, CD-R/W, DVD and high-capacity floppy disk drives, as well as in office equipment, such as facsimile machines, laser printers and photocopy machines; brushless DC fans used in computers, game consoles and other electronic equipment to disperse heat and lower the temperature of critical components; mid-size brushless DC motors used in household appliances, automobiles and industrial equipment; machinery, including semiconductor manufacturing equipment, automatic measuring equipment, image processing equipment, high-speed press machines, industrial robots and card readers; electronic and optical components, such as camera shutters, lens units and optical pick-up units; and other products, including pivot assemblies and automotive parts. Nidec has research and development facilities in Japan, the U.S., Singapore, Taiwan, Vietnam and China, as well as production facilities in China, Thailand, Singapore, Indonesia, the Philippines, Vietnam and Malaysia. Most of the company's research and development facilities are concentrated in Japan, where it focuses on the development of next-generation motor and drive technology products. Most of Nidec's production facilities outside of Japan are located in other Asian countries, offering them more direct access to customers' production facilities in these regions. The company has sales operations throughout Japan, as well as in the U.S., Germany, Taiwan, Singapore, Hong Kong, Korea and China.

FINANCIALS: **Sales and profits are in thousands of dollars—add 000 to get the full amount. 2008 Note: Financial information for 2008 was not available for all companies at press time.**

2008 Sales: $7,407,186 | 2008 Profits: $410,780
2007 Sales: $5,333,901 | 2007 Profits: $338,263
2006 Sales: $4,570,171 | 2006 Profits: $348,591
2005 Sales: $4,524,267 | 2005 Profits: $311,528
2004 Sales: $2,625,575 | 2004 Profits: $152,228

U.S. Stock Ticker: NJ
Int'l Ticker: Int'l Exchange:
Employees: 96,897
Fiscal Year Ends: 3/31
Parent Company:

SALARIES/BENEFITS:

Pension Plan: ESOP Stock Plan: Profit Sharing: Top Exec. Salary: $ Bonus: $
Savings Plan: Stock Purch. Plan: Second Exec. Salary: $ Bonus: $

OTHER THOUGHTS:

Apparent Women Officers or Directors:
Hot Spot for Advancement for Women/Minorities:

LOCATIONS: ("Y" = Yes)

West:	Southwest:	Midwest:	Southeast:	Northeast:	International:
Y	Y	Y		Y	Y

NINTENDO CO LTD

www.nintendo.com

Industry Group Code: 334111 **Ranks within this company's industry group:** Sales: 8 Profits: 4

Techology:		Medical/Drugs:		Engineering:		Transportation:		Chemicals/Petrochemicals:		Specialty:	
Computers:	Y	Manufacturer:		Design:		Aerospace:		Oil/Gas Products:		Special Services:	
Software:	Y	Contract Research:		Construction:		Automotive:		Chemicals:		Consulting:	
Communications:		Medical Services:		Eng. Services:		Shipping:		Oil/Chem. Svcs.:		Specialty Mgmt.:	
Electronics:		Labs:		Consulting:				Gases:		Products:	
Alternative Energy:		Bio. Services:						Other:		Other:	

TYPES OF BUSINESS:

Video Games
Video Game Hardware & Software

BRANDS/DIVISIONS/AFFILIATES:

GameCube
Nintendo DS
Game Boy Advance
Wii
Mario Brothers
Legend of Zelda (The)
Donkey Kong
Pokemon

CONTACTS: *Note: Officers with more than one job title may be intentionally listed here more than once.*

Satoru Iwata, CEO
Satoru Iwata, Pres.
Genyo Takeda, Gen. Mgr.-Integrated R&D Div./Sr. Managing Dir.
Yoshihiro Mori, Sr. Managing Dir.
Shinji Hatano, Sr. Managing Dir.
Shigeru Miyamoto, Sr. Managing Dir.
Nobuo Nagai, Sr. Managing Dir.
Reginald Fils-Aime, COO/Pres., Nintendo of America, Inc.

Phone: 81-75-662-9600 **Fax:** 81-75-662-9620
Toll-Free:
Address: 11-1 Kamitoba, Hokotate-cho, Minami-ku, Kyoto, 601-8116 Japan

GROWTH PLANS/SPECIAL FEATURES:

Nintendo Co., Ltd. makes video game hardware and software, including the well-known video game titles Mario Brothers, Donkey Kong, Pokemon and The Legend of Zelda. Based in Kyoto, Japan, Nintendo owns subsidiaries in the U.S., Canada, Korea, Australia and several European countries, with overseas sales accounting for 48.2% of 2008 sales. Its main products are the video game systems and related software and merchandise for the Nintendo DS and DS Lite, which by the end of 2008 had sold approximately 70.6 million units cumulatively since it was introduced; Game Boy Advance, 81.1 million; GameCube, 21.7 million; and Wii, 24.5 million. Nintendo has recently increased focus on selling the DS and the Game Boy Advance, its portable devices. While the Game Boy Advance is essentially a portable version of home-based video consoles, the DS sports a dual-screen format, an LCD touch screen, wireless connectivity and voice recognition capabilities. Nintendo's newest console and successor to the GameCube, the Wii, features a unique motion-sensitive controller, resembling a TV remote, which allows for point-and-click-style game play. The company's latest products include the Wii system and the new Touch! Generations software line, which includes Nintendo DS titles such as Nintendogs, a virtual pet program, and Brain Age. In December 2007, Nintendo launched the Wii Fit in Japan; in April 2008, Wii Fit launched in Europe; and in May 2008 it launched in Australia and North America. Wii Fit features a unique floor board controller that used in balance related games and activities, including skiing, yoga, meditation and boxing.

FINANCIALS: **Sales and profits are in thousands of dollars—add 000 to get the full amount. 2008 Note: Financial information for 2008 was not available for all companies at press time.**

2008 Sales: $16,724,230	2008 Profits: $2,573,426	**U.S. Stock Ticker: NTDOY**
2007 Sales: $8,183,173	2007 Profits: $1,477,038	**Int'l Ticker: 7974** Int'l Exchange: Tokyo-TSE
2006 Sales: $4,327,100	2006 Profits: $836,600	Employees: 2,977
2005 Sales: $4,788,400	2005 Profits: $812,800	Fiscal Year Ends: 3/31
2004 Sales: $4,869,400	2004 Profits: $314,200	Parent Company:

SALARIES/BENEFITS:

Pension Plan:	ESOP Stock Plan:	Profit Sharing:	Top Exec. Salary: $	Bonus: $
Savings Plan:	Stock Purch. Plan:		Second Exec. Salary: $	Bonus: $

OTHER THOUGHTS:

Apparent Women Officers or Directors:
Hot Spot for Advancement for Women/Minorities:

LOCATIONS: ("Y" = Yes)

West:	Southwest:	Midwest:	Southeast:	Northeast:	International:
Y					Y

NISSAN MOTOR CO LTD

www.nissan-global.com

Industry Group Code: 336111 **Ranks within this company's industry group:** Sales: 7 Profits: 5

Techology:		Medical/Drugs:		Engineering:		Transportation:		Chemicals/Petrochemicals:		Specialty:	
Computers:		Manufacturer:		Design:		Aerospace:		Oil/Gas Products:		Special Services:	
Software:		Contract Research:		Construction:		Automotive:	Y	Chemicals:		Consulting:	
Communications:		Medical Services:		Eng. Services:		Shipping:	Y	Oil/Chem. Svcs.:		Specialty Mgmt.:	
Electronics:		Labs:		Consulting:				Gases:		Products:	
Alternative Energy:		Bio. Services:						Other:		Other:	

TYPES OF BUSINESS:

Automobiles, Manufacturing
Research & Development
Industrial Machinery
Marine Equipment
Logistics Services
Alternative Fuels Research

BRANDS/DIVISIONS/AFFILIATES:

Nissan North America Inc
Nissan Logistics Corp.
Nissan Design America
Nissan-Renault
Nissan Forklift Europe B.V.
Infinity

CONTACTS: *Note: Officers with more than one job title may be intentionally listed here more than once.*

Carlos Ghosn, CEO
Toshiyuki Shiga, COO
Carlos Ghosn, Pres.
Alain Dassas, CFO/Sr. VP
Junichi Endo, Sr. VP-Global Mktg. & Sales
Hitoshi Kawaguchi, Sr. VP-Human Resources
Mitsuhiko Yamashita, Exec. VP-R&D
Minoru Shinohara, Sr. VP-Tech. Dev. Div.
Toshiharu Sakai, Sr. VP-Prod. Eng. Div.
Carlos Tavares, Exec. VP-Corp. Planning
Alain Dassas, Sr. VP-Investor Rel.
Hidetoshi Imazu, Exec. VP-European Oper.
Kazuhiko Toida, Sr. VP-Japan Sales, Fleet Bus. Div.
Colin Dodge, Sr. VP-China Oper.
Carlos Ghosn, Chmn.
Hiroto Saikawa, Exec. VP-American Oper.

Phone: 81-3-3543-5523 **Fax:** 81-3-5565-2228
Toll-Free:
Address: 17-1 Ginza 6-chome, Chuo-ku, Tokyo, 104-8023 Japan

GROWTH PLANS/SPECIAL FEATURES:

Nissan Motor Co., Ltd. develops, manufactures, sells and services automotive products in over 190 countries. The company's products, which are sold both in Japan and overseas, principally in North America and Europe, include passenger cars, busses and trucks, along with related components. Brands include Nissan, Infiniti and Forklift, with model offerings such as the Nissan Sentra, Nissan Versa, Nissan Altima, Nissan Rogue and Nissan Pathfinder. The Forklift brand offers material handling equipment, including pallet trucks, tow tractors and lifts. The company operates worldwide from offices in Japan, North America, Europe, Asia and the Middle East. The firm operates through a variety of business channels, including technical centers, design centers and manufacturing plants in various locations world-wide. Abroad, Nissan and Renault, a French company, manage an alliance that allows each company to maintain its distinct corporate culture and brand identity, while enduring the challenges of market globalization and the accelerating change of technology. Nissan-Renault ranks as one of the world's leading automotive groups, and the two companies operate a joint venture factory in the eastern Indian city of Chennai. The allied firm promotes intensive research and development in alternative fuel technologies. Nissan has been increasing investments in its research and development operations, and plans to produce additional gasoline-electric vehicles as well as subcompact electric cars powered by firm-developed lithium-ion batteries. In late 2008, in response to decreased sales, the firm announced production cuts at a number of plants. In January 2009, Nissan announced plans to move production of its March subcompact model from Japan to Thailand. The company also reduced the number of new and redesigned models it plans to roll out over the next five years, from 60 to 48, along with certain other cost-reduction strategies, such as job cuts at factories, reduced executive pay and the possible elimination of bonuses.

FINANCIALS: **Sales and profits are in thousands of dollars—add 000 to get the full amount. 2008 Note: Financial information for 2008 was not available for all companies at press time.**

2008 Sales: $108,242,000	2008 Profits: $4,823,000	**U.S. Stock Ticker: NSANY**
2007 Sales: $88,717,000	2007 Profits: $3,905,000	**Int'l Ticker: 7201** Int'l Exchange: Tokyo-TSE
2006 Sales: $80,583,700	2006 Profits: $4,427,800	Employees: 180,535
2005 Sales: $79,700,000	2005 Profits: $4,760,000	Fiscal Year Ends: 3/31
2004 Sales: $70,087,000	2004 Profits: $4,751,600	Parent Company:

SALARIES/BENEFITS:

Pension Plan:	ESOP Stock Plan:	Profit Sharing:	Top Exec. Salary: $	Bonus: $
Savings Plan: Y	Stock Purch. Plan:		Second Exec. Salary: $	Bonus: $

OTHER THOUGHTS:

Apparent Women Officers or Directors:
Hot Spot for Advancement for Women/Minorities:

LOCATIONS: ("Y" = Yes)

West:	Southwest:	Midwest:	Southeast:	Northeast:	International:
Y	Y	Y	Y	Y	Y

NITTO DENKO CORPORATION

www.nitto.com

Industry Group Code: 325000 **Ranks within this company's industry group:** Sales: 18 Profits: 12

Techology:		Medical/Drugs:		Engineering:		Transportation:		Chemicals/Petrochemicals:		Specialty:	
Computers:		Manufacturer:	Y	Design:		Aerospace:		Oil/Gas Products:		Special Services:	
Software:		Contract Research:		Construction:		Automotive:		Chemicals:		Consulting:	
Communications:		Medical Services:		Eng. Services:		Shipping:		Oil/Chem. Svcs.:		Specialty Mgmt.:	
Electronics:	Y	Labs:		Consulting:				Gases:		Products:	Y
Alternative Energy:		Bio. Services:						Other:		Other:	

TYPES OF BUSINESS:

Industrial Adhesive Tapes
Semiconductor Materials
Drug Delivery Systems
Water Treatment Membranes
Semiconductor Machinery

BRANDS/DIVISIONS/AFFILIATES:

Nitto Denko America, Inc.
Avevna
Permacel
Hydronautics
Nitto Denko Technology Corporation
Nitto Electronics Kyushu
Nitto Denko Asia Technical Centre

CONTACTS: *Note: Officers with more than one job title may be intentionally listed here more than once.*

Masamichi Takemoto, CEO
Yukio Nagira, COO
Yukio Nagira, Pres.
Tatsunosuke Fujiwara, CFO
Yasuo Ninomiya, CTO
Yoshiyasu Kamiyama, Sr. Exec. Corp. VP
Tetsuo Horiuchi, Exec. Corp. VP
Kaoru Aizawa, Exec. Corp. VP
Katsuhiro Akamatsu, Exec. Corp. VP
Masamichi Takemoto, Chmn.

Phone: 81-6-6452-2101 **Fax:** 81-6-6452-2102
Toll-Free:
Address: Herbis Osaka, 2-5-25, Umeda, Kita-ku, Osaka, 530-0001 Japan

GROWTH PLANS/SPECIAL FEATURES:

Nitto Denko Corporation primarily manufactures industrial adhesive tapes for the electronics, automotive, health care, packaging and construction industries. The company produces industrial, electronic and functional products. Industrial products include bonding and joining products for cellular phones and small LCDs; surface-protection films; and advanced sealing materials. Electronics products include LCD-related items; general and advanced device resins; printed circuit boards; and semiconductor package adhesive sheets. Functional products include medical items such as transdermal therapeutic patches; polymer separation membranes used for water purification and treatment; and plastic engineering products such as information equipment and porous film materials used in cars, electronics, and home appliances. Nitto Denko America, Inc., an opto-electronics subsidiary, manufactures semiconductor encapsulating materials; materials and systems for semiconductor processing; and flexible printed circuits. Nitto Denko's other North American subsidiaries include Aveva Drug Delivery Systems, Inc.; Hydronautics, a producer of membranes for water treatment; and Permacel, a manufacturer of tapes used in the electrical, automobile and aerospace industries. Nitto Denko Technical Corp. serves as the firm's research and development business, focusing on research in biotechnology, optical communications, and nanoceramics industries. Nitto Denko also operates through over 100 other subsidiaries in Europe, East Asia, and Southeast Asia to manufacture and provide adhesive tapes, electronic products and membranes worldwide. In February 2008, the firm announced plans to build a new semiconductor encapsulating resin plant at the location of Nitto Electronics Kyushu, a Japanese subsidiary. Also in February 2008, Nitto Denko and Mitsubishi Rayon Engineering Co., Ltd., made an alliance with the Singapore Public Utility Board to develop wastewater reclamation technology, using supply membrane bioreactor and reverse osmosis technologies. In November 2008, Nitto Denko opened the Nitto Denko Asia Technical Centre in Singapore to develop organic electronic devices. In February 2009, the company terminated its joint venture with Eisai to produce the Alzheimer's patch Aricept.

FINANCIALS: **Sales and profits are in thousands of dollars—add 000 to get the full amount. 2008 Note: Financial information for 2008 was not available for all companies at press time.**

2008 Sales: $7,413,640 | 2008 Profits: $463,900
2007 Sales: $5,758,763 | 2007 Profits: $349,013
2006 Sales: $5,331,719 | 2006 Profits: $470,818
2005 Sales: $4,382,974 | 2005 Profits: $356,202
2004 Sales: $4,285,500 | 2004 Profits: $316,000

U.S. Stock Ticker: NDEKF
Int'l Ticker: 6988 Int'l Exchange: Tokyo-TSE
Employees: 32,101
Fiscal Year Ends: 3/31
Parent Company:

SALARIES/BENEFITS:

Pension Plan: ESOP Stock Plan: Profit Sharing: Top Exec. Salary: $ Bonus: $
Savings Plan: Stock Purch. Plan: Second Exec. Salary: $ Bonus: $

OTHER THOUGHTS:

Apparent Women Officers or Directors:
Hot Spot for Advancement for Women/Minorities:

LOCATIONS: ("Y" = Yes)

West:	Southwest:	Midwest:	Southeast:	Northeast:	International:
Y		Y	Y	Y	Y

NOKIA CORPORATION

www.nokia.com

Industry Group Code: 334220 **Ranks within this company's industry group:** Sales: 1 Profits: 1

Techology:		Medical/Drugs:		Engineering:		Transportation:		Chemicals/Petrochemicals:		Specialty:	
Computers:	Y	Manufacturer:		Design:		Aerospace:		Oil/Gas Products:		Special Services:	
Software:	Y	Contract Research:		Construction:		Automotive:		Chemicals:		Consulting:	
Communications:	Y	Medical Services:		Eng. Services:		Shipping:		Oil/Chem. Svcs.:		Specialty Mgmt.:	
Electronics:		Labs:		Consulting:				Gases:		Products:	
Alternative Energy:		Bio. Services:						Other:		Other:	

TYPES OF BUSINESS:

Telecommunications Equipment-Cellular Telephones
Network Systems & Services
Internet Software & Services
Multimedia Equipment
Research & Development
Venture Capital
Digital Music

BRANDS/DIVISIONS/AFFILIATES:

Vertu
Nokia 6600
Nokia 7600 3G
Symbian Limited
Troltech
NAVTEQ
Plazes
OZ Communications Inc

CONTACTS: *Note: Officers with more than one job title may be intentionally listed here more than once.*

Olli-Pekka Kallasvuo, CEO
Olli-Pekka Kallasvuo, Pres.
Richard Simonson, CFO/Exec. VP
Timo Ihamuotila, Exec. VP-Sales
Hallstein Moerk, Exec. VP-Human Resources
Mary McDowell, Chief Dev. Officer/Exec. VP
Tero Ojanpera, CTO/Exec. VP
Tero Ojanpera, Chief Strategy Officer
Veli Sundback, Exec. VP-Corp. Rel. & Responsibility
Tero Ojanpera, Exec. VP-Entertainment & Communities
Simon Beresford-Wylie, CEO-Nokia Siemens Networks
Niklas Savander, Exec. VP-Svcs. & Software
Robert Andersson, Exec. VP-Devices Finance, Strategy & Sourcing
Olli-Pekka Kallasvuo, Chmn.

Phone: 358-7-1800-8000	**Fax:** 358-7-1803-8503
Toll-Free:	
Address: Keilalahdentie 2-4, Espoo, FIN-02150 Finland	

GROWTH PLANS/SPECIAL FEATURES:

Nokia Corporation is a leading supplier of mobile, fixed and IP networks and related products, as well as being one of the world's top mobile phone manufacturers. Nokia has nine production facilities throughout four countries and a customization and logistics center in the U.S. The company consists of three business segments: mobile phones, multimedia and enterprise solutions. The mobile phones segment develops mobile phones for all major standards and customer segments in over 150 countries. The multimedia segment provides cell phone cameras, video games, MP3 players, satellite receivers and cable/TV receivers. The enterprise solutions segment offers businesses a range of devices and mobile connectivity solutions that manage a customer's mobile communications, Internet access and networks. In addition, Nokia operates through two business units that support its product segments: Customer and Market Operations, and Technology Platforms. The Customer and Market Operations manages Nokia's global sales and marketing organization, logistics and sourcing operations for the mobile phones, multimedia and enterprise solutions segments. The technology platforms segment manages all of Nokia's research and development operations. Nokia Siemens Networks (which began operations in April 2007) is a 50/50 joint venture between Nokia and Siemens, combining Nokia's networks business and Siemens' carrier-related operations. In December 2008, the firm agreed to acquire Symbian Limited, a company that produces software. In November 2008, Nokia acquired OZ Communications Inc. In July 2008, the company acquired Plazes (Plazes.com), a company based out of Berlin. Also in July, the firm acquired NAVTEQ, a firm that offers digital map information. In June 2008, Nokia acquired Troltech, a software provider.

Employees are offered medical, dental and vision coverage; domestic partnership coverage; health and elder care reimbursement; an employee assistance plan; a 401(k) plan; stock purchase plan; legal services; employee discounts; and educational assistance.

FINANCIALS: **Sales and profits are in thousands of dollars—add 000 to get the full amount. 2008 Note: Financial information for 2008 was not available for all companies at press time.**

2008 Sales: $66,957,600	2008 Profits: $9,284,190	**U.S. Stock Ticker: NOK**
2007 Sales: $74,560,000	2007 Profits: $11,660,000	**Int'l Ticker: NOK1V** Int'l Exchange: Helsinki-Euronext
2006 Sales: $54,267,000	2006 Profits: $5,642,000	Employees: 58,874
2005 Sales: $40,465,000	2005 Profits: $4,280,000	Fiscal Year Ends: 12/31
2004 Sales: $39,645,000	2004 Profits: $4,344,000	Parent Company:

SALARIES/BENEFITS:

Pension Plan:	ESOP Stock Plan:	Profit Sharing:	Top Exec. Salary: $1,949,569	Bonus: $4,174,726
Savings Plan: Y	Stock Purch. Plan: Y		Second Exec. Salary: $931,829	Bonus: $1,229,630

OTHER THOUGHTS:

Apparent Women Officers or Directors: 1
Hot Spot for Advancement for Women/Minorities:

LOCATIONS: ("Y" = Yes)

West:	Southwest:	Midwest:	Southeast:	Northeast:	International:
Y	Y	Y	Y	Y	Y

NORTEL NETWORKS CORP

www.nortel.com

Industry Group Code: 334210 **Ranks within this company's industry group:** Sales: 2 Profits: 8

Techology:		Medical/Drugs:		Engineering:		Transportation:		Chemicals/Petrochemicals:		Specialty:	
Computers:		Manufacturer:		Design:		Aerospace:		Oil/Gas Products:		Special Services:	
Software:		Contract Research:		Construction:		Automotive:		Chemicals:		Consulting:	
Communications:	Y	Medical Services:		Eng. Services:		Shipping:		Oil/Chem. Svcs.:		Specialty Mgmt.:	
Electronics:		Labs:		Consulting:				Gases:		Products:	
Alternative Energy:		Bio. Services:						Other:		Other:	

TYPES OF BUSINESS:

Networking Equipment
Wireless & Wireline Networking Equipment
Optical Networking Equipment
Consulting & Outsourcing Services
Nanotechnology Research

BRANDS/DIVISIONS/AFFILIATES:

Enterprise Solutions
Mobility and Converged Core Networks
Metro Ethernet Networks
Global Services
Nortel Government Solutions

CONTACTS: *Note: Officers with more than one job title may be intentionally listed here more than once.*

Mike Zafirovski, CEO
Mike Zafirovski, Pres.
Pavi S. Binning, CFO/Exec. VP
Lauren P. Flaherty, Chief Mktg. Officer
Steven Bandrowczak, CIO
John J. Roese, CTO
David Drinkwater, Chief Legal Officer
Dennis Carey, Exec. VP-Corp. Oper.
George Riedel, Chief Strategy Officer
Bob Bartzokas, Chief Compliance Officer
William J. Donovan, Sr. VP-Bus. Transformation Office
William Nelson, Exec. VP-Global Sales
Joe Flanagan, Sr. VP-Global Oper.
Harry J. Pearce, Chmn.

Phone: 905-863-7000	**Fax:**
Toll-Free: 800-466-7835	
Address: 195 The West Mall, Toronto, ON M9C 5K1 Canada	

GROWTH PLANS/SPECIAL FEATURES:

Nortel Networks Corp. is a global supplier of communication equipment serving small businesses, multinational corporations, government agencies, military and telecommunications and Internet service providers. The firm's technologies support multimedia and business-critical applications, as well as simplify networks, thereby connecting people with information through hardware, software and services. The firm operates in four business segments: Carrier Networks; Enterprise Solutions; Metro Ethernet Networks (MEN); and Global Services. The Carrier Networks segment offers wireline and wireless networks that help service providers and cable operators supply mobile voice, data and multimedia communications services to individuals and enterprises using a variety of computing and communications devices. This segment also offers voice switching products that provide local, toll, long distance and international gateway capabilities for telephone companies, wireless service providers, cable operators and other service providers. Enterprise Solutions offers products that encompass end-to-end network security, unified communications, IP and digital telephony (including phones), wireless LANs, IP and SIP contact centers, self-service solutions, messaging, conferencing, and SIP-based multimedia solutions. The MEN segment delivers carrier-grade Ethernet transport capabilities focused on meeting customer needs for higher performance and lower cost per megabit for emerging video-intensive applications. This includes Carrier Ethernet switching, optical networking and multiservice switching products. Global Services offers solutions to help design, deploy, support and evolve networks for small- and medium-sized businesses and large global enterprises; municipal, regional and federal government agencies; wireline and wireless service providers; cable operators; and mobile virtual network operators. In January 2009, the firm filed for bankruptcy protection while struggling with continuing operating losses and high debt.

Nortel offers employees medical and dental coverage; flexible scheduling and teleworking; and an employee assistance program.

FINANCIALS: **Sales and profits are in thousands of dollars—add 000 to get the full amount. 2008 Note: Financial information for 2008 was not available for all companies at press time.**

2008 Sales: $10,421,000	2008 Profits: $-5,799,000	**U.S. Stock Ticker: NT**
2007 Sales: $10,948,000	2007 Profits: $-957,000	**Int'l Ticker: NT** Int'l Exchange: Toronto-TSX
2006 Sales: $11,418,000	2006 Profits: $28,000	Employees: 30,307
2005 Sales: $10,509,000	2005 Profits: $-2,611,000	Fiscal Year Ends: 12/31
2004 Sales: $9,478,000	2004 Profits: $-296,000	Parent Company:

SALARIES/BENEFITS:

Pension Plan: Y	ESOP Stock Plan:	Profit Sharing:	Top Exec. Salary: $1,272,941	Bonus: $1,288,853
Savings Plan: Y	Stock Purch. Plan:		Second Exec. Salary: $512,486	Bonus: $318,673

OTHER THOUGHTS:

Apparent Women Officers or Directors: 1
Hot Spot for Advancement for Women/Minorities: Y

LOCATIONS: ("Y" = Yes)

West:	Southwest:	Midwest:	Southeast:	Northeast:	International:
Y	Y	Y	Y	Y	Y

Note: Financial information, benefits and other data can change quickly and may vary from those stated here.

NORTHROP GRUMMAN CORP

www.northropgrumman.com

Industry Group Code: 336410 **Ranks within this company's industry group:** Sales: 6 Profits: 20

Techology:		Medical/Drugs:		Engineering:		Transportation:		Chemicals/Petrochemicals:		Specialty:	
Computers:	Y	Manufacturer:		Design:	Y	Aerospace:	Y	Oil/Gas Products:		Special Services:	Y
Software:	Y	Contract Research:		Construction:	Y	Automotive:		Chemicals:		Consulting:	Y
Communications:	Y	Medical Services:		Eng. Services:	Y	Shipping:	Y	Oil/Chem. Svcs.:		Specialty Mgmt.:	
Electronics:	Y	Labs:		Consulting:				Gases:		Products:	Y
Alternative Energy:		Bio. Services:						Other:		Other:	

TYPES OF BUSINESS:

Aerospace & Defense Technology
Shipbuilding & Engineering
Aircraft Manufacturing
Electronic Systems & Components
Hardware & Software Manufacturing
Design & Engineering Services
IT Systems & Services
Nuclear-Powered Aircraft Carriers & Submarines

BRANDS/DIVISIONS/AFFILIATES:

F/A-18
F-35
B-2
Multi-Platform Radar Technology Insertion Program
Global Hawk
James Webb Space Telescope
Airborne Laser
EA-6B

CONTACTS: *Note: Officers with more than one job title may be intentionally listed here more than once.*

Ronald D. Sugar, CEO
Wes Bush, COO
Wes Bush, Pres.
James F. Palmer, CFO/Corp. VP
Ian V. Ziskin, Chief Human Resources Officer/Corp. VP
Linda A. Mills, Corp. VP/Pres., Info. Systems
Alexis Livanos, CTO/Corp. VP
Ian V. Ziskin, Chief Admin. Officer
Stephen D. Yslas, General Counsel/Corp. VP
Darryl M. Fraser, Corp. VP-Comm.
Kenneth N. Heintz, Chief Acct. Officer/Controller/Corp. VP
Robert W. Helm, Corp. VP-Gov't Rel.
James F. Pitts, Corp. VP/Pres., Electronic Systems
Mike Petters, Corp. VP/Pres., Shipbuilding
Gary W. Ervin, Corp. VP/Pres., Aerospace Systems
Ronald D. Sugar, Chmn.

Phone: 310-553-6262 **Fax:** 310-553-2076
Toll-Free:
Address: 1840 Century Park E., Los Angeles, CA 90067-2199 US

GROWTH PLANS/SPECIAL FEATURES:

Northrop Grumman Corp. is a global aerospace and defense technology company. Ninety percent of its revenue comes from the U.S. Government. It has five primary businesses: Information Systems, Aerospace Systems, Electronic Systems, Shipbuilding and Technical Services. Information Systems encompasses two divisions: Mission Systems and Information Technology (IT). Mission Systems offers land forces and global combat support, satellite ground stations and signals intelligence. The IT division offers data analysis; document management; data center, IT security, storage and help desk management; R&D and test centers; and education and training commands. Aerospace Systems encompasses Space Technology and Integrated Systems. The Space Technology division's major projects include the James Webb Space Telescope; Space Tracking and Surveillance System; and the Airborne Laser. The division also includes a missile systems business offering fire control systems, simulation and warfighter operations. Integrated Systems has two business areas. Integrated Systems Western Region is focused on the F/A-18, F-35 and B-2 manned aircraft programs; the Multi-Platform Radar Technology Insertion Program (MP-RTIP); and the Global Hawk and Fire Scout unmanned vehicle programs. Integrated Systems Eastern Region produced the E-2C Hawkeye command plane; and developed the EA-6B (Prowler) offensive tactical radar jamming aircraft. Electronic Systems offers missile tracking and warning systems; fire control radars; advanced simulation systems; infrared detection and countermeasures systems; night vision goggles; laser designators; Chemical, Biological, Radiological, Nuclear and Explosive (CBRNE) material detection and alert systems; U.S. Postal Service bio-detection systems; and power generation systems for aircraft carriers. The Shipbuilding business designs, builds, maintains and refuels nuclear-powered aircraft carriers; and designs and constructs amphibious assault ships, Aegis guided missile destroyers, nuclear-powered submarines and oil tankers. Technical Services offers base support, including civil engineering, and support functions, including space launch services, combat vehicle maintenance and protective and emergency services. It also covers training and simulation services.

FINANCIALS: Sales and profits are in thousands of dollars—add 000 to get the full amount. 2008 Note: Financial information for 2008 was not available for all companies at press time.

2008 Sales: $33,887,000	2008 Profits: $-1,281,000	**U.S. Stock Ticker: NOC**
2007 Sales: $31,828,000	2007 Profits: $1,811,000	**Int'l Ticker:** Int'l Exchange:
2006 Sales: $29,991,000	2006 Profits: $1,593,000	Employees: 123,600
2005 Sales: $29,978,000	2005 Profits: $1,400,000	Fiscal Year Ends: 12/31
2004 Sales: $29,000,000	2004 Profits: $1,080,000	Parent Company:

SALARIES/BENEFITS:

Pension Plan: Y	ESOP Stock Plan:	Profit Sharing:	Top Exec. Salary: $1,510,577	Bonus: $3,090,000
Savings Plan: Y	Stock Purch. Plan:		Second Exec. Salary: $877,501	Bonus: $1,500,000

OTHER THOUGHTS:

Apparent Women Officers or Directors: 3
Hot Spot for Advancement for Women/Minorities: Y

LOCATIONS: ("Y" = Yes)

West:	Southwest:	Midwest:	Southeast:	Northeast:	International:
Y	Y	Y	Y	Y	Y

Note: Financial information, benefits and other data can change quickly and may vary from those stated here.

NOVARTIS AG

www.novartis.com

Industry Group Code: 325412 **Ranks within this company's industry group:** Sales: 4 Profits: 3

Techology:		Medical/Drugs:		Engineering:		Transportation:		Chemicals/Petrochemicals:		Specialty:	
Computers:		Manufacturer:	Y	Design:		Aerospace:		Oil/Gas Products:		Special Services:	
Software:		Contract Research:		Construction:		Automotive:		Chemicals:		Consulting:	
Communications:		Medical Services:		Eng. Services:		Shipping:		Oil/Chem. Svcs.:		Specialty Mgmt.:	
Electronics:		Labs:	Y	Consulting:				Gases:		Products:	Y
Alternative Energy:		Bio. Services:						Other:		Other:	

TYPES OF BUSINESS:

Drugs-Diversified
Therapeutic Drug Discovery
Therapeutic Drug Manufacturing
Generic Drugs
Over-the-Counter Drugs
Ophthalmic Products
Nutritional Products
Veterinary Products

BRANDS/DIVISIONS/AFFILIATES:

CIBA Vision
Chiron Corp
Sandoz
Novartis Institute for Biomedical Research Inc
Novartis Oncology
Alcon Inc

CONTACTS:

Note: Officers with more than one job title may be intentionally listed here more than once.

Daniel Vasella, CEO
Joerg Reinhardt, COO
Daniel Vasella, Pres.
Raymund Breu, CFO
Jurgen Brokatzky-Geiger, Head-Human Resources
Paul Herrling, Head-Corp. Research
Leon V. Schumacher, CIO
Thomas Werlen, General Counsel
Ann Bailey, Head-Corp. Comm.
George Gunn, CEO-Consumer Health
Joseph Jimenez, CEO-Pharmaceuticals
Mark Fishman, Pres., Novartis Institute for Biomedical Research
Jeffrey George, CEO-Sandoz
Daniel Vasella, Chmn.

Phone: 41-61-324-1111	**Fax:** 41-61-324-8001
Toll-Free:	
Address: Lichtstrasse 35, Basel, 4056 Switzerland	

GROWTH PLANS/SPECIAL FEATURES:

Novartis AG researches and develops pharmaceuticals as well as a large number of consumer and animal health products. It operates in four segments: pharmaceuticals; vaccines and diagnostics; consumer health; and Sandoz. The pharmaceuticals division, which accounts for 64% of sales, develops, manufactures, distributes and sells prescription medications in a variety of areas, which include cardiovascular and metabolism, oncology and hematology, neuroscience and ophthalmics, respiratory, immunology and infectious diseases. The segment is organized into global business franchises responsible for the marketing of various products as well as a business unit called Novartis Oncology, responsible for the global development and marketing of oncology products. The vaccines and diagnostics division is focused on the development of preventive vaccine treatments and diagnostic tools. It has two activities: Novartis Vaccines, whose key products include meningococcal and travel vaccines; and Chiron, a blood testing and molecular diagnostics activity dedicated to preventing the spread of infectious diseases through the development of blood-screening tools that protect the world's blood supply. The Sandoz division is a global generic pharmaceuticals company that develops, produces and markets drugs along with pharmaceutical and biotechnological active substances. The segment has activities in retail generics, anti-infectives and biopharmaceuticals. Sandoz offers some 950 compounds in more than 5,000 forms in 130 countries. The most important product groups include antibiotics, treatments for the central nervous system disorders, gastrointestinal medicines, cardiovascular treatments and hormone therapies. The consumer health division consists of three business units: over-the-counter medicines; animal health, which provides veterinary products for farm and companion animals; and CIBA Vision, which markets contact lenses and lens care products. In July 2008, the company raised its stake in Switzerland-based eye car firm Alcon, Inc. to 48%, for approximately $10.4 billion. Novartis has the option to acquire the remaining 52% of Alcon, from Nestle SA, during 2010 or 2011.

FINANCIALS:

Sales and profits are in thousands of dollars—add 000 to get the full amount. 2008 Note: Financial information for 2008 was not available for all companies at press time.

2008 Sales: $41,459,000	2008 Profits: $8,233,000	**U.S. Stock Ticker: NVS**
2007 Sales: $38,072,000	2007 Profits: $11,968,000	**Int'l Ticker: NOVN** Int'l Exchange: Zurich-SWX
2006 Sales: $34,393,000	2006 Profits: $7,202,000	Employees: 96,717
2005 Sales: $31,005,000	2005 Profits: $6,141,000	Fiscal Year Ends: 12/31
2004 Sales: $27,126,000	2004 Profits: $5,601,000	Parent Company:

SALARIES/BENEFITS:

Pension Plan: Y	ESOP Stock Plan:	Profit Sharing:	Top Exec. Salary: $	Bonus: $
Savings Plan:	Stock Purch. Plan:		Second Exec. Salary: $	Bonus: $

OTHER THOUGHTS:

Apparent Women Officers or Directors: 4
Hot Spot for Advancement for Women/Minorities: Y

LOCATIONS: ("Y" = Yes)

West:	Southwest:	Midwest:	Southeast:	Northeast:	International:
Y				Y	Y

NOVELL INC

www.novell.com

Industry Group Code: 511214 **Ranks within this company's industry group:** Sales: 2 Profits: 2

Techology:		Medical/Drugs:		Engineering:		Transportation:		Chemicals/Petrochemicals:		Specialty:	
Computers:		Manufacturer:		Design:		Aerospace:		Oil/Gas Products:		Special Services:	
Software:	Y	Contract Research:		Construction:		Automotive:		Chemicals:		Consulting:	
Communications:		Medical Services:		Eng. Services:		Shipping:		Oil/Chem. Svcs.:		Specialty Mgmt.:	
Electronics:		Labs:		Consulting:				Gases:		Products:	
Alternative Energy:		Bio. Services:						Other:		Other:	

TYPES OF BUSINESS:

Computer Software-Networking & Application
Operational Strategy Consulting Services
E-Business Consulting
Open Source Software
Linux Support & Maintenance
Management Consulting

BRANDS/DIVISIONS/AFFILIATES:

SUSE Linux Enterprise
openSUSE
SUSE Engineering
Identity Manager
Access Manager
SecureLogin
Sentinel
Open Enterprise Server

CONTACTS:

Note: Officers with more than one job title may be intentionally listed here more than once.

Ronald W. Hovespian, CEO
Ronald W. Hovespian, Pres.
Dana C. Russell, CFO
John Dragoon, Chief Mktg. Officer/Sr. VP
Alan J. Friedman, Sr. VP-People
Jose Almandoz, CIO/VP
Jeffrey Jaffe, CTO/Exec. VP
Scott Semel, General Counsel/Sr. VP
Roger Levy, Sr. VP-Strategic Dev.
Bill Smith, VP-Finance
Jim Ebzery, Sr. VP/Gen. Mgr.-Identity & Security Solutions
Kent Erickson, Sr. VP/Gen. Mgr.-Workgroup Solutions
Maarten Koster, Gen. Mgr./Pres., Novell Asia Pacific
Marcus Rex, Acting Sr. VP/Gen. Mgr.-Open Platform Solutions
Richard Crandall, Chmn.
Volker Smid, Pres., EMEA

Phone: 781-464-8000 **Fax:**
Toll-Free: 800-529-3400
Address: 404 Wyman St., Ste. 500, Waltham, MA 02451 US

GROWTH PLANS/SPECIAL FEATURES:

Novell, Inc. provides infrastructure software and services designed to integrate mixed IT environments. The firm operates through four business segments: Open Platform Solutions; Identity and Security Management; Systems and Resource Management; and Workgroup. Novell's primary Open Platform Solutions offerings include SUSE Linux Enterprise Server, an enterprise-class, open source server operating system for professional deployment; SUSE Linux Enterprise Desktop, a business desktop product that combines the Linux operating environment with a set of business applications; openSUSE, a secure home computing product; and SUSE Engineering specialized product development. The firm's identity, security and access management solutions leverage automated, centrally-managed policies to help customers integrate, secure and manage IT assets; reduce complexity; and ensure compliance. Its primary Identity and Security Management offerings are Identity Manager, a data-sharing and synchronization solution; Access Manager, a product for simplifying and safeguarding online asset-sharing; SecureLogin, a directory-integrated authentication solution; and Sentinel, which monitors IT effectiveness. Novell's Workgroup segment provides infrastructure, services and tools for effectively and securely collaborating across numerous devices. Its primary Workgroup products are Open Enterprise Server, a suite of services that provides networking, communication, collaboration and application services; NetWare, its proprietary operating system platform; Novell Cluster Services, a scalable, highly available Storage Area Network resource management tool; GroupWise collaboration products; and BorderManager, a suite of network services used to connect a network securely to the Internet or any other network. In addition to its technology offerings, the firm provides professional services, including discovery workshops, strategy projects and solution implementations; phone-based, web-based and onsite technical support; and training services. In March 2008, Novell acquired PlateSpin Ltd., a provider of workload lifecycle management solutions for the enterprise data center.

FINANCIALS:

Sales and profits are in thousands of dollars—add 000 to get the full amount. 2008 Note: Financial information for 2008 was not available for all companies at press time.

2008 Sales: $956,513	2008 Profits: $-8,745	**U.S. Stock Ticker: NOVL**
2007 Sales: $932,499	2007 Profits: $-44,460	**Int'l Ticker:** Int'l Exchange:
2006 Sales: $919,331	2006 Profits: $18,656	Employees: 4,000
2005 Sales: $986,149	2005 Profits: $376,722	Fiscal Year Ends: 10/31
2004 Sales: $1,165,917	2004 Profits: $57,188	Parent Company:

SALARIES/BENEFITS:

Pension Plan:	ESOP Stock Plan:	Profit Sharing:	Top Exec. Salary: $825,032	Bonus: $2,250,000
Savings Plan: Y	Stock Purch. Plan:		Second Exec. Salary: $501,942	Bonus: $700,000

OTHER THOUGHTS:

Apparent Women Officers or Directors: 4
Hot Spot for Advancement for Women/Minorities: Y

LOCATIONS: ("Y" = Yes)

West:	Southwest:	Midwest:	Southeast:	Northeast:	International:
Y	Y	Y	Y	Y	Y

Note: Financial information, benefits and other data can change quickly and may vary from those stated here.

NOVO-NORDISK AS

www.novonordisk.com

Industry Group Code: 325412 **Ranks within this company's industry group:** Sales: 20 Profits: 19

Techology:		Medical/Drugs:		Engineering:		Transportation:		Chemicals/Petrochemicals:		Specialty:	
Computers:		Manufacturer:	Y	Design:		Aerospace:		Oil/Gas Products:		Special Services:	
Software:		Contract Research:	Y	Construction:		Automotive:		Chemicals:		Consulting:	
Communications:		Medical Services:	Y	Eng. Services:		Shipping:		Oil/Chem. Svcs.:		Specialty Mgmt.:	
Electronics:		Labs:	Y	Consulting:				Gases:		Products:	
Alternative Energy:		Bio. Services:						Other:		Other:	

TYPES OF BUSINESS:

Drugs-Diabetes
Hormone Replacement Therapy
Growth Hormone Drugs
Hemophilia Drugs
Insulin Delivery Systems
Educational & Training Services

BRANDS/DIVISIONS/AFFILIATES:

Levemir
Insulatard
NovoNorm
FlexPen
Norditropin
NovoSeven
Estrofem

CONTACTS: *Note: Officers with more than one job title may be intentionally listed here more than once.*

Lars R. Sorensen, CEO
Kare Schultz, COO/Exec. VP
Lars R. Sorensen, Pres.
Jesper Brandgaard, CFO/Exec. VP
Lise Kingo, Chief of Staff/Exec. VP
Mads K. Thomsen, Chief Science Officer/Exec. VP
Mads Veggerby Lausten, Head-Investor Rel.
Goran A. Ando, Vice Chmn.
Sten Scheibye, Chmn.
Hans Rommer, Dir.-Investor Rel., North America

Phone: 45-4444-8888	**Fax:** 45-4449-0555
Toll-Free:	
Address: Novo Alle, Bagsvaerd, 2880 Denmark	

GROWTH PLANS/SPECIAL FEATURES:

Novo Nordisk A/S is a healthcare company that focuses on developing treatments for diabetes, hemostasis management and hormone therapy. It has two segments: Diabetes care, which generated 73% of 2008 sales; and biopharmaceuticals, 27%. The diabetes care segment manages the firm's insulin franchise, including modern insulins, human insulins, insulin-related sales and oral antidiabetic drugs. Specific products include Levemir and NovoRapid modern insulin; Insulatard and Actrapid human insulin; NovoNorm, an oral antidiabetic drug; NovoPen 4, FlexPen and Innolet insulin injectors; and GlucaGen and NovoFine (needles) diabetic devices. The biopharmaceuticals segment covers hemostasis management, growth hormone therapy, hormone replacement therapy, inflammation therapy and other therapy areas. Specific products include the following. Norditropin is a premixed liquid growth hormone designed to provide a very flexible and accurate dosing, while NordiFlex, NordiFlex PenMate and NordiLet are human growth hormone injection systems. NovoSeven is a hemostasis management product, a hemophilia treatment consisting of a recombinant coagulation factor that enables coagulation to proceed in the absence of natural blood factors. Lastly, the firm's post-menopausal hormone replacement therapy products include Activelle, Novofem, Estrofem and Vagifem. Novo Nordisk has employees in 81 countries and its products are marketed in 179 countries. Besides its products, the company offers educational services and training materials for both patients and health care professionals. Novo Nordisk owns and operates dedicated research centers in the U.S., Denmark and China, as well as clinical development centers in Zurich, Switzerland; Beijing, China; Tokyo, Japan; and in the U.S. in Princeton, New Jersey and Seattle, Washington. In November 2008, the company announced plans to invest $400 million in a new insulin production plant in Tianjin, China, expected to be operational by 2012.

Novo Nordisk offers its U.S. employees health, life, dental and supplemental insurance, as well as tuition reimbursement, among other benefits.

FINANCIALS: **Sales and profits are in thousands of dollars—add 000 to get the full amount. 2008 Note: Financial information for 2008 was not available for all companies at press time.**

2008 Sales: $8,239,030	2008 Profits: $1,744,460	**U.S. Stock Ticker: NVO**
2007 Sales: $8,190,000	2007 Profits: $1,670,000	**Int'l Ticker: NOVO B** Int'l Exchange: Copenhagen-CSE
2006 Sales: $6,913,700	2006 Profits: $1,126,020	Employees: 26,000
2005 Sales: $5,446,472	2005 Profits: $946,073	Fiscal Year Ends: 12/31
2004 Sales: $5,324,285	2004 Profits: $859,229	Parent Company:

SALARIES/BENEFITS:

Pension Plan:	ESOP Stock Plan:	Profit Sharing:	Top Exec. Salary: $	Bonus: $
Savings Plan: Y	Stock Purch. Plan:		Second Exec. Salary: $	Bonus: $

OTHER THOUGHTS:

Apparent Women Officers or Directors: 3
Hot Spot for Advancement for Women/Minorities: Y

LOCATIONS: ("Y" = Yes)

West:	Southwest:	Midwest:	Southeast:	Northeast:	International:
Y				Y	Y

NOVOZYMES

www.novozymes.com

Industry Group Code: 325414 **Ranks within this company's industry group:** Sales: 3 Profits: 2

Techology:		Medical/Drugs:		Engineering:		Transportation:		Chemicals/Petrochemicals:		Specialty:	
Computers:		Manufacturer:		Design:		Aerospace:		Oil/Gas Products:		Special Services:	Y
Software:		Contract Research:		Construction:		Automotive:		Chemicals:		Consulting:	
Communications:		Medical Services:		Eng. Services:		Shipping:		Oil/Chem. Svcs.:		Specialty Mgmt.:	
Electronics:		Labs:	Y	Consulting:				Gases:		Products:	
Alternative Energy:		Bio. Services:	Y					Other:		Other:	

TYPES OF BUSINESS:

Industrial Enzyme & Microorganism Production
Biopharmaceuticals
Enzymes
Microbiology

BRANDS/DIVISIONS/AFFILIATES:

Mannaway
Stainzyme Plus
Spirizyme Ultra
Sucrozyme
Acrylaway
Saczyme
Ultraflo Max
Viscoferm

CONTACTS: *Note: Officers with more than one job title may be intentionally listed here more than once.*

Steen Riisgaard, CEO
Steen Riisgaard, Pres.
Benny Loft, CFO/Exec. VP
Per Falholt, Chief Scientific Officer/Exec. VP
Thomas Nagy, Exec. VP-Stakeholder Rel.
Thomas Videbaek, Exec. VP-Bio Bus.
Peder Holk Nielsen, Exec. VP/Head-Enzyme Bus.
Henrik Gurtler, Chmn.

Phone: 45-88-24-99-99 **Fax:** 45-88-24-99-98
Toll-Free:
Address: Krogshoejvej 36, Bagsvaerd, 2880 Denmark

GROWTH PLANS/SPECIAL FEATURES:

Novozymes is a biotechnology company that specializes in microbiology and enzymes. The firm currently sells over 700 products in 130 countries worldwide. It splits its business into two main areas: microorganisms and enzymes. The enzymes business, which accounts for 93% of sales, is split into technical, food and feed enzymes. The company's technical enzymes include enzymes used in detergents, such as Mannaway and Stainzyme Plus enzymes; enzymes that transform starch in sugar for starch and fuel industries; and enzymes with applications in the textile, leather, forestry and alcohol industries. Technical enzymes include the brand name enzymes Spirizyme Ultra and Sucrozyme. The company's food enzymes increase the quality or production efficiency in the production of food products such as bread, wine, juice, beer, noodles, alcohol and pasta. New food enzyme products include Acrylaway, Saczyme, Ultraflo Max and Viscoferm. Lastly, feed enzymes, such as Ronozyme NP, are designed to increase the nutritional value of feed and to improve phosphorus absorption in animals. This leads to faster growth of animals, while at the same time improving the environment by decreasing the phosphorus that is released through manure. The firm's microorganisms, which generate 4% of sales, have three main applications in wastewater treatment, cleaning products and natural growth enhancements for plants and turf grass. Novozymes also generates 3% of sales from biopharmaceutical products not categorized in its two main business areas. In 2007, the firm acquired the remaining shares of its subsidiary Novozymes Japan from Mitsui. In 2008, the firm announced plans to build a new enzyme production facility in Nebraska.

Novozymes offers all employees medical coverage and life insurance while employees in Demark are offered new parent leave, child care, a fitness center, holiday cottages and in-house counseling. Benefits in the U.S. include flexible spending accounts, tuition reimbursement and an employee assistance plan.

FINANCIALS: Sales and profits are in thousands of dollars—add 000 to get the full amount. 2008 Note: Financial information for 2008 was not available for all companies at press time.

2008 Sales: $1,453,610	2008 Profits: $189,510	**U.S. Stock Ticker: NVZMY**
2007 Sales: $1,327,270	2007 Profits: $185,940	**Int'l Ticker: NZYM** Int'l Exchange: Copenhagen-CSE
2006 Sales: $1,251,490	2006 Profits: $167,610	Employees: 5,000
2005 Sales: $1,079,840	2005 Profits: $148,025	Fiscal Year Ends: 12/31
2004 Sales: $1,029,470	2004 Profits: $133,240	Parent Company:

SALARIES/BENEFITS:

Pension Plan: Y	ESOP Stock Plan:	Profit Sharing:	Top Exec. Salary: $	Bonus: $
Savings Plan: Y	Stock Purch. Plan:		Second Exec. Salary: $	Bonus: $

OTHER THOUGHTS:

Apparent Women Officers or Directors: 1
Hot Spot for Advancement for Women/Minorities: Y

LOCATIONS: ("Y" = Yes)

West:	Southwest:	Midwest:	Southeast:	Northeast:	International:
Y		Y		Y	Y

NTT DATA CORP

www.nttdata.co.jp

Industry Group Code: 541512 **Ranks within this company's industry group:** Sales: 6 Profits: 8

Techology:		**Medical/Drugs:**		**Engineering:**		**Transportation:**		**Chemicals/Petrochemicals:**		**Specialty:**	
Computers:	Y	Manufacturer:		Design:		Aerospace:		Oil/Gas Products:		Special Services:	Y
Software:	Y	Contract Research:		Construction:		Automotive:		Chemicals:		Consulting:	Y
Communications:		Medical Services:		Eng. Services:		Shipping:		Oil/Chem. Svcs.:		Specialty Mgmt.:	
Electronics:		Labs:		Consulting:				Gases:		Products:	
Alternative Energy:		Bio. Services:						Other:		Other:	

TYPES OF BUSINESS:

IT Services
Systems Integration
Consulting Services
Bioinformatics

BRANDS/DIVISIONS/AFFILIATES:

Nippon Telegraph & Telephone Corp. (NTT)
IT PARTNER
NTT Data Hokkaido Corp.
NTT Data Tohoku Corp.
NTT Data Shinetsu Corp.
CoreMount
A.S.I.A.
Cirquent GmbH

CONTACTS: *Note: Officers with more than one job title may be intentionally listed here more than once.*

Toru Yamashita, CEO
Toru Yamashita, Pres.
Takashi Enomoto, Sr. Exec. VP
Hideki Teranishi, Sr. Exec. VP
Toshio Iwamoto, Exec. VP
Mitsuo Muramatsu, Exec. VP

Phone: 81-3-5546-8202 **Fax:** 81-3-5546-2405
Toll-Free:
Address: 3-3 Toyosu 3-chome, Koto-ku, Tokyo, 135-6033 Japan

GROWTH PLANS/SPECIAL FEATURES:

NTT DATA Corporation, originally formed as a division of NTT, is one of the largest information technology providers in Japan, offering a wide array of IT and related services through its 96 subsidiaries and 24 associated companies. NTT DATA is organized into three business segments: system integration (SI), which involves the development, sale, leasing and maintenance of data communication systems; networking system services, which provides information and information processing services related to computer networks; and other related businesses, consisting of the research, analysis, planning and proposals concerning clients' business challenges. NTT DATA has operations in the U.S., the U.K., Hong Kong, Malaysia and China. The company's foreign subsidiaries work in several different areas, including financial clearance and network systems, automated payment systems, information systems for intelligent buildings, e-procurement systems and automated expressway toll collection systems. In addition, the company markets software in China and Southeast Asia, including CoreMount, a web solutions package, and A.S.I.A., a multicurrency, multilingual ERP software package. NTT DATA outsources much of its software design capacity to China and India. Former parent NTT still controls a 55% stake in the firm. In 2008, NTT DATA Europe GmbH & Co. KG, a wholly-owned company subsidiary, sold its stake in Intelligence AG to NTT Communications for $23 million. In August 2008, the company acquired 72.9% of Cirquent GmbH from BMW AG.

FINANCIALS: **Sales and profits are in thousands of dollars—add 000 to get the full amount. 2008 Note: Financial information for 2008 was not available for all companies at press time.**

2008 Sales: $10,744,050 | 2008 Profits: $304,550
2007 Sales: $8,855,237 | 2007 Profits: $429,127
2006 Sales: $7,715,500 | 2006 Profits: $239,700
2005 Sales: $7,982,748 | 2005 Profits: $187,944
2004 Sales: $8,014,900 | 2004 Profits: $255,200

U.S. Stock Ticker:
Int'l Ticker: 9613 Int'l Exchange: Tokyo-TSE
Employees: 23,080
Fiscal Year Ends: 3/31
Parent Company:

SALARIES/BENEFITS:

Pension Plan:	ESOP Stock Plan:	Profit Sharing:	Top Exec. Salary: $	Bonus: $
Savings Plan:	Stock Purch. Plan:		Second Exec. Salary: $	Bonus: $

OTHER THOUGHTS:

Apparent Women Officers or Directors:
Hot Spot for Advancement for Women/Minorities:

LOCATIONS: ("Y" = Yes)

West:	Southwest:	Midwest:	Southeast:	Northeast:	International:
Y		Y			Y

Note: Financial information, benefits and other data can change quickly and may vary from those stated here.

NVIDIA CORP

www.nvidia.com

Industry Group Code: 334119 **Ranks within this company's industry group:** Sales: 8 Profits: 4

Techology:		Medical/Drugs:		Engineering:		Transportation:		Chemicals/Petrochemicals:		Specialty:	
Computers:	Y	Manufacturer:		Design:		Aerospace:		Oil/Gas Products:		Special Services:	
Software:	Y	Contract Research:		Construction:		Automotive:		Chemicals:		Consulting:	
Communications:		Medical Services:		Eng. Services:		Shipping:		Oil/Chem. Svcs.:		Specialty Mgmt.:	
Electronics:		Labs:		Consulting:				Gases:		Products:	
Alternative Energy:		Bio. Services:						Other:		Other:	

TYPES OF BUSINESS:

Computer Accessories-Graphics Cards
Graphics Processors
Graphics Software

BRANDS/DIVISIONS/AFFILIATES:

GeForce
Go
NVIDIA Quadro
NVIDIA nForce
GoForce
ULi Electronics, Inc.

CONTACTS: *Note: Officers with more than one job title may be intentionally listed here more than once.*

Jen-Hsun Huang, CEO
Jen-Hsun Huang, Pres.
Marvin D. Burkett, CFO
Daniel F. Vivoli, Sr. VP-Mktg.
Scott P. Sullivan, VP-Human Resources
David B. Kirk, Chief Scientist
Ranga Jayaraman, CIO
Chris A. Malachowsky, Sr. VP-Eng.
David M. Shannon, General Counsel/Sr. VP/Sec.
Debora Shoquist, Sr. VP-Oper.
Michael W. Hara, VP-Comm.
Michael W. Hara, VP-Investor Rel.
Jonah M. Alben, VP-GPU Eng.
Philip J. Carmack, Sr. VP-Handheld GPU Bus. Unit
Jay Puri, Sr. VP-Worldwide Sales
Jeff Fisher, Sr. VP-GPU Bus. Unit

Phone: 408-486-2000 **Fax:** 408-486-2200
Toll-Free:
Address: 2701 San Tomas Expressway., Santa Clara, CA 95050 US

GROWTH PLANS/SPECIAL FEATURES:

NVIDIA Corporation designs, develops and markets a family of award-winning 3D graphics processors, graphics processing units (GPUs) and related software. The company serves virtually all markets which rely on good visual quality in PC applications, including manufacturing, science, e-business, entertainment and education. The company has four product groups: GPUs, MCPs (media and communications processors), handheld GPUs and consumer electronics. The three major families of the firm's GPUs include GeForce, Go and NVIDIA Quadro. NVIDIA's MCP family (called NVIDIA nForce) supports PCs, professional workstations and servers. The firm's handheld GPU family (called GoForce) supports PDAs and multimedia cellular phones. The consumer electronics product group primarily supports video game consoles. NVIDIA makes the GPUs for the Microsoft Xbox and Sony Computer Entertainment's (SCE) PlayStation 3. In February 2008, the company acquired AGEIA Technologies, Inc., a leader in gaming physics technology.

FINANCIALS: **Sales and profits are in thousands of dollars—add 000 to get the full amount. 2008 Note: Financial information for 2008 was not available for all companies at press time.**

2008 Sales: $4,097,860	2008 Profits: $797,645	**U.S. Stock Ticker: NVDA**
2007 Sales: $3,068,771	2007 Profits: $448,834	**Int'l Ticker:** Int'l Exchange:
2006 Sales: $2,375,687	2006 Profits: $301,176	Employees: 4,985
2005 Sales: $2,010,033	2005 Profits: $88,615	Fiscal Year Ends: 1/31
2004 Sales: $1,822,945	2004 Profits: $74,419	Parent Company:

SALARIES/BENEFITS:

Pension Plan:	ESOP Stock Plan:	Profit Sharing:	Top Exec. Salary: $584,083	Bonus: $2,400,000
Savings Plan: Y	Stock Purch. Plan: Y		Second Exec. Salary: $425,000	Bonus: $637,500

OTHER THOUGHTS:

Apparent Women Officers or Directors: 2
Hot Spot for Advancement for Women/Minorities:

LOCATIONS: ("Y" = Yes)

West:	Southwest:	Midwest:	Southeast:	Northeast:	International:
Y	Y			Y	Y

ORACLE CORP

www.oracle.com

Industry Group Code: 511207 **Ranks within this company's industry group:** Sales: 1 Profits: 1

Techology:		Medical/Drugs:		Engineering:		Transportation:		Chemicals/Petrochemicals:		Specialty:	
Computers:		Manufacturer:		Design:		Aerospace:		Oil/Gas Products:		Special Services:	
Software:	Y	Contract Research:		Construction:		Automotive:		Chemicals:		Consulting:	Y
Communications:		Medical Services:		Eng. Services:		Shipping:		Oil/Chem. Svcs.:		Specialty Mgmt.:	
Electronics:		Labs:		Consulting:				Gases:		Products:	
Alternative Energy:		Bio. Services:						Other:		Other:	

TYPES OF BUSINESS:

Computer Software-Database Management
e-Business Applications Software
Internet-Based Software
Consulting Services
Human Resources Management Software
CRM Software
Middleware

BRANDS/DIVISIONS/AFFILIATES:

BEA Systems Inc
Global Knowledge Software LLC
Advanced Visual Technology Ltd
Primavera Software Inc
Oracle Insurance
Agile Software Corp
Portal Software Inc
Stellant Inc

CONTACTS: *Note: Officers with more than one job title may be intentionally listed here more than once.*

Lawrence J. Ellison, CEO
Charles E. Phillips, Jr., Co-Pres.
Jeff Epstein, CFO/Exec. VP
Judith Sim, Sr. VP/Chief Mktg. Officer
Charles Rozwat, Exec. VP-Prod. Dev.
Dorian Daley, General Counsel/Sr. VP/Sec.
Keith Block, Exec. VP-North America
Mary Ann Davidson, Chief Security Officer
Luiz Meisler, Sr. VP-Latin America
Edward Screven, Chief Corp. Architect
Jeffrey O. Henley, Chmn.
Takao Endo, Pres./CEO-Japan

Phone: 650-506-7000 **Fax:** 650-506-7200
Toll-Free: 800-672-2531
Address: 500 Oracle Pkwy., Redwood Shores, CA 94065 US

GROWTH PLANS/SPECIAL FEATURES:

Oracle Corporation is one of the largest enterprise software companies in the world. The firm markets its software directly to corporations rather than dealing in the consumer market. Oracle's products can be categorized into two broad areas: software (representing 80% of revenue) and services. The company's core software business segment is based upon its prepackaged enterprise data management software and Internet applications including Oracle Database, Oracle Fusion Middleware, Oracle Enterprise Manager, Oracle Collaboration Suite, Oracle Developer Suite and Oracle E-Business Suite. Oracle's services business is comprised of Oracle Consulting and Oracle On Demand. Oracle Consulting specializes in the design, implementation, deployment, upgrade and migration of its database technology and applications software. Oracle On Demand offers distributed application services including E-Business Suite On Demand, Technology On Demand and Collaboration Suite On Demand. Oracle Retail Promotion Planning and Optimization is a data mining application for retail analysis, forecasting and planning. Oracle SQL Developer is an upgrade to Oracle's free database development and debugging application, as well as Oracle Management Pack for Linux. Oracle Manufacturing Execution System for Discrete Manufacturing (Oracle MES for Discrete Manufacturing), is an application that lets manufacturers set up Oracle Applications on the shop floor. Subsidiaries include Agile Software Corp, Portal Software Inc and Stellent Inc. In 2008, the company acquired the e-TEST suite products from Emprix; BEA Systems, Inc.; Global Knowledge Software LLC; Advanced Visual Technology Ltd.; and Primavera Software, Inc. In September of the same year, the firm launched Oracle Insurance, a provider of end-to-end software designed to manage aspects of the insurance business such as technical infrastructure and core insurance processing. In April 2009, Oracle agreed to acquire Sun Microsystems for $7.4 billion.

Employees are offered a 401(k) plan; an employee stock purchase plan; an employee assistance program; and health care benefits.

FINANCIALS: **Sales and profits are in thousands of dollars—add 000 to get the full amount. 2008 Note: Financial information for 2008 was not available for all companies at press time.**

2008 Sales: $22,430,000	2008 Profits: $5,521,000	**U.S. Stock Ticker: ORCL**
2007 Sales: $17,996,000	2007 Profits: $4,274,000	**Int'l Ticker:** Int'l Exchange:
2006 Sales: $14,380,000	2006 Profits: $3,381,000	Employees: 84,233
2005 Sales: $11,799,000	2005 Profits: $2,886,000	Fiscal Year Ends: 5/31
2004 Sales: $10,156,000	2004 Profits: $2,681,000	Parent Company:

SALARIES/BENEFITS:

Pension Plan:	ESOP Stock Plan:	Profit Sharing:	Top Exec. Salary: $1,000,000	Bonus: $10,779,000
Savings Plan: Y	Stock Purch. Plan: Y		Second Exec. Salary: $800,000	Bonus: $6,467,000

OTHER THOUGHTS:

Apparent Women Officers or Directors: 5
Hot Spot for Advancement for Women/Minorities: Y

LOCATIONS: ("Y" = Yes)

West:	Southwest:	Midwest:	Southeast:	Northeast:	International:
Y	Y	Y	Y	Y	Y

Note: Financial information, benefits and other data can change quickly and may vary from those stated here.

OYO CORPORATION

www.oyo.co.jp

Industry Group Code: 541620 **Ranks within this company's industry group:** Sales: Profits:

Techology:		Medical/Drugs:		Engineering:		Transportation:		Chemicals/Petrochemicals:		Specialty:	
Computers:		Manufacturer:		Design:		Aerospace:		Oil/Gas Products:		Special Services:	Y
Software:		Contract Research:		Construction:		Automotive:		Chemicals:		Consulting:	
Communications:		Medical Services:		Eng. Services:	Y	Shipping:		Oil/Chem. Svcs.:		Specialty Mgmt.:	
Electronics:		Labs:		Consulting:				Gases:		Products:	
Alternative Energy:		Bio. Services:						Other:		Other:	

TYPES OF BUSINESS:

Geological Research
Environmental Services
Disaster Prevention
Engineering Consultation
Equipment Manufacturing
Surveying

BRANDS/DIVISIONS/AFFILIATES:

McSEIS-3
SonicViewer-SX
Seismic Starter
McSEIS-SX24
Optical Borehole Camera
Acoustic Borehole Televiewer
OYO Corporation U.S.A.
Klein Associates, Inc.

GROWTH PLANS/SPECIAL FEATURES:

OYO Corporation is a leading Japanese provider of civil engineering consulting, geological investigations, environmental engineering and services involved in various types of problem solving. The company is focused on the creation of geoengineering, localization, globalization, specialization and integration. OYO's business is growing to include environmental services and disaster prevention. The firm is engaged in civil engineering consulting through city planning, architecture, land-use planning and civil engineering structures. The firm's geological investigational services include aerial photographic interpretation, geophysical exploration, field measurement and fossil and rock analysis. Other services the firm provides include environmental engineering, equipment manufacturing and surveys. The company also offers well logging, sea investigation, earthquake monitoring and landslide monitoring. The company's products include seismic, geo-electric, borehole geophysics and in-situ equipment. OYO's seismic instruments include the McSEIS-3, SonicViewer-SX, Seismic Starter and McSEIS-SX24. Borehole imaging tools include the company's Optical Borehole Camera and the Acoustic Borehole Televiewer with data processing software. The corporation is composed of over 20 companies, domestic and overseas.

CONTACTS: *Note: Officers with more than one job title may be intentionally listed here more than once.*

Masaru Narita, Pres.
Satoru Ohya, Exec. Advisor
Kiyoshi Mamiya, Chmn.

Phone: 81-3-3234-0811 **Fax:** 81-3-3234-0383
Toll-Free:
Address: 2-6 Kudan-kita, 4-chrome Chiyoda-ku, Tokyo, 1002-0073 Japan

FINANCIALS: Sales and profits are in thousands of dollars—add 000 to get the full amount. 2008 Note: Financial information for 2008 was not available for all companies at press time.

2008 Sales: $ | 2008 Profits: $
2007 Sales: $ | 2007 Profits: $
2006 Sales: $ | 2006 Profits: $
2005 Sales: $ | 2005 Profits: $
2004 Sales: $ | 2004 Profits: $

U.S. Stock Ticker:
Int'l Ticker: 9755 Int'l Exchange: Tokyo-TSE
Employees: 1,198
Fiscal Year Ends: 12/31
Parent Company:

SALARIES/BENEFITS:

Pension Plan: ESOP Stock Plan: Profit Sharing: Top Exec. Salary: $ Bonus: $
Savings Plan: Stock Purch. Plan: Second Exec. Salary: $ Bonus: $

OTHER THOUGHTS:

Apparent Women Officers or Directors:
Hot Spot for Advancement for Women/Minorities:

LOCATIONS: ("Y" = Yes)

West:	Southwest:	Midwest:	Southeast:	Northeast:	International:
Y				Y	Y

PACCAR INC

www.paccar.com

Industry Group Code: 336111 **Ranks within this company's industry group:** Sales: 19 Profits: 9

Techology:		Medical/Drugs:		Engineering:		Transportation:		Chemicals/Petrochemicals:		Specialty:	
Computers:		Manufacturer:		Design:		Aerospace:		Oil/Gas Products:		Special Services:	
Software:		Contract Research:		Construction:		Automotive:	Y	Chemicals:		Consulting:	
Communications:		Medical Services:		Eng. Services:		Shipping:		Oil/Chem. Svcs.:		Specialty Mgmt.:	
Electronics:		Labs:		Consulting:				Gases:		Products:	
Alternative Energy:		Bio. Services:						Other:		Other:	

TYPES OF BUSINESS:

Truck Manufacturer
Premium Truck Manufacturer
Parts Distribution
Finance, Lease and Insurance Services

BRANDS/DIVISIONS/AFFILIATES:

PACCAR International
DAF Trucks
Peterbilt Motors
Kenworth Truck Company
PACCAR Parts
PACCAR Financial Services
PacLease
Truck Center Hauser GmbH

CONTACTS: *Note: Officers with more than one job title may be intentionally listed here more than once.*

Mark C. Pigott, CEO
Thomas E. Plimpton, Pres.
Janice Skredsvig, CIO/VP
David C. Anderson, General Counsel/VP
Michael T. Barkley, Controller/VP
M. A. Tembreull, Vice Chmn.
James. G. Cardillio, Exec. VP
Kenneth R. Gangl, Sr. VP
Daniel D.Sobic, Sr. VP
Mark C. Pigott, Chmn.

Phone: 425-468-7400	**Fax:** 425-468-8216
Toll-Free:	
Address: 777 106th Ave. NE, Bellevue, WA 98004 US	

GROWTH PLANS/SPECIAL FEATURES:

PACCAR, Inc. is a leading manufacturer of premium light-, medium- and heavy-duty trucks. Subsidiaries include Kenworth Truck Company, Peterbilt Motors and DAF Trucks. The vehicles are used worldwide for over-the-road and off-highway hauling of freight, petroleum, wood products, construction and other materials. The Kenworth and Peterbilt nameplates are manufactured and distributed by separate divisions in the U.S. and foreign plants in Canada, Mexico and Australia. Headquartered in the Netherlands, DAF Trucks comprises the European component of PACCAR, with distribution throughout Europe, Asia and Africa. Products and services are available worldwide through a network of 1,800 locations in more than 100 countries, with customer call centers operating continuously. Substantially all trucks and related parts are sold to independent dealers. The company's financial services segment, which operates through wholly-owned subsidiaries PACCAR Financial and PacLease, maintains a presence in 14 countries and owns a fleet of more than 150,000 vehicles. The company's share of the U.S. and Canadian Class 8 truck market was 26.4% in 2007. Commercial trucks and related replacement parts comprise the largest segment of the company's business, accounting for 91% of 2007 net sales. The firm opened an office in Shanghai early in 2007 to serve as a complimentary facility to an office already existing in Beijing in an effort to bolster its overseas presence. In June 2007, PACCAR Financial acquired German truck rental and leasing company Truck Center Hauser GmbH. In August 2007, the firm announced an agreement with Eaton Corp., an industrial energy manufacturer, to jointly develop hybrid technology for heavy-duty commercial vehicles in North America. In September 2007, the company opened a new Parts Distribution Center near Budapest, Hungary, to support the company's expansion in Central and Eastern Europe.

PACCAR offers employees comprehensive health coverage plans, tuition reimbursement and an interest-free computer purchase program.

FINANCIALS: **Sales and profits are in thousands of dollars—add 000 to get the full amount. 2008 Note: Financial information for 2008 was not available for all companies at press time.**

2008 Sales: $14,972,500	2008 Profits: $1,017,900	**U.S. Stock Ticker: PCAR**
2007 Sales: $15,221,700	2007 Profits: $1,227,300	**Int'l Ticker:** Int'l Exchange:
2006 Sales: $16,454,100	2006 Profits: $1,496,000	Employees: 18,700
2005 Sales: $13,298,400	2005 Profits: $1,133,200	Fiscal Year Ends: 12/31
2004 Sales: $10,833,700	2004 Profits: $906,800	Parent Company:

SALARIES/BENEFITS:

Pension Plan: Y	ESOP Stock Plan:	Profit Sharing:	Top Exec. Salary: $1,300,000	Bonus: $2,059,200
Savings Plan: Y	Stock Purch. Plan:		Second Exec. Salary: $875,000	Bonus: $1,039,500

OTHER THOUGHTS:

Apparent Women Officers or Directors: 1
Hot Spot for Advancement for Women/Minorities:

LOCATIONS: ("Y" = Yes)

West:	Southwest:	Midwest:	Southeast:	Northeast:	International:
Y	Y	Y	Y	Y	Y

PALM INC

www.palm.com

Industry Group Code: 334111 **Ranks within this company's industry group:** Sales: 16 Profits: 15

Techology:		**Medical/Drugs:**		**Engineering:**		**Transportation:**		**Chemicals/Petrochemicals:**		**Specialty:**	
Computers:	Y	Manufacturer:		Design:		Aerospace:		Oil/Gas Products:		Special Services:	
Software:	Y	Contract Research:		Construction:		Automotive:		Chemicals:		Consulting:	
Communications:	Y	Medical Services:		Eng. Services:		Shipping:		Oil/Chem. Svcs.:		Specialty Mgmt.:	
Electronics:	Y	Labs:		Consulting:				Gases:		Products:	
Alternative Energy:		Bio. Services:						Other:		Other:	

TYPES OF BUSINESS:

Computer Hardware-Handheld Organizers
PDAs
Handheld Computer Accessories & Software

BRANDS/DIVISIONS/AFFILIATES:

PalmOne, Inc.
Palm
Treo Smartphones
Tungsten
Zire
Foleo

CONTACTS: *Note: Officers with more than one job title may be intentionally listed here more than once.*

Ed Colligan, CEO
Ed Colligan, Pres.
Andrew (Andy) J. Brown, CFO
Brodie Keast, Sr. VP-Mktg.
Rena Lane, Sr. VP-Human Resources
Mike Bell, Sr. VP-Prod. Dev.
Mary E. Doyle, General Counsel/Corp. Sec./Sr. VP
Jeff Devine, Sr. VP-Global Oper.
Mark Bercow, Sr. VP-Bus. Dev.
Michael Abbott, Sr. VP-Application Software & Svcs.
Way Ting, Sr. VP-System Software
Jon Rubinstein, Exec. Chmn.

Phone: 408-617-7000	**Fax:** 408-617-0100
Toll-Free: 800-881-7256	
Address: 950 W. Maude Ave., Sunnyvale, CA 94085 US	

GROWTH PLANS/SPECIAL FEATURES:

Palm, Inc. is a leading global provider of handheld computing devices, or personal digital assistants (PDAs), add-ons and accessories as well as related services and software. The company develops, designs and markets its Palm-branded handheld devices in two areas: smartphones and handheld computers. Its product lines provide a wide range of business productivity tools and personal and entertainment applications designed for mobile professionals and business customers as well as entry-level consumers. Palm offers its smartphones, handheld computers and accessories through a network of wireless carriers, as well as retail and business outlets worldwide. In the U.S. wireless carriers offering Palm products include Sprint, Verizon Wireless and AT&T. Sprint represents approximately 41% of the firm's 2008 revenue; Verizon represents 13%; and AT&T represents 11%. Some products and services offered include the Treo and Centro Smartphones; Palm OS Platform; Windows Mobile OS Platform; and the Tungsten and Palm handheld computers. Palm's products are differentiated in terms of price, design, functionality and software applications that are delivered with the device. All products offer features such as instant-on one-touch access to the most frequently used applications and non-volatile flash memory that protects stored data even if the charge and power run out. Additional features found in some of the firms products include wireless communication capabilities, such as Bluetooth and wireless fidelity, or Wi-Fi; messaging capabilities, e-mail, web browsing, wireless synchronization and telephone communications; multimedia features; a slot for stamp-sized expansion cards for storage, content and input/output devices; and productivity software. All products run on the Palm systems platform or Windows Mobile OS platform. However, the firm is currently developing a new OS and related next-generation systems software. Palm expects this new OS and software to be completed in time to ship products based on this platform in 2009.

FINANCIALS: **Sales and profits are in thousands of dollars—add 000 to get the full amount. 2008 Note: Financial information for 2008 was not available for all companies at press time.**

2008 Sales: $1,318,691	2008 Profits: $-105,419	**U.S. Stock Ticker: PALM**
2007 Sales: $1,560,507	2007 Profits: $56,383	**Int'l Ticker:** Int'l Exchange:
2006 Sales: $1,578,509	2006 Profits: $336,170	Employees: 1,050
2005 Sales: $1,270,410	2005 Profits: $66,387	Fiscal Year Ends: 5/31
2004 Sales: $949,654	2004 Profits: $-21,849	Parent Company:

SALARIES/BENEFITS:

Pension Plan:	ESOP Stock Plan:	Profit Sharing:	Top Exec. Salary: $757,500	Bonus: $
Savings Plan: Y	Stock Purch. Plan:		Second Exec. Salary: $427,500	Bonus: $

OTHER THOUGHTS:

Apparent Women Officers or Directors: 2
Hot Spot for Advancement for Women/Minorities: Y

LOCATIONS: ("Y" = Yes)

West:	Southwest:	Midwest:	Southeast:	Northeast:	International:
Y				Y	Y

PALO ALTO RESEARCH CENTER

www.parc.xerox.com

Industry Group Code: 541710 **Ranks within this company's industry group:** Sales: Profits:

Techology:		Medical/Drugs:		Engineering:		Transportation:		Chemicals/Petrochemicals:		Specialty:	
Computers:	Y	Manufacturer:		Design:		Aerospace:		Oil/Gas Products:		Special Services:	
Software:	Y	Contract Research:		Construction:		Automotive:		Chemicals:		Consulting:	
Communications:	Y	Medical Services:		Eng. Services:		Shipping:		Oil/Chem. Svcs.:		Specialty Mgmt.:	
Electronics:	Y	Labs:	Y	Consulting:				Gases:		Products:	
Alternative Energy:	Y	Bio. Services:	Y					Other:		Other:	

TYPES OF BUSINESS:

Research & Development-Office Technology
Computing
Software
Networks
Materials Science
Renewable Energy Technology
Biomedical Science
Environmental Technologies

BRANDS/DIVISIONS/AFFILIATES:

Xerox Corporation
Office of the Future
Scripps-PARC Institute
Startup@PARC
WikiDashboard

CONTACTS:

Note: Officers with more than one job title may be intentionally listed here more than once.

Mark Bernstein, Managing Dir.
Mark Bernstein, Pres.
Linda Jacobson, Mgr.-Mktg.
John Pauksta, VP-Human Resources
Dana Bloomberg, VP-Oper.
Jennifer Ernst, Dir.-Bus. Dev.
Linda Jacobson, Mgr.-Comm.
John Pauksta, VP-Finance
Damon C. Matteo, VP-Intellectual Capital Mgmt.
Ross Bringans, Mgr.-Electronic Materials & Devices
Scott Elrod, Mgr.-Hardware Systems
Markus Fromherz, Mgr.-Intelligent Systems

Phone: 650-812-4000	**Fax:** 650-812-4028
Toll-Free:	
Address: 3333 Coyote Hill Rd., Palo Alto, CA 94304 US	

GROWTH PLANS/SPECIAL FEATURES:

The Palo Alto Research Center (PARC) was founded by Xerox Corporation in 1970, and incorporated as a subsidiary of Xerox Corporation in 2002. The company's aim is to develop a concept it calls the Office of the Future. PARC has had a serious impact upon computer and office technology by creating technologies such as laser printing, Ethernet, the graphical user interface and ubiquitous computing. Almost every Xerox product on the market today incorporates or has been influenced by PARC inventions. Since its inception, PARC has spawned 30 new technology companies, licensed its technologies across the world and has made significant contributions in such scientific fields as materials, computing, linguistics and sociology. The company is currently divided into four research and development organizations: Computing science, electronic materials and devices, hardware systems and intelligent systems. It also runs an intellectual capital management division. Together with the Scripps Research Institute, PARC founded the Scripps-PARC Institute for Advanced Biomedical Science. The institute's research centers on such areas as drug discovery, cancer screening, protein purification and cell monitoring. The company's areas of focus in research and innovation include biomedical systems; cleantech; nanotechnology; natural language processing; ethnography; networking; human information interaction; optoelectronics and optical systems; intelligent control and autonomous systems; printing; intelligent image recognition; security and privacy; and large area electronic. Entrepreneurs who wish to take advantage of PARC research can access the Startup@PARC program, which creates customized partnerships for selected ventures, providing access to high-end technical expertise and facilities resources such as office-lab space and operational support. In early 2009, the company developed WikiDashboard, a tool that helps readers further examine the validity and credibility of information and articles derived from Wikipedia.com.

Employee benefits include medical, dental and vision coverage; flexible spending accounts; disability benefits; and 401(k).

FINANCIALS:

Sales and profits are in thousands of dollars—add 000 to get the full amount. 2008 Note: Financial information for 2008 was not available for all companies at press time.

2008 Sales: $	2008 Profits: $	**U.S. Stock Ticker: Subsidiary**
2007 Sales: $	2007 Profits: $	**Int'l Ticker:** Int'l Exchange:
2006 Sales: $	2006 Profits: $	Employees:
2005 Sales: $	2005 Profits: $	Fiscal Year Ends: 12/31
2004 Sales: $	2004 Profits: $	Parent Company: XEROX CORP

SALARIES/BENEFITS:

Pension Plan:	ESOP Stock Plan:	Profit Sharing:	Top Exec. Salary: $	Bonus: $
Savings Plan: Y	Stock Purch. Plan:		Second Exec. Salary: $	Bonus: $

OTHER THOUGHTS:

Apparent Women Officers or Directors: 3
Hot Spot for Advancement for Women/Minorities: Y

LOCATIONS: ("Y" = Yes)

West:	Southwest:	Midwest:	Southeast:	Northeast:	International:
Y					

PANASONIC CORPORATION

www.panasonic.net

Industry Group Code: 334310 **Ranks within this company's industry group:** Sales: 2 Profits: 3

Techology:		Medical/Drugs:		Engineering:		Transportation:		Chemicals/Petrochemicals:		Specialty:	
Computers:	Y	Manufacturer:		Design:		Aerospace:		Oil/Gas Products:		Special Services:	
Software:		Contract Research:		Construction:		Automotive:		Chemicals:		Consulting:	
Communications:	Y	Medical Services:		Eng. Services:		Shipping:		Oil/Chem. Svcs.:		Specialty Mgmt.:	
Electronics:	Y	Labs:		Consulting:				Gases:		Products:	
Alternative Energy:		Bio. Services:						Other:		Other:	

TYPES OF BUSINESS:

Audio & Video Equipment, Manufacturing
Batteries
Home Appliances
Electronic Components
Cellular Phones
Medical Equipment
Photovoltaic Equipment

BRANDS/DIVISIONS/AFFILIATES:

Matsushita Electric Industrial Co., Ltd
Quasar
Technics
JVC
National
Toray Industries, Inc.
Matsushita PDP Company Ltd.

CONTACTS: *Note: Officers with more than one job title may be intentionally listed here more than once.*

Koshi Kitadai, Sr. Managing Exec. Officer
Fumio Ohtsubo, Pres.
Shunzo Ushimaru, Sr. Managing Dir.-Mktg.
Shinichi Fukushima, Managing Dir.-Personnel & Gen. Affairs
Takae Makita, Exec. Officer-Info. Systems
Susumu Koike, Exec. VP-Tech. & Semiconductors
Ikusaburo Kashima, Dir.-Corp. Legal Affairs
Takahiro Mori, Managing Dir.-Planning
Yoichi Nagata, Dir.-Overseas Investor Rel.
Tetsuya Kawakami, Exec. VP-Acct.
Joachim Reinhart, COO-Panasonic Europe Ltd.
Koshi Kitadai, Pres., Panasonic Electronic Devices Co., Ltd.
Yoshiaki Kushiki, Pres., Panasonic Mobile Communications Co., Ltd.
Toru Ishida, Pres., Matsushita Battery Industrial Co., Ltd.
Kunio Nakamura, Chmn.
Nobutane Yamamoto, Exec. Officer-Corp. Procurement

Phone: 81-6-6908-1121 **Fax:** 81-6-6908-2351
Toll-Free:
Address: 1006 Kadoma, Kadoma City, Osaka, 571-8501 Japan

GROWTH PLANS/SPECIAL FEATURES:

Panasonic Corporation, formerly Matsushita Electric Industrial Co., Ltd, produces consumer electronics products marketed under brand names such as Panasonic, National, Quasar, Technics and JVC. The company's primary business areas include audio, visual and communications (AVC Networks); home appliances; components and devices; Panasonic Electric Works; PanaHome, which is a residential construction group; and JVC. MEI's AVC products include computers; monitors; optical disk drives; cell phones; copying machines and printers; plasma, LCD and CRT TVs; VCRs; camcorders; DVD players and recorders; and audio equipment. Home appliance products include refrigerators, air conditioners, washing machines, dryers, vacuum cleaners, dishwashers, microwave ovens, cooking appliances, medical equipment, electric lamps, vending machines and electric and gas heating equipment. Components and devices include semiconductors, batteries, electric motors and general components such as circuit boards and speakers. The Panasonic Electric Works and PanaHome segment supplies lighting fixtures, interior furnishing materials, automation controls, rental apartment housing, home remodeling, residential real estate and medical and nursing care facilities. The JVC segment produces business-use AV equipment; AV software for DVDs, video tapes and CDs; and other equipment similar to the AVC division's. Additional business operations include industrial robots, bicycles and electronic-components-mounting machines. Panasonic is one of the world's largest makers of plasma TVs. In 2008, the company announced that it would launch fuel-cell systems for domestic use in Japan in the year starting April 2009, taking aim at demand for cleaner energy sources. In late 2008, the firm announced its intention to acquire Sanyo Electric Co., Ltd. This will give Panasonic a big boost in the rechargeable battery segment and position it to grow in the renewable energy area.

FINANCIALS: **Sales and profits are in thousands of dollars—add 000 to get the full amount. 2008 Note: Financial information for 2008 was not available for all companies at press time.**

2008 Sales: $93,428,320	2008 Profits: $2,905,150	**U.S. Stock Ticker: MC**
2007 Sales: $81,831,200	2007 Profits: $1,949,650	**Int'l Ticker: 6752** Int'l Exchange: Tokyo-TSE
2006 Sales: $75,601,800	2006 Profits: $1,312,500	Employees: 305,828
2005 Sales: $81,298,000	2005 Profits: $546,000	Fiscal Year Ends: 3/31
2004 Sales: $71,920,600	2004 Profits: $405,200	Parent Company:

SALARIES/BENEFITS:

Pension Plan:	ESOP Stock Plan:	Profit Sharing:	Top Exec. Salary: $	Bonus: $
Savings Plan:	Stock Purch. Plan:		Second Exec. Salary: $	Bonus: $

OTHER THOUGHTS:

Apparent Women Officers or Directors:
Hot Spot for Advancement for Women/Minorities:

LOCATIONS: ("Y" = Yes)

West:	Southwest:	Midwest:	Southeast:	Northeast:	International:
Y	Y	Y	Y	Y	Y

PANASONIC MOBILE COMMUNICATIONS CO LTD

panasonic.co.jp/pmc/en

Industry Group Code: 334210 **Ranks within this company's industry group:** Sales: Profits:

Techology:		Medical/Drugs:		Engineering:		Transportation:		Chemicals/Petrochemicals:		Specialty:	
Computers:		Manufacturer:		Design:		Aerospace:		Oil/Gas Products:		Special Services:	
Software:		Contract Research:		Construction:		Automotive:		Chemicals:		Consulting:	
Communications:	Y	Medical Services:		Eng. Services:		Shipping:		Oil/Chem. Svcs.:		Specialty Mgmt.:	
Electronics:	Y	Labs:		Consulting:				Gases:		Products:	
Alternative Energy:		Bio. Services:						Other:		Other:	

TYPES OF BUSINESS:

Electronics Manufacturing
Mobile Phones
Wireless Equipment
Automotive Navigation Systems
Audio & Visual Equipment
Scientific Measurement Equipment

BRANDS/DIVISIONS/AFFILIATES:

Matsushita Electric Industrial Co Ltd
Visual Slim (VS)
Sporty and Active (SA)
Maximum Endurance (MX)
Stylish Camera Phone (SC) 3
A210
X800 Smartphone
X700

CONTACTS: *Note: Officers with more than one job title may be intentionally listed here more than once.*

Osamu Waki, Pres.
Toshinori Hoshi, VP
Ryoichi Wada, VP
Eiji Hagiwara, Managing Dir.
Tomozo Hiroki, Sr. Corp. Auditor

Phone: 81-45-932-1231	**Fax:** 81-45-542-5105
Toll-Free:	
Address: 600 Saedo-cho, Tsuzuki-ku, Yokohama, 224-8539 Japan	

GROWTH PLANS/SPECIAL FEATURES:

Panasonic Mobile Communications Co., Ltd., a subsidiary of Panasonic Corporation (formerly Matsushita Electric Industrial), is a global provider of mobile communications products and services, including mobile phones, infrastructure and terminals. Panasonic Mobile's primary product line consists of its selection of cellular phones. Current cellular phone models sold by the company include the Visual Slim (VS) series, the Sporty and Active (SA) series, the Maximum Endurance (MX) series, the Stylish Camera Phone (SC) 3, the A210, the P906i, the X800 Smartphone and the X700. Panasonic Mobile has ISO9001 certified plants in several countries, including Japan, China, the Philippines, and the Czech Republic, operating through direct ownership and strategic partnerships. In addition, the company has research facilities worldwide, including locations in China, Japan and the U.K. The research facility based in Japan is a joint venture between the company, government and regional universities; the research team is currently studying third generation (3G) features such as multimedia services and high-speed packet data transmission. Panasonic Mobile is also currently working on the development of a global platform based on the Linux Operating System currently used in mobile terminals in the Japanese market. In February 2008, Panasonic Mobile launched seven new handset models for NTT DoCoMo, Inc.; SoftBank Mobile Corp.; and KDDI Corp., featuring reduced thickness, enhanced picture quality and 1seg reception sensitivity. In April 2008, the firm reached the record for 100 million units shipped to Japanese phone carriers.

FINANCIALS: **Sales and profits are in thousands of dollars—add 000 to get the full amount. 2008 Note: Financial information for 2008 was not available for all companies at press time.**

2008 Sales: $	2008 Profits: $	**U.S. Stock Ticker: Subsidiary**
2007 Sales: $	2007 Profits: $	**Int'l Ticker:** Int'l Exchange:
2006 Sales: $	2006 Profits: $	Employees:
2005 Sales: $	2005 Profits: $	Fiscal Year Ends: 3/31
2004 Sales: $	2004 Profits: $	Parent Company: PANASONIC CORPORATION

SALARIES/BENEFITS:

Pension Plan:	ESOP Stock Plan:	Profit Sharing:	Top Exec. Salary: $	Bonus: $
Savings Plan:	Stock Purch. Plan:		Second Exec. Salary: $	Bonus: $

OTHER THOUGHTS:

Apparent Women Officers or Directors:
Hot Spot for Advancement for Women/Minorities:

LOCATIONS: ("Y" = Yes)

West:	Southwest:	Midwest:	Southeast:	Northeast:	International:
					Y

PARAMETRIC TECHNOLOGY CORP

www.ptc.com

Industry Group Code: 511215 **Ranks within this company's industry group:** Sales: 4 Profits: 4

Techology:		Medical/Drugs:		Engineering:		Transportation:		Chemicals/Petrochemicals:		Specialty:	
Computers:		Manufacturer:		Design:		Aerospace:		Oil/Gas Products:		Special Services:	
Software:	Y	Contract Research:		Construction:		Automotive:		Chemicals:		Consulting:	
Communications:		Medical Services:		Eng. Services:		Shipping:		Oil/Chem. Svcs.:		Specialty Mgmt.:	
Electronics:		Labs:		Consulting:	Y			Gases:		Products:	
Alternative Energy:		Bio. Services:						Other:		Other:	

TYPES OF BUSINESS:

Computer Software-Engineering & Manufacturing
Engineering Consulting Services
Enterprise Publishing Software
Product Data Management

BRANDS/DIVISIONS/AFFILIATES:

Pro/ENGINEER
Arbortext, Inc.
Arbortext Advanced Print Publisher
Mathsoft Engineering & Education, Inc.
Mathcad
ITEDO Software LLC
CoCreate Software GmbH
Pro/ENGINEER Manikin

CONTACTS: *Note: Officers with more than one job title may be intentionally listed here more than once.*

C. Richard (Dick) Harrison, CEO
C. Richard (Dick) Harrison, Pres.
Neil F. Moses, CFO/Exec. VP
Paul J. Cunningham, Exec. VP-Worldwide Sales
Steve Horan, CIO/Corp. VP
James E. (Jim) Heppelmann, Chief Prod. Officer/Exec. VP-Software Solutions
Aaron C. von Staats, General Counsel/Sr. VP
Barry F. Cohen, Exec. VP-Strategic Svcs. & Partners
Anita Berryman, Sr. Mgr.-Corp. Comm.
Kristian P. Talvitie, VP-Investor Rel.
Anthony (Tony) DiBona, Exec. VP-Global Maintenance Support
Noel G. Posternak, Chmn.
Paul J. Cunningham, Exec. VP-Dist.

Phone: 781-370-5000	**Fax:** 781-370-6000
Toll-Free: 877-275-4782	
Address: 140 Kendrick St., Needham, MA 02494 US	

GROWTH PLANS/SPECIAL FEATURES:

Parametric Technology Corp. (PTC) develops, markets and supports product lifecycle management (PLM) and enterprise content management (ECM) software that help companies improve their product development processes. It offers product data management, dynamic publishing solutions, supplier management, digital mockup, enterprise application integration, project management, after-market service, customer needs management and manufacturing planning. PTC's leading product family, Pro/ENGINEER, is a 3D modeling software used by large enterprises including NASA. The Pro/ENGINEER family includes Pro/ENGINEER CAD, CAM and CAE. The firm's Windchill Software enables users to enhance their businesses via the Internet through digital mock-up collaboration, internal library design, product data management tools and cross-application integration. PTC owns Arbortext, Inc., a leader in the dynamic enterprise publishing market, and subsequently released Arbortext Advanced Print Publisher 9.0, designed assist in the production of technical documentation; financial reports; scientific, technical and medical journals; legislation and amendments; marketing brochures; telephone directories; and product catalogs. PTC also owns Mathsoft Engineering & Education, Inc., which creates Mathcad software essential to the PLM process; and ITEDO Software GmbH and ITEDO Software LLC, designers of software which creates technical illustrations. PTC has partnered with many companies in recent years, including Autodesk, Inc., to expand its manufacturing capabilities; International Business Machines Corp. (IBM), to integrate with the IBM Rational Software Development platform and focus on the PLM market in China; and IHS, Inc., to deliver electronic components content to users of PTC Windchill. In November 2008, PTC launched Pro/ENGINEER Manikin, a program than can insert 3D human models into a CAD model to assess human-product interactions, such as ergonomic issues. In December 2008, the company acquired Synapsis Technology, Inc., and plans to integrate Synapsis' technology into Windchill.

Parametric provides its employees with tuition reimbursement; paid time off; medical, dental and vision plans; life insurance; and short- and long-term disability coverage.

FINANCIALS: **Sales and profits are in thousands of dollars—add 000 to get the full amount. 2008 Note: Financial information for 2008 was not available for all companies at press time.**

2008 Sales: $1,070,330	2008 Profits: $79,702	**U.S. Stock Ticker: PMTC**
2007 Sales: $941,279	2007 Profits: $143,656	**Int'l Ticker:** Int'l Exchange:
2006 Sales: $847,983	2006 Profits: $56,804	Employees: 5,087
2005 Sales: $707,975	2005 Profits: $73,187	Fiscal Year Ends: 9/30
2004 Sales: $660,029	2004 Profits: $34,813	Parent Company:

SALARIES/BENEFITS:

Pension Plan:	ESOP Stock Plan:	Profit Sharing:	Top Exec. Salary: $520,000	Bonus: $
Savings Plan: Y	Stock Purch. Plan:		Second Exec. Salary: $487,000	Bonus: $

OTHER THOUGHTS:

Apparent Women Officers or Directors:
Hot Spot for Advancement for Women/Minorities:

LOCATIONS: ("Y" = Yes)

West:	Southwest:	Midwest:	Southeast:	Northeast:	International:
Y	Y	Y	Y	Y	Y

Note: Financial information, benefits and other data can change quickly and may vary from those stated here.

PAREXEL INTERNATIONAL CORP

www.parexel.com

Industry Group Code: 541710 **Ranks within this company's industry group:** Sales: 3 Profits: 3

Techology:		**Medical/Drugs:**		**Engineering:**		**Transportation:**		**Chemicals/Petrochemicals:**		**Specialty:**	
Computers:		Manufacturer:		Design:		Aerospace:		Oil/Gas Products:		Special Services:	
Software:		Contract Research:	Y	Construction:		Automotive:		Chemicals:		Consulting:	
Communications:		Medical Services:	Y	Eng. Services:		Shipping:		Oil/Chem. Svcs.:		Specialty Mgmt.:	
Electronics:		Labs:		Consulting:				Gases:		Products:	
Alternative Energy:		Bio. Services:	Y					Other:		Other:	Y

TYPES OF BUSINESS:

Clinical Trial & Data Management
Biostatistical Analysis & Reporting
Medical Communications Services
Clinical Pharmacology Services
Consulting Services

BRANDS/DIVISIONS/AFFILIATES:

Clinical Research Services
PAREXEL Consulting & Medical Communications Svcs.
Perceptive Informatics, Inc.
Synchron Research
ClinPhone plc
Safe Implementation of Treatments in Stroke

CONTACTS: *Note: Officers with more than one job title may be intentionally listed here more than once.*

Josef H. von Rickenbach, CEO
Mark A. Goldberg, COO
James F. Winschel, Jr., CFO/Sr. VP
Ulf Schneider, Chief Admin. Officer/Sr. VP
Douglas A. Batt, General Counsel/Corp. Sec./Sr. VP
Jill L. Baker, VP-Investor Rel.
Kurt A. Brykman, Pres., PAREXEL Consulting & Medical Comm. Svcs.
Josef H. von Rickenbach, Chmn.

Phone: 781-487-9900	**Fax:** 781-768-5512
Toll-Free:	
Address: 200 West St., Waltham, MA 02451 US	

GROWTH PLANS/SPECIAL FEATURES:

PAREXEL International is a biopharmaceutical services company providing clinical research, medical communications services, consulting and informatics and advanced technology products and services to the worldwide pharmaceutical, biotechnology and medical device industries. Operating in 71 locations throughout 52 countries, PAREXEL has three business segments: Clinical Research Services (CRS); PAREXEL Consulting and Medical Communications Services (PCMS); and Perceptive Informatics, Inc. PAREXEL's core business, CRS, provides clinical trials management and biostatistics; data management; clinical pharmacology; and related medical advisory, patient recruitment and investigator site services. PCMS provides technical expertise and advice for drug development, regulatory affairs and biopharmaceutical process consulting; offers product launch support, including market development, product development and targeted communications services; identifies alternatives and solutions regarding product development, registration and commercialization; and provides health policy consulting and strategic reimbursement services. Lastly, Perceptive provides information technology designed to improve clients' product development processes, including medical imaging services, IVRS, CTMS, web-based portals, systems integration, and patient diary applications. In March 2008, the company sold a bioanalytical laboratory in Poitiers, France, to a subsidiary of Synchron Research. Also in March 2008, PAREXEL increased its minority stake in clinical pharmacology business of Synchron from 19.5% to 31%. In August 2008, the firm acquired ClinPhone plc, a clinical technology organization. In November 2008, PAREXEL opened an office in Lima, Peru. In December 2008, the company established an alliance with Safe Implementation of Treatments in Stroke (SITS) International to provide PAREXEL clients access to SITS' 800 investigator sites in 40 countries.

FINANCIALS: **Sales and profits are in thousands of dollars—add 000 to get the full amount. 2008 Note: Financial information for 2008 was not available for all companies at press time.**

2008 Sales: $964,283	2008 Profits: $64,640	**U.S. Stock Ticker: PRXL**
2007 Sales: $741,955	2007 Profits: $37,289	**Int'l Ticker:** Int'l Exchange:
2006 Sales: $614,947	2006 Profits: $23,544	Employees: 8,050
2005 Sales: $544,726	2005 Profits: $-35,177	Fiscal Year Ends: 6/30
2004 Sales: $540,983	2004 Profits: $13,791	Parent Company:

SALARIES/BENEFITS:

Pension Plan:	ESOP Stock Plan:	Profit Sharing:	Top Exec. Salary: $550,000	Bonus: $633,600
Savings Plan:	Stock Purch. Plan:		Second Exec. Salary: $409,679	Bonus: $178,882

OTHER THOUGHTS:

Apparent Women Officers or Directors: 1
Hot Spot for Advancement for Women/Minorities: Y

LOCATIONS: ("Y" = Yes)

West:	Southwest:	Midwest:	Southeast:	Northeast:	International:
Y				Y	Y

PARSONS BRINCKERHOFF INC

www.pbworld.com

Industry Group Code: 234000 **Ranks within this company's industry group:** Sales: 24 Profits: 20

Techology:		Medical/Drugs:		Engineering:		Transportation:		Chemicals/Petrochemicals:		Specialty:	
Computers:		Manufacturer:		Design:	Y	Aerospace:		Oil/Gas Products:		Special Services:	
Software:		Contract Research:		Construction:	Y	Automotive:		Chemicals:		Consulting:	
Communications:		Medical Services:		Eng. Services:	Y	Shipping:		Oil/Chem. Svcs.:		Specialty Mgmt.:	Y
Electronics:		Labs:		Consulting:	Y			Gases:		Products:	
Alternative Energy:		Bio. Services:						Other:		Other:	

TYPES OF BUSINESS:

Engineering Services
Planning, Design & Construction
Civic Construction Projects
Commercial Construction
Transportation Consulting
Program Management Services
Telecommunications & Environmental Projects

BRANDS/DIVISIONS/AFFILIATES:

PB Facilities, Inc.
PB Aviation, Inc.
PB Farradyne, Inc.
PB Buildings, Inc.
PB Constructors, Inc.
PB Telecommunications, Inc.
Parsons Brinckerhoff Power, Inc.
PB Research Library

CONTACTS:

Note: Officers with more than one job title may be intentionally listed here more than once.

Keith Hawksworth, CEO
Richard A. Schrader, CFO/Exec. VP
John J. Ryan, Exec. VP/Dir.-Human Resources
Lisa M. Palumbo, General Counsel
Hugh Inglis, Sr. VP-Alltech
Gay Knipper, Dir.-National Program Management, PB Americas
Paul Skoutelas, Market Leader-Transit, PB Americas
James L. Lammie, Chmn.
Patrick Lun, Deputy COO-PB Int'l

Phone: 212-465-5000 **Fax:** 212-465-5096
Toll-Free:
Address: 1 Penn Plaza, New York, NY 10119 US

GROWTH PLANS/SPECIAL FEATURES:

Parsons Brinckerhoff, Inc. provides engineering, consulting, and management services to local governments and the transportation, energy, and commercial market sectors. The company also offers construction services, program and project management, and facilities management. Parsons Brinckerhoff has taken on projects for clients such as Bangkok Mass Transit System Corporation and the City of Austin, Texas; and its signature works include the design of New York City's first subway and the reconfiguration of the Fort Washington Way interstate connector in Cincinnati. The company also worked with the Delhi Metro Rail Corporation to build a mass transit system designed as an urban transport system to move over 3 million passengers a day. Other relevant projects have included contracts to build a gas fired power station in Kuwait; to design a website and communications plan for lower Manhattan, known as lowermanhatten.info; and to design and engineer the Greater Cairo Metro system. Potential clients can view the company's work through the PB Research Library, a body that showcases and publishes the details of important projects. The firm is organized into three divisions: Americas, International and Facilities. The company is employee-owned with 150 offices worldwide. In August 2008, the company entered a joint venture with The Maryland Transportation Authority for inspection and construction management services on an on call-basis. In October 2008, the company was awarded a five-year joint venture contract with The North Texas Tollway Authority for construction management services.

FINANCIALS:

Sales and profits are in thousands of dollars—add 000 to get the full amount. 2008 Note: Financial information for 2008 was not available for all companies at press time.

2008 Sales: $2,343,117	2008 Profits: $73,882
2007 Sales: $1,853,741	2007 Profits: $62,117
2006 Sales: $1,689,964	2006 Profits: $46,386
2005 Sales: $1,447,756	2005 Profits: $27,160
2004 Sales: $1,389,400	2004 Profits: $18,400

U.S. Stock Ticker: Private
Int'l Ticker: Int'l Exchange:
Employees: 13,010
Fiscal Year Ends: 10/31
Parent Company:

SALARIES/BENEFITS:

Pension Plan:	ESOP Stock Plan:	Profit Sharing:	Top Exec. Salary: $	Bonus: $
Savings Plan:	Stock Purch. Plan:		Second Exec. Salary: $	Bonus: $

OTHER THOUGHTS:

Apparent Women Officers or Directors: 3
Hot Spot for Advancement for Women/Minorities: Y

LOCATIONS: ("Y" = Yes)

West:	Southwest:	Midwest:	Southeast:	Northeast:	International:
Y	Y	Y	Y	Y	Y

PCL CONSTRUCTION GROUP INC

www.pcl.com

Industry Group Code: 234000 **Ranks within this company's industry group:** Sales: Profits:

Techology:		Medical/Drugs:		Engineering:		Transportation:		Chemicals/Petrochemicals:		Specialty:	
Computers:		Manufacturer:		Design:		Aerospace:		Oil/Gas Products:		Special Services:	
Software:		Contract Research:		Construction:		Automotive:		Chemicals:		Consulting:	
Communications:		Medical Services:		Eng. Services:	Y	Shipping:		Oil/Chem. Svcs.:		Specialty Mgmt.:	Y
Electronics:		Labs:		Consulting:				Gases:		Products:	
Alternative Energy:		Bio. Services:						Other:		Other:	Y

TYPES OF BUSINESS:

Construction
Financial and Accounting Reporting
Development, Support and Project Management
Engineering Services

BRANDS/DIVISIONS/AFFILIATES:

Melloy Industrial Services
Monad Industrial Constructors
PCL Civil Constructors
PCL Industrial Services
PCL Intracon Power
Teton Industrial Construction

CONTACTS: *Note: Officers with more than one job title may be intentionally listed here more than once.*

Ross Grieve, CEO
Paul Douglas, COO
Ross Grieve, Pres.
Gordon Maron, CFO
Glen Anderson, VP-Admin. & Finance
Doug Stollery, Legal Counsel
Paul Douglas, COO/Pres., Canadian Oper.
Joe Watson, Dir.-Corp. Bus. Dev., Canadian Oper.
Gordon Stephenson, VP-Corp. Finance
Brad Nelson, COO/Pres., Canadian Buildings
Peter Stalenhoef, COO/Pres., Heavy Industrial
Al Troppmann, Pres., US Buildings
Joseph D. Thompson, Chmn.
Peter Beaupre, COO/Pres., U.S. Oper.

Phone: 780-733-5000	**Fax:** 780-733-5075
Toll-Free:	
Address: 5410 99 St., Edmonton, AB T6E 3P4 Canada	

GROWTH PLANS/SPECIAL FEATURES:

PCL Construction Group, Inc., founded in 1906, is an employee-owned group of construction companies in 27 locations throughout Canada, the U.S. and the Bahamas, with operations in the buildings, infrastructure and heavy industrial sectors. The firm focuses on three main areas of construction: buildings, infrastructure and heavy industrial. The buildings segment conducts projects throughout North America and is able to work on an array of projects including commercial; institutional; educational; residential; adaptive reuse, which entails upgrading and converting an existing facility; cultural consideration, including on-site and on-the-job employment and training opportunities; green building; high-tech projects, for meeting cleanliness protocols in the medical, bio-tech and research working environments; historical preservation, including repair, exterior masonry and renovations; and theming, combining typical construction methods with scenic construction technology. The infrastructure segment undertakes various civil structure projects including bridges, overpasses, tunnels, interchanges, water treatment facilities, interchanges and light rail transportation projects. The heavy industrial division offers construction assistance to the petrochemical; oil and gas; pulp and paper; mining; and power and generation industries. PCL's building operations include larger projects, such as airports, sports facilities and office towers, and smaller projects, such as renovations, restorations and repairs. Subsidiaries include Melloy Industrial Services, Monad Industrial Constructors, PCL Civil Constructors, PCL Industrial Services, PCL Intracon Power and Teton Industrial Construction.

PCL offers employees medical, vision and dental insurance; flexible spending accounts; a prescription drug plan; a 401(k); a profit sharing bonus; and an employee assistance programs. Additionally, in 2009, the firm ranked among the top 100 companies to work for according to Fortune Magazine.

FINANCIALS: **Sales and profits are in thousands of dollars—add 000 to get the full amount. 2008 Note: Financial information for 2008 was not available for all companies at press time.**

2008 Sales: $	2008 Profits: $	**U.S. Stock Ticker: Private**
2007 Sales: $	2007 Profits: $	**Int'l Ticker:** Int'l Exchange:
2006 Sales: $	2006 Profits: $	Employees: 9,989
2005 Sales: $3,120,000	2005 Profits: $	Fiscal Year Ends:
2004 Sales: $	2004 Profits: $	Parent Company:

SALARIES/BENEFITS:

Pension Plan:	ESOP Stock Plan:	Profit Sharing:	Top Exec. Salary: $	Bonus: $
Savings Plan: Y	Stock Purch. Plan:		Second Exec. Salary: $	Bonus: $

OTHER THOUGHTS:

Apparent Women Officers or Directors:
Hot Spot for Advancement for Women/Minorities:

LOCATIONS: ("Y" = Yes)

West:	Southwest:	Midwest:	Southeast:	Northeast:	International:
Y	Y	Y	Y		Y

PERINI CORPORATION

www.perini.com

Industry Group Code: 234000 **Ranks within this company's industry group:** Sales: 18 Profits: 27

Techology:		Medical/Drugs:		Engineering:		Transportation:		Chemicals/Petrochemicals:		Specialty:	
Computers:		Manufacturer:		Design:	Y	Aerospace:		Oil/Gas Products:		Special Services:	Y
Software:		Contract Research:		Construction:	Y	Automotive:		Chemicals:		Consulting:	
Communications:		Medical Services:		Eng. Services:	Y	Shipping:		Oil/Chem. Svcs.:		Specialty Mgmt.:	
Electronics:		Labs:		Consulting:	Y			Gases:		Products:	
Alternative Energy:		Bio. Services:						Other:		Other:	

TYPES OF BUSINESS:

Construction Services
Hospitality & Casino Construction
Construction Management Services
Civic & Infrastructure Construction
Design Services
Health Care Facility Construction

BRANDS/DIVISIONS/AFFILIATES:

Perini Building Co., Inc.
James A. Cummings, Inc.
Rudolph and Sletten, Inc.
Perini Civil Construction
Cherry Hill Construction, Inc.
Tutor-Saliba Corporation
Keating Building Corporation

CONTACTS: *Note: Officers with more than one job title may be intentionally listed here more than once.*

Ronald N. Tutor, CEO
Robert Band, COO
Robert Band, Pres.
Kenneth R. Burk, CFO/Sr. VP
Anthony J. Buccitelli, VP-Legal
Susan C. Mellace, Treas./VP
Robert Band, Chmn./Pres., Perini Mgmt. Services, Inc.
Craig D. Shaw, Chmn.-Perini Building Co., Inc.
Martin B. Sisemore, Pres./CEO-Rudolpf & Sletten, Inc.
William R. Derrer, Pres./CEO-James A. Cummings, Inc.
Ronald N. Tutor, Chmn.

Phone: 508-628-2000 **Fax:** 508-628-2357
Toll-Free:
Address: 73 Mt. Wayte Ave., Framingham, MA 01701 US

GROWTH PLANS/SPECIAL FEATURES:

Perini Corporation and its subsidiaries provide general contracting, construction management and design/build services throughout the world. It operates in three segments: Building, civil and management services. The building segment, comprised of Perini Building Co., James A. Cummings Inc. and Rudolph and Sletten Inc., focuses on large, complex projects in the hospitality and gaming, sports and entertainment, educational, transportation, corrections, health care, biotech, pharmaceutical and high-tech markets. The civil segment is comprised of Perini Civil Construction and Cherry Hill Construction, Inc. The segment focuses on public works construction primarily in the Northeastern and Mid-Atlantic U.S., including the repair, replacement and reconstruction of public infrastructure such as highways, bridges, mass transit systems and wastewater treatment facilities. The company's customers primarily award contracts through one of two methods: Public competitive bid, in which price is the major determining factor, or through a request for proposals where contracts are awarded based on a combination of technical capability and price. The management services segment provides diversified construction, design-build and maintenance services to the U.S. military and government agencies as well as surety companies and multi-national corporations in the U.S. and overseas. In September 2008, the company acquired Tutor-Saliba Corporation, a civil infrastructure and commercial building construction company. In January 2009, the firm acquired Keating Building Corporation, a private construction management and designing and building company.

Employees are offered medical and dental insurance; a 401(k) plan; medical and dependent care spending accounts; life and accident insurance; disability coverage; educational assistance; and an employee assistance program.

FINANCIALS: Sales and profits are in thousands of dollars—add 000 to get the full amount. 2008 Note: Financial information for 2008 was not available for all companies at press time.

2008 Sales: $5,660,286	2008 Profits: $-75,140	**U.S. Stock Ticker: PCR**
2007 Sales: $4,628,358	2007 Profits: $97,114	**Int'l Ticker:** Int'l Exchange:
2006 Sales: $3,042,839	2006 Profits: $41,536	Employees: 8,000
2005 Sales: $1,733,477	2005 Profits: $4,049	Fiscal Year Ends: 12/31
2004 Sales: $1,842,315	2004 Profits: $36,007	Parent Company:

SALARIES/BENEFITS:

Pension Plan:	ESOP Stock Plan:	Profit Sharing:	Top Exec. Salary: $538,500	Bonus: $976,900
Savings Plan: Y	Stock Purch. Plan:		Second Exec. Salary: $500,000	Bonus: $628,750

OTHER THOUGHTS:

Apparent Women Officers or Directors: 2
Hot Spot for Advancement for Women/Minorities:

LOCATIONS: ("Y" = Yes)

West:	Southwest:	Midwest:	Southeast:	Northeast:	International:
Y	Y	Y	Y	Y	

PEROT SYSTEMS CORP

www.perotsystems.com

Industry Group Code: 541512 **Ranks within this company's industry group:** Sales: 15 Profits: 10

Techology:		Medical/Drugs:		Engineering:		Transportation:		Chemicals/Petrochemicals:		Specialty:	
Computers:		Manufacturer:		Design:		Aerospace:		Oil/Gas Products:		Special Services:	Y
Software:		Contract Research:		Construction:		Automotive:		Chemicals:		Consulting:	Y
Communications:		Medical Services:		Eng. Services:		Shipping:		Oil/Chem. Svcs.:		Specialty Mgmt.:	
Electronics:		Labs:		Consulting:				Gases:		Products:	
Alternative Energy:		Bio. Services:						Other:		Other:	

TYPES OF BUSINESS:

IT Consulting
Business Process Outsourcing
Management Consulting
Government Services
Infrastructure Services
Systems & Software Development

BRANDS/DIVISIONS/AFFILIATES:

QSS Group Inc
JJWild Inc
Original Solutions Limited

CONTACTS: *Note: Officers with more than one job title may be intentionally listed here more than once.*

Peter Altabef, CEO
Russell Freeman, COO
Peter Altabef, Pres.
John Harper, CFO
Jeff Renzi, Exec. VP-Mktg. & Sales
Darcy Anderson, Chief People Officer/VP-Corp. Support
Susan Nolan, CIO
Del Williams, General Counsel/VP/Corp. Sec
Raj Asava, Chief Strategy Officer
John King, VP
James Champy, Chmn.-Consulting
Scott Barnes, VP-Infrastructure Solutions
Atul Vohra, Chief Mktg. Officer
Ross Perot, Jr., Chmn.

Phone: 972-577-0000	**Fax:**
Toll-Free: 888-317-3768	
Address: 2300 W. Plano Pkwy., Plano, TX 75075 US	

GROWTH PLANS/SPECIAL FEATURES:

Perot Systems Corp. is a worldwide provider of information technology (IT) services and business solutions to a broad range of customers. The firm offers integrated solutions designed around specific business objectives, with services including technology outsourcing, business process outsourcing, development and integration of systems and applications, and business and technology consulting services. Services are divided into four primary segments: infrastructure services, applications services, business process services and consulting services. The infrastructure services segment forms multi-year contracts through which it assumes operational responsibility for various aspects of customers' businesses. Perot Systems can take charge of a company's data center management, web hosting and Internet access, desktop solutions, messaging services, network management, program management and security. The applications services segment includes services such as application development and maintenance, including the development and maintenance of custom and packaged application software for customers, and application systems migration and testing, which includes the migration of applications from legacy environments to current technologies, as well as performing quality assurance functions on custom applications. The division also provides other applications services such as application assessment and evaluation, hardware and architecture consulting, systems integration, and web-based services. The business process services segment includes services such as product engineering, claims processing, life insurance policy administration, call center management, payment and settlement management, security, and services to improve the collection of receivables. In addition, this group also provides engineering support and other technical and administrative services to the U.S. government. Consulting services include strategy, enterprise and technology consulting, research and software implementation. The firm's clients include government agencies, healthcare providers, the construction and manufacturing industries and financial services companies. In May 2008, the firm acquired Original Solutions Limited, an IT services company.

FINANCIALS: **Sales and profits are in thousands of dollars—add 000 to get the full amount. 2008 Note: Financial information for 2008 was not available for all companies at press time.**

2008 Sales: $2,779,000	2008 Profits: $117,000	**U.S. Stock Ticker: PER**
2007 Sales: $2,612,000	2007 Profits: $115,000	**Int'l Ticker:** Int'l Exchange:
2006 Sales: $2,298,000	2006 Profits: $81,000	Employees: 23,100
2005 Sales: $1,998,286	2005 Profits: $111,120	Fiscal Year Ends: 12/31
2004 Sales: $1,773,452	2004 Profits: $94,347	Parent Company:

SALARIES/BENEFITS:

Pension Plan:	ESOP Stock Plan:	Profit Sharing:	Top Exec. Salary: $650,000	Bonus: $
Savings Plan:	Stock Purch. Plan:		Second Exec. Salary: $585,495	Bonus: $

OTHER THOUGHTS:

Apparent Women Officers or Directors:
Hot Spot for Advancement for Women/Minorities:

LOCATIONS: ("Y" = Yes)

West:	Southwest:	Midwest:	Southeast:	Northeast:	International:
Y	Y	Y	Y	Y	Y

Note: Financial information, benefits and other data can change quickly and may vary from those stated here.

PETROCHINA COMPANY

www.petrochina.com.cn

Industry Group Code: 211111 **Ranks within this company's industry group:** Sales: 8 Profits: 6

Techology:		Medical/Drugs:		Engineering:		Transportation:		Chemicals/Petrochemicals:		Specialty:	
Computers:		Manufacturer:		Design:		Aerospace:		Oil/Gas Products:	Y	Special Services:	
Software:		Contract Research:		Construction:		Automotive:		Chemicals:	Y	Consulting:	
Communications:		Medical Services:		Eng. Services:		Shipping:		Oil/Chem. Svcs.:	Y	Specialty Mgmt.:	
Electronics:		Labs:		Consulting:				Gases:		Products:	
Alternative Energy:		Bio. Services:						Other:		Other:	

TYPES OF BUSINESS:

Oil & Gas Exploration & Production
Chemicals, Lubricants & Petroleum Products
Oil Refining, Transportation & Marketing
Gas Stations

BRANDS/DIVISIONS/AFFILIATES:

China National Petroleum Company
PetroKazakhstan, Inc.
Daqing Oilfield Co., Ltd.
CNPC Exploration and Development Co., Ltd.
Daqing Yu Shu Lin Oilfield Co., Ltd.

CONTACTS:

Note: Officers with more than one job title may be intentionally listed here more than once.

Jiang Jiemin, Pres.
Zhou Mingchun, CFO
Lin Aiguo, Chief Engineer
Zhou Mingchun, Gen. Mgr.-Finance Dept.
Shen Diancheng, VP/General Mgr.-Refining & Chemical Co.
Huang Weihe, General Mgr.-Petroleum & Pipeline Co.
Zhao Zhengzhang, VP/General Mgr.-Exploration & Prod. Co.
Wang Daofu, Chief Geologist
Jiang Jiemen, Chmn.

Phone: 86-10-8488-6270 **Fax:** 86-10-8488-6260
Toll-Free:
Address: 16 Andelu, Dongcheng District, Beijing, 100011 China

GROWTH PLANS/SPECIAL FEATURES:

PetroChina Company, headquartered in Beijing, is one of the largest oil and gas producers and distributors in China. The company is involved in a broad range of crude oil and natural gas operations, including exploration, development, production and marketing of crude oil and natural gas; refining, transportation, storage and marketing of crude oil and oil products; production and marketing of primary petrochemical products, derivative chemicals and other chemicals; transportation of natural gas, crude oil and refined oil; and the marketing of natural gas. The company markets refined petroleum products, including transportation of natural gas, crude oil and refined oil, and marketing of natural gas, through 430 regional wholesale distribution outlets and thousands of service stations nationwide. The company also produces and sells chemical products, including polyethylene, synthetic fiber, synthetic rubber and polypropylene. PetroChina has oil exploration units in the Erdos, Tarim, Sichuan and Song-Liao Basins. The company's subsidiaries involved in the exploration, production and sale of natural gas and crude oil include Daqing Oilfield Co., Ltd., CNPC Exploration and Development Co., Ltd., Daqing Yu Shu Lin Oilfield Co., Ltd., and PetroKazakhstan, Inc. As of January 2008, PetroChina had accumulated proven oil reserves of approximately 20,529 MMboe (million barrels of oil equivalent). The company is 86%-owned by China National Petroleum Company (CNPC). Recently, the company acquired a 67% interest in PetroKazakhstan from CNPC for approximately $2.74 billion. In March 2007, the company launched the Beijing Oil and Gas Pipeline Network Dispatching Center, which will assist in the centralized dispatching and controlling operation and integration of oil and gas transmission lines.

FINANCIALS:

Sales and profits are in thousands of dollars—add 000 to get the full amount. 2008 Note: Financial information for 2008 was not available for all companies at press time.

2008 Sales: $156,490,000	2008 Profits: $18,503,200	**U.S. Stock Ticker: PTR**
2007 Sales: $122,188,000	2007 Profits: $22,670,600	**Int'l Ticker: 0857** Int'l Exchange: Hong Kong-HKEX
2006 Sales: $89,221,840	2006 Profits: $18,417,270	Employees: 422,554
2005 Sales: $68,476,396	2005 Profits: $17,095,260	Fiscal Year Ends: 12/31
2004 Sales: $46,956,000	2004 Profits: $13,065,000	Parent Company:

SALARIES/BENEFITS:

Pension Plan:	ESOP Stock Plan:	Profit Sharing:	Top Exec. Salary: $	Bonus: $
Savings Plan:	Stock Purch. Plan:		Second Exec. Salary: $	Bonus: $

OTHER THOUGHTS:

Apparent Women Officers or Directors:
Hot Spot for Advancement for Women/Minorities:

LOCATIONS: ("Y" = Yes)

West:	Southwest:	Midwest:	Southeast:	Northeast:	International:
					Y

PETROLEO BRASILEIRO SA (PETROBRAS)

www.petrobras.com.br

Industry Group Code: 211111 **Ranks within this company's industry group:** Sales: 10 Profits: 5

Techology:		Medical/Drugs:		Engineering:		Transportation:		Chemicals/Petrochemicals:		Specialty:	
Computers:		Manufacturer:		Design:		Aerospace:		Oil/Gas Products:	Y	Special Services:	
Software:		Contract Research:		Construction:		Automotive:		Chemicals:	Y	Consulting:	
Communications:		Medical Services:		Eng. Services:		Shipping:		Oil/Chem. Svcs.:	Y	Specialty Mgmt.:	
Electronics:		Labs:		Consulting:				Gases:	Y	Products:	
Alternative Energy:	Y	Bio. Services:						Other:		Other:	

TYPES OF BUSINESS:

Oil & Gas Exploration & Production
Oil Refineries
Service Stations
Transportation & Pipelines
Energy Trading

BRANDS/DIVISIONS/AFFILIATES:

Petrobras
Petrobras Distribudora SA
Petrobras International Finance Company
Petrobras Transporte SA
Petrobras Energia Participaciones SA
Petrobras Gas SA

CONTACTS: *Note: Officers with more than one job title may be intentionally listed here more than once.*

Jose S. G. de Azevedo, CEO
Jose S. G. de Azevedo, Pres.
Almir G. Barbassa, CFO
Diego Hernandes, Dir.-Human Resources
Nilton Antonio de Almeida Maia, Dir.-Legal
Celso Fernando Lucchesi, Dir.-Bus. Strategy & Performance
Wilson Santarosa, Dir.-Institutional Comm.
Almir G. Barbassa, Officer-Investor Rel.
Daniel Lima de Oliveira, Dir.-Corp. Finance
Guilherme de O. Estrella, Dir.-Exploration & Prod.
Paulo R. Costa, Dir.-Downstream
Maria das G.S. Foster, Dir.-Gas & Energy
Renato de S. Duque, Dir.-Svcs.
Dilma V. Rousseff, Chmn.
Jorge L. Zelada, Dir.-Int'l

Phone: 55-21-3224-4477 **Fax:**
Toll-Free:
Address: 65 Ave. Republica do Chile, Rio de Janeiro, 20031-912 Brazil

GROWTH PLANS/SPECIAL FEATURES:

Petroleo Brasileiro SA, known as Petrobras, is owned primarily by the Brazilian government and is Brazil's largest energy company. It refines, produces and distributes oil and oil-based products both nationally and internationally. The firm divides company activities into a number of business sectors, including exploration and production; downstream; gas and energy; and international. Petrobras is one of the largest companies in the global downstream sector, which includes refining, transportation and marketing. The firm's downstream business includes 15 oil refineries and more than 18,000 miles of pipeline. Petrobras supplies almost the entire demand for petroleum byproducts in Brazil, which are distributed through more than 8,000 service stations by subsidiary Petrobras Distribudora. The exploration and production unit of Petrobras researches, identifies, develops, produces and incorporates oil and natural gas reserves in Brazil. The gas and energy segment markets domestic and imported natural gas and implements project with the private sector to guarantee fuel throughout Brazil. This division also develops and invests in alternative energy sources, such as wind, solar and biofuel energy. Internationally, Petrobras operates in 26 countries outside of Brazil, maintaining international operations including exploration and petroleum procurement. Subsidiary Petrobras Transporte S.A. is responsible for the transportation and storage of the firm's oil and gas. The firm sells fuels and lubricants for the auto, aviation, marine, railroad, and other industries. In 2008, Petrobas became the leading shareholder in the Nansei Sekiyu Kabushiki Kaisha Refinery and signed an equity partnership with Peroleo de Venezuela for a refinery in Brazil. Petrobras has a research staff of more than 1,800 people and a massive exploration budget. It will invest $174.5 billion from 2009 through 2013 in improvements and new fields, concentrating on finds in deep offshore waters, including the new Tupi field, which may contain as many as 8 billion barrels of oil.

FINANCIALS: **Sales and profits are in thousands of dollars—add 000 to get the full amount. 2008 Note: Financial information for 2008 was not available for all companies at press time.**

2008 Sales: $118,257,000	2008 Profits: $18,879,000	**U.S. Stock Ticker: PBR**
2007 Sales: $87,735,000	2007 Profits: $13,138,000	**Int'l Ticker:** Int'l Exchange:
2006 Sales: $93,893,000	2006 Profits: $12,826,000	Employees: 62,266
2005 Sales: $74,065,000	2005 Profits: $10,344,000	Fiscal Year Ends: 12/31
2004 Sales: $51,954,000	2004 Profits: $6,726,400	Parent Company:

SALARIES/BENEFITS:

Pension Plan:	ESOP Stock Plan:	Profit Sharing:	Top Exec. Salary: $	Bonus: $
Savings Plan:	Stock Purch. Plan:		Second Exec. Salary: $	Bonus: $

OTHER THOUGHTS:

Apparent Women Officers or Directors: 2
Hot Spot for Advancement for Women/Minorities:

LOCATIONS: ("Y" = Yes)

West:	Southwest:	Midwest:	Southeast:	Northeast:	International:
	Y			Y	Y

PETROLEOS MEXICANOS (PEMEX)

www.pemex.com

Industry Group Code: 211111 **Ranks within this company's industry group:** Sales: 13 Profits: 12

Techology:		Medical/Drugs:		Engineering:		Transportation:		Chemicals/Petrochemicals:		Specialty:	
Computers:		Manufacturer:		Design:		Aerospace:		Oil/Gas Products:	Y	Special Services:	
Software:		Contract Research:		Construction:		Automotive:		Chemicals:	Y	Consulting:	
Communications:		Medical Services:		Eng. Services:		Shipping:		Oil/Chem. Svcs.:	Y	Specialty Mgmt.:	
Electronics:		Labs:		Consulting:				Gases:	Y	Products:	
Alternative Energy:		Bio. Services:						Other:	Y	Other:	

TYPES OF BUSINESS:

Oil & Gas Exploration & Production
Oil & Gas Transportation & Storage
Gas Stations
Refining
Petrochemicals

BRANDS/DIVISIONS/AFFILIATES:

Pemex Petroquimica
PMI Comercio Internacional
Pemex International

CONTACTS: *Note: Officers with more than one job title may be intentionally listed here more than once.*

Jesus Reyes Heroles G.G., CEO
Raul Alejandro Llavas Elizondo, COO
Esteban Levin Balcells, CFO
Ernesto Rios Montero, Chief Eng. Officer
Rosendo Alfredo Villarreal Davila, Chief Admin. Officer
Ernesto Rios Montero, Chief Dev. Officer
Roberto Ramirez Soberon, Dir.-Gas & Basic Petrochemicals
Carlos Arnoldo Morales Gil, Dir.-Exploration & Prod.
Jose Antonio Ceballos Soberanis, Dir.-Refining Unit
Rafael Beverido Lomelin, Dir.-Petrochemicals Unit
Fernando E. Barragan, Chmn.

Phone: 52-55-1944--2500 | **Fax:** 52-55-1944-8768
Toll-Free:
Address: Avenida Marina Nacional 329, Colonia Huasteca, 11311 Mexico

GROWTH PLANS/SPECIAL FEATURES:

Petroleos Mexicanos (Pemex) is Mexico's national petroleum company and an essential source of revenue for the country's government. The company is organized into four divisions: exploration and production; refining; gas and basic petrochemicals; and international services. The exploration and production segment has operations throughout Mexico and produces roughly 3.1 million barrels of crude oil daily. The refinery segment owns and manages the firm's six refineries and petrochemical plants. This segment also operates the Petroleos Mexicanos gas stations, with thousands of franchised locations. Pemex Petroquimica, Pemex's chemical division, operates eight important petrochemical complexes. In an effort to increase the value of its chemicals segment, Pemex is investing in new processes to produce polyethylene, PVC and ammonia fertilizers. The company's PMI Comercio Internacional subsidiary (Pemex International) provides administrative and commercial services for the international sale of oil and for cooperation with foreign companies. The U.S. purchases approximately 80% of the total of the company's crude oil exports, about 1.9 million barrels of oil per day. In March 2008, Pemex announced plans to drill 300 new natural gas wells in the Burgos Basin that comprise a production level of 1.5 billion cubic feet of natural gas. In March 2009, the company announced plans to drill an additional 500 oil wells.

FINANCIALS: **Sales and profits are in thousands of dollars—add 000 to get the full amount. 2008 Note: Financial information for 2008 was not available for all companies at press time.**

2008 Sales: $98,200,000	2008 Profits: $-8,100,000	**U.S. Stock Ticker: Government-Owned**
2007 Sales: $104,548,000	2007 Profits: $-1,685,000	**Int'l Ticker:** Int'l Exchange:
2006 Sales: $105,115,540	2006 Profits: $4,201,160	Employees: 141,146
2005 Sales: $90,852,170	2005 Profits: $-7,369,020	Fiscal Year Ends: 12/31
2004 Sales: $70,110,400	2004 Profits: $-2,277,800	Parent Company:

SALARIES/BENEFITS:

Pension Plan:	ESOP Stock Plan:	Profit Sharing:	Top Exec. Salary: $	Bonus: $
Savings Plan:	Stock Purch. Plan:		Second Exec. Salary: $	Bonus: $

OTHER THOUGHTS:

Apparent Women Officers or Directors: 1
Hot Spot for Advancement for Women/Minorities:

LOCATIONS: ("Y" = Yes)

West:	Southwest:	Midwest:	Southeast:	Northeast:	International:
					Y

PFIZER INC

www.pfizer.com

Industry Group Code: 325412 **Ranks within this company's industry group:** Sales: 2 Profits: 4

Techology:		Medical/Drugs:		Engineering:		Transportation:		Chemicals/Petrochemicals:		Specialty:	
Computers:		Manufacturer:	Y	Design:		Aerospace:		Oil/Gas Products:		Special Services:	
Software:		Contract Research:		Construction:		Automotive:		Chemicals:		Consulting:	
Communications:		Medical Services:		Eng. Services:		Shipping:		Oil/Chem. Svcs.:		Specialty Mgmt.:	
Electronics:		Labs:		Consulting:				Gases:		Products:	
Alternative Energy:		Bio. Services:						Other:		Other:	

TYPES OF BUSINESS:

Pharmaceutical Drugs
Prescription Pharmaceuticals
Veterinary Pharmaceuticals

BRANDS/DIVISIONS/AFFILIATES:

Norvasc
Viagra
Zoloft
Revolution/Stronghold
Sutent
Lipitor
Chantix
Rimadyl

CONTACTS: *Note: Officers with more than one job title may be intentionally listed here more than once.*

Jeffrey B. Kindler, CEO
Frank D'Amelio, CFO
Mary S. McLeod, Sr. VP-Worldwide Human Resources
Martin Mackay, Pres., Pfizer Global R&D
Natale Ricciardi, Pres./Team Leader-Pfizer Global Mfg.
Amy Schulman, General Counsel/Corp. Sec./Sr. VP
William Ringo, Sr. VP-Strategy & Bus. Dev.
Sally Susman, Chief Comm. Officer/Sr. VP
Charles E. Triano, Sr. VP-Investor Rel.
Joe Feckzo, Chief Medical Officer
Corey Goodman, Pres., Biotherapeutics & Bioinnovation Center
Ian Read, Sr. VP/Pres., Worldwide Pharmaceutical Oper.
Jeffrey B. Kindler, Chmn.

Phone: 212-573-2323	**Fax:**
Toll-Free:	
Address: 235 E. 42nd St., New York, NY 10017 US	

GROWTH PLANS/SPECIAL FEATURES:

Pfizer, Inc. is a research-based, global pharmaceutical company. It discovers, develops, manufactures and markets prescription medicines for humans and animals. The company operates in two segments: pharmaceutical and animal health. The pharmaceutical business is one of the largest in the world, with medicines across 11 therapeutic areas: cardiovascular and metabolic diseases; central nervous system disorders; arthritis and pain; infectious and respiratory diseases; urology; oncology; ophthalmology; and endocrine disorders. Major pharmaceutical products include Lipitor, for the treatment of LDL-cholesterol levels in the blood; Norvasc, for treating hypertension; Zoloft, for the treatment of major depressive disorder and other conditions; and Viagra, a treatment for erectile dysfunction. Pfizer's latest drugs include Chantix, an anti-smoking agent; and Sutent, which kills cancer-infected cells and prevents blood flow from reaching existing tumors. The animal health segment develops and sells products for the prevention and treatment of diseases in livestock/companion animals. Among the products it markets are parasiticides, anti-inflammatories, antibiotics, vaccines, and anti-obesity agents. Brands include Revolution/Stronghold, a parasiticide for dogs and cats; Rimadyl, an arthritis pain medication; and Draxxin, an antibiotic used to treat infections in cattle and swine. In March 2008, the firm agreed to acquire Serenex, Inc. In June 2008, the company acquired Encysive Pharmaceuticals, Inc. In September 2008, Pfizer partnered with Medivation, Inc., to market Dimebon, potential inhibitor of Alzheimer's and Huntington's disease; and bought several European animal product franchises from Schering-Plough Corporation. In January 2009, the company agreed to acquire pharmaceuticals company Wyeth. In March 2009, Pfizer signed licensing agreements with India-based pharmaceutical company Aurobindo Pharma Ltd., expanding its generic medicines market; the firm also partnered with Bausch & Lomb to promote opthamalic pharmaceuticals. Also in March 2009, Pfizer agreed to sell its German insulin plant and assets to MannKind Corporation, and opened a new development plant in Dalian, Liaoning, China.

FINANCIALS: **Sales and profits are in thousands of dollars—add 000 to get the full amount. 2008 Note: Financial information for 2008 was not available for all companies at press time.**

2008 Sales: $48,296,000	2008 Profits: $8,104,000	**U.S. Stock Ticker: PFE**
2007 Sales: $48,418,000	2007 Profits: $8,144,000	**Int'l Ticker:** Int'l Exchange:
2006 Sales: $48,371,000	2006 Profits: $19,337,000	Employees: 81,800
2005 Sales: $47,405,000	2005 Profits: $8,085,000	Fiscal Year Ends: 12/31
2004 Sales: $48,988,000	2004 Profits: $11,361,000	Parent Company:

SALARIES/BENEFITS:

Pension Plan: Y	ESOP Stock Plan:	Profit Sharing:	Top Exec. Salary: $1,462,500	Bonus: $3,100,000
Savings Plan: Y	Stock Purch. Plan:		Second Exec. Salary: $1,056,875	Bonus: $951,200

OTHER THOUGHTS:

Apparent Women Officers or Directors: 4
Hot Spot for Advancement for Women/Minorities: Y

LOCATIONS: ("Y" = Yes)

West:	Southwest:	Midwest:	Southeast:	Northeast:	International:
Y	Y	Y	Y	Y	Y

PHARMACEUTICAL PRODUCT DEVELOPMENT INC www.ppdi.com

Industry Group Code: 541710 **Ranks within this company's industry group:** Sales: 2 Profits: 2

Techology:		Medical/Drugs:		Engineering:		Transportation:		Chemicals/Petrochemicals:		Specialty:	
Computers:		Manufacturer:		Design:		Aerospace:		Oil/Gas Products:		Special Services:	
Software:	Y	Contract Research:	Y	Construction:		Automotive:		Chemicals:		Consulting:	
Communications:		Medical Services:	Y	Eng. Services:		Shipping:		Oil/Chem. Svcs.:		Specialty Mgmt.:	
Electronics:		Labs:	Y	Consulting:				Gases:		Products:	
Alternative Energy:		Bio. Services:	Y					Other:		Other:	

TYPES OF BUSINESS:

Contract Research
Drug Discovery & Development Services
Clinical Data Consulting Services
Medical Marketing & Information Support Services
Drug Development Software
Medical Device Development

BRANDS/DIVISIONS/AFFILIATES:

PPD Discovery Sciences
PPD Development
CSS Informatics
PPD Medical Communications
PPD Virtual
InnoPharm Ltd

CONTACTS: *Note: Officers with more than one job title may be intentionally listed here more than once.*

Fred N. Eshelman, CEO
William J. Sharbaugh, COO
Daniel Darazsdi, CFO
Christine A. Dingivan, Chief Medical Officer/Exec. VP
B. Judd Hartman, General Counsel/Corp. Sec.
William W. Richardson, Sr. VP-Global Bus. Dev.
Louise Caudle, Dir.-Corp. Comm.
Luke Heagle, Dir.-Investor Rel.
Sue Ann Pentecost, Mgr.-Corp. Comm.
Michael O. Wilkinson, Exec. VP-Global Clinical Dev.
Ernest Mario, Chmn.

Phone: 910-251-0081 **Fax:** 910-762-5820
Toll-Free:
Address: 929 N. Front St., Wilmington, NC 28401-3331 US

GROWTH PLANS/SPECIAL FEATURES:

Pharmaceutical Product Development, Inc. (PPD) provides drug discovery and development services to pharmaceutical and biotechnology companies as well as academic and government organizations. PPD's services are primarily divided into two company segments: Discovery Sciences and Development. Through the combined services of these segments, PPD helps pharmaceutical companies through all stages of clinical testing. The stages of testing can be specifically divided into preclinical, phase I, phase II-IIIb and post-approval. In the preclinical stages of drug testing, PPD provides information concerning the pharmaceutical composition of a new drug, its safety, its formulaic design and how it will be administered to children and adults. During phase I of testing, PPD conducts healthy volunteer clinics, provides data management services and guides companies/laboratories through regulatory affairs. In phase II and III tests, PPD oversees the later stages of product development and government approval, providing project management and clinical monitoring. In the post-approval stage of a drug's development, PPD provides technology and marketing services aimed to maximize the new drug's lifecycle. PPD has experience conducting research and drug development in the areas of antiviral studies, cardiovascular diseases, critical care studies, endocrine/metabolic studies, vaccine development, hematology/oncology studies, immunology studies and ophthalmology studies. The firm conducts regional, national and global studies and research projects through offices in 33 countries worldwide. In June 2008, the company opened an office in Istanbul. In October of the same year, PPD acquired Russia-based independent contract research organization, InnoPharm. In February 2009, the firm agreed to acquire AbC.R.O., Inc., a contract research organization that serves Central and Eastern Europe.

Employees are offered health insurance; life insurance; wellness programs; and a 401(k) savings plan.

FINANCIALS: **Sales and profits are in thousands of dollars—add 000 to get the full amount. 2008 Note: Financial information for 2008 was not available for all companies at press time.**

2008 Sales: $1,569,901	2008 Profits: $187,519	**U.S. Stock Ticker: PPDI**
2007 Sales: $1,414,465	2007 Profits: $163,401	**Int'l Ticker:** Int'l Exchange:
2006 Sales: $1,247,682	2006 Profits: $156,652	Employees: 10,500
2005 Sales: $1,037,090	2005 Profits: $119,897	Fiscal Year Ends: 12/31
2004 Sales: $841,256	2004 Profits: $91,684	Parent Company:

SALARIES/BENEFITS:

Pension Plan:	ESOP Stock Plan:	Profit Sharing:	Top Exec. Salary: $709,167	Bonus: $500,000
Savings Plan: Y	Stock Purch. Plan:		Second Exec. Salary: $327,688	Bonus: $172,500

OTHER THOUGHTS:

Apparent Women Officers or Directors: 4
Hot Spot for Advancement for Women/Minorities: Y

LOCATIONS: ("Y" = Yes)

West:	Southwest:	Midwest:	Southeast:	Northeast:	International:
Y	Y	Y	Y	Y	Y

PININFARINA SPA

www.pininfarina.it

Industry Group Code: 336111 **Ranks within this company's industry group:** Sales: 24 Profits: 21

Techology:		Medical/Drugs:		Engineering:		Transportation:		Chemicals/Petrochemicals:		Specialty:	
Computers:		Manufacturer:		Design:	Y	Aerospace:	Y	Oil/Gas Products:		Special Services:	
Software:		Contract Research:		Construction:		Automotive:	Y	Chemicals:		Consulting:	
Communications:		Medical Services:		Eng. Services:	Y	Shipping:		Oil/Chem. Svcs.:		Specialty Mgmt.:	
Electronics:		Labs:		Consulting:	Y			Gases:		Products:	
Alternative Energy:		Bio. Services:						Other:		Other:	

TYPES OF BUSINESS:

Automotive Design & Engineering Services
Aeronautics Design
Mass Transit Design
Consumer Products Design
Retractable Roof Systems
Engineering Services
Prototype Testing
Automobile Design

BRANDS/DIVISIONS/AFFILIATES:

Pininfarina Studi e Riceerche
Matra Automobile Engineering
Pininfarina Deutschland
Pininfarina Extra
Matra Development
Pininfarina Sverige
D3 S.a.S.
Ceram S.a.S.

CONTACTS: *Note: Officers with more than one job title may be intentionally listed here more than once.*

Silvio Angori, COO
Gianfranco Albertini, CFO
Paolo Pininfarina, Chmn.

Phone: 39-011-9438111	**Fax:** 39-011-5175011
Toll-Free:	
Address: Strada Nazionale 30, Turin, 10020 Italy	

GROWTH PLANS/SPECIAL FEATURES:

Pininfarina SpA specializes in providing automotive and general manufacturers with services through all stages of product development, from planning, designing and development to engineering, manufacturing and end product consultation. The firm's subsidiaries include Pininfarina Sverige; Matra Automobile Engineering; D3 S.a.S.; Ceram S.a.S.; Pininfarina Deutschland; and Pininfarina Extra. The firm has collaborated with Fiat, Mitsubishi, Peugot, General Motors, Ferrari, Maserati, Alfa, Bentley and Rolls Royce. In the aeronautics and aeroacoustics industry, the company designs the interior and exterior forms of its vehicles using its own automotive wind tunnels. It does design work for trains, planes and boats, as well as non-transportation products such as shoes, cellular phones, coffee machines, ski boots and watches. Through the recent initiative leading to the production of the Alfa Romeo Brera and Volvo C70 the company has established new subsidiary companies. Pininfarina established itself in Sweden through Pininfarina Sverige, a joint venture with the Volvo Car Corporation, and in France through the companies Matra Automobile Engineering Maroc and Matra Development. Currently the firm is continuing the development of five new models: the Alfa Romeo Brera, Volvo C70, Alfa Romeo Spider, Mitsubishi Colt CZC and Ford Focus CC. In 2007, the company signed an agreement to supply automotive design services to Sonalika Group, an Indian industrial group. In December 2007, the company began collaborating with the Bollere Group to design and manufacture an electric car. In April 2008, Pininfarina announced plans to establish a research, design and engineering center in Pune, India with the Tata Group.

FINANCIALS: **Sales and profits are in thousands of dollars—add 000 to get the full amount. 2008 Note: Financial information for 2008 was not available for all companies at press time.**

2008 Sales: $711,720	2008 Profits: $-275,520	**U.S. Stock Ticker:**
2007 Sales: $962,300	2007 Profits: $-154,580	**Int'l Ticker: PINF** Int'l Exchange: Milan-BI
2006 Sales: $713,570	2006 Profits: $-29,670	Employees: 2,768
2005 Sales: $629,085	2005 Profits: $-11,047	Fiscal Year Ends: 12/31
2004 Sales: $692,300	2004 Profits: $4,400	Parent Company:

SALARIES/BENEFITS:

Pension Plan:	ESOP Stock Plan:	Profit Sharing:	Top Exec. Salary: $	Bonus: $
Savings Plan:	Stock Purch. Plan:		Second Exec. Salary: $	Bonus: $

OTHER THOUGHTS:

Apparent Women Officers or Directors:
Hot Spot for Advancement for Women/Minorities:

LOCATIONS: ("Y" = Yes)

West:	Southwest:	Midwest:	Southeast:	Northeast:	International:
					Y

PIONEER CORPORATION

www.pioneer.co.jp

Industry Group Code: 334310 **Ranks within this company's industry group:** Sales: 7 Profits: 6

Techology:		Medical/Drugs:		Engineering:		Transportation:		Chemicals/Petrochemicals:		Specialty:	
Computers:	Y	Manufacturer:		Design:		Aerospace:		Oil/Gas Products:		Special Services:	
Software:		Contract Research:		Construction:		Automotive:		Chemicals:		Consulting:	
Communications:		Medical Services:		Eng. Services:		Shipping:		Oil/Chem. Svcs.:		Specialty Mgmt.:	
Electronics:	Y	Labs:		Consulting:				Gases:		Products:	
Alternative Energy:		Bio. Services:						Other:		Other:	

TYPES OF BUSINESS:

Consumer Electronics
Audio/Video Equipment
CD/DVD Players
Automotive Electronics
Telecommunications Equipment
Research & Development
Software Development

BRANDS/DIVISIONS/AFFILIATES:

Pioneer Electronics (USA), Inc.
Discovision Associates
Pioneer Display Products Corp.
Pioneer Home Entertainment Co.
Tohoku Pioneer Corporation
Pioneer Europe
Pioneer China Holding Co., Ltd.
Pioneer India Electronics Private Ltd.

CONTACTS: *Note: Officers with more than one job title may be intentionally listed here more than once.*

Susumu Kotani, CEO
Susumu Kotani, Pres.
Hideki Okayasu, CFO
Masanori Koshoubu, General Mgr.-R&D
Hajime Ishizuka, Exec. VP/Dir.-Corp. Mgmt. & Corp. Planning
Hideki Okayasu, Gen. Mgr.-Finance & Acct.
Akira Haeno, General Mgr.-Mobile Entertainment Business Group
Satoshi Matsumoto, Managing Dir.-Quality Control
Masanori Koshoubu, General Mgr.-Network Media Platform
Akira Haeno, Gen. Mgr.-Procurement

Phone: 81-3-3494-1111 **Fax:** 81-3-3495-4428
Toll-Free:
Address: 4-1, Meguro 1-chome, Meguro-ku, Tokyo, 153-8654 Japan

GROWTH PLANS/SPECIAL FEATURES:

Pioneer Corporation is one of the leading manufacturers of consumer electronics in the world, operating mainly in four segments: home electronics, car electronics, patent licensing and others. Headquartered in Japan and originally a speaker manufacturer, Pioneer now develops, designs, and manufactures (in its 30-plus facilities worldwide) amplifiers, hi-fi stereos, car electronics, cable-TV systems, audio and video equipment, CD players, and factory automation systems and parts. Pioneer was the first company to release global positioning systems (GPS) to the consumer market. The firm also makes DVD, CD-R/RW and DVD-R/RW drives, plasma-screen TVs and OLED displays. The company's primary markets are Japan, North America, Europe and Asia. Additionally, the company sells its products to customers in consumer and business markets through sales offices in Japan and through sales subsidiaries of Pioneer and independent distributors outside of Japan. In addition, on an OEM basis, Pioneer markets certain products, such as car electronics products, recordable DVD drives, plasma displays and OLED displays to other companies. Subsidiaries include Pioneer Electronics (USA), Inc.; Discovision Associates; Pioneer Display Products Corp; Pioneer Home Entertainment Co.; Tohoku Pioneer Corporation; Pioneer Europe; and Pioneer China Holding Co., Ltd. In November 2008, the company announced plans to enter the Indian market by creating an India based subsidiary, Pioneer India Electronics Private Ltd.

FINANCIALS: **Sales and profits are in thousands of dollars—add 000 to get the full amount. 2008 Note: Financial information for 2008 was not available for all companies at press time.**

2008 Sales: $7,753,300	2008 Profits: $-179,900	**U.S. Stock Ticker:**
2007 Sales: $7,978,100	2007 Profits: $-67,600	**Int'l Ticker: 6773** Int'l Exchange: Tokyo-TSE
2006 Sales: $7,549,600	2006 Profits: $-849,900	Employees: 42,775
2005 Sales: $7,110,400	2005 Profits: $-87,900	Fiscal Year Ends: 3/31
2004 Sales: $6,612,100	2004 Profits: $234,300	Parent Company:

SALARIES/BENEFITS:

Pension Plan:	ESOP Stock Plan:	Profit Sharing:	Top Exec. Salary: $	Bonus: $
Savings Plan:	Stock Purch. Plan:		Second Exec. Salary: $	Bonus: $

OTHER THOUGHTS:

Apparent Women Officers or Directors:
Hot Spot for Advancement for Women/Minorities:

LOCATIONS: ("Y" = Yes)

West:	Southwest:	Midwest:	Southeast:	Northeast:	International:
Y					Y

PITNEY BOWES INC

www.pb.com

Industry Group Code: 333313 **Ranks within this company's industry group:** Sales: 3 Profits: 2

Techology:		Medical/Drugs:		Engineering:		Transportation:		Chemicals/Petrochemicals:		Specialty:	
Computers:	Y	Manufacturer:		Design:		Aerospace:		Oil/Gas Products:		Special Services:	Y
Software:	Y	Contract Research:		Construction:		Automotive:		Chemicals:		Consulting:	
Communications:		Medical Services:		Eng. Services:		Shipping:		Oil/Chem. Svcs.:		Specialty Mgmt.:	
Electronics:		Labs:		Consulting:				Gases:		Products:	
Alternative Energy:		Bio. Services:						Other:		Other:	

TYPES OF BUSINESS:

Business Machines-Mail and Messaging
Business Equipment
Outsourced Services
Mail Logistics Services

BRANDS/DIVISIONS/AFFILIATES:

Pitney Bowes Legal Services
Pitney Bowes Marketing Services
Pitney Bowes Management Services
Pitney Bowes Mail Services
Pitney Bowes Business Insight
Pitney Bowes Software Inc
MapInfo Corp
Group 1 Software, Inc.

CONTACTS: *Note: Officers with more than one job title may be intentionally listed here more than once.*

Murray D. Martin, CEO
Murray D. Martin, Pres.
Michael Monahan, CFO/Exec. VP
Mark Cattini, Pres., Pitney Bowes Mktg. Svcs.
Johnna G. Torsone, Chief Human Resources Officer/Exec. VP
Gregory E. Buoncontri, CIO/Exec. VP
Vicki A. O'Meara, Chief Legal & Compliance Officer/Exec. VP
David C. Dobson, Chief Strategy & Innovation Officer
Juanita T. James, Chief Mktg. & Comm. Officer/VP
Charles F. McBride, VP-Investor Rel.
Steven J. Green, Chief Acct. Officer/VP-Finance
Leslie Abi-Karam, Exec. VP/Pres., Mailing Solutions Mgmt.
Elise R. DeBois, Exec. VP/Pres., Global Financial Svcs.
Amy C. Corn, VP-Chief Governance Officer/Sec.
Helen Shan, VP/Treas.
Murray D. Martin, Chmn.
Patrick Keddy, Exec. VP/Pres., Mailstream Int'l
Neil Metviner, Exec. VP/Pres., Global Mainstream Europe

Phone: 203-356-5000	**Fax:**
Toll-Free: 800-672-6937	
Address: 1 Elmcroft Rd., Stamford, CT 06926-0700 US	

GROWTH PLANS/SPECIAL FEATURES:

Pitney Bowes, Inc. is a global provider of informed mail and messaging management for corporations and businesses of all sizes. The company conducts business in seven segments. The U.S. Mailing segment includes the U.S. revenue and related expenses from the firm's sale, rental and financing of mail finishing; mail creation; shipping equipment and software; supplies; support; and other professional services. The International Mailing division consists of non-U.S. revenue, expenses and mail-related services. Production Mail focuses on the worldwide sale, financing, support and services of the company's high-speed, production mail systems and sorting equipment. The Software unit consists of the sale and services of non-equipment-based mailing, customer communication and location intelligence software. The Management Services segment involves secure mail services; reprographic, document management services; and litigation support and eDiscovery services. The Mail Services division includes presort mail and cross-border mail services. The Marketing Services division consists of direct marketing services for targeted customers; web-tools for the customization of promotional mail and marketing collateral; and other marketing consulting services. In January 2009, subsidiary, Pitney Bowes Software Inc. created a new business unit composed of Group 1 software and Pitney Bowes Mapinfo called Pitney Bowes Business Insight.

Employees are offered medical, dental and life insurance; short-and long-term disability coverage; travel accident insurance; a stock purchase plan; a 401(k) plan; a college savings plan; and health and dependent care accounts.

FINANCIALS: Sales and profits are in thousands of dollars—add 000 to get the full amount. 2008 Note: Financial information for 2008 was not available for all companies at press time.

2008 Sales: $6,262,305	2008 Profits: $419,793	**U.S. Stock Ticker: PBI**
2007 Sales: $6,129,795	2007 Profits: $366,781	**Int'l Ticker:** Int'l Exchange:
2006 Sales: $5,730,018	2006 Profits: $105,347	Employees: 26,267
2005 Sales: $5,366,936	2005 Profits: $508,611	Fiscal Year Ends: 12/31
2004 Sales: $4,832,304	2004 Profits: $461,996	Parent Company:

SALARIES/BENEFITS:

Pension Plan:	ESOP Stock Plan:	Profit Sharing:	Top Exec. Salary: $931,250	Bonus: $2,214,950
Savings Plan: Y	Stock Purch. Plan: Y		Second Exec. Salary: $837,500	Bonus: $1,336,000

OTHER THOUGHTS:

Apparent Women Officers or Directors: 10
Hot Spot for Advancement for Women/Minorities: Y

LOCATIONS: ("Y" = Yes)

West:	Southwest:	Midwest:	Southeast:	Northeast:	International:
Y	Y	Y	Y	Y	Y

PLANTRONICS INC

www.plantronics.com

Industry Group Code: 334200 **Ranks within this company's industry group:** Sales: 4 Profits: 3

Techology:		Medical/Drugs:		Engineering:		Transportation:		Chemicals/Petrochemicals:		Specialty:	
Computers:		Manufacturer:		Design:		Aerospace:		Oil/Gas Products:		Special Services:	
Software:		Contract Research:		Construction:		Automotive:		Chemicals:		Consulting:	
Communications:	Y	Medical Services:		Eng. Services:		Shipping:		Oil/Chem. Svcs.:		Specialty Mgmt.:	
Electronics:		Labs:		Consulting:				Gases:		Products:	
Alternative Energy:		Bio. Services:						Other:		Other:	

TYPES OF BUSINESS:

Communications Headsets
Communications Accessories
Specialty Telephone Products
Wireless Headsets

BRANDS/DIVISIONS/AFFILIATES:

Clarity
Volume Logic
Altec Lansing

CONTACTS: *Note: Officers with more than one job title may be intentionally listed here more than once.*

Ken Kannappan, CEO
Ken Kannappan, Pres.
Barbara Scherer, CFO
Donald Houston, Sr. VP-Sales
Owen Brown, CTO/VP
Mike Perkins, VP-Prod. Dev. & Tech.
Barbara Scherer, Sr. VP-Admin.
Larry Wuerz, Sr. VP-Worldwide Oper.
Barry Margerum, Chief Strategy Officer
Dan Race, Dir.-Corp. Comm.
Greg Klaben, VP-Investor Rel.
Barbara Scherer, Sr. VP-Finance
Clay Hausmann, VP-Corp. Mktg.
Renee Niemi, VP/General Mgr.-Mobile & Entertainment
Joyce Shimizu, VP/General Mgr.-Home & Home Office
Carsten Trads, Pres., Clarity Div.
Marvin Tseu, Chmn.
Philip Vanhoutte, Managing Dir.-EMEA

Phone: 831-426-5858 | **Fax:** 831-426-6098
Toll-Free: 800-544-4660
Address: 345 Encinal St., Santa Cruz, CA 95060 US

GROWTH PLANS/SPECIAL FEATURES:

Plantronics, Inc. is a worldwide designer, manufacturer and marketer of lightweight communications headsets, telephone headset systems and accessories for the business and consumer markets under the Plantronics brand. The company is organized in two segments: The audio entertainment group (AEG) and the audio communications group (ACG). The AEG segment, the firm's core business, designs, manufactures, markets and sells headsets for business and consumer applications and other specialty products. The segment also designs, manufactures, sells and markets audio solutions and related technologies. Plantronics manufactures and markets computer and home entertainment sound systems; docking audio products; and a line of headsets and headphones for personal digital media under Altec Landing brand. In addition, the company manufactures and markets under the Clarity brand specialty telephone products, such as telephones for the hearing impaired and other related products for people with special communicated needs. The firm also provides audio enhancement solutions to consumers, audio professionals and businesses under the Volume Logic brand. The company ships a broad range of communications products to over 80 countries through a worldwide network of distributors, retailers, wireless carriers, original equipment manufacturers (OEMs) and telephony service providers. The firm has well-developed distribution channels in North America, Europe, Australia and New Zeeland. In January 2009, the company announced plans to reduce its worldwide workforce by 18%.

Employees are offered medical, dental and vision insurance; life insurance; business travel and accident insurance; short- and long-term disability coverage; access to company sponsored cafeterias; onsite credit union; onsite massage and dry cleaning services; discounts for exercise facility memberships; a 401(k) plan; profit sharing; a stock purchase plan; and educational assistance.

FINANCIALS: **Sales and profits are in thousands of dollars—add 000 to get the full amount. 2008 Note: Financial information for 2008 was not available for all companies at press time.**

2008 Sales: $856,286	2008 Profits: $68,395	**U.S. Stock Ticker: PLT**
2007 Sales: $800,154	2007 Profits: $50,143	**Int'l Ticker:** Int'l Exchange:
2006 Sales: $750,394	2006 Profits: $81,150	Employees: 5,000
2005 Sales: $559,995	2005 Profits: $97,520	Fiscal Year Ends: 3/31
2004 Sales: $417,000	2004 Profits: $62,300	Parent Company:

SALARIES/BENEFITS:

Pension Plan:	ESOP Stock Plan:	Profit Sharing: Y	Top Exec. Salary: $613,000	Bonus: $723,318
Savings Plan: Y	Stock Purch. Plan: Y		Second Exec. Salary: $368,958	Bonus: $311,099

OTHER THOUGHTS:

Apparent Women Officers or Directors: 5
Hot Spot for Advancement for Women/Minorities: Y

LOCATIONS: ("Y" = Yes)

West:	Southwest:	Midwest:	Southeast:	Northeast:	International:
Y					Y

Note: Financial information, benefits and other data can change quickly and may vary from those stated here.

PLEXUS CORP

www.plexus.com

Industry Group Code: 334419 **Ranks within this company's industry group:** Sales: 9 Profits: 5

Techology:		Medical/Drugs:		Engineering:		Transportation:		Chemicals/Petrochemicals:		Specialty:	
Computers:		Manufacturer:		Design:		Aerospace:		Oil/Gas Products:		Special Services:	
Software:		Contract Research:		Construction:		Automotive:		Chemicals:		Consulting:	
Communications:		Medical Services:		Eng. Services:	Y	Shipping:		Oil/Chem. Svcs.:		Specialty Mgmt.:	
Electronics:	Y	Labs:		Consulting:				Gases:		Products:	
Alternative Energy:		Bio. Services:						Other:		Other:	

TYPES OF BUSINESS:

Contract Manufacturing-Diversified Electronics
Hardware & Software Design
Printed Circuit Board Design
Prototyping Services
Material Procurement & Management

BRANDS/DIVISIONS/AFFILIATES:

CONTACTS: *Note: Officers with more than one job title may be intentionally listed here more than once.*

Dean Foate, CEO
Dean Foate, Pres.
Ginger Jones, CFO/VP
Joe Mauthe, VP-Global Human Resources
Tom Czajkowski, CIO/VP
Steve Frisch, Sr. VP-Global Eng. Svcs.
Mike Buseman, Sr. VP-Global Mfg. Oper.
Angelo Ninivaggi, General Counsel/VP/Sec.
Bob Kronser, Chief Strategy Officer
George Setton, Chief Treasury Officer/Corp. Treas.
David A. Clark, Sr. VP-Global Customer Svcs.
Mike Verstegen, Sr. VP-Global Market Dev.
John L. Nussbaum, Chmn.
David A. Clark, VP-Supply Chain

Phone: 920-722-3451 **Fax:**
Toll-Free:
Address: 55 Jewelers Park Dr., Neenah, WI 54957-0156 US

GROWTH PLANS/SPECIAL FEATURES:

Plexus Corp. is a global provider of electronics manufacturing services. The company's customers may outsource all stages of the product realization process, including development and design, materials procurement and management, prototyping and new product introduction, testing, manufacturing configuration, logistics and repair. Additionally, the company provides its customers with fulfillment and logistics services including direct order fulfillment, build to order, configure to order, global logistics management and after-market service and repair. Plexus offers a complete menu of engineering services, including project management, feasibility studies, product conceptualization, specification development for product features and functions, circuit design (such as digital, microprocessor, power, analog, radio frequency, optical and micro-electronics), field programmable gate array design, printed circuit board layout, embedded software design, mechanical design (including thermal analysis, plastic components, sheet metal enclosures, and castings), development of test specifications and product validation testing. Other than certain test equipment and software used for internal operations, the firm does not design or manufacture its own proprietary products, although its product realization services have created complex, high-tech products for large original equipment manufacturers and start-ups. Plexus serves companies from industries including wireline/networking, 44% net sales; medical, 21%; industrial/commercial, 16%; defense/security/aerospace, 10%; and wireless infrastructure, 9%. The company's 10 largest customers accounted for roughly 60% of net sales. Within the top 10 customers, Juniper Networks, Inc. accounts for approximately 20% of sales. As of 2008, Plexus had 19 active facilities throughout 14 locations in Malaysia, Mexico, China, Scotland, and the U.S.

Plexus offers employees medical, dental and vision coverage; a 401(k) plan; complimentary onsite investment and financial planning services; tuition reimbursement; relocation assistance; bonus and success share programs; life insurance; long term disability; an employee assistance program; health and dependant care flexible spending accounts; a scholarship program for children of employees; and various employee discounts.

FINANCIALS: **Sales and profits are in thousands of dollars—add 000 to get the full amount. 2008 Note: Financial information for 2008 was not available for all companies at press time.**

2008 Sales: $1,841,622
2007 Sales: $1,546,264
2006 Sales: $1,460,557
2005 Sales: $1,228,882
2004 Sales: $1,040,858

2008 Profits: $84,144
2007 Profits: $65,718
2006 Profits: $100,025
2005 Profits: $-12,417
2004 Profits: $-31,580

U.S. Stock Ticker: PLXS
Int'l Ticker: Int'l Exchange:
Employees: 7,900
Fiscal Year Ends: 9/30
Parent Company:

SALARIES/BENEFITS:

Pension Plan: ESOP Stock Plan: Profit Sharing: Top Exec. Salary: $672,981 Bonus: $764,452
Savings Plan: Y Stock Purch. Plan: Second Exec. Salary: $302,057 Bonus: $169,418

OTHER THOUGHTS:

Apparent Women Officers or Directors: 1
Hot Spot for Advancement for Women/Minorities:

LOCATIONS: ("Y" = Yes)

West:	Southwest:	Midwest:	Southeast:	Northeast:	International:
Y		Y	Y	Y	Y

Note: Financial information, benefits and other data can change quickly and may vary from those stated here.

PORSCHE AUTOMOBIL HOLDING SE

www.porsche-se.com

Industry Group Code: 336111 **Ranks within this company's industry group:** Sales: 22 Profits: 2

Techology:		Medical/Drugs:		Engineering:		Transportation:		Chemicals/Petrochemicals:		Specialty:	
Computers:		Manufacturer:		Design:		Aerospace:		Oil/Gas Products:		Special Services:	Y
Software:		Contract Research:		Construction:		Automotive:	Y	Chemicals:		Consulting:	
Communications:		Medical Services:		Eng. Services:	Y	Shipping:		Oil/Chem. Svcs.:		Specialty Mgmt.:	
Electronics:		Labs:		Consulting:				Gases:		Products:	
Alternative Energy:		Bio. Services:						Other:		Other:	

TYPES OF BUSINESS:

Automobile Manufacturing
Sports Cars
Engineering Services
Financial Services
Consulting Services
Driving School
Racing
Apparel & Accessories

BRANDS/DIVISIONS/AFFILIATES:

Volkswagen AG
Dr. Ing. h.c. F. Porsche AG
Porsche Cars North America
Cayenne
911 Turbo
911 Carerra
Cayman S
Panamera

CONTACTS: *Note: Officers with more than one job title may be intentionally listed here more than once.*

Wendelin Wiedeking, CEO
Wendelin Wiedeking, Pres.
Holger P. Harter, Dir.-Finance & Controlling
Klaus Berning, Dir.-Sales & Mktg.
Harro Harmel, Dir.-Human Resources & Labor Rel.
Wolfgang Porsche, Chmn.
Detlev von Platen, Pres./CEO-Porsche Cars North America

Phone: 49-711-911-0 **Fax:** 49-711-911-5777
Toll-Free:
Address: Porscheplatz 1, Stuttgart, D-70435 Germany

GROWTH PLANS/SPECIAL FEATURES:

Porsche Automobil Holding SE is a holding company that controls 100% of Dr. Ing. h.c. F. Porsche AG (Porsche) and approximately 31% of Volkswagen AG. The company, through its Porsche subsidiary, is a leading global manufacturer of sports cars. The company's production has been streamlined to four model lines: the 911, the newly introduced Cayman, the Boxster and the Cayenne SUV. The 911 is available in a wide range of model variations: Carrera, Carrera 4, Carrera S, Carrera Cabriolet, Carrera S Cabriolet, Carrera 4 Cabriolet, Carrera 4S, Carrera 4S Cabriolet and Turbo. Most are priced between $73,500 and approximately $125,000. The Boxster, a mid-engined roadster, was introduced in the 1997 model year and revitalized the firm's sales, especially in North America. The vehicle ranges in price up to $60,000. Its models include the Boxster and Boxster S. The Cayman line offers the Cayman and Cayman S priced up to $60,000. Cayenne SUVs are available in three different models: Cayenne, Cayenne S and Cayenne Turbo, which range in price from to $95,000. The firm's U.S. division, Porsche Cars North America, had U.S. sales of 36,680 cars in 2007, accounting for almost 40% of the firm's global sales. The firm has a driving school, called Porsche Sport Driving School in the U.S. and Porsche Sportfahrschule in Europe, that offers one- and two-day driving programs at world-class tracks with professional instructors that have won top racing competitions. Porsche AG is controlled by descendants of its founding family. In recent news, the automaker announced plans for a Cayenne model with a hybrid engine, as well as plans for the Panamera, scheduled to enter the market in 2009. Also, Porsche has been pursuing increased stock ownership in Volkswagen. With the 2007 acquisition of a 31% stake in Volkswagen AG, the company underwent a restructuring resulting in Dr. Ing. h.c. F. Porsche AG becoming a subsidiary of newly formed holding company Porsche Automobil Holding SE. The company has recently launched an initiative to acquire a controlling stake in Volkswagen AG.

FINANCIALS: **Sales and profits are in thousands of dollars—add 000 to get the full amount. 2008 Note: Financial information for 2008 was not available for all companies at press time.**

2008 Sales: $9,935,620	2008 Profits: $8,371,000	**U.S. Stock Ticker: PSEPF**
2007 Sales: $9,804,510	2007 Profits: $5,644,870	**Int'l Ticker: POR3** Int'l Exchange: Frankfurt-Euronext
2006 Sales: $9,655,630	2006 Profits: $1,888,380	Employees: 11,668
2005 Sales: $7,971,600	2005 Profits: $948,900	Fiscal Year Ends: 7/31
2004 Sales: $7,644,600	2004 Profits: $293,300	Parent Company:

SALARIES/BENEFITS:

Pension Plan:	ESOP Stock Plan:	Profit Sharing:	Top Exec. Salary: $	Bonus: $
Savings Plan: Y	Stock Purch. Plan:		Second Exec. Salary: $	Bonus: $

OTHER THOUGHTS:

Apparent Women Officers or Directors:
Hot Spot for Advancement for Women/Minorities:

LOCATIONS: ("Y" = Yes)

West:	Southwest:	Midwest:	Southeast:	Northeast:	International:
					Y

PSA PEUGEOT CITROEN SA

www.psa-peugeot-citroen.com

Industry Group Code: 336111 **Ranks within this company's industry group:** Sales: 9 Profits: 22

Techology:		Medical/Drugs:		Engineering:		Transportation:		Chemicals/Petrochemicals:		Specialty:	
Computers:		Manufacturer:		Design:		Aerospace:		Oil/Gas Products:		Special Services:	
Software:		Contract Research:		Construction:		Automotive:	Y	Chemicals:		Consulting:	
Communications:		Medical Services:		Eng. Services:		Shipping:	Y	Oil/Chem. Svcs.:		Specialty Mgmt.:	
Electronics:		Labs:		Consulting:				Gases:		Products:	
Alternative Energy:		Bio. Services:						Other:		Other:	

TYPES OF BUSINESS:

Automobiles, Manufacturing
Automotive Equipment & Components
Transportation & Logistics Services
Motorcycles
Financial Services
Industrial Equipment
Engines
Clean Diesel & Hybrid Engine Technology

BRANDS/DIVISIONS/AFFILIATES:

Peugeot
Citroen
Faurecia
Gefco
Banque PSA Finance
Peugeot Motocycles
Dongfeng Peugeot Citroen Automobile

CONTACTS: *Note: Officers with more than one job title may be intentionally listed here more than once.*

Philippe Varin, CEO
Jean-Luc Vergne, VP-Human Resources
Pascal Henault, VP-Research & Automotive Innovation
Alain Sartoris, VP-IT & Exec. Dev.
Roland Vardanega, Managing Dir.-Tech.
Roland Vardanega, Managing Dir.-Mfg.
Jean-Claude Hanus, VP-Legal Affairs/Institutional Rel./Internal Audit
Liliane Lacourt, VP-Corp. Comm.
Isabel Marey-Semper, VP-Finance
Jean-Philippe Collin, Managing Dir.-Automobiles Peugeot
Gregoire Olivier, Exec. VP/Managing Dir.-Programs
Daniel Marteau, Dir.-Replacement Parts
Roland Vardanega, Interim Chmn.
Claude Vajsman, Dir.-China
Jean-Christophe Quemard, Dir.-Purchasing

Phone: 01-40-66-55-11	**Fax:**
Toll-Free:	
Address: 75 Ave. de la Grande-Armee, Paris, 75116 France	

GROWTH PLANS/SPECIAL FEATURES:

PSA Peugeot Citroen S.A. (PSAPC) is a leading automobile manufacturer in Europe, producing cars and light commercial vehicles under the Peugeot and Citroen brand names. With a presence in over 150 countries, it sold almost 2 million Peugeot vehicles and CKDs (Complete Knock Down, typically a complete car kit sold to foreign affiliates for local assembly) and nearly 1.5 million Citroen vehicles and CKDs in 2007. PSAPC is focusing on producing more environmentally friendly vehicles. To this end, the company premiered six new vehicles featuring HDi (High-pressure Direct Injection) diesel engine technology, which helps the diesel burn more effectively, thus greatly reducing solid particles in emissions. The firm also developed the Diesel Particulate Filter System (DPFS), which it claims eliminates virtually all fine particle diesel emissions by burning them while still in the cylinder, and trapping any resulting soot in the exhaust system. Besides creating cleaner diesel engines, the company developed a hybrid Citroen engine equipped with its Stop & Start system, which turns the engine off when the vehicle reaches a full stop and starts the engine again when the accelerator is pressed. In addition to car manufacturing, PSAPC also operates the following four subsidiaries. Faurecia is a European leader in manufacturing automotive equipment and components, such as seats and exhaust systems. Gefco is one of France's top providers of transportation and logistics services. Banque PSA Finance is a federation of the group's finance companies. Peugeot Motocycles is one of the largest manufacturers of 50cc-125cc scooters and motorcycles in Europe. Additionally, the firm has a joint venture with Chinese automaker Dongfeng Motor, called Dongfeng Peugeot Citroen Automobile (DPCA). This joint venture operates two manufacturing facilities in Hubei. In May 2008, the company agreed to form a joint venture with Mitsubishi Motors Corporation to produce Peugeot, Citroen and Mitsubishi vehicles in Russia.

FINANCIALS: **Sales and profits are in thousands of dollars—add 000 to get the full amount. 2008 Note: Financial information for 2008 was not available for all companies at press time.**

2008 Sales: $73,365,900	2008 Profits: $-462,960	**U.S. Stock Ticker:**
2007 Sales: $79,196,800	2007 Profits: $1,194,510	**Int'l Ticker: UG** Int'l Exchange: Paris-Euronext
2006 Sales: $75,428,100	2006 Profits: $234,960	Employees: 207,800
2005 Sales: $72,260,021	2005 Profits: $1,321,479	Fiscal Year Ends: 12/31
2004 Sales: $72,065,303	2004 Profits: $2,113,870	Parent Company:

SALARIES/BENEFITS:

Pension Plan:	ESOP Stock Plan:	Profit Sharing: Y	Top Exec. Salary: $	Bonus: $
Savings Plan:	Stock Purch. Plan:		Second Exec. Salary: $	Bonus: $

OTHER THOUGHTS:

Apparent Women Officers or Directors: 3
Hot Spot for Advancement for Women/Minorities: Y

LOCATIONS: ("Y" = Yes)

West:	Southwest:	Midwest:	Southeast:	Northeast:	International:
				Y	Y

QUALCOMM INC

www.qualcomm.com

Industry Group Code: 334413 **Ranks within this company's industry group:** Sales: 3 Profits: 3

Techology:		Medical/Drugs:		Engineering:		Transportation:		Chemicals/Petrochemicals:		Specialty:	
Computers:		Manufacturer:		Design:		Aerospace:		Oil/Gas Products:		Special Services:	
Software:	Y	Contract Research:		Construction:		Automotive:		Chemicals:		Consulting:	
Communications:	Y	Medical Services:		Eng. Services:		Shipping:		Oil/Chem. Svcs.:		Specialty Mgmt.:	
Electronics:	Y	Labs:		Consulting:				Gases:		Products:	
Alternative Energy:		Bio. Services:						Other:		Other:	

TYPES OF BUSINESS:

Telecommunications Equipment
Digital Wireless Communications Products
Integrated Circuits
Mobile Communications Systems
Wireless Software & Services
E-Mail Software
Code Division Multiple Access

BRANDS/DIVISIONS/AFFILIATES:

MediaFLO USA, Inc.
Qualcomm Flarion Technologies, Inc.
Qualcomm MEMS Technologies, Inc.
Firethorn Holdings, LLC
SoftMax, Inc.
Xiam Technologies Limited
Ronda Grupo Consultor, S.L.

CONTACTS: *Note: Officers with more than one job title may be intentionally listed here more than once.*

Paul E. Jacobs, CEO
Len J. Lauer, COO/Exec. VP
Steven R. Altman, Pres.
William E. Keitel, CFO/Exec. VP
William F. Davidson, Jr., Sr. VP-Global Mktg.
Daniel L. Sullivan, Exec. VP-Human Resources
Norm Fjeldheim, CIO/Sr. VP
Roberto Padovani, CTO/Exec. VP
Donald J. Rosenberg, General Counsel/Exec. VP/Corp. Sec.
William Bold, Sr. VP-Gov't Affairs
William F. Davidson, Jr., Sr. VP-Investor Rel.
Margaret L. Johnson, Exec. VP-Americas & India
Derek Aberle, Exec. VP/Pres., Qualcomm Tech. Licensing
Robert Walton, Sr. VP/Pres., Qualcomm Enterprise Svcs.
Paul E. Jacobs, Chmn.
Jing Wang, Exec. VP-Asia Pacific, Middle East & Africa

Phone: 858-587-1121 **Fax:** 858-658-2100
Toll-Free:
Address: 5775 Morehouse Dr., San Diego, CA 92121 US

GROWTH PLANS/SPECIAL FEATURES:

Qualcomm, Inc. provides digital wireless communications products, technologies and services. It designs application-specific integrated circuits based on Code Division Multiple Access (CDMA) technology and licenses its technology to domestic and international telecommunications equipment suppliers. CDMA technology is an industry standard for all forms of digital wireless communications networks. The company also produces the e-mail software Eudora and sells Binary Runtime Environment for Wireless (BREW) software to network operators, handset manufacturers and application developers. BREW is an open-standard platform that can interface with many different wireless applications. The firm's wireless business services, which consist of satellite and terrestrial-based two-way data messaging and position reporting, serve transportation companies, private and construction equipment fleets and U.S. government agencies through its government technologies division. Subsidiary Qualcomm MEMS Technologies develops improved graphical systems for handheld devices. Subsidiary MediaFLO USA, Inc. offers services over a nationwide multicast network based on the MediaFLO Media Distribution System (MDS) and Forward Link Only (FLO) technology This network is utilized as a shared resource for wireless operators and partners. Subsidiary Qualcomm Flarion Technologies is a developer and provider of FLASH-OFDM (Orthogonal Frequency Division Multiplexing Access). The firm offers mobile entertainment services via partnerships with a variety of media networks including NBC; CBS; FOX; and MTV. In 2008, the company acquired Xiam Technologies Limited, an Irish wireless content discovery and recommendations discovery provider, and the majority of the assets of Ronda Grupo Consultor, S.L., a provider of fleet management systems in Spain and Portugal. In 2009, the firm acquired the handheld graphics and multimedia assets from Advanced Micro Devices.

Employees are offered medical, dental and vision insurance; dependent and health care reimbursement accounts; tuition reimbursement; adoption assistance; and a wireless device subsidy program.

FINANCIALS: **Sales and profits are in thousands of dollars—add 000 to get the full amount. 2008 Note: Financial information for 2008 was not available for all companies at press time.**

2008 Sales: $11,142,000	2008 Profits: $3,160,000	**U.S. Stock Ticker: QCOM**
2007 Sales: $8,871,000	2007 Profits: $3,303,000	**Int'l Ticker:** Int'l Exchange:
2006 Sales: $7,526,000	2006 Profits: $2,470,000	Employees: 15,400
2005 Sales: $5,673,000	2005 Profits: $2,143,000	Fiscal Year Ends: 9/30
2004 Sales: $4,880,000	2004 Profits: $1,720,000	Parent Company:

SALARIES/BENEFITS:

Pension Plan:	ESOP Stock Plan:	Profit Sharing:	Top Exec. Salary: $1,112,218	Bonus: $9,100,000
Savings Plan: Y	Stock Purch. Plan: Y		Second Exec. Salary: $817,351	Bonus: $2,909,000

OTHER THOUGHTS:

Apparent Women Officers or Directors: 4
Hot Spot for Advancement for Women/Minorities: Y

LOCATIONS: ("Y" = Yes)

West:	Southwest:	Midwest:	Southeast:	Northeast:	International:
Y	Y	Y	Y	Y	Y

Note: Financial information, benefits and other data can change quickly and may vary from those stated here.

QUANTUM CORP

www.quantum.com

Industry Group Code: 334112 **Ranks within this company's industry group:** Sales: 7 Profits: 7

Techology:		Medical/Drugs:		Engineering:		Transportation:		Chemicals/Petrochemicals:		Specialty:	
Computers:	Y	Manufacturer:		Design:		Aerospace:		Oil/Gas Products:		Special Services:	
Software:		Contract Research:		Construction:		Automotive:		Chemicals:		Consulting:	
Communications:		Medical Services:		Eng. Services:		Shipping:		Oil/Chem. Svcs.:		Specialty Mgmt.:	
Electronics:		Labs:		Consulting:				Gases:		Products:	
Alternative Energy:		Bio. Services:						Other:		Other:	

TYPES OF BUSINESS:

Data Storage Equipment
Tape Drives
Media Cartridges
Tape Automation Systems

BRANDS/DIVISIONS/AFFILIATES:

Advanced Digital Information Corp
SuperLoader 3
Scalar i500
Scalar i2000

CONTACTS: *Note: Officers with more than one job title may be intentionally listed here more than once.*

Richard Belluzzo, CEO
Jon Gacek, CFO/Exec. VP
Bill Britts, Exec. VP-Sales, Mktg. & Service
Barbara Barrett, VP-Human Resources
Jerry Lopatin, Sr. VP-Eng.
Shawn Hall, General Counsel/VP/Sec.
Richard Belluzzo, Chmn.

Phone: 408-944-4000 **Fax:** 408-944-4040
Toll-Free:
Address: 1650 Technology Dr., Ste. 700, San Jose, CA 95110 US

GROWTH PLANS/SPECIAL FEATURES:

Quantum Corp. is a global storage company specializing in backup, recovery and archive solutions. It provides an integrated range of disk, tape and software solutions. The company's solutions are designed to provide information technology (IT) departments in a wide variety of organizations with tools for protecting, retaining and accessing digital assets. The firm's products are divided into three categories: Tape automation systems; data management software and disk-based backup systems; and devices and media. The tape automation systems portfolio include autoloaders and entry-level, midrange and enterprise libraries. These products integrate tape drives into a system with automation technology, advanced connectivity and management tools. The SuperLoader 3 autoloader has one tape drive and up to 16 cartridges, whereas Quantum's large enterprise-class libraries can hold up to hundreds of drives and thousands of cartridges. The midrange and enterprise libraries, such as the Scalar i500 and Scalar i2000, leverage a common, integrated software management approach called iLayer, which provides monitoring, alerts and diagnostics. The disk-based backup systems products include the DXi-Series disk-based backup appliances featuring data de-duplication and replication technologies. Data de-duplication technology increases effective disk capacity, enabling users to retain backup data on fast recovery disk for a longer time. Data management software products, designed for open system computing environments, allow multiple applications to rapidly access a single data set. They also transparently move data based on business value. Devices and media products include removable disk devices, as well as a broad family of tape drives and media representing all major tape technology formats. Quantum sells its products via its branded channels and through original equipment manufacturers such as Dell, Inc.; Hewlett-Packard Co.; International Business Machines Corp.; and Sun Microsystems, Inc. The company provides services to customers in approximately 100 countries, with multi-language technical support centers in North America, Europe and Asia.

FINANCIALS: **Sales and profits are in thousands of dollars—add 000 to get the full amount. 2008 Note: Financial information for 2008 was not available for all companies at press time.**

2008 Sales: $975,702	2008 Profits: $-60,234	**U.S. Stock Ticker: QTM**
2007 Sales: $1,016,174	2007 Profits: $-64,094	**Int'l Ticker:** Int'l Exchange:
2006 Sales: $834,287	2006 Profits: $-41,479	Employees: 2,050
2005 Sales: $794,168	2005 Profits: $-3,496	Fiscal Year Ends: 3/31
2004 Sales: $808,384	2004 Profits: $-62,022	Parent Company:

SALARIES/BENEFITS:

Pension Plan:	ESOP Stock Plan:	Profit Sharing:	Top Exec. Salary: $694,231	Bonus: $
Savings Plan: Y	Stock Purch. Plan:		Second Exec. Salary: $350,004	Bonus: $

OTHER THOUGHTS:

Apparent Women Officers or Directors: 2
Hot Spot for Advancement for Women/Minorities:

LOCATIONS: ("Y" = Yes)

West:	Southwest:	Midwest:	Southeast:	Northeast:	International:
Y		Y		Y	Y

Note: Financial information, benefits and other data can change quickly and may vary from those stated here.

QUINTILES TRANSNATIONAL CORP

www.quintiles.com

Industry Group Code: 541710 **Ranks within this company's industry group:** Sales: Profits:

Techology:		Medical/Drugs:		Engineering:		Transportation:		Chemicals/Petrochemicals:		Specialty:	
Computers:		Manufacturer:		Design:		Aerospace:		Oil/Gas Products:		Special Services:	Y
Software:		Contract Research:	Y	Construction:		Automotive:		Chemicals:		Consulting:	
Communications:		Medical Services:	Y	Eng. Services:		Shipping:		Oil/Chem. Svcs.:		Specialty Mgmt.:	
Electronics:		Labs:		Consulting:				Gases:		Products:	
Alternative Energy:		Bio. Services:	Y					Other:		Other:	

TYPES OF BUSINESS:

Contract Research
Pharmaceutical, Biotech & Medical Device Research
Consulting & Training Services
Sales & Marketing Services

BRANDS/DIVISIONS/AFFILIATES:

Novaquest
Innovex
Eidetics

CONTACTS:

Note: Officers with more than one job title may be intentionally listed here more than once.

Dennis Gillings, CEO
John Ratliff, COO
Mike Troullis, CFO
Christopher Cabell, Chief Medical & Scientific Officer
William R. Deam, CIO/Exec. VP
Ron Wooten, Exec. VP-Corp. Dev.
Oren Cohen, Sr. VP-Clinical Research Strategies
Dennis Gillings, Chmn.

Phone: 919-998-2000 **Fax:** 919-998-2094
Toll-Free:
Address: 4709 Creekstone Dr. Ste. 200, Durham, NC 27703 US

GROWTH PLANS/SPECIAL FEATURES:

Quintiles Transnational Corp. provides full-service contract research, sales and marketing services to the global pharmaceutical, biotechnology and medical device industries. The company is one of the world's top contract research organizations, and it provides a broad range of contract services to speed the process from development to peak sales of a new drug or medical device. The firm operates through offices in 50 countries, organized in three primary business segments, including the product development group, the Innovex commercialization group and the Novaquest strategic partnering solutions group. The product development group provides a full range of drug development services from strategic planning and preclinical services to regulatory submission and approval. The commercial services group, which operates under the Innovex brand, engages in sales solutions such as recruitment, training and deployment of Innovex managed sales teams; and medical communications, which provides and promotes physician education. The Novaquest strategic partnering solutions segment attempts to optimize portfolio development, company growth and profits for pharmaceutical and biotech companies through a variety of solutions such as structured finance, strategic resourcing and eBio. In January 2009, the firm announced plans to open a Phase I clinical trial unit in India through a partnership with Apollo Hospitals Group. In May 2008, the firm agreed to acquire Eidetics, a decision-analytics and market research firm.

The company offers its employees a comprehensive benefits package including on-the-job training, recreational activities and community support activities.

FINANCIALS:

Sales and profits are in thousands of dollars—add 000 to get the full amount. 2008 Note: Financial information for 2008 was not available for all companies at press time.

2008 Sales: $	2008 Profits: $	**U.S. Stock Ticker: Private**
2007 Sales: $	2007 Profits: $	**Int'l Ticker:** Int'l Exchange:
2006 Sales: $	2006 Profits: $	Employees: 16,000
2005 Sales: $2,398,583	2005 Profits: $ 648	Fiscal Year Ends: 12/31
2004 Sales: $1,956,254	2004 Profits: $-7,427	Parent Company:

SALARIES/BENEFITS:

Pension Plan:	ESOP Stock Plan:	Profit Sharing:	Top Exec. Salary: $706,061	Bonus: $825,000
Savings Plan:	Stock Purch. Plan:		Second Exec. Salary: $471,224	Bonus: $709,000

OTHER THOUGHTS:

Apparent Women Officers or Directors:
Hot Spot for Advancement for Women/Minorities:

LOCATIONS: ("Y" = Yes)

West:	Southwest:	Midwest:	Southeast:	Northeast:	International:
Y	Y	Y	Y	Y	Y

RAILWORKS CORP

www.railworks.com

Industry Group Code: 234000 **Ranks within this company's industry group:** Sales: Profits:

Techology:		Medical/Drugs:		Engineering:		Transportation:		Chemicals/Petrochemicals:		Specialty:	
Computers:		Manufacturer:		Design:		Aerospace:		Oil/Gas Products:		Special Services:	
Software:		Contract Research:		Construction:		Automotive:		Chemicals:		Consulting:	
Communications:		Medical Services:		Eng. Services:	Y	Shipping:	Y	Oil/Chem. Svcs.:		Specialty Mgmt.:	
Electronics:		Labs:		Consulting:				Gases:		Products:	
Alternative Energy:		Bio. Services:						Other:		Other:	

TYPES OF BUSINESS:

Railroad Construction & Maintenance
Rail Technologies
Leasing
Electrical & Mechanical Installations

BRANDS/DIVISIONS/AFFILIATES:

Railworks Transit, Inc.
Railworks Track Systems, Inc.
RailWorks Track-Texas, Inc.
HSQ Technology
L.K. Comstock & Company, Inc.
PNR Railworks, Inc.
PNR Leasing, Ltd.
Railworks Track Services, Inc.

CONTACTS: *Note: Officers with more than one job title may be intentionally listed here more than once.*

Jeffrey M. Levy, CEO
Jeffrey M. Levy, Pres.
Michael Mermelstein, CFO/Exec. VP
Michele Bodnar, VP-Human Resources
Steven G. Milewicz, General Counsel/Sec./Exec. VP
Kean Smith, VP-Bus. Dev.
Gene Cellini, VP-Tax
John August, Exec. VP
Joseph Spirito, VP-Risk Management
Ben D'Alessandro, Pres., Railworks Transit, Inc.
Scott Brace, Exec. VP-Track Systems
Raymond List, Chmn.

Phone: 212-502-7900	**Fax:** 212-502-1865
Toll-Free:	
Address: 5 Penn Plaza, 17th Fl., New York, NY 10001 US	

GROWTH PLANS/SPECIAL FEATURES:

RailWorks Corporation and its network of affiliated companies provide specialized construction, maintenance and materials for the rail and rail-transit industries in the U.S. and Canada. In May 2007, the firm was acquired by Wind Point Partners, a private equity investment firm. Prior to the acquisition, the company had been owned by MatlinPatterson Global Opportunities Partners for five years. The company's business serves a range of railroads, transit authorities and commuter railroads, as well as municipalities, industrial manufacturing facilities and power plants. The firm divides its operations into two business units, transit systems and tracks. In total, RailWorks has eight subsidiaries: HSQ Technology; L.K. Comstock & Company, Inc.; PNR Railworks, Inc.; PNR Leasing, Ltd.; RailWorks Track Services, Inc.; RailWorks Track Systems, Inc.; RailWorks Track-Texas, Inc.; and RailWorks Transit, Inc. The transit systems segment handles electrical and mechanical installations (such as power supply, overhead systems, signal, and fire and safety equipment), construction (including power generation, instrumentation and control). In addition to these contracted services, the transit systems unit includes a specialized systems management group that designs, integrates, builds and supports a range of supervisory control and data acquisition systems. The track segment designs, builds, maintains and rehabilitates railways. This business involves, in addition to advanced rail and tie installation techniques, the development of signals and crossings, bridge construction, communication systems, scheduled maintenance work and emergency repairs, which include derailment response. In April 2008, PNR RailWorks Inc. acquired Quebec's largest railway contractor, Entretien de Voies Ferrees Coyle Inc., dba E.V.F. Coyle Inc.

FINANCIALS: **Sales and profits are in thousands of dollars—add 000 to get the full amount. 2008 Note: Financial information for 2008 was not available for all companies at press time.**

2008 Sales: $	2008 Profits: $	**U.S. Stock Ticker: Private**
2007 Sales: $	2007 Profits: $	**Int'l Ticker:** Int'l Exchange:
2006 Sales: $	2006 Profits: $	Employees: 1,300
2005 Sales: $350,000	2005 Profits: $	Fiscal Year Ends: 12/31
2004 Sales: $	2004 Profits: $	Parent Company:

SALARIES/BENEFITS:

Pension Plan:	ESOP Stock Plan:	Profit Sharing:	Top Exec. Salary: $	Bonus: $
Savings Plan:	Stock Purch. Plan:		Second Exec. Salary: $	Bonus: $

OTHER THOUGHTS:

Apparent Women Officers or Directors: 1
Hot Spot for Advancement for Women/Minorities:

LOCATIONS: ("Y" = Yes)

West:	Southwest:	Midwest:	Southeast:	Northeast:	International:
Y	Y	Y	Y	Y	Y

RAYTHEON CO

www.raytheon.com

Industry Group Code: 336410 **Ranks within this company's industry group:** Sales: 9 Profits: 9

Techology:		Medical/Drugs:		Engineering:		Transportation:		Chemicals/Petrochemicals:		Specialty:	
Computers:		Manufacturer:		Design:		Aerospace:	Y	Oil/Gas Products:		Special Services:	Y
Software:	Y	Contract Research:		Construction:		Automotive:		Chemicals:		Consulting:	Y
Communications:	Y	Medical Services:		Eng. Services:		Shipping:		Oil/Chem. Svcs.:		Specialty Mgmt.:	
Electronics:	Y	Labs:		Consulting:				Gases:		Products:	Y
Alternative Energy:		Bio. Services:						Other:		Other:	Y

TYPES OF BUSINESS:

Aerospace & Defense Technology
Commercial Electronics
Technical Services
Communications & Information Systems
Sensors & Surveillance Equipment
Missile Systems
Space Exploration Devices
Software Engineering

BRANDS/DIVISIONS/AFFILIATES:

Patriot Air & Missile Defense System
Raytheon Systems Limited
Raytheon Australia
Raytheon Canada Limited

CONTACTS: *Note: Officers with more than one job title may be intentionally listed here more than once.*

William H. Swanson, CEO
David C. Wajsgras, CFO/Sr. VP
Keith J. Peden, Sr. VP-Human Resources
Rebecca R. Rhoads, CIO/VP
Mark E. Russell, VP-Tech. & Mission Assurance
Mark E. Russell, VP-Eng.
Jay B. Stephens, General Counsel/Sec./Sr. VP
Richard A. Goglia, VP-Corp. Dev./Treas.
Pamela A. Wickham, VP-Corp. Affairs & Comm.
Michael J. Wood, Chief Acct. Officer/VP
Jon C. Jones, VP/Pres., Space & Airborne Systems
Taylor W. Lawrence, VP/Pres., Missile Systems
Colin Schottlaender, VP/Pres., Network Centric Systems
Daniel L. Smith, VP/Pres., Integrated Defense Systems
William H. Swanson, Chmn.
Thomas M. Culligan, CEO-Raytheon Int'l, Inc./Exec. VP-Bus. Dev.
John D. Harris, II, VP-Contracts & Supply Chain

Phone: 781-522-3000 **Fax:** 781-522-3001
Toll-Free:
Address: 870 Winter St., Waltham, MA 02451-1449 US

GROWTH PLANS/SPECIAL FEATURES:

Raytheon Co. offers aerospace systems, defense and government electronics, IT equipment and technical services. Raytheon operates six segments: Integrated Defense Systems (IDS); Intelligence and Information Systems (IIS); Missile Systems (MS); Network Centric Systems (NCS); Space and Airborne Systems (SAS); and Technical Services (TS). IDS provides integrated space, air, surface, subsurface and homeland security products, including advanced radar and sonar systems; surveillance equipment; sensors; air and missile defense systems, including the Patriot Air & Missile Defense System; and technical services. IIS offers commercial and government customers weather and environmental management; geospatial intelligence; signal and image processing; and ground engineering support. MS produces various missiles, including one anti-satellite system, as well as smart projectiles, missile defense guns and even a microwave-based anti-missile system. NCS develops and produces mission solutions for networking and communications; command and control; battlefield awareness; and transportation management. SAS provides electro-optic/infrared sensors, airborne radars, high-energy lasers, precision guidance systems and space-qualified systems for civil and military applications. Lastly, TS provides technical, scientific and professional services, including training and outsourcing, for defense, federal and commercial customers worldwide. Raytheon's international subsidiaries include Raytheon Systems Limited, which works with IIS, SAS and NCS in the U.K.; Raytheon Australia, which works with IDS and TS in Australia, including managing operations and maintenance for the Canberra Deep Space Communication Complex; and Raytheon Canada Limited, which works with NCS offering air traffic control systems. Its customers include the Department of Homeland Security, all branches of the U.S. military, the National Guard, the F.A.A., the Japanese Defense Agency and the Royal Saudi Air Defense Forces. The U.S. government accounted for 87% of its 2008 sales.

Raytheon employees receive dental, prescription drug and vision care coverage; life and AD&D insurance; short- and long-term disability benefits; paid time off; adoption assistance; educational assistance; and investment services.

FINANCIALS: **Sales and profits are in thousands of dollars—add 000 to get the full amount. 2008 Note: Financial information for 2008 was not available for all companies at press time.**

2008 Sales: $23,174,000	2008 Profits: $1,672,000	**U.S. Stock Ticker: RTN**
2007 Sales: $21,301,000	2007 Profits: $2,578,000	**Int'l Ticker:** Int'l Exchange:
2006 Sales: $19,707,000	2006 Profits: $1,283,000	Employees: 73,000
2005 Sales: $18,491,000	2005 Profits: $871,000	Fiscal Year Ends: 12/31
2004 Sales: $17,825,000	2004 Profits: $417,000	Parent Company:

SALARIES/BENEFITS:

Pension Plan:	ESOP Stock Plan:	Profit Sharing:	Top Exec. Salary: $1,229,544	Bonus: $3,050,000
Savings Plan: Y	Stock Purch. Plan:		Second Exec. Salary: $725,846	Bonus: $870,000

OTHER THOUGHTS:

Apparent Women Officers or Directors: 4
Hot Spot for Advancement for Women/Minorities: Y

LOCATIONS: ("Y" = Yes)

West:	Southwest:	Midwest:	Southeast:	Northeast:	International:
Y	Y	Y	Y	Y	Y

RENAULT SA

www.renault.com

Industry Group Code: 336111 **Ranks within this company's industry group:** Sales: 12 Profits: 12

Techology:		Medical/Drugs:		Engineering:		Transportation:		Chemicals/Petrochemicals:		Specialty:	
Computers:		Manufacturer:		Design:		Aerospace:		Oil/Gas Products:		Special Services:	
Software:		Contract Research:		Construction:		Automotive:	Y	Chemicals:		Consulting:	
Communications:		Medical Services:		Eng. Services:		Shipping:		Oil/Chem. Svcs.:		Specialty Mgmt.:	
Electronics:		Labs:		Consulting:				Gases:		Products:	
Alternative Energy:		Bio. Services:						Other:		Other:	

TYPES OF BUSINESS:

Automobiles, Manufacturing
Financial Services
Commercial Vehicles
Two-Wheelers
Farm Machinery
Automotive Maintenance Service

BRANDS/DIVISIONS/AFFILIATES:

Renault Samsung Motors
Dacia
RCI Banque
Renault-Nissan B.V.
Renault Agriculture
Renault Minute
Nissan Motor Co Ltd
AvtoVAZ OAO

CONTACTS: *Note: Officers with more than one job title may be intentionally listed here more than once.*

Carlos Ghosn, CEO
Patrick Pelata, COO
Carlos Ghosn, Pres.
Thierry Moulonguet, CFO
Patrick Blain, Exec. VP-Sales & Mktg.
Gerard Leclercq, Sr. VP-Human Resources
Jean-Pierre Corniou, CIO
Jean-Louis Ricaud, Exec. VP-Eng. & Quality
Michel Gornet, Exec. VP-Mfg.
Michel de Virville, Corp. Sec./Exec. VP
Patrick Pelata, Exec. VP-Product & Strategic Planning & Programs
Marie-Francoise Damesin, Sr. VP-Corp. Comm.
Jean-Baptiste Duzan, Corp. Controller/Sr. VP
Jacques Chauvet, Sr. VP-Market Area France
Stephen Norman, Sr. VP-Global Mktg.
Odile Desforges, Sr. VP-Purchasing/CEO-Renault Nissan Purchasing
Phillippe Gamba, Chmn./CEO-RCI Banque
Louis Schweitzer, Chmn.
Marie-Christine Caubet, Sr. VP-Market Area Europe
Michel Gornet, Exec. VP-Logistics

Phone: 33-1-76-84-50-50	**Fax:** 33-1-41-04-51-49
Toll-Free:	
Address: 13-15 Quai le Gallo, Boulogne Billancourt, F-92512 France	

GROWTH PLANS/SPECIAL FEATURES:

Renault S.A. is one of the largest automobile manufacturers in France. The company's automobile division consists of the Renault, Renault Samsung Motors (RSM) and Dacia brands based in South Korea and Romania, respectively. It designs, develops and markets a line of small to mid-size cars, including hatchbacks and minivans, as well as light commercial vehicles and two-wheelers, such as scooters. Renault's brands include the Twingo, Clio, Megane and Megane II, Scenic, Modus, Espace, Laguna, Kangoo, Vel Satis and Avantime. The Kangoo Express, Trafic and Master are all light commercial vehicles; while almost all its remaining brands are passenger cars such as hatchbacks and sedans. Dacia's models are limited to Logan, a 4-door sedan, and Logan MCV, a station-wagon-like version of the Logan. RSM brands include the SM3, SM5 and SM7, all 4-door sedans. Renault's sales and finance division is comprised of RCI Banque and its subsidiaries, a total of approximately 60 companies, which provide sales, services and cash management for the group. In addition, the firm operates Renault Agriculture, a subsidiary that manufactures and markets farm machinery. The firm also has an agreement with Claas, a leader in harvesting and haymaking machinery, making Claas the majority shareholder in Renault Agriculture. Renault operates a host of automotive maintenance locations that run under the name Renault Minute centers. There are 481 centers in France, 365 elsewhere in Europe and 74 internationally. Through its joint venture Renault-Nissan B.V., Renault owns approximately 44% of Japan-based Nissan Motor Co. Ltd. Nissan, in turn, owns approximately 15% of Renault. The French government has a 16% stake in Renault, down considerably from the 45% owned a decade ago. In February 2008, the company acquired a stake in Russian automaker AvtoVAZ OAO.

Employees at Renault are offered training and continuing development. In addition, the firm offers internships.

FINANCIALS: **Sales and profits are in thousands of dollars—add 000 to get the full amount. 2008 Note: Financial information for 2008 was not available for all companies at press time.**

2008 Sales: $47,578,900	2008 Profits: $754,140	**U.S. Stock Ticker: RNSDF**
2007 Sales: $64,891,000	2007 Profits: $4,360,950	**Int'l Ticker: RNO** Int'l Exchange: Paris-Euronext
2006 Sales: $54,787,900	2006 Profits: $3,882,700	Employees: 130,179
2005 Sales: $52,749,800	2005 Profits: $4,406,240	Fiscal Year Ends: 12/31
2004 Sales: $55,535,300	2004 Profits: $4,843,600	Parent Company:

SALARIES/BENEFITS:

Pension Plan:	ESOP Stock Plan:	Profit Sharing:	Top Exec. Salary: $	Bonus: $
Savings Plan:	Stock Purch. Plan:		Second Exec. Salary: $	Bonus: $

OTHER THOUGHTS:

Apparent Women Officers or Directors: 3
Hot Spot for Advancement for Women/Minorities: Y

LOCATIONS: ("Y" = Yes)

West:	Southwest:	Midwest:	Southeast:	Northeast:	International:
					Y

Note: Financial information, benefits and other data can change quickly and may vary from those stated here.

RENESAS TECHNOLOGY CORP

www.renesas.com

Industry Group Code: 334413 **Ranks within this company's industry group:** Sales: Profits:

Techology:		Medical/Drugs:		Engineering:		Transportation:		Chemicals/Petrochemicals:		Specialty:	
Computers:		Manufacturer:		Design:	Y	Aerospace:		Oil/Gas Products:		Special Services:	
Software:		Contract Research:		Construction:		Automotive:		Chemicals:		Consulting:	
Communications:		Medical Services:		Eng. Services:		Shipping:		Oil/Chem. Svcs.:		Specialty Mgmt.:	
Electronics:	Y	Labs:		Consulting:				Gases:		Products:	Y
Alternative Energy:		Bio. Services:						Other:		Other:	Y

TYPES OF BUSINESS:

Semiconductor Systems
System in Package Technology
Microcontrollers
Smartcard Products

BRANDS/DIVISIONS/AFFILIATES:

Hitachi Ltd
Mitsubishi Electric Corporation
Renesas Technology (China) Co Ltd
Renesas Technology Canada Limited
Renesas Technology (Shanghai) Co Ltd
Renesas Technology Europe Limited
Renesas Technology Europe GmbH
Renesas Technology America Inc

CONTACTS: *Note: Officers with more than one job title may be intentionally listed here more than once.*

Satoru Ito, CEO
Katsuhiro Tsukamoto, COO
Katsuhiro Tsukamoto, Pres.
Takeo Kawano, CFO/Sr. VP
Shigeo Uoya, Exec. VP
Shiro Baba, Sr. VP
Shunsuke Hosomi, Managing Officer
Isao Shimura, General Mgr.-Power Supply Devices Bus. Unit
Satoru Ito, Chmn.

Phone: 81-3-5201-5111	**Fax:** 81-3-3270-5003
Toll-Free:	
Address: Nippon Bldg., 2-6-2, Ote-machi, Chiyoda-ku, Tokyo, 100-0004 Japan	

GROWTH PLANS/SPECIAL FEATURES:

Renesas Technology Corporation is a provider of an array of semiconductors, including application-specific integrated circuits (ASICs), discrete devices, microcomputers, logic/analog devices, microcontrollers and memory products (such as SRAM and flash memory). Established in April 2003 through the merger of the semiconductor divisions of Hitachi Ltd. and Mitsubishi Electric Corporation, Renesas is headquartered in Tokyo and operates through a group of 43 companies, including 21 in Japan and 22 overseas. Hitachi owns 55% of Renesas, while Mitsubishi owns 45%. Renesas's products include a variety of microprocessors and microcontrollers (MPUs and MCUs); a range of software and tools; memory products; standard ICs (integrated circuits); power MOS FETs (metal-oxide-semiconductor field-effect transistors) and diodes; key components with ASSPs (application specific standard products); system in package (SiP) products; USB devices; Bluetooth LSI (large scale integration) products; source drivers for organic light-emitting diodes (OLEDs); Smartcards; and SuperH core licensing. The firm's products are primarily used in the following markets: automotive, for air bag control, cruise control and dashboard information; digital home electronics, for use in DVD players, LCD-TV and vacuum cleaners; inverter applications, for use in air conditioners and dishwashers; motor control, for use in fitness equipment and power tools; networks, in Bluetooth devices and network terminals; and wireless, specifically in cellular phones. In January 2008, Renesas established a new analog and discrete semiconductor design company in Malaysia and announced plans to expand its back-end process plant in Malaysia. In February 2008, the company announced a partnership with Sharp Corporation and Powerchip Semiconductor Corp.; the joint venture is focused on the development of drivers and controllers for small- and mid-size LCDs. In July 2008, the firm announced plans to reorganize its operations in China by merging several of its sales and technical support subsidiaries in Hong Kong, Shanghai and Beijing.

FINANCIALS: **Sales and profits are in thousands of dollars—add 000 to get the full amount. 2008 Note: Financial information for 2008 was not available for all companies at press time.**

2008 Sales: $	2008 Profits: $	**U.S. Stock Ticker: Joint Venture**
2007 Sales: $	2007 Profits: $	**Int'l Ticker:** Int'l Exchange:
2006 Sales: $	2006 Profits: $	Employees: 26,000
2005 Sales: $8,349,726	2005 Profits: $	Fiscal Year Ends: 3/31
2004 Sales: $	2004 Profits: $	Parent Company:

SALARIES/BENEFITS:

Pension Plan:	ESOP Stock Plan:	Profit Sharing:	Top Exec. Salary: $	Bonus: $
Savings Plan:	Stock Purch. Plan:		Second Exec. Salary: $	Bonus: $

OTHER THOUGHTS:

Apparent Women Officers or Directors:
Hot Spot for Advancement for Women/Minorities:

LOCATIONS: ("Y" = Yes)

West:	Southwest:	Midwest:	Southeast:	Northeast:	International:
Y		Y		Y	Y

RHEINMETALL AG

www.rheinmetall.com

Industry Group Code: 336300 **Ranks within this company's industry group:** Sales: 20 Profits: 8

Techology:		Medical/Drugs:		Engineering:		Transportation:		Chemicals/Petrochemicals:		Specialty:	
Computers:		Manufacturer:		Design:		Aerospace:	Y	Oil/Gas Products:		Special Services:	
Software:		Contract Research:		Construction:		Automotive:	Y	Chemicals:		Consulting:	
Communications:		Medical Services:		Eng. Services:	Y	Shipping:		Oil/Chem. Svcs.:		Specialty Mgmt.:	
Electronics:		Labs:		Consulting:				Gases:		Products:	
Alternative Energy:		Bio. Services:						Other:		Other:	

TYPES OF BUSINESS:

Automotive Components Manufacturing
Military Vehicles
Weapons & Ammunition
Defense Electronics
Air Defense Systems

BRANDS/DIVISIONS/AFFILIATES:

Kolbenschmidt Pierburg
Pierburg Gmbh
KS Kolbenschmidt
KS Gleitlager GmbH
KS Aluminum-Technologie AG
MS Motor Systems International GmbH

CONTACTS: *Note: Officers with more than one job title may be intentionally listed here more than once.*

Klaus Eberhardt, CEO/Chmn.-Defense Sector
Herbert Mueller, CFO
Ingo Hecke, Head-Human Resources
Ludwig Dammer, Head-Tech./Prod. System, Pierburg Gmbh
Andreas Beyer, Head-Law
Peter Rucker, Head-Corp. Comm.
Franz-Bernd Reich, Head-Investor Rel.
Joachim Stoeber, Vice-Chmn.
Gerd Kleinert, Chmn.-Automotive/CEO-Kolbenschmidt Pierburg AG
Klaus Greinert, Chmn.

Phone: 49-211-473-01	**Fax:** 49-211-473-4727
Toll-Free:	
Address: Rheinmetall Platz 1, Dusseldorf, 40476 Germany	

GROWTH PLANS/SPECIAL FEATURES:

Rheinmetall AG, established in 1889, makes automotive components and military defense equipment. The automotive sector, run by Kolbenschmidt Pierburg AG, specializes in module and systems production. This sector exclusively supplies the new Audi A6 gasoline engine block. Kolbenschmidt operates the following divisions. Pierburg GmbH manufactures air management, actuator, emission control systems and solenoid valves. Pierburg Pump Technology offers oil, vacuum and water pumps. KS Kolbenschmidth manufactures various pistons. KS Gleitlager GmbH manufactures various bearings, permaglide and continuous casting products. KS Aluminum-Technologie AG manufactures aluminum engine blocks. Lastly, MS Motor Service International GmbH mainly sells parts for the aftermarket sector. Rheinmetall's defense sector business, one of Europe's top land forces equipment suppliers, supplying many European military bases, operates the following six divisions. The land systems division mainly manufactures combat vehicles including bridge-laying tanks, mine-clearing systems and armored recovery vehicles, as well as offering turrets and weapons stations. The weapons and munitions division manufactures lethal ammunition, such as the 120 millimeter shells for the Leopard 2 tank, and non-lethal weapons such as medium-energy lasers. The air defense division manufactures short-range antiaircraft systems. The propellants division mainly manufactures artillery charges, but also develops automotive, aviation, medical and fastening applications for its products. The C4ISTAR division manufactures technology packages that assist reconnaissance systems, command and control systems, fire control units, ground surveillance sensors and thermal-imaging systems. Lastly, the defense sector also operates a simulation and training division, which manufactures air, land and sea training simulators. In February 2008, Rheinmetall agreed to acquire 51% of Denel Munitions, a division of South African firm Denel (Pty) Ltd. In March 2008, the firm agreed to acquire Dutch armored vehicle manufacturer Stork PWV B.V. for an undisclosed amount. In June 2008, KS Aluminum-Technologie expanded its operations to Pune, India, signing a licensing agreement with Jaya Hind Industries Ltd.

FINANCIALS: **Sales and profits are in thousands of dollars—add 000 to get the full amount. 2008 Note: Financial information for 2008 was not available for all companies at press time.**

2008 Sales: $5,154,670	2008 Profits: $179,860	**U.S. Stock Ticker:**
2007 Sales: $5,335,860	2007 Profits: $199,850	**Int'l Ticker: RHM** Int'l Exchange: Frankfurt-Euronext
2006 Sales: $4,830,920	2006 Profits: $163,870	Employees: 21,020
2005 Sales: $4,413,870	2005 Profits: $150,790	Fiscal Year Ends: 12/31
2004 Sales: $4,655,300	2004 Profits: $130,900	Parent Company:

SALARIES/BENEFITS:

Pension Plan:	ESOP Stock Plan:	Profit Sharing:	Top Exec. Salary: $	Bonus: $
Savings Plan:	Stock Purch. Plan:		Second Exec. Salary: $	Bonus: $

OTHER THOUGHTS:

Apparent Women Officers or Directors:
Hot Spot for Advancement for Women/Minorities:

LOCATIONS: ("Y" = Yes)

West:	Southwest:	Midwest:	Southeast:	Northeast:	International:
		Y		Y	Y

Note: Financial information, benefits and other data can change quickly and may vary from those stated here.

RICOH COMPANY LTD

www.ricoh.com

Industry Group Code: 333313 **Ranks within this company's industry group:** Sales: 1 Profits: 1

Techology:		Medical/Drugs:		Engineering:		Transportation:		Chemicals/Petrochemicals:		Specialty:	
Computers:		Manufacturer:		Design:		Aerospace:		Oil/Gas Products:		Special Services:	
Software:		Contract Research:		Construction:		Automotive:		Chemicals:		Consulting:	
Communications:		Medical Services:		Eng. Services:		Shipping:		Oil/Chem. Svcs.:		Specialty Mgmt.:	
Electronics:	Y	Labs:		Consulting:				Gases:		Products:	
Alternative Energy:		Bio. Services:						Other:		Other:	

TYPES OF BUSINESS:

Manufacturing-Business Machines
Network Systems
Printers, Copiers & Fax Machines
PCs & Servers
Accessories
Software
Electronic Devices
Managed Print Services

BRANDS/DIVISIONS/AFFILIATES:

Ricoh Printing Systems
Nashuatec
Rex-Rotary
Gestetner
Ricoh Europe B.V.
Danka Business Systems PLC
IKON Office Solutions Inc

CONTACTS: *Note: Officers with more than one job title may be intentionally listed here more than once.*

Shiro Kondo, CEO
Shiro Kondo, Pres.
Masayuki Matsumoto, Exec. VP
Takashi Nakamura, Exec. VP
Kazunori Azuma, Exec. VP
Zenji Miura, Exec. VP
Masamitsu Sakurai, Chmn.

Phone: 81-3-6278-2111 **Fax:**
Toll-Free:
Address: Ricoh Bldg., 8-13-1 Ginza, Chuo-ku, Tokyo, 104-8222 Japan

GROWTH PLANS/SPECIAL FEATURES:

Ricoh Company, Ltd. is a global developer of office automation equipment. The firm manufactures and markets copiers, including plain paper copiers (PPCs); multi-functional printers (MFPs), scanners, fax machines, CD, CD-R/RW and DVD drives, and media supplies and services. The company has three business segments: office solutions, industrial products and other businesses. The office solutions product category, accounting for approximately 86% of 2008 sales, consists of imaging and network systems, including monochrome and color digital copiers, MFPs, laser printers, digital duplicators, fax machines, analog PPCs and diazo copiers. The industrial product category, accounting for approximately 6.5% of sales, consists of thermal media, optical equipments, semiconductor devices, electronic components and measuring equipment. The other category offers digital cameras, optical discs, financing and logistics services and accounted for 7.5% of 2008 sales. The firm's services include "managed print services," an outsourcing service whereby the company takes over ownership and/or operation of a client's desktop printers, faxes and copiers, with a goal of creating significant savings for the client. Through Ricoh Printing Systems, the company has entered the super high-speed printing capabilities market, a product line in which it previously did not have any market share. The company has manufacturing facilities in Japan, Europe, North America and Asia and markets products under the Ricoh, Nashuatec, Rex Rotary and Gestetner brands, as well as the Savin and Lanier brands in the U.S. Sales in Japan, the Americas and Europe accounted for 45.8%, 19.6% and 27.2% of total sales respectively in 2008. In 2007, the firm's subsidiary, Ricoh Europe B.V., completed the acquisition of Danka Business Systems PLC for $250 million. In February 2008, Ricoh announced plans to build a $110 million production plant for laser printers and MFPs in Taiwan, in order to reinforce its manufacturing network in Asia. In November 2008, Ricoh acquired U.S.-based IKON Office Solutions, Inc., a provider of document management systems and services, for approximately $1.63 billion.

Ricoh offers its employees a variety of benefits, including medical and life insurance; 401(k) and pension plans; and tuition assistance.

FINANCIALS: **Sales and profits are in thousands of dollars—add 000 to get the full amount. 2008 Note: Financial information for 2008 was not available for all companies at press time.**

2008 Sales: $22,199,890	2008 Profits: $1,815,060	**U.S. Stock Ticker: RICOY**
2007 Sales: $17,533,263	2007 Profits: $946,814	**Int'l Ticker: 7752** Int'l Exchange: Tokyo-TSE
2006 Sales: $16,368,291	2006 Profits: $829,547	Employees: 83,456
2005 Sales: $16,867,600	2005 Profits: $773,100	Fiscal Year Ends: 3/31
2004 Sales: $16,851,800	2004 Profits: $868,700	Parent Company:

SALARIES/BENEFITS:

Pension Plan: Y	ESOP Stock Plan:	Profit Sharing:	Top Exec. Salary: $	Bonus: $
Savings Plan: Y	Stock Purch. Plan:		Second Exec. Salary: $	Bonus: $

OTHER THOUGHTS:

Apparent Women Officers or Directors:
Hot Spot for Advancement for Women/Minorities:

LOCATIONS: ("Y" = Yes)

West:	Southwest:	Midwest:	Southeast:	Northeast:	International:
Y	Y	Y	Y	Y	Y

Note: Financial information, benefits and other data can change quickly and may vary from those stated here.

ROBERT BOSCH GMBH

www.bosch.com

Industry Group Code: 336300 **Ranks within this company's industry group:** Sales: Profits:

Techology:		Medical/Drugs:		Engineering:		Transportation:		Chemicals/Petrochemicals:		Specialty:	
Computers:		Manufacturer:		Design:		Aerospace:		Oil/Gas Products:		Special Services:	
Software:		Contract Research:		Construction:		Automotive:	Y	Chemicals:		Consulting:	
Communications:		Medical Services:		Eng. Services:		Shipping:		Oil/Chem. Svcs.:		Specialty Mgmt.:	
Electronics:	Y	Labs:		Consulting:				Gases:		Products:	Y
Alternative Energy:		Bio. Services:						Other:		Other:	

TYPES OF BUSINESS:

Auto Parts Manufacturing
Gasoline Systems
Motor, Control & Motion Products
Chassis Systems
Electronics & Multimedia
Energy & Body Systems
Security Systems
Power Tools

BRANDS/DIVISIONS/AFFILIATES:

Bosch Security Systems
Telex Communications Inc
ZF Steering Systems GmbH
Bosch Rexroth
Blaupunkt
Bosch-Siemens Hausgerate
Accu Industries Inc
Shenzhen Wei Ning Da Industrial Co Ltd

CONTACTS: *Note: Officers with more than one job title may be intentionally listed here more than once.*

Franz Fehrenbach, Managing Dir.
Gerhard Kummel, Dir.-Finance & Financial Statements
Rudolf Colm, Dir.-Sales & Mktg.
Wolfgang Malchow, Dir.-Human Resources & Social Svcs.
Siegfried Dais, Dir.-Research
Siegfried Dais, Dir.-IT
Siegfried Dais, Dir.-Advance Eng.
Peter J. Marks, Dir.-Mfg. Coordination
Gerhard Kummel, Dir.-Bus. Admin.
Wolfgang Malchow, Dir.-Legal Svcs., Taxes & Internal Auditing
Franz Fehrenbach, Dir.-Corp. Planning, Real Estate & Facilities
Franz Fehrenbach, Dir.-Corp. Comm.
Gerhard Kummel, Dir.-Planning & Controlling
Peter Tyroller, Dir.-Original Equipment Sales
Bernd Bohr, Chmn.-Automotive Group & Systems Integration
Peter J. Marks, Regional Dir.-North & South America
Volkmar Denner, Dir.-Electrical Drives & Automotive Electronics
Hermann Scholl, Supervisory Chmn.
Uwe Raschke, Dir.-Asia Pacific
Rudolf Colm, Dir.-Purchasing, Logistics & Insurance

Phone: 49-711-811-0	**Fax:** 49-711-811-6630
Toll-Free:	
Address: Postfach 106050, Stuttgart, 70049 Germany	

GROWTH PLANS/SPECIAL FEATURES:

Robert Bosch GmbH is one of the world's leading manufacturers of automotive components. It has operations in more than 50 countries. The company operates in three business sectors: automotive technology; industrial technology; and consumer goods and building technology. Its automotive divisions deal in gasoline systems; diesel systems; chassis systems; energy and body systems; car multimedia; automotive electronics; and automotive aftermarket products. Bosch's products include braking and fuel injection systems, starters and alternators. The segment is also involved in a joint venture with ZH Friedrichshafen AG called ZF Steering Systems GmbH, which develops, produces and sells steering technology for passenger and commercial vehicles. The industrial technology unit includes Bosch Rexroth, which supplies a range of motor, control and motion products, and the packaging technology division. The consumer goods and building technology group deals in power tools, thermotechnology, household appliances, security systems and broadband networks. The Blaupunkt unit is a major name in car audio equipment. The firm also owns 50% of European appliance maker Bosch-Siemens Hausgerate. Bosch is a leader in antilock brake technology, clean diesel technology and factory automation. In March 2008, the company acquired U.S.-based Accu Industries Inc., a vehicle workshop equipment manufacturer, and Shenzhen Wei Ning Da Industrial Co Ltd (Weicon), a Shenzhen, China-based diagnostics equipment specialist.

Bosch offers its U.S. employees a variety of benefits, including medical, dental and vision coverage; long-term care insurance; life and accidental death and dismemberment insurance; travel accident insurance; paid vacations; short and long-term disability coverage; a 401(k) plan and a pension plan; and an educational assistance program.

FINANCIALS: **Sales and profits are in thousands of dollars—add 000 to get the full amount. 2008 Note: Financial information for 2008 was not available for all companies at press time.**

2008 Sales: $	2008 Profits: $	**U.S. Stock Ticker: Private**
2007 Sales: $72,214,300	2007 Profits: $4,443,240	**Int'l Ticker:** Int'l Exchange:
2006 Sales: $68,104,700	2006 Profits: $3,383,100	Employees: 271,000
2005 Sales: $64,638,900	2005 Profits: $3,819,620	Fiscal Year Ends: 12/31
2004 Sales: $50,801,000	2004 Profits: $2,270,410	Parent Company:

SALARIES/BENEFITS:

Pension Plan: Y	ESOP Stock Plan:	Profit Sharing:	Top Exec. Salary: $	Bonus: $
Savings Plan: Y	Stock Purch. Plan:		Second Exec. Salary: $	Bonus: $

OTHER THOUGHTS:

Apparent Women Officers or Directors:
Hot Spot for Advancement for Women/Minorities:

LOCATIONS: ("Y" = Yes)

West:	Southwest:	Midwest:	Southeast:	Northeast:	International:
Y	Y	Y	Y	Y	Y

ROCHE HOLDING LTD

www.roche.com

Industry Group Code: 325412 **Ranks within this company's industry group:** Sales: 3 Profits: 6

Techology:		Medical/Drugs:		Engineering:		Transportation:		Chemicals/Petrochemicals:		Specialty:	
Computers:		Manufacturer:	Y	Design:		Aerospace:		Oil/Gas Products:		Special Services:	
Software:		Contract Research:		Construction:		Automotive:		Chemicals:		Consulting:	
Communications:		Medical Services:		Eng. Services:		Shipping:		Oil/Chem. Svcs.:		Specialty Mgmt.:	
Electronics:		Labs:	Y	Consulting:				Gases:		Products:	
Alternative Energy:		Bio. Services:						Other:		Other:	

TYPES OF BUSINESS:

Pharmaceuticals Manufacturing
Antibiotics
Diagnostics
Cancer Drugs
Virology Products
HIV/AIDS Treatments
Transplant Drugs

BRANDS/DIVISIONS/AFFILIATES:

Genentech Inc
454 Life Sciences
NimbleGen Systems Inc
Therapeutic Human Polyclonals Inc
Ventana Medical Systems Inc
Chugai Pharmaceuticals
Gilead Sciences
Memory Pharmaceuticals Corp

CONTACTS: *Note: Officers with more than one job title may be intentionally listed here more than once.*

Severin Schwan, CEO
Erich Hunziker, CFO
Sylvia Ayyoubi, Head-Human Resources
Jonathan Knowles, Head-Group Research
Gottlieb Keller, General Counsel/Head-Corp. Svcs.
Per-Olof Attinger, Head-Global Corp. Comm.
William M. Burns, CEO-Roche Pharmaceuticals
Jurgen Schwiezer, CEO-Roche Diagnostics
Osamu Nagayama, Pres./CEO-Chugai
Pascal Soriot, Head-Commercial Oper., Pharmaceuticals
Franz B. Humer, Chmn.

Phone: 41-61-688-1111 **Fax:** 41-61-691-9391
Toll-Free:
Address: Grenzacherstrasse 124, Basel, 4070 Switzerland

GROWTH PLANS/SPECIAL FEATURES:

Roche Holding, Ltd. is one of the world's largest health care companies, occupying an industry-leading position in the global diagnostics market and ranking as one of the top producers of pharmaceuticals, with particular recognition in the areas of cancer drugs, autoimmune disease and metabolic disorder treatments, virology and transplantation medicine. The company's operations currently extend to over 150 countries, with additional alliances and research and development agreements with corporate and institutional partners, furthering Roche's collective reach. Among the company's related corporate interests are majority ownership holdings in U.S.-based Genentech and Japanese pharmaceutical firm Chugai. The firm operates through two divisions, Pharmaceuticals and Diagnostics, and its products include the cancer drugs Avastin, Bondronat, Xeloda, Herceptin and Tarceva; the antibiotic Rocephin; the HIV/AIDS treatments Viracept, Invirase and Fuzeon; and Tamiflu, which is used to prevent and treat influenza. Roche companies control proprietary diagnostic technologies across a range of areas, including advanced DNA tests, leading consumer diabetes monitoring devices and applied sciences methodologies for laboratory research. As part of the mobilization of Tamiflu, the company has maintained a long-term strategic partnership with Gilead Sciences to coordinate the licensing and manufacture of the drug, important in the case of a flu pandemic. In January 2008, the firm agreed to acquire Ventana Medical Systems, Inc. for $3.4 billion. In April 2008, Roche's Actemra, a treatment for adult rheumatoid arthritis and juvenile idiopathic arthritis, received approval for use in Japan. In July 2008, the firm announced that it hopes to acquire the remaining shares of biotech giant Genentech. In November 2008, Roche announced that it would acquire Memory Pharmaceuticals Corp., a developer of drug treatments for disorders of the central nervous system such as Alzheimer's, for approximately $50 million.

FINANCIALS: **Sales and profits are in thousands of dollars—add 000 to get the full amount. 2008 Note: Financial information for 2008 was not available for all companies at press time.**

2008 Sales: $41,676,500	2008 Profits: $7,803,000	**U.S. Stock Ticker: RHHBY**
2007 Sales: $40,650,000	2007 Profits: $8,600,000	**Int'l Ticker: RO** Int'l Exchange: Zurich-SWX
2006 Sales: $34,851,500	2006 Profits: $7,116,030	Employees: 68,218
2005 Sales: $27,385,668	2005 Profits: $5,189,777	Fiscal Year Ends: 12/31
2004 Sales: $22,767,021	2004 Profits: $5,446,567	Parent Company:

SALARIES/BENEFITS:

Pension Plan: Y	ESOP Stock Plan:	Profit Sharing:	Top Exec. Salary: $	Bonus: $
Savings Plan:	Stock Purch. Plan:		Second Exec. Salary: $	Bonus: $

OTHER THOUGHTS:

Apparent Women Officers or Directors: 4
Hot Spot for Advancement for Women/Minorities: Y

LOCATIONS: ("Y" = Yes)

West:	Southwest:	Midwest:	Southeast:	Northeast:	International:
Y	Y	Y	Y	Y	Y

ROCKWELL AUTOMATION INC

www.rockwellautomation.com

Industry Group Code: 334500 **Ranks within this company's industry group:** Sales: 3 Profits: 3

Techology:		Medical/Drugs:		Engineering:		Transportation:		Chemicals/Petrochemicals:		Specialty:	
Computers:	Y	Manufacturer:		Design:		Aerospace:		Oil/Gas Products:		Special Services:	Y
Software:	Y	Contract Research:		Construction:		Automotive:		Chemicals:		Consulting:	
Communications:		Medical Services:		Eng. Services:		Shipping:		Oil/Chem. Svcs.:		Specialty Mgmt.:	
Electronics:		Labs:		Consulting:				Gases:		Products:	Y
Alternative Energy:		Bio. Services:						Other:		Other:	

TYPES OF BUSINESS:

Architecture & Software Products
Control Products & Services

BRANDS/DIVISIONS/AFFILIATES:

Allen-Bradley
Rockwell Software
ProsCon Holdings Ltd.
Control Services Group, Ltd.
ICS Triplex
Pavilion Technologies, Inc.
Incuity Software Inc
CEDES Safety & Automation AG

CONTACTS: *Note: Officers with more than one job title may be intentionally listed here more than once.*

Keith Nosbusch, CEO
Theodore D. Crandall, CFO/Sr. VP
John McDermott, Sr. VP-Global Sales & Mktg.
Susan Schmitt, Sr. VP-Human Resources
Bob Honor, Info. Svcs.
Sujeet Chand, CTO/Sr. VP-Advanced Tech.
Marty Thomas, Sr. VP-Eng. Svcs.
Douglas Hagerman, General Counsel/Sr. VP/Corp. Sec.
Marty Thomas, Sr. VP-Oper.
John Cohn, Sr. VP-Strategic Dev.
John Cohn, Sr. VP-Comm.
Rondi Rohr-Dralle, VP-Investor Rel.
Bob Becker, VP-Latin America Region
Lee Tschanz, VP-North America Region
Steve Eisenbrown, Sr. VP-Architecture & Software
Keith Nosbusch, Chmn.
Keiran Coulton, Pres., Asia Pacific Region

Phone: 414-382-2000 **Fax:** 414-382-4444
Toll-Free:
Address: 1201 S. 2nd St., Milwaukee, WI 53204-2496 US

GROWTH PLANS/SPECIAL FEATURES:

Rockwell Automation is a global provider of industrial automation power, control and information products and services. It operates in two segments: Architecture & software; and control products & solutions. The architecture & software operating segment contains all elements of the company's integrated control and information architecture capable of connecting the customer's entire manufacturing enterprise. The division's integrated architecture and Logix controllers perform multiple types of control and monitoring applications, including discrete, batch, continuous process, drive system, motion and machine safety across various industrial machinery, plants and processes; and supply real time information to supervisory software and plant-wide information systems. Products include control platforms, software, I/O devices, communication networks, high performance rotary and linear motion control systems, electronic operator interface devices, condition based monitoring systems, sensors, industrial computers and machine safety components. These products are marketed primarily under the Allen-Bradley and Rockwell Software brand names. Major markets served include food and beverage, automotive, water/wastewater, oil and gas, and home and personal care. The control products & solutions segment's portfolio includes low voltage and medium voltage electro-mechanical and electronic motor starters, motor and circuit protection devices, AC/DC variable frequency drives, contractors, push buttons, signaling devices, termination and protection devices, relays and timers and condition sensors; value-added packaged solutions, including configured drives, motor control centers and custom engineered panels; automation and information solutions, including custom engineered hardware and software systems for discrete, process, motion, drives and manufacturing information applications; and services designed to help maximize a customer's automation investment and provide life-cycle support, including multi-vendor customer technical support and repair, asset management, training and predictive and preventative maintenance. In 2008, the company acquired Incuity Software, Inc.; CEDES Safety & Automation AG; and Pavilion Technologies, Inc. In early 2009, the firm agreed to acquire the majority of the assets of Rutter Hinz, Inc.

FINANCIALS: **Sales and profits are in thousands of dollars—add 000 to get the full amount. 2008 Note: Financial information for 2008 was not available for all companies at press time.**

2008 Sales: $5,697,800
2007 Sales: $5,003,900
2006 Sales: $4,556,400
2005 Sales: $4,111,500
2004 Sales: $4,411,100

2008 Profits: $577,600
2007 Profits: $1,487,800
2006 Profits: $607,000
2005 Profits: $540,000
2004 Profits: $414,900

U.S. Stock Ticker: ROK
Int'l Ticker: Int'l Exchange:
Employees: 21,000
Fiscal Year Ends: 9/30
Parent Company:

SALARIES/BENEFITS:

Pension Plan: ESOP Stock Plan: Profit Sharing: Top Exec. Salary: $1,030,840 Bonus: $561,600
Savings Plan: Stock Purch. Plan: Second Exec. Salary: $531,931 Bonus: $196,200

OTHER THOUGHTS:

Apparent Women Officers or Directors: 2
Hot Spot for Advancement for Women/Minorities:

LOCATIONS: ("Y" = Yes)

West:	Southwest:	Midwest:	Southeast:	Northeast:	International:
Y	Y	Y	Y	Y	Y

Note: Financial information, benefits and other data can change quickly and may vary from those stated here.

ROHM CO LTD

www.rohm.com

Industry Group Code: 334413 **Ranks within this company's industry group:** Sales: 11 Profits: 8

Techology:		Medical/Drugs:		Engineering:		Transportation:		Chemicals/Petrochemicals:		Specialty:	
Computers:		Manufacturer:		Design:		Aerospace:		Oil/Gas Products:		Special Services:	
Software:		Contract Research:		Construction:		Automotive:		Chemicals:		Consulting:	
Communications:		Medical Services:		Eng. Services:		Shipping:		Oil/Chem. Svcs.:		Specialty Mgmt.:	
Electronics:	Y	Labs:		Consulting:				Gases:		Products:	
Alternative Energy:		Bio. Services:						Other:		Other:	

TYPES OF BUSINESS:

Electronic Components Manufacturing
Integrated Circuits
Discrete Semiconductor Devices
Passive Components
Resistors & Capacitors
Display Devices
LED Displays

BRANDS/DIVISIONS/AFFILIATES:

OKI Semiconductor Co., Ltd.

CONTACTS: *Note: Officers with more than one job title may be intentionally listed here more than once.*

Ken Sato, CEO
Ken Sato, Pres.
Satoshi Sawamura, Chief Sr. Dir.-Sales/Managing Dir.
Nobuo Hatta, Chief Dir.-Admin.
Eiichi Sasayama, Chief Dir.-Acct.
Naotoshi Watanabe, Managing Dir./Chief Sr. Dir.-Discrete Modules Prod
Toru Okada, Chief Dir.-Quality & Environment
Osamu Hattori, Chief Dir.-Asia Sales

Phone: 81-75-311-2121 **Fax:** 81-75-315-0172
Toll-Free:
Address: 21 Saiin Mizosaki-cho, Ukyo-ku, Kyoto, 615-8585 Japan

GROWTH PLANS/SPECIAL FEATURES:

Rohm Co., Ltd. is a Japanese manufacturer of electronic components and component systems. Rohm makes components for a number of applications, including car electronics, mobile phones, FPD TVs and DVD recorders. The firm's products include integrated circuits (ICs), discrete semiconductor devices, passive components and display components. Its ICs, which generated approximately 43.7% of the firm's sales in 2008, include monolithic ICs, power modules and photo link modules. Rohm's discrete semiconductor devices, which generated approximately 41.6% of its 2008 sales, include transistors, diodes, LEDs and laser diodes. The firm's passive components, which generated approximately 6.3% of its 2008 sales, include resistors and tantalum capacitors. Rohm's display components, which generated approximately 8.4% of its 2008 sales, include thermal heads, image sensor heads and LED displays. Of its 2008 sales, 55.2% were in Asia, 36.9% in Japan, 4.3% in Europe and 3.6% in the Americas. Rohm has 10 manufacturing centers in Japan and eight others throughout Korea, China, Thailand, Malaysia and the Philippines; 12 research and development centers worldwide, including one in San Diego; 10 quality assurance centers worldwide, including one in Novi, Michigan; and 50 sales offices worldwide, including eight in the U.S. In October 2008, Rohm acquired OKI Semiconductor Co., Ltd., the semiconductor business of OKI Electric Industry Co., Ltd.

FINANCIALS: **Sales and profits are in thousands of dollars—add 000 to get the full amount. 2008 Note: Financial information for 2008 was not available for all companies at press time.**

2008 Sales: $3,734,100	2008 Profits: $319,300	**U.S. Stock Ticker: ROHCF.PK**
2007 Sales: $3,950,800	2007 Profits: $474,500	**Int'l Ticker: 6963** Int'l Exchange: Tokyo-TSE
2006 Sales: $3,877,900	2006 Profits: $483,000	Employees: 20,279
2005 Sales: $3,690,200	2005 Profits: $451,400	Fiscal Year Ends: 3/31
2004 Sales: $3,355,000	2004 Profits: $601,104	Parent Company:

SALARIES/BENEFITS:

Pension Plan:	ESOP Stock Plan:	Profit Sharing:	Top Exec. Salary: $	Bonus: $
Savings Plan:	Stock Purch. Plan:		Second Exec. Salary: $	Bonus: $

OTHER THOUGHTS:

Apparent Women Officers or Directors:
Hot Spot for Advancement for Women/Minorities:

LOCATIONS: ("Y" = Yes)

West:	Southwest:	Midwest:	Southeast:	Northeast:	International:
Y	Y	Y	Y	Y	Y

ROLLSROYCE PLC

www.rolls-royce.com

Industry Group Code: 336410 **Ranks within this company's industry group:** Sales: 14 Profits: 21

Techology:		Medical/Drugs:		Engineering:		Transportation:		Chemicals/Petrochemicals:		Specialty:	
Computers:		Manufacturer:		Design:	Y	Aerospace:	Y	Oil/Gas Products:		Special Services:	Y
Software:		Contract Research:		Construction:	Y	Automotive:		Chemicals:		Consulting:	
Communications:		Medical Services:		Eng. Services:	Y	Shipping:		Oil/Chem. Svcs.:	Y	Specialty Mgmt.:	
Electronics:		Labs:		Consulting:				Gases:		Products:	
Alternative Energy:		Bio. Services:						Other:		Other:	

TYPES OF BUSINESS:

Aerospace Engines
Power Generation Solutions
Marine Propulsion Systems
Aftermarket & Support Services

BRANDS/DIVISIONS/AFFILIATES:

Rolls-Royce North America
Syncrolift, Inc.
Allen Gears
Clayton Equipment
Sourcerer
Rolls-Royce Fuel Cell Systems, Inc.
Rolls-Royce Deutschland

CONTACTS: *Note: Officers with more than one job title may be intentionally listed here more than once.*

John Rose, CEO
Mike J. Terrett, COO
Tom Brown, Dir.-Human Resources
Colin P Smith, Dir.-Tech.
Colin P Smith, Dir.-Eng.
Tim Rayner, General Counsel/Company Sec.
Charles E. Blundell, Dir.-Public Affairs
Andrew Shilston, Dir.-Finance
Miles Cowdry, Pres., Svcs.
Mark King, Pres., Civilian Aerospace
John Paterson, Pres., Marine
Axel Arendt, Pres., Defense Aerospace
Simon Robertson, Chmn.
James M. Guyette, CEO/Pres., Rolls-Royce North America, Inc.
Mike Orris, Chief Procurement Officer

Phone: 44-20-7222-9020	**Fax:** 44-20-7227-9170
Toll-Free:	
Address: 65 Buckingham Gate, London, SW1E 6AT UK	

GROWTH PLANS/SPECIAL FEATURES:

Rolls-Royce plc designs and produces engines and power systems for civilian aerospace, defense aerospace, marine and energy markets worldwide. It has offices and operations in 50 countries and customers in 150 countries. In civilian aerospace, it supplies over 600 airlines and 2,100 corporate and utility operators, with approximately 12,500 jet engines in service. Defense aerospace operations serve 160 customers in 103 countries, with offerings including military transport aircraft, helicopters and combat aircraft. In the marine sector, it serves more than 2,000 customers, including 70 navies and the U.K.'s nuclear submarine fleet, with equipment installed on approximately 20,000 commercial and naval vessels operating around the world. Energy solutions include power generation and distribution equipment sold in 120 countries. Rolls-Royce also offers support services for its engines through a global network of 70 maintenance centers. Services include operation management; repairs and overhauls; and customer training. In general, civilian aerospace operations generate 19% of sales; defense, 10%; marine, 13%; energy, 3%; and aftermarket services, 55%. Rolls-Royce has separate operating subsidiaries for China, Germany, India, Korea, Malaysia, Singapore and North America; as well as subsidiaries from various acquisitions. These include Syncrolift, Inc., which manufactures equipment for lifting ships out of and into water; Allen Gears, which designs and manufactures high-performance gearboxes; and Sourcerer, which uses procurement services to integrate supply chains. Rolls-Royce won, among others, the following engine-supply contracts in 2008: an $880 million contract with Synergy Aerospace for 10 to 20 A350XWBs; a $500 million contract with a MatlinPatterson Global Advisers LLC affiliate, for six A330 freighters; a $600 million contract with Iberia for 3-6 A340-600s; and a $1.2 billion contract with Hong Kong Airlines for 20 A330-300s. The company has announced that it will eliminate between 1,500 and 2,000 jobs during 2009.

FINANCIALS: **Sales and profits are in thousands of dollars—add 000 to get the full amount. 2008 Note: Financial information for 2008 was not available for all companies at press time.**

2008 Sales: $13,323,400	2008 Profits: $-1,973,130	**U.S. Stock Ticker: RYCEY**
2007 Sales: $10,907,200	2007 Profits: $880,210	**Int'l Ticker: RR** Int'l Exchange: London-LSE
2006 Sales: $13,953,500	2006 Profits: $1,937,200	Employees: 36,200
2005 Sales: $12,338,640	2005 Profits: $648,748	Fiscal Year Ends: 12/31
2004 Sales: $1,102,996	2004 Profits: $493,572	Parent Company:

SALARIES/BENEFITS:

Pension Plan:	ESOP Stock Plan:	Profit Sharing:	Top Exec. Salary: $907,500	Bonus: $283,500
Savings Plan: Y	Stock Purch. Plan:		Second Exec. Salary: $607,500	Bonus: $189,000

OTHER THOUGHTS:

Apparent Women Officers or Directors: 1
Hot Spot for Advancement for Women/Minorities:

LOCATIONS: ("Y" = Yes)

West:	Southwest:	Midwest:	Southeast:	Northeast:	International:
Y	Y	Y	Y	Y	Y

ROSETTA INPHARMATICS LLC

www.rii.com

Industry Group Code: 541710 **Ranks within this company's industry group:** Sales: Profits:

Techology:		Medical/Drugs:		Engineering:		Transportation:		Chemicals/Petrochemicals:		Specialty:	
Computers:		Manufacturer:		Design:		Aerospace:		Oil/Gas Products:		Special Services:	Y
Software:	Y	Contract Research:	Y	Construction:		Automotive:		Chemicals:		Consulting:	
Communications:		Medical Services:		Eng. Services:		Shipping:		Oil/Chem. Svcs.:		Specialty Mgmt.:	
Electronics:		Labs:	Y	Consulting:				Gases:		Products:	
Alternative Energy:		Bio. Services:						Other:		Other:	

TYPES OF BUSINESS:

Biotechnology Research
Bioinformatics Software
Gene Expression Research
DNA Microarrays

BRANDS/DIVISIONS/AFFILIATES:

Rosetta Biosoftware
Rosetta Resolver
Rosetta Syllego
Rosetta Elucidator

CONTACTS: *Note: Officers with more than one job title may be intentionally listed here more than once.*

S.J. Rupert Vessey, Site Head
Douglas E. Bassett, Jr., Co-Site Head
Stephen H. Friend, Pres.
Eric Schadt, Exec. Scientific Dir.-Genetics
S.J. Rupert Vessey, VP-Molecular Profiling
Douglas E. Bassett, Jr., Exec. Dir.-Molecular Profiling

Phone: 206-802-7000 **Fax:** 206-802-6501
Toll-Free:
Address: 401 Terry Ave. N., Seattle, WA 98109 US

GROWTH PLANS/SPECIAL FEATURES:

Rosetta Inpharmatics, a wholly-owned subsidiary of Merck and Co., uses gene expression research and DNA microarray technologies to support Merck's drug discovery efforts and to enhance drug development activities. Through its Rosetta Biosoftware business unit, the company continues the commercial release of the Rosetta Resolver gene expression data analysis system, an enterprise-level bioinformatics software package launched in 2000 and currently in its seventh version. The software remains the firm's flagship product, licensed to many of the world's leading academic research institutions and life sciences corporations. The firm also offers two other software packages: Rosetta Syllego, for genetic data management; and Rosetta Elucidator, for protein expression analysis. The company's expertise has led to new applications of gene expression technologies in areas including molecular toxicology, biomarker discovery and disease classification. Rosetta Inpharmatics is committed to using genomic research and data analysis to enable more accurate selection of drug targets and more efficient drug development, while also developing new tools to extend the analysis of gene expression data generated by DNA microarrays. These developments not only support the pharmaceutical industry, but also bring new capabilities to other sectors, including agrochemical research and biotechnology. In June 2008, the firm released version 2.0 of its Rosetta Syllego software, with an expanded set of data analysis tools. In December 2008, Rosetta released version 3.2 of its Rosetta Elucidator software.

Rosetta's work atmosphere includes clubs for rock climbers and theater goers, as well as a post-doctorate program to facilitate the transition of fellows to independent scientific investigators in a rigorous research setting. Employees benefits include education assistance; scholarship programs; paid vacation; wellness centers; daycare centers; flexible work arrangements; a 401(k) plan and a pension plan; flexible spending accounts; and medical, dental, prescription, and vision insurance.

FINANCIALS: **Sales and profits are in thousands of dollars—add 000 to get the full amount. 2008 Note: Financial information for 2008 was not available for all companies at press time.**

2008 Sales: $	2008 Profits: $	**U.S. Stock Ticker: Subsidiary**
2007 Sales: $	2007 Profits: $	**Int'l Ticker:** Int'l Exchange:
2006 Sales: $	2006 Profits: $	Employees: 266
2005 Sales: $	2005 Profits: $	Fiscal Year Ends: 12/31
2004 Sales: $	2004 Profits: $	Parent Company: MERCK & CO INC

SALARIES/BENEFITS:

Pension Plan: Y	ESOP Stock Plan:	Profit Sharing:	Top Exec. Salary: $	Bonus: $
Savings Plan: Y	Stock Purch. Plan:		Second Exec. Salary: $	Bonus: $

OTHER THOUGHTS:

Apparent Women Officers or Directors:
Hot Spot for Advancement for Women/Minorities:

LOCATIONS: ("Y" = Yes)

West:	Southwest:	Midwest:	Southeast:	Northeast:	International:
Y					

ROYAL DUTCH SHELL (SHELL GROUP)

www.shell.com

Industry Group Code: 211111 **Ranks within this company's industry group:** Sales: 2 Profits: 2

Techology:		Medical/Drugs:		Engineering:		Transportation:		Chemicals/Petrochemicals:		Specialty:	
Computers:		Manufacturer:		Design:		Aerospace:		Oil/Gas Products:	Y	Special Services:	Y
Software:		Contract Research:		Construction:		Automotive:		Chemicals:	Y	Consulting:	Y
Communications:		Medical Services:		Eng. Services:		Shipping:	Y	Oil/Chem. Svcs.:	Y	Specialty Mgmt.:	
Electronics:		Labs:		Consulting:				Gases:	Y	Products:	
Alternative Energy:	Y	Bio. Services:						Other:	Y	Other:	

TYPES OF BUSINESS:

Oil & Gas-Exploration & Production
Gas Stations
Refineries
Solar & Wind Power
Chemicals
Consulting & Technology Services
Hydrogen & Fuel Cell Technology

BRANDS/DIVISIONS/AFFILIATES:

Shell Oil Co
Shell Canada Limited
Shell Chemicals Limited
Shell WindEnergy BV
Shell Trading
Shell Hydrogen
Shell Global Solutions
Duvernay Oil Corporation

CONTACTS: *Note: Officers with more than one job title may be intentionally listed here more than once.*

Jeroen van der Veer, CEO
Peter Voser, CFO
Hugh Mitchell, Dir.-Human Resources
Beat Hess, Dir.-Legal
Linda Cook, Exec. Dir.-Gas & Power
Mark Williams, Dir.-Downstream
Malcom Brinded, Exec. Dir.-Exploration & Prod.
Roxanne Decyk, Dir.-Corp. Affairs
Jorma Ollila, Chmn.

Phone: 31-70-377-9111 **Fax:** 31-70-377-3115
Toll-Free:
Address: Carel van Bylandtlaan 16, The Hague, 2596 HR The Netherlands

GROWTH PLANS/SPECIAL FEATURES:

Royal Dutch Shell (Shell) is one of the world's largest oil and gas groups, with operations in over 110 countries. It operates five core businesses: Exploration & Production (E&P; Gas & Power (G&P); Oil Products; Chemicals; and Oil Sands. E&P has oil and gas activities in nearly 40 countries producing 3.3 million barrels of oil equivalent (BOE) daily. G&P works closely with E&P to produce, process and transport natural gas and also oversees Shell's wind and solar power operations. The Oil Products division manufactures and markets petroleum products worldwide; and includes the operation of Shell's network of approximately 45,000 gasoline stations. The Chemicals business produces petrochemicals and derivatives through a number of business units, including aromatics, solvents and detergent alcohols. Lastly, Oil Sands harvests bitumen from Muskeg River Mine, in Canada, which it transforms into synthetic crude oil products. Shell operates numerous companies outside its core business areas. Shell Trading trades about 14 million BOE per day, including crude oil, refined products, natural gas and chemicals. Shell Hydrogen researches hydrogen and fuel cells. Shell Global Solutions provides consulting and technology services to the petrochemical and processing industries. In July 2008, the firm sold its stake in the London Array, an offshore wind farm located in the outer Thames estuary. In August 2008, subsidiary Shell Canada Limited completed its acquisition of Duvernay Oil Corporation. In December 2008, Shell sold its interests in seven North Sea oil fields to a subsidiary of Abu Dhabi National Energy Company, in a transaction valued at approximately $631 million. In February 2009, the company announced a partnership with Mitsubishi Corporation for the development of natural gas infrastructure in the oil fields of southern Iraq.

Employees of Shell receive telecommuting opportunities; flexible schedules; maternity/paternity leave; a pension plan; and medical and dental care, among other benefits.

FINANCIALS: **Sales and profits are in thousands of dollars—add 000 to get the full amount. 2008 Note: Financial information for 2008 was not available for all companies at press time.**

2008 Sales: $458,361,000 2008 Profits: $26,476,000
2007 Sales: $355,782,000 2007 Profits: $31,926,000
2006 Sales: $318,845,000 2006 Profits: $26,311,000
2005 Sales: $306,731,000 2005 Profits: $25,311,000
2004 Sales: $265,190,000 2004 Profits: $18,183,000

U.S. Stock Ticker: RDSA
Int'l Ticker: RDSA Int'l Exchange: Amsterdam-Euronext
Employees: 102,000
Fiscal Year Ends: 12/31
Parent Company:

SALARIES/BENEFITS:

Pension Plan: Y ESOP Stock Plan: Profit Sharing: Top Exec. Salary: $ Bonus: $
Savings Plan: Stock Purch. Plan: Y Second Exec. Salary: $ Bonus: $

OTHER THOUGHTS:

Apparent Women Officers or Directors: 3
Hot Spot for Advancement for Women/Minorities: Y

LOCATIONS: ("Y" = Yes)

West:	Southwest:	Midwest:	Southeast:	Northeast:	International:
Y	Y	Y	Y	Y	Y

ROYAL PHILIPS ELECTRONICS NV

www.philips.com

Industry Group Code: 334310 **Ranks within this company's industry group:** Sales: 4 Profits: 7

Techology:		Medical/Drugs:		Engineering:		Transportation:		Chemicals/Petrochemicals:		Specialty:	
Computers:		Manufacturer:		Design:		Aerospace:		Oil/Gas Products:		Special Services:	
Software:		Contract Research:		Construction:		Automotive:		Chemicals:		Consulting:	
Communications:		Medical Services:		Eng. Services:		Shipping:		Oil/Chem. Svcs.:		Specialty Mgmt.:	
Electronics:	Y	Labs:		Consulting:				Gases:		Products:	
Alternative Energy:		Bio. Services:						Other:		Other:	

TYPES OF BUSINESS:

Manufacturing-Electrical & Electronic Equipment
Consumer Electronics & Appliances
Lighting Systems
Medical Imaging Equipment
Semiconductors
Consulting Services
Nanotech Research
MEMS

BRANDS/DIVISIONS/AFFILIATES:

Koninklijke Philips Electronics N.V.
Philips Electronics North America Corp.
Power Sentry
Witt Biomedical Corporation
Intermagnetics General Corporation
Bodine Company (The)
Partners in Lighting
Lumileds Lighting

CONTACTS: *Note: Officers with more than one job title may be intentionally listed here more than once.*

Gerard Kleisterlee, CEO
Gerard Kleisterlee, Pres.
Pierre-Jean Sivignon, CFO/Exec. VP
Rick Harwig, CTO
Steve Rusckowski, CEO-Philips Healthcare
Theo van Deursen, CEO-Lighting
Gottfried Dutine, Exec. VP
Andrea Ragnetti, CEO-Phillips Consumer Lifestyle
W. De Kleuver, Chmn.

Phone: 31-20-59-77-777 **Fax:** 31-20-59-77-070
Toll-Free: 877-248-4237
Address: Breitner Center, Amstelplein 2, Amsterdam, 1096 BC The Netherlands

GROWTH PLANS/SPECIAL FEATURES:

Royal Philips Electronics N.V. (Philips) is an electronics company organized into three divisions: Philips Healthcare, Philips Lighting and Philips Consumer Lifestyle. The Philips Healthcare division includes x-ray, ultrasound, magnetic resonance, nuclear medicine and positron emission tomography equipment. Furthermore, this division offers training and education, business consultancy, finance, leasing and e-business services in the health care sector. The Philips Lighting division offers a range of products including incandescent, halogen and fluorescent lighting, as well as fixtures and automotive headlights. The Philips Consumer Lifestyle division manufactures and markets products such as wide-screen televisions, optical disc products, digital television systems, digital cameras and LCD projectors. Additionally, the segment produces domestic appliances such as electric shavers, kitchen appliances, vacuum cleaners and irons. The firm's research initiatives include a wide range of nanotechnology and MEMS applications, such as soft lithography, silicon nanowires for microelectrical devices, nanoLEDs, quantum dot composites, 10-nanometer scale transistors, carbon nanotube field emitters for electron microscopes and more. Recent activity includes the acquisitions of Lumileds Lighting, Partners in Lighting and Intermagnetics General Corporation, as well as the sale of FEI Company, Philips Sound Solutions, Advanced Metrology Systems, its remaining Mobile Phone activities and the manufacturing operations of the Philips Automotive Playback Modules. In 2008, the company acquired The Genlyte Group Incorporated; VISICU Inc.; Respironics, Inc.; Shenzhen Goldway Industrial, Inc.; Dixtal Biomedica e Tecnologia; Alpha X-Ray Technologies; and the aerosol business of Medel SpA. Also in 2008, the firm sold its 90% stake in High Tech Plastics (HTP) Optics; Set-Top Boxes; Connectivity Solutions; and its 69.5% interest in MedQuist Inc.

Philips' U.S. employees receive benefits including flexible spending accounts and employee assistance. The company is working to develop green products in an effort to increase Philips' ecological sustainability; it has introduced more than 100 such products to date.

FINANCIALS: **Sales and profits are in thousands of dollars—add 000 to get the full amount. 2008 Note: Financial information for 2008 was not available for all companies at press time.**

2008 Sales: $37,183,000	2008 Profits: $-262,000	**U.S. Stock Ticker: PHG**
2007 Sales: $39,459,000	2007 Profits: $6,138,000	**Int'l Ticker: PHIA** Int'l Exchange: Amsterdam-Euronext
2006 Sales: $35,537,000	2006 Profits: $7,091,000	Employees: 121,000
2005 Sales: $35,972,000	2005 Profits: $3,395,000	Fiscal Year Ends: 12/31
2004 Sales: $41,070,000	2004 Profits: $3,842,000	Parent Company:

SALARIES/BENEFITS:

Pension Plan:	ESOP Stock Plan:	Profit Sharing:	Top Exec. Salary: $1,235,219	Bonus: $
Savings Plan:	Stock Purch. Plan:		Second Exec. Salary: $1,017,239	Bonus: $

OTHER THOUGHTS:

Apparent Women Officers or Directors: 1
Hot Spot for Advancement for Women/Minorities:

LOCATIONS: ("Y" = Yes)

West:	Southwest:	Midwest:	Southeast:	Northeast:	International:
Y	Y	Y	Y	Y	Y

Note: Financial information, benefits and other data can change quickly and may vary from those stated here.

SAAB AB

www.saabgroup.com

Industry Group Code: 336410 **Ranks within this company's industry group:** Sales: Profits:

Techology:		Medical/Drugs:		Engineering:		Transportation:		Chemicals/Petrochemicals:		Specialty:	
Computers:		Manufacturer:		Design:	Y	Aerospace:	Y	Oil/Gas Products:		Special Services:	
Software:		Contract Research:		Construction:	Y	Automotive:		Chemicals:		Consulting:	
Communications:		Medical Services:		Eng. Services:	Y	Shipping:		Oil/Chem. Svcs.:		Specialty Mgmt.:	
Electronics:		Labs:		Consulting:	Y			Gases:		Products:	
Alternative Energy:		Bio. Services:						Other:		Other:	

TYPES OF BUSINESS:

Aerospace Manufacturing
Security System Development
Electronic Warfare
Aeronautics Training

BRANDS/DIVISIONS/AFFILIATES:

SAAB Aerostructures
SAAB Aerosystems
SAAB Aerotech
SAAB Air Craft Leasing
SAAB Security
SAAB Surveillance Systems
SAAB Training Systems
Vingtech Saab AS

CONTACTS: *Note: Officers with more than one job title may be intentionally listed here more than once.*

Ake Svensson, CEO
Ake Svensson, Pres.
Lars Granlof, CFO/Sr. VP
Mats Warstedt, Sr. VP-Mktg.
Mikael Grodzinsky, Sr. VP-Human Resources
Anne Gynnerstedt, Sr. VP-Legal Affairs/Sec.
Dan Jangblad, Sr. VP-Strategy & Bus. Dev.
Cecilia Schön Jansson, Sr. VP-Corp. Comm. & Public Affairs
Ann-Sofi Jönsson, Gen. Mgr.-Investor Rel.
Peter Sandehed, Sr. VP-Treasury
Lennart Sindahl, Exec. VP/Head-Aeronautics
Dan-Ake Enstedt, Exec. VP/Head-Defense & Security
Lena Olving, Exec. VP/Head-Systems & Products
Peter Sandehed, Sr. VP-Mergers & Acquisitions
Marcus Wallenberg, Chmn.
Riaz Saloojee, Pres., Saab South Africa

Phone: 46-8-463-0000	**Fax:** 46-8-463-0152
Toll-Free:	
Address: Box 70 363, Stockholm, 107 24 Sweden	

GROWTH PLANS/SPECIAL FEATURES:

SAAB AB is a Sweden-based aerospace and defense company that designs and manufactures military and civilian aircraft; aeronautical systems; and defense and security technology. The company operates in three segments: aeronautics; systems and products; and defense and security solutions. The aeronautics segment designs airframe structures for companies such as Airbus and Boeing; develops systems for the JAS 39 Gripen aircraft; and leases the Saab 340 and Saab 2000 regional aircraft. The systems and products segment designs and manufactures avionics and electronic warfare systems; camouflage systems; missles and short-range weapons; microwave and radar systems; military equipment simulators; and underwater military systems. The defense and security solutions segment offers military-grade telecommunication infrastructures, surveillance systems, technical support for aircraft ground operations; servicing of Saab aircraft; and consultancy services. Saab AB operates via 17 subsidiaries: SAAB Aerostructures; SAAB Aerosystems; SAAB Aerotech; SAAB Air Craft Leasing; Saab Avitronics; SAAB Barracuda; SAAB Bofors Dynamics; SAAB Grintek; SAAB Microwave Systems; SAAB Security; SAAB Surveillance Systems; SAAB Systems; SAAB Training Systems; SAAB Transponder Tech; SAAB Underwater Systems; Combitech; and Gripen International. Late in 2008, the firm formed a new joint venture, Vingtech Saab AS., with Simrad Optronics ASA for the purpose of furthering its research and development of products associated with high tech optronics. Additionally, the company sold its Saab Space AB subsidiary to Swiss firm RUAG Holding AG.

FINANCIALS: Sales and profits are in thousands of dollars—add 000 to get the full amount. 2008 Note: Financial information for 2008 was not available for all companies at press time.

2008 Sales: $	2008 Profits: $	**U.S. Stock Ticker:**
2007 Sales: $	2007 Profits: $	**Int'l Ticker: SAAB** Int'l Exchange: Stockholm-SSE
2006 Sales: $	2006 Profits: $	Employees:
2005 Sales: $	2005 Profits: $	Fiscal Year Ends: 12/31
2004 Sales: $	2004 Profits: $	Parent Company:

SALARIES/BENEFITS:

Pension Plan:	ESOP Stock Plan:	Profit Sharing:	Top Exec. Salary: $	Bonus: $
Savings Plan:	Stock Purch. Plan:		Second Exec. Salary: $	Bonus: $

OTHER THOUGHTS:

Apparent Women Officers or Directors: 5
Hot Spot for Advancement for Women/Minorities: Y

LOCATIONS: ("Y" = Yes)

West:	Southwest:	Midwest:	Southeast:	Northeast:	International:
			Y		Y

SAFRAN SA

www.safran-group.com

Industry Group Code: 336410 **Ranks within this company's industry group:** Sales: 13 Profits: 18

Techology:		Medical/Drugs:		Engineering:		Transportation:		Chemicals/Petrochemicals:		Specialty:	
Computers:		Manufacturer:		Design:	Y	Aerospace:	Y	Oil/Gas Products:		Special Services:	
Software:		Contract Research:		Construction:		Automotive:		Chemicals:		Consulting:	
Communications:	Y	Medical Services:		Eng. Services:	Y	Shipping:		Oil/Chem. Svcs.:		Specialty Mgmt.:	
Electronics:		Labs:		Consulting:				Gases:		Products:	
Alternative Energy:		Bio. Services:						Other:		Other:	

TYPES OF BUSINESS:

Aerospace-Engines
Aircraft Equipment
Defense Security Equipment
Communications Equipment
Aerospace Propulsion

BRANDS/DIVISIONS/AFFILIATES:

SAGEM SA
Snecma
Turbomeca
Microturbo
Aircelle
Messier-Dowty
Sagem Defense Securite
Sagem Mobiles

CONTACTS: *Note: Officers with more than one job title may be intentionally listed here more than once.*

Jean-Pual Herteman, CEO
Xavier Lagarde, Exec. VP-Comm.
Marc Ventre, Exec. VP-Propulsion
Yves Leclere, Exec. VP-Equipment
Jean-Paul Herteman, Exec. VP-Defense Security
Francis Mer, Chmn.

Phone: 33-1-40-60-80-80 **Fax:** 33-1-40-60-81-02
Toll-Free:
Address: 2 Blvd. du General Martial Valin, Paris, 75724 France

GROWTH PLANS/SPECIAL FEATURES:

Safran SA, formerly SAGEM SA, is a Paris-based international group of high-technology companies. The group has industrial, design and commercial operations in more than 30 countries. Safran operates in four divisions. The Aerospace Propulsion division produces engines and parts for civil and military aircraft, helicopter turbines and the ballistics and space industries. The division operates through several subsidiaries, including Snecma, Turbomeca and Microturbo. The Aicraft Equipment division provides mechanical, hydro-mechanical and electro-mechanical equipment for the aeronautics industry through its subsidiaries, including Aircelle and Messier-Dowty. The Defense Security division produces a range of defense and security equipment, including military avionics and aeronautic systems, navigation equipment, optronic systems, biometric identification systems and secure transaction terminals. Defense Security subsidiaries include Sagem Defense Securite, Sagem Monetel and Sagem Morpho. The Communications division consolidates Sagem Mobiles and its subsidiaries' mobile phones businesses. The subsidiary designs, develops, manufactures and markets a wide range of Sagem brand mobile phones and associated accessories. Sagem Mobiles also offers original design manufacturer (ODM) capabilities, to develop mobile phones sold by its partners under their brand names. In February 2008, subsidiary Sagem Securite announced an agreement with Interpol to supply it and its 186 member states with the MetaMorpho automated fingerprint identification system.

FINANCIALS: **Sales and profits are in thousands of dollars—add 000 to get the full amount. 2008 Note: Financial information for 2008 was not available for all companies at press time.**

2008 Sales: $13,666,700
2007 Sales: $15,881,600
2006 Sales: $15,461,300
2005 Sales: $14,433,600
2004 Sales: $

2008 Profits: $206,410
2007 Profits: $537,200
2006 Profits: $241,560
2005 Profits: $605,950
2004 Profits: $

U.S. Stock Ticker:
Int'l Ticker: SAF Int'l Exchange: Paris-Euronext
Employees: 61,400
Fiscal Year Ends: 12/31
Parent Company:

SALARIES/BENEFITS:

Pension Plan:	ESOP Stock Plan:	Profit Sharing:	Top Exec. Salary: $	Bonus: $
Savings Plan:	Stock Purch. Plan:		Second Exec. Salary: $	Bonus: $

OTHER THOUGHTS:

Apparent Women Officers or Directors: 2
Hot Spot for Advancement for Women/Minorities:

LOCATIONS: ("Y" = Yes)

West:	Southwest:	Midwest:	Southeast:	Northeast:	International:
Y	Y	Y	Y	Y	Y

SAIC INC

www.saic.com

Industry Group Code: 541512 **Ranks within this company's industry group:** Sales: 7 Profits: 6

Techology:		**Medical/Drugs:**		**Engineering:**		**Transportation:**		**Chemicals/Petrochemicals:**		**Specialty:**	
Computers:		Manufacturer:		Design:		Aerospace:		Oil/Gas Products:		Special Services:	
Software:	Y	Contract Research:		Construction:		Automotive:		Chemicals:		Consulting:	Y
Communications:		Medical Services:		Eng. Services:	Y	Shipping:		Oil/Chem. Svcs.:		Specialty Mgmt.:	
Electronics:		Labs:		Consulting:	Y			Gases:		Products:	
Alternative Energy:		Bio. Services:						Other:		Other:	

TYPES OF BUSINESS:

Systems Integration Services
Consulting Services
Research & Development
Software Development
Venture Capital
Engineering

BRANDS/DIVISIONS/AFFILIATES:

Icon Systems, Inc.
SM Consulting, Inc.

CONTACTS: *Note: Officers with more than one job title may be intentionally listed here more than once.*

Kenneth C. (Ken) Dahlberg, CEO
Lawrence B. Prior, III, COO
Mark W. Sopp, CFO/Exec. VP
Brian F. Keenan, Exec. VP-Human Resources
Charles F. Koontz, Pres., IT & Network Solutions Group
Amy E. Alving, CTO
Joseph W. Craver, III, Pres., Prod. Solutions Group
Douglas E. Scott, General Counsel/Exec. VP/Corp. Sec.
Greg Henson, Sr. VP/Dir.-Bus. Dev.
Arnold L. Punaro, Exec. VP
Joseph P. Walkush, Exec. VP-Strategic Initiatives
Deborah H. Alderson, Pres., Defense Solutions Group
K. Stuart Shea, Pres., Intelligence, Security & Tech. Group
Kenneth C. (Ken) Dahlberg, Chmn.
Donald H. Foley, Exec. VP, Special Int'l Assignment
Joseph W. Craver, III, Pres., Logistics & Infrastructure Group

Phone: 858-826-6000	**Fax:**
Toll-Free:	
Address: 10260 Campus Point Dr., San Diego, CA 92121 US	

GROWTH PLANS/SPECIAL FEATURES:

SAIC, Inc., formerly Science Applications International Corporation, provides scientific, engineering, systems integration and technical services for all branches of the U.S. military, agencies of the U.S. Department of Defense (DoD), the intelligence community, the U.S. Department of Homeland Security (DHS), other U.S. government agencies, foreign governments and customers in selected commercial markets. SAIC offers products and solutions in three segments: government, commercial and corporate. The government segment, which generated 94% of the firm's revenues in 2008, offers services and solutions in the areas of defense; intelligence; homeland security; logistics and product support; systems engineering and integration; and research and development. SAIC's commercial segment, which generated 6% of its revenue in 2008, primarily targets commercial customers worldwide in selected industry markets, which currently include oil and gas; utilities; and life sciences. While the commercial segment provides a number of IT systems integration and advanced technical services, the focused offerings include applications and IT infrastructure management; data lifecycle management; and business transformation services. During 2008, SAIC disposed of its 55% interest in AMSEC LLC, a provider of maintenance engineering and technical support services to the U.S. Navy and marine industry customers, in exchange for the acquisition of certain divisions and subsidiaries of AMSEC. In April 2008, the company acquired Icon Systems, Inc., a designer, developer and producer of laser-based systems and products for military training and testing. In May 2008, SAIC acquired SM Consulting, Inc., a provider or language, intelligence, IT, management consulting, business process outsourcing, training and logistics to federal, state and local governments and private industry.

SAIC offers its employees education assistance, access to SAIC University, a commuting program, an employee assistance plan, backup childcare, onsite fitness centers, domestic partner benefits and medical, dental, vision, life, accident and disability insurance.

FINANCIALS: **Sales and profits are in thousands of dollars—add 000 to get the full amount. 2008 Note: Financial information for 2008 was not available for all companies at press time.**

2008 Sales: $8,935,000	2008 Profits: $415,000	**U.S. Stock Ticker: SAI**
2007 Sales: $8,061,000	2007 Profits: $391,000	**Int'l Ticker:** Int'l Exchange:
2006 Sales: $7,518,000	2006 Profits: $927,000	Employees: 43,800
2005 Sales: $6,910,000	2005 Profits: $409,000	Fiscal Year Ends: 1/31
2004 Sales: $6,720,000	2004 Profits: $351,000	Parent Company:

SALARIES/BENEFITS:

Pension Plan:	ESOP Stock Plan:	Profit Sharing:	Top Exec. Salary: $1,000,000	Bonus: $1,050,000
Savings Plan: Y	Stock Purch. Plan:		Second Exec. Salary: $519,231	Bonus: $485,000

OTHER THOUGHTS:

Apparent Women Officers or Directors: 5
Hot Spot for Advancement for Women/Minorities: Y

LOCATIONS: ("Y" = Yes)

West:	Southwest:	Midwest:	Southeast:	Northeast:	International:
Y	Y	Y	Y	Y	Y

SAIC-GM-WULING AUTOMOBILE COMPANY

www.sgmw.com.cn

Industry Group Code: 336111 **Ranks within this company's industry group:** Sales: Profits:

Techology:		Medical/Drugs:		Engineering:		Transportation:		Chemicals/Petrochemicals:		Specialty:	
Computers:		Manufacturer:		Design:		Aerospace:		Oil/Gas Products:		Special Services:	
Software:		Contract Research:		Construction:		Automotive:	Y	Chemicals:		Consulting:	
Communications:		Medical Services:		Eng. Services:		Shipping:		Oil/Chem. Svcs.:		Specialty Mgmt.:	
Electronics:		Labs:		Consulting:				Gases:		Products:	
Alternative Energy:		Bio. Services:						Other:		Other:	

TYPES OF BUSINESS:

Automobile Manufacturing

BRANDS/DIVISIONS/AFFILIATES:

Spark
Newsunshine
Sunshine
SAIC
PLN
PSN
General Motors Corp (GM)
Wuling Automotive

CONTACTS:

Note: Officers with more than one job title may be intentionally listed here more than once.

Shen Yang, Gen. Mgr.
Dylan Wu, Sales-Africa
Tom Chen, Sales-America
Jason Ding, Sales-Asia & Europe

Phone: 0772-3750656	**Fax:** 0772-3719805
Toll-Free:	
Address: No. 18 He Xi Rd., Liu Zhou City, 545007 China	

GROWTH PLANS/SPECIAL FEATURES:

SAIC-GM-Wuling Automobile Company Limited (SGMW) is owned and operated by three partners: Shanghai Automobile Industry Corp. (SAIC); General Motors; and Wuling Automobile Co. Ltd. SAIC has a 50.1% stake, General Motors China has a 34% stake and Wuling Automotive has a 15.9% stake in the joint venture. Wuling Automotive is 75% owned by SAIC. The three-way partnership was established to produce mini-vehicles. SGMW produces over 200 models that fall into the categories of commercial vehicles, rear box mini-van, double-cab pickup, single-cab pickup and mini passenger cars. The firm currently produces six brands of mini-vehicles, including Newsunshine, Sunshine, 6360, Chevrolet Spark, PLN and PSN. The Newsunshine, Sunshine and 6360 are similar to the mini-van, but have higher gas mileage and considerably less horsepower. The Sunshine and Newsunshine, which are rear box mini-vans, seat five to seven passengers, while the 6360, which is a commercial vehicle, can only seat five to seven. The Spark is a Chevrolet mini passenger car that has a seating capacity of five passengers. PLN is a single-cab pickup and the PSN is the firm's double-cab pickup. SGMW is highly focused on exporting the company's product, and is currently sold in 30 countries including Chile, India, Poland, Thailand, Ukraine, Philippines and Syria. The firm has regional sales contacts in Africa; America; and Asia and Europe.

FINANCIALS:

Sales and profits are in thousands of dollars—add 000 to get the full amount. 2008 Note: Financial information for 2008 was not available for all companies at press time.

2008 Sales: $	2008 Profits: $	**U.S. Stock Ticker: Joint Venture**
2007 Sales: $1,685,100	2007 Profits: $	**Int'l Ticker:** Int'l Exchange:
2006 Sales: $	2006 Profits: $	Employees: 8,000
2005 Sales: $	2005 Profits: $	Fiscal Year Ends:
2004 Sales: $	2004 Profits: $	Parent Company: SHANGHAI AUTOMOTIVE INDUSTRY CORP (SAIC)

SALARIES/BENEFITS:

Pension Plan:	ESOP Stock Plan:	Profit Sharing:	Top Exec. Salary: $	Bonus: $
Savings Plan:	Stock Purch. Plan:		Second Exec. Salary: $	Bonus: $

OTHER THOUGHTS:

Apparent Women Officers or Directors:
Hot Spot for Advancement for Women/Minorities:

LOCATIONS: ("Y" = Yes)

West:	Southwest:	Midwest:	Southeast:	Northeast:	International:
					Y

SAMSUNG ADVANCED INSTITUTE OF TECHNOLOGY (SAIT)

www.sait.samsung.com

Industry Group Code: 541710 **Ranks within this company's industry group:** Sales: Profits:

Techology:		Medical/Drugs:		Engineering:		Transportation:		Chemicals/Petrochemicals:		Specialty:	
Computers:		Manufacturer:	Y	Design:		Aerospace:		Oil/Gas Products:		Special Services:	
Software:		Contract Research:		Construction:		Automotive:		Chemicals:		Consulting:	
Communications:	Y	Medical Services:		Eng. Services:		Shipping:		Oil/Chem. Svcs.:		Specialty Mgmt.:	
Electronics:	Y	Labs:		Consulting:				Gases:		Products:	Y
Alternative Energy:		Bio. Services:						Other:		Other:	

TYPES OF BUSINESS:

Research & Development
Computers & Software
Opto/Display
Energy
Biotechnology & Health
Communications & Networks
Semiconductor Materials
Nanotubes and Nanoelectronics

BRANDS/DIVISIONS/AFFILIATES:

Samsung Group
SAIT

GROWTH PLANS/SPECIAL FEATURES:

Samsung Advanced Institute of Technology (SAIT) is the central research and development organization of the Samsung Group in South Korea. As such, SAIT is the lead developer of new technologies for all of Samsung's business operations, including electronics, machinery, chemicals and financial services. SAIT's primary function, however, is the development of cutting-edge technologies for Samsung's consumer electronics business, which includes products such as LCD panels, DVD players and cell phones. Related technologies falling under SAIT's purview include nanotubes and semiconductor materials. SAIT also provides Samsung and its affiliates with mid- and long-term technology strategies and consulting. In the past, the institute's projects have included the development of a 10-hour battery for laptops using methanol.

CONTACTS: *Note: Officers with more than one job title may be intentionally listed here more than once.*

Hyung-Kyu Lim, CEO
Hyung-Kyu Lim, Pres.

Phone: 82-31-280-9114	**Fax:** 82-31-280-9099
Toll-Free:	
Address: Mt. 14-1 Nongseo-Dong, Giheung-gu, Yonggin-si, Gyunggi-Do, 449-712 Korea	

FINANCIALS: **Sales and profits are in thousands of dollars—add 000 to get the full amount. 2008 Note: Financial information for 2008 was not available for all companies at press time.**

2008 Sales: $	2008 Profits: $	**U.S. Stock Ticker: Subsidiary**
2007 Sales: $	2007 Profits: $	**Int'l Ticker:** Int'l Exchange:
2006 Sales: $	2006 Profits: $	Employees: 1,030
2005 Sales: $	2005 Profits: $	Fiscal Year Ends: 12/31
2004 Sales: $	2004 Profits: $	Parent Company: SAMSUNG GROUP

SALARIES/BENEFITS:

Pension Plan:	ESOP Stock Plan:	Profit Sharing:	Top Exec. Salary: $	Bonus: $
Savings Plan:	Stock Purch. Plan:		Second Exec. Salary: $	Bonus: $

OTHER THOUGHTS:

Apparent Women Officers or Directors:
Hot Spot for Advancement for Women/Minorities:

LOCATIONS: ("Y" = Yes)

West:	Southwest:	Midwest:	Southeast:	Northeast:	International:
					Y

SAMSUNG ELECTRONICS CO LTD

www.samsung.com

Industry Group Code: 334310 **Ranks within this company's industry group:** Sales: 1 Profits: 1

Techology:		Medical/Drugs:		Engineering:		Transportation:		Chemicals/Petrochemicals:		Specialty:	
Computers:	Y	Manufacturer:		Design:		Aerospace:		Oil/Gas Products:		Special Services:	
Software:		Contract Research:		Construction:		Automotive:		Chemicals:		Consulting:	
Communications:	Y	Medical Services:		Eng. Services:		Shipping:		Oil/Chem. Svcs.:		Specialty Mgmt.:	
Electronics:	Y	Labs:		Consulting:				Gases:		Products:	
Alternative Energy:		Bio. Services:						Other:		Other:	

TYPES OF BUSINESS:

Consumer Electronics
Semiconductors
Cellular Phones
Computers & Accessories
Digital Cameras
Fuel-Cell Technology
LCD Displays
Memory Products

BRANDS/DIVISIONS/AFFILIATES:

Samsung Group (The)
Samsung NEC Mobile Displays Co., Ltd.
Samsung Austin Semiconductor
Samsung Electro-Mechanics
Samsung Opto-Electronics America, Inc.
Samsung Electronics America
Samsung SDS
Samsung Networks

CONTACTS: *Note: Officers with more than one job title may be intentionally listed here more than once.*

Jong-Yong Yun, CEO/Vice Chmn.
In Joo Kim, Co-Pres.
Doh-Seok Choi, CFO
Choi Gee-sung, CEO-Consumer Products Div.
Dale Sohn, Pres. Samsung Telecom America
Jon Kang, Pres., Samsung Semiconductor
Kun-Hee Lee, Chmn.
Don-Jin Oh, Pres./CEO-Samsung Electronics America

Phone: 82-2-727-7114 **Fax:** 82-2-727-7892
Toll-Free:
Address: 250, 2-ga, Taepyung-ro, Jung-gu, Seoul, 100-742 Korea

GROWTH PLANS/SPECIAL FEATURES:

Samsung Electronics Co., Ltd., part of The Samsung Group, is a global leader in semiconductor, telecommunications and digital convergence technology. The digital media segment produces color monitors, DVD and Blu-ray players, notebook PCS, printers, camcorders and mp3 players. The telecommunication networks segment has activities in both telecommunication systems and mobile telephones. The digital appliance segment makes air conditioners, vacuum cleaners, refrigerators, washers, ovens and other appliances. The semiconductor segment consists of three divisions: memory, system LSI and storage. In the semiconductor segment, sales of high-capacity devices grew due to the application of 90nm and 80nm processing in the DRAM lineup and 60nm processing in the NAND flash memory products. The system LSI portion produces smart card ICs used in European mobile phones and CPUs used in automobile navigation systems. Finally, the LCD segment makes products used in televisions, monitors and displays for mobile products. The company offers one of the largest plasma TVs in the world, a high-definition flat-screen measuring a full 80 inches across, and one of the largest LCD TVs with a 70-inch screen. The firm's Green Management initiative focuses on reducing the environmental impact of its products and processing techniques and eliminating workplace pollutants. Samsung has over 100 subsidiaries worldwide. The company invests at least 9% of its revenues in research and development activities annually. Samsung announced in early 2009 that it will reorganize into two units. The CEO will be in direct charge of the Components Division, which will include memory chips, LCDs and other computer parts or accessories. The Consumer Products Division will include cell phones, cameras, TVs and other household items. It will be managed by Choi Gee-sung.

FINANCIALS: **Sales and profits are in thousands of dollars—add 000 to get the full amount. 2008 Note: Financial information for 2008 was not available for all companies at press time.**

2008 Sales: $97,035,500	2008 Profits: $4,420,700	**U.S. Stock Ticker: SSNLF.PK**
2007 Sales: $92,260,000	2007 Profits: $8,560,000	**Int'l Ticker: 000830** Int'l Exchange: Seoul-KRX
2006 Sales: $63,495,000	2006 Profits: $8,535,460	Employees: 64,000
2005 Sales: $61,863,800	2005 Profits: $8,227,470	Fiscal Year Ends: 12/31
2004 Sales: $56,892,753	2004 Profits: $10,648,314	Parent Company:

SALARIES/BENEFITS:

Pension Plan:	ESOP Stock Plan:	Profit Sharing:	Top Exec. Salary: $	Bonus: $
Savings Plan:	Stock Purch. Plan:		Second Exec. Salary: $	Bonus: $

OTHER THOUGHTS:

Apparent Women Officers or Directors:
Hot Spot for Advancement for Women/Minorities:

LOCATIONS: ("Y" = Yes)

West:	Southwest:	Midwest:	Southeast:	Northeast:	International:
Y	Y	Y	Y	Y	Y

Note: Financial information, benefits and other data can change quickly and may vary from those stated here.

SANDISK CORP

www.sandisk.com

Industry Group Code: 334413 **Ranks within this company's industry group:** Sales: 12 Profits: 17

Techology:		Medical/Drugs:		Engineering:		Transportation:		Chemicals/Petrochemicals:		Specialty:	
Computers:		Manufacturer:		Design:		Aerospace:		Oil/Gas Products:		Special Services:	
Software:		Contract Research:		Construction:		Automotive:		Chemicals:		Consulting:	
Communications:		Medical Services:		Eng. Services:		Shipping:		Oil/Chem. Svcs.:		Specialty Mgmt.:	
Electronics:	Y	Labs:		Consulting:				Gases:		Products:	
Alternative Energy:		Bio. Services:						Other:		Other:	

TYPES OF BUSINESS:

Flash-Based Data Storage Products
Flash Memory Cards

BRANDS/DIVISIONS/AFFILIATES:

SanDisk Ultra II
SanDisk Extreme
FlashVision, Ltd.
Memory Stick PRO
CompactFlash
miniSD
SmartMedia
FlashDisk

CONTACTS: *Note: Officers with more than one job title may be intentionally listed here more than once.*

Eli Harari, CEO
Sanjay Mehrotra, COO
Sanjay Mehrotra, Pres.
Judy Bruner, CFO
Yoram Cedar, Exec. VP-Corp. Eng.
Judy Bruner, Exec. VP-Admin.
Yoram Cedar, Exec. VP-Mobile Bus. Unit
Eli Harari, Chmn.

Phone: 408-801-1000	**Fax:** 408-801-8657
Toll-Free:	
Address: 601 McCarthy Blvd., Milpitas, CA 95035 US	

GROWTH PLANS/SPECIAL FEATURES:

SanDisk Corp. is a supplier of flash-based data storage products for the consumer, mobile communications and industrial markets. It designs, develops, markets and manufactures products and solutions in a variety of form factors using flash memory, controller and firmware technologies. The firm's products are used in a wide range of consumer electronics devices such as digital camera, mobile phones, gaming consoles, MP3 players and other digital devices. SanDisk's products are also embedded in a variety of systems for the enterprise, industrial, military and other markets. The company manufactures and sells every major flash card format including CompactFlash; Secure Digital; miniSD; SmartMedia; FlashDisk; MultiMediaCards; Memory Stick PRO (which it co-owns with Sony Corp.); as well as other Memory Stick products such as xD-Picture cards; and USB flash drives. In addition to its standard grade products, SanDisk offers Ultra II and SanDisk Extreme memory cards, designed for faster write times and improved operation in harsh conditions. The company does not operate fabrication facilities but does control a significant portion of its flash memory wafer manufacturing through its FlashVision, Ltd. joint venture with Toshiba, as well as through sourcing agreements. SanDisk's customers include retailers such as Best Buy, OEMs such as Canon and distributors such as Ingram Micro. SanDisk also licenses its technologies to several companies, including Intel, Sony and Toshiba. The firm currently holds over 860 U.S. and 550 foreign patents. The company's top ten customers account for 46% of its revenues. In October 2008, SanDisk entered into agreement to sell 30% of its manufacturing capacity to Toshiba Corp. In June 2008, the firm acquired MusicGremlin, a company that develops digital content distribution technologies.

SanDisk offers employees medical, dental and vision insurance; an employee assistance program; income protection; flexible spending accounts; stock options plans; employee stock purchase plan; onsite health club; commuter vouchers; employee discounts; and tuition reimbursement.

FINANCIALS: **Sales and profits are in thousands of dollars—add 000 to get the full amount. 2008 Note: Financial information for 2008 was not available for all companies at press time.**

2008 Sales: $3,351,352	2008 Profits: $-2,056,776	**U.S. Stock Ticker: SNDK**
2007 Sales: $3,896,366	2007 Profits: $218,357	**Int'l Ticker:** Int'l Exchange:
2006 Sales: $3,257,525	2006 Profits: $198,896	Employees: 3,565
2005 Sales: $2,306,069	2005 Profits: $386,384	Fiscal Year Ends: 12/31
2004 Sales: $1,777,055	2004 Profits: $266,616	Parent Company:

SALARIES/BENEFITS:

Pension Plan:	ESOP Stock Plan:	Profit Sharing:	Top Exec. Salary: $763,493	Bonus: $911,600
Savings Plan: Y	Stock Purch. Plan: Y		Second Exec. Salary: $459,750	Bonus: $416,670

OTHER THOUGHTS:

Apparent Women Officers or Directors: 2
Hot Spot for Advancement for Women/Minorities:

LOCATIONS: ("Y" = Yes)

West:	Southwest:	Midwest:	Southeast:	Northeast:	International:
Y					Y

Note: Financial information, benefits and other data can change quickly and may vary from those stated here.

SANMINA-SCI CORPORATION

www.sanmina-sci.com

Industry Group Code: 334419 **Ranks within this company's industry group:** Sales: 6 Profits: 10

Techology:		Medical/Drugs:		Engineering:		Transportation:		Chemicals/Petrochemicals:		Specialty:	
Computers:		Manufacturer:		Design:		Aerospace:		Oil/Gas Products:		Special Services:	Y
Software:		Contract Research:		Construction:		Automotive:		Chemicals:		Consulting:	Y
Communications:		Medical Services:		Eng. Services:		Shipping:		Oil/Chem. Svcs.:		Specialty Mgmt.:	
Electronics:	Y	Labs:		Consulting:				Gases:		Products:	
Alternative Energy:		Bio. Services:						Other:		Other:	

TYPES OF BUSINESS:

Contract Manufacturing-Electronics
Assembly & Testing
Logistics Services
Support Services
Product Design & Engineering
Repair & Maintenance Services

BRANDS/DIVISIONS/AFFILIATES:

CONTACTS:

Note: Officers with more than one job title may be intentionally listed here more than once.

Jure Sola, CEO
Hari Pillai, COO
Hari Pillai, Pres.
David L. White, CFO/Exec. VP
Dennis Young, Exec. VP-Worldwide Sales & Mktg.
Michael R. Tyler, General Counsel/Corp. Sec./Exec. VP
Walter (Walt) Hussey, Pres., Electro-Mechanical Systems
Hari Pillai, Pres., Global EMS Oper.
Jure Sola, Chmn.

Phone: 408-964-3500 **Fax:** 408-964-3636
Toll-Free:
Address: 2700 N. 1st St., San Jose, CA 95134 US

GROWTH PLANS/SPECIAL FEATURES:

Sanmina-SCI Corp. is an independent global provider of customized, integrated electronics manufacturing services (EMS) primarily to original equipment manufacturers (OEMs) in the communications, computing, storage, multimedia, industrial, semiconductor capital equipment, defense, aerospace, medical and automotive industries. With production facilities in 18 countries on five continents, the firm is one of the largest global EMS providers. The company's service segments include product design and engineering; volume manufacturing of complete systems, components and subassemblies; final system assembly and testing; direct order fulfillment; and global supply chain management. The product design and engineering segment provides services for initial product development, detailed product design and pre-production for a wide range of products, including switches, personal computers and servers. The volume manufacturing segment produces components and subassemblies including printed circuit boards, printed circuit board assemblies, backplanes and backplane assemblies, enclosures, cable assemblies, optical modules and memory modules. The final system assembly and test unit combines the company's various products and modules to form finished products, and then tests these products for conformity to applicable industry, product integrity and regulatory standards. The direct order fulfillment segment receives customer orders, configures products to quickly fill the orders and delivers the products either to the OEM, a distribution channel (such as a retail outlet) or directly to the end customer. The global supply chain management segment plans, purchases and warehouses product components. Sales to its 10 largest customers generated 48.2% of Sanmina-SCI's revenue for 2008. In February 2008, the company agreed to sell its personal computing business and associated logistics services located in Hungary, Mexico and the U.S. to Foxteq Holdings, Inc.

Sanmina-SCI offers its employees tuition reimbursement, credit union membership, a work-life balance program, an employee assistance program, business travel accident insurance, flexible spending accounts and medical, dental, vision, prescription, life and AD&D insurance.

FINANCIALS:

Sales and profits are in thousands of dollars—add 000 to get the full amount. 2008 Note: Financial information for 2008 was not available for all companies at press time.

2008 Sales: $7,303,403	2008 Profits: $-486,349	**U.S. Stock Ticker: SANM**
2007 Sales: $7,137,793	2007 Profits: $-1,134,657	**Int'l Ticker:** Int'l Exchange:
2006 Sales: $7,645,118	2006 Profits: $-141,557	Employees: 45,610
2005 Sales: $7,644,932	2005 Profits: $-1,033,946	Fiscal Year Ends: 9/30
2004 Sales: $12,204,607	2004 Profits: $-51,629	Parent Company:

SALARIES/BENEFITS:

Pension Plan:	ESOP Stock Plan:	Profit Sharing:	Top Exec. Salary: $800,000	Bonus: $440,000
Savings Plan: Y	Stock Purch. Plan:		Second Exec. Salary: $500,000	Bonus: $247,500

OTHER THOUGHTS:

Apparent Women Officers or Directors:
Hot Spot for Advancement for Women/Minorities:

LOCATIONS: ("Y" = Yes)

West:	Southwest:	Midwest:	Southeast:	Northeast:	International:
Y	Y	Y	Y	Y	Y

SANOFI-AVENTIS SA

www.en.sanofi-aventis.com

Industry Group Code: 325412 **Ranks within this company's industry group:** Sales: 5 Profits: 8

Techology:		Medical/Drugs:		Engineering:		Transportation:		Chemicals/Petrochemicals:		Specialty:	
Computers:		Manufacturer:	Y	Design:		Aerospace:		Oil/Gas Products:		Special Services:	
Software:		Contract Research:		Construction:		Automotive:		Chemicals:		Consulting:	
Communications:		Medical Services:	Y	Eng. Services:		Shipping:		Oil/Chem. Svcs.:		Specialty Mgmt.:	
Electronics:		Labs:	Y	Consulting:				Gases:		Products:	
Alternative Energy:		Bio. Services:						Other:		Other:	

TYPES OF BUSINESS:

Pharmaceuticals Development & Manufacturing
Over-the-Counter Drugs
Cardiovascular Drugs
CNS Drugs
Oncology Drugs
Diabetes Drugs
Generics
Vaccines

BRANDS/DIVISIONS/AFFILIATES:

Aprovel
Plavix
Allegra
Depakine
Stilnox
Sanofi Pasteur
Eloxatin
Lantus

CONTACTS: *Note: Officers with more than one job title may be intentionally listed here more than once.*

Chris Viehbacher, CEO
Laurence Debroux, CFO/Sr. VP/Chief Strategic Officer
Pierre Chancel, Sr. VP-Global Mktg.
Gilles Lhernould, Sr. VP-Human Resources
Marc Cluzel, Sr. VP-R&D
Karen Linehan, General Counsel/Sr. VP-Legal Affairs
Hanspeter Spek, Exec. VP-Pharmaceutical Oper.
Philippe Fauchet, Sr. VP-Bus. Dev.
Michel Labie, Sr. VP-Comm./VP-Institutional & Professional Rel.
Philippe Peyre, Sr. VP-Corp. Affairs
Olivier Charmeil, Sr. VP-Pharmaceutical Oper., Asia-Pacific & Japan
Philippe Luscan, Sr. VP-Industrial Affairs
Gregory Irace, Sr. VP-Pharmaceutical Oper., U.S.
Jean-Francois Dehecq, Chmn.
Antoine Ortoli, Sr. VP-Pharmaceuticals Oper., Int'l

Phone: 33-1-53-77-4000	**Fax:**
Toll-Free:	
Address: 174 Ave. de France, Paris, 75365 France	

GROWTH PLANS/SPECIAL FEATURES:

Sanofi-Aventis SA is an international pharmaceutical group engaged in the research, development, manufacturing and marketing of primarily prescription pharmaceutical products. The firm conducts research and produces pharmaceutical products in seven therapeutic areas: cardiovascular diseases, thrombosis, metabolic disorders (especially diabetes), oncology, central nervous system (CNS) disorders, internal medicine and vaccines. Cardiovascular medications include the blood pressure medication, Aprovel. One of the company's thrombosis medications is the anti-clotting agent, Plavix. In the field of oncology, Sanofi-Aventis manufactures Eloxatin, a treatment for colon-rectal cancer, and Taxotere, a medication for breast cancer patients. CNS medications include Stilnox, an insomnia medication, and Depakine, a treatment for epilepsy. Products in the internal medicine sector include the antihistamine, Allegra, as well as Xatral, a treatment for enlarged prostrates. The firm has three metabolism/diabetes treatments: Amaryl, Apidra and Lantus. Subsidiary Sanofi Pasteur produces vaccines that fight 20 diseases, immunizing over 500 million people annually. In September 2008, the company acquired Symbion Consumer, Australian distributor of vitamins and mineral supplements, from Primary Health Care Limited for approximately $363 million. In February 2009, the firm agreed to partner with the Salk Institute for Biological Studies, forming the Sanofi-Aventis Regenerative Medicine Program.

FINANCIALS: **Sales and profits are in thousands of dollars—add 000 to get the full amount. 2008 Note: Financial information for 2008 was not available for all companies at press time.**

2008 Sales: $36,751,700	2008 Profits: $5,721,790	**U.S. Stock Ticker: SNY**
2007 Sales: $37,397,000	2007 Profits: $7,574,840	**Int'l Ticker: SAN** Int'l Exchange: Paris-Euronext
2006 Sales: $38,722,100	2006 Profits: $6,003,540	Employees: 98,213
2005 Sales: $37,272,700	2005 Profits: $3,538,800	Fiscal Year Ends: 12/31
2004 Sales: $20,377,000	2004 Profits: $-4,890,000	Parent Company:

SALARIES/BENEFITS:

Pension Plan:	ESOP Stock Plan:	Profit Sharing:	Top Exec. Salary: $	Bonus: $
Savings Plan:	Stock Purch. Plan:		Second Exec. Salary: $	Bonus: $

OTHER THOUGHTS:

Apparent Women Officers or Directors: 4
Hot Spot for Advancement for Women/Minorities: Y

LOCATIONS: ("Y" = Yes)

West:	Southwest:	Midwest:	Southeast:	Northeast:	International:
Y	Y	Y	Y	Y	Y

SANYO ELECTRIC COMPANY LTD

www.sanyo.com

Industry Group Code: 334310 **Ranks within this company's industry group:** Sales: 6 Profits: 5

Techology:		Medical/Drugs:		Engineering:		Transportation:		Chemicals/Petrochemicals:		Specialty:	
Computers:		Manufacturer:		Design:		Aerospace:		Oil/Gas Products:		Special Services:	
Software:		Contract Research:		Construction:		Automotive:		Chemicals:		Consulting:	
Communications:	Y	Medical Services:		Eng. Services:		Shipping:		Oil/Chem. Svcs.:		Specialty Mgmt.:	
Electronics:	Y	Labs:		Consulting:				Gases:		Products:	
Alternative Energy:	Y	Bio. Services:						Other:		Other:	

TYPES OF BUSINESS:

Consumer Electronics
Fuel-Cell Technology
Communications Equipment
Industrial Equipment
Home Appliances
Batteries & Electronic Components
Photovoltaic Technology
Research & Development

BRANDS/DIVISIONS/AFFILIATES:

SANYO Semiconductor Co., Ltd.
SANYO Tokyo Manufacturing Co., Ltd.
SANYO Consumer Electronics Co., Ltd.
SANYO Electric Sales Co., Ltd.
Kyocera Corp
Volkswagen AG
Panasonic Corporation
Matsushita Electric Industrial Co Ltd

CONTACTS: *Note: Officers with more than one job title may be intentionally listed here more than once.*

Seiichiro Sano, Pres.
Koichi Maeda, Exec. VP
Kazuhiko Suruta, Exec. VP
Kentaro Yamagishi, Exec. VP
Mitsuru Honma, Sr. VP

Phone: 81-6-6991-1181	**Fax:** 81-81-6992-0009
Toll-Free:	
Address: 5-5 Keihan-Hondori 2-Chome, Moriguchi, Osaka, 570-8077 Japan	

GROWTH PLANS/SPECIAL FEATURES:

Sanyo Electric Co., Ltd., a worldwide conglomerate with approximately 245 subsidiaries and affiliates, conducts manufacturing, sales, maintenance and service activities in four primary business segments: Consumer, Commercial, Component and Other. The Consumer business segment accounts for approximately 36% of revenues and covers audio, video and communications equipment, such as digital cameras, TVs and car navigation systems, as well as home appliances such as washing machines and air conditioners. The Commercial business segment accounts for approximately 13% of revenues and deals with commercial equipment, including showcases for supermarkets and convenience stores, commercial air conditioners, including package air conditioners, and computer systems for medical applications. The Component business segment accounts for approximately 46% of revenues and covers electronic components, such as capacitors and motors, rechargeable batteries including lithium-ion batteries, photovoltaic systems, semiconductors, optical pickups and other products. The remaining Other segment accounts for approximately 5% of revenues and comprises nonmanufacturing businesses, including the logistics business and the maintenance service business. In addition, the firm conducts research on batteries, flash memory, semiconductors, systems-on-a-chip and photonic devices using nanotechnology. Sanyo invests heavily in research and development and is focused on becoming a world technological leader in LCDs, electronic devices and environmental technology, including a joint venture with Samsung to develop fuel-cell technology. In April 2008, Sanyo sold its mobile phone business to Kyocera Corporation. In May 2008 the company reached an agreement with Volkswagen Group on co-development of a lithium-ion battery system for hybrid electric vehicles. In late 2008, Panasonic Corporation (formerly Matsushita Electric Industrial Co Ltd) announced plans to take over Sanyo.

FINANCIALS: **Sales and profits are in thousands of dollars—add 000 to get the full amount. 2008 Note: Financial information for 2008 was not available for all companies at press time.**

2008 Sales: $20,389,900	2008 Profits: $287,000	**U.S. Stock Ticker: SANYY**
2007 Sales: $19,650,000	2007 Profits: $-390,000	**Int'l Ticker: 6764** Int'l Exchange: Tokyo-TSE
2006 Sales: $21,804,658	2006 Profits: $-1,757,786	Employees: 99,875
2005 Sales: $24,173,700	2005 Profits: $-1,603,200	Fiscal Year Ends: 3/31
2004 Sales: $24,527,700	2004 Profits: $126,400	Parent Company:

SALARIES/BENEFITS:

Pension Plan:	ESOP Stock Plan:	Profit Sharing:	Top Exec. Salary: $	Bonus: $
Savings Plan: Y	Stock Purch. Plan:		Second Exec. Salary: $	Bonus: $

OTHER THOUGHTS:

Apparent Women Officers or Directors:
Hot Spot for Advancement for Women/Minorities:

LOCATIONS: ("Y" = Yes)

West:	Southwest:	Midwest:	Southeast:	Northeast:	International:
Y					Y

SAP AG

www.sap.com

Industry Group Code: 511207 **Ranks within this company's industry group:** Sales: 2 Profits: 2

Techology:		Medical/Drugs:		Engineering:		Transportation:		Chemicals/Petrochemicals:		Specialty:	
Computers:		Manufacturer:		Design:		Aerospace:		Oil/Gas Products:		Special Services:	
Software:	Y	Contract Research:		Construction:		Automotive:		Chemicals:		Consulting:	
Communications:		Medical Services:		Eng. Services:		Shipping:		Oil/Chem. Svcs.:		Specialty Mgmt.:	
Electronics:		Labs:		Consulting:				Gases:		Products:	
Alternative Energy:		Bio. Services:						Other:		Other:	

TYPES OF BUSINESS:

Enterprise Management Software
Consulting & Training Services
Hosting Services

BRANDS/DIVISIONS/AFFILIATES:

SAP Business Suite
SAP ERP
SAP Customer Relationship Management
SAP Product Lifecycle Management
SAP Business ByDesign
SAP Business One
SAP Business All-in-One
Business Objects SA

CONTACTS: *Note: Officers with more than one job title may be intentionally listed here more than once.*

Henning Kagerman, Co-CEO
Erwin Gunst, COO
Werner Brandt, CFO
Ernie Gunst, Dir.-Global Human Resources
Ernie Gunst, Dir.-Internal IT
Leo Apotheker, Co-CEO
Bill McDermott, Dir.-Global Field Oper.
Gerhard Oswald, Dir.- Global Service & Support
John Schwarz, CEO-Business Objects
Hasso Plattner, Chmn.

Phone: 49-6227-74-7474	**Fax:** 49-6227-75-7575
Toll-Free:	
Address: Dietmar-Hopp-Allee 16, Walldorf, 69190 Germany	

GROWTH PLANS/SPECIAL FEATURES:

SAP AG is a leading provider of enterprise software solutions worldwide and a major independent software producer. The company's products include general-purpose applications as well as industry-specific applications, providing a software foundation with which customers can address their various business issues. General-purpose applications include the SAP Business Suite family of business applications which consists of SAP ERP, SAP Customer Relationship Management, SAP Product Lifecycle Management, SAP Supply Chain Management and SAP Supplier Relationship Management. These applications can be licensed individually or together as a suite. Various cross-industry applications are also available, including SAP Global Trade Management and SAP solutions for radio frequency identification (RFID). The firm's industry-specific applications perform defined business functions in particular industries. These applications often are delivered as add-ons to general-purpose applications. Examples of industry-specific applications include the SAP Apparel and Footwear application for the consumer products industry and the SAP Reinsurance Management application for the insurance industry. For large enterprises, SAP offers more than 25 tailored solution portfolios. Solution portfolios for industries are created by SAP through the assembly of general-purpose applications, industry-specific applications, and, potentially, partner products. Solution portfolios encompass the following industry segments: process industries, such as chemicals, oil & gas and mining; discrete industries, such as aerospace, defense, high-tech and automotive; consumer industries, such as retail, distribution and life sciences; services industries, such as media, postal services, railways and utilities; financial services, such as banking and insurance; and public services, such as healthcare, education and security. For small and midsize enterprises, the firm offers the SAP Business One application, the SAP Business All-in-One solutions, and the SAP Business ByDesign solution. SAP also offers a portfolio of services, including consulting, education, support, custom development, and application management and hosting. In January 2008, SAP acquired Business Objects SA, for approximately $6.78 billion.

FINANCIALS: **Sales and profits are in thousands of dollars—add 000 to get the full amount. 2008 Note: Financial information for 2008 was not available for all companies at press time.**

2008 Sales: $15,005,600	2008 Profits: $2,449,260	**U.S. Stock Ticker: SAP**
2007 Sales: $16,387,200	2007 Profits: $3,070,400	**Int'l Ticker: SAP** Int'l Exchange: Frankfurt-Euronext
2006 Sales: $15,028,800	2006 Profits: $2,993,600	Employees: 51,500
2005 Sales: $13,614,400	2005 Profits: $2,393,600	Fiscal Year Ends: 12/31
2004 Sales: $10,178,000	2004 Profits: $1,776,000	Parent Company:

SALARIES/BENEFITS:

Pension Plan: Y	ESOP Stock Plan:	Profit Sharing:	Top Exec. Salary: $	Bonus: $
Savings Plan: Y	Stock Purch. Plan:		Second Exec. Salary: $	Bonus: $

OTHER THOUGHTS:

Apparent Women Officers or Directors:
Hot Spot for Advancement for Women/Minorities:

LOCATIONS: ("Y" = Yes)

West:	Southwest:	Midwest:	Southeast:	Northeast:	International:
Y	Y	Y	Y	Y	Y

Note: Financial information, benefits and other data can change quickly and may vary from those stated here.

SAS INSTITUTE INC

www.sas.com

Industry Group Code: 511207 **Ranks within this company's industry group:** Sales: 4 Profits:

Techology:		Medical/Drugs:		Engineering:		Transportation:		Chemicals/Petrochemicals:		Specialty:	
Computers:		Manufacturer:		Design:		Aerospace:		Oil/Gas Products:		Special Services:	
Software:	Y	Contract Research:		Construction:		Automotive:		Chemicals:		Consulting:	
Communications:		Medical Services:		Eng. Services:		Shipping:		Oil/Chem. Svcs.:		Specialty Mgmt.:	
Electronics:		Labs:		Consulting:				Gases:		Products:	
Alternative Energy:		Bio. Services:						Other:		Other:	

TYPES OF BUSINESS:

Software-Statistical Analysis
Business Intelligence Software
Data Warehousing
Online Bookstore

BRANDS/DIVISIONS/AFFILIATES:

SAS9
SAS Enterprise BI Server
DataFlux
SAS Revenue Optimization
SAS Promotion Optimization
SAS Enterprise Intelligence Platform

CONTACTS: *Note: Officers with more than one job title may be intentionally listed here more than once.*

James Goodnight, CEO
James Goodnight, Pres.
Don Parker, CFO/Sr. VP
Jim Davis, Chief Mktg. Officer/Sr. VP
Jennifer Mann, VP-Human Resources
Suzanne Gordon, CIO/VP-IT
Keith Collins, CTO/Sr. VP
John Sall, Exec. VP
James Goodnight, Chmn.
Mikael Hagstrom, Exec. VP-EMEA & APAC

Phone: 919-677-8000 **Fax:** 919-677-4444
Toll-Free: 800-727-0025
Address: 100 SAS Campus Dr., Cary, NC 27513-2414 US

GROWTH PLANS/SPECIAL FEATURES:

SAS Institute, Inc. provides statistical analysis software. The company's products are designed to extract, manage and analyze large volumes of data, often assisting in financial reporting and credit analysis. Individual contracts can be tailored to specific global and local industries, such as banking, manufacturing and government. SAS's top products are SAS9 and SAS Enterprise BI Server. The SAS9 platform is centered on providing extensive data management and analytics integration. It also features predictive applications, a highly adaptable interface and unique grid computing capabilities. SAS Enterprise BI Server is an enhanced reporting and analysis system for the organization and reporting of business intelligence. SAS also provides data warehousing services for large amounts of data, as well as consulting, training and technical support through its SAS Services unit. The company's DataFlux subsidiary helps it deliver quality capabilities in SAS Data Integration solutions. In addition, the firm operates an online bookstore offering a library of SAS-produced books, documentation and training materials. SAS serves more than 45,000 business, government and university sites in 111 different countries, including 91 of the top 100 companies on the Fortune Global 500 list. Some of the firm's more prominent clients are Hewlett Packard; Brooks Brothers; the U.S. Department of Defense; Staples, Subway; and Allstate Financial. In March 2008, the firm acquired Teragram, a natural language processing and linguistic technology company. In August 2008, the company acquired IDeaS Revenue Optimization, which provides revenue management software for the hospitality industry.

The SAS headquarters features on-site childcare centers, an eldercare information and referral program, an employee health care center, wellness programs and a 58,000 square foot recreation and fitness center. The firm has been listed in Fortune's Top 100 Companies to Work For in America for 11 consecutive years.

FINANCIALS: Sales and profits are in thousands of dollars—add 000 to get the full amount. 2008 Note: Financial information for 2008 was not available for all companies at press time.

2008 Sales: $2,260,000	2008 Profits: $	**U.S. Stock Ticker: Private**
2007 Sales: $2,150,000	2007 Profits: $	**Int'l Ticker:** Int'l Exchange:
2006 Sales: $1,900,000	2006 Profits: $	Employees: 11,139
2005 Sales: $1,680,000	2005 Profits: $	Fiscal Year Ends: 12/31
2004 Sales: $1,530,000	2004 Profits: $	Parent Company:

SALARIES/BENEFITS:

Pension Plan:	ESOP Stock Plan:	Profit Sharing: Y	Top Exec. Salary: $	Bonus: $
Savings Plan: Y	Stock Purch. Plan:		Second Exec. Salary: $	Bonus: $

OTHER THOUGHTS:

Apparent Women Officers or Directors: 2
Hot Spot for Advancement for Women/Minorities: Y

LOCATIONS: ("Y" = Yes)

West:	Southwest:	Midwest:	Southeast:	Northeast:	International:
Y	Y	Y	Y	Y	Y

SASOL LIMITED

www.sasol.com

Industry Group Code: 325000 **Ranks within this company's industry group:** Sales: 9 Profits: 2

Techology:		Medical/Drugs:		Engineering:		Transportation:		Chemicals/Petrochemicals:		Specialty:	
Computers:		Manufacturer:		Design:		Aerospace:		Oil/Gas Products:	Y	Special Services:	
Software:		Contract Research:		Construction:		Automotive:		Chemicals:	Y	Consulting:	
Communications:		Medical Services:		Eng. Services:		Shipping:		Oil/Chem. Svcs.:	Y	Specialty Mgmt.:	
Electronics:		Labs:		Consulting:				Gases:	Y	Products:	
Alternative Energy:		Bio. Services:						Other:		Other:	

TYPES OF BUSINESS:

Synthetic Fuels Manufacturing
Crude Oil Refining
Natural Gas Production
Coal Mining
Polymers
Solvents

BRANDS/DIVISIONS/AFFILIATES:

Sasol Mining
Sasol Synfuels
Sasol Oil
Sasol Gas
Sasol Synfuels International
Sasol Petroleum International
Sasol Polymers
Sasol Olefins & Surfactants

CONTACTS: *Note: Officers with more than one job title may be intentionally listed here more than once.*

Lawrence Patrick Davies, CEO
Kandimathie Christine Ramon, CFO
Victoria Nolitha Fakude, Dir.-Human Resources
Nereus Louis Joubert, Corp. Sec.
Thembalihle Hixonia Nyasulu, Chmn.
Anthony Madimetja Mokaba, Dir.-Energy Bus., South Africa

Phone: 27-11-441-3563	**Fax:** 27-11-441-3481
Toll-Free:	
Address: 1 Sturdee Ave., Rosebank, 2196 South Africa	

GROWTH PLANS/SPECIAL FEATURES:

Sasol Limited is an integrated oil and gas company with substantial chemicals interests based in South Africa and with international operations throughout Europe, Asia and the Americas. The company uses in-house technology for the commercial production of synthetic fuels and chemicals from low-grade coal and manufactures a variety of fuel and chemical products sold in over 90 countries. In South Africa, liquid fuels are sold through a network of approximately 406 Sasol retail convenience centers and Exel service stations. Sasol additionally operates coal mines to provide feedstock for its synthetic fuel and chemical plants; manufactures and markets synthetic gas; and operates the only inland crude oil refinery in South Africa. The company supplements its coal mining activities by marketing Mozambican natural gas. Domestic subsidiaries include Sasol Mining, which mines over 40 million tons of saleable coal per year; Sasol Synfuels, operator of the world's only commercial coal-based synthetic fuels manufacturing facility; Sasol Oil, a marketer of petrol, diesel, jet fuel, illuminating paraffin, fuel oils, bitumen and lubricants; and Sasol Gas, a distributor of Mozambican-produced natural gas and Secunda-produced methane-rich gas. The company's international subsidiaries include Sasol Synfuels International, which develops and implements international joint ventures with Sasol Chevron; and Sasol Petroleum International, which develops and manages upstream interests in oil and gas exploration and production in Mozambique, South Africa, Gabon, Nigeria and the Joint Development Zone between Nigeria and Sao Tome. Sasol's chemicals portfolio includes monomers, polymers, solvents, olefins, surfactants, surfactant intermediates, comonomers, waxes, phenolics and nitrogenous products. Chemical subsidiaries include Sasol Polymers, Sasol Solvents and Sasol Olefins & Surfactants. The company has one operational GTL (gas to liquids) plant outside South Africa, with additional interests in a GTL plant in Nigeria. In March 2008, Sasol acquired the remaining 50% interest in U.S.-based Luxco Wax, making it a wholly-owned subsidiary.

FINANCIALS: **Sales and profits are in thousands of dollars—add 000 to get the full amount. 2008 Note: Financial information for 2008 was not available for all companies at press time.**

2008 Sales: $15,618,000	2008 Profits: $2,828,000	**U.S. Stock Ticker: SSL**
2007 Sales: $13,910,000	2007 Profits: $2,410,000	**Int'l Ticker: SOL** Int'l Exchange: Johannesburg-JSE
2006 Sales: $7,973,000	2006 Profits: $1,456,000	Employees: 30,004
2005 Sales: $10,141,000	2005 Profits: $1,472,000	Fiscal Year Ends: 6/30
2004 Sales: $9,480,142	2004 Profits: $858,887	Parent Company:

SALARIES/BENEFITS:

Pension Plan:	ESOP Stock Plan:	Profit Sharing:	Top Exec. Salary: $544,620	Bonus: $597,209
Savings Plan:	Stock Purch. Plan:		Second Exec. Salary: $515,488	Bonus: $412,390

OTHER THOUGHTS:

Apparent Women Officers or Directors: 5
Hot Spot for Advancement for Women/Minorities: Y

LOCATIONS: ("Y" = Yes)

West:	Southwest:	Midwest:	Southeast:	Northeast:	International:
Y	Y	Y	Y	Y	Y

SAUDI ARAMCO (SAUDI ARABIAN OIL CO)

www.saudiaramco.com

Industry Group Code: 211111 **Ranks within this company's industry group:** Sales: 4 Profits:

Techology:		Medical/Drugs:		Engineering:		Transportation:		Chemicals/Petrochemicals:		Specialty:	
Computers:		Manufacturer:		Design:		Aerospace:		Oil/Gas Products:	Y	Special Services:	
Software:		Contract Research:		Construction:		Automotive:		Chemicals:	Y	Consulting:	
Communications:		Medical Services:		Eng. Services:		Shipping:		Oil/Chem. Svcs.:	Y	Specialty Mgmt.:	
Electronics:		Labs:		Consulting:				Gases:	Y	Products:	
Alternative Energy:		Bio. Services:						Other:		Other:	

TYPES OF BUSINESS:

Oil & Gas-Exploration & Production
Oil Refining
Crude Oil Distribution
Pipelines
Oil Tankers

BRANDS/DIVISIONS/AFFILIATES:

California Arabian Standard Oil Company

CONTACTS:

Note: Officers with more than one job title may be intentionally listed here more than once.

Abdallah S. Jum'ah, CEO
Abdallah S. Jum'ah, Pres.
Khalid G. Al-Buainain, Sr. VP-Mktg. & Refining
Salim S. Al-Aydh, Sr. VP-Eng. & Project Mgmt.
Stanley E. McGinley, General Counsel/Sec.
Khalid A. Al-Falih, Exec. VP-Oper.
Abdulaziz F. Al-Khayyal, Sr. VP-Industrial Rel.
Abdullatif A. Al-Othman, Sr. VP-Finance
M. Yusof Rafie, Sr. VP-Special Assignment
Adbulrahman F. Al-Wuhalb, Sr. VP-Oper. Svcs.
Ali I. Al-Naimi, Chmn.
Khalid G. Al-Buainain, Sr. VP-Int'l

Phone: 966-3-872-0115 **Fax:** 966-3-873-8190
Toll-Free:
Address: R-2220 E. Administration Bldg., P.O. Box 5000, Dhahran, 31311 Saudi Arabia

GROWTH PLANS/SPECIAL FEATURES:

Saudi Aramco (Saudi Arabian Oil Co.) is one of the world's largest holders and producers of crude oil and natural gas, with reserves of about 259.9 billion barrels of oil and 253.8 trillion cubic feet of gas. Originally founded in 1933, Saudi Aramco's 2007 oil production averaged approximately 8.5 million barrels per day (bpd), totaling 3.11 billion barrels; natural gas production averaged 8 billion cubic feet per day, totaling 2.919 trillion cubic feet; and natural gas liquids production averaged 1.1 million bpd, totaling 394.6 million barrels. The company conducts extensive surveying and exploration activities while harvesting oil from some of the largest oil fields in the world, such as the Dhahran, Khurais, Shaybah, Ghawar and Safaniya fields. The company also operates an extensive network of pipelines, refineries and oil tankers. Its main domestic refineries include Ras Tanura, processing 550,000 bpd; Rabigh, 385,000 bpd; Yanbu', 237,000 bpd; Jiddah, 85,000 bpd; and Riyadh, 122,000 bpd. It also owns 50% of two domestic refineries, which together process 705,000 bpd; and owns primarily minority interests in four international refineries that collectively process 2 million bpd. Each year about 3,375 tankers make port at Ras Tanura and Ju'aymah on the Arabian Gulf; and at Yanbu', Jiddah and Rabigh on the Red Sea. Oil is primarily exported to the Far East and to the U.S. through overseas refineries and distribution hubs in New York, Houston, London, Leiden, Beijing, Tokyo and Hong Kong. Saudi Aramco recently launched the Haradh-III Increment in the Ghawar oilfield, producing 300,000 bpd of light crude oil. Additionally, the firm plans to start production soon at new locations in Khurais, adding 1.2 million bpd; Nuayyim, adding 100,000 bpd; and Abu Hadriya, Fadhili and Khursaniyah (AFK), adding 500,000 bpd.

Employees of Saudi Aramco receive free health care at company-owned or designated hospitals; suburban-style low-cost housing; and 30 days of vacation per year.

FINANCIALS:

Sales and profits are in thousands of dollars—add 000 to get the full amount. 2008 Note: Financial information for 2008 was not available for all companies at press time.

2008 Sales: $280,000,000	2008 Profits: $	**U.S. Stock Ticker: Government-Owned**
2007 Sales: $240,000,000	2007 Profits: $	**Int'l Ticker:** Int'l Exchange:
2006 Sales: $200,000,000	2006 Profits: $	Employees: 54,487
2005 Sales: $150,000,000	2005 Profits: $	Fiscal Year Ends: 12/31
2004 Sales: $116,000,000	2004 Profits: $	Parent Company:

SALARIES/BENEFITS:

Pension Plan:	ESOP Stock Plan:	Profit Sharing:	Top Exec. Salary: $	Bonus: $
Savings Plan:	Stock Purch. Plan:		Second Exec. Salary: $	Bonus: $

OTHER THOUGHTS:

Apparent Women Officers or Directors:
Hot Spot for Advancement for Women/Minorities:

LOCATIONS: ("Y" = Yes)

West:	Southwest:	Midwest:	Southeast:	Northeast:	International:
	Y			Y	Y

SCHERING-PLOUGH CORP

www.schering-plough.com

Industry Group Code: 325412 **Ranks within this company's industry group:** Sales: 13 Profits: 17

Techology:		Medical/Drugs:		Engineering:		Transportation:		Chemicals/Petrochemicals:		Specialty:	
Computers:		Manufacturer:	Y	Design:		Aerospace:		Oil/Gas Products:		Special Services:	
Software:		Contract Research:		Construction:		Automotive:		Chemicals:		Consulting:	
Communications:		Medical Services:		Eng. Services:		Shipping:		Oil/Chem. Svcs.:		Specialty Mgmt.:	
Electronics:		Labs:		Consulting:				Gases:		Products:	
Alternative Energy:		Bio. Services:						Other:		Other:	

TYPES OF BUSINESS:

Drugs-Diversified
Anti-Infective & Anti-Cancer Drugs
Dermatologicals
Cardiovascular Drugs
Animal Health Products
Over-the-Counter Drugs
Foot & Sun Care Products

BRANDS/DIVISIONS/AFFILIATES:

Bovilis/Vista
HOMEAGAIN
Dr. Scholl's
Coppertone
Nuflor
Livial
Vytorin
Lotrimin

CONTACTS: *Note: Officers with more than one job title may be intentionally listed here more than once.*

Fred Hassan, CEO
Robert J. Bertolini, CFO/Exec. VP
C. Ron Cheeley, Sr. VP-Global Human Resources
Thomas P. Koestler, Exec. VP/Pres., Schering-Plough Research Institute
Thomas Sabatino, Jr., General Counsel/Exec. VP
Janet M. Barth, VP-Investor Rel.
Steven H. Koehler, Chief Acct. Officer/Controller/VP
Richard S. Bowles III, Sr. VP-Global Quality Oper.
Carrie S. Cox, Exec. VP/Pres., Global Pharmaceuticals
Lori Queisser, Sr. VP-Global Compliance & Bus. Practices
Brent Saunders, Sr. VP/Pres., Consumer Health Care
Fred Hassan, Chmn.
Ian McInnes, Sr. VP/Pres., Global Supply Chain

Phone: 908-298-4000	**Fax:** 908-298-7653
Toll-Free:	
Address: 2000 Galloping Hill Rd., Kenilworth, NJ 07033 US	

GROWTH PLANS/SPECIAL FEATURES:

Schering-Plough Corp. is a science-centered global health care company. The company operates in three segments: human prescription pharmaceuticals, animal health and consumer health care. The human prescription pharmaceuticals segment discovers, develops, manufactures and markets human pharmaceutical products. Within the segment, the firm has a broad range of research projects and marketed products in six therapeutic areas: cardiovascular, central nervous system, immunology and infectious disease, oncology, respiratory and women's health. Marketed products include Vytorin, a cholesterol-lowering tablet; Remeron, an antidepressant; Livial, a menopausal therapy; and Temodar capsules for certain types of brain tumors including newly diagnosed glioblastoma multiforme. The animal health segment discovers, develops, manufactures and markets animal health products, including vaccines. Principal marketed products in this segment include Nuflor fish, bovine and swine antibiotics; Bovilis/Vista vaccine lines for infectious diseases in cattle; Innovax ND-SB vaccine for poultry; Otomax, a canine ear treatment; and HOMEAGAIN, which identifies pet cats and dogs and makes them easier to recover if lost. The consumer health care segment develops, manufactures and markets various over-the-counter, foot care and sun care products. Principal products in this division include Claritin non-sedating antihistamines; Dr. Scholl's foot care products; Lotrimin topical antifungal products; and Coppertone sun care lotions, sprays, dry oils, lip protection products and sunless tanning products. Throughout 2008, the firm continued the integration of its 2007 acquisition, Organon BioSciences, into its operations. In February 2008, the company partnered with OraSure Technologies, Inc., to develop a rapid oral hepatitis C test. In April 2008, Schering-Plough agreed to sell a combined 12 European animal product franchises to Virbac, S.A., and Pfizer Animal Health. In August 2008, the firm founded Shanghai Schering-Plough Pharmaceutical Co. Ltd., to expand its Chinese allergy and skincare product market. In March 2009, the firm agreed to be acquired by Merck & Co. for $41.1 billion.

FINANCIALS: **Sales and profits are in thousands of dollars—add 000 to get the full amount. 2008 Note: Financial information for 2008 was not available for all companies at press time.**

2008 Sales: $18,502,000	2008 Profits: $1,903,000	**U.S. Stock Ticker: SGP**
2007 Sales: $12,690,000	2007 Profits: $-1,473,000	**Int'l Ticker:** Int'l Exchange:
2006 Sales: $10,594,000	2006 Profits: $1,143,000	Employees: 51,000
2005 Sales: $9,508,000	2005 Profits: $269,000	Fiscal Year Ends: 12/31
2004 Sales: $8,272,000	2004 Profits: $-947,000	Parent Company:

SALARIES/BENEFITS:

Pension Plan:	ESOP Stock Plan:	Profit Sharing:	Top Exec. Salary: $1,670,000	Bonus: $4,033,050
Savings Plan:	Stock Purch. Plan:		Second Exec. Salary: $1,037,500	Bonus: $1,327,200

OTHER THOUGHTS:

Apparent Women Officers or Directors: 8
Hot Spot for Advancement for Women/Minorities: Y

LOCATIONS: ("Y" = Yes)

West:	Southwest:	Midwest:	Southeast:	Northeast:	International:
Y	Y	Y	Y	Y	Y

SCHERING-PLOUGH RESEARCH INSTITUTE www.schering-plough.com/research-development/index.aspx

Industry Group Code: 541710 **Ranks within this company's industry group:** Sales: Profits:

Techology:		Medical/Drugs:		Engineering:		Transportation:		Chemicals/Petrochemicals:		Specialty:	
Computers:		Manufacturer:		Design:		Aerospace:		Oil/Gas Products:		Special Services:	
Software:		Contract Research:		Construction:		Automotive:		Chemicals:		Consulting:	
Communications:		Medical Services:	Y	Eng. Services:		Shipping:		Oil/Chem. Svcs.:		Specialty Mgmt.:	
Electronics:		Labs:	Y	Consulting:				Gases:		Products:	
Alternative Energy:		Bio. Services:	Y					Other:		Other:	

TYPES OF BUSINESS:

Drug Discovery
Genomics & Gene Therapy
Informatics

BRANDS/DIVISIONS/AFFILIATES:

Schering-Plough Corp
Customer-Centered Product Flow (CCPF)
ALIS (Automated Ligand Identification System)
Schering-Plough Biopharma
SARASAR
Vicriviroc
NASONEX

CONTACTS: *Note: Officers with more than one job title may be intentionally listed here more than once.*

Thomas P. Koestler, Pres./Exec. VP
John T. Curnutte, Pres., Schering-Plough Biopharma
Fred Hassan, Chmn./CEO-Schering-Plough Corp.

Phone: 908-298-4000	**Fax:** 908-740-7101
Toll-Free:	
Address: 2015 Galloping Hill Rd., Kenilworth, NJ 07033-1300 US	

GROWTH PLANS/SPECIAL FEATURES:

Schering-Plough Research Institute (SPRI) is the pharmaceutical research and development division of Schering-Plough Corporation. The firm's research is focused on discovering and developing new small molecules and biologics to treat various cancers, infectious diseases, respiratory conditions, inflammatory diseases, cardiovascular diseases, metabolic diseases and neurodegenerative diseases, with nearly $3 billion invested in research and development annually. SPRI's largest facility, in Kenilworth, NJ, conducts research in small molecule drug discovery, as does its newest facility in Cambridge, MA. The Kenilworth facility additionally conducts high-throughput screening of SPRI's compound libraries using robotics and microfluidics to increase throughput and decrease compound utilization, and has areas devoted to drug metabolism, pharmacokinetics, clinical development and pharmaceutical sciences. The Kenilworth facility is also where drug development decisions are made using the company's proprietary Customer-Centered Product Flow (CCPF) process. At its Cambridge facility, the company's ALIS (Automated Ligand Identification System) technology uses affinity selection of mass-encoded compound libraries for lead identification and optimization. SPRI conducts biologics research on monoclonal antibodies and therapeutic proteins at its Schering-Plough Biopharma laboratories in Palo Alto, CA. Biopharma's operations are comprised of its discovery research; experimental pathology and pharmacology; protein engineering; and bioanalytical and protein chemistry departments. SPRI's Milan, Italy facility is engaged in the discovery of small molecules, focusing on neurobiological indications for the treatment of pain. The company has invested in structural chemistry, including X-ray crystallography, mass spectrometry and NMR (nuclear magnetic resonance), which it has integrated with computer-assisted drug design to facilitate compound optimization for soluble protein targets. SPRI conducts pharmaceutical sciences development work at three locations in New Jersey and one in Lucerne, Switzerland. It develops its products both in-house and through collaborations with outside companies and organizations. Products currently under development include SARASAR, for breast cancer; Vicriviroc, for HIV; and NASONEX, for allergies.

FINANCIALS: **Sales and profits are in thousands of dollars—add 000 to get the full amount. 2008 Note: Financial information for 2008 was not available for all companies at press time.**

2008 Sales: $	2008 Profits: $	**U.S. Stock Ticker: Subsidiary**
2007 Sales: $	2007 Profits: $	**Int'l Ticker:** Int'l Exchange:
2006 Sales: $	2006 Profits: $	Employees: 102
2005 Sales: $	2005 Profits: $	Fiscal Year Ends: 12/31
2004 Sales: $	2004 Profits: $	Parent Company: SCHERING-PLOUGH CORP

SALARIES/BENEFITS:

Pension Plan:	ESOP Stock Plan:	Profit Sharing:	Top Exec. Salary: $	Bonus: $
Savings Plan: Y	Stock Purch. Plan:		Second Exec. Salary: $	Bonus: $

OTHER THOUGHTS:

Apparent Women Officers or Directors:
Hot Spot for Advancement for Women/Minorities:

LOCATIONS: ("Y" = Yes)

West:	Southwest:	Midwest:	Southeast:	Northeast:	International:
Y				Y	Y

SCHLUMBERGER LIMITED

www.slb.com

Industry Group Code: 213111 **Ranks within this company's industry group:** Sales: 1 Profits: 1

Techology:		Medical/Drugs:		Engineering:		Transportation:		Chemicals/Petrochemicals:		Specialty:	
Computers:		Manufacturer:		Design:	Y	Aerospace:		Oil/Gas Products:		Special Services:	Y
Software:		Contract Research:		Construction:		Automotive:		Chemicals:		Consulting:	Y
Communications:		Medical Services:		Eng. Services:	Y	Shipping:		Oil/Chem. Svcs.:	Y	Specialty Mgmt.:	
Electronics:		Labs:		Consulting:				Gases:		Products:	Y
Alternative Energy:		Bio. Services:						Other:	Y	Other:	

TYPES OF BUSINESS:

Oil & Gas Drilling Support Services
Seismic Services
Reservoir Imaging
Data & IT Consulting Services
Outsourcing
Stimulation Services

BRANDS/DIVISIONS/AFFILIATES:

Schlumberger Oilfield Services
WesternGeco
Framo Engineering
M-I Drilling Fluids
Extreme Engineering Limited
Saxon Energy Services Inc

CONTACTS: *Note: Officers with more than one job title may be intentionally listed here more than once.*

Andrew Gould, CEO
Simon Ayat, CFO/Exec. VP
Ashok Belani, CTO
Satish Pai, VP-Oper., Oilfield Svcs.
Malcolm Theobald, VP-Investor Rel.
Chakib Sbiti, Exec. VP-Oilfield Svcs.
Dalton Boutte, Pres., WesternGeco
Imran Kizilbash, Pres., Reservoir Characterization Group
Doug Pferdehirt, Pres., Reservoir Product Group
Andrew Gould, Chmn.

Phone: 713-513-2000	**Fax:** 281-285-8548
Toll-Free:	
Address: 5599 San Felipe St., Fl. 17, Houston, TX 77056 US	

GROWTH PLANS/SPECIAL FEATURES:

Schlumberger, Ltd. (SLB) is a leading oil field service company offering technology, project management and information solutions for customers in the international oil and gas industry. Schlumberger operates in 80 countries throughout North America, Latin America, Europe, Africa, the Middle East and Asia in 31 oilfield service GeoMarket regions and 20 research and engineering facilities. The SLB Oilfield Services segment is divided into eight technology-based service lines, which include wireline, drilling and measurements, well testing, well services, completions, artificial lift, data and consulting services and SLB information solutions. The overall purpose of the Oilfield Services sector is to provide proper exploration with production services and technologies throughout the entire life cycle of a reservoir. Another SLB service is its Integrated Project Management (IPM) line, which provides consulting, project management and engineering services for well construction using SLB technology. The company owns 40% of M-I Drilling Fluids along with Smith International, which offers drilling and completion fluids to stabilize rock and minimize formation damage. In addition, the firm owns a majority stake in Framo Engineering, a Norwegian-based company that provides multiphase booster pumps, flow metering equipment and swivel stack systems. Another subsidiary of SLB, WesternGeco, offers worldwide marine and seismic reservoir imaging, data processing centers and a multi-client seismic library for monitoring and development services. Additional services include 3-D, time-lapse and multicomponent surveys for delineating prospects and reservoir management. In June 2008, SLB acquired Extreme Engineering Limited, a supplier of unmanned measurement-while-drilling (MWD) systems. Also during 2008, in partnership with U.S. private equity firm First Reserve, the company acquired Saxon Energy Services, Inc., a Canadian provider of oil field equipment and services.

FINANCIALS: **Sales and profits are in thousands of dollars—add 000 to get the full amount. 2008 Note: Financial information for 2008 was not available for all companies at press time.**

2008 Sales: $27,163,000	2008 Profits: $5,435,000	**U.S. Stock Ticker: SLB**
2007 Sales: $23,277,000	2007 Profits: $5,177,000	**Int'l Ticker:** Int'l Exchange:
2006 Sales: $19,230,000	2006 Profits: $3,710,000	Employees: 87,000
2005 Sales: $14,309,000	2005 Profits: $2,207,000	Fiscal Year Ends: 12/31
2004 Sales: $11,480,200	2004 Profits: $1,223,900	Parent Company:

SALARIES/BENEFITS:

Pension Plan: Y	ESOP Stock Plan:	Profit Sharing:	Top Exec. Salary: $2,500,000	Bonus: $3,750,000
Savings Plan: Y	Stock Purch. Plan: Y		Second Exec. Salary: $964,516	Bonus: $1,401,907

OTHER THOUGHTS:

Apparent Women Officers or Directors:
Hot Spot for Advancement for Women/Minorities:

LOCATIONS: ("Y" = Yes)

West:	Southwest:	Midwest:	Southeast:	Northeast:	International:
Y	Y	Y		Y	Y

Note: Financial information, benefits and other data can change quickly and may vary from those stated here.

SCHNEIDER ELECTRIC SA

www.schneider-electric.com

Industry Group Code: 335000 **Ranks within this company's industry group:** Sales: 5 Profits: 3

Techology:		Medical/Drugs:		Engineering:		Transportation:		Chemicals/Petrochemicals:		Specialty:	
Computers:		Manufacturer:		Design:		Aerospace:		Oil/Gas Products:		Special Services:	
Software:		Contract Research:		Construction:		Automotive:		Chemicals:		Consulting:	
Communications:		Medical Services:		Eng. Services:	Y	Shipping:		Oil/Chem. Svcs.:		Specialty Mgmt.:	
Electronics:	Y	Labs:		Consulting:				Gases:		Products:	Y
Alternative Energy:		Bio. Services:						Other:		Other:	

TYPES OF BUSINESS:

Electrical Distribution Products
Infrastructure Products
Building Automation & Control Products

BRANDS/DIVISIONS/AFFILIATES:

BEI Technologies Inc
Systron Donner Inertial
American Power Conversion Corp
Merlin Gerin
Square D
Telemecanique
Wessen

CONTACTS: *Note: Officers with more than one job title may be intentionally listed here more than once.*

Jean-Pascal Tricoire, CEO
Pierre Bouchut, CFO
Aaron Davis, Chief Mktg. Officer
Karen Ferguson, Exec. VP-Human Resources
Herve Coureil, CIO
Eric Pilaud, Exec. VP-Tech.
Eric Pilaud, Exec. VP-Strategy
Russell Stocker, Exec. VP-Asia-Pacific
Chris Curtis, Exec. VP-North America
Julio Rodriguez, Exec. VP-Europe
Serge Goldenberg, Sr. VP-Corp. Quality
Jean-Pascal Tricoire, Chmn.
Christian Wiest, Exec. VP-Int'l

Phone: 33-1-41-29-70-00	**Fax:** 33-1-41-29-71-00
Toll-Free:	
Address: 35 rue Joseph Monier, Rueil-Malmaison, 92500 France	

GROWTH PLANS/SPECIAL FEATURES:

Schneider Electric S.A. manufactures and markets a range of products and services for the energy and infrastructure markets in residential buildings and industry areas. Schneider Electric has operations in nearly 200 countries worldwide, with approximately 15,000 sales outlets; 25 research and development sites; 205 manufacturing facilities; and 60 logistics centers. The company works through three core business segments: electrical distribution; automation & control; and critical power & cooling services. The firm's electrical distribution segment, accounting for 63% of annual revenues, offers products, equipment and systems covering all phases of transmission and electrical distribution, classified according to their voltage level. Low-voltage products, including circuit breakers, switches, security lighting, prefabricated electrical wiring, modular switchgear and communication products, are used in the building market. Medium-voltage equipment is designed to transform electricity and then deliver it to an end user. The company's electrical distribution segment has two primary brand names: Merlin Gerin and Square D. The Merlin Gerin brand supplies intermediaries with modular and autonomous components that are organized as systems designed to increase and optimize distribution. The Square D brand aids companies in meeting market requirements for products that must comply with NEMA (National Electrical Manufacturers Association) standards. The company's automation & control segment, accounting for 29% of annual revenues, specializes in developing platforms and products for human-machine interaction including contractors, overload relays, soft starters, speed drives, sensors and operator terminals. This segment includes company Telemecanique, which develops products and systems for automation that include abilities in detection, man-machine dialogue and process supervision. The recently-created critical power & cooling services segment, accounting for a growing portion of annual revenues, focuses on providing solutions for energy-critical applications, such as data centers and hospitals. In April 2008, the firm acquired Wessen, a manufacturer of wiring devices based in Russia.

FINANCIALS: **Sales and profits are in thousands of dollars—add 000 to get the full amount. 2008 Note: Financial information for 2008 was not available for all companies at press time.**

2008 Sales: $24,395,700	2008 Profits: $2,240,930	**U.S. Stock Ticker:**
2007 Sales: $23,060,800	2007 Profits: $2,109,030	**Int'l Ticker: SU** Int'l Exchange: Paris-Euronext
2006 Sales: $18,113,600	2006 Profits: $1,776,600	Employees: 46,500
2005 Sales: $14,226,400	2005 Profits: $1,210,800	Fiscal Year Ends: 12/31
2004 Sales: $14,138,300	2004 Profits: $770,100	Parent Company:

SALARIES/BENEFITS:

Pension Plan:	ESOP Stock Plan:	Profit Sharing:	Top Exec. Salary: $	Bonus: $
Savings Plan:	Stock Purch. Plan:		Second Exec. Salary: $	Bonus: $

OTHER THOUGHTS:

Apparent Women Officers or Directors: 1
Hot Spot for Advancement for Women/Minorities:

LOCATIONS: ("Y" = Yes)

West:	Southwest:	Midwest:	Southeast:	Northeast:	International:
					Y

SCIENTIFIC ATLANTA INC

www.scientificatlanta.com

Industry Group Code: 334220 **Ranks within this company's industry group:** Sales: Profits:

Techology:		Medical/Drugs:		Engineering:		Transportation:		Chemicals/Petrochemicals:		Specialty:	
Computers:		Manufacturer:		Design:		Aerospace:		Oil/Gas Products:		Special Services:	
Software:		Contract Research:		Construction:		Automotive:		Chemicals:		Consulting:	
Communications:	Y	Medical Services:		Eng. Services:		Shipping:		Oil/Chem. Svcs.:		Specialty Mgmt.:	
Electronics:	Y	Labs:		Consulting:				Gases:		Products:	
Alternative Energy:		Bio. Services:						Other:		Other:	

TYPES OF BUSINESS:

Radio & Television Broadcasting Equipment
Terrestrial & Satellite Communications Network Products
Transmission & Distribution Equipment
Equipment Design & Implementation
Optoelectronic Technologies
Broadband Access Products
Fiber-Optic Networks
Installation, Integration & Support Services

BRANDS/DIVISIONS/AFFILIATES:

Cisco Systems Inc
SciCare Broadband Services
Explorer 8300 Home Entertainment Server
PowerVu
Barconet
Scientific-Atlanta (Shanghai) Company, Ltd.

CONTACTS: *Note: Officers with more than one job title may be intentionally listed here more than once.*

James McDonald, CEO
Patrick M. Tylka, Sr. VP/Pres., Worldwide Sales
Brian C. Koenig, Sr. VP-Human Resources
Robert C. McIntyre, CTO/Sr. VP
Michael C. Veysey, General Counsel/Corp. Sec./Sr. VP
John A. Buckett, II, VP-Corp. Dev.
H. Allen Ecker, Exec. VP
J. Lawrence Bradner, Corp. Sr. VP/Pres., SciCare Broadband Svcs.
Dwight B. Duke, Corp. Sr. VP/Pres., Transmission Network Systems
Michael Harney, Corp. Sr. VP/Pres., Subscriber Networks
Bill Katherman, VP/Managing Dir.-Asia Pacific Region

Phone: 678-277-1000 **Fax:** 770-236-5477
Toll-Free: 800-722-2009
Address: 5030 Sugarloaf Pkwy., Lawrenceville, GA 30044-2869 US

GROWTH PLANS/SPECIAL FEATURES:

Scientific Atlanta, Inc., a subsidiary of Cisco Systems, Inc., provides equipment for telecommunications, wireless, cable and satellite service providers. It has three main classes of products: Subscriber Products, Broadband Access Products and Content Distribution Products; it also offers SciCare Broadband Services. Subscriber Products include solutions for cable operators seeking to grow their subscriber base. These products chiefly consist of digital interactive solutions, which let operators provide customers with e-mail, video-on-demand, telephony, web browsing and electronic commerce over a TV set. To enhance these solutions, the firm also offers the PowerTV operating system, Explorer digital set-tops and two-way digital networks, all of which can combine with Scientific Atlanta's broadband access products. Broadband Access Products include headend (central office) systems, RF electronics and optoelectronics equipment. These products also include distribution systems such as amplifiers, trunk stations and line extenders. Content Distribution Products consist mainly of PowerVu Plus digital compression products, serving satellite and broadband digital television providers. SciCare Broadband Services include basic installation services, telephone support, comprehensive training, complete turnkey installation and system monitoring and management. The firm's Switched Digital Video platform allows different vendor technologies and applications to be used at one time to further enhance television viewing. The firm's IPTV offerings include the delivery and support of digital video networks. Scientific Atlanta's customers include cable operators like Time Warner, SES Americom, Comcast, Rogers Cable, Cox Communications, AT&T and Charter Communications; notable programmers and broadcasters such as A&E, CNN, The History Channel, Toon Disney, Shanghai Cable TV, ESPN and Discovery Channel; and satellite service providers, including PanAmSat. The firm's primary manufacturing facility is located in Juarez, Mexico.

FINANCIALS: **Sales and profits are in thousands of dollars—add 000 to get the full amount. 2008 Note: Financial information for 2008 was not available for all companies at press time.**

2008 Sales: $ | 2008 Profits: $
2007 Sales: $ | 2007 Profits: $
2006 Sales: $ | 2006 Profits: $
2005 Sales: $1,910,892 | 2005 Profits: $210,760
2004 Sales: $1,708,004 | 2004 Profits: $218,001

U.S. Stock Ticker: Subsidiary
Int'l Ticker: Int'l Exchange:
Employees: 7,652
Fiscal Year Ends: 7/31
Parent Company: CISCO SYSTEMS INC

SALARIES/BENEFITS:

Pension Plan: Y | ESOP Stock Plan: | Profit Sharing: | Top Exec. Salary: $971,539 | Bonus: $1,186,400
Savings Plan: Y | Stock Purch. Plan: Y | | Second Exec. Salary: $469,615 | Bonus: $489,500

OTHER THOUGHTS:

Apparent Women Officers or Directors:
Hot Spot for Advancement for Women/Minorities:

LOCATIONS: ("Y" = Yes)

West:	Southwest:	Midwest:	Southeast:	Northeast:	International:
Y	Y		Y		Y

SEAGATE TECHNOLOGY INC

www.seagate.com

Industry Group Code: 334112 **Ranks within this company's industry group:** Sales: 2 Profits: 2

Techology:		Medical/Drugs:		Engineering:		Transportation:		Chemicals/Petrochemicals:		Specialty:	
Computers:	Y	Manufacturer:		Design:		Aerospace:		Oil/Gas Products:		Special Services:	
Software:	Y	Contract Research:		Construction:		Automotive:		Chemicals:		Consulting:	
Communications:		Medical Services:		Eng. Services:		Shipping:		Oil/Chem. Svcs.:		Specialty Mgmt.:	
Electronics:		Labs:		Consulting:				Gases:		Products:	
Alternative Energy:		Bio. Services:						Other:		Other:	

TYPES OF BUSINESS:

Computer Storage Equipment-Disk & Tape Drives
Driver Components
Business Intelligence Software

BRANDS/DIVISIONS/AFFILIATES:

Maxtor Corp
Cheetah
Barracuda
Momentus

CONTACTS: *Note: Officers with more than one job title may be intentionally listed here more than once.*

Stephen J. Luczo, CEO
David Wickersham, COO
David Wickersham, Pres.
Patrick O'Malley, CFO/Exec. VP
Pat King, Sr. VP-Global Mktg.
Karen Hanlon, Sr. VP-Global Human Resources
Mark Brewer, CIO/Sr. VP
Bob Whitmore, CTO/Exec. VP
Ken Massaroni, General Counsel/Sr. VP
Charles C. Pope, Exec. VP-Strategic Planning & Corp. Dev.
Brian Dexheimer, Pres., Consumer Solutions Div.
Sherman Black, Sr. VP-Core Mktg. & Strategy
Phil Pollok, Sr. VP-Solid State Dev. & Alternative Tech.
Kurt Richarz, Exec. VP-Sales & Customer Service
Stephen J. Luczo, Chmn.
Pornchai Piemsomboon, Sr. VP-Asia Mfg. Oper.

Phone: 831-438-6550	**Fax:** 831-438-4127
Toll-Free:	
Address: 920 Disc Dr., Scotts Valley, CA 95066 US	

GROWTH PLANS/SPECIAL FEATURES:

Seagate Technology, Inc. manufactures rigid disk drives, often called disk drives or hard drives, used for storing electronic information in desktop and notebook computers, consumer electronic devices and data centers. Seagate sells its products primarily to OEMs, including Hewlett-Packard, Dell, IBM, EMC and Lenovo Group Limited, as well as to independent distributors and retailers. Sales to OEMs accounted for approximately 67% of disc drive revenues in 2008. Seagate's branded storage solutions are sold under both the Seagate and Maxtor brand names. In addition to the manufacture and sale of disc drives, Seagate provides data storage services for small- to medium-sized businesses, including online backup, data protection and recovery solutions. The company produces multiple rigid disk drive products used in enterprise servers, mainframes, workstations, PCs, digital video recorders, gaming platforms and digital music players. Its product lines include the Cheetah brand, used for Internet and e-commerce servers, data mining, data warehousing, workstations, transaction processing and medical imaging; the Barracuda brand, used in desktop storage, workstations and low-end servers; and the Momentus brand of mobile computing products, used in home notebook computers, tablet computers and digital audio equipment. Seagate also produces disk components for read/write heads, recording media, printed circuit boards, spindle motors, interface controllers and disc drive assemblies. Seagate's OEM customers typically enter into master purchase agreements with the firm, which provide for pricing, volume discounts, order lead times, product support obligations and other terms and conditions. The firm maintains sales offices throughout the U.S., as well as in Australia, China, France, Germany, Japan, Singapore, Taiwan and the U.K. It has manufacturing facilities in the U.S., China, Malaysia, Northern Ireland, Singapore and Thailand.

Seagate offers employees tuition assistance, adoption assistance and an employee assistance program, as well as comprehensive medical coverage and life insurance.

FINANCIALS: **Sales and profits are in thousands of dollars—add 000 to get the full amount. 2008 Note: Financial information for 2008 was not available for all companies at press time.**

2008 Sales: $12,708,000	2008 Profits: $1,262,000	**U.S. Stock Ticker: STX**
2007 Sales: $11,360,000	2007 Profits: $913,000	**Int'l Ticker:** Int'l Exchange:
2006 Sales: $9,206,000	2006 Profits: $840,000	Employees: 54,000
2005 Sales: $7,553,000	2005 Profits: $707,000	Fiscal Year Ends: 6/30
2004 Sales: $6,224,000	2004 Profits: $529,000	Parent Company:

SALARIES/BENEFITS:

Pension Plan:	ESOP Stock Plan:	Profit Sharing:	Top Exec. Salary: $1,000,002	Bonus: $3,000,000
Savings Plan: Y	Stock Purch. Plan: Y		Second Exec. Salary: $786,928	Bonus: $2,015,000

OTHER THOUGHTS:

Apparent Women Officers or Directors: 1
Hot Spot for Advancement for Women/Minorities:

LOCATIONS: ("Y" = Yes)

West:	Southwest:	Midwest:	Southeast:	Northeast:	International:
Y		Y	Y	Y	Y

SEGA SAMMY HOLDINGS INC

www.segasammy.co.jp/english

Industry Group Code: 511208 **Ranks within this company's industry group:** Sales: 1 Profits: 6

Techology:		Medical/Drugs:		Engineering:		Transportation:		Chemicals/Petrochemicals:		Specialty:	
Computers:		Manufacturer:		Design:		Aerospace:		Oil/Gas Products:		Special Services:	
Software:	Y	Contract Research:		Construction:		Automotive:		Chemicals:		Consulting:	
Communications:		Medical Services:		Eng. Services:		Shipping:		Oil/Chem. Svcs.:		Specialty Mgmt.:	
Electronics:		Labs:		Consulting:				Gases:		Products:	Y
Alternative Energy:		Bio. Services:						Other:		Other:	

TYPES OF BUSINESS:

Computer Software-Games
Arcade Games
Amusement Centers
Toys
Ring Tones & Mobile Phone Media
Animation Production
Karaoke Machines
Display Design & Construction Services

BRANDS/DIVISIONS/AFFILIATES:

Sega Corporation
Sammy NetWorks Co., Ltd.
H-I System Corporation
Nissho Inter Life Co., Ltd.
SI Electronics, Ltd.
TMS Entertainment, Ltd.
SEGA Music Networks Co., Ltd.

CONTACTS: *Note: Officers with more than one job title may be intentionally listed here more than once.*

Hajime Satomi, CEO
Hajime Satomi, Pres.
Norio Uchida, Gen. Mgr.-R&D & Prod. Control-Sammy Corp.
Kazutada Ieda, Standing Corp. Auditor
Okitane Usui, Pres./CEO/COO-Sega Corporation
Keishi Nakayama, Exec. VP/Pres./CEO/COO-Sammy Corporation
Hisao Oguchi, Chief Creative Officer
Hideo Yoshizawa, Sr. Exec. Officer
Hajime Satomi, Chmn.

Phone: 81-3-621-59955 **Fax:** 81-3-5736-7066
Toll-Free:
Address: Shiodome Sumitomo Bldg 21F,1-9-2 Higashi Shimbashi, Tokyo, 105-0021 Japan

GROWTH PLANS/SPECIAL FEATURES:

Sega Sammy Holdings, Inc. (SSH), the product of a merger between Sega Corporation and Sammy Corporation, operates amusement centers and produces game software and arcade games. The company is organized into four principle segments: Pachislot and Pachinko Machines (PPM), similar to slot machines, which generated 31.7% of 2008 sales; Amusement Machine Sales (AMS), 15.5%; Amusement Center Operations (ACO), 19.9%; and Consumer Business, 30.9%. Other operations accounted for the remaining 2%. During 2008, the PPM segment installed 380,688 pachislot and 108,184 pachinko machines, down from previous years. In the AMS segment, the company uses the ALL.Net P-ras business model, wherein it sells game hardware and provides mother board and software at no cost. SSH is paid by content use. This model allows operators of amusement centers to introduce new arcade machines with a small initial investment. The ACO segment owns and operates 363 amusement centers, including those operated by TMS Entertainment, opening 12 and closing 92 stores in 2008. Lastly, the Consumer Business segment manufactures software for home video game consoles (including producing the Incredible Hulk and Iron Man games for XBOX 360), Internet game play and mobile phones, as well as having operations in the traditional toy market. Some of the company's 29 domestic and 25 overseas subsidiaries and affiliates include Sega Corporation; Sammy NetWorks Co., LTD., developer of ring tones and games for mobile phones; TMS Entertainment, LTD., an animation planning and production firm; H-I System Corporation, which makes amusement hall computers and prize POS systems; Nissho Inter Life Co., Ltd., which engages in planning, design, management and construction of displays and commercial facilities; and Sega Music Networks Co., Ltd., involved in the production and sales of karaoke machines.

FINANCIALS: **Sales and profits are in thousands of dollars—add 000 to get the full amount. 2008 Note: Financial information for 2008 was not available for all companies at press time.**

2008 Sales: $4,589,800	2008 Profits: $-524,700	**U.S. Stock Ticker: SGAMY.PK**
2007 Sales: $5,282,400	2007 Profits: $434,600	**Int'l Ticker: 6460** Int'l Exchange: Tokyo-TSE
2006 Sales: $5,532,400	2006 Profits: $662,200	Employees: 6,416
2005 Sales: $5,156,700	2005 Profits: $505,700	Fiscal Year Ends: 3/31
2004 Sales: $1,810,400	2004 Profits: $82,900	Parent Company:

SALARIES/BENEFITS:

Pension Plan:	ESOP Stock Plan:	Profit Sharing:	Top Exec. Salary: $	Bonus: $
Savings Plan:	Stock Purch. Plan:		Second Exec. Salary: $	Bonus: $

OTHER THOUGHTS:

Apparent Women Officers or Directors:
Hot Spot for Advancement for Women/Minorities:

LOCATIONS: ("Y" = Yes)

West:	Southwest:	Midwest:	Southeast:	Northeast:	International:
Y		Y	Y		Y

SEIKO EPSON CORPORATION

www.epson.com

Industry Group Code: 334119 **Ranks within this company's industry group:** Sales: 2 Profits: 9

Techology:		Medical/Drugs:		Engineering:		Transportation:		Chemicals/Petrochemicals:		Specialty:	
Computers:	Y	Manufacturer:		Design:		Aerospace:		Oil/Gas Products:		Special Services:	
Software:		Contract Research:		Construction:		Automotive:		Chemicals:		Consulting:	
Communications:		Medical Services:		Eng. Services:		Shipping:		Oil/Chem. Svcs.:		Specialty Mgmt.:	
Electronics:	Y	Labs:		Consulting:				Gases:		Products:	Y
Alternative Energy:		Bio. Services:						Other:		Other:	

TYPES OF BUSINESS:

Electronic Device Manufacturing
Computers & Peripherals
Business Machines
Precision Components
Semiconductors
Printer Consumables
Contract Manufacturing
Printer Software

BRANDS/DIVISIONS/AFFILIATES:

Seiko Group
Epson Software Development Laboratory, Inc.
Epson Stylus Photo
Epson Toyocom Corp.
PictureMate
Livingstation
Orient Watch Co., Ltd.
Epson (China) Co., Ltd.

CONTACTS: *Note: Officers with more than one job title may be intentionally listed here more than once.*

Minoru Usui, Pres.
Akio Mori, COO-Watch Oper.
Kenji Kubota, Gen. Admin. Mgr.-Corp. Strategy Office
Akihiko Sakai, COO-Imaging Prod. Oper.
Torao Yajima, Pres., Tohoku Epson Corporation
Kiyofumi Koike, Pres., Epson (China) Co., Ltd.
Kaname Miyazawa, Pres., Epson Toyocom Corporation
Seiji Hanaoka, Chmn.
John Lang, Pres./CEO-Epson America, Inc.
Norio Niwa, Exec. VP-Logistics, Sales & Mktg.

Phone: 81-266-52-3131 **Fax:** 81-266-53-4844
Toll-Free:
Address: 3-3-5 Owa, Suwa, Nagano, 392-8502 Japan

GROWTH PLANS/SPECIAL FEATURES:

Seiko Epson Corporation develops, markets, manufactures and services information-related products, electronic devices and precision products. Seiko's main product lines are printers and projectors, displays, liquid crystal displays (LCDs), monitors, projectors, scanners, semiconductors and precision instruments such as watches. The company also manufactures precision products, watch parts, lenses, motors and magnets for its parent company, Seiko Group. Seiko Epson has five main product segments: printing technology, projection technology, high-temperature polysilicon (HTPS) projection panels, electronic components and precision machines. The printing technology group features the firm's Epson Stylus Photo series of printers, as well as the PictureMate series, which are both popular for printing photographs. In addition, the segment includes print cartridges, print heads and printer paper. The projection technology group consists primarily of the 3LCD series projectors. The electronic components segment includes display screens for cell phones and personal digital assistants, integrated circuits and timing devices for use in a wide range of electronic devices. The precision machines section includes corrective lenses for eyeglasses, high quality industrial robotics and the firm's well-known watches. Other products include Epson Perfection and Expression series scanners, 3LCD series projectors and Livingstation LCD projection televisions. Other electronic devices include point-of-sale monitors and printers, semiconductors and quartz devices such as oscillators. In 2007, information related equipment accounted for roughly 64% of sales; electronic devices accounted for 28%; precision products accounted for 5.9%; and other products accounted for the remaining 2.1%. As part of a business realignment, the company spent 2008 consolidating several subsidiaries. In January 2008, the company absorbed the operations of Seiko Epson Contactlens Corp., a wholly-owned subsidiary. In November 2008, the company acquired the remaining interests in Orient Watch Co., Ltd., making the company a wholly-owned subsidiary.

FINANCIALS: **Sales and profits are in thousands of dollars—add 000 to get the full amount. 2008 Note: Financial information for 2008 was not available for all companies at press time.**

2008 Sales: $13,478,400 | 2008 Profits: $190,900
2007 Sales: $14,160,300 | 2007 Profits: $-70,900
2006 Sales: $15,495,700 | 2006 Profits: $-179,200
2005 Sales: $14,797,500 | 2005 Profits: $556,900
2004 Sales: $13,377,800 | 2004 Profits: $360,000

U.S. Stock Ticker:
Int'l Ticker: 6724 Int'l Exchange: Tokyo-TSE
Employees: 87,626
Fiscal Year Ends: 3/31
Parent Company:

SALARIES/BENEFITS:

Pension Plan: ESOP Stock Plan: Profit Sharing: Top Exec. Salary: $ Bonus: $
Savings Plan: Stock Purch. Plan: Second Exec. Salary: $ Bonus: $

OTHER THOUGHTS:

Apparent Women Officers or Directors:
Hot Spot for Advancement for Women/Minorities:

LOCATIONS: ("Y" = Yes)

West:	Southwest:	Midwest:	Southeast:	Northeast:	International:
Y	Y	Y	Y	Y	Y

SEMBCORP INDUSTRIES LTD

www.sembcorp.com.sg

Industry Group Code: 234000 **Ranks within this company's industry group:** Sales: 14 Profits: 7

Techology:		Medical/Drugs:		Engineering:		Transportation:		Chemicals/Petrochemicals:		Specialty:	
Computers:		Manufacturer:		Design:		Aerospace:		Oil/Gas Products:		Special Services:	Y
Software:		Contract Research:		Construction:	Y	Automotive:		Chemicals:		Consulting:	
Communications:		Medical Services:		Eng. Services:	Y	Shipping:	Y	Oil/Chem. Svcs.:	Y	Specialty Mgmt.:	Y
Electronics:		Labs:		Consulting:				Gases:		Products:	
Alternative Energy:		Bio. Services:						Other:		Other:	

TYPES OF BUSINESS:

Heavy Construction
Marine Construction & Shipbuilding
Utilities Services
Environmental Engineering & Waste Management
Industrial Parks
Internet Service Provider
Floating Oil Production Platforms
Pipelines

BRANDS/DIVISIONS/AFFILIATES:

SembCorp Marine
SembCorp Environmental Management
SembCorp Utilities
SembCorp Gas
SembCorp Cogen
SembCorp Power
SembCorp Parks Holdings
Pacific Internet

CONTACTS: *Note: Officers with more than one job title may be intentionally listed here more than once.*

Tang Kin Fei, CEO
Tang Kin Fei, Pres.
Lim Joke Mui, CFO
Tan Cheng Guan, Exec. VP-Group Bus. & Strategic Dev.
April Lee, Sr. VP-Corp. Rel.
Koh Chiap Khiong, Deputy Group CFO
Francis Joseph Gomez, Exec. VP-Energy
Peter Seah Lim Huat, Chmn.

Phone: 65-6723-3113	**Fax:** 65-6822-3254
Toll-Free:	
Address: 30 Hill St., #05-04, Singapore, 179360 Singapore	

GROWTH PLANS/SPECIAL FEATURES:

Sembcorp Industries, Ltd. is one of Singapore's leading utilities and marine groups and has assets in excess of $5.8 billion. The firm's primary businesses include Sembcorp Utilities, Sembcorp Marine, Sembcorp Environment, and Sembcorp Industrial Parks. Sembcorp Utilities provides integrated utilities, energy and water solutions to the chemical and petrochemical industry in Singapore, the U.K. and China. The firm offers a variety of industrial utilities services including, but not limited to, water supply and wastewater treatment; power generation; process stream production and distribution; chemical feedstock; and asset protection. Sembcorp Marine has one of the largest ship repair, shipbuilding and ship conversion operations in East Asia. The company offers a full range of marine and offshore engineering solutions including container ships, chemical tankers, production platforms; and converts Floating Production, Storage and Offloading units (FPSO) for the oil and gas industry. Sembcorp Environment offers integrated environmental services and handles more than one million customers, including private residences, healthcare organizations and commercial and industrial clients. The Sembcorp Industrial Parks segment owns, develops markets and manages more than 400 multinational industrial parks predominately located in China, Indonesia and Vietnam. Sembcorp Industries operates several additional subsidiaries including Sembcorp Gas, Sembcorp Cogen, Sembcorp Power, Singapore Mint; SembCorp Parks Holdings and Pacific Internet, an Internet service provider in Singapore. In June 2008, Sembcorp Industries and Nanyang Technological University signed a R&D agreement to develop new water management technologies. In September 2008, the firm was ordered (under Section 98 of the Gas Act) to transfer its transmission and distribution pipeline assets to PowerGas Ltd, the licensed gas transporter under the Gas Act. In October 2008, the firm signed an agreement to invest in an industrial township project in China.

Sembcorp offers employees health benefits; loan/interest subsidy; a stock ownership plan; a bonus program; and a job development program.

FINANCIALS: **Sales and profits are in thousands of dollars—add 000 to get the full amount. 2008 Note: Financial information for 2008 was not available for all companies at press time.**

2008 Sales: $6,548,910	2008 Profits: $482,170	**U.S. Stock Ticker: SCRPF**
2007 Sales: $5,990,000	2007 Profits: $370,000	**Int'l Ticker: U96** Int'l Exchange: Singapore-SIN
2006 Sales: $4,880,000	2006 Profits: $670,000	Employees: 12,000
2005 Sales: $4,604,000	2005 Profits: $258,000	Fiscal Year Ends: 12/31
2004 Sales: $3,629,400	2004 Profits: $241,500	Parent Company:

SALARIES/BENEFITS:

Pension Plan:	ESOP Stock Plan: Y	Profit Sharing:	Top Exec. Salary: $443,071	Bonus: $1,165,529
Savings Plan:	Stock Purch. Plan:		Second Exec. Salary: $	Bonus: $

OTHER THOUGHTS:

Apparent Women Officers or Directors: 1
Hot Spot for Advancement for Women/Minorities: Y

LOCATIONS: ("Y" = Yes)

West:	Southwest:	Midwest:	Southeast:	Northeast:	International:
					Y

SHANGHAI AUTOMOTIVE INDUSTRY CORP (SAIC)

www.saicgroup.com

Industry Group Code: 336111 **Ranks within this company's industry group:** Sales: Profits:

Techology:		Medical/Drugs:		Engineering:		Transportation:		Chemicals/Petrochemicals:		Specialty:	
Computers:		Manufacturer:		Design:		Aerospace:		Oil/Gas Products:		Special Services:	Y
Software:		Contract Research:		Construction:		Automotive:	Y	Chemicals:		Consulting:	
Communications:		Medical Services:		Eng. Services:		Shipping:		Oil/Chem. Svcs.:		Specialty Mgmt.:	
Electronics:		Labs:		Consulting:				Gases:		Products:	
Alternative Energy:		Bio. Services:						Other:		Other:	

TYPES OF BUSINESS:

Automobile Manufacturing
Motorcycle Manufacturing
Bus Manufacturing
Car Rental Services
Tractor & Heavy Equipment Manufacturing
Parts Manufacturing, Distribution & Retailing
Consumer Finance & Leasing
Insurance

BRANDS/DIVISIONS/AFFILIATES:

SAIC Motor Corporation, Ltd. (SAIC Motor)
Shanghai Motor Manufacturing Co., Ltd.
Shanghai Automobile Import and Export Corp.
Shanghai General Motors
Shanghai Volkswagen Automotive Co., Ltd.
SAIC GM Wuling Automobile Co.
Wuling
Istana

CONTACTS:

Note: Officers with more than one job title may be intentionally listed here more than once.

Shen Jianhua, Pres.
Zhe Genlin, VP-Finance
Zhang Guangsheng, Vice Chmn.
Chen Hong, Vice Chmn.-SAIC Group/Pres., SAIC Motor
Chen Zhixin, Exec. VP-SAIC Motor
Ye Yongming, VP
Hu Maoyuan, Chmn.

Phone: 86-21-2201-1688	**Fax:** 86-21-2201-1188
Toll-Free:	
Address: 489 WeiHai Rd., Shanghai, 200041 China	

GROWTH PLANS/SPECIAL FEATURES:

Shanghai Automotive Industry Corporation (SAIC), a state-owned entity, is one of China's largest automotive companies. The group operates roughly 50 manufacturing facilities, mainly near Shanghai, that make passenger cars, tractors, motorcycles, trucks, buses and automotive parts. SAIC has branches in Korea, the U.S., the U.K. and Japan. During 2007, it sold nearly 1.7 million vehicles, comprising 1.1 million passenger cars and 553,000 commercial vehicles. Additional group operations include automotive service, insurance, parts distribution and retail, consumer automotive financing and car rental services. SAIC's primary operating subsidiary is 83.83%-owned SAIC Motor Corporation, Ltd. (SAIC Motor). Subsidiaries under SAIC Motor include Shanghai Motor Manufacturing Co., Ltd.; 51.33%-owned Ssangyong Motor of South Korea; and Sunwin Motor Group. Its manufacturing operations include SAIC Yizheng Automotive Co., Ltd., used for the production of a light utility passenger car with the nameplate Sabre, based on the platform of GM's Opel S4200. Additional vehicle and parts exporting is managed by subsidiary Shanghai Automobile Import and Export Corp. (SACO), which also oversees importation of high-precision machines, testing and inspection devices and other related items to support advanced manufacturing technologies. SAIC Motor's main joint ventures are Shanghai General Motors, a 50-50 joint venture with General Motors Corp. (GM); and Shanghai Volkswagen Automotive Co., Ltd., a 50-50 joint venture with Volkswagen AG. SAIC GM Wuling Automobile Co., a three-way joint venture between SAIC Group, General Motors and Liuzhou Wuling Motors Co., has the capability to manufacture more than 340,000 vehicles annually. Finished vehicles are branded under the Wuling name for sale domestically and under export to more than 19 countries in Southeast Asia, the Middle East, South America and Western Europe. 1,000 of SAIC's Istana brand commercial vehicles, and other models, served as some of the official transportation for the 2008 Beijing Olympics.

FINANCIALS:

Sales and profits are in thousands of dollars—add 000 to get the full amount. 2008 Note: Financial information for 2008 was not available for all companies at press time.

2008 Sales: $	2008 Profits: $	**U.S. Stock Ticker:**
2007 Sales: $	2007 Profits: $	**Int'l Ticker: SAIC** Int'l Exchange: Shanghai-SHE
2006 Sales: $	2006 Profits: $	Employees: 64,343
2005 Sales: $	2005 Profits: $	Fiscal Year Ends: 12/31
2004 Sales: $	2004 Profits: $	Parent Company:

SALARIES/BENEFITS:

Pension Plan:	ESOP Stock Plan:	Profit Sharing:	Top Exec. Salary: $	Bonus: $
Savings Plan:	Stock Purch. Plan:		Second Exec. Salary: $	Bonus: $

OTHER THOUGHTS:

Apparent Women Officers or Directors:
Hot Spot for Advancement for Women/Minorities:

LOCATIONS: ("Y" = Yes)

West:	Southwest:	Midwest:	Southeast:	Northeast:	International:
		Y			Y

SHARP CORPORATION

www.sharp-world.com

Industry Group Code: 334310 **Ranks within this company's industry group:** Sales: 5 Profits: 4

Techology:		Medical/Drugs:		Engineering:		Transportation:		Chemicals/Petrochemicals:		Specialty:	
Computers:		Manufacturer:		Design:		Aerospace:		Oil/Gas Products:		Special Services:	
Software:	Y	Contract Research:		Construction:		Automotive:		Chemicals:		Consulting:	
Communications:	Y	Medical Services:		Eng. Services:		Shipping:		Oil/Chem. Svcs.:		Specialty Mgmt.:	
Electronics:	Y	Labs:		Consulting:				Gases:		Products:	
Alternative Energy:		Bio. Services:						Other:		Other:	

TYPES OF BUSINESS:

Audiovisual & Communications Equipment
Electronic Components
Solar Cells & Advanced Batteries
Home Appliances
Computers & Information Equipment
Consumer Electronics
LCD Flat Panel TVs, Monitors & Displays
Managed Print Services

BRANDS/DIVISIONS/AFFILIATES:

Kameyama Plant No. 2
LB-1085

CONTACTS:

Note: Officers with more than one job title may be intentionally listed here more than once.

Katsuhiko Machida, CEO
Mikio Katayama, COO
Mikio Katayama, Pres.
Kohichi Takamori, Group Gen. Mgr.-Domestic Mktg.
Nobuyuki Taniguchi, Group Gen. Mgr.-Human Resources
Shigeaki Mizushima, Group Gen. Mgr.-Corp. R&D
Hirohide Nakagawa, Group Gen. Mgr.-Info. Systems
Kenji Ohta, CTO
Toshishige Hamano, Chief Gen. Admin. Officer/Exec. VP
Takashi Nakagawa, Exec. Managing Officer-Legal Affairs
Masafumi Matsumoto, Exec. VP-Bus. Oper.
Tetsuo Onishi, Group Gen. Mgr.-Corporate Acct. & Control
Toshio Adachi, Exec. VP/Group Gen. Mgr.-Tokyo Branch
Yoshiaki Ibuchi, Exec. VP-Electronic Components and Devices Bus.
Nobuyuki Sugano, Group Gen. Mgr.-Int'l Sales & Mktg.
Toshihiko Hirobe, Group Gen. Mgr.-Audio/Visual Systems
Katsuhiko Machida, Chmn.

Phone: 81-6-6621-1221 **Fax:** 81-6-6627-1759
Toll-Free:
Address: 22-22 Nagaike-cho, Abeno-ku, Osaka, 545-8522 Japan

GROWTH PLANS/SPECIAL FEATURES:

Sharp Corporation designs, manufactures and distributes electronic products, information system products and home appliances. Its electronic products include LCD TVs, video projectors, digital audio products, mobile phones and Blu-ray Disc players. Sharp information system products include digital copier/printers, electronic cash registers, fax machines, scientific calculators, electronic organizers, POS systems, LCD monitors and wireless PDAs. Home appliances include superheated steam ovens, small cooking appliances, microwave ovens, air conditioners, washing machines, air purifiers, humidifiers and refrigerators/freezers. Electronic Components business produces such items as CCD/CMOS imagers, microcomputers, flash memories, LCD modules, components for satellite broadcasting, laser diodes and regulators. The firm is also a leading manufacturer of solar cells. Sharp has 28 sales subsidiaries in 23 countries, 24 manufacturing bases in 14 countries and four research and development bases in three countries. The firm's Kameyama Plant No. 2 features an energy supply system based on integrating diverse power sources distributed within the plant into a single large-scale system independent of the utility power grid. These sources include one of the world's largest photovoltaic power systems. The company operates its own manufacturing plants for LCD TVs and makes large investments in research and development for LCD technology, including its triple directional viewing technology, which allows one screen to produce three different images. In addition, Sharp offers managed print services outsourcing, where it can take over the complete operation of a client's desktop printers and copiers with the goal of creating significant savings. In September 2008, the company began producing solar-powered street lights combining its proprietary photovoltaic modules with long-life, white LEDs. In October 2008, Sharp announced a new nationwide electronics recycling program in the U.S., which will accept televisions and other consumer audio and video products. In November 2008, Sharp unveiled its new LB-1085, a 108-inch widescreen LCD monitor, the largest produced to-date. The product is intended for professional use in such venues as shopping malls, financial institutions, educational institutions and transportation hubs. The company is also working on high-capacity lithium-ion battery technology.

FINANCIALS:

Sales and profits are in thousands of dollars—add 000 to get the full amount. 2008 Note: Financial information for 2008 was not available for all companies at press time.

2008 Sales: $34,177,400 — 2008 Profits: $1,019,200
2007 Sales: $26,620,000 — 2007 Profits: $870,000
2006 Sales: $24,113,009 — 2006 Profits: $764,405
2005 Sales: $23,960,934 — 2005 Profits: $724,953
2004 Sales: $21,367,300 — 2004 Profits: $574,700

U.S. Stock Ticker: SHCAY
Int'l Ticker: 6753 Int'l Exchange: Tokyo-TSE
Employees: 53,708
Fiscal Year Ends: 3/31
Parent Company:

SALARIES/BENEFITS:

Pension Plan: ESOP Stock Plan: Profit Sharing: Top Exec. Salary: $ Bonus: $
Savings Plan: Stock Purch. Plan: Second Exec. Salary: $ Bonus: $

OTHER THOUGHTS:

Apparent Women Officers or Directors:
Hot Spot for Advancement for Women/Minorities:

LOCATIONS: ("Y" = Yes)

West:	Southwest:	Midwest:	Southeast:	Northeast:	International:
Y		Y	Y	Y	Y

SHAW GROUP INC (THE)

www.shawgrp.com

Industry Group Code: 234000 **Ranks within this company's industry group:** Sales: 12 Profits: 18

Techology:		Medical/Drugs:		Engineering:		Transportation:		Chemicals/Petrochemicals:		Specialty:	
Computers:		Manufacturer:		Design:	Y	Aerospace:		Oil/Gas Products:		Special Services:	Y
Software:		Contract Research:		Construction:	Y	Automotive:		Chemicals:		Consulting:	Y
Communications:		Medical Services:		Eng. Services:	Y	Shipping:		Oil/Chem. Svcs.:		Specialty Mgmt.:	
Electronics:		Labs:		Consulting:	Y			Gases:		Products:	
Alternative Energy:		Bio. Services:						Other:		Other:	

TYPES OF BUSINESS:

Pipe Manufacturing
Construction & Engineering
Consulting Services
Environmental Services
Facilities Management
Power Plant Construction
Nuclear Power Plant Construction

BRANDS/DIVISIONS/AFFILIATES:

Westinghouse Electric Company, L.L.C
Ezeflow, Inc.
Shaw Capital, Inc.

CONTACTS: *Note: Officers with more than one job title may be intentionally listed here more than once.*

James M. Bernhard, Jr., CEO
Gary P. Graphia, COO/Exec. VP
James M. Bernhard, Jr., Pres.
Brian K. Ferraioli, CFO/Exec. VP
David L. Chapman Sr., Pres., Fabrication & Mfg. Group
Dirk J. Wild, Sr. VP-Admin.
Cliff S. Rankin, General Counsel/Corp. Sec.
Michael J. Kershaw, Sr. VP/Chief Acct. Officer
Robert L. Belk, Exec. VP
Louis J. Pucher, Pres., Energy & Chemicals Group
George P. Bevan, Pres., Environmental & Infrastructure Group
David P. Barry, Pres., Nuclear Div.
James M. Bernhard, Jr., Chmn.
Ronald W. Oakley, Managing Dir.-Europe

Phone: 225-932-2500	**Fax:** 225-987-3328
Toll-Free:	
Address: 4171 Essen Ln., Baton Rouge, LA 70809 US	

GROWTH PLANS/SPECIAL FEATURES:

The Shaw Group, Inc. is a construction and engineering contractor firm. It is involved in engineering; technology; construction; fabrication; and environmental and industrial services. The company operates in six segments: power; energy & chemicals (E&C); environmental & infrastructure (E&I); power maintenance; fabrication & manufacturing (F&M); and project development, finance and investments (PDF&I). The power segment provides a range of project-related services, primarily to the global fossil and nuclear power generation industries. The E&C division's offerings include design, engineering, construction, procurement, technology and consulting services, primarily to the oil and gas, refinery, petrochemical and chemical industries. The E&I segment designs and executes remediation solutions involving contaminants in soil, air and water. It also provides project/facilities management for non-environmental construction, watershed restoration, emergency response services, program management and solutions to support and enhance domestic and global land, water and air transportation systems. The maintenance segment performs routine and outage/turnaround maintenance, engineering, construction, recovery and specialty services. The power maintenance sector' services include fossil/nuclear maintenance and turbine generator repair. The F&M segment supplies fabricated piping systems. The PDF&I segment is operated by Shaw Group's wholly-owned subsidiary, Shaw Capital, Inc.; this sector handles the evaluation of energy, chemical, infrastructural and environmental investments. The company's customer base includes multinational oil companies and industrial corporations; regulated utilities; independent and merchant power producers; government agencies; and other equipment manufacturers. Shaw recently acquired Ezeflow, Inc., a manufacturer of pipe fittings. In June 2008, the firm agreed to sell the assets of Shaw Energy Delivery Services, Inc., to Pike Electric, Inc., for approximately $24 million. In August 2008, Shaw Group partnered with Westinghouse Electric Company, L.L.C., to build a new fabrication plant in Lake Charles, Louisiana.

FINANCIALS: **Sales and profits are in thousands of dollars—add 000 to get the full amount. 2008 Note: Financial information for 2008 was not available for all companies at press time.**

2008 Sales: $6,998,011	2008 Profits: $140,717	**U.S. Stock Ticker: SGR**
2007 Sales: $5,723,712	2007 Profits: $-19,000	**Int'l Ticker:** Int'l Exchange:
2006 Sales: $4,775,649	2006 Profits: $50,226	Employees: 26,000
2005 Sales: $3,267,702	2005 Profits: $15,671	Fiscal Year Ends: 8/31
2004 Sales: $3,014,709	2004 Profits: $-33,075	Parent Company:

SALARIES/BENEFITS:

Pension Plan:	ESOP Stock Plan:	Profit Sharing:	Top Exec. Salary: $1,735,386	Bonus: $264,000
Savings Plan: Y	Stock Purch. Plan:		Second Exec. Salary: $603,891	Bonus: $135,400

OTHER THOUGHTS:

Apparent Women Officers or Directors:
Hot Spot for Advancement for Women/Minorities:

LOCATIONS: ("Y" = Yes)

West:	Southwest:	Midwest:	Southeast:	Northeast:	International:
Y	Y	Y	Y	Y	Y

SHELL OIL CO

www.shell.us

Industry Group Code: 211111 **Ranks within this company's industry group:** Sales: Profits:

Techology:		Medical/Drugs:		Engineering:		Transportation:		Chemicals/Petrochemicals:		Specialty:	
Computers:		Manufacturer:		Design:		Aerospace:		Oil/Gas Products:	Y	Special Services:	
Software:		Contract Research:		Construction:		Automotive:		Chemicals:	Y	Consulting:	
Communications:		Medical Services:		Eng. Services:		Shipping:	Y	Oil/Chem. Svcs.:	Y	Specialty Mgmt.:	
Electronics:		Labs:		Consulting:				Gases:	Y	Products:	
Alternative Energy:	Y	Bio. Services:						Other:	Y	Other:	

TYPES OF BUSINESS:

Oil & Gas Exploration & Production
Chemicals
Power Generation
Nanocomposites
Nanocatalysts
Refineries
Pipelines & Shipping
Hydrogen Storage Technology

BRANDS/DIVISIONS/AFFILIATES:

Shell Oil Products US
Shell Chemicals Limited
Shell Gas and Power
Shell Exploration and Production
Royal Dutch Shell (Shell Group)
Motiva Enterprises LLC
Perdido Development

CONTACTS:

Note: Officers with more than one job title may be intentionally listed here more than once.

Marvin E. Odum, Pres.
William C. (Bill) Lowrey, General Counsel/Sr. VP/Corp. Sec.
Allen Kirkley, VP-Strategy & Portfolio
Curtis R. Frasier, Exec. VP-Americas Shell Gas & Power
Marvin E. Odum, Exec. VP-Shell Exploration & Production, Americas
Mark Quartermain, Pres., Shell Energy North America (US) L.P.

Phone: 713-241-6161	**Fax:** 713-241-4044
Toll-Free:	
Address: 1 Shell Plaza, 910 Louisiana St., Houston, TX 77002 US	

GROWTH PLANS/SPECIAL FEATURES:

Shell Oil Company, an affiliate of the Shell Group, is a chemical, oil and natural gas producer in the U.S., with operations in all 50 states. Shell Oil has a number of division and operations, including Shell Oil Products U.S., Motiva Enterprises, Shell Chemicals, Shell Gas and Power, Shell Exploration and Production (SEPCo) and others. These companies discover, develop, manufacture, transport and market crude oil, natural gas and chemical products. Specifically, Shell Oil Products has four refineries which produce a total of 753,000 barrels of oil per day, as well as a network of approximately 6,000 branded gasoline stations in the western U.S. Shell Oil Products also maintains 50% ownership of Motiva Enterprises LLC, with whom the firm refines and ships gasoline to approximately 7,900 Shell-branded stations in the eastern and southern U.S. Shell Chemicals is involved in manufacturing chemicals, including ethylene and propylene, for use in cars, computers, packaging and paints. SEPCo explores and develops natural gas in the U.S, with interests in five states and the Gulf of Mexico. Shell Oil's Gas and Power business is involved in power generation, gas pipeline transmission, receiving terminals, liquefied natural gas (LNG), shipping and coal gasification. Other divisions include Shell Hydrogen, focused on the development of hydrogen and fuel cell technologies from regional bases in Houston and Tokyo; and Shell Renewables, which invests heavily in wind and solar power research. During 2008, the firm began work on its Perdido Development project, currently the world's deepest offshore well at 9,365 feet below the water's surface. In December 2008, subsidiary Shell Energy North America acquired the assets of Enspire Energy LLC, a Virginia-based energy marketing firm. In March 2009, the company launched a new nitrogen-enriched gasoline for automotive use, formulated to remove carbon deposits and remain stable at the high operating temperatures common in modern engines.

FINANCIALS:

Sales and profits are in thousands of dollars—add 000 to get the full amount. 2008 Note: Financial information for 2008 was not available for all companies at press time.

2008 Sales: $	2008 Profits: $	**U.S. Stock Ticker: Subsidiary**
2007 Sales: $87,548,000	2007 Profits: $	**Int'l Ticker:** Int'l Exchange:
2006 Sales: $80,974,000	2006 Profits: $	Employees: 24,008
2005 Sales: $70,000,000	2005 Profits: $	Fiscal Year Ends: 12/31
2004 Sales: $60,000,000	2004 Profits: $	Parent Company: ROYAL DUTCH SHELL (SHELL GROUP)

SALARIES/BENEFITS:

Pension Plan:	ESOP Stock Plan:	Profit Sharing:	Top Exec. Salary: $	Bonus: $
Savings Plan: Y	Stock Purch. Plan:		Second Exec. Salary: $	Bonus: $

OTHER THOUGHTS:

Apparent Women Officers or Directors:
Hot Spot for Advancement for Women/Minorities:

LOCATIONS: ("Y" = Yes)

West:	Southwest:	Midwest:	Southeast:	Northeast:	International:
Y	Y	Y	Y	Y	Y

Note: Financial information, benefits and other data can change quickly and may vary from those stated here.

SHIN ETSU CHEMICAL CO LTD

www.shinetsu.co.jp

Industry Group Code: 325000 **Ranks within this company's industry group:** Sales: 10 Profits: 5

Techology:		**Medical/Drugs:**		**Engineering:**		**Transportation:**		**Chemicals/Petrochemicals:**		**Specialty:**	
Computers:		Manufacturer:		Design:		Aerospace:		Oil/Gas Products:		Special Services:	
Software:		Contract Research:		Construction:	Y	Automotive:		Chemicals:	Y	Consulting:	
Communications:		Medical Services:		Eng. Services:	Y	Shipping:		Oil/Chem. Svcs.:		Specialty Mgmt.:	
Electronics:		Labs:		Consulting:				Gases:		Products:	Y
Alternative Energy:		Bio. Services:						Other:		Other:	

TYPES OF BUSINESS:

Organic & Inorganic Chemicals
PVC
Silicones
Semiconductor Silicon
Rare Earth Magnets & Refined Rare Earth Elements
Synthetic Quartz
Construction & Plant Engineering
Importing & Exporting Goods

BRANDS/DIVISIONS/AFFILIATES:

Shintech, Inc.
CIRES S.A.

CONTACTS: *Note: Officers with more than one job title may be intentionally listed here more than once.*

Chihiro Kanagawa, CEO
Chihiro Kanagawa, Pres.
Toshiyuki Kasahara, Dir./Gen. Mgr.-Finance & Acct.
Shunzo Mori, Sr. Managing Dir.
Fumio Akiya, Sr. Managing Dir.
Yasuhiko Saitoh, Sr. Managing Dir.
Kiichi Habata, Managing. Dir.

Phone: 81-3-3246-5091 **Fax:** 81-3-3246-5096
Toll-Free:
Address: 6-1, Ohtemachi 2-chome, Chiyoda-ku, Tokyo, 100-0004 Japan

GROWTH PLANS/SPECIAL FEATURES:

Shin-Etsu Chemical Co. Ltd. mainly manufactures advanced electronics and industrial materials, including PVC (polyvinyl chloride), semiconductor silicon and synthetic quartz, a key component in fiber optic cables. Founded in 1926, Shin-Etsu is divided into three segments: organic and inorganic chemicals, which generated 51% of 2008 sales; electronics materials, 41%; and functional materials and others, 8%. The organic and inorganic chemicals segment manufactures PVC (52% of this segment's business), silicones (28%) and cellulose derivatives and other products (20%), including methanol, synthetic pheromones, caustic soda and silicon metal. The electronics materials business segment produces semiconductor silicon (85.5% of this segment's business) and other materials (14.5%), including epoxy molding compounds, photoresists and organic materials and rare earth magnets for the electronics industry. Rare earth magnets are typically 10 times stronger than iron-based or ferrite magnets. Lastly, the functional materials and others business segment offers synthetic quartz products (26.7% of this segment's business); rare earth magnets and rare earth elements (33.8%); and other materials (39.5%), including liquid fluoroelastomers, flexible copper-clad laminates and pellicles. Refined rare earth elements, sometimes called rare earths, consist of 17 atomic elements (atomic numbers 21, 39 and 57-71) mainly used in rare earth magnets, superconductors, hybrid car components and other modern, technologically advanced products, including fuel cells. Services of this segment include importing and exporting goods; plant engineering and construction; exporting technology and plants; and information processing. The firm operates 26 domestic and 47 overseas subsidiaries, including U.S.-based Shintech, Inc., which manufactures PVC resin. During 2008, Japan generated around 31.7% of Shin-Etsu's sales; Asia/Oceania, 29.9%; North America, 20.2%; Europe, 12.9%; and other regions, 5.3%. In December 2008, Shin-Etsu announced its plan to transform Portuguese-based affiliate CIRES S.A., which manufactures and distributes PVC, into a wholly-owned subsidiary.

FINANCIALS: **Sales and profits are in thousands of dollars—add 000 to get the full amount. 2008 Note: Financial information for 2008 was not available for all companies at press time.**

2008 Sales: $13,763,650	2008 Profits: $1,835,800	**U.S. Stock Ticker: SHECF**
2007 Sales: $11,100,000	2007 Profits: $1,310,000	**Int'l Ticker: 4063** Int'l Exchange: Tokyo-TSE
2006 Sales: $9,470,000	2006 Profits: $965,900	Employees: 20,241
2005 Sales: $8,995,700	2005 Profits: $866,200	Fiscal Year Ends: 3/31
2004 Sales: $7,883,300	2004 Profits: $708,100	Parent Company:

SALARIES/BENEFITS:

Pension Plan:	ESOP Stock Plan:	Profit Sharing:	Top Exec. Salary: $	Bonus: $
Savings Plan:	Stock Purch. Plan:		Second Exec. Salary: $	Bonus: $

OTHER THOUGHTS:

Apparent Women Officers or Directors:
Hot Spot for Advancement for Women/Minorities:

LOCATIONS: ("Y" = Yes)

West:	Southwest:	Midwest:	Southeast:	Northeast:	International:
					Y

SHOWA DENKO KK

www.sdk.co.jp

Industry Group Code: 325000 **Ranks within this company's industry group:** Sales: 12 Profits: 22

Techology:		Medical/Drugs:		Engineering:		Transportation:		Chemicals/Petrochemicals:		Specialty:	
Computers:	Y	Manufacturer:		Design:		Aerospace:		Oil/Gas Products:		Special Services:	
Software:		Contract Research:		Construction:		Automotive:		Chemicals:	Y	Consulting:	
Communications:		Medical Services:		Eng. Services:		Shipping:		Oil/Chem. Svcs.:		Specialty Mgmt.:	
Electronics:	Y	Labs:		Consulting:				Gases:		Products:	Y
Alternative Energy:		Bio. Services:						Other:	Y	Other:	Y

TYPES OF BUSINESS:

Petrochemical Manufacturing
Aluminum
Electronic Components
Basic & Specialty Chemicals
Ceramic Materials
Carbon Nanofiber
Graphite

BRANDS/DIVISIONS/AFFILIATES:

Fuyo Group
F2 Chemicals Limited

CONTACTS: *Note: Officers with more than one job title may be intentionally listed here more than once.*

Kyohei Takahashi, CEO
Kyohei Takahashi, Pres.
Ichiro Nomura, CFO
Norikuni Imoto, Dir.-Human Resources
Ichiro Nomura, Managing Corp. Officer-Info. Systems
Shinji Sakai, Dir.-Corp. Strategy
Ichiro Nomura, Managing Corp. Officer-Public Rel.
Ichiro Nomura, Managing Corp. Officer-Investor Rel.
Takashi Miyazaki, Exec. Officer-Petrochemicals Sector
Shunichi Shiraishi, Exec. Officer-Aluminum Sector
Akira Ebinuma, Exec. Officer-Electronics Sector
Masakazu Maki, Exec. Officer-Inorganics Sector
Mitsuo Ohashi, Chmn.
Norikuni Imoto, Sr. Managing Corp. Officer-Purchasing

Phone: 81-3-5470-3284 **Fax:** 81-3-3436-2625
Toll-Free:
Address: 13-9 Shiba Daimon 1-chome, Minato-ku, Tokyo, 105-8518 Japan

GROWTH PLANS/SPECIAL FEATURES:

Showa Denko K.K., a part of the Fuyo Group, is a leading Japanese chemicals and industrial materials production firm. It operates in five major sectors: petrochemicals, accounting for 38.6% of annual sales; aluminum, 25.2%; electronics, 19.6%; chemicals, 8.3%; and inorganics, 8.3%. Showa's chief petrochemical products are plastic products; olefins, including propylene and ethylene; and organic chemicals, such as vinyl acetate monomer, acetic acid and ethyl acetate. Aluminum products include extruded products, sheets, ingots, high-purity capacitor foils and fabricated products, such as beverage cans, heat exchangers, forged products and aluminum cylinders for laser printers. Electronic products include specialty gases, rare earth magnetic alloys, compound semiconductors, hard disks, ceramic materials for semiconductors, fine carbons and high-purity chemicals such as alternatives to chlorinated solvents. Chemical products include oxygen, hydrogen, nitrogen and fluorocarbon gasses; specialty chemicals, such as analytical columns, specialized polymers, amino acids and stabilized vitamin C; and basic chemicals, such as chlorine, ammonia, caustic soda and acrylonitrile. Lastly, inorganic products consist of ceramics, such as abrasives, alumina, aluminum hydroxide and refractories; and carbons, such as graphite electrodes, carbon nanofiber and artificial graphite powder. The firms' highly crystalline carbon nanofibers, which are easier to handle than carbon nanotubes, can be used to manufacture batteries, to reinforce resin parts and resin sheets, to make electrically conductive paints and adhesives and to improve thermal conductivity and corrosion resistance of metals. In September 2008, the company acquired U.K.-based F2 Chemicals Limited. In November 2008, Showa Denko announced its plan to dissolve a Tokyo-based subsidiary engaged in the manufacture and sale of synthetic resin products. In February 2009, the company announced that it would acquire a hard disk memory media business from a subsidiary of Fujitsu Limited.

FINANCIALS: **Sales and profits are in thousands of dollars—add 000 to get the full amount. 2008 Note: Financial information for 2008 was not available for all companies at press time.**

2008 Sales: $11,027,972
2007 Sales: $8,963,975
2006 Sales: $6,910,100
2005 Sales: $6,872,460
2004 Sales: $7,184,100

2008 Profits: $26,925
2007 Profits: $289,668
2006 Profits: $133,200
2005 Profits: $132,100
2004 Profits: $73,700

U.S. Stock Ticker: SHWDF
Int'l Ticker: 4004 Int'l Exchange: Tokyo-TSE
Employees: 11,118
Fiscal Year Ends: 12/31
Parent Company:

SALARIES/BENEFITS:

Pension Plan:	ESOP Stock Plan:	Profit Sharing:	Top Exec. Salary: $	Bonus: $
Savings Plan:	Stock Purch. Plan:		Second Exec. Salary: $	Bonus: $

OTHER THOUGHTS:

Apparent Women Officers or Directors:
Hot Spot for Advancement for Women/Minorities:

LOCATIONS: ("Y" = Yes)

West:	Southwest:	Midwest:	Southeast:	Northeast:	International:
Y				Y	Y

SIEMENS AG

www.siemens.com

Industry Group Code: 335000 **Ranks within this company's industry group:** Sales: 1 Profits: 1

Techology:		Medical/Drugs:		Engineering:		Transportation:		Chemicals/Petrochemicals:		Specialty:	
Computers:		Manufacturer:		Design:	Y	Aerospace:		Oil/Gas Products:		Special Services:	
Software:		Contract Research:		Construction:	Y	Automotive:		Chemicals:		Consulting:	
Communications:	Y	Medical Services:		Eng. Services:		Shipping:		Oil/Chem. Svcs.:		Specialty Mgmt.:	
Electronics:	Y	Labs:		Consulting:				Gases:		Products:	
Alternative Energy:	Y	Bio. Services:						Other:		Other:	Y

TYPES OF BUSINESS:

Electrical Equipment Manufacturing
Energy & Power Plant Systems & Consulting
IT Systems & Consulting
Lighting & Optical Systems
Automation Systems
Transportation & Logistics Systems
Photovoltaic Equipment
Medical and Health Care Services and Equipment

BRANDS/DIVISIONS/AFFILIATES:

CTI Molecular Imaging
Siemens Corporate Technology
Siemens VDO Automotive
Siemens Canada
Siemens Limited
Siemens Healthcare
Siemens Healthcare Diagnostics

CONTACTS: *Note: Officers with more than one job title may be intentionally listed here more than once.*

Peter H. Loescher, CEO
Peter H. Loescher, Pres.
Joe Kaeser, Head-Finance
Siegfried Russwurm, Head-Human Resources/Dir.-Labor
Heinrich Hiesinger, CIO
Hermann Requardt, Head-Corp. Tech.
Peter Y. Solmssen, Head-Legal & Compliance
Joe Kaeser, Controller
Erin R. Reinhardt, CEO-Healthcare
Heinrich Hiesinger, CEO-Industry
Wolfgang Dehen, CEO-Energy
Gerhard Cromme, Chmn.
Peter Y. Solmssen, Dir.-The Americas
Barbara Kux, Head-Supply Chain Mgmt. & Global Shared Svcs.

Phone: 49-69-797-6660	**Fax:**
Toll-Free:	
Address: Wittelsbacherplatz 2, Munich, 80333 Germany	

GROWTH PLANS/SPECIAL FEATURES:

Siemens AG is one of the largest electrical engineering and manufacturing companies in the world. Based in Germany, the firm sells products and services to approximately 190 countries around the globe, including all 50 states in the U.S., its largest single source of income. As of 2008, the company has reorganized itself to operate in three primary sectors: Industry, Energy and Healthcare. The Industry sector's portfolio ranges from industry automation and drives products and services to building, lighting and mobility solutions and services, as well as system integration and solutions for plant business. Additionally, this sector provides networking and other solutions for transportation systems, including airport logistics, postal automation and railway electrification. The Energy sector offers a broad range of products, services and solutions for the generation, transmission and distribution of power, as well as for the extraction, conversion and transport of oil and gas. The Healthcare sector develops, manufactures and markets diagnostic and therapeutic systems, devices and consumables, as well as information technology systems for clinical and administrative purposes. Besides these activities, subsidiaries Siemens IT Solutions & Services as well as Siemens Financial Services support sector activities as business partners, meanwhile continuing to build up their own business with external customers. During 2008, Siemens acquired BJC, a leading Spain-based supplier of switches and socket-outlets; Innotec GmbH, a provider of lifecycle management solutions software; and U.S-based rolling mill technology specialist Morgan Construction Co. In July 2008, the company announced layoffs of approximately 4.2% of its workforce, totaling nearly 16,750 jobs. The firm has also begun to consolidate its more than 1,800 separate businesses to fewer than 1,000, realigning its operations regionally as cost-saving measures. The company has sold much of its telecommunications industry businesses in order to focus on its core sectors of health care, energy and industrial equipment.

FINANCIALS: **Sales and profits are in thousands of dollars—add 000 to get the full amount. 2008 Note: Financial information for 2008 was not available for all companies at press time.**

2008 Sales: $107,580,000	2008 Profits: $8,189,070	**U.S. Stock Ticker: SI**
2007 Sales: $115,406,000	2007 Profits: $3,535,760	**Int'l Ticker: SIE** Int'l Exchange: Frankfurt-Euronext
2006 Sales: $113,740,000	2006 Profits: $3,950,360	Employees: 427,000
2005 Sales: $90,670,000	2005 Profits: $2,702,000	Fiscal Year Ends: 9/30
2004 Sales: $93,455,000	2004 Profits: $4,233,000	Parent Company:

SALARIES/BENEFITS:

Pension Plan:	ESOP Stock Plan:	Profit Sharing:	Top Exec. Salary: $	Bonus: $
Savings Plan:	Stock Purch. Plan:		Second Exec. Salary: $	Bonus: $

OTHER THOUGHTS:

Apparent Women Officers or Directors: 3
Hot Spot for Advancement for Women/Minorities: Y

LOCATIONS: ("Y" = Yes)

West:	Southwest:	Midwest:	Southeast:	Northeast:	International:
Y	Y	Y	Y	Y	Y

Note: Financial information, benefits and other data can change quickly and may vary from those stated here.

SIEMENS CORPORATE TECHNOLOGY

www.ct.siemens.com/en/

Industry Group Code: 541710 **Ranks within this company's industry group:** Sales: Profits:

Techology:		Medical/Drugs:		Engineering:		Transportation:		Chemicals/Petrochemicals:		Specialty:	
Computers:		Manufacturer:		Design:	Y	Aerospace:		Oil/Gas Products:		Special Services:	Y
Software:	Y	Contract Research:		Construction:		Automotive:	Y	Chemicals:		Consulting:	
Communications:	Y	Medical Services:		Eng. Services:		Shipping:		Oil/Chem. Svcs.:		Specialty Mgmt.:	
Electronics:	Y	Labs:		Consulting:				Gases:		Products:	Y
Alternative Energy:	Y	Bio. Services:						Other:		Other:	

TYPES OF BUSINESS:

Research & Development
Materials
Microsystems
Production Processes
Power & Sensor Systems
Software Products
Communications

BRANDS/DIVISIONS/AFFILIATES:

Siemens Corporate Intellectual Property
Siemens Corporate Research
Siemens Technology-to-Business Center
Siemens Technology Accelerator

CONTACTS: *Note: Officers with more than one job title may be intentionally listed here more than once.*

Herman Requardt, Unit Head
Peter Loscher, Pres./CEO-Siemens AG

Phone: 49-89-636-49030	**Fax:** 49-89-636-49220
Toll-Free:	
Address: Otto-Hahn-Ring 6, Bldg. 53, Munich, 81739 Germany	

GROWTH PLANS/SPECIAL FEATURES:

Siemens Corporate Technology brings together a worldwide network of research facilities and expert scientists to promote and develop new technologies that will help to achieve the strategic goals of its parent company, Siemens AG. Working in close collaboration with Siemens' core business units, Siemens Corporate Technology analyzes company data to develop blueprints for future developments, while also watching research trends to link scientific advances with potential new business applications. The Corporate Technology unit also works to safeguard new technologies on behalf of the company through its Corporate Intellectual Property subdivision. Research is organized into five broad technology divisions: information and communications; transportation; automation and control; medical; and lighting and power. Collectively, these technology divisions encompass more than 40 core technologies which are considered to have strategic value for the company. Siemens Corporate Technology also works in direct partnership with separately managed research and development bodies in the U.S., Europe and Asia, such as Siemens Corporate Research in Princeton, New Jersey and Roke Manor Research, Ltd. in the U.K. The unit also oversees the operation of two business incubators: Siemens Technology-to-Business Center, with locations in Berkeley, California and Shanghai, China; and Siemens Technology Accelerator, located in Munich, Germany. The Technology-to-Business Centers focus on developing ideas into new Siemens products or subsidiaries, while Siemens Technology Accelerator works to create successful spin-off businesses from technologies that have been developed within Siemens Corporate Technology but are not chosen for further development within the Siemens Group. During 2008, Siemens registered approximately 5,000 new patents.

FINANCIALS: **Sales and profits are in thousands of dollars—add 000 to get the full amount. 2008 Note: Financial information for 2008 was not available for all companies at press time.**

2008 Sales: $	2008 Profits: $	**U.S. Stock Ticker: Subsidiary**
2007 Sales: $	2007 Profits: $	**Int'l Ticker:** Int'l Exchange:
2006 Sales: $	2006 Profits: $	Employees:
2005 Sales: $	2005 Profits: $	Fiscal Year Ends: 9/30
2004 Sales: $	2004 Profits: $	Parent Company: SIEMENS AG

SALARIES/BENEFITS:

Pension Plan:	ESOP Stock Plan:	Profit Sharing:	Top Exec. Salary: $	Bonus: $
Savings Plan:	Stock Purch. Plan:		Second Exec. Salary: $	Bonus: $

OTHER THOUGHTS:

Apparent Women Officers or Directors:
Hot Spot for Advancement for Women/Minorities:

LOCATIONS: ("Y" = Yes)

West:	Southwest:	Midwest:	Southeast:	Northeast:	International:
Y				Y	Y

Note: Financial information, benefits and other data can change quickly and may vary from those stated here.

SIEMENS HEALTHCARE

medical.siemens.com

Industry Group Code: 339113 **Ranks within this company's industry group:** Sales: Profits:

Techology:		**Medical/Drugs:**		**Engineering:**		**Transportation:**		**Chemicals/Petrochemicals:**		**Specialty:**	
Computers:		Manufacturer:	Y	Design:		Aerospace:		Oil/Gas Products:		Special Services:	Y
Software:		Contract Research:		Construction:		Automotive:		Chemicals:		Consulting:	Y
Communications:		Medical Services:		Eng. Services:		Shipping:		Oil/Chem. Svcs.:		Specialty Mgmt.:	
Electronics:		Labs:		Consulting:				Gases:		Products:	
Alternative Energy:		Bio. Services:						Other:		Other:	

TYPES OF BUSINESS:

Medical Equipment Manufacturing
Information Systems
Management Consulting
Ultrasound Systems
Hearing Aids

BRANDS/DIVISIONS/AFFILIATES:

Siemens AG
Siemens Healthcare Diagnostics
ADVIA
Sonoline
Acuson
Somatom Sensation 16
Dade Behring Holdings Inc
Siemens Medical Solutions Diagnostics

CONTACTS: *Note: Officers with more than one job title may be intentionally listed here more than once.*

Jim Reid-Anderson, CEO
Jim Reid-Anderson, Pres.
Klaus Stegemann, CFO
Norbert Kleinjohann, Corporate IT
Bernd Montag, CEO-Imaging & IT Division
Thomas Miller, CEO-Workflow & Solutions Division
Donal Quinn, CEO-Diagnostics Division

Phone: 49 69 797 6602 **Fax:**
Toll-Free:
Address: Henkestr 127, Erlangen, D-91052 Germany

GROWTH PLANS/SPECIAL FEATURES:

Siemens Healthcare, a business segment of Siemens AG, is one of the largest suppliers to the health care industry with operations in over 130 countries. Siemens Healthcare and its subsidiaries, including Siemens Healthcare Diagnostics in the U.S., offer innovative medical technologies, health care information systems, management consulting and support services. The firm manufactures and markets a wide range of medical equipment including MRI systems, radiation therapy equipment and patient monitoring systems. With 75% of all of the company's products less than five years old, the firm devotes 10% of its budget to research and development and launches numerous new products every year. Siemens Healthcare ultrasound division is a global supplier of ultrasound systems and also offers general imaging systems. The company produces imaging equipment for cardiology, gynecology, radiology and urology under the Sonoline and Acuson brand-name product lines. Through its health services division, the firm offers information technology support to doctors, hospitals and clinics. Through its hearing instruments division, the segment makes a variety of hearing aids. Some of Siemens Healthcare's products include the Somatom Sensation 16 spiral CT scanner, an imaging system that enables previously unavailable applications such as virtual flight through the heart or intestine, and TRIANO, the firm's newest generation hearing aid, made up of a combination of three microphones that permit directional hearing. In July 2007, the company acquired Dade Behring, Inc., a leading clinical laboratory diagnostics company. The firm acquired CAS Innovations AG in February 2008. In 2008, Siemens Healthcare Diagnostics entered a joint marketing agreement with Bio-Rad Laboratories, Inc.

SMS offers its employees work/life initiatives including child care discounts, emergency child care, mothers' rooms, financial planning resources, tuition reimbursement and flexible spending accounts.

FINANCIALS: **Sales and profits are in thousands of dollars—add 000 to get the full amount. 2008 Note: Financial information for 2008 was not available for all companies at press time.**

2008 Sales: $	2008 Profits: $	**U.S. Stock Ticker: Subsidiary**
2007 Sales: $	2007 Profits: $	**Int'l Ticker:** Int'l Exchange:
2006 Sales: $11,121,700	2006 Profits: $	Employees: 33,000
2005 Sales: $10,309,236	2005 Profits: $1,163,063	Fiscal Year Ends: 9/30
2004 Sales: $8,423,794	2004 Profits: $1,246,014	Parent Company: SIEMENS AG

SALARIES/BENEFITS:

Pension Plan:	ESOP Stock Plan:	Profit Sharing:	Top Exec. Salary: $	Bonus: $
Savings Plan: Y	Stock Purch. Plan:		Second Exec. Salary: $	Bonus: $

OTHER THOUGHTS:

Apparent Women Officers or Directors:
Hot Spot for Advancement for Women/Minorities:

LOCATIONS: ("Y" = Yes)

West:	Southwest:	Midwest:	Southeast:	Northeast:	International:
				Y	Y

Note: Financial information, benefits and other data can change quickly and may vary from those stated here.

SIEMENS PLM SOFTWARE

www.plm.automation.siemens.com

Industry Group Code: 511215 **Ranks within this company's industry group:** Sales: Profits:

Techology:		Medical/Drugs:		Engineering:		Transportation:		Chemicals/Petrochemicals:		Specialty:	
Computers:		Manufacturer:		Design:		Aerospace:		Oil/Gas Products:		Special Services:	
Software:	Y	Contract Research:		Construction:		Automotive:		Chemicals:		Consulting:	Y
Communications:		Medical Services:		Eng. Services:	Y	Shipping:		Oil/Chem. Svcs.:		Specialty Mgmt.:	
Electronics:		Labs:		Consulting:				Gases:		Products:	
Alternative Energy:		Bio. Services:						Other:		Other:	

TYPES OF BUSINESS:

Software-Product Lifecycle Management
Engineering Outsourcing

BRANDS/DIVISIONS/AFFILIATES:

Unigraphics Solutions
D-Cubed, Ltd.
NX
UGS Velocity Series
Tecnomatix
PLM Components
Teamcenter

CONTACTS: *Note: Officers with more than one job title may be intentionally listed here more than once.*

Anthony J. Affuso, CEO
Helmuth Ludwig, Pres.
Peter Bichara, CFO/Exec. VP
Dave Shirk, Exec. VP-Global Mktg.
Dan Malliet, Sr. VP-Human Resources
Craig J. Berry, CIO/Sr. VP
Chuck Grindstaff, CTO
Chuck. Grindstaff, Exec. VP-Prod.
Rose Marie E. Glazer, General Counsel/Sr. VP
David Punter, VP-Exec. Oper.
Mike Sayen, VP-Strategy
John Graham, Exec. VP-Global Sales & Svc.
Dave Shook, Sr. VP/Managing Dir.-Americas
Paul Vogel, Exec. VP-Global Sales & Svcs.
Anthony J. Affuso, Chmn.
Hans-Kurt Lubberstedt, Exec. VP-Asia-Pacific

Phone: 972-987-3000 **Fax:** 972-605-2643
Toll-Free: 800-498-5351
Address: 5800 Granite Pkwy., Ste. 600, Plano, TX 75024-3199 US

GROWTH PLANS/SPECIAL FEATURES:

Siemens PLM Software, (SPS) formerly UGS Corp., is a leading global provider of product lifecycle management (PLM) products and services, with more than 6 million licensed seats of its technology in use and 56,000 clients worldwide. PLM products help customers accelerate their time to market, improve quality and increase revenue by allowing organizations to digitally manage a product's complete lifecycle, from its concept and design to its retirement. The firm's portfolio of software and service solutions includes: Product development; enterprise collaboration; data management; and factory and manufacturing planning tools. SPS's four primary product suites and business initiatives are: Teamcenter, which focuses on economizing business operations by helping employees communicate more effectively; NX, which contains primarily Computer Aided Design (CAD) software and other design software; Tecnomatix, which aids in industrial design and assembly; UGS Velocity Series, which is a modular set of solutions to assist small and medium businesses with their PLM; and PLM Components, which helps companies share data with customers and partners. Some of the company's main customers include a few of the world's largest automakers, such as GM, DaimlerChrysler and Ford. The firm's subsidiary D-Cubed, Ltd. is an India based engineering outsourcer.

Siemens PLM Software offers its employees health insurance, flexible spending accounts, life insurance, disability coverage and tuition reimbursement.

FINANCIALS: **Sales and profits are in thousands of dollars—add 000 to get the full amount. 2008 Note: Financial information for 2008 was not available for all companies at press time.**

2008 Sales: $	2008 Profits: $	**U.S. Stock Ticker: Private**
2007 Sales: $	2007 Profits: $	**Int'l Ticker:** Int'l Exchange:
2006 Sales: $1,218,747	2006 Profits: $-10,338	Employees: 6,800
2005 Sales: $1,154,621	2005 Profits: $-10,024	Fiscal Year Ends: 12/31
2004 Sales: $977,982	2004 Profits: $-18,743	Parent Company:

SALARIES/BENEFITS:

Pension Plan:	ESOP Stock Plan:	Profit Sharing:	Top Exec. Salary: $	Bonus: $
Savings Plan: Y	Stock Purch. Plan:		Second Exec. Salary: $	Bonus: $

OTHER THOUGHTS:

Apparent Women Officers or Directors: 1
Hot Spot for Advancement for Women/Minorities:

LOCATIONS: ("Y" = Yes)

West:	Southwest:	Midwest:	Southeast:	Northeast:	International:
Y	Y	Y	Y	Y	Y

Note: Financial information, benefits and other data can change quickly and may vary from those stated here.

SINGAPORE TECHNOLOGIES ENGINEERING LIMITED

www.stengg.com

Industry Group Code: 336410 **Ranks within this company's industry group:** Sales: 21 Profits: 15

Techology:		Medical/Drugs:		Engineering:		Transportation:		Chemicals/Petrochemicals:		Specialty:	
Computers:		Manufacturer:		Design:		Aerospace:	Y	Oil/Gas Products:		Special Services:	
Software:		Contract Research:		Construction:		Automotive:	Y	Chemicals:		Consulting:	Y
Communications:		Medical Services:		Eng. Services:		Shipping:	Y	Oil/Chem. Svcs.:		Specialty Mgmt.:	
Electronics:	Y	Labs:		Consulting:				Gases:		Products:	Y
Alternative Energy:		Bio. Services:						Other:		Other:	

TYPES OF BUSINESS:

Aerospace & Electronics
Aircraft Repair & Development
Electronic Systems
Military Equipment & Vehicles
Industrial, Commercial & Construction Vehicles
Shipbuilding

BRANDS/DIVISIONS/AFFILIATES:

ST Aeropace
ST Electronics
iDirect
ST Kinetics
ST Marine
VT Halter Marine

CONTACTS: *Note: Officers with more than one job title may be intentionally listed here more than once.*

Tan Pheng Hock, CEO
Tan Pheng Hock, Pres.
Tan Ai Ching, CFO
Patrick Choy, Exec. VP-Int'l Mktg.
Tan Nga Kok, Sr. VP-Human Resources
Tan Hock Hai, CIO
Fong Saik Hay, CTO
Low Meng Wai, VP-Legal
Robin Thevathasan, Sr. VP-Strategic Plans
Sharolyn Choy, Sr. VP-Corp. Comm.
Joseph Chia, Manager-Investor Rel.
John G. Coburn, Chmn./CEO-U.S. Oper.
Seah Moon Ming, Deputy CEO-Electronics & Land Systems
Wee Siew Kim, Deputy CEO-Aerospace & Marine/Pres., Defense
Augustine Syn, Sr. VP-Europe Oper.
Peter Seah Lim Huat, Chmn.
Seah Moon Ming, Pres., Int'l Bus.
Goh Bak Nguan, Chief Procurement Officer/VP

Phone: 65-6722-1818 **Fax:** 65-6720-2293
Toll-Free:
Address: 51 Cuppage Rd. #09-08, StarHub Centre, Singapore, 229469 Singapore

GROWTH PLANS/SPECIAL FEATURES:

Singapore Technologies Engineering Limited (ST Engineering) is an international engineering firm. The company has over 100 subsidiaries in 24 countries in Asia, Oceania, Europe and North America, with a customer base spanning over 70 countries. Business is divided into four main groups: Aerospace, electronics, land systems and marine technology. ST (Singapore Technologies) Aerospace, the aerospace group, specializes in the repair and overhaul of aircraft owned by air forces, commercial airlines and freight forwarding companies. Besides standard components supply and support, this group can also repair helicopters and advanced military aircraft, offer engine support and assist in the design, development and upgrading process. ST Electronics provides electronics systems to a variety of different sectors, with services including broadband radio frequency and microwave communication; rail and traffic management; military services such as command and control operations and training and simulation systems; and IT security and mobile commerce support. Among its many international divisions is iDirect, based in the U.S., which is a developer of broadband satellite systems. The land systems group, ST Kinetics, primarily designs and builds weapons, munitions systems and specialty vehicles for military and industrial applications. Products include ammunition and firearms; armored vehicles; emergency vehicles; construction vehicles, such as excavators, dump trucks and asphalt pavers; distribution vehicles, including refrigerated trailers; and other vehicles. ST Marine offers shipbuilding, conversion and repair services to both navies and commercial fleets. Its two Singaporean shipyards are equipped to dock ships up to 70,000 deadweight tons, and are equipped with vessel transfer space; wharf space; building berths; plate-cutting and pipe-bending apparatuses; diesel engine workshops; and blasting chambers, among other features. It also owns a shipyard in Mississippi, through VT Halter Marine. In February 2009, the firm established STET Centre Pte Ltd as a professional education and training school.

FINANCIALS: **Sales and profits are in thousands of dollars—add 000 to get the full amount. 2008 Note: Financial information for 2008 was not available for all companies at press time.**

2008 Sales: $3,523,310	2008 Profits: $356,420	**U.S. Stock Ticker: SGGKF**
2007 Sales: $3,510,000	2007 Profits: $350,000	**Int'l Ticker: S63** Int'l Exchange: Singapore-SIN
2006 Sales: $2,922,900	2006 Profits: $	Employees: 15,912
2005 Sales: $2,113,255	2005 Profits: $260,368	Fiscal Year Ends: 12/31
2004 Sales: $1,866,489	2004 Profits: $227,406	Parent Company:

SALARIES/BENEFITS:

Pension Plan:	ESOP Stock Plan:	Profit Sharing:	Top Exec. Salary: $1,090,275	Bonus: $1,711,991
Savings Plan:	Stock Purch. Plan:		Second Exec. Salary: $	Bonus: $

OTHER THOUGHTS:

Apparent Women Officers or Directors: 1
Hot Spot for Advancement for Women/Minorities:

LOCATIONS: ("Y" = Yes)

West:	Southwest:	Midwest:	Southeast:	Northeast:	International:
	Y		Y	Y	Y

SKIDMORE OWINGS & MERRILL LLP

www.som.com

Industry Group Code: 541330 **Ranks within this company's industry group:** Sales: Profits:

Techology:		Medical/Drugs:		Engineering:		Transportation:		Chemicals/Petrochemicals:		Specialty:	
Computers:		Manufacturer:		Design:	Y	Aerospace:		Oil/Gas Products:		Special Services:	
Software:		Contract Research:		Construction:		Automotive:		Chemicals:		Consulting:	
Communications:		Medical Services:		Eng. Services:	Y	Shipping:		Oil/Chem. Svcs.:		Specialty Mgmt.:	
Electronics:		Labs:		Consulting:	Y			Gases:		Products:	
Alternative Energy:		Bio. Services:						Other:		Other:	

TYPES OF BUSINESS:

Architectural & Engineering Services
Urban Design Services
Transportation Planning
Seismic Analysis & Consulting
Environmental Engineering

BRANDS/DIVISIONS/AFFILIATES:

Mechanical and Electrical Engineering Group
MEP Engineering
SOM Interiors

CONTACTS: *Note: Officers with more than one job title may be intentionally listed here more than once.*

Jeffrey J. McCarthy, Managing Partner-Chicago
Carl Galioto, Partner-Technical
Gene Schnair, Managing Partner-West Coast
Gary P. Haney, Design Partner
William F. Baker, Partner-Civil & Structural Eng.

Phone: 312-554-9090	**Fax:** 312-360-4545
Toll-Free: 866-269-2688	
Address: 224 S. Michigan Ave., Ste. 1000, Chicago, IL 60604 US	

GROWTH PLANS/SPECIAL FEATURES:

Skidmore, Owings & Merrill, LLP (SOM) is one of the world's leading architecture, urban design, engineering and interior architecture firms. Its services span architectural design and engineering of individual buildings to the master planning and design of entire communities. The firm's projects include corporate offices, banking and financial institutions, government buildings, public and private institutions, health care facilities, religious buildings, airports, recreational and sports facilities, university buildings and residential developments. SOM's graphics group provides branding, corporate identity and graphic design services, with expansive projects for clients including the Bay Area Discovery Museum and Dublin Airport. The SOM Interiors group provides interior design solutions for corporate facilities, educational facilities, retail spaces, performing arts spaces, hotels and residential complexes among others. SOM's Mechanical and Electrical Engineering Group (MEP Engineering) provides design engineering services for new and existing buildings, such as developing solar heating and cooling for new and existing buildings; modeling energy consumption patterns; forecasting probable operating costs; and developing energy recovery systems. Additionally, the firm offers structural and civil engineering services; sustainable design services; and urban design and planning services. Signature projects include 7 World Trade Center, the Willis Tower (formerly known as the Sears Tower) and the John Hancock Tower. The firm's 73-story residential Infinity Tower in Dubai, expected completion by 2010, features a twisting helix shape that gradually rotates 90 degrees while maintaining a consistent structural and architectural floor plate throughout its height. The company's Burj Dubai is the world's tallest structure, reaching 150 floors. The ultimate height of the building has not been disclosed.

FINANCIALS: **Sales and profits are in thousands of dollars—add 000 to get the full amount. 2008 Note: Financial information for 2008 was not available for all companies at press time.**

2008 Sales: $	2008 Profits: $	**U.S. Stock Ticker: Private**
2007 Sales: $228,000	2007 Profits: $	**Int'l Ticker:** Int'l Exchange:
2006 Sales: $228,000	2006 Profits: $	Employees: 1,131
2005 Sales: $225,000	2005 Profits: $	Fiscal Year Ends: 9/30
2004 Sales: $	2004 Profits: $	Parent Company:

SALARIES/BENEFITS:

Pension Plan:	ESOP Stock Plan:	Profit Sharing:	Top Exec. Salary: $	Bonus: $
Savings Plan:	Stock Purch. Plan:		Second Exec. Salary: $	Bonus: $

OTHER THOUGHTS:

Apparent Women Officers or Directors: 2
Hot Spot for Advancement for Women/Minorities:

LOCATIONS: ("Y" = Yes)

West:	Southwest:	Midwest:	Southeast:	Northeast:	International:
Y		Y		Y	Y

Note: Financial information, benefits and other data can change quickly and may vary from those stated here.

SMITH & NEPHEW PLC

www.smith-nephew.com

Industry Group Code: 339113 **Ranks within this company's industry group:** Sales: 10 Profits: 9

Techology:		Medical/Drugs:		Engineering:		Transportation:		Chemicals/Petrochemicals:		Specialty:	
Computers:		Manufacturer:	Y	Design:		Aerospace:		Oil/Gas Products:		Special Services:	
Software:		Contract Research:		Construction:		Automotive:		Chemicals:		Consulting:	
Communications:		Medical Services:		Eng. Services:		Shipping:		Oil/Chem. Svcs.:		Specialty Mgmt.:	
Electronics:		Labs:		Consulting:				Gases:		Products:	Y
Alternative Energy:		Bio. Services:						Other:		Other:	

TYPES OF BUSINESS:

Medical Device Manufacturing-Orthopedics
Reconstructive Joint Implants
Endoscopy Products
Wound Management Products

BRANDS/DIVISIONS/AFFILIATES:

Smith & Nephew Group
Genesis II
Supartz
Trivex
Allevyn
Versajet
Iodosorb
Arthrograde Hip Access Cannula

CONTACTS: *Note: Officers with more than one job title may be intentionally listed here more than once.*

David Illingworth, CEO
David Illingworth, Pres.
Adrian Hennah, CFO
Elizabeth Bolgiano, Group Dir.-Human Resources
Sal Chiovari, CIO
Jim Ralston, Chief Legal Officer
R. Gordon Howe, Sr. VP-Global Planning & Dev.
Liz Hewitt, Group Dir.-Corporate Affairs
Michael Frazzette, Pres., Endoscopy
Joe Woody, Pres., Advanced Wound Mgmt.
Mark Augusti, Pres., Orthopaedic Trauma & Clinical Therapies
Joseph DeVivo, Pres., Orthopaedic Reconstruction Div.
John Buchanan, Chmn.

Phone: 44-20-7401-7646 **Fax:** 44-20-7960-2350
Toll-Free:
Address: 15 Adam St., London, WC2N 6LA UK

GROWTH PLANS/SPECIAL FEATURES:

Smith & Nephew PLC, founded in 1856, develops and markets advanced medical devices for healthcare professionals. It is the parent company of the Smith & Nephew Group, an international medical devices business organized into four global business units: Orthopedic Reconstruction; Orthopedic Trauma & Clinical Therapies; Endoscopy; and Advanced Wound Management. Orthopedic products include reconstructive joint implants; trauma products that help repair broken bones; and other pain relieving and healing products. Reconstructive joint implants include hip, knee and shoulder joints as well as ancillary products like bone cement used in reconstructive surgery. Product lines include the GENESIS II and PROFIX knee replacements, SUPARTZ joint fluid therapy, and EXOGEN ultrasound bone healing system. Smith & Nephew's Endoscopy unit develops and markets a range of minimally invasive surgery techniques and educational programs to repair soft tissues, articulating joints, spinal discs and vascular structures. It focuses principally on arthroscopy. Arthroscopy is the minimally invasive surgery of joints, in particular the knee, hip and shoulder. Products include fluid management systems, cameras, scopes, light sources, radiofrequency ablation devices, powered shaver systems, soft tissue reattachment devices, blades and tissue regeneration products. The company has developed a new technique for removing varicose veins, called TRIVEX. The Advanced Wound Management unit supplies products for chronic and acute wounds. Chronic wounds, such as pressure, leg or diabetic foot ulcers, are generally difficult to heal; and acute wounds, such as burns and post-operative wounds, are generally life threatening, with potential scarring and infection. The division's products include Allevyn foam dressings; Acticoad, dressings that contain silver; the Versajet hydrosurgery system; and Iodosorb, a dressing and ointment that contains iodine. In May 2008, the company launched the Arthrograde Hip Access Cannula, designed to prevent damage, which normally occurs during arthroscopic hip repair surgery, to soft tissue.

FINANCIALS: **Sales and profits are in thousands of dollars—add 000 to get the full amount. 2008 Note: Financial information for 2008 was not available for all companies at press time.**

2008 Sales: $3,801,000 | 2008 Profits: $377,000
2007 Sales: $3,369,000 | 2007 Profits: $316,000
2006 Sales: $2,779,000 | 2006 Profits: $745,000
2005 Sales: $2,552,000 | 2005 Profits: $333,000
2004 Sales: $2,301,000 | 2004 Profits: $245,000

U.S. Stock Ticker: SNN
Int'l Ticker: SN Int'l Exchange: London-LSE
Employees: 9,757
Fiscal Year Ends: 12/31
Parent Company:

SALARIES/BENEFITS:

Pension Plan: ESOP Stock Plan: Profit Sharing: Top Exec. Salary: $ Bonus: $
Savings Plan: Stock Purch. Plan: Second Exec. Salary: $ Bonus: $

OTHER THOUGHTS:

Apparent Women Officers or Directors: 2
Hot Spot for Advancement for Women/Minorities:

LOCATIONS: ("Y" = Yes)

West:	Southwest:	Midwest:	Southeast:	Northeast:	International:
			Y	Y	Y

SMITHS GROUP PLC

www.smiths-group.com

Industry Group Code: 333000 **Ranks within this company's industry group:** Sales: 8 Profits: 6

Techology:		Medical/Drugs:		Engineering:		Transportation:		Chemicals/Petrochemicals:		Specialty:	
Computers:		Manufacturer:	Y	Design:	Y	Aerospace:	Y	Oil/Gas Products:		Special Services:	
Software:		Contract Research:		Construction:	Y	Automotive:		Chemicals:		Consulting:	
Communications:		Medical Services:		Eng. Services:		Shipping:		Oil/Chem. Svcs.:	Y	Specialty Mgmt.:	
Electronics:	Y	Labs:		Consulting:				Gases:		Products:	
Alternative Energy:		Bio. Services:						Other:		Other:	

TYPES OF BUSINESS:

Machinery, Manufacturing
Medical Devices, Manufacturing

BRANDS/DIVISIONS/AFFILIATES:

John Crane
Interconnect
Flexible Technologies
Kelvin Hughes Limited
Fiber Composite Company Inc
Allrizon Tongguang
Triasx Pty Ltd
Zhejiang Zheda Medical Instrument Co. Ltd.

CONTACTS: *Note: Officers with more than one job title may be intentionally listed here more than once.*

Philip Bowman, CEO
John Langston, Dir.-Finance
David P. Lillycrop, General Counsel
Russell Plumley, Dir.-Investor Rel.
John Langston, Dir.-Finance
Donald H. Brydon, Chmn.

Phone: 44-20-7808-5500 **Fax:** 44-20-7808-5533
Toll-Free:
Address: 80 Victoria St., 2nd Fl., Cardinal Pl., London, SW1E 5JL UK

GROWTH PLANS/SPECIAL FEATURES:

Smiths Group plc is a global technology company with five main divisions: Smiths Detection; Smiths Medical; Smiths Interconnect; John Crane; and Flex-Tek. Smiths Detection provides security equipment for the detection and identification of explosives; chemical and biological agents; weapons; and contraband. This equipment is used by military forces, airport security, customs officers and emergency services. Smiths Medical focuses on critical care and medication delivery, which include airway management; pain management; needle safety; temperature monitoring; hospital and ambulatory infusion; insulin infusion; vascular access; and in-vitro fertilization. Smiths Interconnect manufactures electronic connectors, coaxial, cable and connector assemblies, antennae, as well as lightning and surge protectors. John Crane manufactures mechanical seals and related products for the petrochemical and transportation industries. Flex-Tek provides flexible hose and ducting for commercial and consumer air moving products and for conveying gas, liquid and airborne solids in industrial processes. In 2008, the company completed a restructuring in which it disbanded its specialty engineering division, creating the Smiths Interconnect; John Crane; and Flex-Tek division. In May 2008, the company acquired Fiber Composite Company, Inc., a specialist in oil and gas lifting equipment. That same month, the firm purchased Allrizon Tongguang, a Shanghai-based communications equipment firm. In July 2008, Smiths Group acquired Triasx Pty Ltd., wireless communications components manufacturer. In November 2008, the company acquired Zhejiang Zheda Medical Instrument Co. Ltd., medical instruments manufacturer.

FINANCIALS: **Sales and profits are in thousands of dollars—add 000 to get the full amount. 2008 Note: Financial information for 2008 was not available for all companies at press time.**

2008 Sales: $3,410,420	2008 Profits: $394,930	**U.S. Stock Ticker:**
2007 Sales: $3,174,900	2007 Profits: $2,539,000	**Int'l Ticker: SMIN** Int'l Exchange: London-LSE
2006 Sales: $6,564,200	2006 Profits: $45,100	Employees: 31,324
2005 Sales: $5,302,900	2005 Profits: $388,100	Fiscal Year Ends:
2004 Sales: $4,974,800	2004 Profits: $387,500	Parent Company:

SALARIES/BENEFITS:

Pension Plan:	ESOP Stock Plan:	Profit Sharing:	Top Exec. Salary: $	Bonus: $
Savings Plan:	Stock Purch. Plan:		Second Exec. Salary: $	Bonus: $

OTHER THOUGHTS:

Apparent Women Officers or Directors:
Hot Spot for Advancement for Women/Minorities:

LOCATIONS: ("Y" = Yes)

West:	Southwest:	Midwest:	Southeast:	Northeast:	International:
Y	Y	Y	Y	Y	Y

SNC-LAVALIN GROUP INC

www.snc-lavalin.com

Industry Group Code: 234000 **Ranks within this company's industry group:** Sales: 17 Profits: 15

Techology:		Medical/Drugs:		Engineering:		Transportation:		Chemicals/Petrochemicals:		Specialty:	
Computers:		Manufacturer:		Design:	Y	Aerospace:		Oil/Gas Products:		Special Services:	
Software:		Contract Research:		Construction:	Y	Automotive:		Chemicals:		Consulting:	
Communications:		Medical Services:		Eng. Services:	Y	Shipping:		Oil/Chem. Svcs.:	Y	Specialty Mgmt.:	
Electronics:		Labs:		Consulting:	Y			Gases:		Products:	
Alternative Energy:		Bio. Services:						Other:		Other:	

TYPES OF BUSINESS:

Construction
Engineering
Chemicals & Petroleum
Mining & Metallurgy
Operations & Maintenance
Infrastructure Concessions
Training
Pharmaceuticals & Biotechnology Facilities

BRANDS/DIVISIONS/AFFILIATES:

SNC-Lavalin ProFac
Queformat Ltd.
Laboratoire Sol et Beton L.S.B.
C.J. MacLellan & Associates
Groupe Techmat
DTI Telecom Inc

CONTACTS:

Note: Officers with more than one job title may be intentionally listed here more than once.

Jacques Lamarre, CEO
Jacques Lamarre, Pres.
Gilles Laramee, CFO/Exec. VP
Marylynne Campbell, Exec. VP-Global Human Resources
Louis Dagenais, VP-Global IT & Project Mgmt. Systems
Pierre Mailhot, VP-Admin.
Rejean Goulet, VP-Law
Marylynne Campbell, Exec. VP-Oper. & Maintenance
Gillian MacCormack, VP-Public Rel.
Denis Jasmin, VP-Investor Rel.
Gerry Grigoropoulos, Controller/VP
Pierre Anctil, Exec. VP-Investment, Infrastructure & Environment
Jean Beaudoin, Exec. VP-Chemicals & Petroleum
Pierre Duhaime, Exec. VP-Mining, Metallurgy, & Industrial
Riadh Ben Aissa, Exec. VP-Infrastructure, Water & Construction
Gwyn Morgan, Chmn.
Klaus Triendl, Exec VP-Int'l, Power & Transportation
Michael C. Novak, Exec. VP-Global Procurement & Defense Contractors

Phone: 514-393-1000 **Fax:** 514-866-0795
Toll-Free:
Address: 455 Rene-Levesque Blvd. W., Montreal, QC H2Z 1Z3 Canada

GROWTH PLANS/SPECIAL FEATURES:

SNC-Lavalin Group, Inc. is a construction, engineering, maintenance and operations company present in over 100 countries. Its activities are generally divided into seven operating divisions: Infrastructure and Environment; Power; Operations and Maintenance; Chemicals and Petroleum; Mining and Metallurgy; Infrastructure Concession Investments; and All Other. Infrastructure projects have included institutional, commercial and industrial buildings, such as courthouses, concert halls and museums; medical infrastructure, including hospitals and pharmaceuticals and biotechnology facilities; sports facilities, including pools, stadiums and parks; water facilities, including pipelines, well drilling and water treatment plants; and transportation, such as airports, railways, tunnels, bridges, ports and traffic analysis. Environmental projects include geotechnical engineering; solid and industrial waste management; auditing and environmental management systems; and climate change, acoustics and air quality studies. The Power segment provides engineering, construction and procurement services as well as participating in ownership and arranging financing for nuclear, thermal and hydroelectric plants. It has experience working with transmission and distribution systems; power system studies; and power sector reform. The Operations and Maintenance segment, working through SNC-Lavalin ProFac, has five main business lines: Logistics; Naval and Marine Support; Facilities Management; and Industrial and Infrastructure. The Chemicals and Petroleum segment has worked on numerous petroleum-related facilities, including those for gas processing; pipelines, field facilities and gathering systems; refining and sulfur recovery; fertilizer production; oil sands mining and extraction; bitumen production; and chemicals and biochemicals. The Mining and Metallurgy segment has worked with iron ore, potash and industrial minerals processing; smelting; mine planning and closure; electrorefining; and cyanidation (used in gold recovery). The firm's Infrastructure Concession Investments mainly cover airports, mass transit systems, energy, roads and bridges. Lastly, the All Other segment includes projects in agriculture; project management and financing; and training and development. Recent acquisitions include Laboratoire Sol et Beton L.S.B.; C.J. MacLellan & Associates; Groupe Techmat; and DTI Telecom, Inc.

FINANCIALS:

Sales and profits are in thousands of dollars—add 000 to get the full amount. 2008 Note: Financial information for 2008 was not available for all companies at press time.

2008 Sales: $5,737,200	2008 Profits: $252,270	**U.S. Stock Ticker:**
2007 Sales: $5,434,150	2007 Profits: $123,680	**Int'l Ticker: SNC** Int'l Exchange: Toronto-TSX
2006 Sales: $4,877,129	2006 Profits: $149,969	Employees: 13,297
2005 Sales: $3,267,427	2005 Profits: $123,019	Fiscal Year Ends: 12/31
2004 Sales: $3,264,104	2004 Profits: $98,591	Parent Company:

SALARIES/BENEFITS:

Pension Plan: Y	ESOP Stock Plan:	Profit Sharing:	Top Exec. Salary: $	Bonus: $
Savings Plan:	Stock Purch. Plan:		Second Exec. Salary: $	Bonus: $

OTHER THOUGHTS:

Apparent Women Officers or Directors: 3
Hot Spot for Advancement for Women/Minorities: Y

LOCATIONS: ("Y" = Yes)

West:	Southwest:	Midwest:	Southeast:	Northeast:	International:
Y	Y			Y	Y

Note: Financial information, benefits and other data can change quickly and may vary from those stated here.

SOLVAY SA

www.solvay.com

Industry Group Code: 325000 **Ranks within this company's industry group:** Sales: 11 Profits: 9

Techology:		Medical/Drugs:		Engineering:		Transportation:		Chemicals/Petrochemicals:		Specialty:	
Computers:		Manufacturer:	Y	Design:		Aerospace:		Oil/Gas Products:		Special Services:	Y
Software:		Contract Research:		Construction:		Automotive:	Y	Chemicals:	Y	Consulting:	
Communications:		Medical Services:		Eng. Services:		Shipping:		Oil/Chem. Svcs.:		Specialty Mgmt.:	
Electronics:		Labs:		Consulting:				Gases:		Products:	Y
Alternative Energy:		Bio. Services:						Other:		Other:	

TYPES OF BUSINESS:

Pharmaceuticals
Chemicals & Plastics
Pipeline Systems
Detergents
Automotive Systems

BRANDS/DIVISIONS/AFFILIATES:

Inergy Automotive Systems
Pipelife
Cetrorelix
Solvay Engineered Polymers
Pipelife Jet Stream Inc
Solvay Pharmaceuticals
Solvac
Alexandria Sodium Carbonate Company

CONTACTS: *Note: Officers with more than one job title may be intentionally listed here more than once.*

Christian Jourquin, Chmn.-Exec. Committee
Bernard de Laguiche, CFO
Daniel Broens, Gen. Mgr.-Human Resources
Jean-Michel Mesland, Gen. Mgr.-Research
Jean-Michel Mesland, Gen. Mgr.-Tech.
Dominique Dussard, General Counsel
Bernard de Laguiche, Gen. Mgr.-Finance
Werner Cautreels, Gen. Mgr.-Pharmaceuticals
Jacques van Rijckevorsel, Gen. Mgr.-Plastics
Marc Duhem, Regional Mgr.-Europe
Roger Kearns, Regional Mgr.-Asia-Pacific
Alois Michielsen, Chmn.
Rene Degreve, Regional Mgr.-U.S., Canada & Mexico

Phone: 32-2-509-61-11 **Fax:** 32-2-509-66-17
Toll-Free:
Address: Rue Du Prince Albert, 33, Brussels, B-1050 Belgium

GROWTH PLANS/SPECIAL FEATURES:

Solvay SA, headquartered in Brussels, Belgium, is an international specialty chemicals and pharmaceutical company. It boasts nearly 400 sales and production facilities in 50 countries. The company operates in three sectors: pharmaceuticals, chemicals and plastics. Pharmaceutical products are developed for a wide range of therapeutic areas, including cardiology, gastroenterology, gynecology/andrology and mental health. Products include Teveten, Physiotens, Aceon and Omacor to treat hypertension; Creon, Rowasa, Dicetel, Duspatalin, Duphalac, Pantoloc, Cilansetron to treat gastrointestinal disorders; Androgel, Presomen, Zumenon, Femoston, Zumeston, Presomen Compositum, Estratest and Prometrium to treat gynecological and andrological disorders; and Luvox, Floxyfral, Faverin, Marinol and Serc to treat mental disorders. The chemicals segment focuses on mineral products, such as soda ash and its derivatives, barium strontium carbonates and advanced functional minerals; halogens, including chlorine and fluorinated gas products; and oxygen products, such as peroxygens, detergent and caprolactones. Plastic products include vinyls, performance compounds and specialty polymers. Solvay's joint venture with Plastic Omnium, Inergy Automotive Systems, creates integrated fuel systems designed for the higher operating temperatures and increased vapor generation found in modern vehicles. Pipelife, a joint venture with Wienerberger of Austria, produces and distributes pipes and fittings system for water supply, sewage, gas supply, cable protection, irrigation and draining, heating and domestic chimney flues. Belgian holding company Solvac owns approximately 30% of Solvay. In March 2008, the company sold its subsidiary, Solvay Engineered Polymers, to Lyondell Basell Industries, a Netherlands-based polymers and fuels company. In the same month, Simcor, a combination lipid therapy developed by Abbott in the U.S., received approval from the U.S. Food and Drug Administration (FDA). In October 2008, the firm acquired Egypt-based Alexandria Sodium Carbonate Company from Holding Company for Chemical Industries. In December 2008, the FDA approved Solvay's TriLipixit, a cholesterol management medication, for sale in the U.S.

FINANCIALS: **Sales and profits are in thousands of dollars—add 000 to get the full amount. 2008 Note: Financial information for 2008 was not available for all companies at press time.**

2008 Sales: $13,207,000	2008 Profits: $625,000	**U.S. Stock Ticker: SVYSY**
2007 Sales: $13,970,000	2007 Profits: $1,140,000	**Int'l Ticker: SOLB** Int'l Exchange: Brussels-Euronext
2006 Sales: $12,378,000	2006 Profits: $1,076,000	Employees: 29,433
2005 Sales: $10,429,000	2005 Profits: $993,980	Fiscal Year Ends: 12/31
2004 Sales: $8,856,950	2004 Profits: $659,000	Parent Company:

SALARIES/BENEFITS:

Pension Plan:	ESOP Stock Plan:	Profit Sharing:	Top Exec. Salary: $	Bonus: $
Savings Plan:	Stock Purch. Plan:		Second Exec. Salary: $	Bonus: $

OTHER THOUGHTS:

Apparent Women Officers or Directors:
Hot Spot for Advancement for Women/Minorities:

LOCATIONS: ("Y" = Yes)

West:	Southwest:	Midwest:	Southeast:	Northeast:	International:
Y	Y	Y	Y	Y	Y

SONY CORPORATION

www.sony.net

Industry Group Code: 334310 **Ranks within this company's industry group:** Sales: 3 Profits: 2

Techology:		Medical/Drugs:		Engineering:		Transportation:		Chemicals/Petrochemicals:		Specialty:	
Computers:	Y	Manufacturer:		Design:		Aerospace:		Oil/Gas Products:		Special Services:	
Software:	Y	Contract Research:		Construction:		Automotive:		Chemicals:		Consulting:	
Communications:	Y	Medical Services:		Eng. Services:		Shipping:		Oil/Chem. Svcs.:		Specialty Mgmt.:	
Electronics:		Labs:		Consulting:				Gases:		Products:	Y
Alternative Energy:		Bio. Services:						Other:		Other:	

TYPES OF BUSINESS:

Consumer Electronics Manufacturer
Film & Television Production
Music Production
Personal Computers
Semiconductors
Technology Research
Video Games
Financial Services, Banking & Insurance

BRANDS/DIVISIONS/AFFILIATES:

Sony Style
Sony Computer Entertainment, Inc.
PlayStation
Sony Pictures Entertainment
Columbia TriStar
Sony Financial Holdings
Sony BMG
Epic Records

CONTACTS: *Note: Officers with more than one job title may be intentionally listed here more than once.*

Howard Stringer, CEO
Ryoji Chubachi, Pres.
Nobuyuki Oneda, CFO/Exec. VP
Kiyoshi Shikano, Sr. Gen. Mgr.-Global Mktg.
Kunitaka Fujita, Sr. VP-Group Human Resources
Keiji Kimura, Exec. VP-Tech. Strategies & Intellectual Property
Nicole Seligman, General Counsel/Exec. VP
Keiji Kimura, Exec. VP-Electronics Bus. Strategies
Naofumi Hara, Sr. VP-Corp. Comm. & External Rel.
Ryoji Chubachi, CEO-Electronics
Yutaka Nakagawa, Exec. Deputy Pres., Semiconductor & Component
Katsumi Ihara, Exec. Deputy Pres., Consumer Products Group
Shuhei Yoshida, Pres., Computer Entertainment Worldwide Studios
Howard Stringer, Chmn.
Yutaka Nakagawa, Exec. Deputy Pres., Supply Chain & Prod. Strategy

Phone: 81-3-6748-2111 **Fax:** 81-3-6748-2244
Toll-Free: 800-566-3411
Address: 7-1 Konan, 1-Chome, Minato-Ku, Tokyo, 108-0075 Japan

GROWTH PLANS/SPECIAL FEATURES:

Sony Corporation, a leading consumer electronics firm, produces consumer and industrial electronic products and entertainment. Sony Corporation has five business segments: Electronics, generating 66.9% of the firm's 2008 revenues; Games, 13.7%; Pictures, 9.7%; Financial Services, 6.2%; and Other, 3.5. The Electronics segment divides its products between audio; video; televisions; information and communications; semiconductors; components; and other, such as manufacturing CDs and DVDs. The Games section, through Sony Computer Entertainment, Inc., manufactures and markets hardware and related software for Sony's PlayStation products, including the PlayStation 3. The Pictures segment, through Sony Pictures Entertainment, produces and distributes movies and television programs; acquires and distributes home videos; and operates studio facilities. The division operates Columbia TriStar, Columbia Pictures, Sony Pictures Classics and Columbia TriStar Home Entertainment. Sony Financial Holdings owns companies involved in insurance, banking and brokerage. The Other segment includes the company's music division, which produces and distributes music and releases music under the Columbia Records, Epic Records and RCA Records labels. In February 2008, Sony announced plans to sell Sony Berlin GmbH, which owns The Sony Center am Potsdamer Platz, to Morgan Stanly, Corpus Sireo and an affiliate of The John Buck Company. In April 2008, the firm and Samsung Electronics Co. agreed to build a LCD manufacturing plant in the Tangjeong complex in Seoul, Korea. In May 2008, Sony, Axis and Bosch entered into a development agreement in which the three will create a global standard for the interface of network video products such as cameras, video encoders and video management systems. In September 2008, NEC Corporation agreed to transfer its stock in Sony NEC Opiarc to Sony Corporation. In October 2008, Sony acquired the remaining 50% stake in Sony BMG from Bertelsmann AG. The music group is now a 100% owned subsidiary called Sony Music Entertainment, Inc.

FINANCIALS: **Sales and profits are in thousands of dollars—add 000 to get the full amount. 2008 Note: Financial information for 2008 was not available for all companies at press time.**

2008 Sales: $88,714,100	2008 Profits: $3,694,400	**U.S. Stock Ticker: SNE**
2007 Sales: $70,513,400	2007 Profits: $1,073,800	**Int'l Ticker: 6758** Int'l Exchange: Tokyo-TSE
2006 Sales: $64,021,000	2006 Profits: $1,047,270	Employees: 180,500
2005 Sales: $66,912,000	2005 Profits: $1,531,000	Fiscal Year Ends: 3/31
2004 Sales: $71,215,714	2004 Profits: $840,854	Parent Company:

SALARIES/BENEFITS:

Pension Plan: Y	ESOP Stock Plan:	Profit Sharing:	Top Exec. Salary: $	Bonus: $
Savings Plan:	Stock Purch. Plan:		Second Exec. Salary: $	Bonus: $

OTHER THOUGHTS:

Apparent Women Officers or Directors: 1
Hot Spot for Advancement for Women/Minorities:

LOCATIONS: ("Y" = Yes)

West:	Southwest:	Midwest:	Southeast:	Northeast:	International:
Y	Y	Y	Y	Y	Y

SONY ERICSSON MOBILE COMMUNICATIONS AB

www.sonyericsson.com

Industry Group Code: 334220 **Ranks within this company's industry group:** Sales: 5 Profits: 4

Techology:		Medical/Drugs:		Engineering:		Transportation:		Chemicals/Petrochemicals:		Specialty:	
Computers:		Manufacturer:		Design:		Aerospace:		Oil/Gas Products:		Special Services:	
Software:		Contract Research:		Construction:		Automotive:		Chemicals:		Consulting:	
Communications:	Y	Medical Services:		Eng. Services:		Shipping:		Oil/Chem. Svcs.:		Specialty Mgmt.:	
Electronics:	Y	Labs:		Consulting:				Gases:		Products:	
Alternative Energy:		Bio. Services:						Other:		Other:	

TYPES OF BUSINESS:

Cellular Telephones
Mobile Phone Accessories
PC Cards
Machine-to-Machine Communications Systems
Communications Products

BRANDS/DIVISIONS/AFFILIATES:

Sony Corporation
Ericsson (Telefon AB LM Ericsson)
PC300
W710 WALKMAN Phone
Z710 Phone
Smartphone
Cyber-shot

CONTACTS: *Note: Officers with more than one job title may be intentionally listed here more than once.*

Hideki Komiyama, Pres.
Anders Runevad, Exec. VP/Head-Sales

Phone: 44-208-762-58-00	**Fax:** 44-208-762-58-87
Toll-Free:	
Address: Sony Ericsson House, 202 Hammersmith Rd., London, W6 7DN UK	

GROWTH PLANS/SPECIAL FEATURES:

Sony Ericsson Mobile Communications AB is a 50-50 joint venture between consumer electronics giants Sony Corp. and Ericsson AB, a provider of network infrastructure and telecommunications. Sony Ericsson Mobile uses these combined resources to globally provide mobile multimedia devices including mobile phones and accessories, PC cards and business products. The firm is based in London, with research and development operations in the U.K., U.S., Sweden, Japan and China. Sony Ericsson's product portfolio includes phones that support GSM, TDMA, CDMA and satellite technologies; accessories including batteries, micro travel phone chargers, messaging, connectivity, entertainment and hands-free products (Bluetooth devices); and PC cards compatible with CSD, EDGE, GPRS, GSM and WLAN networks. The company's business products include Smartphones (featuring a PDA and phone in one device), GPS-based navigation systems, security applications and business software. The firm's best known products include the Cyber-shot camera phone, Walkman music phone and the T610 mobile phone. The firm's web site features downloadable ring tones, picture messaging and applications to create mobile movies. Additionally, software and service packages can be accessed online and added to consumer phones; add-on features include portable photo albums, picture messaging, image editors and navigation systems.

FINANCIALS: **Sales and profits are in thousands of dollars—add 000 to get the full amount. 2008 Note: Financial information for 2008 was not available for all companies at press time.**

2008 Sales: $14,980,380	2008 Profits: $-97,260	**U.S. Stock Ticker: Joint Venture**
2007 Sales: $17,208,000	2007 Profits: $1,484,180	**Int'l Ticker:** Int'l Exchange:
2006 Sales: $17,219,730	2006 Profits: $1,566,700	Employees: 5,000
2005 Sales: $	2005 Profits: $	Fiscal Year Ends: 12/31
2004 Sales: $	2004 Profits: $	Parent Company:

SALARIES/BENEFITS:

Pension Plan:	ESOP Stock Plan:	Profit Sharing:	Top Exec. Salary: $	Bonus: $
Savings Plan:	Stock Purch. Plan:		Second Exec. Salary: $	Bonus: $

OTHER THOUGHTS:

Apparent Women Officers or Directors: 1
Hot Spot for Advancement for Women/Minorities:

LOCATIONS: ("Y" = Yes)

West:	Southwest:	Midwest:	Southeast:	Northeast:	International:
			Y	Y	Y

SPIRIT AEROSYSTEMS HOLDINGS INC

www.spiritaero.com

Industry Group Code: 336410 **Ranks within this company's industry group:** Sales: 20 Profits: 17

Techology:		Medical/Drugs:		Engineering:		Transportation:		Chemicals/Petrochemicals:		Specialty:	
Computers:		Manufacturer:		Design:		Aerospace:	Y	Oil/Gas Products:		Special Services:	
Software:		Contract Research:		Construction:		Automotive:		Chemicals:		Consulting:	
Communications:		Medical Services:		Eng. Services:		Shipping:		Oil/Chem. Svcs.:		Specialty Mgmt.:	
Electronics:		Labs:		Consulting:				Gases:		Products:	
Alternative Energy:		Bio. Services:						Other:		Other:	

TYPES OF BUSINESS:

Aircraft Manufacturing
Aerostructures
Fuselages
Wings & Flight Control Components
Engineering, Design & Materials Testing
Custom Tool Fabrication
Spare Parts & Maintenance Services
Supply Chain Management

BRANDS/DIVISIONS/AFFILIATES:

Taikoo Spirit AeroSystems Composite Co

CONTACTS: *Note: Officers with more than one job title may be intentionally listed here more than once.*

Jeff Turner, CEO
Ron Brunton, COO/Exec. VP
Jeff Turner, Pres.
Rick Schmidt, CFO/Exec. VP
H. D. Walker, Sr. VP-Mktg. & Sales
Gloria Flentje, Sr. VP-Human Resources
Peter Wu, Chief Scientist/VP
John Pilla, CTO/Sr. VP
Gloria Flentje, Sr. VP-Admin.
Jonathan Greenberg, General Counsel/Sr. VP/Sec.
Buck Buchanan, Sr. VP/Gen. Mgr.-Fuselage Segment
Mike King, Sr. VP/Gen. Mgr.-Propulsion Segment
John Lewelling, Sr. VP/Gen. Mgr.-AeroStructures Segment

Phone: 316-526-9000 **Fax:**
Toll-Free: 800-501-7597
Address: 3801 S. Oliver St., Wichita, KS 67210 US

GROWTH PLANS/SPECIAL FEATURES:

Spirit Aerosystems Holdings, Inc. is an independent original parts designer and manufacturer of aerostructures in the world. Aerostructures are structural components such as fuselages, propulsion systems and wing systems for commercial and military aircraft. It operates through three principal segments corresponding to its three main products: Fuselages, propulsion systems and wing systems. The fuselages segment produces forward, mid- and rear fuselage sections and offers services that include numerical control programming, materials testing, on-site planning and global supply chain management. The propulsion systems segment primarily produces nacelles (aerodynamic engine enclosures which enhance propulsion installation efficiency, dampen engine noise and provide thrust reversing capabilities), struts/pylons (structures that attach engines to airplane wings) and engine structural components. Propulsion system services include engineering design, numerical control programming, materials testing, on-site planning, process improvement consulting and global supply chain management. The wing systems segment produces wings, wing components and flight control components. A key aspect of the company's business, vital to all three segments of the company, is tooling (the fabrication of custom tools). The firm's tooling capabilities include tool design, CNC programming, machining, composite, aluminum and invar tooling. Another facet of Spirit Aerosystems' business is its aftermarket customer support. The company offers spare parts and components for all items of which it is the original production supplier and provides maintenance, repair and overhaul work for nacelles, fuselage doors, structural components and modification kits. The firm supplies its products to Boeing and Airbus. In April 2008, the company joined a joint venture partnership with several aviation companies for a metal bond repair station called Taikoo Spirit AeroSystems Composite Co. in Xiamen, China. The construction of the facility is expected to be completed in mid-2009. In September 2008, the firm opened a new Maintenance, Repair and Overhaul station in Prestwick, Scotland.

Employees are offered medical, dental and vision insurance, as well as a 401(k) plan.

FINANCIALS: **Sales and profits are in thousands of dollars—add 000 to get the full amount. 2008 Note: Financial information for 2008 was not available for all companies at press time.**

2008 Sales: $3,772,000	2008 Profits: $265,000	**U.S. Stock Ticker: SPR**
2007 Sales: $3,860,800	2007 Profits: $296,900	**Int'l Ticker:** Int'l Exchange:
2006 Sales: $3,207,700	2006 Profits: $16,800	Employees: 13,089
2005 Sales: $1,207,600	2005 Profits: $-90,300	Fiscal Year Ends: 12/31
2004 Sales: $	2004 Profits: $	Parent Company:

SALARIES/BENEFITS:

Pension Plan:	ESOP Stock Plan:	Profit Sharing:	Top Exec. Salary: $432,494	Bonus: $638,561
Savings Plan: Y	Stock Purch. Plan:		Second Exec. Salary: $375,003	Bonus: $368,045

OTHER THOUGHTS:

Apparent Women Officers or Directors: 1
Hot Spot for Advancement for Women/Minorities:

LOCATIONS: ("Y" = Yes)

West:	Southwest:	Midwest:	Southeast:	Northeast:	International:
	Y	Y			Y

Note: Financial information, benefits and other data can change quickly and may vary from those stated here.

ST JUDE MEDICAL INC

www.sjm.com

Industry Group Code: 339113 **Ranks within this company's industry group:** Sales: 8 Profits: 8

Techology:		Medical/Drugs:		Engineering:		Transportation:		Chemicals/Petrochemicals:		Specialty:	
Computers:		Manufacturer:	Y	Design:		Aerospace:		Oil/Gas Products:		Special Services:	
Software:		Contract Research:		Construction:		Automotive:		Chemicals:		Consulting:	
Communications:		Medical Services:		Eng. Services:		Shipping:		Oil/Chem. Svcs.:		Specialty Mgmt.:	
Electronics:		Labs:		Consulting:				Gases:		Products:	
Alternative Energy:		Bio. Services:						Other:		Other:	

TYPES OF BUSINESS:

Cardiovascular Medical Devices
Cardiac Rhythm Management Devices
Cardiac Surgery Devices
Cardiology Devices
Atrial Fibrillation Devices

BRANDS/DIVISIONS/AFFILIATES:

Atlas II ICD
Atlas II HF CRT-D
Eon
TigerWire
Reflexion Spiral X
EP MedSystems, Inc.

CONTACTS: *Note: Officers with more than one job title may be intentionally listed here more than once.*

Daniel J. Starks, CEO
Daniel J. Starks, Pres.
John C. Heinmiller, CFO/Exec. VP
Paul Bae, VP-Human Resources
Thomas R. Northenscold, CIO/VP-IT
Thomas R. Northenscold, VP-Admin.
Pamela S. Krop, General Counsel/VP/Sec.
Angela D. Craig, VP-Corp. Rel.
Mark D. Carlson, Chief Medical Officer/Sr. VP-Clinical Affairs
Christopher G. Chavez, Pres., Neuromodulation Division
Eric S. Fain, Pres., Cardiac Rhythm Mgmt. Division
Frank J. Callaghan, Pres., Cardiovascular Division
Daniel J. Starks, Chmn.
Denis M. Gestin, Pres., Int'l Div.

Phone: 651-483-2000	**Fax:** 651-482-8318
Toll-Free: 800-328-9634	
Address: 1 Lillehei Plaza, St. Paul, MN 55117 US	

GROWTH PLANS/SPECIAL FEATURES:

St. Jude Medical, Inc. develops, manufactures and distributes cardiovascular medical devices for global cardiac rhythm management, cardiac surgery, cardiology and atrial fibrillation therapy and implantable neuromodulation devices for the management of chronic pain. The company operates in four segments: cardiac rhythm management, whose products include tachycardia implantable cardioverter defribrillator systems and bradycardia pacemaker systems; cardiovascular, whose products include vascular closure devices, heart valves and valve repair products; advanced neuromodulation systems, whose products include neurostimulation devices; and atrial fibrillation, whose products include electrophysiology introducers and catheters, advanced cardiac mapping and navigation systems and ablation systems. St. Jude's Neuromodulation Division focuses its efforts on the related therapy areas. Neuromodulation is the delivery of very small, precise doses of electric current or drugs directly to nerve sites and is aimed at treating patients suffering from chronic pain or other disabling nervous system disorders. The firm markets and sells its products through a direct sales force and independent distributors. The principal geographic markets for its products are the U.S., Europe, Japan and the Asia-Pacific region. St. Jude also sells products in Canada and Latin America. The cardiac rhythm management products generated 62.7% of revenue in 2007. In recent news, St. Jude received clearance in the U.S., Canada and Europe on a large variety of products, including the Eon neurostimulator line to treat chronic pain. In 2008, the firm launched its TigerWire steerable guidewire and Reflexion Spiral X variable radius mapping catheter in the U.S. In July 2008, the company acquired EP MedSystems, Inc., which develops, manufactures and markets products for cardiac rhythm management.

The company offers its employees medical, dental and vision insurance; flexible spending accounts; access to a credit union; disability insurance; life insurance; a physical fitness program; a matching gift program; and tuition reimbursement.

FINANCIALS: **Sales and profits are in thousands of dollars—add 000 to get the full amount. 2008 Note: Financial information for 2008 was not available for all companies at press time.**

2008 Sales: $4,363,251	2008 Profits: $384,327	**U.S. Stock Ticker: STJ**
2007 Sales: $3,779,277	2007 Profits: $559,038	**Int'l Ticker:** Int'l Exchange:
2006 Sales: $3,302,447	2006 Profits: $548,251	Employees: 14,000
2005 Sales: $2,915,280	2005 Profits: $393,490	Fiscal Year Ends: 12/31
2004 Sales: $2,294,173	2004 Profits: $409,934	Parent Company:

SALARIES/BENEFITS:

Pension Plan:	ESOP Stock Plan:	Profit Sharing: Y	Top Exec. Salary: $975,000	Bonus: $1,205,100
Savings Plan: Y	Stock Purch. Plan: Y		Second Exec. Salary: $610,000	Bonus: $628,300

OTHER THOUGHTS:

Apparent Women Officers or Directors: 5
Hot Spot for Advancement for Women/Minorities: Y

LOCATIONS: ("Y" = Yes)

West:	Southwest:	Midwest:	Southeast:	Northeast:	International:
Y	Y	Y	Y	Y	Y

STATOILHYDRO ASA

www.statoilhydro.com

Industry Group Code: 211111 **Ranks within this company's industry group:** Sales: 12 Profits: 10

Techology:		Medical/Drugs:		Engineering:		Transportation:		Chemicals/Petrochemicals:		Specialty:	
Computers:		Manufacturer:		Design:		Aerospace:		Oil/Gas Products:	Y	Special Services:	
Software:		Contract Research:		Construction:		Automotive:		Chemicals:		Consulting:	
Communications:		Medical Services:		Eng. Services:		Shipping:		Oil/Chem. Svcs.:		Specialty Mgmt.:	
Electronics:		Labs:		Consulting:				Gases:		Products:	
Alternative Energy:		Bio. Services:						Other:		Other:	

TYPES OF BUSINESS:

Oil & Gas Exploration & Production
Refining
Pipelines
Energy Marketing
Oil Sands Production

BRANDS/DIVISIONS/AFFILIATES:

North American Oil Sands Corp.
Norsk Hydro ASA
Statoil ASA
Statoil Canada Limited

CONTACTS: *Note: Officers with more than one job title may be intentionally listed here more than once.*

Helge Lund, CEO
Helge Lund, Pres.
Jon Arnt Jacobsen, Exec. VP-Mktg.
Hilde Merete Aasheim, Exec. VP-Staffs & Corp. Svcs.
Margareth Ovrum, Exec. VP-Tech. & New Energy
Jon Arnt Jacobsen, Exec. VP-Mfg.
Oystein Michelsen, Acting Exec. VP-Exploration & Prod.
Helga Nes, Exec. VP-Projects
Rune Bjornson, Exec. VP-Natural Gas
Svein Rennemo, Chmn.
Peter Mellbye, Exec. VP-Int'l Exploration & Prod.

Phone: 47-51-99-00-00	**Fax:** 47-51-99-00-50
Toll-Free:	
Address: Forusbeen 50, Stavanger, N-4035 Norway	

GROWTH PLANS/SPECIAL FEATURES:

StatoilHydro ASA, formerly known as Statoil ASA, is an international oil and gas company and one of the largest companies in Scandinavia. At the end of 2007, the company had proved reserves of around 2389 million barrels (mmbbls) of oil and 20.3 trillion cubic feet of natural gas, which represents an aggregate of 6,010 million barrels of oil equivalent (MMboe). StatoilHydro maintains operations in 34 countries. The company's retail gasoline business operates through four divisions: exploration and production in Norway (E&P Norway); international exploration and production (International E&P); natural gas; and manufacturing and marketing. E&P Norway explores, develops and produces petroleum products on the Norwegian continental shelf. The company's pipelines extend from the offshore outposts to locations in Norway and other countries. International E&P includes all exploration, development and production operations outside Norway, with interests in fields in the Caspian Sea, North Africa, Western Africa, Western Europe, China, the Middle East, North and South America. Statoil's natural gas segment transports, processes and sells natural gas from upstream positions offshore of Norway and abroad. The manufacturing and marketing segment includes the group's operations in transporting oil, processing, sale of crude oil and refined products and retailing. The company also operates a business area service unit, Technology and Projects, in order to develop distinct technology positions and strengthen project execution. In March 2008, StaoilHydro signed an agreement with Anadarko to acquire the remaining 50% in the Brazilian Peregrino development, giving the company complete operatorship in the project. The company also acquired Anadarko's 25% interest in the Kaskida discovery in deep water of U.S Gulf of Mexico.

StaoilHydro offers its employees onsite childcare at the majority of its office locations; yoga and relaxation sessions during the workday; reduced ticket prices to a selection of concerts and shows; and vacation stays at company-owned cabins.

FINANCIALS: **Sales and profits are in thousands of dollars—add 000 to get the full amount. 2008 Note: Financial information for 2008 was not available for all companies at press time.**

2008 Sales: $98,337,900	2008 Profits: $6,530,720	**U.S. Stock Ticker: STO**
2007 Sales: $89,000,000	2007 Profits: $7,520,000	**Int'l Ticker: STL** Int'l Exchange: Oslo-OBX
2006 Sales: $71,295,100	2006 Profits: $6,810,630	Employees: 29,500
2005 Sales: $64,964,000	2005 Profits: $5,153,040	Fiscal Year Ends: 12/31
2004 Sales: $50,548,300	2004 Profits: $4,178,100	Parent Company:

SALARIES/BENEFITS:

Pension Plan: Y	ESOP Stock Plan: Y	Profit Sharing:	Top Exec. Salary: $	Bonus: $
Savings Plan:	Stock Purch. Plan:		Second Exec. Salary: $	Bonus: $

OTHER THOUGHTS:

Apparent Women Officers or Directors: 6
Hot Spot for Advancement for Women/Minorities: Y

LOCATIONS: ("Y" = Yes)

West:	Southwest:	Midwest:	Southeast:	Northeast:	International:
	Y			Y	Y

STMICROELECTRONICS NV

www.st.com

Industry Group Code: 334413 **Ranks within this company's industry group:** Sales: 5 Profits: 15

Techology:		Medical/Drugs:		Engineering:		Transportation:		Chemicals/Petrochemicals:		Specialty:	
Computers:	Y	Manufacturer:		Design:		Aerospace:		Oil/Gas Products:		Special Services:	
Software:		Contract Research:		Construction:		Automotive:		Chemicals:		Consulting:	
Communications:		Medical Services:		Eng. Services:		Shipping:		Oil/Chem. Svcs.:		Specialty Mgmt.:	
Electronics:	Y	Labs:		Consulting:				Gases:		Products:	
Alternative Energy:		Bio. Services:						Other:		Other:	

TYPES OF BUSINESS:

Semiconductor Manufacturing
Integrated Circuits
Transistors & Diodes

BRANDS/DIVISIONS/AFFILIATES:

Genesis Microchip, Inc.

CONTACTS: *Note: Officers with more than one job title may be intentionally listed here more than once.*

Carlo Bozotti, CEO
Alain Dutheil, COO
Carlo Bozotti, Pres.
Carlo Ferro, CFO/Exec. VP
Patrice Chastagner, VP-Human Resources
Jean-Marc Chery, CTO/Exec. VP
Orio Bellezza, Exec. VP-Front-End Mfg.
Pierre Ollivier, General Counsel/VP
Loic Lietar, VP-Corp. Bus. Dev.
Carlo Emanuele Ottaviani, VP-Corp. Comm.
Celine Berthier, Dir.-Investor Rel.
Otto Kosgalwies, VP-Company Infrastructure & Svcs.
Georges Auguste, Exec. VP/Dir.-Total Quality & Corp. Responsibility
Alisia Grenville, VP/Chief Compliance Officer
Jeffrey See, Exec. VP/Gen. Mgr.-Packaging & Test Mfg.
Gerald Arbola, Chmn.
Reza Kazerounian, VP/Gen. Mgr.-North America Region

Phone: 41-22-929-29-29 **Fax:** 41-22-929-29-88
Toll-Free:
Address: 39 Chemin du Champ des Filles, Plan-Les-Ouates, 1228 Switzerland

GROWTH PLANS/SPECIAL FEATURES:

STMicroelectronics N.V. (STM) is one of the world's largest semiconductor companies. It is a leading chip manufacturer in Europe, as well as a top maker of analog chips globally. The company also makes a variety of discrete devices such as transistors and diodes as well as integrated circuits (ICs), including microcontrollers, memory chips and application-specific and custom ICs. The company is organized into three product segments: Application Specific Group, Flash Memory Group and Industrial Multisegment Sector (IMS). The Application Specific Group is responsible for the design, development and manufacture of application-specific products, as well as mixed analog/digital semicustom devices, using advanced bipolar, CMOS, BiCMOS mixed-signal and power technologies. The segment is further comprised of groups focused on home entertainment & displays; automotive products; mobile, multimedia & communications products; and computer peripherals. The Flash Memory Group designs, develops and manufactures a broad range of semiconductor memory products. The segment also conducts research and development, front-end and back-end manufacturing and worldwide sales and marketing. The Industrial and Multisegment Sector is responsible for the design, development and manufacture of discrete power devices, such as power transistors; standard linear and logic ICs; and radio frequency products. In addition, this segment spearheads ongoing efforts to maintain and develop high-end analog products. The firm sells to manufacturers in the telecommunications, computer, consumer electronics, industrial and automotive markets. One of STM's top clients, Nokia, accounts for as much as 22% of annual revenues. The firm's top ten OEM clients account for roughly 50% of net revenues. The firm has research and development partnerships with Freescale Semiconductor, Inc., Hynix Semiconductor, Inc. and Intel Corporation. STM operates 15 main manufacturing sites worldwide. In January 2008, the company acquired Genesis Microchip, Inc.

FINANCIALS: **Sales and profits are in thousands of dollars—add 000 to get the full amount. 2008 Note: Financial information for 2008 was not available for all companies at press time.**

2008 Sales: $9,842,000
2007 Sales: $10,001,000
2006 Sales: $9,854,000
2005 Sales: $8,882,000
2004 Sales: $8,760,000

2008 Profits: $-786,000
2007 Profits: $-477,000
2006 Profits: $782,000
2005 Profits: $266,000
2004 Profits: $601,000

U.S. Stock Ticker: STM
Int'l Ticker: STM Int'l Exchange: Paris-Euronext
Employees: 50,000
Fiscal Year Ends: 12/31
Parent Company:

SALARIES/BENEFITS:

Pension Plan:	ESOP Stock Plan:	Profit Sharing:	Top Exec. Salary: $770,000	Bonus: $423,500
Savings Plan:	Stock Purch. Plan:		Second Exec. Salary: $	Bonus: $

OTHER THOUGHTS:

Apparent Women Officers or Directors: 1
Hot Spot for Advancement for Women/Minorities:

LOCATIONS: ("Y" = Yes)

West:	Southwest:	Midwest:	Southeast:	Northeast:	International:
Y	Y	Y	Y	Y	Y

STRYKER CORP

www.stryker.com

Industry Group Code: 339113 **Ranks within this company's industry group:** Sales: 7 Profits: 5

Techology:		Medical/Drugs:		Engineering:		Transportation:		Chemicals/Petrochemicals:		Specialty:	
Computers:		Manufacturer:	Y	Design:		Aerospace:		Oil/Gas Products:		Special Services:	
Software:		Contract Research:		Construction:		Automotive:		Chemicals:		Consulting:	
Communications:		Medical Services:		Eng. Services:		Shipping:		Oil/Chem. Svcs.:		Specialty Mgmt.:	
Electronics:		Labs:		Consulting:				Gases:		Products:	
Alternative Energy:		Bio. Services:						Other:		Other:	

TYPES OF BUSINESS:

Equipment-Orthopedic Implants
Powered Surgical Instruments
Endoscopic Systems
Patient Care & Handling Equipment
Outpatient Physical Therapy Services
Imaging Software

BRANDS/DIVISIONS/AFFILIATES:

Stryker Orthopaedics
Stryker Osteosynthesis
Stryker Spine
Stryker Biotech
Stryker Instruments
Stryker Endoscopy
Stryker Medical
Sightline Technologies

CONTACTS: *Note: Officers with more than one job title may be intentionally listed here more than once.*

Stephen P. MacMillan, CEO
Stephen P. MacMillan, Pres.
Dean H. Bergy, CFO/VP
Michael W. Rude, VP-Human Resources
Curtis E. Hall, General Counsel/VP
Bryant S. Zanko, VP-Corp. Bus. Dev.
J. Patrick Anderson, VP-Corp. Affairs
Katherine A. Owen, VP-Investor Rel. & Strategy
Jeanne M. Blondia, Treas./VP
James E. Kemler, VP/Group Pres., Biotech, Osteosynthesis & Dev.
Stephen Si Johnson, VP/Group Pres., MedSurg Equipment
Edward B. Lipes, Exec. VP
Bronwen R. Taylor, VP-Internal Audit & Compliance
John W. Brown, Chmn.
Andrew G. Fox-Smith, Pres., Int'l

Phone: 269-385-2600 **Fax:** 269-385-1062
Toll-Free:
Address: 2825 Airview Blvd., Kalamazoo, MI 49002 US

GROWTH PLANS/SPECIAL FEATURES:

Stryker Corp. develops, manufactures and markets specialty surgical and medical products for the global market. These products include orthopedic implants, patient care and handling equipment, powered surgical instruments and endoscopic systems. Founded in 1941, the firm's products are produced by two segments: Orthopaedic Implants, which generated approximately 60% of Stryker's 2007 sales; and MedSurg equipment, the remaining 40%. The Orthopaedic Implant segment's products include reconstructive implants for knee, hip, elbow, shoulder and other joint surgeries; nailing, plating and external fixation systems to mend trauma injuries; spine implants; micro implants for craniomaxillofacial and hand surgery; bone cement; and OP-1, a natural protein that induces bone formation. These products are designed and manufactured by subsidiaries Stryker Orthopaedics, Stryker Osteosynthesis, Stryker Spine and Stryker Biotech. Stryker MedSurg Equipment provides powered surgical instruments, surgical navigation systems, hospital beds and stretchers, endoscopic products, emergency medical equipment and medical video imaging equipment. These devices are produced by Stryker Instruments, Stryker Endoscopy, Stryker Medical and Sightline Technologies Ltd., a recently acquired Israeli company that develops flexible endoscopes. Stryker maintains administrative, sales, warehousing and distribution sites in 41 countries in Europe, Asia, Africa and the Americas; and exports products to numerous international destinations. Geographically, domestic regions generated 64% of the 2007 sales; international regions, the remaining 36%. In June 2007, Physiotherapy Associates was sold for $150 million to Water Street Healthcare Partners. Physiotherapy Associates provided outpatient physical therapy services in the U.S.

Employees of Stryker receive benefits including medical, dental, vision, prescription, disability and life insurance; flexible spending accounts; an employee assistance program; onsite fitness centers and cafeterias; tuition reimbursement; adoption assistance; and paid vacations, holidays and maternity leave.

FINANCIALS: **Sales and profits are in thousands of dollars—add 000 to get the full amount. 2008 Note: Financial information for 2008 was not available for all companies at press time.**

2008 Sales: $6,718,200	2008 Profits: $1,147,800	**U.S. Stock Ticker: SYK**
2007 Sales: $6,000,500	2007 Profits: $1,017,400	**Int'l Ticker:** Int'l Exchange:
2006 Sales: $5,147,200	2006 Profits: $777,700	Employees: 17,694
2005 Sales: $4,871,500	2005 Profits: $643,600	Fiscal Year Ends: 12/31
2004 Sales: $4,262,300	2004 Profits: $440,000	Parent Company:

SALARIES/BENEFITS:

Pension Plan:	ESOP Stock Plan:	Profit Sharing:	Top Exec. Salary: $950,000	Bonus: $1,098,300
Savings Plan: Y	Stock Purch. Plan: Y		Second Exec. Salary: $900,000	Bonus: $877,500

OTHER THOUGHTS:

Apparent Women Officers or Directors: 5
Hot Spot for Advancement for Women/Minorities: Y

LOCATIONS: ("Y" = Yes)

West:	Southwest:	Midwest:	Southeast:	Northeast:	International:
Y	Y	Y	Y	Y	Y

STV GROUP INC

www.stvinc.com

Industry Group Code: 541330 **Ranks within this company's industry group:** Sales: Profits:

Techology:		Medical/Drugs:		Engineering:		Transportation:		Chemicals/Petrochemicals:		Specialty:	
Computers:		Manufacturer:		Design:	Y	Aerospace:		Oil/Gas Products:		Special Services:	Y
Software:		Contract Research:		Construction:	Y	Automotive:		Chemicals:		Consulting:	
Communications:		Medical Services:		Eng. Services:	Y	Shipping:		Oil/Chem. Svcs.:		Specialty Mgmt.:	Y
Electronics:		Labs:		Consulting:	Y			Gases:		Products:	
Alternative Energy:		Bio. Services:						Other:		Other:	

TYPES OF BUSINESS:

Architectural & Engineering Services
Construction management
Infrastructure Design
Defense Systems Engineering
Industrial Process Engineering

BRANDS/DIVISIONS/AFFILIATES:

STV Security Solutions
STV Architects
STV Construction

CONTACTS:

Note: Officers with more than one job title may be intentionally listed here more than once.

Dominick M. Servedio, CEO
Milo E. Riverso, Pres.
Peter W. Knipe, CFO
Linda Rosenberg, Sr. VP-Mktg. & Comm.
Sydney Koerner, VP-Human Resources
Ronald Wiseman, CIO
Sydney Koerner, VP-Admin.
Judith Held, General Counsel/Sr. VP
Nadine Roper, VP-Corp. Comm.
Maher Z. Labib, COO-Buildings & Facilities Division /Exec. VP
William F. Matts, COO-Transportation & Infrastructure/Exec. VP
John A. Agro Jr., Sr. VP/Deputy Dir.-Transportation & Infrastructure
Anthony G. Cracchiolo, Sr. VP-Specialty Practices Div.
Dominick M. Servedio, Chmn.

Phone: 610-385-8200 **Fax:** 610-385-8500
Toll-Free:
Address: 205 W. Welsh Dr., Douglassville, PA 19518 US

GROWTH PLANS/SPECIAL FEATURES:

STV Group, Inc. is an architectural, engineering, planning, environmental and construction management firm. It operates through four divisions: Construction Management; Buildings/Facilities; Transportation and Infrastructure; and Specialty Practices. The firm specializes in constructing airports, highways, bridges, ports, railroad systems and schools, almost all of which are in the U.S. STV Construction Management undertakes design and building contracts in nearly every field of industry; the firm's personnel oversees construction programs through administrative, inspection and surveillance. The Buildings/Facilities division works directly with architects, to address the safety, practicality, cost and efficiency of its buildings. STV's Transportation and Infrastructure sector focuses on the management, planning and design of transportation systems and facilities. The Special Practices division is made up of two parts: STV Security Solutions Group and aviation/transportation architecture. This division provides all levels of security management and offers planning to the aviation/public transportation industry. Some of the STV Group's representative projects include the MetroLink in St. Louis, Missouri; the Villanova University Center for Engineering Education and Research; Sprint PCS Environmental Site Assessments in seven states; the Metra Inner Circumferential Rail Study in Chicago, Illinois; Shea Stadium in Queens, New York; and engineering and technical services for the U.S. Naval Air Warfare Center in Patuxent River, Maryland. In January 2008, a new service and inspection facility at New Jersey Transit's Morrisville Yard, designed by STV, opened for operation. In June 2008, the company created a new subsidiary, STV Security Solutions Group, Inc., to offer security, as well as risk, crisis and emergency management to its clients. In September 2008, STV opened a new office in Harrisburg, Pennsylvania and a second Boston, Massachusetts office in November.

FINANCIALS:

Sales and profits are in thousands of dollars—add 000 to get the full amount. 2008 Note: Financial information for 2008 was not available for all companies at press time.

2008 Sales: $	2008 Profits: $	**U.S. Stock Ticker: Private**
2007 Sales: $205,000	2007 Profits: $	**Int'l Ticker:** Int'l Exchange:
2006 Sales: $	2006 Profits: $	Employees: 1,400
2005 Sales: $	2005 Profits: $	Fiscal Year Ends: 9/30
2004 Sales: $	2004 Profits: $	Parent Company:

SALARIES/BENEFITS:

Pension Plan:	ESOP Stock Plan: Y	Profit Sharing:	Top Exec. Salary: $	Bonus: $
Savings Plan: Y	Stock Purch. Plan:		Second Exec. Salary: $	Bonus: $

OTHER THOUGHTS:

Apparent Women Officers or Directors: 6
Hot Spot for Advancement for Women/Minorities: Y

LOCATIONS: ("Y" = Yes)

West:	Southwest:	Midwest:	Southeast:	Northeast:	International:
Y	Y	Y	Y	Y	

SUMITOMO CHEMICAL CO LTD

www.sumitomo-chem.co.jp

Industry Group Code: 325000 **Ranks within this company's industry group:** Sales: 7 Profits: 8

Techology:		Medical/Drugs:		Engineering:		Transportation:		Chemicals/Petrochemicals:		Specialty:	
Computers:		Manufacturer:	Y	Design:		Aerospace:		Oil/Gas Products:	Y	Special Services:	
Software:		Contract Research:		Construction:		Automotive:		Chemicals:	Y	Consulting:	
Communications:		Medical Services:		Eng. Services:		Shipping:		Oil/Chem. Svcs.:		Specialty Mgmt.:	
Electronics:	Y	Labs:		Consulting:				Gases:		Products:	
Alternative Energy:		Bio. Services:						Other:		Other:	

TYPES OF BUSINESS:

Chemicals Manufacture
Basic Chemicals
Petrochemicals
Fine Chemicals
Agricultural Chemicals
IT-Related Chemicals
Pharmaceuticals

BRANDS/DIVISIONS/AFFILIATES:

Sumitomo Pharmaceuticals Company
Nihon Medi-physics Co., Ltd.
Dainippon Sumitomo Pharma
Sumitomo Chemical Agro Europe S.A.S.
Interfarm (UK), Ltd.
Cambridge Display Technology, Inc.

CONTACTS: *Note: Officers with more than one job title may be intentionally listed here more than once.*

Hiromasa Yonekura, Pres.
Yoshimasa Takao, Managing Exec. Officer-Human Resources Dept.
Naoya Kanda, Managing Exec. Officer-R&D
Kiyohiko Nakae, Exec. VP-Tech.
Yoshimasa Takao, Managing Exec. Officer-Legal Dept.
Kiyohiko Nakae, Exec. Officer-Corp. Planning & Coordination
Hiroshi Hirose, Exec. VP-Corp. Comm.
Hiroshi Hirose, Exec. VP-Finance & Acct.
Yasuo Kamei, Sr. Managing Exec. Officer-Basic Chemicals
Hideaki Watanabe, Sr. Managing Exec. Officer-Petrochemicals
Takatsugu Enami, Sr. Managing Exec. Officer-Fine Chemicals
Kenjiro Fukubayashi, Sr. Managing Exec. Officer-Agricultural Chemicals
Yoshimasa Takao, Exec. VP-Procurement & Logistics

Phone: 81-3-5543-5500 **Fax:** 81-3-5543-5901
Toll-Free:
Address: 27-1, Shinkawa 2-chome, Chuo-ku, Tokyo, 104-8260 Japan

GROWTH PLANS/SPECIAL FEATURES:

Sumitomo Chemical Co., Ltd., part of the Sumitomo Group, is a Japanese chemicals manufacturer. The company operates in six segments. The basic chemical segment provides alumina products, methyl methacrylate monomer and polymer products, optical materials, aluminum and inorganic and organic industrial chemicals. The petrochemicals and plastics segment supplies organic chemicals, plastics, polymer alloys, synthetic resins, synthetic rubber and downstream plastic products. The fine chemicals segment offers specialty and pharmaceutical products used in adhesives for wood, tire cords and flame retardants; rubber antioxidants; and polymer additives in synthetic resins. The IT-related chemicals segment is comprised of the optical materials division, the semiconductor process materials division and the electronic materials division. Products include positive-type photoresists, high purity chemicals, super engineering chemicals and composite molding materials. The agricultural chemicals segment has products including plant protection chemicals such as insecticides, fungicides and herbicides and new types of products such as amino acid feed additives. Finally, the pharmaceutical segment produces synthetic medicines. Dainippon Sumitomo Pharma, which produces prescription drugs to treat diabetes and the central nervous system, and Nihon Medi-Physics Co., Ltd., which makes diagnostic radio-pharmaceuticals, operate Sumitomo Chemical's pharmaceutical division. Sumitomo Chemical includes roughly 100 companies and markets its products in more than 110 countries worldwide. In September 2008, the company established a new device development center to develop technologies for high-resolution displays using polymer organic LEDs.

FINANCIALS: **Sales and profits are in thousands of dollars—add 000 to get the full amount. 2008 Note: Financial information for 2008 was not available for all companies at press time.**

2008 Sales: $18,929,424	2008 Profits: $629,634	**U.S. Stock Ticker:**
2007 Sales: $15,230,000	2007 Profits: $800,000	**Int'l Ticker: 4005** Int'l Exchange: Tokyo-TSE
2006 Sales: $13,327,400	2006 Profits: $771,000	Employees: 24,160
2005 Sales: $13,251,094	2005 Profits: $771,814	Fiscal Year Ends: 3/31
2004 Sales: $10,965,400	2004 Profits: $324,900	Parent Company:

SALARIES/BENEFITS:

Pension Plan:	ESOP Stock Plan:	Profit Sharing:	Top Exec. Salary: $	Bonus: $
Savings Plan:	Stock Purch. Plan:		Second Exec. Salary: $	Bonus: $

OTHER THOUGHTS:

Apparent Women Officers or Directors:
Hot Spot for Advancement for Women/Minorities:

LOCATIONS: ("Y" = Yes)

West:	Southwest:	Midwest:	Southeast:	Northeast:	International:
	Y			Y	Y

SUN MICROSYSTEMS INC

www.sun.com

Industry Group Code: 334111 **Ranks within this company's industry group:** Sales: 11 Profits: 9

Techology:		Medical/Drugs:		Engineering:		Transportation:		Chemicals/Petrochemicals:		Specialty:	
Computers:	Y	Manufacturer:		Design:		Aerospace:		Oil/Gas Products:		Special Services:	
Software:	Y	Contract Research:		Construction:		Automotive:		Chemicals:		Consulting:	
Communications:		Medical Services:		Eng. Services:		Shipping:		Oil/Chem. Svcs.:		Specialty Mgmt.:	
Electronics:		Labs:		Consulting:				Gases:		Products:	
Alternative Energy:		Bio. Services:						Other:		Other:	

TYPES OF BUSINESS:

Computer Hardware
UNIX-Based Workstation Computers
Multiprocessing Servers
Operating System Software
Systems Integration
Office Application Software
Network Products
Consulting Services

BRANDS/DIVISIONS/AFFILIATES:

NetBeans IDE
UltraSPARC
Sun Fire
Solaris OS
Java
StorEdge
SunSpectrum
Tarantella Inc

CONTACTS: *Note: Officers with more than one job title may be intentionally listed here more than once.*

Jonathan I. Schwartz, CEO
Jonathan I. Schwartz, Pres.
Michael E. Lehman, CFO/Exec. VP-Corp. Resources
Anil Gadre, Chief Mktg. Officer/Exec. VP
William N. MacGowan, Chief Human Resources Officer/Exec. VP
Greg Papadopoulos, Exec. VP-R&D
Robert Worrall, CIO
Greg Papadopoulos, CTO
Michael A. Dillon, General Counsel/Exec. VP
Brian Sutphin, Exec. VP-Corp. Dev. & Alliances
Ingrid Van Den Hoogen, Sr. VP-Brand, Global Comm. & Integrated Mktg.
David W. Yen, Ph.D., Exec. VP-Microelectronics
Bill Vass, COO/Pres., Sun Microsystems Federal
Rich Green, Exec. VP-Software
Scott G. McNealy, Chmn.
Eugene McCabe, Exec. VP-Worldwide Oper.

Phone: 650-960-1300	**Fax:** 408-276-3804
Toll-Free: 800-786-0404	
Address: 4150 Network Cir., Santa Clara, CA 95054 US	

GROWTH PLANS/SPECIAL FEATURES:

Sun Microsystems, Inc. (Sun) provides scalable computer systems, networks, storage systems, software, microprocessors and support services. The products segment encompasses computer systems and data management products. Sun's services segment consists maintenance contracts and client solutions; and educational services, which consist of technical consulting to help customers plan, implement, and manage distributed network computing environments and developing integrated learning solutions for enterprises, IT organizations and individual IT professionals. Sun's desktops and workstations, including the Sun Ultra series, facilitate a wide range of activities such as software development, mechanical design, financial analysis and education. Sun's proprietary microprocessor, the 64-bit UltraSPARC, powers most Sun platforms, including the Sun Fire series. The software segment of the computer systems group consists of Solaris OS and Java, Sun's universal software platform. Solaris OS is a secure operating system for Sun platforms. Sun's storage systems segment includes the StorEdge system and StorEdge software, offering multi-level storage solutions. SunSpectrum support service products allow customers to customize their services, choosing among four levels of support that range from mission-critical to self-support. The company employs independent distributors in over 100 countries; its channel partners account for 63% of revenues. Sun recently announced a broad strategic partnership with Intel Corporation based on Intel's endorsement of the Solaris Operating System and Sun's commitment to deliver a comprehensive family of enterprise and telecommunications servers and workstations based on Intel's Xeon processor. Late in 2007, Sun partnered with Dell in a multi-year original equipment manufacturer agreement to combine Sun's Solaris Operating System (OS) and support services with Dell's PowerEdge servers. In 2008, the company acquired Vaau, a provider of Enterprise Role Management (ERM) and identity compliance solutions; MySQL, which developed an open source database; and innotek, which provides open source virtualization software, VirtualBox. In April 2009, the firm agreed to be acquired by Oracle for $7.4 billion.

Sun offers employees fitness centers, adoption assistance and discounted computer equipment.

FINANCIALS: **Sales and profits are in thousands of dollars—add 000 to get the full amount. 2008 Note: Financial information for 2008 was not available for all companies at press time.**

2008 Sales: $13,880,000	2008 Profits: $403,000	**U.S. Stock Ticker: SUNW**
2007 Sales: $13,873,000	2007 Profits: $473,000	**Int'l Ticker:** Int'l Exchange:
2006 Sales: $13,068,000	2006 Profits: $-864,000	Employees: 34,900
2005 Sales: $11,070,000	2005 Profits: $-107,000	Fiscal Year Ends: 6/30
2004 Sales: $11,185,000	2004 Profits: $-388,000	Parent Company:

SALARIES/BENEFITS:

Pension Plan: Y	ESOP Stock Plan:	Profit Sharing:	Top Exec. Salary: $1,000,000	Bonus: $1,043,000
Savings Plan: Y	Stock Purch. Plan: Y		Second Exec. Salary: $995,040	Bonus: $389,185

OTHER THOUGHTS:

Apparent Women Officers or Directors: 1
Hot Spot for Advancement for Women/Minorities: Y

LOCATIONS: ("Y" = Yes)

West:	Southwest:	Midwest:	Southeast:	Northeast:	International:
Y	Y	Y	Y	Y	Y

Note: Financial information, benefits and other data can change quickly and may vary from those stated here.

SUZUKI MOTOR CORPORATION

www.globalsuzuki.com

Industry Group Code: 336111 **Ranks within this company's industry group:** Sales: Profits:

Techology:		Medical/Drugs:		Engineering:		Transportation:		Chemicals/Petrochemicals:		Specialty:	
Computers:		Manufacturer:		Design:		Aerospace:		Oil/Gas Products:		Special Services:	
Software:		Contract Research:		Construction:		Automotive:	Y	Chemicals:		Consulting:	
Communications:		Medical Services:		Eng. Services:		Shipping:		Oil/Chem. Svcs.:		Specialty Mgmt.:	
Electronics:		Labs:		Consulting:				Gases:		Products:	
Alternative Energy:		Bio. Services:						Other:		Other:	

TYPES OF BUSINESS:

Automobiles, Manufacturing
Motorcycles
ATVs
Marine Products
Generators
Engines
Wheelchairs
Ultrasonic Products

BRANDS/DIVISIONS/AFFILIATES:

SVB Automotores Do Brasil Ltda.
Suzuki Malaysia Automobile Sdn. Bhd.
Marauder
Suzuki International Europe GmbH
Suzuki Italia S.p.A.
Suzuki Motor Poland SP.Z.O.O.
American Suzuki Motor Corp.
Maruti Suzuki India, Ltd.

CONTACTS: *Note: Officers with more than one job title may be intentionally listed here more than once.*

Osamu Suzuki, CEO
Hiroshi Tsuda, COO
Hiroshi Tsuda, Pres.
Takashi Nakayama, Sr. Managing Exec. Officer
Shinzo Nakanishi, Sr. Managing Exec. Officer
Takao Hirosawa, Sr. Managing Exec. Officer
Minoru Tamura, Sr. Managing Exec. Officer
Osamu Suzuki, Chmn.

Phone: 81-53-440-2061 **Fax:** 81-53-440-2776
Toll-Free:
Address: 300 Takatsuka, Minami-ku, Shizuoka, 432-8611 Japan

GROWTH PLANS/SPECIAL FEATURES:

Suzuki Motor Corporation designs and manufactures all terrain vehicles (ATVs), commercial vehicles, motorcycles, outboard motors, passenger cars and other products. The firm also manufactures boats, generators, welders, general-purpose engines, electric scooters, motorized wheelchairs, ultrasonic products (such as cleaners and cutters) and prefabricated houses. The company is one of the largest manufacturer of minicars and motorcycles in Japan. Suzuki's main production facilities are spread throughout 23 countries. The company's network serves 192 countries and areas. The firm's U.S. products include the Vitara and Grand Vitara SUVs (sport utility vehicles); the XL-7; and the Aerio and Aerio SX sedans. Motorcycle models include the Bandit, Katana and Marauder. Suzuki has partnered with General Motors and Kawasaki to make automobiles, ATVs and motorcycles. Suzuki has developed an ultra-low-emission, direct-injection turbo engine for the minicar category in Japan, as well as a line of motorcycles incorporating an electronically controlled, continuously variable transmission. Major overseas subsidiaries include Suzuki International Europe GmbH in Germany; Suzuki Italia S.p.A. in Italy; Suzuki Motor Poland SP.Z.O.O. in Poland; American Suzuki Motor Corp. in California, U.S.; Maruti Suzuki India, Ltd. in India; and Suzuki New Zealand, Ltd. in New Zealand. General Motors owns a minority interest in Suzuki. One of Suzuki's most recent products is the Palette, a new wagon-type minicar available in Japan. In June 2007, the firm announced plans to build an industrial assembly production plant in Russia. In 2008, the company established SVB Automotores Do Brasil Ltda. to import and distribute cars in Brazil. The firm also acquired an additional interest in Suzuki Malaysia Automobile Sdn. Bhd., Suzuki's distribution partner in Malaysia.

FINANCIALS: **Sales and profits are in thousands of dollars—add 000 to get the full amount. 2008 Note: Financial information for 2008 was not available for all companies at press time.**

2008 Sales: $	2008 Profits: $	**U.S. Stock Ticker:**
2007 Sales: $26,799,405	2007 Profits: $635,394	**Int'l Ticker: 7269** Int'l Exchange: Tokyo-TSE
2006 Sales: $23,380,045	2006 Profits: $561,379	Employees: 45,510
2005 Sales: $20,806,000	2005 Profits: $415,000	Fiscal Year Ends:
2004 Sales: $20,815,600	2004 Profits: $414,900	Parent Company:

SALARIES/BENEFITS:

Pension Plan:	ESOP Stock Plan:	Profit Sharing:	Top Exec. Salary: $	Bonus: $
Savings Plan:	Stock Purch. Plan:		Second Exec. Salary: $	Bonus: $

OTHER THOUGHTS:

Apparent Women Officers or Directors:
Hot Spot for Advancement for Women/Minorities:

LOCATIONS: ("Y" = Yes)

West:	Southwest:	Midwest:	Southeast:	Northeast:	International:
Y			Y		Y

SYBASE INC

www.sybase.com

Industry Group Code: 511207 **Ranks within this company's industry group:** Sales: 8 Profits: 6

Techology:		Medical/Drugs:		Engineering:		Transportation:		Chemicals/Petrochemicals:		Specialty:	
Computers:		Manufacturer:		Design:		Aerospace:		Oil/Gas Products:		Special Services:	
Software:	Y	Contract Research:		Construction:		Automotive:		Chemicals:		Consulting:	Y
Communications:		Medical Services:		Eng. Services:		Shipping:		Oil/Chem. Svcs.:		Specialty Mgmt.:	
Electronics:		Labs:		Consulting:				Gases:		Products:	
Alternative Energy:		Bio. Services:						Other:		Other:	

TYPES OF BUSINESS:

Software-Database Management
Enterprise Portal Products
Consulting Services
Wireless Software Solutions

BRANDS/DIVISIONS/AFFILIATES:

Infrastructure Platform Group
iAnywhere Solutions
Sybase 365
Adaptive Server Enterprise
Sybase IQ
PowerDesigner
PowerBuilder
WorkSpace

CONTACTS: *Note: Officers with more than one job title may be intentionally listed here more than once.*

John S. Chen, CEO
John S. Chen, Pres.
Jeffrey G. (Jeff) Ross, CFO/Sr. VP
Raj Nathan, Chief Mktg. Officer-Worldwide Mktg. Oper.
Nita C. White-Ivy, VP-Human Resources
Billy Ho, Sr. VP-Tech. Oper.
Billy Ho, Sr. VP-Prod. Oper.
Daniel R. (Dan) Carl, General Counsel/Corp. Sec./VP
Steven M. Capelli, Pres., Worldwide Field Oper.
Keith F. Jensen, Corp. Controller/VP
Marty J. Beard, Pres., Sybase 365
Terry Stepien, Pres., Sybase iAnywhere
John S. Chen, Chmn.
Pieter A. Van der Vorst, Sr. VP/Gen. Mgr.-EMEA

Phone: 925-236-5000 **Fax:** 925-236-4468
Toll-Free: 800-879-2273
Address: 1 Sybase Dr., Dublin, CA 94568 US

GROWTH PLANS/SPECIAL FEATURES:

Sybase, Inc. is a global enterprise software and services company exclusively focused on managing and mobilizing information from the data-center to the point of action. The firm operates through three segments: Infrastructure Platform Group (IPG), iAnywhere Solutions (iAS) and Sybase 365. IPG focuses on information management, offering two lines of enterprise class data servers: Adaptive Server Enterprise (ASE), a relational database management system for mission-critical transactions, and Sybase IQ, a specialized column-based analytic server, for business intelligence applications such as accelerated reporting, advanced analytics and analytics services. IPG also produces solutions for business continuity, including the Sybase Replication Server and the Sybase Mirror Activator for very high availability data environments. Products include PowerDesigner, a modeling tool; PowerBuilder, a Rapid Application Development tool; and WorkSpace for integrated development environments. IPG generated approximately 69% of Sybase's revenue during 2007. iAS, which generated approximately 31% of the firm's 2007 revenue, provides mobile and embedded databases; mobile management and security; mobile middleware and synchronization; and Bluetooth and infrared protocol technologies. iAS's technologies include SQL Anywhere, Information Anywhere Suite, Afaria and OneBridge. Sybase 365 provides mobile messaging interoperability; the delivery and settlement of Short Message Service (SMS) and Multimedia Messaging Service (MMS) content; mobile commerce; and enterprise-class messaging services. Sybase 365 utilizes an operator-grade, secure messaging platform connected by a global private network of IP and SS7 connections to more than 700 mobile operators worldwide. In 2007, Sybase 365 processed over 89 billion messages. In May 2008, the Sybase IQ analytics server set a new Guinness World Record for the world's largest data warehouse.

Sybase offers its employees an education assistance program; credit union membership; commuter benefits; national child care discounts; onsite child care centers; onsite fitness centers; travel assistance; flexible spending accounts; and medical, dental, vision, life, AD&D and disability insurance.

FINANCIALS: **Sales and profits are in thousands of dollars—add 000 to get the full amount. 2008 Note: Financial information for 2008 was not available for all companies at press time.**

2008 Sales: $1,131,930	2008 Profits: $138,571	**U.S. Stock Ticker: SY**
2007 Sales: $1,025,530	2007 Profits: $148,850	**Int'l Ticker:** Int'l Exchange:
2006 Sales: $876,163	2006 Profits: $95,064	Employees: 3,995
2005 Sales: $818,695	2005 Profits: $85,583	Fiscal Year Ends: 12/31
2004 Sales: $788,536	2004 Profits: $67,950	Parent Company:

SALARIES/BENEFITS:

Pension Plan:	ESOP Stock Plan:	Profit Sharing:	Top Exec. Salary: $990,000	Bonus: $1,527,500
Savings Plan: Y	Stock Purch. Plan: Y		Second Exec. Salary: $415,800	Bonus: $281,563

OTHER THOUGHTS:

Apparent Women Officers or Directors: 3
Hot Spot for Advancement for Women/Minorities: Y

LOCATIONS: ("Y" = Yes)

West:	Southwest:	Midwest:	Southeast:	Northeast:	International:
Y	Y	Y	Y	Y	Y

Note: Financial information, benefits and other data can change quickly and may vary from those stated here.

SYMANTEC CORP

www.symantec.com

Industry Group Code: 511211 **Ranks within this company's industry group:** Sales: 1 Profits: 1

Techology:		Medical/Drugs:		Engineering:		Transportation:		Chemicals/Petrochemicals:		Specialty:	
Computers:		Manufacturer:		Design:		Aerospace:		Oil/Gas Products:		Special Services:	
Software:	Y	Contract Research:		Construction:		Automotive:		Chemicals:		Consulting:	
Communications:		Medical Services:		Eng. Services:		Shipping:		Oil/Chem. Svcs.:		Specialty Mgmt.:	
Electronics:		Labs:		Consulting:				Gases:		Products:	
Alternative Energy:		Bio. Services:						Other:		Other:	

TYPES OF BUSINESS:

Software-Security
Remote Management Products
IT Consulting Services

BRANDS/DIVISIONS/AFFILIATES:

nSuite Technologies, Inc.
LiveUpdate
Norton AntiVirus
Norton Internet Security
AppStream, Inc.
SwapDrive, Inc.
Transparent Logic Technologies
MessageLabs

CONTACTS: *Note: Officers with more than one job title may be intentionally listed here more than once.*

John W. Thompson, CEO
Enrique T. Salem, COO
James Beer, CFO/Exec. VP
Carine Clark, Sr. VP-Mktg.
Rebecca Ranninger, Chief Human Resources Officer/Exec. VP
David Thompson, CIO/Exec. VP
Mark Bregman, CTO/Exec. VP
Scott Taylor, General Counsel/Exec. VP/Sec.
Greg Hughes, Chief Strategy Officer
David Thompson, Pres., IT & Services Group
Janice Chaffin, Pres., Consumer Bus. Unit
Brad Kingsbury, Sr. VP-Endpoint Security & Mgmt.
Francis deSouza, Sr. VP-Info. Risk Mgmt. Group
John W. Thompson, Chmn.
John Brigden, Sr. VP-EMEA

Phone: 408-517-8000 **Fax:** 408-517-8186
Toll-Free:
Address: 20330 Stevens Creek Blvd., Cupertino, CA 95014 US

GROWTH PLANS/SPECIAL FEATURES:

Symantec Corp. provides a range of software, appliances and services designed to secure and manage information technology (IT) infrastructure. The company provides customers worldwide with software and services that protect, manage and control information risks related to security, data protection, storage, compliance, and systems management. The firm has five operating segments: consumer products; security and compliance; storage and server management; services; and other. The consumer products segment delivers Internet security, PC tuneup and backup products. The company's Norton brand provides protection for Windows and Macintosh platforms. Primary consumer products include Norton Antivirus and Norton Internet Security, which helps defend home and home office users by blocking online identity theft, detecting and eliminating spyware and protecting against hackers from entering a user's system. The security and compliance segment provides solutions for compliance and security management, endpoint security, messaging management and data protection management software solutions that allow customers to secure, provision, backup and remotely access laptops, PCs, mobile devices and servers. The storage and server management segment provides storage and server management, data protection, and application performance services that manage IT risk on an ongoing basis. The other segment includes sunset products and products nearing the end of their life cycle. During 2008, the firm acquired nSuite Technologies, Inc., a provider of connection broker technology; AppStream, Inc., a provider of endpoint virtualization software; SwapDrive, Inc., a provider of online storage products; MessageLabs, provider of online messaging, PC Tools, provider of security software; and Transparent Logic Technologies, provider of business automation products. In February 2008, Symantec formed the joint venture Huawei-Symantec, Inc. with a subsidiary of Huawei Technologies Co., Ltd. The joint venture operates in Chengdu, China.

The company offers employees medical, dental and vision insurance; a 401(k) plan; stock options; life and dismemberment insurance; tuition reimbursement; and an employee assistance program.

FINANCIALS: **Sales and profits are in thousands of dollars—add 000 to get the full amount. 2008 Note: Financial information for 2008 was not available for all companies at press time.**

2008 Sales: $5,874,419	2008 Profits: $463,850	**U.S. Stock Ticker: SYMC**
2007 Sales: $5,199,370	2007 Profits: $404,380	**Int'l Ticker:** Int'l Exchange:
2006 Sales: $4,143,392	2006 Profits: $156,852	Employees: 17,600
2005 Sales: $2,582,849	2005 Profits: $536,159	Fiscal Year Ends: 3/31
2004 Sales: $1,870,129	2004 Profits: $370,619	Parent Company:

SALARIES/BENEFITS:

Pension Plan:	ESOP Stock Plan:	Profit Sharing:	Top Exec. Salary: $800,000	Bonus: $1,150,000
Savings Plan: Y	Stock Purch. Plan: Y		Second Exec. Salary: $660,000	Bonus: $1,079,700

OTHER THOUGHTS:

Apparent Women Officers or Directors: 3
Hot Spot for Advancement for Women/Minorities: Y

LOCATIONS: ("Y" = Yes)

West:	Southwest:	Midwest:	Southeast:	Northeast:	International:
Y	Y	Y	Y	Y	Y

SYNGENTA AG

www.syngenta.com

Industry Group Code: 115112 **Ranks within this company's industry group:** Sales: 1 Profits: 2

Techology:		Medical/Drugs:		Engineering:		Transportation:		Chemicals/Petrochemicals:		Specialty:	
Computers:		Manufacturer:		Design:		Aerospace:		Oil/Gas Products:		Special Services:	
Software:		Contract Research:		Construction:		Automotive:		Chemicals:	Y	Consulting:	
Communications:		Medical Services:		Eng. Services:		Shipping:		Oil/Chem. Svcs.:		Specialty Mgmt.:	
Electronics:		Labs:		Consulting:				Gases:		Products:	Y
Alternative Energy:		Bio. Services:						Other:		Other:	

TYPES OF BUSINESS:

Agricultural Biotechnology Products & Chemicals Manufacturing
Crop Protection Products
Seeds

BRANDS/DIVISIONS/AFFILIATES:

Dual Gold
Bicept Magnum
Acanto
Score
Syngenta Biotechnology, Inc.
Wageningen Agricultural University
Fischer Group
Zeraim Gedera Ltd.

CONTACTS: *Note: Officers with more than one job title may be intentionally listed here more than once.*

Michael Mack, CEO
John Ramsay, CFO
David Lawrence, VP-R&D
Christoph Mader, Head-Legal & Taxes/Corp. Sec.
Mark Peacock, Head-Global Oper.
Robert Berendes, Head-Bus. Dev.
John Atkin, COO-Crop Protection
Davor Pisk, COO-Syngenta Seeds
Martin Taylor, Chmn.

Phone: 41-61-697-1111	**Fax:** 41-61-323-2324
Toll-Free:	
Address: Schwarzwaldallee 215, Basel, 4058 Switzerland	

GROWTH PLANS/SPECIAL FEATURES:

Syngenta AG is one of the world's largest agrochemical companies and a leading worldwide supplier of conventional and bioengineered crop protection and seeds. Products designed for crop protection include herbicides, fungicides and insecticides. Additionally, the firm produces seeds for field crops, vegetables and flowers. Its leading marketed products include the following: Dual Gold and Bicept Magnum herbicides; Acanto, Score and Amistar fungicides; and Proclaim, an insecticide. The seeds that Syngenta markets are for field crops, such as corn, soybeans, sugar beets, sunflowers and oilseed rape (canola); fruits and vegetables, including tomatoes, lettuce, melons, squash, cabbages, peppers, beans and radishes; and a wide variety of garden plants such as begonias, lavender, sage and many other seasonal flowers and herbs, some of which can also be purchased as plugs or full-grown plants. The company spends a significant amount of resources on research and development, with major laboratories located in Basel and Stein, Switzerland; Jealott's Hill, in the U.K.; and Syngenta Biotechnology, Inc., in North Carolina. Spending on research and development efforts regularly exceeds $800 million annually. Syngenta's plant science division is engaged in collaborations with several companies and universities, including Wageningen Agricultural University in the Netherlands. The research and development activities at Syngenta are currently devoted to advances in genomics, crop protection, health assessment, environmental issues, genetic mapping and traits development. The company's gene technology has become so refined that single genes can be isolated from a type of plant material and transferred to the DNA of another. This process allows manipulation of such traits as nutrient composition, appearance, and even the specifics of the taste of a certain crop. In March 2007, the firm acquired the Fischer Group, a vegetative flower company, for roughly $67 million. In July 2007, Syngenta acquired Zeraim Gedera Ltd., an Israeli seeds company, for $95 million.

FINANCIALS: **Sales and profits are in thousands of dollars—add 000 to get the full amount. 2008 Note: Financial information for 2008 was not available for all companies at press time.**

2008 Sales: $11,624,000	2008 Profits: $1,385,000	**U.S. Stock Ticker: SYT**
2007 Sales: $9,240,000	2007 Profits: $1,109,000	**Int'l Ticker: SYNN** Int'l Exchange: Zurich-SWX
2006 Sales: $8,046,000	2006 Profits: $634,000	Employees: 24,000
2005 Sales: $8,104,000	2005 Profits: $622,000	Fiscal Year Ends: 12/31
2004 Sales: $7,269,000	2004 Profits: $428,000	Parent Company:

SALARIES/BENEFITS:

Pension Plan: Y	ESOP Stock Plan:	Profit Sharing:	Top Exec. Salary: $	Bonus: $
Savings Plan: Y	Stock Purch. Plan: Y		Second Exec. Salary: $	Bonus: $

OTHER THOUGHTS:

Apparent Women Officers or Directors: 1
Hot Spot for Advancement for Women/Minorities:

LOCATIONS: ("Y" = Yes)

West:	Southwest:	Midwest:	Southeast:	Northeast:	International:
Y	Y	Y	Y	Y	Y

Note: Financial information, benefits and other data can change quickly and may vary from those stated here.

SYNOPSYS INC

www.synopsys.com

Industry Group Code: 511215 **Ranks within this company's industry group:** Sales: 3 Profits: 3

Techology:		Medical/Drugs:		Engineering:		Transportation:		Chemicals/Petrochemicals:		Specialty:	
Computers:		Manufacturer:		Design:		Aerospace:		Oil/Gas Products:		Special Services:	
Software:	Y	Contract Research:		Construction:		Automotive:		Chemicals:		Consulting:	Y
Communications:		Medical Services:		Eng. Services:		Shipping:		Oil/Chem. Svcs.:		Specialty Mgmt.:	
Electronics:		Labs:		Consulting:				Gases:		Products:	
Alternative Energy:		Bio. Services:						Other:		Other:	

TYPES OF BUSINESS:

Computer Software-Electronic Design Automation
Consulting & Support Services

BRANDS/DIVISIONS/AFFILIATES:

Galaxy Design Platform
Discovery Verification Platform
ArchPro Design Automation, Inc.
Sandwork Design
MOSAID Technologies Incorporated
Synplicity Inc
CHIPit

CONTACTS: *Note: Officers with more than one job title may be intentionally listed here more than once.*

Aart de Geus, CEO
Chi-Foon Chan, COO
Chi-Foon Chan, Pres.
Brian Beattie, CFO
John Chilton, Sr. VP-Mktg.
Jan Collinson, Sr. VP-Human Resources & Facilities
Brian Cabrera, General Counsel/VP/Corp. Sec.
John Chilton, Sr. VP-Strategic Dev.
Deirdre Hanford, Sr. VP-Global Tech. Svcs.
Antun Domic, Sr. VP/Gen. Mgr.-Implementation Group
Manoj Gandhi, Sr. VP/Gen. Mgr.-Verification Group
Howard Ko, Sr. VP/Gen. Mgr.-Silicon Engineering Group
Aart de Geus, Chmn.
Joe Logan, Sr. VP-Worldwide Sales

Phone: 650-584-5000 **Fax:**
Toll-Free: 800-541-7737
Address: 700 E. Middlefield Rd., Mountain View, CA 94043 US

GROWTH PLANS/SPECIAL FEATURES:

Synopsys, Inc. is a supplier of electronic design automation (EDA) software and related services for semiconductor design companies. The firm offers semiconductor design and verification software platforms and integrated circuit (IC) manufacturing software products to the global electronics market, enabling the development and production of complex systems-on-chips (SoCs). Additionally, Synopsys provides intellectual property (IP), system-level design hardware and software products and design. Finally, the company provides software and services that help customers prepare and optimize their designs for manufacturing. The firm's products offer customers the opportunity to design ICs that are optimized for speed, area, power consumption and production cost, while reducing overall design time. Products offered are categorized into five groupings. The Galaxy Design Platform, which provides customers with many diverse common design requirements in a single application; the Discovery Verification Platform, which combines simulation and verification products and design-for-verification methodologies to provide a consistent control environment; IP and Systems-Level Solutions group, which responds to the portfolio demands of designers seeking solutions to reduce their risk and time-to-market; the Manufacturing Solutions group, which addresses the mask-making and yield enhancement of very small geometry IC, as well as very high-level modeling of physical effects within the ICs; and lastly, the Professional Services group, which provides consulting and design services covering all critical phases of the SoC development process. In addition, Synopsys provides consulting services to assist customers with their IC designs, as well as training and support services. The firm has licensed products to most of the world's leading semiconductor, computer, communications and electronics companies. In 2008, the firm acquired Synplicity, Inc. as well as the CHIPit business of ProDesigns.

Employees are offered medical, dental and vision coverage; an employee assistance program; educational assistance; adoption benefits; shopping discounts; flexible spending accounts; a wellness program; and telecommuting options.

FINANCIALS: **Sales and profits are in thousands of dollars—add 000 to get the full amount. 2008 Note: Financial information for 2008 was not available for all companies at press time.**

2008 Sales: $1,336,951	2008 Profits: $189,978	**U.S. Stock Ticker: SNPS**
2007 Sales: $1,212,469	2007 Profits: $130,491	**Int'l Ticker:** Int'l Exchange:
2006 Sales: $1,095,560	2006 Profits: $24,742	Employees: 5,691
2005 Sales: $991,931	2005 Profits: $-17,114	Fiscal Year Ends: 10/31
2004 Sales: $1,092,104	2004 Profits: $74,337	Parent Company:

SALARIES/BENEFITS:

Pension Plan:	ESOP Stock Plan:	Profit Sharing:	Top Exec. Salary: $458,654	Bonus: $1,610,000
Savings Plan: Y	Stock Purch. Plan: Y		Second Exec. Salary: $428,077	Bonus: $1,080,000

OTHER THOUGHTS:

Apparent Women Officers or Directors: 2
Hot Spot for Advancement for Women/Minorities: Y

LOCATIONS: ("Y" = Yes)

West:	Southwest:	Midwest:	Southeast:	Northeast:	International:
Y	Y	Y	Y	Y	Y

Note: Financial information, benefits and other data can change quickly and may vary from those stated here.

TAIWAN SEMICONDUCTOR MANUFACTURING CO LTD (TSMC)

www.tsmc.com.tw

Industry Group Code: 334413 **Ranks within this company's industry group:** Sales: 4 Profits: 2

Techology:		Medical/Drugs:		Engineering:		Transportation:		Chemicals/Petrochemicals:		Specialty:	
Computers:	Y	Manufacturer:		Design:	Y	Aerospace:		Oil/Gas Products:		Special Services:	
Software:	Y	Contract Research:		Construction:		Automotive:		Chemicals:		Consulting:	
Communications:		Medical Services:		Eng. Services:		Shipping:		Oil/Chem. Svcs.:		Specialty Mgmt.:	
Electronics:	Y	Labs:		Consulting:				Gases:		Products:	Y
Alternative Energy:		Bio. Services:						Other:		Other:	

TYPES OF BUSINESS:

Contract Manufacturing-Semiconductors
Assembly & Testing Services
Software Products

BRANDS/DIVISIONS/AFFILIATES:

WaferTech LLC
Systems on Silicon Manufacturing Company Pte Ltd
Nexsys
eFoundry
CyberShuttle

CONTACTS: *Note: Officers with more than one job title may be intentionally listed here more than once.*

Rick Tsai, CEO
Rick Tsai, Pres.
Lora Ho, CFO/VP
Jason C.S. Chen, VP-Worldwide Sales & Mktg.
P. H. Chang, VP-Human Resources
Wei-Jen Lo, VP-R&D
Stephen T. Tso, CIO/Sr. VP
Fu-Chieh Hsu, VP-Design & Tech. Platform
Richard Thurston, General Counsel/VP
M.C. Tzeng, VP-Oper.
Kenneth Kin, Sr. VP-Special Project
C.C. Wei, Sr. VP-Mainstream Tech. Bus.
Mark Liu, Sr. VP-Advanced Tech. Bus.
N.S.Tsai, VP-Quality & Reliability
Morris Chang, Chmn.
Rick Cassidy, Pres., TSMC North America

Phone: 886-3-563-6688	**Fax:** 886-3-563-7000
Toll-Free:	
Address: No. 8, Li-Hsin Rd. VI, Hsinchu Science Park, Hsinchu, 300 Taiwan	

GROWTH PLANS/SPECIAL FEATURES:

Taiwan Semiconductor Manufacturing Co., Ltd. (TSMC) is one of the world's largest dedicated foundries in the semiconductor industry. The company manufactures semiconductors, using either its advanced or mainstream manufacturing processes, for its customers and based on their own or third parties' proprietary integrated circuit designs. TSMC offers a comprehensive range of wafer fabrication processes, including processes to manufacture CMOS logic, mixed-signal, radio frequency, embedded memory, BiCMOS mixed-signal and other semiconductors. The company operates two 300 mm wafer facilities, four 8-inch wafer facilities and one 6-inch wafer facility. Operations are centralized in Taiwan near the firm's headquarters, with additional production facilities located in China, Singapore (Systems on Silicon Manufacturing Company Pte. Ltd), and the U.S. (WaferTech LLC). The company also operates account management and engineering service offices in Taiwan, Japan, China, India, Korea, the Netherlands and the U.S. Besides semiconductors, the company provides mask making, probing, testing and assembly services. It also offers a suite of software programs called eFoundry, which aids the semiconductor manufacturing process from design to completion, and offers CyberShuttle, a prototyping service. The firm serves a number of leading semiconductor companies, ranging from fabless semiconductor and systems companies such as Altera Corporation, Broadcom Corporation, Marvell Semiconductor Inc., Microsoft Corporation and nVidia Corporation, to integrated device manufacturers such as Advanced Micro Devices Inc., Analog Devices, Inc., Freescale Semiconductor Inc. and NXP Semiconductors. Sales to fabless semiconductor and system companies account for approximately two-thirds of company revenues, while sales to integrated device manufacturers account for approximately one-third. In recent years the firm has launched its 0.13 micron process technology, as well as its 65-nanometer and 55-nanometer Nexsys brand process technology. In 2008 TSMC began commercial production of its 45-nanometer process technology circuits.

TSMC offers its employees health and fitness programs; incentive plans; tuition assistance; and an employee assistance program.

FINANCIALS: **Sales and profits are in thousands of dollars—add 000 to get the full amount. 2008 Note: Financial information for 2008 was not available for all companies at press time.**

2008 Sales: $10,608,000	2008 Profits: $3,201,000	**U.S. Stock Ticker: TSM**
2007 Sales: $9,967,000	2007 Profits: $2,210,000	**Int'l Ticker: 2330** Int'l Exchange: Taipei-TPE
2006 Sales: $9,739,400	2006 Profits: $3,902,900	Employees: 23,020
2005 Sales: $8,141,100	2005 Profits: $2,852,900	Fiscal Year Ends: 12/31
2004 Sales: $8,103,700	2004 Profits: $2,908,500	Parent Company:

SALARIES/BENEFITS:

Pension Plan:	ESOP Stock Plan:	Profit Sharing: Y	Top Exec. Salary: $	Bonus: $
Savings Plan:	Stock Purch. Plan:		Second Exec. Salary: $	Bonus: $

OTHER THOUGHTS:

Apparent Women Officers or Directors: 2
Hot Spot for Advancement for Women/Minorities: Y

LOCATIONS: ("Y" = Yes)

West:	Southwest:	Midwest:	Southeast:	Northeast:	International:
Y					Y

Note: Financial information, benefits and other data can change quickly and may vary from those stated here.

TAKEDA PHARMACEUTICAL COMPANY LTD

www.takeda.com

Industry Group Code: 325412 **Ranks within this company's industry group:** Sales: 16 Profits: 13

Techology:		Medical/Drugs:		Engineering:		Transportation:		Chemicals/Petrochemicals:		Specialty:	
Computers:		Manufacturer:	Y	Design:		Aerospace:		Oil/Gas Products:		Special Services:	Y
Software:		Contract Research:		Construction:		Automotive:		Chemicals:		Consulting:	
Communications:		Medical Services:	Y	Eng. Services:		Shipping:		Oil/Chem. Svcs.:		Specialty Mgmt.:	
Electronics:		Labs:	Y	Consulting:				Gases:		Products:	Y
Alternative Energy:		Bio. Services:						Other:		Other:	

TYPES OF BUSINESS:

Pharmaceuticals Discovery & Development
Over-the-Counter Drugs
Vitamins
Chemicals
Agricultural & Food Products

BRANDS/DIVISIONS/AFFILIATES:

Takeda America Holdings, Inc.
Takeda Research Investment, Inc.
TAP Pharmaceutical Products Inc.
Takeda Europe Research and Development Center Ltd.
Takeda Ireland Limited
Boie-Takeda Chemicals, Inc.
Paradigm Therapeutics Ltd.
Millennium Pharmaceuticals, Inc.

CONTACTS: *Note: Officers with more than one job title may be intentionally listed here more than once.*

Yasuchika Hasegawa, Pres.
Tsudoi Miyoshi, Gen. Mgr.-Human Resources Dept.
Shigenori Ohkawa, Gen. Mgr.-Pharmaceutical Research Div.
Hiroshi Takahara, Gen. Mgr.-Finance & Acct.
Kanji Negi, Gen. Mgr.-Admin. Mgmt., Pharmaceutical
Hiroshi Sakiyama, Gen. Mgr.-Tokyo Branch
Teruo Sakurada, Gen. Mgr.-Osaka Branch
Hiroshi Ohtsuki, Pres., Consumer Healthcare Company
Kunio Takeda, Chmn.
Naohisa Takeda, Gen. Mgr.-Overseas Bus. Planning Dept.

Phone: 81-6-6204-2111 **Fax:** 81-6-6204-2880
Toll-Free:
Address: 1-1, Doshomachi 4-chome, Chuo-ku,, Osaka, 540-8645 Japan

GROWTH PLANS/SPECIAL FEATURES:

Takeda Pharmaceutical Company Ltd., based in Japan, is an international research-based company focused on pharmaceuticals. One of the largest pharmaceutical companies in Japan, it operates research and development facilities in four countries and production facilities in five countries. Takeda discovers, develops, manufactures and markets pharmaceutical products in two categories: ethical and consumer health care drugs. Ethical drugs, as the firm denominates them, are marketed in about 90 countries worldwide. This segment includes the anti-prostatic cancer agent leuprolide acetate, marketed as Lupron Depot, Enantone, Prostap and Leuplin; the anti-peptic ulcer agent lansoprazole, marketed as Prevacid, Ogast, Takepron and other names; the anti-hypertensive agent candesartan cilexetil, marketed as Blopress, Kenzen and Amias; and the anti-diabetic agent pioglitazone hydrochloride, marketed as Actos. The company's consumer health care division focuses on the over-the-counter drug market. Takeda's main consumer brands include Alinamin, a vitamin B1 derivative; Benza, a cold remedy; and Hicee, a vitamin C preparation. Outside Japan, Takeda's subsidiaries include development, production, and sales and marketing companies, as well as holding companies in the U.S. and Europe. The company also operates subsidiaries with the agro, food, urethane chemicals and bulk vitamin businesses. Within research and development, Takeda focuses on the life-style related diseases, oncology, urologic diseases, central nervous system diseases and gastroenterology life cycle management. The company pursues alliances with other pharmaceutical manufacturers, biotechnology companies, universities and other research institutions to efficiently introduce key technologies. In May 2008, the company acquired Millennium Pharmaceuticals, Inc.

FINANCIALS: **Sales and profits are in thousands of dollars—add 000 to get the full amount. 2008 Note: Financial information for 2008 was not available for all companies at press time.**

2008 Sales: $13,748,020 | 2008 Profits: $3,554,540
2007 Sales: $11,060,737 | 2007 Profits: $2,845,805
2006 Sales: $10,360,744 | 2006 Profits: $2,677,342
2005 Sales: $10,441,300 | 2005 Profits: $2,579,600
2004 Sales: $10,284,200 | 2004 Profits: $2,700,300

U.S. Stock Ticker: TKPHF
Int'l Ticker: 4502 Int'l Exchange: Tokyo-TSE
Employees: 15,717
Fiscal Year Ends: 3/31
Parent Company:

SALARIES/BENEFITS:

Pension Plan: ESOP Stock Plan: Profit Sharing: Top Exec. Salary: $ Bonus: $
Savings Plan: Stock Purch. Plan: Second Exec. Salary: $ Bonus: $

OTHER THOUGHTS:

Apparent Women Officers or Directors:
Hot Spot for Advancement for Women/Minorities:

LOCATIONS: ("Y" = Yes)

West:	Southwest:	Midwest:	Southeast:	Northeast:	International:
Y		Y		Y	Y

TAKE-TWO INTERACTIVE SOFTWARE INC

www.take2games.com

Industry Group Code: 511208 **Ranks within this company's industry group:** Sales: 5 Profits: 2

Techology:		Medical/Drugs:		Engineering:		Transportation:		Chemicals/Petrochemicals:		Specialty:	
Computers:		Manufacturer:		Design:		Aerospace:		Oil/Gas Products:		Special Services:	
Software:	Y	Contract Research:		Construction:		Automotive:		Chemicals:		Consulting:	
Communications:		Medical Services:		Eng. Services:		Shipping:		Oil/Chem. Svcs.:		Specialty Mgmt.:	
Electronics:		Labs:		Consulting:				Gases:		Products:	
Alternative Energy:		Bio. Services:						Other:		Other:	

TYPES OF BUSINESS:

Computer Software-Video Games
Software Distribution

BRANDS/DIVISIONS/AFFILIATES:

Rockstar Games
Bioshock
2K Games
2K Sports
2K Play
Rock Banc
Civilization
Grand Theft Auto

CONTACTS: *Note: Officers with more than one job title may be intentionally listed here more than once.*

Benjamin Feder, CEO
Gary Dale, COO
Lainie Goldstein, CFO
Seth Krauss, General Counsel/Exec. VP
Strauss Zelnick, Chmn.

Phone: 646-536-2842	**Fax:** 646-536-2926
Toll-Free:	
Address: 622 Broadway, New York, NY 10012 US	

GROWTH PLANS/SPECIAL FEATURES:

Take-Two Interactive Software, Inc. is a global publisher, developer and distributor of interactive entertainment software, hardware and accessories. Its publishing segment consists of Rockstar Games, 2K Games, 2K Sports and 2K Play publishing labels. The firm develops, markets and publishes software titles for the leading gaming and entertainment hardware platforms, including Sony's PlayStation 2 & 3; Sony's PSP system; Microsoft's Xbox 360; Nintendo's Wii and GameCube; DS and Game Boy Advance handheld systems; and personal computer (PC) games using Windows. The interactive software that it develops and publishes is broken down into two major categories: games developed by internal development studios, and games that it publishes with, or markets and distributes on behalf of, third party developers. The firm has internal development studios located in the U.S., Canada, the U.K., France, Australia and China. In 2007, it had a research and development staff of roughly 1,178 employees with the technical capabilities to develop software titles for all major prior and next-generation consoles, handheld hardware platforms and PCs in several languages. The Rockstar Games titles are primarily internally developed and include the Grand Theft Auto series. Most of the firms third party developed titles are published by its 2K Games label. 2K Games has actively secured rights to publish popular entertainment properties including The Elder Scrolls IV: Oblivion, and its internally developed BioShock and Civilization franchises. Its 2K Sports titles include Major League Baseball 2K and NBA 2K. Its 2K Play titles include Deal or No Deal and Dora the Explorer. The firm's distribution segment, which includes its Jack of All Games subsidiary, distributes products as well as software, hardware and accessories produced by others to retail outlets in North America. In November 2008, Kalypso Media acquired the worldwide rights to the firm's Tropico 3 PC game series.

FINANCIALS: **Sales and profits are in thousands of dollars—add 000 to get the full amount. 2008 Note: Financial information for 2008 was not available for all companies at press time.**

2008 Sales: $1,537,530	2008 Profits: $97,097	**U.S. Stock Ticker: TTWO**
2007 Sales: $981,791	2007 Profits: $-138,406	**Int'l Ticker:** Int'l Exchange:
2006 Sales: $1,037,840	2006 Profits: $-184,889	Employees: 2,100
2005 Sales: $1,201,220	2005 Profits: $35,314	Fiscal Year Ends: 10/31
2004 Sales: $1,127,751	2004 Profits: $62,119	Parent Company:

SALARIES/BENEFITS:

Pension Plan:	ESOP Stock Plan:	Profit Sharing:	Top Exec. Salary: $347,019	Bonus: $
Savings Plan: Y	Stock Purch. Plan:		Second Exec. Salary: $326,967	Bonus: $

OTHER THOUGHTS:

Apparent Women Officers or Directors: 1
Hot Spot for Advancement for Women/Minorities:

LOCATIONS: ("Y" = Yes)

West:	Southwest:	Midwest:	Southeast:	Northeast:	International:
				Y	Y

Note: Financial information, benefits and other data can change quickly and may vary from those stated here.

TATA CONSULTANCY SERVICES (TCS)

www.tcs.com

Industry Group Code: 541512 **Ranks within this company's industry group:** Sales: 13 Profits:

Techology:		Medical/Drugs:		Engineering:		Transportation:		Chemicals/Petrochemicals:		Specialty:	
Computers:		Manufacturer:		Design:		Aerospace:		Oil/Gas Products:		Special Services:	
Software:	Y	Contract Research:		Construction:		Automotive:		Chemicals:		Consulting:	Y
Communications:		Medical Services:		Eng. Services:	Y	Shipping:		Oil/Chem. Svcs.:		Specialty Mgmt.:	
Electronics:	Y	Labs:		Consulting:				Gases:		Products:	
Alternative Energy:		Bio. Services:						Other:		Other:	

TYPES OF BUSINESS:

IT Consulting
Software Engineering
Business Process Outsourcing
Research

BRANDS/DIVISIONS/AFFILIATES:

TATA Group
Tata Research, Design and Development Centre
Tata Consultancy Services (China) Co.
Tata Infotech
Comicrom
Tata Sons, Ltd.
Tata Infotech, Ltd.
Tata Consultancy Services Asia Pacific Pte

CONTACTS:

Note: Officers with more than one job title may be intentionally listed here more than once.

S. Ramadorai, CEO/Managing Dir.
N. Chandrasekaran, COO/Exec. Dir.
S. Mahalingam, CFO/Exec. VP
N. Chandrasekaran, Exec. VP-Global Sales
Ajoy Mukherjee, Exec. VP-Global Human Resources
Mathai Joseph, Exec. VP-Global R&D
Kesav Nori, CIO
Satyanarayan S. Hegde, General Counsel/Sr. VP-Legal
N. Chandrasekaran, Exec. VP-Oper.
Phiroz Vandrevala, Exec. VP-Global Corp. Affairs
S. Mahalingam, Exec. VP-Global Finance
Surya Kant, Pres., TCS Americas
Gabriel Rozman, Pres., TCS Iberoamerica
Jayant V. Pendharkar, VP-Global Mktg.
J. R. Bhandari, VP-Financial Svcs.
Ratan N. Tata, Chmn.
Girija Pande, Exec. VP-Asia Pacific

Phone: 91-22-5668-9999 **Fax:** 91-22-5550-9333
Toll-Free:
Address: Air India Bldg., 11th Fl., Nariman Point, Mumbai, 400021 India

GROWTH PLANS/SPECIAL FEATURES:

Tata Consultancy Services (TCS) is India's largest consulting company and one of Asia's largest independent software and services organizations, with a presence in 42 countries. TCS primarily provides IT consulting, services and business process outsourcing (BPO) for international businesses. The firm is a subsidiary of the TATA Group, one of Asia's largest conglomerates with interests in energy, telecommunications, financial services, chemicals, engineering and materials. TCS' services are divided into several divisions: consulting, IT services, asset based solutions, IT infrastructure, engineering and industrial services and BPO (transaction based IT enabled services). The company focuses on software engineering practices and standards, software quality assurance, software project management, software processes, and research and development in software engineering and technology. TCS operates the Tata Research, Design and Development Centre and the Advanced Technology Centre, both located in India. Core research areas are systems and software engineering, process engineering, embedded systems, VLSI, bioinformatics and security. The firm has formed alliances with some of the world's leading technology companies, academic institutions and consulting firms to provide customers with expertise in technology fields in which it does not specialize. Development of new strategies and technologies occurs in the firm's global centers of excellence, located in several nations. The firm has 50 offices in North America, with a regional headquarters in New York City, a performance engineering center in Minneapolis, Minnesota and an RFID lab in Chicago, Illinois. In 2008, TCS began construction of its largest development center, TCS Sahyadri Park in Pune, India. In October 2008, the firm agreed to acquire Citigroup Global Services for $505 million.

The firm offers its employees holiday homes across India; on-site gym and recreation facilities; medical insurance for children and dependant parents; office banks; and personal loans for housing, computers and automobiles.

FINANCIALS:

Sales and profits are in thousands of dollars—add 000 to get the full amount. 2008 Note: Financial information for 2008 was not available for all companies at press time.

2008 Sales: $4,597,100	2008 Profits: $	**U.S. Stock Ticker: Subsidiary**
2007 Sales: $4,320,000	2007 Profits: $970,000	**Int'l Ticker:** Int'l Exchange:
2006 Sales: $4,300,000	2006 Profits: $950,000	Employees: 111,000
2005 Sales: $2,970,000	2005 Profits: $649,170	Fiscal Year Ends: 3/31
2004 Sales: $1,614,000	2004 Profits: $365,400	Parent Company: TATA GROUP

SALARIES/BENEFITS:

Pension Plan:	ESOP Stock Plan:	Profit Sharing:	Top Exec. Salary: $	Bonus: $
Savings Plan:	Stock Purch. Plan:		Second Exec. Salary: $	Bonus: $

OTHER THOUGHTS:

Apparent Women Officers or Directors: 1
Hot Spot for Advancement for Women/Minorities:

LOCATIONS: ("Y" = Yes)

West:	Southwest:	Midwest:	Southeast:	Northeast:	International:
Y	Y	Y	Y	Y	Y

TATA GROUP

www.tata.com

Industry Group Code: 551110 **Ranks within this company's industry group:** Sales: 1 Profits:

Techology:		Medical/Drugs:		Engineering:		Transportation:		Chemicals/Petrochemicals:		Specialty:	
Computers:	Y	Manufacturer:	Y	Design:	Y	Aerospace:		Oil/Gas Products:		Special Services:	Y
Software:	Y	Contract Research:		Construction:	Y	Automotive:	Y	Chemicals:	Y	Consulting:	Y
Communications:	Y	Medical Services:		Eng. Services:	Y	Shipping:		Oil/Chem. Svcs.:		Specialty Mgmt.:	
Electronics:	Y	Labs:		Consulting:	Y			Gases:		Products:	
Alternative Energy:	Y	Bio. Services:						Other:		Other:	

TYPES OF BUSINESS:

Engineering Products
Communication & Information Systems
Steel
Energy Utilities
Solar Power
Automobiles
Hotels & Resorts
Pharmaceuticals & Chemicals

BRANDS/DIVISIONS/AFFILIATES:

General Chemical Industrial Products Inc
Tata Tea
Tata Strategic Management Group
Taj Hotels, Resorts & Palaces
Tata Motors Limited
Tata Communications Lts
Tata Consultancy Services (TCS)
Tata Chemicals

CONTACTS: *Note: Officers with more than one job title may be intentionally listed here more than once.*

Ishaat Hussain, Dir.-Finance
R. Gopalakrishnan, Member-Group Exec. Office & Group Corp. Center
Srinath Narasimhan, CEO-Tata Communications
Kishor A. Chaukar, Managing Dir.-Tata Industries
Patrick McGoldrick, CEO-Tata Technologies
Ratan N. Tata, Chmn.

Phone: 91-22-6665-8282 **Fax:** 91-22-6665-8160
Toll-Free:
Address: Bombay House, 24, Homi Mody St., Mumbai, 400 001 India

GROWTH PLANS/SPECIAL FEATURES:

Tata Group comprises approximately 116 companies operating worldwide across seven business sectors: information technology and communications; engineering; materials; services; energy; consumer products; and chemicals. One of India's largest business conglomerates, Tata Group has operations in over 80 countries spanning six continents. The group's 27 publicly listed companies include Tata Steel, Tata Consultancy Services, Tata Motors and Tata Tea. Tata's engineering sector includes automotive company Tata AutoComp Systems and engineering products company TAL Manufacturing Solutions. The group's materials sector includes Tata Advanced Materials, a manufacturer of armor products, telecommunication products and composite panels for cargo containers. Tata's energy sector includes power companies Tata BP Solar and Tata Power. Tata's chemicals companies include Rallis India, Tata Chemicals, Tata Pigments and pharmaceutical company Advinus Therapeutics. The group's services sector includes Indian Hotels Company Limited (IHCL) and financial services companies such as Tata AIG General Insurance and Tata Financial Services. Tata consumer products companies include Infiniti Retail, Tata Ceramics and Alliance Coffee. Tata's information systems and communications sector includes information systems companies Nelito Systems and Tata Technologies; communications partnership company Virgin Mobile India; and Nelco, a manufacturer of consumer electronic products. Tata Sons promotes and holds majority shares in Tata Group's key companies. Tata Industries is a promoter company of Tata Group which focuses in particular on high-tech business areas. In 2008, Tata Communications International Pte Ltd, a wholly owned subsidiary of Tata Communications Limited, signed an equity joint venture agreement with China Enterprise Communications Limited (CEC) for the acquisition of 50% equity interest in CEC. The firm also recently partnered with Etisalat and HSBC India to launch a mobile phone-based money remittance service to its subscribers in India. In November 2008, the company announced a strategic partnership with Tokyo-based NTT Docomo focused on the growth of mobile communications in India.

FINANCIALS: **Sales and profits are in thousands of dollars—add 000 to get the full amount. 2008 Note: Financial information for 2008 was not available for all companies at press time.**

2008 Sales: $62,500,000	2008 Profits: $	**U.S. Stock Ticker: Private**
2007 Sales: $28,500,000	2007 Profits: $	**Int'l Ticker:** Int'l Exchange:
2006 Sales: $21,675,600	2006 Profits: $	Employees: 350,000
2005 Sales: $17,878,000	2005 Profits: $	Fiscal Year Ends: 3/31
2004 Sales: $13,920,900	2004 Profits: $	Parent Company:

SALARIES/BENEFITS:

Pension Plan:	ESOP Stock Plan:	Profit Sharing:	Top Exec. Salary: $	Bonus: $
Savings Plan:	Stock Purch. Plan:		Second Exec. Salary: $	Bonus: $

OTHER THOUGHTS:

Apparent Women Officers or Directors:
Hot Spot for Advancement for Women/Minorities:

LOCATIONS: ("Y" = Yes)

West:	Southwest:	Midwest:	Southeast:	Northeast:	International:
				Y	Y

TATA MOTORS LIMITED

www.tatamotors.com

Industry Group Code: 336111 **Ranks within this company's industry group:** Sales: 21 Profits: 15

Techology:		Medical/Drugs:		Engineering:		Transportation:		Chemicals/Petrochemicals:		Specialty:	
Computers:		Manufacturer:		Design:	Y	Aerospace:		Oil/Gas Products:		Special Services:	
Software:		Contract Research:		Construction:	Y	Automotive:	Y	Chemicals:		Consulting:	
Communications:		Medical Services:		Eng. Services:	Y	Shipping:	Y	Oil/Chem. Svcs.:		Specialty Mgmt.:	
Electronics:		Labs:		Consulting:				Gases:		Products:	
Alternative Energy:	Y	Bio. Services:						Other:		Other:	Y

TYPES OF BUSINESS:

Automobile Manufacturing
Light & Medium Commercial Vehicles Manufacturing
Heavy Commercial Vehicles Manufacturing
Passenger Vehicles Manufacturing

BRANDS/DIVISIONS/AFFILIATES:

Tata Daewoo Commercial Vehicles Company
Daewoo Novus Truck
Tata Ace
Jaguar Cars Ltd
Land Rover
Nano

CONTACTS: *Note: Officers with more than one job title may be intentionally listed here more than once.*

Ravi Kant, CEO/Managing Dir.
C. Ramakrishnan, CFO/Exec. Dir.
Ravi Pisharody, VP-Mktg. & Sales
S.J. Tambe, VP-Human Resources
H.K. Sethna, Corp. Sec.
Debasis Ray, Head-Corp. Comm.
H.K. Sethna, Investor Rel./Sec.
P.Y. Gurav, VP-Corp. Finance
P.M. Telang, Exec. Dir.-Commercial Vehicles
S.B. Borwankar, Head-Jamshedpur Plant
Akshaykumar Mankad, Head-Car Plant
Rajiv Dube, Pres., Passenger Cars
Ratan N. Tata, Chmn.

Phone: 91-22-6665-8282 **Fax:** 91-22-6665-7260
Toll-Free:
Address: Bombay House, 24, Homi Mody St., Mumbai, 400 001 India

GROWTH PLANS/SPECIAL FEATURES:

Tata Motors Limited is one of India's largest automobile manufacturers. The company manufactures commercial and passenger vehicles, and is a provider of automobile financing services. Tata's product portfolio encompasses passenger vehicles, including compact and midsize cars, in which the firm held a 14.1% Indian market share in 2008; utility vehicles, in which Tata held a 20% market share; light commercial vehicles, with a 64.3% market share; and medium and heavy commercial vehicles, with a market share of 61.3%. Through its subsidiaries, the firm is also engaged in areas such as engineering services; construction equipment manufacturing; vehicle components manufacturing; supply chain activities; machine tools and factory automation solutions; automotive services; and research and development (R&D) operations. The company boasts over 2,500 engineers and scientists and has R&D centers in the Indian cities of Pune, Jamshedpur and Lucknow, as well as in South Korea, Spain and the U.K. Tata is among the world's leading bus manufacturers, and the company has expanded these activities through strategic partnerships with Hispano Carrocera, a Spanish bus and coach manufacturer, as well as Marcopolo, a Brazil-based company engaged in the manufacture of bodies for buses and coaches. The firm has expanded its international presence by marketing Fiat-branded cars in Argentina and pick-up vehicles in Thailand, South America, Central America and select European markets. In January 2008, Tata Motors announced plans to unveil the most inexpensive automobile in the market, the Tata Nano, slated for release in July 2009. The Nano, a small four-seat vehicle, is slated to cost only 100,000 Rupees (approximately $2,000), a price that is expected to fundamentally affect the availability of passenger cars in India. Also in 2008, Tata Motors acquired the Jaguar and Land Rover brands from Ford Motor Co. for approximately $2 billion. In February 2009, Tata launched its Xenon XT, a 4-door, 5-seat pickup.

FINANCIALS: **Sales and profits are in thousands of dollars—add 000 to get the full amount. 2008 Note: Financial information for 2008 was not available for all companies at press time.**

2008 Sales: $9,998,600	2008 Profits: $355,100	**U.S. Stock Ticker: TTM**
2007 Sales: $7,270,000	2007 Profits: $500,000	**Int'l Ticker: 500570** Int'l Exchange: Bombay-BSE
2006 Sales: $5,409,500	2006 Profits: $337,400	Employees: 36,364
2005 Sales: $4,548,100	2005 Profits: $304,000	Fiscal Year Ends: 3/31
2004 Sales: $	2004 Profits: $	Parent Company: TATA GROUP

SALARIES/BENEFITS:

Pension Plan:	ESOP Stock Plan:	Profit Sharing:	Top Exec. Salary: $612,394	Bonus: $
Savings Plan:	Stock Purch. Plan:		Second Exec. Salary: $373,126	Bonus: $

OTHER THOUGHTS:

Apparent Women Officers or Directors:
Hot Spot for Advancement for Women/Minorities:

LOCATIONS: ("Y" = Yes)

West:	Southwest:	Midwest:	Southeast:	Northeast:	International:
					Y

TATE & LYLE PLC

www.tateandlyle.com

Industry Group Code: 325000 **Ranks within this company's industry group:** Sales: 24 Profits: 16

Techology:		Medical/Drugs:		Engineering:		Transportation:		Chemicals/Petrochemicals:		Specialty:	
Computers:		Manufacturer:		Design:		Aerospace:		Oil/Gas Products:		Special Services:	
Software:		Contract Research:		Construction:		Automotive:		Chemicals:	Y	Consulting:	
Communications:		Medical Services:		Eng. Services:		Shipping:		Oil/Chem. Svcs.:		Specialty Mgmt.:	
Electronics:		Labs:		Consulting:				Gases:		Products:	Y
Alternative Energy:		Bio. Services:						Other:		Other:	

TYPES OF BUSINESS:

Sugar & Confectionery Product Manufacturing
Animal Feed
Bulk Storage
Starches & Proteins
Sweeteners
Ethanol
Flavors & Ingredients
Cosmetic Ingredients

BRANDS/DIVISIONS/AFFILIATES:

McNeil Nutritionals, LLC
DuPont
Splenda
Orsan
PROMITOR
BioFilm, Ltd.
ENRICH
REBALANCE

CONTACTS:

Note: Officers with more than one job title may be intentionally listed here more than once.

Iain Ferguson, CEO
Timothy Lodge, Acting Group Dir.-Finance
Robert Fisher, Head-Global R&D
Robert Gibber, General Counsel/Company Sec.
Timothy Lodge, Dir.-Investor Rel.
Ian Bacon, CEO-Sugars
Olivier Rigaud, CEO-Food & Industrial Ingredients, Europe
Karl Kramer, Pres., Sucralose
Matthew Wineinger, Pres., Food & Industrial Ingredients, Americas
David Lees, Chmn.

Phone: 44-20-7626-6525	**Fax:** 44-20-7623-5213
Toll-Free:	
Address: Sugar Quay, Lower Thames St., London, EC3R 6DQ UK	

GROWTH PLANS/SPECIAL FEATURES:

Tate & Lyle plc is a global leader in the processing of renewable food and industrial ingredients. Its product portfolio includes sweeteners, molasses, starches, biogums, proteins and acidulants, as well as ethanol, animal feed and bulk liquid storage facilities. The company's ingredients can be found in sugars and syrups, ointments, creams, toothpaste, animal feeds, biofuels and pharmaceuticals. Tate & Lyle operates four main divisions: Food and Industrial Ingredients in the Americas and Europe; Sucralose; and Sugars. The firm has alliances with McNeil Nutritionals, LLC, a Johnson & Johnson company, and DuPont, to develop bio-based polymers. Through its alliance with McNeil, Tate & Lyle is the sole manufacturer of Splenda Sucralose sweetener. The company's principle subsidiaries include Orsan SA, Ltd.; United Molasses; Tate & Lyle Holdings, Ltd.; Tate & Lyle Investments, Ltd.; and Tate & Lyle International Finance plc. Tate & Lyle also operates more than 50 facilities throughout the Americas, Southeast Asia and Europe. In January 2007, the firm unveiled the ENRICH brand, a normal tasting, nutrient rich supplement. In May 2007, it expanded its REBALANCE brand, adding no-sugar or reduced sugar sauces and desserts to its product line. In April 2007, it agreed to acquire 80% of G.C. Hahn & Co., a German specialty food ingredients group. In June 2007, Tate & Lyle launched PROMITOR Resistant Starch, the first product in its PROMITOR line of dietary fibers. In October 2007, the company sold its starch facilities in Europe. Also in October, Tate & Lyle opened a research and development in Shanghai, China. In December 2007, Tate & Lyle sold its 49% shareholding in the Mexican sugar business Grupo Industrial Azucarero de Occidente, S.A. de C.V. In January 2008, Tate & Lyle Ventures, a venture capital fund, and Scottish Enterprise's Scottish Venture Fund acquired BioFilm, Ltd.

FINANCIALS:

Sales and profits are in thousands of dollars—add 000 to get the full amount. 2008 Note: Financial information for 2008 was not available for all companies at press time.

2008 Sales: $5,136,000	2008 Profits: $291,000	**U.S. Stock Ticker: TATYY**
2007 Sales: $4,837,500	2007 Profits: $321,000	**Int'l Ticker: TATE** Int'l Exchange: London-LSE
2006 Sales: $5,197,500	2006 Profits: $-45,000	Employees: 6,488
2005 Sales: $5,008,500	2005 Profits: $219,000	Fiscal Year Ends: 3/31
2004 Sales: $5,782,300	2004 Profits: $281,200	Parent Company:

SALARIES/BENEFITS:

Pension Plan:	ESOP Stock Plan:	Profit Sharing:	Top Exec. Salary: $1,236,600	Bonus: $1,026,000
Savings Plan:	Stock Purch. Plan:		Second Exec. Salary: $880,200	Bonus: $659,700

OTHER THOUGHTS:

Apparent Women Officers or Directors: 1
Hot Spot for Advancement for Women/Minorities:

LOCATIONS: ("Y" = Yes)

West:	Southwest:	Midwest:	Southeast:	Northeast:	International:
		Y			Y

Note: Financial information, benefits and other data can change quickly and may vary from those stated here.

TECHNIP

www.technip.com

Industry Group Code: 213111 **Ranks within this company's industry group:** Sales: 4 Profits: 4

Techology:		Medical/Drugs:		Engineering:		Transportation:		Chemicals/Petrochemicals:		Specialty:	
Computers:		Manufacturer:		Design:	Y	Aerospace:		Oil/Gas Products:		Special Services:	
Software:		Contract Research:		Construction:	Y	Automotive:		Chemicals:		Consulting:	
Communications:		Medical Services:		Eng. Services:	Y	Shipping:		Oil/Chem. Svcs.:	Y	Specialty Mgmt.:	
Electronics:		Labs:		Consulting:				Gases:		Products:	
Alternative Energy:		Bio. Services:						Other:		Other:	

TYPES OF BUSINESS:

Construction Services-Oil & Gas Wells
Marine & Subsea Construction
Refinery Construction
Pipeline Construction
Petrochemical Plant Construction
Maintenance Services
Metallurgical Facility Construction
Power Generation Systems

BRANDS/DIVISIONS/AFFILIATES:

Technip USA, Inc.

CONTACTS:

Note: Officers with more than one job title may be intentionally listed here more than once.

Thierry Pilenko, CEO
Bernard di Tullio, COO
Olivier Dubois, Pres.
Olivier Dubois, CFO
Anne Decressac, Pres., Human Resources
Anne Decressac, Pres., Comm.
Arnaud Real, Sr. VP-Finance
Guy Arlette, Pres., Global Processes & Dev.
Thierry Pilenko, Chmn.

Phone: 33-1-47-78-21-21 **Fax:** 33-1-47-78-33-40
Toll-Free:
Address: 6-8 Allee de l'Arche, Paris, 92973 France

GROWTH PLANS/SPECIAL FEATURES:

Technip is a Paris-based oil, gas and petrochemical engineering and construction services company with operations worldwide. The firm has operations in Europe, the U.S., Brazil, the Middle East and Asia. It is active in a wide variety of both offshore and onshore industry sectors. The firm is organized into four divisions: Offshore SURF, Offshore Facilities, Onshore Downstream and Industries. Offshore SURF activities include the design, engineering, manufacturing and installation of subsea umbilical, risers and flowlines (SURF) that connect underwater wells to surface platforms. Offshore Facilities activities include offshore oil field development, platform construction, maintenance and mooring services. Onshore and downstream activities include field development, gas treatment and liquefaction, oil refining, pipelines, petrochemicals and advanced systems engineering. The Onshore segment also develops onshore oil fields and constructs pipeline systems. The Industries division constructs systems and facilities for fertilizers, life sciences, agro-industries, metals, aeronautic and space, cement, chemicals and power generation businesses. In July 2008, the company acquired Eurodim, an engineering and consulting company specializing in offshore oil and fluid transfer industry. In July 2008, Technip acquired BV Ingenieursbureau EPG, an engineering firm based in the Netherlands.

The company offers its employees career training and opportunities to travel abroad.

FINANCIALS:

Sales and profits are in thousands of dollars—add 000 to get the full amount. 2008 Note: Financial information for 2008 was not available for all companies at press time.

2008 Sales: $9,898,940
2007 Sales: $10,434,940
2006 Sales: $11,082,400
2005 Sales: $8,601,800
2004 Sales: $6,964,000

2008 Profits: $592,770
2007 Profits: $167,110
2006 Profits: $320,200
2005 Profits: $149,300
2004 Profits: $6,400

U.S. Stock Ticker: TKP
Int'l Ticker: TECF Int'l Exchange: Paris-Euronext
Employees: 23,000
Fiscal Year Ends: 12/31
Parent Company:

SALARIES/BENEFITS:

Pension Plan: ESOP Stock Plan: Profit Sharing: Top Exec. Salary: $ Bonus: $
Savings Plan: Stock Purch. Plan: Second Exec. Salary: $ Bonus: $

OTHER THOUGHTS:

Apparent Women Officers or Directors: 1
Hot Spot for Advancement for Women/Minorities:

LOCATIONS: ("Y" = Yes)

West:	Southwest:	Midwest:	Southeast:	Northeast:	International:
Y	Y		Y		Y

TELCORDIA TECHNOLOGIES

www.telcordia.com

Industry Group Code: 511214 **Ranks within this company's industry group:** Sales: Profits:

Techology:		Medical/Drugs:		Engineering:		Transportation:		Chemicals/Petrochemicals:		Specialty:	
Computers:		Manufacturer:		Design:		Aerospace:		Oil/Gas Products:		Special Services:	
Software:	Y	Contract Research:		Construction:		Automotive:		Chemicals:		Consulting:	Y
Communications:	Y	Medical Services:		Eng. Services:		Shipping:		Oil/Chem. Svcs.:		Specialty Mgmt.:	
Electronics:		Labs:		Consulting:				Gases:		Products:	
Alternative Energy:		Bio. Services:						Other:		Other:	

TYPES OF BUSINESS:

Telecommunications Software Services
Consulting & Professional Services
Network Systems & Services
Engineering & Research Services
Systems Integration Services

BRANDS/DIVISIONS/AFFILIATES:

Network Engineer
Fulfillment Portfolio
Service Delivery
Telcordia Service Management
Providence Equity Partners
Warburg Pincus

CONTACTS: *Note: Officers with more than one job title may be intentionally listed here more than once.*

Mark Greenquist, CEO
Mark Greenquist, Pres.
Steve Noonan, CFO/Exec. VP
Linda DeLukey, Exec. VP-Human Resources
Adam Drobot, Pres./CTO-Advanced Tech. Solutions
Steve Noonan, Exec. VP-Admin.
Joseph Giordano, General Counsel/Corp. Sec.
Rich Marano, Exec. VP-Oper.
Rolando R. Ramirez, VP-Corp. & Mktg. Comm.
Steve Noonan, Exec. VP-Finance
Richard Jacowleff, Pres., Interconnect Solutions
William J. Wanke, Pres., Oper. Solutions
Mike Wojcik, Pres., Service Delivery Solutions

Phone: 732-699-2000 **Fax:** 732-336-2320
Toll-Free: 800-521-2673
Address: 1 Telcordia Dr., Piscataway, NJ 08854-4157 US

GROWTH PLANS/SPECIAL FEATURES:

Telcordia Technologies (Telcordia), a holding of private equity firms Providence Equity Partners and Warburg Pincus, is a global leader in network systems, operations support systems, business support systems and related services for communications carriers. It is one of the largest employee-owned research and engineering firms in the U.S. The company serves: Wireless and wireline service providers; cable operators; and large enterprises. Telcordia invents, develops, implements and maintains software that approximately 80% of the fixed access lines, 100% of the toll-free traffic, and 90% of the wireless number portability market require. The firm is dedicated to helping customers use technology to streamline operations, advance network flexibility, add new services, reduce operating and capital expenditures, and increase profits. Telcordia's products include: Network Engineer, which manages company information through spatial representation; Fulfillment Portfolio, which allows companies to direct a customer's experience interacting with those companies; Service Delivery, which allows companies to converge many aspect of customer relations in a single platform; Telcordia Service Management, which allows companies to refine new technology offerings to improve customer interaction; and various OSS software systems. In addition, the firm offers consulting and testing services for a variety of software applications and software training courses.

Telcordia offers its employees a benefits package that includes a 401(k) savings plan; a cash balance pension; an employee assistance program; work-life resources and referrals; adoption benefits; flexible spending accounts; educational assistance; and matching charity gifts.

FINANCIALS: Sales and profits are in thousands of dollars—add 000 to get the full amount. 2008 Note: Financial information for 2008 was not available for all companies at press time.

2008 Sales: $
2007 Sales: $
2006 Sales: $
2005 Sales: $1,000,000
2004 Sales: $892,000

2008 Profits: $
2007 Profits: $
2006 Profits: $
2005 Profits: $
2004 Profits: $

U.S. Stock Ticker: Private
Int'l Ticker: Int'l Exchange:
Employees: 3,245
Fiscal Year Ends: 1/31
Parent Company: PROVIDENCE EQUITY PARTNERS

SALARIES/BENEFITS:

Pension Plan: Y
Savings Plan: Y
ESOP Stock Plan:
Stock Purch. Plan:
Profit Sharing:
Top Exec. Salary: $
Second Exec. Salary: $
Bonus: $
Bonus: $

OTHER THOUGHTS:

Apparent Women Officers or Directors: 1
Hot Spot for Advancement for Women/Minorities: Y

LOCATIONS: ("Y" = Yes)

West:	Southwest:	Midwest:	Southeast:	Northeast:	International:
Y	Y		Y	Y	Y

TELEDYNE TECHNOLOGIES INCORPORATED www.teledyne.com

Industry Group Code: 336410 **Ranks within this company's industry group:** Sales: 23 Profits: 19

Techology:		Medical/Drugs:		Engineering:		Transportation:		Chemicals/Petrochemicals:		Specialty:	
Computers:		Manufacturer:		Design:		Aerospace:	Y	Oil/Gas Products:		Special Services:	
Software:		Contract Research:		Construction:		Automotive:		Chemicals:	Y	Consulting:	
Communications:		Medical Services:		Eng. Services:		Shipping:		Oil/Chem. Svcs.:		Specialty Mgmt.:	
Electronics:		Labs:		Consulting:				Gases:	Y	Products:	Y
Alternative Energy:		Bio. Services:						Other:		Other:	

TYPES OF BUSINESS:

Electronics & Communications Products
Systems Engineering Solutions
Aerospace Engines & Components
Energy Systems

BRANDS/DIVISIONS/AFFILIATES:

Teledyne Isco Inc
Teledyne Brown Engineering
Teledyne Tekmar Co
Teledyne Solutions Inc
Teledyne Energy Systems Inc
Teledyne Cougar Inc
Teledyne Titan
Tindall Technologies Inc

CONTACTS: *Note: Officers with more than one job title may be intentionally listed here more than once.*

Robert Mehrabian, CEO
Robert Mehrabian, Pres.
Dale A. Schnittjer, CFO/Sr. VP
Robyn E. McGowan, VP-Human Resources
Robert W. Steenberge, CTO/VP
Robyn E. McGowan, VP-Admin.
John T. Kuelbs, General Counsel/Exec. VP/Sec.
Jason VanWees, VP-Corp. Dev.
Jason VanWees, VP-Investor Rel.
Susan L. Main, Controller/VP
Ivars R. Blukis, Chief Bus. Risk Assurance Officer
Aldo Pichelli, COO/Sr. VP-Electronics & Comm. Segment
Bryan R. Lewis, Pres., Teledyne Continental Motors
Rex Geveden, Pres., Teledyne Brown Eng.
Robert Mehrabian, Chmn.

Phone: 805-373-4545 **Fax:** 805-373-4775
Toll-Free:
Address: 1049 Camino Dos Rios, Thousand Oaks, CA 91360 US

GROWTH PLANS/SPECIAL FEATURES:

Teledyne Technologies, Inc. provides electronic components, instruments and communications products including defense electronics, monitoring and control instrumentation for marine, environmental and industrial applications; data acquisition and communications equipment for airlines and business aircraft and components; and subsystems for wireless and satellite communications. The company also provides systems engineering and information technology services for defense, space and environmental applications, and manufactures general aviation engines and components, supply energy generation, energy storage and small propulsion products. The firm operates in four segments, electronics and communications, responsible for 66% of revenue in 2007; engineered systems, which accounted for 19% of revenue in 2007; aerospace engines and components, which generated 11% of revenue; and energy and power systems, 4%. Subsidiaries include Teledyne Isco, Inc., a producer of water quality monitoring products such as wastewater samplers and open channel flow meters; Teledyne Brown Engineering, a full-service missile defense contractor; Teledyne Solutions, Inc., a missile defense systems engineering contractor for the U.S. Army; Teledyne Energy Systems, Inc., a provider of Teledyne Titan hydrogen gas generators and thermoelectric and fuel cell-based power sources; and Teledyne Tekmar Co., a manufacturer of instruments that automate the preparation and concentrations of drinking water and wastewater. Teledyne Technologies operates the Rapid Response System, a mobile chemical waste treatment system used to process chemical agents. Customers include government agencies; aerospace prime contractors; major industrial, communications and aviation companies. In 2007, the firm acquired Storm Products Co and the assets of Impulse Enterprise. In February 2008, it acquired assets of Judson Technologies, LLC, which manufactures infrared detectors. In January 2008, the firm acquired S G Brown Limited and its wholly-owned subsidiary TSS (International) Limited, which is headquartered in Watford, U. K. In July 2008, it acquired assets of Webb Research Corp. In August 2008, it acquired Filtronic PLC in the U.K.

FINANCIALS: **Sales and profits are in thousands of dollars—add 000 to get the full amount. 2008 Note: Financial information for 2008 was not available for all companies at press time.**

2008 Sales: $1,893,000	2008 Profits: $111,300	**U.S. Stock Ticker: TDY**
2007 Sales: $1,622,300	2007 Profits: $98,500	**Int'l Ticker:** Int'l Exchange:
2006 Sales: $1,433,200	2006 Profits: $80,300	Employees: 8,800
2005 Sales: $1,206,500	2005 Profits: $64,200	Fiscal Year Ends: 12/31
2004 Sales: $1,016,600	2004 Profits: $41,700	Parent Company:

SALARIES/BENEFITS:

Pension Plan:	ESOP Stock Plan:	Profit Sharing:	Top Exec. Salary: $768,269	Bonus: $1,300,000
Savings Plan:	Stock Purch. Plan:		Second Exec. Salary: $403,677	Bonus: $426,031

OTHER THOUGHTS:

Apparent Women Officers or Directors: 3
Hot Spot for Advancement for Women/Minorities: Y

LOCATIONS: ("Y" = Yes)

West:	Southwest:	Midwest:	Southeast:	Northeast:	International:
Y	Y	Y	Y	Y	Y

TELEFON AB LM ERICSSON (ERICSSON)

www.ericsson.com

Industry Group Code: 334220 **Ranks within this company's industry group:** Sales: 4 Profits: 3

Techology:		Medical/Drugs:		Engineering:		Transportation:		Chemicals/Petrochemicals:		Specialty:	
Computers:		Manufacturer:		Design:		Aerospace:		Oil/Gas Products:		Special Services:	
Software:		Contract Research:		Construction:		Automotive:		Chemicals:		Consulting:	
Communications:	Y	Medical Services:		Eng. Services:		Shipping:		Oil/Chem. Svcs.:		Specialty Mgmt.:	
Electronics:		Labs:		Consulting:				Gases:		Products:	
Alternative Energy:		Bio. Services:						Other:		Other:	

TYPES OF BUSINESS:

Telecommunications Equipment
Mobile Phones
Pagers
Networking Equipment
Defense Electronics
Telecommunications Software
Professional Services
Research & Development

BRANDS/DIVISIONS/AFFILIATES:

Sony Ericsson Mobile Communications
Drutt Corporation
Redback Networks, Inc.
LHS
Tandberg Television
Entrisphere
HyC Group
Mobeon AB

CONTACTS: *Note: Officers with more than one job title may be intentionally listed here more than once.*

Carl-Henric Svanberg, CEO
Carl-Henric Svanberg, Pres.
Hans Vestberg, CFO/Exec. VP
Torbjorn Possne, Sr. VP-Sales & Mktg.
Marita Hellberg, Sr. VP-Human Resources & Organization
Hakan Eriksson, CTO/Sr. VP
Carl Olof Blomqvist, General Counsel/Sr. VP-Legal Affairs
Joakim Westh, Sr. VP-Oper. Excellence
Joakim Westh, Sr. VP-Strategy
Henry Stenson, Sr. VP-Comm.
Johan Wibergh, Sr. VP/Head-Networks
Jan Wareby, Sr. VP-Multimedia
Jan Frykhammar, Sr. VP-Global Svcs.
Michael Treschow, Chmn.

Phone: 46-8-719-00-00	**Fax:** 46-8-18-40-85
Toll-Free:	
Address: Torshamnsgatan 23, Kista, Stockholm, 164 83 Sweden	

GROWTH PLANS/SPECIAL FEATURES:

Telefon AB LM Ericsson (Ericsson) is a leading global supplier of mobile phone handsets and equipment for mobile and fixed-line telecommunications operators. The company is structured into three business units: networks, global services and multimedia. The networks unit is grouped into mobile and fixed access, core and transmission networks and next generation IP-networks. The mobile networks division provides radio base stations, base station controllers and radio network controllers, mobile switching centers, service application nodes and other nodes for billing and operations support for GSM, CDMA and EDGE networks. Fixed network operators are moving from single-service networks toward new multi-service networks that have the ability to simultaneously handle multiple services, such as voice, text and images. The global services unit consists of professional services as well as network rollout, and supports operators with technology evolution and efficient operations. The multimedia unit consists of the multimedia units of Ericsson's former Business Unit Systems, Business Units Enterprise and Ericsson Mobile Platforms, as well as Ericsson Consumer and Enterprise Lab. Other operations include research and development of mobile systems, licensing of brand names and intellectual property, military microwave communications systems and radar network technologies, enterprise systems and other miscellaneous units. Subsidiaries include HyC Group, a leading Spanish TV consultancy and systems integration company; Entrisphere, a company providing fiber access technology, Drutt Corporation, a Service Delivery Platform (SDP) solutions provider; Redback Networks, Inc., a U.S. supplier of multi-service routing platform for broadband services; LHS, a German provider of post-paid billing and customer care systems for wireless markets; Tandberg Television, a Norwegian global provider of digital TV products; and Mobeon AB, a supplier of IP-messaging components.

FINANCIALS: **Sales and profits are in thousands of dollars—add 000 to get the full amount. 2008 Note: Financial information for 2008 was not available for all companies at press time.**

2008 Sales: $26,120,660	2008 Profits: $1,412,940	**U.S. Stock Ticker: ERICY**
2007 Sales: $31,375,900	2007 Profits: $3,698,510	**Int'l Ticker: ERIC** Int'l Exchange: Stockholm-SSE
2006 Sales: $30,046,000	2006 Profits: $4,417,150	Employees: 74,011
2005 Sales: $21,732,200	2005 Profits: $3,501,290	Fiscal Year Ends: 12/31
2004 Sales: $19,954,000	2004 Profits: $2,876,000	Parent Company:

SALARIES/BENEFITS:

Pension Plan:	ESOP Stock Plan:	Profit Sharing:	Top Exec. Salary: $	Bonus: $
Savings Plan:	Stock Purch. Plan:		Second Exec. Salary: $	Bonus: $

OTHER THOUGHTS:

Apparent Women Officers or Directors: 7
Hot Spot for Advancement for Women/Minorities: Y

LOCATIONS: ("Y" = Yes)

West:	Southwest:	Midwest:	Southeast:	Northeast:	International:
Y	Y			Y	Y

TELLABS INC

www.tellabs.com

Industry Group Code: 334210 **Ranks within this company's industry group:** Sales: 5 Profits: 7

Techology:		Medical/Drugs:		Engineering:		Transportation:		Chemicals/Petrochemicals:		Specialty:	
Computers:		Manufacturer:		Design:		Aerospace:		Oil/Gas Products:		Special Services:	Y
Software:	Y	Contract Research:		Construction:		Automotive:		Chemicals:		Consulting:	Y
Communications:	Y	Medical Services:		Eng. Services:		Shipping:		Oil/Chem. Svcs.:		Specialty Mgmt.:	Y
Electronics:	Y	Labs:		Consulting:				Gases:		Products:	
Alternative Energy:		Bio. Services:						Other:		Other:	

TYPES OF BUSINESS:

Wireline & Wireless Products & Services
Consulting

BRANDS/DIVISIONS/AFFILIATES:

Tellabs DynamicHome
Tellabs MultiservicePLus
Tellabs IntegratedMobile
Tellabs Assured-Ethernet

CONTACTS: *Note: Officers with more than one job title may be intentionally listed here more than once.*

Robert W. Pullen, CEO
Robert W. Pullen, Pres.
Timothy J. Wiggins, CFO/Exec. VP
Rizwan Khan, Exec. VP-Global Mktg.
Jean K. Holley, CIO/Exec. VP
Vikram Saksena, CTO
Daniel P. Kelly, Exec. VP-Prod. Dev.
James M. Sheehan, Chief Admin. Officer
James M. Sheehan, General Counsel/Exec. VP/Sec.
John M. Brots, Exec. VP-Global Oper.
Carl A. DeWilde, Exec. VP-Strategy
Ariana Nikitas, Media Contact
Tom Scottino, Investor Contact
Thomas P. Minichiello, VP-Finance/Chief Acct. Officer
Roger J. Heinz, Exec. VP-Sales & Svcs.
Michael J. Birck, Chmn.

Phone: 630-798-8800 **Fax:** 630-798-2000
Toll-Free:
Address: 1415 W. Diehl Rd., Naperville, IL 60563 US

GROWTH PLANS/SPECIAL FEATURES:

Tellabs, Inc. provides products and services that enable customers to deliver wireline and wireless voice, data and video services to business and residential customers. It operates in three segments: broadband, transport and services. Within the broadband segment, the company markets its products in three areas: access, marketed as the Tellabs DynamicHome solution, which includes products that enable service providers to deliver bundled voice, video and high-speed Internet/data services over copper or fiber networks; managed access, marketed as the Tellabs IntegratedMobile solution, which includes aggregation and transport products that deliver wireless and business services outside of the U.S.; and data, marketed as the Tellabs Assured-Ethernet solution, the Tellabs MultiservicePLus solution and the Tellabs IntegratedMobile solution, which include packet-switched products that enable wireline and wireless carriers to deliver business services and wireless services to their customers. The transport segment, marketed as the Tellabs DynamicHome solution, the Tellabs Assured-Ethernet solution and the Tellabs Integrated Mobile solution, includes solutions that enable service providers to transport services and manage bandwidth by adding capacity when and where it is needed. Products include the Tellabs 3000 voice-quality enhancement products, the Tellabs 5000 series of digital cross-connect systems and the Tellabs 7100 optical transport system. The services segment delivers deployment, training, support services and professional consulting to Tellabs' customers. Through these offerings, the firm supports its customers through all phases of running a network: planning, building and operating. Tellabs' customers are primarily communication service providers, including local exchange carriers; national post, telephone and telegraph administrators; wireless service providers; multi system operators; and competitive service providers. The customer base also includes distributors, original equipment manufacturers, system integrators and government agencies.

In 2008, Tellabs was selected by Computerworld as one of the best places for IT professionals to work.

FINANCIALS: **Sales and profits are in thousands of dollars—add 000 to get the full amount. 2008 Note: Financial information for 2008 was not available for all companies at press time.**

2008 Sales: $1,729,000	2008 Profits: $-930,000	**U.S. Stock Ticker: TLAB**
2007 Sales: $1,913,400	2007 Profits: $65,000	**Int'l Ticker:** Int'l Exchange:
2006 Sales: $2,041,200	2006 Profits: $194,100	Employees: 3,228
2005 Sales: $1,883,000	2005 Profits: $176,000	Fiscal Year Ends: 12/31
2004 Sales: $1,231,800	2004 Profits: $-29,800	Parent Company:

SALARIES/BENEFITS:

Pension Plan:	ESOP Stock Plan:	Profit Sharing:	Top Exec. Salary: $900,000	Bonus: $
Savings Plan:	Stock Purch. Plan:		Second Exec. Salary: $365,200	Bonus: $

OTHER THOUGHTS:

Apparent Women Officers or Directors: 3
Hot Spot for Advancement for Women/Minorities: Y

LOCATIONS: ("Y" = Yes)

West:	Southwest:	Midwest:	Southeast:	Northeast:	International:
Y	Y	Y	Y	Y	Y

TENNECO INC

www.tenneco.com

Industry Group Code: 336300 **Ranks within this company's industry group:** Sales: 19 Profits: 16

Techology:		Medical/Drugs:		Engineering:		Transportation:		Chemicals/Petrochemicals:		Specialty:	
Computers:		Manufacturer:		Design:		Aerospace:		Oil/Gas Products:		Special Services:	
Software:		Contract Research:		Construction:		Automotive:	Y	Chemicals:		Consulting:	
Communications:		Medical Services:		Eng. Services:		Shipping:		Oil/Chem. Svcs.:		Specialty Mgmt.:	
Electronics:		Labs:		Consulting:				Gases:		Products:	
Alternative Energy:		Bio. Services:						Other:		Other:	

TYPES OF BUSINESS:

Automotive Parts Manufacturer
Advanced Suspension Technologies
Ride Control Products
Emissions Systems
Performance Mufflers
Noise Control Systems

BRANDS/DIVISIONS/AFFILIATES:

Tenneco Automotive, Inc.
Combustion Components Associates, Inc.
Walker
Gillet
DynoMax
Thrush
Kinetic
Gabilan Manufacturing, Inc.

CONTACTS: *Note: Officers with more than one job title may be intentionally listed here more than once.*

Gregg Sherrill, CEO
Kenneth R. Trammell, CFO/Exec. VP
H. William Haser, CIO/VP
Timothy E. Jackson, CTO/Sr. VP
Alain Michaelis, Sr. VP-Mfg.
Richard P. Schneider, Sr. VP-Global Admin.
David A. Wardell, General Counsel/Sr. VP/ Corp. Sec.
Maritza Gibbons, VP-Strategic Planning & Bus. Dev.
James K. Spangler, VP-Global Comm.
John Kunz, Treas./VP-Tax
Brent Bauer, Sr. VP/Gen. Mgr.-North American Original Equipment
Michael Charlton, Managing Dir.-India
Jeff Jarrell, VP-Japan & Korea Global OEM Bus.
Josep Fornos, VP-European Original Equipment Emission Control
Gregg Sherrill, Chmn.
Hari N. Nair, Exec. VP/Pres., Int'l
Alain Michaelis, Sr. VP-Global Supply Chain Mgmt.

Phone: 847-482-5000	**Fax:** 847-482-5940
Toll-Free:	
Address: 500 N. Field Dr., Lake Forest, IL 60045 US	

GROWTH PLANS/SPECIAL FEATURES:

Tenneco, Inc. is a manufacturer of automotive emissions control and ride control products and systems for both original equipment manufacturers (OEMs) and aftermarket retailers. The firm designs, engineers, manufactures, markets and sells individual components for vehicles as well as groups of components that are combined as modules or systems within vehicles. The firm maintains 80 manufacturing plants and 14 engineering institutions in 24 countries around the world. Tenneco's primary brands are Monroe ride control products and Walker exhaust products. Other brands include Rancho shock absorbers; Gillet and Walker exhaust systems; Monroe shocks and struts; DynoMax; and Thrush performance mufflers and Kinetic advanced suspension technology. Tenneco sells to over 39 OEMs, mainly to General Motors with 20% of net sales in 2007, Ford 14% and Volkswagen 9%. In the aftermarket, Tenneco's customers include NAPA, O'Reilly Automotive, Kwik-fit Europe, Uni-Select and Pep Boys. Its systems are included on eight of the top 10 passenger car models sold in Europe; and nine of the top 10 SUV and light truck models produced in North America. The company's software prediction programs enable its engineers to improve designs and predict outcome, which shortens development cycle time. The firm's products are sold primarily in North America (47% of 2007 sales) and Europe, South America and India (51%). The remaining sales come from the Asian Pacific market. In September 2007, Tenneco acquired Combustion Components Associates, Inc., a manufacturer of air pollution control technologies, for approximately $16 million. In April 2008, Tenneco launched its emission control business with the 2008 Toyota Sequoia, for which it will supply the full exhaust system. In May 2008, Tenneco acquired parts of Delphi Automotive Systems LLC, including ride control components for $10 million and certain machinery and equipment for $9 million.

FINANCIALS: **Sales and profits are in thousands of dollars—add 000 to get the full amount. 2008 Note: Financial information for 2008 was not available for all companies at press time.**

2008 Sales: $5,916,000	2008 Profits: $-415,000	**U.S. Stock Ticker: TEN**
2007 Sales: $6,184,000	2007 Profits: $-5,000	**Int'l Ticker:** Int'l Exchange:
2006 Sales: $4,682,000	2006 Profits: $49,000	Employees: 21,000
2005 Sales: $4,441,000	2005 Profits: $58,000	Fiscal Year Ends: 12/31
2004 Sales: $4,213,000	2004 Profits: $15,000	Parent Company:

SALARIES/BENEFITS:

Pension Plan: Y	ESOP Stock Plan:	Profit Sharing:	Top Exec. Salary: $841,856	Bonus: $1,587,000
Savings Plan: Y	Stock Purch. Plan: Y		Second Exec. Salary: $466,720	Bonus: $81,900

OTHER THOUGHTS:

Apparent Women Officers or Directors: 1
Hot Spot for Advancement for Women/Minorities:

LOCATIONS: ("Y" = Yes)

West:	Southwest:	Midwest:	Southeast:	Northeast:	International:
Y		Y	Y	Y	Y

Note: Financial information, benefits and other data can change quickly and may vary from those stated here.

TEREX CORPORATION

www.terex.com

Industry Group Code: 333000 **Ranks within this company's industry group:** Sales: 7 Profits: 9

Techology:		Medical/Drugs:		Engineering:		Transportation:		Chemicals/Petrochemicals:		Specialty:	
Computers:		Manufacturer:		Design:		Aerospace:		Oil/Gas Products:		Special Services:	Y
Software:		Contract Research:		Construction:	Y	Automotive:		Chemicals:		Consulting:	
Communications:		Medical Services:		Eng. Services:		Shipping:		Oil/Chem. Svcs.:		Specialty Mgmt.:	
Electronics:		Labs:		Consulting:				Gases:		Products:	
Alternative Energy:		Bio. Services:						Other:		Other:	Y

TYPES OF BUSINESS:

Heavy Equipment
Cranes
Mining Equipment
Aerial Work Platforms
Roadbuilding Equipment
Utility Products
Construction Equipment
Materials Handling Equipment

BRANDS/DIVISIONS/AFFILIATES:

Terex
Genie Lifts
Bid-Well Paving Machines

CONTACTS: *Note: Officers with more than one job title may be intentionally listed here more than once.*

Ronald M. DeFeo, CEO
Tom Riordan, COO
Tom Riordan, Pres.
Phillip C. Widman, CFO/Sr. VP
Katia Facchetti, Sr. VP/Chief Mktg. Officer
Kevin A. Barr, Sr. VP-Human Resources
Eric I Cohen, General Counsel/Sr. VP/Corp. Sec.
Laura Kiernan, Dir.-Investor Rel.
Jonathan D. Carter, Controller/VP/Chief Acct. Officer
Tim Ford, Pres., Terex Aerial Work Platforms
Colin Fox, Sr. VP-Terex Bus. Systems
Robert Isaman, Pres., Terex Construction
Richard Nichols, Pres., Terex Cranes
Ronald M. DeFeo, Chmn.

Phone: 203-222-7170 **Fax:** 203-222-7976
Toll-Free:
Address: 200 Nyala Farm Rd., Westport, CT 06880 US

GROWTH PLANS/SPECIAL FEATURES:

Terex Corporation is a diversified global manufacturer of capital equipment focused on solutions for the construction, infrastructure, quarrying, surface mining, shipping, transportation, refining and utility industries. The company operates in five business segments: Terex Aerial Work Platforms; Terex Construction; Terex Cranes; Terex Materials Processing & Mining; and Terex Roadbuilding, Utility Products and Other. The Terex Aerial Work Platforms segment designs, manufactures and markets products such as material lifts, portable aerial work platforms, trailer-mounted articulating booms, self-propelled articulating and telescopic booms, scissor lifts, construction trailers, generators, and related components and parts. The Terex Construction segment designs, manufactures and markets heavy and compact construction equipment. Heavy equipment includes such products as off-highway trucks, hydraulic excavators, large wheel loaders and truck-mounted articulated hydraulic cranes. Compact equipment includes products such as loader backhoes, compaction equipment, excavators, site dumpers and skid steer loaders. The Terex Cranes segment produces mobile telescopic cranes, tower cranes, lattice boom crawler cranes, truck-mounted cranes and telescopic container stackers, as well as their related replacement parts and components. The Terex Materials Processing & Mining segment produces crushing and screening equipment; hydraulic mining excavators; highwall mining equipment; high capacity surface mining trucks; drilling equipment; and related components and replacement parts. The Terex Roadbuilding, Utility Products and Other segment produces products such as asphalt and concrete equipment; landfill compactors; and utility equipment, including digger derricks, aerial devices and cable placers. Terex sells its products worldwide and operates manufacturing facilities in North and South America, Europe, Australia and Asia. Current strategic initiatives include the further growth of the company's international business, with increased emphasis on developing markets including China, India, Russia, the Middle East and Latin America. In April 2008, Terex acquired South Carolina-based Hydra Platforms Mfg., Inc., a manufacturer of under-bridge access equipment used in bridge construction, maintenance and inspection.

FINANCIALS: **Sales and profits are in thousands of dollars—add 000 to get the full amount. 2008 Note: Financial information for 2008 was not available for all companies at press time.**

2008 Sales: $9,889,600	2008 Profits: $71,900	**U.S. Stock Ticker: TEX**
2007 Sales: $9,137,700	2007 Profits: $613,900	**Int'l Ticker:** Int'l Exchange:
2006 Sales: $	2006 Profits: $	Employees:
2005 Sales: $	2005 Profits: $	Fiscal Year Ends: 12/31
2004 Sales: $	2004 Profits: $	Parent Company:

SALARIES/BENEFITS:

Pension Plan:	ESOP Stock Plan:	Profit Sharing:	Top Exec. Salary: $1,025,000	Bonus: $2,507,713
Savings Plan:	Stock Purch. Plan:		Second Exec. Salary: $744,231	Bonus: $857,849

OTHER THOUGHTS:

Apparent Women Officers or Directors: 4
Hot Spot for Advancement for Women/Minorities: Y

LOCATIONS: ("Y" = Yes)

West:	Southwest:	Midwest:	Southeast:	Northeast:	International:
Y	Y	Y	Y	Y	Y

TEXAS INSTRUMENTS INC (TI)

www.ti.com

Industry Group Code: 334413 **Ranks within this company's industry group:** Sales: 2 Profits: 4

Techology:		Medical/Drugs:		Engineering:		Transportation:		Chemicals/Petrochemicals:		Specialty:	
Computers:	Y	Manufacturer:		Design:		Aerospace:		Oil/Gas Products:		Special Services:	
Software:		Contract Research:		Construction:		Automotive:		Chemicals:		Consulting:	
Communications:	Y	Medical Services:		Eng. Services:		Shipping:		Oil/Chem. Svcs.:		Specialty Mgmt.:	
Electronics:		Labs:		Consulting:				Gases:		Products:	
Alternative Energy:		Bio. Services:						Other:		Other:	

TYPES OF BUSINESS:

Chips-Digital Signal Processors
Semiconductors
Calculators

BRANDS/DIVISIONS/AFFILIATES:

DLP
POWERCASE Solutions, Inc.

CONTACTS: *Note: Officers with more than one job title may be intentionally listed here more than once.*

Richard K. (Rich) Templeton, CEO
Richard K. (Rich) Templeton, Pres.
Kevin P. March, CFO/Sr. VP
Darla Whitaker, Sr. VP/Dir.-Worldwide Human Resources
Kevin Ritchie, Sr. VP-Tech.
Kevin Ritchie, Sr. VP-Mfg.
Joseph F. (Joe) Hubach, General Counsel/Sec./Sr. VP
Terri West, Sr. VP/Mgr.-Comm.
Terri West, Sr. VP/Mgr.-Investor Rel.
Steve Anderson, Sr. VP/Worldwide Mgr.-Power Mgmt.
Greg Delagi, Sr. VP/Gen. Mgr.-Wireless Terminals Bus. Unit
Mike Hames, Sr. VP/Mgr.-Application Specific Prod.
Melendy Lovett, Sr. VP/Pres., Education Tech.
Richard K. (Rich) Templeton, Chmn.
Art George, Sr. VP/Worldwide Mgr.-High-Performance Analog

Phone: 972-995-2011 **Fax:** 972-927-6377
Toll-Free: 800-336-5236
Address: 12500 TI Blvd., P.O. Box 660199, Dallas, TX 75266-0199 US

GROWTH PLANS/SPECIAL FEATURES:

Texas Instruments, Inc. (TI) is a technology company with sales and manufacturing operations in more than 25 countries. It operates in two segments: Semiconductor, which accounted for 96% of revenue in 2007; and Education Technology, the remaining 4%. The Semiconductor segment's core products enhance and often make possible a variety of applications that serve the communications, computer, consumer electronics, medical, automotive and industrial markets. The segment is divided into four sub-segments: Analog semiconductors, digital signal processing (DSP), wireless and DLP technology. Analog semiconductors process real world inputs such as sound, temperature, pressure and visual images, conditions them, amplifies them and converts them into digital signals. They also assist in the management of power distribution and consumption. DSP products use complex algorithms and compression techniques to alter and improve a data stream. They perform these functions instantaneously and power-efficiently. These products are ideal for applications that require precise, real-time processing of real-world analog signals that have been converted into digital form. TI's wireless semiconductors are mainly used in mobile phones, including standard voice-centric and more advanced multimedia-rich data handsets. Lastly, the firm's proprietary DLP optical semiconductor products enable clear video and microprocessors that serve as the brains of everything from high-end computer servers to high definition televisions (HDTVs). The Education Technology segment is mainly a supplier of handheld graphing calculators manufactured by third-party suppliers. It also provides customers with business and scientific calculators and a wide range of advanced classroom tools and professional development resources to help students and teachers interactively explore math and science. In October 2007, TI acquired POWERPRECISE Solutions, Inc., a portable power management integrated circuit solutions firm. In January 2009, the company announced plans to eliminate roughly 3,400 jobs.

The company offers its employees medical, dental and vision insurance; life and AD&D insurance; short- and long-term disability insurance; business travel accident insurance; an employee assistance program; and educational assistance.

FINANCIALS: **Sales and profits are in thousands of dollars—add 000 to get the full amount. 2008 Note: Financial information for 2008 was not available for all companies at press time.**

2008 Sales: $12,501,000	2008 Profits: $1,920,000	**U.S. Stock Ticker: TXN**
2007 Sales: $13,835,000	2007 Profits: $2,657,000	**Int'l Ticker:** Int'l Exchange:
2006 Sales: $14,255,000	2006 Profits: $4,341,000	Employees: 29,537
2005 Sales: $12,335,000	2005 Profits: $2,324,000	Fiscal Year Ends: 12/31
2004 Sales: $11,552,000	2004 Profits: $1,861,000	Parent Company:

SALARIES/BENEFITS:

Pension Plan:	ESOP Stock Plan:	Profit Sharing: Y	Top Exec. Salary: $932,120	Bonus: $2,395,822
Savings Plan: Y	Stock Purch. Plan: Y		Second Exec. Salary: $502,535	Bonus: $1,151,661

OTHER THOUGHTS:

Apparent Women Officers or Directors: 3
Hot Spot for Advancement for Women/Minorities: Y

LOCATIONS: ("Y" = Yes)

West:	Southwest:	Midwest:	Southeast:	Northeast:	International:
Y	Y	Y	Y	Y	Y

Note: Financial information, benefits and other data can change quickly and may vary from those stated here.

TEXTRON INC

www.textron.com

Industry Group Code: 336410 **Ranks within this company's industry group:** Sales: 12 Profits: 12

Techology:		Medical/Drugs:		Engineering:		Transportation:		Chemicals/Petrochemicals:		Specialty:	
Computers:		Manufacturer:		Design:		Aerospace:	Y	Oil/Gas Products:		Special Services:	Y
Software:		Contract Research:		Construction:		Automotive:	Y	Chemicals:		Consulting:	
Communications:	Y	Medical Services:		Eng. Services:		Shipping:		Oil/Chem. Svcs.:		Specialty Mgmt.:	
Electronics:		Labs:		Consulting:				Gases:		Products:	Y
Alternative Energy:		Bio. Services:						Other:		Other:	Y

TYPES OF BUSINESS:

Aerospace Related Manufacturing
Helicopters & General Aviation Aircraft Manufacturing
Electrical Test & Measurement Equipment
Fiber Optic Equipment
Off-Road Vehicles
Financing

BRANDS/DIVISIONS/AFFILIATES:

Bell Helicopters
Textron Systems
Cessna Aircraft Co.
Textron Financial Corp.
Jacobsen
Kautex
Greenlee
Fluid & Power

CONTACTS: *Note: Officers with more than one job title may be intentionally listed here more than once.*

Lewis B. Campbell, CEO
Scott Donnelly, COO/Exec. VP
Lewis B. Campbell, Pres.
Ted R. French, CFO/Exec. VP
R. Siisi Adu-Gyamfi, Sr. VP-Mktg.
John D. Butler, Chief Human Resources Officer
Gary Cantrell, CIO/VP
John D. Butler, Exec. VP-Admin.
Terrence O'Donnell, General Counsel/Exec. VP
Stuart Grief, VP-Strategy & Bus. Dev.
Susan M. Tardanico, VP-Comm.
Douglas R. Wilburne, VP-Investor Rel.
Richard Yates, Controller/Sr. VP
Mary L. Howell, Exec. VP
Ken C. Bohlen, Exec. VP/Chief Innovation Officer
Cathy Streker, VP-Human Resources
Mary F. Lovejoy, Treas./VP
Lewis B. Campbell, Chmn.
R. Siisi Adu-Gyamfi, Exec. VP-Int'l

Phone: 401-421-2800 **Fax:** 401-457-2220
Toll-Free:
Address: 40 Westminster St., Providence, RI 02903 US

GROWTH PLANS/SPECIAL FEATURES:

Textron, Inc. is a global multi-industry company operating in 34 countries. The company participates in four business segments: Bell, Cessna, industrial and finance. The Bell segment includes Bell Helicopter and Textron Systems. Bell Helicopter supplies helicopters, tilt rotor aircraft and helicopter-related spare parts and services for military and commercial applications. Bell Helicopter also supplies commercially certified helicopters to corporate, offshore petroleum exploration and development, utility, charter, police, fire, rescue, and emergency medical helicopter operators. Revenues from Bell Helicopter accounted for roughly 19% of net sales in 2007. Textron Systems manufactures smart weapons; airborne and ground-based surveillance systems; aircraft landing systems; hovercraft; search and rescue vessels; and aircraft and missile controls actuators to the defense, aerospace and general aviation markets. The Cessna segment is comprised of the Cessna Aircraft Co., a manufacturer of general aviation aircraft. Cessna has four major product lines: Citation business jets; single engine turboprop Caravans; Cessna single engine piston aircraft; and aftermarket parts and services. Cessna accounted for 38% of 2007 revenues. The Industrial segment is composed of the E-Z-GO, Jacobsen, Kautex, Greenlee and Fluid & Power businesses. These businesses design, manufacture and sell diverse products such as golf cars; off-road utility vehicles; turf maintenance equipment; blow-molded fuel systems; electrical test and measurement instruments; fiber optic connectors; and industrial gears and pumps. The finance segment consists of Textron Financial Corp. and its subsidiaries, with core operations in six markets: Asset-based lending; aviation finance; distribution finance; gold finance; resort finance; and structured capital.

Textron offers its employees scholarships, matching gift contributions, employee award and recognitions, discounts on Textron products, financial counseling, college coaches, educational assistance, adoption assistance and employee assistance.

FINANCIALS: Sales and profits are in thousands of dollars—add 000 to get the full amount. 2008 Note: Financial information for 2008 was not available for all companies at press time.

2008 Sales: $14,246,000 | 2008 Profits: $486,000
2007 Sales: $12,615,000 | 2007 Profits: $917,000
2006 Sales: $10,973,000 | 2006 Profits: $601,000
2005 Sales: $10,043,000 | 2005 Profits: $203,000
2004 Sales: $10,242,000 | 2004 Profits: $365,000

U.S. Stock Ticker: TXT
Int'l Ticker: Int'l Exchange:
Employees: 43,000
Fiscal Year Ends: 12/31
Parent Company:

SALARIES/BENEFITS:

Pension Plan: Y | ESOP Stock Plan: | Profit Sharing: | Top Exec. Salary: $1,100,000 | Bonus: $2,200,000
Savings Plan: Y | Stock Purch. Plan: | | Second Exec. Salary: $700,000 | Bonus: $1,050,000

OTHER THOUGHTS:

Apparent Women Officers or Directors: 7
Hot Spot for Advancement for Women/Minorities: Y

LOCATIONS: ("Y" = Yes)

West:	Southwest:	Midwest:	Southeast:	Northeast:	International:
				Y	

THQ INC

www.thq.com

Industry Group Code: 511208 **Ranks within this company's industry group:** Sales: 6 Profits: 3

Techology:		Medical/Drugs:		Engineering:		Transportation:		Chemicals/Petrochemicals:		Specialty:	
Computers:		Manufacturer:		Design:		Aerospace:		Oil/Gas Products:		Special Services:	
Software:	Y	Contract Research:		Construction:		Automotive:		Chemicals:		Consulting:	
Communications:		Medical Services:		Eng. Services:		Shipping:		Oil/Chem. Svcs.:		Specialty Mgmt.:	
Electronics:		Labs:		Consulting:				Gases:		Products:	
Alternative Energy:		Bio. Services:						Other:		Other:	

TYPES OF BUSINESS:

Software-Video Games
Mobile Gaming Software

BRANDS/DIVISIONS/AFFILIATES:

Relic Entertainment
Vigil Games
Paradigm Entertainment
Kaos Studios
Destroy All Humans!
THQ Wireless Inc
Big Huge Games
ICE Entertainment

CONTACTS: *Note: Officers with more than one job title may be intentionally listed here more than once.*

Brian J. Farrell, CEO
Brian J. Farrell, Pres.
Colin Slade, CFO/Exec. VP
Bob Aniello, Sr. VP-Worldwide Mktg.
Bill Goodmen, Exec. VP-Human Resources
Bill Goodmen, Exec. VP-Admin.
James M. Kennedy, Sec./Exec. VP-Bus. & Legal Affairs
Liz Pieri, VP-Mktg. Comm.
Julie MacMedan, VP-Investor Rel.
Jack Sorensen, Exec. VP-Worldwide Studios
Doug Clemmer, Pres., THQ Wireless, Inc.
Marko Hein, Gen. Manager-THQ Int'l GmbH
Brian J. Farrell, Chmn.
Ian Curran, Exec. VP-Int'l

Phone: 818-871-5000	**Fax:** 818-871-7590
Toll-Free:	
Address: 29903 Agoura Rd., Aguora Hills, CA 91301 US	

GROWTH PLANS/SPECIAL FEATURES:

THQ, Inc. is a worldwide publisher, marketer and developer of proprietary and licensed video game software for Sony PSP, PlayStation 2 and PlayStation 3; Microsoft Xbox and Xbox 360;, Nintendo GameCube, Game Boy Advance, DS and Wii; PCs; and mobile devices. It develops titles through 16 development studios under a new strategy called Studio located in the U.S., Australia, Canada and the U.K. The strategy is designed to leverage resources across the entire organization to benefit each of the separate studios. Its studios include Relic Entertainment; Sandblast Games; Locomotive Games; Mass Media; Heavy Iron Studios; Incinerator Studios; Concrete Games; Rainbow Studios; Vigil Games; Paradigm Entertainment; Volition, Inc.; Kaos Studios; Helixe; Juice Games; THQ Studio Australia; and Blue Tongue Entertainment. Games based on the company's own intellectual property include Company of Heroes, Destroy All Humans!, Juiced, MX vs. ATV, Red Faction and Saints Row. Its games based on properties it licenses from third parties include Hot Wheels, Scooby-Doo, Sonic the Hedgehog, SpongeBob SquarePants, World Wrestling Entertainment, Bratz, Warhammer 40,000 and several Disney/Pixar properties, including Finding Nemo, Cars and Ratatouille. The firm also has software and artwork developed for it by third parties. Subsidiary THQ Wireless, Inc. produces ringtones and videogames for mobile phones, including products related to the Star Wars franchise, which the firm only develops for wireless applications. The company's corporate strategy focuses on improving its internal development capabilities and technology base, increasing its international presence and exploring the potential of the mobile interactive entertainment segment. In 2008, THQ acquired Big Huge Games, a development studio focused on Role-Playing-Games. In the same year, the firm announced a joint venture with ICE Entertainment, an operator of online games based in Shanghai. The venture plans to launch Dragonica, a multiplayer online casual game, in North America in 2009.

FINANCIALS: **Sales and profits are in thousands of dollars—add 000 to get the full amount. 2008 Note: Financial information for 2008 was not available for all companies at press time.**

2008 Sales: $1,030,467	2008 Profits: $-35,337	**U.S. Stock Ticker: THQI**
2007 Sales: $1,026,856	2007 Profits: $68,038	**Int'l Ticker:** Int'l Exchange:
2006 Sales: $806,560	2006 Profits: $32,106	Employees: 2,400
2005 Sales: $756,731	2005 Profits: $34,072	Fiscal Year Ends: 3/31
2004 Sales: $640,846	2004 Profits: $35,839	Parent Company:

SALARIES/BENEFITS:

Pension Plan:	ESOP Stock Plan:	Profit Sharing:	Top Exec. Salary: $651,087	Bonus: $165,000
Savings Plan: Y	Stock Purch. Plan:		Second Exec. Salary: $432,539	Bonus: $156,261

OTHER THOUGHTS:

Apparent Women Officers or Directors: 2
Hot Spot for Advancement for Women/Minorities: Y

LOCATIONS: ("Y" = Yes)

West:	Southwest:	Midwest:	Southeast:	Northeast:	International:
Y	Y	Y		Y	Y

TIETOENATOR

www.tietoenator.com

Industry Group Code: 541512 **Ranks within this company's industry group:** Sales: 16 Profits: 11

Techology:		Medical/Drugs:		Engineering:		Transportation:		Chemicals/Petrochemicals:		Specialty:	
Computers:		Manufacturer:		Design:		Aerospace:		Oil/Gas Products:		Special Services:	Y
Software:	Y	Contract Research:		Construction:		Automotive:		Chemicals:		Consulting:	Y
Communications:	Y	Medical Services:		Eng. Services:		Shipping:		Oil/Chem. Svcs.:		Specialty Mgmt.:	
Electronics:		Labs:		Consulting:				Gases:		Products:	
Alternative Energy:		Bio. Services:						Other:		Other:	

TYPES OF BUSINESS:

IT Services
Human Resources Services
Software Development
Telecommunications Consulting

BRANDS/DIVISIONS/AFFILIATES:

Tieto
Service Design Center

CONTACTS:

Note: Officers with more than one job title may be intentionally listed here more than once.

Hannu Syrjala, CEO
Hannu Syrjala, Pres.
Seppo Haapalainen, CFO/Exec. VP
Johanna Pyykonen-Walker, Exec. VP-Human Resources
Ari Vanhanen, Exec. VP-Industry Group
Bengt Moller, Exec. VP-Telecom & Media
Kavilesh Gupta, Exec. VP-Global Svcs. & IT Svcs.
Eva Gidlof, Exec. VP/Country Head-Sweden
Anders Ullberg, Chmn.
Pekka Viljakainen, Exec. VP-Int'l

Phone: 358-207-2010 **Fax:** 358-207-2688-98
Toll-Free:
Address: Aku Korhosen tie 2-6, P.O. Box 38, Helsinki, 00441 Finland

GROWTH PLANS/SPECIAL FEATURES:

TietoEnator is one of the largest IT services companies in the Nordic region. It provides IT services primarily to companies in nine business sectors through offices across 26 countries. Primary business sectors served by the company include financial services; telecom & media; forestry; healthcare; energy; public; welfare; retail & logistics; and manufacturing. For example, the company's financial services segment provides value-added IT services that involve close collaboration with customers in the banking, finance and insurance industries. The company's telecommunications division provides IT and research and development services to the European telecom and media industry. It works with customers across the entire range of media applications, from content providers to manufacturers and network operators. TietoEnator's public and welfare divisions offer services and products for building new electronic networks for social programs, governments, health care and educational organizations, as well as libraries, hospitals, laboratories and other institutions. The company's production segment services forest, energy, manufacturing, retail and logistics providers across the entire value chain, from procurement to customer relationship management. TietoEnator offers all of its clients ongoing processing, data centers, server management and network support services. Some of the company's largest customers include Nordea, Swedbank, Royal Bank of Scotland, Alcatel-Lucent, Nokia, Siemens and Sony Ericsson. In January 2008, TietoEnator opened a new office in Chengdu, China, focused on the areas of mobile devices, networks and operations. In February 2008, the firm announced that it would partner with Microsoft Corporation to establish the Service Design Center, with location in Amsterdam, Helsinki, Munich, Oslo, Stockholm and Moscow. In January 2009, TietoEnator opened a new data center in St. Petersburg, which will allow more comprehensive service for customers with operations in Russia. In February 2009, the company announced that it would provide enterprise architecture consulting services to the City of Helsinki in Finland.

FINANCIALS:

Sales and profits are in thousands of dollars—add 000 to get the full amount. 2008 Note: Financial information for 2008 was not available for all companies at press time.

2008 Sales: $2,485,670	2008 Profits: $80,600	**U.S. Stock Ticker:**
2007 Sales: $2,361,270	2007 Profits: $-41,570	**Int'l Ticker: TIE1V** Int'l Exchange: Helsinki-Euronext
2006 Sales: $2,552,100	2006 Profits: $378,000	Employees:
2005 Sales: $2,434,100	2005 Profits: $211,300	Fiscal Year Ends: 12/31
2004 Sales: $	2004 Profits: $	Parent Company:

SALARIES/BENEFITS:

Pension Plan:	ESOP Stock Plan:	Profit Sharing:	Top Exec. Salary: $	Bonus: $
Savings Plan:	Stock Purch. Plan:		Second Exec. Salary: $	Bonus: $

OTHER THOUGHTS:

Apparent Women Officers or Directors: 3
Hot Spot for Advancement for Women/Minorities: Y

LOCATIONS: ("Y" = Yes)

West:	Southwest:	Midwest:	Southeast:	Northeast:	International:
Y	Y			Y	Y

Note: Financial information, benefits and other data can change quickly and may vary from those stated here.

TOSHIBA CORPORATE R&D CENTER

www.toshiba.co.jp/rdc/index.htm

Industry Group Code: 541710 **Ranks within this company's industry group:** Sales: Profits:

Techology:		Medical/Drugs:		Engineering:		Transportation:		Chemicals/Petrochemicals:		Specialty:	
Computers:	Y	Manufacturer:	Y	Design:		Aerospace:		Oil/Gas Products:		Special Services:	
Software:	Y	Contract Research:		Construction:		Automotive:		Chemicals:		Consulting:	
Communications:	Y	Medical Services:		Eng. Services:		Shipping:		Oil/Chem. Svcs.:		Specialty Mgmt.:	
Electronics:	Y	Labs:		Consulting:				Gases:		Products:	Y
Alternative Energy:	Y	Bio. Services:						Other:		Other:	

TYPES OF BUSINESS:

Research & Development
Semiconductor Processes
MEMS Applications
Biotechnology Tools
Electronic Devices
Software
Medical Devices
Speech Recognition Technology

BRANDS/DIVISIONS/AFFILIATES:

Toshiba Corp.
Toshiba Research Europe Limited
Toshiba China R&D Center
Toshiba America Research, Inc

CONTACTS:

Note: Officers with more than one job title may be intentionally listed here more than once.

Akira Sudo, Dir.-Corp. R&D Center
Kazuaki Kawabata, Sec.-Toshiba Research Europe
Atsutoshi Nishida, CEO/Pres., Toshiba Corporation
Ichiro Tai, Exec. VP-Toshiba Corporation

Phone: 81-44-549-2056	**Fax:**
Toll-Free:	
Address: 1 Komukai Toshiba-cho, Saiwai-ku, Kawasaki-shi, 212-8582 Japan	

GROWTH PLANS/SPECIAL FEATURES:

Toshiba Corporate R&D Center (CRDC) manages a global network of research laboratories, test facilities and planning groups that support the ongoing commercialization of products and technologies for Toshiba Corporation, its parent company. Toshiba is a global leader in the manufacture of consumer, industrial, medical and communications electronics. CRDC has focused the bulk of its short-term research and development initiatives on digital products and electronic devices, while its scientists and engineers continue to develop a range of platform technologies, including new nanometric semiconductor processes, innovative microelectromechanical systems (MEMS) applications and chip-based biotech tools. The firm has facilities in Japan, the U.K., the U.S. and China. Its research and development areas include: wireless and network (examples include holding teleconferences with people in remote locations.); human interface (or the firm's Yubi de Komimi Hasander Ontology-Based Technology which is used for gathering word-of-mouth information from blogs); LSI and Storage (which involves the development of Magnetoresistive Random Access Memory, MRAM) the only nonvolatile memory that has no rewriting limitation; advance materials and devices (which includes, among others, the commercialization of a DNA chip for medical applications; and systems and environment (which includes the development of an Incident and Accident Report System that utilizes a Risk Failure Mode and Effects Analysis, RFMEA, to better deliver medical care in a more timely and efficient manner.

FINANCIALS:

Sales and profits are in thousands of dollars—add 000 to get the full amount. 2008 Note: Financial information for 2008 was not available for all companies at press time.

2008 Sales: $	2008 Profits: $	**U.S. Stock Ticker: Subsidiary**
2007 Sales: $	2007 Profits: $	**Int'l Ticker:** Int'l Exchange:
2006 Sales: $	2006 Profits: $	Employees:
2005 Sales: $	2005 Profits: $	Fiscal Year Ends: 3/31
2004 Sales: $	2004 Profits: $	Parent Company: TOSHIBA CORPORATION

SALARIES/BENEFITS:

Pension Plan:	ESOP Stock Plan:	Profit Sharing:	Top Exec. Salary: $	Bonus: $
Savings Plan:	Stock Purch. Plan:		Second Exec. Salary: $	Bonus: $

OTHER THOUGHTS:

Apparent Women Officers or Directors:
Hot Spot for Advancement for Women/Minorities:

LOCATIONS: ("Y" = Yes)

West:	Southwest:	Midwest:	Southeast:	Northeast:	International:
				Y	Y

Note: Financial information, benefits and other data can change quickly and may vary from those stated here.

TOSHIBA CORPORATION

www.toshiba.co.jp/index.htm

Industry Group Code: 334111 **Ranks within this company's industry group:** Sales: 3 Profits: 6

Techology:		Medical/Drugs:		Engineering:		Transportation:		Chemicals/Petrochemicals:		Specialty:	
Computers:	Y	Manufacturer:	Y	Design:		Aerospace:		Oil/Gas Products:		Special Services:	Y
Software:		Contract Research:		Construction:		Automotive:	Y	Chemicals:		Consulting:	
Communications:	Y	Medical Services:		Eng. Services:	Y	Shipping:		Oil/Chem. Svcs.:		Specialty Mgmt.:	
Electronics:	Y	Labs:		Consulting:				Gases:		Products:	
Alternative Energy:	Y	Bio. Services:						Other:		Other:	Y

TYPES OF BUSINESS:

Electronics Manufacturing
Computers & Accessories
Telecommunications Equipment
Semiconductors
Consumer Electronics
Medical & Industrial Equipment
Satellite Radio
Internet Services

BRANDS/DIVISIONS/AFFILIATES:

Mobile Communications Company
Digital Media Network Company
Personal Computer & Network Company
Semiconductor Company
Industrial Systems Company
Social Infrastructure Systems Company
Toshiba TEC Corporation
Toshiba Matsushita Display Technology Co., Ltd.

CONTACTS: *Note: Officers with more than one job title may be intentionally listed here more than once.*

Norio Sasaki, CEO
Kosei Okamoto, VP/Pres./CEO-Mobile Comm. Co.
Yoshihide Fujii, Sr. VP/Pres./CEO-Digital Medial Network Co.
Hidejiro Shimomitsu, Sr. VP/Pres./CEO-Personal Computer & Network Co.
Shozo Saito, Sr. VP/Pres./CEO-Semiconductor Group
Atsutoshi Nishida, Chmn.

Phone: 81-3-3457-4511 **Fax:** 81-3-3456-1631
Toll-Free:
Address: 1-1, Shibaura 1-chome, Minato-ku, Tokyo, 105-8001 Japan

GROWTH PLANS/SPECIAL FEATURES:

Toshiba Corporation is a diversified technology firm. It has 519 consolidated subsidiaries and seven in-house companies that are active in four business segments: Digital Products; Electronic Devices & Components; Social Infrastructure Systems; and Home Appliances and Other. Digital Products consists of the Mobile Communications Company, which develops mobile phones, Smartphones and data terminals; Digital Media Network Company, which manufactures LCD TVs, surveillance cameras and hard disk drives; and Personal Computer & Network Company, which mainly manufactures notebook PCs. It also works with Toshiba TEC Corporation, which creates peripheral equipment such as fax machines and cash registers. Electronic Devices & Components consists of the Semiconductor Company, which manufactures circuits such as NAND flash memory, power devices and cell phone components. It also works with the Display Devices & Components Control Center, which manufactures direct methanol fuel cells and various materials and components; and Toshiba Matsushita Display Technology Co., Ltd., which mainly manufactures organic LED displays. Social Infrastructure Systems includes the Power Systems Company, which develops nuclear, hydroelectric, geothermal and thermal power plants and related equipment; Industrial Systems Company, which manufactures face recognition security systems, automatic letter-processing systems and industrial computers; and Social Infrastructure Systems Company, which manufactures broadcasting systems, air-traffic control systems and power distribution systems. It also works with Toshiba Elevator and Building Systems Corporation; Toshiba Solutions Corporation, an IT company; and Toshiba Medical Systems Corporation, developing CT scanners, ultrasound equipment and X-ray systems. The Home Appliances & Other division works with Toshiba Consumer Marketing Corporation supplying home appliances, lighting solutions and batteries. The division also includes MBCo's satellite broadcasting center; automotive systems; and a TV program recording recommendation service. In February 2009, the company, partnering with Tokyo Electric Power and Japan Bank for International Cooperation, acquired 19.95% equity interest in Uranium One of Canada.

FINANCIALS: **Sales and profits are in thousands of dollars—add 000 to get the full amount. 2008 Note: Financial information for 2008 was not available for all companies at press time.**

2008 Sales: $76,680,800	2008 Profits: $1,274,100	**U.S. Stock Ticker: TOSBF**
2007 Sales: $64,330,700	2007 Profits: $1,242,340	**Int'l Ticker: 6502** Int'l Exchange: Tokyo-TSE
2006 Sales: $53,945,200	2006 Profits: $664,900	Employees: 190,708
2005 Sales: $54,264,400	2005 Profits: $428,100	Fiscal Year Ends: 3/31
2004 Sales: $52,815,600	2004 Profits: $272,900	Parent Company:

SALARIES/BENEFITS:

Pension Plan:	ESOP Stock Plan:	Profit Sharing:	Top Exec. Salary: $	Bonus: $
Savings Plan:	Stock Purch. Plan:		Second Exec. Salary: $	Bonus: $

OTHER THOUGHTS:

Apparent Women Officers or Directors:
Hot Spot for Advancement for Women/Minorities:

LOCATIONS: ("Y" = Yes)

West:	Southwest:	Midwest:	Southeast:	Northeast:	International:
Y	Y			Y	Y

TOTAL SA

www.total.com

Industry Group Code: 211111 **Ranks within this company's industry group:** Sales: 7 Profits: 7

Techology:		Medical/Drugs:		Engineering:		Transportation:		Chemicals/Petrochemicals:		Specialty:	
Computers:		Manufacturer:		Design:		Aerospace:		Oil/Gas Products:	Y	Special Services:	Y
Software:		Contract Research:		Construction:		Automotive:		Chemicals:	Y	Consulting:	
Communications:		Medical Services:		Eng. Services:		Shipping:		Oil/Chem. Svcs.:	Y	Specialty Mgmt.:	
Electronics:		Labs:		Consulting:				Gases:		Products:	
Alternative Energy:	Y	Bio. Services:						Other:	Y	Other:	

TYPES OF BUSINESS:

Oil & Gas Exploration & Production
Petrochemicals
Specialty Chemicals
Hydrocarbons
Service Stations
Photovoltaic Cells

BRANDS/DIVISIONS/AFFILIATES:

Total
Elan
Elf

CONTACTS:

Note: Officers with more than one job title may be intentionally listed here more than once.

Christophe de Margerie, CEO
Patrick de la Chevardiere, CFO
Michel Benezit, Pres., Mktg. & Refining
Jean-Jaques Guilbaud, Pres., Human Resources
Patrick de la Chevardiere, IT
Jean-Jacques Guilbaud, Chief Admin. Officer
Peter Herbel, General Counsel
Bruno Weymuller, Exec. VP/Pres., Strategy & Risk Assessment
Jean-Jaques Guilbaud, VP-Corp. Comm.
Yves-Louis Darricarrere, Pres., Exploration & Prod.
Franxois Cornelis, Pres., Chemicals
Marc Blaizot, Sr. VP-Geosciences Exploration & Prod.
Philippe Boisseau, Pres., Gas & Power
Thierry Desmarest, Chmn.
Jacques Marraud des Grottes, Sr. VP-Exploration & Prod., Africa
Jean Bie, VP-Purchasing

Phone: 33-1-47-44-58-53 **Fax:** 33-1-47-44-58-24
Toll-Free:
Address: 2 Place Jean Miller, La Defense 6, Courbevoie, 92400 France

GROWTH PLANS/SPECIAL FEATURES:

Total S.A. is one of the world's largest energy companies, with operations in more than 130 countries. The firm's activities are divided into three segments: Upstream, Downstream and Chemicals. The Upstream sector handles oil and gas exploration and production. Total produces 2.35 million barrels of oil (BOE) per day, with proven reserves of 10.46 billion BOE. Exploration activities take place in 42 countries, and production in 30. The Downstream segment does trading, shipping, refining and marketing of petroleum and other fuels; it is a leader in Europe and Africa in the refining and service station market. Total has a worldwide network of over 16,000 service stations under the Total, Elf and Elan brand names. The Chemicals division prepares petrochemicals and fertilizers for the industrial/commercial markets; it is also involved in rubber processing, resins, adhesives and electroplating. The company is focusing on high-growth zones (such as Africa, the Mediterranean Basin and Asia) as well as specialty products such as liquefied petroleum gas, aviation fuel, lubricants, waxes, bitumens and solvents. Total, Electrabel and IMEC have collaborated to form a company for the production of photovoltaic cells and modules, called Photovoltech. In January 2008, the company partnered with Suez and Areva with the intent to build a nuclear power plant in the United Arab Emirates. In March 2008, Total acquired ExxonMobil's marketing assets in Puerto Rico, Jamaica and the U.S. Virgin Islands. In May 2008, Total and the Saudi Arabian Oil Company agreed to create the Jubail Refining and Petrochemical Company in Saudi Arabia by 2012. In July 2008, Total Canada agreed to acquire Syneco Energy, Inc. In September 2008, the company agreed to acquire Goal Petroleum (Netherlands) B.V. from Talisman Energy for $480 million. In January 2009, Total acquired 50% stake in American Shale Oil, LLC, subsidiary of IDT Corporation.

FINANCIALS:

Sales and profits are in thousands of dollars—add 000 to get the full amount. 2008 Note: Financial information for 2008 was not available for all companies at press time.

2008 Sales: $213,742,000	2008 Profits: $14,117,800	**U.S. Stock Ticker: TOT**
2007 Sales: $182,404,000	2007 Profits: $17,572,000	**Int'l Ticker: FP** Int'l Exchange: Paris-Euronext
2006 Sales: $208,359,000	2006 Profits: $16,439,500	Employees: 96,959
2005 Sales: $186,419,000	2005 Profits: $17,127,700	Fiscal Year Ends: 12/31
2004 Sales: $158,288,000	2004 Profits: $16,049,400	Parent Company:

SALARIES/BENEFITS:

Pension Plan:	ESOP Stock Plan:	Profit Sharing:	Top Exec. Salary: $1,535,838	Bonus: $1,457,656
Savings Plan:	Stock Purch. Plan:		Second Exec. Salary: $	Bonus: $

OTHER THOUGHTS:

Apparent Women Officers or Directors: 1
Hot Spot for Advancement for Women/Minorities:

LOCATIONS: ("Y" = Yes)

West:	Southwest:	Midwest:	Southeast:	Northeast:	International:
Y	Y				Y

TOYODA GOSEI CO LTD

www.toyoda-gosei.com

Industry Group Code: 336300 **Ranks within this company's industry group:** Sales: 16 Profits: 7

Techology:		Medical/Drugs:		Engineering:		Transportation:		Chemicals/Petrochemicals:		Specialty:	
Computers:		Manufacturer:		Design:		Aerospace:		Oil/Gas Products:		Special Services:	
Software:		Contract Research:		Construction:		Automotive:	Y	Chemicals:		Consulting:	
Communications:		Medical Services:		Eng. Services:		Shipping:		Oil/Chem. Svcs.:		Specialty Mgmt.:	
Electronics:		Labs:		Consulting:				Gases:		Products:	
Alternative Energy:		Bio. Services:						Other:		Other:	

TYPES OF BUSINESS:

Automotive Components
LEDs & Optoelectronics
Consumer Products
Airbags

BRANDS/DIVISIONS/AFFILIATES:

Toyota Group
Toyota Motor Corporation

CONTACTS:

Note: Officers with more than one job title may be intentionally listed here more than once.

Takashi Matsuura, Pres.
Fujiwara Nobuo, Dir./Mgr.-Bus. Dept./Dept. Mgr.-Quality Assurance
Noboru Kato, Managing Dir.
Ikehata Hiroshi, Managing Dir.
Akio Matsubara, Chmn.

Phone: 81-52-400-1055	**Fax:** 81-52-409-7491
Toll-Free:	
Address: 1 Nagahata, Ochiai, Haruhi-cho, Nishikasugai-gun, Aichi, 452 8564 Japan	

GROWTH PLANS/SPECIAL FEATURES:

Toyoda Gosei Co., Ltd., a member of the Toyota Group, produces and distributes several categories of automotive components. The company has 16 locations in Japan, 15 in the U.S., 22 in Asia and six in Europe, for a total of 59 locations. Its business segments include interior and exterior parts, body sealing products, functional parts, safety system products and optoelectronic products, as well as general industry parts and various other products. In automotive components, the company's interior and exterior parts division produces instrument panels and controls, door trims, hubcaps, radiator grills and spoilers. The body sealing products division primarily makes weather stripping for vehicles. The functional parts division develops fuel tanks and components, valve and head covers, hoses and gaskets. The safety system products division makes steering wheels and airbags. In optoelectronic products, Toyoda offers blue, green and white LEDs, which are used in multi-colored lighting for center consoles and instrument panels, large outdoor color displays, traffic signals and cell phone displays. The company also produces a variety of other consumer products, including cell phone cases, air purifiers and weight-dispersing mattresses. In addition, the company recently entered an agreement with OSRAM GmbH to share patents for LED technologies.

Toyoda Gosei offers its employees in Japan a health care center and company dormitories.

FINANCIALS:

Sales and profits are in thousands of dollars—add 000 to get the full amount. 2008 Note: Financial information for 2008 was not available for all companies at press time.

2008 Sales: $6,612,408	2008 Profits: $307,443	**U.S. Stock Ticker:**
2007 Sales: $5,027,145	2007 Profits: $135,059	**Int'l Ticker: 7282** Int'l Exchange: Tokyo-TSE
2006 Sales: $4,243,021	2006 Profits: $91,833	Employees: 23,925
2005 Sales: $4,055,673	2005 Profits: $98,567	Fiscal Year Ends: 3/31
2004 Sales: $3,757,800	2004 Profits: $120,000	Parent Company:

SALARIES/BENEFITS:

Pension Plan:	ESOP Stock Plan:	Profit Sharing:	Top Exec. Salary: $	Bonus: $
Savings Plan:	Stock Purch. Plan:		Second Exec. Salary: $	Bonus: $

OTHER THOUGHTS:

Apparent Women Officers or Directors:
Hot Spot for Advancement for Women/Minorities:

LOCATIONS: ("Y" = Yes)

West:	Southwest:	Midwest:	Southeast:	Northeast:	International:
Y	Y	Y			Y

TOYOTA MOTOR CORPORATION

www.toyota.co.jp/en

Industry Group Code: 336111 **Ranks within this company's industry group:** Sales: 1 Profits: 1

Techology:		Medical/Drugs:		Engineering:		Transportation:		Chemicals/Petrochemicals:		Specialty:	
Computers:		Manufacturer:		Design:		Aerospace:		Oil/Gas Products:		Special Services:	Y
Software:		Contract Research:		Construction:		Automotive:	Y	Chemicals:		Consulting:	
Communications:	Y	Medical Services:		Eng. Services:		Shipping:		Oil/Chem. Svcs.:		Specialty Mgmt.:	
Electronics:		Labs:		Consulting:				Gases:		Products:	
Alternative Energy:		Bio. Services:						Other:		Other:	

TYPES OF BUSINESS:

Automobiles, Manufacturing
Manufactured Housing
Advertising & e-Commerce Services
Financial Services
Telecommunications Services
Information Technology
Nanotechnology Research

BRANDS/DIVISIONS/AFFILIATES:

Lexus
Wesco Investments
Central Motor Co. Ltd.
Toyota South Africa (Pty) Ltd.
Toyota Motor Credit Corp
Toyota Auto Body Co Ltd
Hino Motors Ltd
Delphys Inc

CONTACTS: *Note: Officers with more than one job title may be intentionally listed here more than once.*

Akio Toyoda, Pres./Representative Dir.
Masatami Takimoto, Exec. VP-R&D Center
Koichi Ina, Sr. Managing Dir.-Strategic Prod. Planning Group
Iwao Nihashi, Sr. Managing Dir.-TQM Promotion Div.
Takeshi Suzuki, Sr. Managing Dir.-Finance & Acct. Group
Katsuaki Watanabe, Vice Chmn./Representative Dir.
Takahiko Ijichi, Sr. Managing Dir.-Bus. Dev. Group
Takeshi Uchiyamada, Exec. VP/Representative Dir.
Mitsuo Kinoshita, Exec. VP/Representative Dir.
Fujio Cho, Chmn./Representative Dir.

Phone: 81-0565-28-2121	**Fax:** 81-0565-23-5800
Toll-Free:	
Address: 1 Toyota-Cho, Toyota City, Aichi, 471-8571 Japan	

GROWTH PLANS/SPECIAL FEATURES:

Toyota Motor Corporation (TMC) designs, manufactures, assemblies and sells automobiles in over 170 countries under the Toyota, Lexus, Daihatsu and Hino brands. The firm operates in three segments: automotive, financial and other. The automotive segment includes the manufacturing of passenger vehicles, minivans and trucks, related parts and accessories. The financial segment consists primarily of providing financing for the purchase of Toyota vehicles. Subsidiary Toyota Financial Services Corp. oversees the management of the firm's finance companies worldwide and the expansion into new automobile-related product areas. Subsidiary Toyota Motor Credit Corp., the principal financial services subsidiary in the U.S., provides a wide range of financial services, including retail financing, retail leasing, wholesale financing and insurance. Toyota Finance Corp. provides a range of financial services, including retail financing, retail leasing, credit cards and housing loans. The other segment includes non-automotive business activities such as the manufacture and sale of prefabricated housing and the development of IT related products and services. The majority of vehicle sales, 33.2%, are to the North American market; 24.6% vehicles sold are in Japan; 14.4%throughout Europe; 10.7% within the remainder of Asia; and 17.1% are scattered through various other regions. In July 2008, the company agreed to acquire Central Motor Co. Ltd. In August 2008, the firm signed an agreement to acquire the remaining shares in joint venture Toyota South Africa (Pty) Ltd. Toyota suffered a serious global drop in unit sales in 2008.

FINANCIALS: **Sales and profits are in thousands of dollars—add 000 to get the full amount. 2008 Note: Financial information for 2008 was not available for all companies at press time.**

2008 Sales: $262,394,000	2008 Profits: $17,146,000	**U.S. Stock Ticker: TM**
2007 Sales: $185,752,000	2007 Profits: $13,927,000	**Int'l Ticker: 7203** Int'l Exchange: Tokyo-TSE
2006 Sales: $179,083,000	2006 Profits: $11,681,000	Employees: 316,121
2005 Sales: $159,046,000	2005 Profits: $10,037,000	Fiscal Year Ends: 3/31
2004 Sales: $148,240,000	2004 Profits: $9,961,000	Parent Company:

SALARIES/BENEFITS:

Pension Plan:	ESOP Stock Plan:	Profit Sharing:	Top Exec. Salary: $	Bonus: $
Savings Plan:	Stock Purch. Plan:		Second Exec. Salary: $	Bonus: $

OTHER THOUGHTS:

Apparent Women Officers or Directors:
Hot Spot for Advancement for Women/Minorities:

LOCATIONS: ("Y" = Yes)

West:	Southwest:	Midwest:	Southeast:	Northeast:	International:
Y	Y	Y	Y	Y	Y

TPV TECHNOLOGY LTD

www.tpvholdings.com

Industry Group Code: 334119 **Ranks within this company's industry group:** Sales: 5 Profits: 10

Techology:		Medical/Drugs:		Engineering:		Transportation:		Chemicals/Petrochemicals:		Specialty:	
Computers:		Manufacturer:		Design:		Aerospace:		Oil/Gas Products:		Special Services:	
Software:		Contract Research:		Construction:		Automotive:		Chemicals:		Consulting:	
Communications:		Medical Services:		Eng. Services:		Shipping:		Oil/Chem. Svcs.:		Specialty Mgmt.:	
Electronics:	Y	Labs:		Consulting:				Gases:		Products:	Y
Alternative Energy:		Bio. Services:						Other:		Other:	

TYPES OF BUSINESS:

Computer Accessories-Monitors
LCD Products
LCD & Plasma Televisions
Contract Manufacturing

BRANDS/DIVISIONS/AFFILIATES:

Envision
AOC
CMO

CONTACTS:

Note: Officers with more than one job title may be intentionally listed here more than once.

Jason Hsuan, CEO
Houng Yu-Te, CFO/Sr. VP
Lu Being-Chang, CTO/Sr. VP
Liao Jen Tsung, VP-Mfg.
Jason Hsuan, Chmn.
Hsieh Chi Tsung, Chief Procurement Officer/Sr. VP

Phone: 852-2858-5736	**Fax:** 852-2546-8884
Toll-Free:	
Address: Canon's Ct., 22 Victoria St., Hamilton, HM 12 Bermuda	

GROWTH PLANS/SPECIAL FEATURES:

TPV Technology, Ltd. is a leading contract manufacturer of more than 100 monitor models. The firm sells CRT (cathode ray tube) PC monitors, which generate approximately 13.2% of its revenue, and TFT-LCD monitors, which generate approximately 86.8%, ranging from 15-inch to 42-inch. TPV's 19-inch monitors generate approximately 24.2% of its sales, while its 32-inch models generate 19.7%, its 15-inch generate 13%, its 42-inch generate 10.7%, its 20-inch generate 9.7%, its 37-inch generate 8.3%, its 26-inch generate 6.9% and its other sizes together generate 7.3%. Its customers have included IBM, Hewlett-Packard, Compaq and Dell. The company also sells its own CRT monitors in over 30 countries worldwide under the Envision brand name, as well as both CRT and LCD monitors under the AOC brand name. In addition to its monitors, TPV manufactures LCD TVs and PDP (plasma multimedia) TVs. The firm is incorporated in Bermuda, conducts its manufacturing operations primarily in China and sells to Europe, the Americas, China and other Asian countries. During 2008, sales in China generated approximately 25.7% of TPV's revenue, while sales in North America generated approximately 26.9%, sales in Europe generated approximately 23.2% and sales throughout the rest of the world generated approximately 24.2%. In March 2008, TPV acquired a business operation from CMO, one of its major shareholders, for approximately $32.9 million.

FINANCIALS:

Sales and profits are in thousands of dollars—add 000 to get the full amount. 2008 Note: Financial information for 2008 was not available for all companies at press time.

2008 Sales: $9,247,020	2008 Profits: $97,580	**U.S. Stock Ticker:**
2007 Sales: $8,455,151	2007 Profits: $183,396	**Int'l Ticker: T18** Int'l Exchange: Singapore-SIN
2006 Sales: $7,176,300	2006 Profits: $154,400	Employees: 27,320
2005 Sales: $5,053,950	2005 Profits: $149,580	Fiscal Year Ends: 12/31
2004 Sales: $3,738,180	2004 Profits: $103,590	Parent Company:

SALARIES/BENEFITS:

Pension Plan:	ESOP Stock Plan:	Profit Sharing:	Top Exec. Salary: $	Bonus: $
Savings Plan:	Stock Purch. Plan:		Second Exec. Salary: $	Bonus: $

OTHER THOUGHTS:

Apparent Women Officers or Directors:
Hot Spot for Advancement for Women/Minorities:

LOCATIONS: ("Y" = Yes)

West:	Southwest:	Midwest:	Southeast:	Northeast:	International:
					Y

TRC COMPANIES INC

www.trcsolutions.com

Industry Group Code: 230000 **Ranks within this company's industry group:** Sales: 2 Profits: 2

Techology:		Medical/Drugs:		Engineering:		Transportation:		Chemicals/Petrochemicals:		Specialty:	
Computers:		Manufacturer:		Design:		Aerospace:		Oil/Gas Products:		Special Services:	Y
Software:		Contract Research:		Construction:	Y	Automotive:		Chemicals:		Consulting:	Y
Communications:		Medical Services:		Eng. Services:	Y	Shipping:		Oil/Chem. Svcs.:		Specialty Mgmt.:	Y
Electronics:		Labs:		Consulting:	Y			Gases:		Products:	
Alternative Energy:		Bio. Services:						Other:		Other:	

TYPES OF BUSINESS:

Infrastructure Services
Financial Risk Management
Technical Services
Environmental Engineering
Energy Services
Security Services
Hazardous Waste Disposal
Construction

BRANDS/DIVISIONS/AFFILIATES:

TRC Exit Strategy

CONTACTS:

Note: Officers with more than one job title may be intentionally listed here more than once.

Christopher P. Vincze, CEO
Michael C. Salmon, Pres.
Thomas W.Bennet, Jr., CFO/Sr. VP
Martin H. Dodd, General Counsel/Sr. VP/Sec.
Glenn Harkness, Sr. VP
Christopher Vincze, Chmn.

Phone: 860-298-9692 **Fax:** 860-298-6291
Toll-Free:
Address: 21 Griffin Rd. N., Windsor, CT 06095 US

GROWTH PLANS/SPECIAL FEATURES:

TRC Companies, Inc. is a national consulting, engineering and construction management firm. Its services are focused on four principal market areas: real estate, energy, environmental and infrastructure. In the real estate sector, the company offers the Exit Strategy program, which forms the platform of its overall real estate business. The program offers clients an alternative to the traditional management of contaminated sites and the perpetual retention of financial liability and risk. Under the program, the firm assumes responsibility and liability for remediation of the site, with clients paying a fixed price usually backed by insurance. Services provided to companies in the energy sector include support in the licensing and engineering design of new sources of power generation, electric transmission system upgrades and natural gas and petroleum pipelines and terminals. TRC's scientists, engineers and other technical professionals provide services to a wide range of clients including industrial and natural resource companies, railroads, real estate companies, and federal and state agencies. In many instances, services to these clients are channeled to the company by leading law firms or financial institutions. The firm's practice is organized to focus upon key areas of demand: building sciences, air quality measurements and air quality modeling, environmental assessment and remediation, and natural and cultural resource management. TRC's services for infrastructure clients are primarily related to expansion of infrastructure capacity in geographic areas where population growth and demographic change is occurring; rehabilitation of overburdened and deteriorating infrastructure systems; and management of risks related to security of public and private facilities. In March 2008, the company announced the completion of the new Long Island to Connecticut cable line, replacing the nearly 40 year-old original.

FINANCIALS:

Sales and profits are in thousands of dollars—add 000 to get the full amount. 2008 Note: Financial information for 2008 was not available for all companies at press time.

2008 Sales: $465,079	2008 Profits: $-109,149	**U.S. Stock Ticker: TRR**
2007 Sales: $441,643	2007 Profits: $-3,634	**Int'l Ticker:** Int'l Exchange:
2006 Sales: $396,091	2006 Profits: $-23,847	Employees: 2,500
2005 Sales: $358,522	2005 Profits: $-7,262	Fiscal Year Ends: 6/30
2004 Sales: $354,400	2004 Profits: $9,737	Parent Company:

SALARIES/BENEFITS:

Pension Plan:	ESOP Stock Plan:	Profit Sharing:	Top Exec. Salary: $465,000	Bonus: $
Savings Plan:	Stock Purch. Plan:		Second Exec. Salary: $309,402	Bonus: $

OTHER THOUGHTS:

Apparent Women Officers or Directors:
Hot Spot for Advancement for Women/Minorities:

LOCATIONS: ("Y" = Yes)

West:	Southwest:	Midwest:	Southeast:	Northeast:	International:
Y	Y	Y	Y	Y	

Note: Financial information, benefits and other data can change quickly and may vary from those stated here.

TREVI-FINANZIARIA INDUSTRIALE SPA (TREVI GROUP)

www.trevifin.com

Industry Group Code: 541330 **Ranks within this company's industry group:** Sales: 8 Profits: 6

Techology:		Medical/Drugs:		Engineering:		Transportation:		Chemicals/Petrochemicals:		Specialty:	
Computers:		Manufacturer:		Design:		Aerospace:		Oil/Gas Products:		Special Services:	
Software:		Contract Research:		Construction:	Y	Automotive:		Chemicals:		Consulting:	
Communications:		Medical Services:		Eng. Services:	Y	Shipping:		Oil/Chem. Svcs.:		Specialty Mgmt.:	
Electronics:		Labs:		Consulting:				Gases:		Products:	Y
Alternative Energy:	Y	Bio. Services:						Other:		Other:	

TYPES OF BUSINESS:

Engineering & Construction Services
Underground Construction Services
Foundation & Drilling Machinery & Services
Wind Farms

BRANDS/DIVISIONS/AFFILIATES:

Trevi Group
TREVI S.p.A.
SOILMEC S.p.A.
DRILLMEC S.p.A.
Trevi Energy S.p.A.
Galante SA
Arabian Soil Contractors Ltd

CONTACTS:

Note: Officers with more than one job title may be intentionally listed here more than once.

Gianluigi Trevisani, Managing Dir./VP
Stefano Trevisani, Managing Dir.
Cesare Trevisani, Managing Dir.
Davide Trevisani, Chmn.

Phone: 39-05-473-19111	**Fax:** 39-05-473-19313
Toll-Free:	
Address: 201 via Larga, Cesena, 47023 Italy	

GROWTH PLANS/SPECIAL FEATURES:

Trevi-Finanziaria Industriale (Trevi Group) is a global leader in foundation engineering and drilling and provides project management services supporting related projects around the world. It has branches in as over 30 countries. The group operates through four subsidiaries: Trevi, Petreven, Soilmec and Drillmec. Trevi provides construction services for underground engineering projects, such as special foundations for bridges, railways, dams, industrial systems and tunnels. Petreven is the company's segment in charge of oil drilling. Soilmec manufactures plants and rigs used for foundation engineering. Drillmec specializes in drilling projects and manufactures hydraulic rigs for oil, geothermal and water drilling. The company, through its subsidiaries, also has operations in well drilling for water research, as well as having completed numerous automated car park projects. Trevi Group's strong worldwide presence is illustrated by such past projects as the foundation works for the Third Mainland Bridge of Lagos in Nigeria; the Alicura in Argentina; the Port of Bandar Abbas in Iran; and the Khao dam in Thailand. In early 2008, Trevi Group announced the formation of a new company, Trevi Energy S.p.A., for the design, development and engineering of offshore wind farms. In February 2009, the company acquired Galante S.A. in Colombia and Arabian Soil Contractors Ltd in Saudi Arabia.

FINANCIALS:

Sales and profits are in thousands of dollars—add 000 to get the full amount. 2008 Note: Financial information for 2008 was not available for all companies at press time.

2008 Sales: $1,443,130	2008 Profits: $100,830	**U.S. Stock Ticker:**
2007 Sales: $1,323,600	2007 Profits: $87,600	**Int'l Ticker: TFI** Int'l Exchange: Milan-BI
2006 Sales: $1,019,100	2006 Profits: $42,000	Employees: 2,445
2005 Sales: $676,728	2005 Profits: $18,623	Fiscal Year Ends: 12/31
2004 Sales: $	2004 Profits: $	Parent Company:

SALARIES/BENEFITS:

Pension Plan:	ESOP Stock Plan:	Profit Sharing:	Top Exec. Salary: $	Bonus: $
Savings Plan:	Stock Purch. Plan:		Second Exec. Salary: $	Bonus: $

OTHER THOUGHTS:

Apparent Women Officers or Directors:
Hot Spot for Advancement for Women/Minorities:

LOCATIONS: ("Y" = Yes)

West:	Southwest:	Midwest:	Southeast:	Northeast:	International:
Y	Y		Y	Y	Y

TRW AUTOMOTIVE HOLDINGS CORP

www.trw.com

Industry Group Code: 336300 **Ranks within this company's industry group:** Sales: 8 Profits: 21

Techology:		Medical/Drugs:		Engineering:		Transportation:		Chemicals/Petrochemicals:		Specialty:	
Computers:		Manufacturer:		Design:		Aerospace:		Oil/Gas Products:		Special Services:	
Software:		Contract Research:		Construction:		Automotive:	Y	Chemicals:		Consulting:	
Communications:		Medical Services:		Eng. Services:		Shipping:		Oil/Chem. Svcs.:		Specialty Mgmt.:	
Electronics:	Y	Labs:		Consulting:				Gases:		Products:	
Alternative Energy:		Bio. Services:						Other:		Other:	

TYPES OF BUSINESS:

Automotive Systems & Components
Safety Systems

BRANDS/DIVISIONS/AFFILIATES:

TRW Integrated Chassis Systems LLC
TRW Technar Inc
EnTire Solutions LLC
LucasVarity Automotive Holding Company
TRW Automotive Global Receivables LLC
TRW Occupant Restraint Systems (Ventures) Ltd
TRW Intellectual Property Corp
TRW Overseas Inc

CONTACTS: *Note: Officers with more than one job title may be intentionally listed here more than once.*

John C. Plant, CEO
Steven Lunn, COO/Exec. VP
John C. Plant, Pres.
Joseph S. Cantie, CFO/Exec. VP
Peter J. Lake, Exec. VP-Sales
Neil E. Marchuk, Exec. VP-Human Resources
David L. Bialosky, General Counsel/Exec. VP
Peter J. Lake, Exec. VP-Bus. Dev.
Neil P. Simpkins, Chmn.

Phone: 734-855-2600	**Fax:** 734-855-2999
Toll-Free:	
Address: 12001 Tech Ctr. Dr., Livonia, MI 48150 US	

GROWTH PLANS/SPECIAL FEATURES:

TRW Automotive Holdings Corp. is one of the world's largest suppliers of automotive systems, modules and components to global automotive original equipment manufacturers (OEMs) and related aftermarkets. Through an extensive network of subsidiaries, TRW supplies products and services to more than 40 major vehicle manufacturers. With more than 200 facilities around the world, the company is a market leader in the production of braking, steering, suspension, cruise control, commercial steering, airbag, seat belt and body control (heating and air conditioning) systems. In addition, the firm develops a comprehensive line of safety products for the automobile industry, including both active safety systems, such as tire pressure monitoring systems and vehicle rollover sensors; and passive safety systems, such as airbag sensors. TRW uses cutting-edge tire pressure monitoring systems that can tell drivers which tires are under-inflated, by how much and how fast they are losing pressure. The company also uses advanced technology in its occupant weight sensing system. The system uses strain gauges at each corner of the front passenger seat frame to directly measure the occupant's seating weight and classify them to determine the appropriate air bag deployment strength. In addition to products and systems it produces on behalf of new vehicle manufacturers, the company is also a leading provider of automotive service, parts, technical support and diagnostic support through its aftermarket business unit, which serves customers in more than 120 countries worldwide. Customers that accounted for 10% or more of sales in 2008 include Volkswagen, Ford and General Motors. In early 2008, subsidiary TRW Integrated Chassis Systems, LLC acquired a portion of Delphi Corp.'s North American brake component machining and module assembly assets. In June 2008, subsidiary TRW Airbag Systems GmbH reached an agreement to acquire certain initiator machining and intellectual property rights from France-based Davey Bickford SNC.

FINANCIALS: **Sales and profits are in thousands of dollars—add 000 to get the full amount. 2008 Note: Financial information for 2008 was not available for all companies at press time.**

2008 Sales: $14,995,000	2008 Profits: $-779,000	**U.S. Stock Ticker: TRW**
2007 Sales: $14,702,000	2007 Profits: $90,000	**Int'l Ticker:** Int'l Exchange:
2006 Sales: $13,144,000	2006 Profits: $176,000	Employees: 65,200
2005 Sales: $12,643,000	2005 Profits: $204,000	Fiscal Year Ends: 12/31
2004 Sales: $12,011,000	2004 Profits: $29,000	Parent Company:

SALARIES/BENEFITS:

Pension Plan: Y	ESOP Stock Plan:	Profit Sharing:	Top Exec. Salary: $1,594,167	Bonus: $3,904,000
Savings Plan: Y	Stock Purch. Plan:		Second Exec. Salary: $974,152	Bonus: $1,519,045

OTHER THOUGHTS:

Apparent Women Officers or Directors: 1
Hot Spot for Advancement for Women/Minorities: Y

LOCATIONS: ("Y" = Yes)

West:	Southwest:	Midwest:	Southeast:	Northeast:	International:
	Y	Y	Y	Y	Y

TTM TECHNOLOGIES INC

www.ttmtech.com

Industry Group Code: 334419 **Ranks within this company's industry group:** Sales: 11 Profits: 8

Techology:		Medical/Drugs:		Engineering:		Transportation:		Chemicals/Petrochemicals:		Specialty:	
Computers:		Manufacturer:		Design:		Aerospace:		Oil/Gas Products:		Special Services:	
Software:		Contract Research:		Construction:		Automotive:		Chemicals:		Consulting:	
Communications:		Medical Services:		Eng. Services:		Shipping:		Oil/Chem. Svcs.:		Specialty Mgmt.:	
Electronics:	Y	Labs:		Consulting:				Gases:		Products:	
Alternative Energy:		Bio. Services:						Other:		Other:	

TYPES OF BUSINESS:

Printed Circuit Board Manufacturing
Backplane Assemblies
Quick-Turn Manufacturing Services

BRANDS/DIVISIONS/AFFILIATES:

CONTACTS:

Note: Officers with more than one job title may be intentionally listed here more than once.

Kenton K. Alder, CEO
Shane Whiteside, COO/Exec. VP
Kenton K. Alder, Pres.
Steven W. Richards, CFO/Exec. VP
Jeanette Newman, VP-Human Resources
Dale Knecht, VP-IT
Douglas Soder, Exec. VP
Robert Klatell, Chmn.

Phone: 714-241-0303	**Fax:** 714-241-0708
Toll-Free:	
Address: 2630 S. Harbor Blvd., Santa Ana, CA 92704 US	

GROWTH PLANS/SPECIAL FEATURES:

TTM Technologies, Inc. is a one-stop provider of complex printed circuit boards (PCBs) used in electronic equipment and provides backplane and sub-system assembly services for both standard and specialty products in defense and commercial operations. The primary raw materials that the firm uses in PCB manufacturing include copper-clad laminate; chemical solutions such as copper and gold for plating operations; photographic film; carbide drill bits; and plastic for testing fixtures. The primary raw materials used in backplane assembly include PCBs, connectors, capacitors, resistors, diodes and integrated circuits. The firm is capable of manufacturing high-layer count PCBs, stacked microvias, copper and epoxy-filled vias, flex and rigid flex circuits, multiple surface finishes, mixed dielectrics, embedded passives and oversize panel formats, among others. TTM also offers thermal management and custom assembly solutions, as well as design, modeling and simulation services. The company has over 1 million square feet of manufacturing space across 11 facilities, located in California, Washington, Wisconsin, Utah, Connecticut and Shanghai, China. TTM also maintains an on-call global customer support network. The company can function as a one-stop manufacturing solution, because its facilities are specialized and integrated, each focusing on a different stage of an electronic product's life cycle. TTM's specialty is quick-turn services, which enable customers to shorten the time required to develop new products and bring them to market, and technologically advanced PCBs and the backplane and sub-system assembly business. The company serves high-end commercial markets and aerospace markets, providing PCBs and backplane assemblies for applications including networking/communications infrastructure; high-end computing; defense systems; industrial controls; and medical testing equipment. Customers include both OEMs and electronic manufacturing services (EMS) providers.

The company offers its employees medical, dental and vision insurance; life and AD&D insurance; short- and long-term disability insurance; a 401(k) plan; and access to a credit union.

FINANCIALS:

Sales and profits are in thousands of dollars—add 000 to get the full amount. 2008 Note: Financial information for 2008 was not available for all companies at press time.

2008 Sales: $680,981	2008 Profits: $-35,270	**U.S. Stock Ticker: TTMI**
2007 Sales: $669,458	2007 Profits: $34,683	**Int'l Ticker:** Int'l Exchange:
2006 Sales: $369,316	2006 Profits: $35,039	Employees: 3,585
2005 Sales: $240,209	2005 Profits: $30,841	Fiscal Year Ends: 12/31
2004 Sales: $240,650	2004 Profits: $28,330	Parent Company:

SALARIES/BENEFITS:

Pension Plan:	ESOP Stock Plan:	Profit Sharing:	Top Exec. Salary: $487,692	Bonus: $416,952
Savings Plan: Y	Stock Purch. Plan:		Second Exec. Salary: $337,896	Bonus: $200,000

OTHER THOUGHTS:

Apparent Women Officers or Directors: 1
Hot Spot for Advancement for Women/Minorities:

LOCATIONS: ("Y" = Yes)

West:	Southwest:	Midwest:	Southeast:	Northeast:	International:
Y		Y		Y	Y

TYCO INTERNATIONAL LTD

www.tyco.com

Industry Group Code: 561610 **Ranks within this company's industry group:** Sales: 1 Profits: 1

Techology:		Medical/Drugs:		Engineering:		Transportation:		Chemicals/Petrochemicals:		Specialty:	
Computers:		Manufacturer:		Design:		Aerospace:		Oil/Gas Products:		Special Services:	Y
Software:		Contract Research:		Construction:		Automotive:		Chemicals:		Consulting:	Y
Communications:	Y	Medical Services:		Eng. Services:		Shipping:		Oil/Chem. Svcs.:		Specialty Mgmt.:	
Electronics:	Y	Labs:		Consulting:				Gases:		Products:	Y
Alternative Energy:		Bio. Services:						Other:		Other:	

TYPES OF BUSINESS:

Fire & Security Systems & Services
Security Monitoring Services
Specialty Valves

BRANDS/DIVISIONS/AFFILIATES:

ADT Security Services Inc.
M/A-Com Inc.
Tyco Flow Control
Tyco Fire and Security Services
SimplexGrinnell

CONTACTS: *Note: Officers with more than one job title may be intentionally listed here more than once.*

Edward D. Breen, CEO
Christopher J. Coughlin, CFO/Exec. VP
Laurie Siegel, Sr. VP-Human Resources
Judith A. Reinsdorf, General Counsel/Exec. VP
Edward C. Arditte, Sr. VP-Strategy
Edward C. Arditte, Sr. VP-Investor Rel.
Carol Anthony Davidson, Chief Acct. Officer/Controller/Sr. VP
Patrick Decker, Pres., Flow Control
George R. Oliver, Pres., Safety, Electrical & Metal Prod.
Jim Spicer, Pres., SimplexGrinnell
Naren K. Gursahaney, Pres., ADT Worldwide
Edward D. Breen, Chmn.
Shelley Stewart, Jr., Chief Procurement Officer

Phone: 441-292-8674 **Fax:** 441-295-9647
Toll-Free:
Address: 90 Pitts Bay Rd, 2nd Fl., Pembroke, HM 08 Bermuda

GROWTH PLANS/SPECIAL FEATURES:

Tyco International, Ltd. is a diversified, global company that provides products and services to customers in more than 60 countries. The company operates in five segments: ADT Worldwide; fire protection services; safety products; flow control; and electrical and metal products. ADT Worldwide is an electronic security and alarm monitoring provider for residential, commercial, industrial and governmental clientele. The fire protection services segment offers solutions in the fields of fire detection, fire suppression and special-hazard solutions. The safety products category supplies breathing apparatuses for firefighters, intrusion security, access control, video management and electronic surveillance systems. The flow control segment provides valves, pipes, fittings, valve automation and heat tracing solutions for an array of industries, including oil and gas, food, energy and chemical. The electrical and metal products group provides galvanized steel tubes, armored wire and cable, and other metal products for the construction, electrical, fire and security industries. Key company brands include ADT, Sensormatic, SimplexGrinnell, Keystone, Vanessa, Wormald, Scott, Ansul, Allied Tube & Conduit and AFC Cable. In 2008, Tyco sold Nippon Dry-Chemical Co. Ltd., a subsidiary, to Daiwa Securities SMBC Principal Investments Co. Ltd. It then sold its Infrastructure Services business (which operated under the name Earth Tech, Inc.) to AECOM Technology Corp. and its Ancon Building Products business to CRH plc. In addition, the company's ADT Worldwide segment acquired Sensormatic Security Corp., Winner Security Services LLC and First Service Security, a division of First Service Corporation. In October 2008, Sensormatic Electronics Corporation acquired Vue Technology, Inc., an item-level RFID software solutions firm.

The firm offers its employees a 401(k); employee stock purchase plan; life, accident and disability insurance; employee assistance programs; and tuition reimbursement.

FINANCIALS: Sales and profits are in thousands of dollars—add 000 to get the full amount. 2008 Note: Financial information for 2008 was not available for all companies at press time.

2008 Sales: $20,199,000	2008 Profits: $1,553,000	**U.S. Stock Ticker: TYC**
2007 Sales: $18,477,000	2007 Profits: $-1,742,000	**Int'l Ticker:** Int'l Exchange:
2006 Sales: $17,066,000	2006 Profits: $3,590,000	Employees: 113,000
2005 Sales: $16,665,000	2005 Profits: $3,094,000	Fiscal Year Ends: 9/30
2004 Sales: $29,886,000	2004 Profits: $2,820,000	Parent Company:

SALARIES/BENEFITS:

Pension Plan:	ESOP Stock Plan:	Profit Sharing:	Top Exec. Salary: $1,625,000	Bonus: $3,250,000
Savings Plan: Y	Stock Purch. Plan: Y		Second Exec. Salary: $800,000	Bonus: $1,600,000

OTHER THOUGHTS:

Apparent Women Officers or Directors: 2
Hot Spot for Advancement for Women/Minorities: Y

LOCATIONS: ("Y" = Yes)

West:	Southwest:	Midwest:	Southeast:	Northeast:	International:
Y	Y	Y	Y	Y	Y

UCB SA

www.ucb-group.com

Industry Group Code: 325412 **Ranks within this company's industry group:** Sales: 23 Profits: 26

Techology:		Medical/Drugs:		Engineering:		Transportation:		Chemicals/Petrochemicals:		Specialty:	
Computers:		Manufacturer:	Y	Design:		Aerospace:		Oil/Gas Products:		Special Services:	
Software:		Contract Research:		Construction:		Automotive:		Chemicals:	Y	Consulting:	
Communications:		Medical Services:		Eng. Services:		Shipping:		Oil/Chem. Svcs.:		Specialty Mgmt.:	
Electronics:		Labs:		Consulting:				Gases:		Products:	
Alternative Energy:		Bio. Services:						Other:		Other:	

TYPES OF BUSINESS:

Pharmaceuticals Development
Industrial Chemical Products
Allergy & Respiratory Treatments
Central Nervous System Disorder Treatments

BRANDS/DIVISIONS/AFFILIATES:

Keppra
Neupro
Cimzia
Lortab
Xyzal
Zyrtec
Schwarz Pharma AG
Otsuka Pharmaceuticals Co., Ltd.

CONTACTS: *Note: Officers with more than one job title may be intentionally listed here more than once.*

Roch Doliveux, CEO
Detlef Thielgen, CFO/Exec. VP
Fabrice Enderlin, Exec. VP-Human Resources
Melanie Lee, Exec. VP-Research
Bob Trainor, General Counsel/Exec. VP
Bill Robinson, Exec. VP-Global Oper.
Antje Witte, VP-Corp. Comm.
Antje Witte, VP-Investor Rel.
Iris Low-Friedrich, Chief Medical Officer
Iris Low-Friedrich, Exec. VP-Dev.
Roch Doliveux, Chmn.

Phone: 32-2-559-99-99	**Fax:** 32-2-599-99-00
Toll-Free:	
Address: Allee de la Recherche, 60, Brussels, 1070 Belgium	

GROWTH PLANS/SPECIAL FEATURES:

UCB S.A. is a Belgian biopharmaceutical firm with operations in more than 40 countries, focusing on severe diseases in the fields of the central nervous system (CNS), including epilepsy and Parkinson's disease; inflammation, including allergy; and oncology. Keppra, the firm's lead product, is used in both monotherapy and adjunctive therapy for the treatment of epilepsy. Another CNS product is Neupro, approved in Europe for the treatment of early-stage Parkinson's disease. UCB's anti-allergics include Xyzal, an anti-allergic designed to treat and prevent persistent rhinitis in children, characterized by severe and long-lasting allergic symptoms with a tendency to evolve towards allergic asthma; Cimzia, approved in the U.S. and Switzerland for the treatment of Crohn's disease; and Zyrtec, an antihistamine approved in 100 countries for use in children from the age of six months. Other products include Nootropil, a cerebral function regulator used to treat adults and the elderly; Lortab, an analgesic approved in the U.S. for the relief of moderate to moderately severe pain; Tussionex, a 12-hour cough suppressant approved in the U.S.; Metadate CD/Equasym XL, used in the treatment of Attention Deficit Hyperactivity Disorder (ADHD); Innovair, a combination therapy for asthma; Isoket, used to treat coronary heart disease; and BUP-4, a once-daily treatment for urinary incontinence. In January 2007, UCB acquired more than 88% of Schwarz Pharma AG's shares. In March 2007, the company sold its stake in Cytec Industries, Inc. In February 2008, the U.S. FDA approved Xyzal for the relief of allergy symptoms and the treatment of chronic idiopathic urticaria. In April 2008, the FDA also approved Cimzia for treatment of moderate to severe Crohn's disease. In June 2008, UCB signed a collaboration agreement with Otsuka Pharmaceuticals Co., Ltd., of Japan, to co-promote Keppra and Cimzia.

FINANCIALS: **Sales and profits are in thousands of dollars—add 000 to get the full amount. 2008 Note: Financial information for 2008 was not available for all companies at press time.**

2008 Sales: $4,860,380	2008 Profits: $-58,040	**U.S. Stock Ticker:**
2007 Sales: $4,894,120	2007 Profits: $295,590	**Int'l Ticker: UCB** Int'l Exchange: Brussels-Euronext
2006 Sales: $2,987,500	2006 Profits: $501,100	Employees: 11,403
2005 Sales: $2,602,500	2005 Profits: $961,760	Fiscal Year Ends: 12/31
2004 Sales: $2,132,440	2004 Profits: $419,100	Parent Company:

SALARIES/BENEFITS:

Pension Plan: Y	ESOP Stock Plan:	Profit Sharing:	Top Exec. Salary: $	Bonus: $
Savings Plan:	Stock Purch. Plan:		Second Exec. Salary: $	Bonus: $

OTHER THOUGHTS:

Apparent Women Officers or Directors: 2
Hot Spot for Advancement for Women/Minorities:

LOCATIONS: ("Y" = Yes)

West:	Southwest:	Midwest:	Southeast:	Northeast:	International:
		Y	Y	Y	Y

UNIDEN CORPORATION

www.uniden.co.jp

Industry Group Code: 334200 **Ranks within this company's industry group:** Sales: 5 Profits: 4

Techology:		Medical/Drugs:		Engineering:		Transportation:		Chemicals/Petrochemicals:		Specialty:	
Computers:		Manufacturer:		Design:		Aerospace:		Oil/Gas Products:		Special Services:	
Software:		Contract Research:		Construction:		Automotive:		Chemicals:		Consulting:	
Communications:	Y	Medical Services:		Eng. Services:		Shipping:		Oil/Chem. Svcs.:		Specialty Mgmt.:	
Electronics:	Y	Labs:		Consulting:				Gases:		Products:	
Alternative Energy:		Bio. Services:						Other:		Other:	

TYPES OF BUSINESS:

Communications Equipment-Wireless Devices
Cordless Phones
Networking Equipment
Scanners
Radar Detectors
Electronic Products
Business Phones
Marine Electronics

BRANDS/DIVISIONS/AFFILIATES:

Uniden America Corporation
Uniden European Corporation
Uniden Electronics Products Co
Uniden New Zealand Ltd
Uniden Canada
Uniden Australia Pty Ltd
Uniden Hong Kong Ltd

CONTACTS: *Note: Officers with more than one job title may be intentionally listed here more than once.*

Hiroyuki Maeda, Pres.
Larry Johannes, Dir.-Media Rel.
Yasutaka Sagiyama, Sr. Managing Dir.
Yoshinori Matsuoka, Sr. Managing Dir.
Hidero Fujimoto, Chmn.
Rich Tosi, Pres., Uniden America

Phone: 81-3-5543-2800	**Fax:** 81-3-5543-2921
Toll-Free:	
Address: 2-12-7 Hatchobori, Chuo-ku, Tokyo, 104-8512 Japan	

GROWTH PLANS/SPECIAL FEATURES:

Uniden Corporation, based in Japan, is a leading producer of wireless communications devices. It manufactures and markets wireless consumer electronic products including cordless phones, networking equipment, general transceivers, scanners, marine electronics, telecommunications systems, radar detectors and CB radios. Additionally, the company offers business phones and business networking equipment, including wireless, multi-line and VoIP (voice over Internet protocol) phones, routers and switches. Uniden has subsidiaries operating in the U.S., Canada, China, Vietnam, Australia and New Zealand, as well as a European liaison office in Belgium. In the U.S., Uniden operates through Uniden America Corporation and is headquartered in Fort Worth, Texas. Recently the company partnered with Microsoft Corp. to create a line of digital cordless phones that also serve as a traditional landline phone and offers Internet calls via the Windows Live Messenger service. In January 2008, the firm began production of DECT (Digital Enhanced Cordless Telecommunications) cordless telephones for an original equipment manufacturer serving the European market. Also in January, Uniden completed construction of a new manufacturing facility at Jiangxi in China. The facility will supply a number of products, including AC adaptors. In March 2008, the company released its TRAX350 portable car navigation system in the North American market. In February 2009, Uniden announced that it would cease manufacturing activities at its plant in Shenzhen in order to focus more of its production in Vietnam.

FINANCIALS: **Sales and profits are in thousands of dollars—add 000 to get the full amount. 2008 Note: Financial information for 2008 was not available for all companies at press time.**

2008 Sales: $611,598	2008 Profits: $-74,768	**U.S. Stock Ticker:**
2007 Sales: $714,600	2007 Profits: $-27,300	**Int'l Ticker: 6815** Int'l Exchange: Tokyo-TSE
2006 Sales: $788,700	2006 Profits: $46,200	Employees: 19,496
2005 Sales: $772,400	2005 Profits: $116,200	Fiscal Year Ends: 3/31
2004 Sales: $773,700	2004 Profits: $-132,200	Parent Company:

SALARIES/BENEFITS:

Pension Plan:	ESOP Stock Plan:	Profit Sharing:	Top Exec. Salary: $	Bonus: $
Savings Plan:	Stock Purch. Plan:		Second Exec. Salary: $	Bonus: $

OTHER THOUGHTS:

Apparent Women Officers or Directors:
Hot Spot for Advancement for Women/Minorities:

LOCATIONS: ("Y" = Yes)

West:	Southwest:	Midwest:	Southeast:	Northeast:	International:
	Y				Y

UNION CARBIDE CORPORATION

www.unioncarbide.com

Industry Group Code: 325000 **Ranks within this company's industry group:** Sales: Profits:

Techology:		Medical/Drugs:		Engineering:		Transportation:		Chemicals/Petrochemicals:		Specialty:	
Computers:		Manufacturer:		Design:		Aerospace:		Oil/Gas Products:		Special Services:	
Software:		Contract Research:		Construction:		Automotive:		Chemicals:	Y	Consulting:	
Communications:		Medical Services:		Eng. Services:		Shipping:		Oil/Chem. Svcs.:		Specialty Mgmt.:	
Electronics:		Labs:		Consulting:				Gases:		Products:	Y
Alternative Energy:		Bio. Services:						Other:		Other:	

TYPES OF BUSINESS:

Basic Chemicals, Manufacturing
Polymers

BRANDS/DIVISIONS/AFFILIATES:

Dow Chemical

CONTACTS:

Note: Officers with more than one job title may be intentionally listed here more than once.

Patrick E. Gottschalk, CEO
Patrick E. Gottschalk, Pres.
Edward W. Rich, CFO/VP
Edward W. Rich, Treas.

Phone: 713-978-2016 **Fax:** 713-978-2394
Toll-Free:
Address: 400 W. Sam Houston Pkwy. S., Houston, TX 77042 US

GROWTH PLANS/SPECIAL FEATURES:

Union Carbide Corporation (UCC) manufactures basic chemicals and polymers primarily for commercial manufacturers. UCC produces ethylene from crude oil and natural gas and converts it to polyethylene or ethylene oxide, a precursor to many of the company's products. The firm operates 12 manufacturing sites in four countries, where it produces a broad range of chemicals, including ethylene glycol, solvents, alcohols, surfactants, amines, specialty products, polypropylene, polyethylene, biocides, anti-icing fluids and solution vinyl resins for industrial coatings. These chemicals produced by UCC provide vital functions for various businesses, such as deicing airplanes and coating pills to make them easier to swallow. Customers who buy these products include companies with operations in paints and coatings; packaging; wire and cable; household products; personal care; pharmaceuticals; automotive; textiles; agriculture; and oil and gas. UCC primarily sells its products to its parent company, Dow Chemicals. Dow Chemicals, a chemical, plastics and agricultural products supplier, markets UCC's products to customers who make food containers, toys, automotive antifreeze, rubbing alcohol, paper towels, cosmetics and cleaning products.

Union Carbide offers its employees a comprehensive medical plan, life insurance, long-term care insurance, personal lines insurance, a pension and a 401(k) plan.

FINANCIALS:

Sales and profits are in thousands of dollars—add 000 to get the full amount. 2008 Note: Financial information for 2008 was not available for all companies at press time.

2008 Sales: $	2008 Profits: $	**U.S. Stock Ticker: Subsidiary**
2007 Sales: $	2007 Profits: $	**Int'l Ticker:** Int'l Exchange:
2006 Sales: $7,528,000	2006 Profits: $1,046,000	Employees: 3,800
2005 Sales: $6,388,000	2005 Profits: $1,311,000	Fiscal Year Ends: 12/31
2004 Sales: $5,864,000	2004 Profits: $687,000	Parent Company: DOW CHEMICAL COMPANY (THE)

SALARIES/BENEFITS:

Pension Plan: Y	ESOP Stock Plan:	Profit Sharing:	Top Exec. Salary: $	Bonus: $
Savings Plan: Y	Stock Purch. Plan:		Second Exec. Salary: $	Bonus: $

OTHER THOUGHTS:

Apparent Women Officers or Directors:
Hot Spot for Advancement for Women/Minorities:

LOCATIONS: ("Y" = Yes)

West:	Southwest:	Midwest:	Southeast:	Northeast:	International:
Y	Y	Y	Y	Y	Y

UNISYS CORP

www.unisys.com

Industry Group Code: 541512 **Ranks within this company's industry group:** Sales: 11 Profits: 15

Techology:		Medical/Drugs:		Engineering:		Transportation:		Chemicals/Petrochemicals:		Specialty:	
Computers:	Y	Manufacturer:		Design:		Aerospace:		Oil/Gas Products:		Special Services:	Y
Software:	Y	Contract Research:		Construction:		Automotive:		Chemicals:		Consulting:	Y
Communications:	Y	Medical Services:		Eng. Services:		Shipping:		Oil/Chem. Svcs.:		Specialty Mgmt.:	
Electronics:		Labs:		Consulting:				Gases:		Products:	
Alternative Energy:		Bio. Services:						Other:		Other:	

TYPES OF BUSINESS:

Consulting-Systems Integration & Technology Support
Enterprise Systems & Servers
Outsourcing Services
Infrastructure Services
Security Technology
Server Software & Middleware

BRANDS/DIVISIONS/AFFILIATES:

ClearPath Plus
ES7000 Server
Atex Group Limited

CONTACTS: *Note: Officers with more than one job title may be intentionally listed here more than once.*

J. Edward Coleman, CEO
Janet B. Haugen, CFO/Sr. VP
Patricia A. Bradford, Sr. VP-Human Resources
Richard C. Marcello, Sr. VP/Pres., Systems & Tech.
Nancy S. Sundheim, General Counsel/Corp. Sec./Sr. VP
Dominick Cavuoto, Pres., Worldwide Strategic Svcs.
Jack F. McHale, VP-Investor Rel.
Scott A. Battersby, Treas./VP
Scott W. Hurley, VP/Corp. Controller
Ted Davies, Pres., Federal Systems
Anthony P. Doyle, Pres., Global Outsourcing & Infrastructure Svcs.
Dominick Cavuoto, Pres., Global Industries
J. Edward Coleman, Chmn.

Phone: 215-986-4011	**Fax:** 215-986-6850
Toll-Free:	
Address: Unisys Way, Blue Bell, PA 19424 US	

GROWTH PLANS/SPECIAL FEATURES:

Unisys Corp. is a worldwide information technology services and solutions company. The firm offers services for systems integration, outsourcing, infrastructure, server technology and consulting to commercial businesses and governments. Unisys operates in two business segments: services and technology. In the services segment, the company provides end-to-end services and solutions designed to help clients improve their competitiveness and efficiency in the global marketplace. The Unisys portfolio of solutions and services includes systems integrations and consulting, including check processing systems, public welfare systems, airline reservations and communications messaging solutions; outsourcing, including the management of a customer's internal information systems and management of specific business processes, such as insurance claims processing, health claims processing, mortgage administration and cargo management; infrastructure services involving the design and support of customers' IT infrastructure, including desktops, servers, mobile and wireless systems and networks; enterprise-wide security solutions to protect systems, networks, applications and data; and core maintenance services, including the maintenance of Unisys proprietary products. In the technology segment, the company designs and develops servers and related products. Major technology offerings include enterprise-class servers based on Cellular Multi-Processing architecture, such as the ClearPath family of servers, and the ES7000 family of servers, providing enterprise-class attributes on Intel-based servers; operating system software and middleware; and specialized technologies such as payment systems and third-party products. Primary markets served by Unisys include the financial services, communications, transportation, commercial and public sectors. The company maintains working partnerships with Cisco, Dell, EMC, IBM, Intel, Microsoft, Oracle and SAP, among others. In March 2007, Unisys sold its media business to Atex Group, Ltd. In May 2008, the firm won a $179 million contract to provide a new Medicaid Management Information System to the state of Maine.

Unisys offers its employees flexible spending accounts, an employee assistance program and medical, dental, disability and life insurance.

FINANCIALS: **Sales and profits are in thousands of dollars—add 000 to get the full amount. 2008 Note: Financial information for 2008 was not available for all companies at press time.**

2008 Sales: $5,233,200	2008 Profits: $-130,100	**U.S. Stock Ticker: UIS**
2007 Sales: $5,652,500	2007 Profits: $-79,100	**Int'l Ticker:** Int'l Exchange:
2006 Sales: $5,757,200	2006 Profits: $-278,700	Employees: 29,000
2005 Sales: $5,758,700	2005 Profits: $-1,731,900	Fiscal Year Ends: 12/31
2004 Sales: $5,820,700	2004 Profits: $38,600	Parent Company:

SALARIES/BENEFITS:

Pension Plan:	ESOP Stock Plan:	Profit Sharing:	Top Exec. Salary: $959,297	Bonus: $
Savings Plan: Y	Stock Purch. Plan:		Second Exec. Salary: $530,410	Bonus: $

OTHER THOUGHTS:

Apparent Women Officers or Directors: 3
Hot Spot for Advancement for Women/Minorities: Y

LOCATIONS: ("Y" = Yes)

West:	Southwest:	Midwest:	Southeast:	Northeast:	International:
Y	Y	Y	Y	Y	Y

Note: Financial information, benefits and other data can change quickly and may vary from those stated here.

UNITED MICROELECTRONICS CORP

www.umc.com

Industry Group Code: 334413 **Ranks within this company's industry group:** Sales: 13 Profits: 14

Techology:		Medical/Drugs:		Engineering:		Transportation:		Chemicals/Petrochemicals:		Specialty:	
Computers:		Manufacturer:		Design:		Aerospace:		Oil/Gas Products:		Special Services:	
Software:		Contract Research:		Construction:		Automotive:		Chemicals:		Consulting:	
Communications:		Medical Services:		Eng. Services:		Shipping:		Oil/Chem. Svcs.:		Specialty Mgmt.:	
Electronics:	Y	Labs:		Consulting:				Gases:		Products:	
Alternative Energy:		Bio. Services:						Other:		Other:	

TYPES OF BUSINESS:

Chips/Semiconductors

BRANDS/DIVISIONS/AFFILIATES:

CONTACTS:

Note: Officers with more than one job title may be intentionally listed here more than once.

Shih Wei Sun, CEO
Po Wen Yen, Pres., 12-inch Oper.
Wen Yang Chen, Pres., 8-inch Oper.
Stan Hung, Chmn.

Phone: 886-3-578-2258 **Fax:** 886-3-577-9392
Toll-Free:
Address: 3 Li-Hsin 2nd Rd., Hsinchu Science Park, Hsinchu, Taiwan

GROWTH PLANS/SPECIAL FEATURES:

United Microelectronics Corp. (UMC), based in Taiwan, is a leading manufacturer of high-speed semiconductor products, such as advanced process ICs for applications spanning the major sectors of the semiconductor industry. The microchips are generally contract manufactured, and customers incorporate the company's products into a range of electronic devices, including 3G cell phones and digital consumer products. The company design sizes are offered in a range from 65 nanometers (nm) to .25 microns, and its products include 90nm, 65nm and mixed signal/RFCMOS technologies, as well as a range of specialty technologies. UMC's 90 nm copper technology has been in volume production since 2004, and the 65 nm technology entered mass production in 2007. UMC produced functional 45nm SRAM chips in late 2006 and continues to develop the technology. The company has ten manufacturing facilities throughout the world. In recent years, focus has shifted to System on Chip or SoC designs, which incorporate and integrate all the components of a computing system onto one chip. To this end, UMC has developed high-yield 0.13 micron 1T-SRAM, 6T-SRAM and embedded flash memory products. The company also provides product yield management services to assist customers with product qualification, manufacturing, development and support. The firm has locations in Japan, Singapore, Europe and the U.S. The company's top ten customers account for roughly 58% of its net operating revenues. In December 2007, UMC was ranked the top semiconductor company in Taiwan in the Asian Corporate Governance Association (ACGA) and CLSA Limited's Clean & Green Watch 2007 report.

UMC offers counseling services and the use of a reaction center at its Hsinchu headquarters, which features sports facilities, a performance venue and meeting space. In addition, employees are encouraged to communicate with management through opinion boxes, meetings and symposia.

FINANCIALS:

Sales and profits are in thousands of dollars—add 000 to get the full amount. 2008 Note: Financial information for 2008 was not available for all companies at press time.

2008 Sales: $2,824,000	2008 Profits: $-681,000	**U.S. Stock Ticker: UMC**
2007 Sales: $3,440,000	2007 Profits: $1,000,000	**Int'l Ticker: 2303** Int'l Exchange: Taipei-TPE
2006 Sales: $3,437,000	2006 Profits: $1,001,000	Employees: 11,935
2005 Sales: $3,058,400	2005 Profits: $-477,700	Fiscal Year Ends: 12/31
2004 Sales: $4,070,282	2004 Profits: $1,003,257	Parent Company:

SALARIES/BENEFITS:

Pension Plan:	ESOP Stock Plan:	Profit Sharing:	Top Exec. Salary: $	Bonus: $
Savings Plan:	Stock Purch. Plan:		Second Exec. Salary: $	Bonus: $

OTHER THOUGHTS:

Apparent Women Officers or Directors:
Hot Spot for Advancement for Women/Minorities:

LOCATIONS: ("Y" = Yes)

West:	Southwest:	Midwest:	Southeast:	Northeast:	International:
Y					Y

Note: Financial information, benefits and other data can change quickly and may vary from those stated here.

UNITED TECHNOLOGIES CORPORATION

www.utc.com

Industry Group Code: 336410 **Ranks within this company's industry group:** Sales: 2 Profits: 1

Techology:		**Medical/Drugs:**		**Engineering:**		**Transportation:**		**Chemicals/Petrochemicals:**		**Specialty:**	
Computers:		Manufacturer:		Design:		Aerospace:	Y	Oil/Gas Products:		Special Services:	Y
Software:	Y	Contract Research:		Construction:		Automotive:		Chemicals:		Consulting:	
Communications:	Y	Medical Services:		Eng. Services:		Shipping:		Oil/Chem. Svcs.:		Specialty Mgmt.:	
Electronics:	Y	Labs:		Consulting:				Gases:		Products:	
Alternative Energy:	Y	Bio. Services:						Other:		Other:	

TYPES OF BUSINESS:

Aerospace Technology
Elevator & Escalator Systems
HVAC Systems
Fuel Cells & Power Generation
Industrial Systems
Aircraft Parts & Maintenance
Flight Systems
Security Products & Services

BRANDS/DIVISIONS/AFFILIATES:

Otis Elevator Company
Carrier Corp.
Sikorsky
Pratt & Whitney
Hamilton Sundstrand
UTC Fire and Security
UTC Power
Architectural Energy Corp

CONTACTS: *Note: Officers with more than one job title may be intentionally listed here more than once.*

Louis R. Chenevert, CEO
Louis R. Chenevert, Pres.
Gregory J. Hayes, CFO/Sr. VP
J. Thomas Bowler, Jr., Sr. VP-Human Resources & Organization
J. Michael McQuade, Sr. VP-Science & Tech.
John Doucette, CIO/VP
Charles D. Gill, General Counsel/Sr. VP
Jothi Purushotaman, VP-Oper.
James E. Geisler, VP-Corp. Strategy & Planning
Nancy T. Lintner, VP-Corp. Comm.
Ari Bousbib, Corp. Exec. VP/Pres., Commercial Companies
William M. Brown, Pres., UTC Fire & Security
Geraud Darnis, Pres., Carrier
Didier Michaud-Daniel, Pres., Otis
George David, Chmn.

Phone: 860-728-7000	**Fax:** 860-728-7028
Toll-Free:	
Address: 1 Financial Plz., Hartford, CT 06101 US	

GROWTH PLANS/SPECIAL FEATURES:

United Technologies Corporation (UTC) provides high-technology products and services to the building systems and aerospace industries worldwide. The company operates through seven companies: Carrier Corp., Hamilton Sundstrand, Otis Elevator Company, Pratt & Whitney, Sikorsky, UTC Fire & Security and UTC Power. Carrier manufactures commercial and residential heating, ventilation and air conditioning (HVAC) systems and equipment. It also produces, sells, services and provides components for commercial and transport refrigeration equipment. Hamilton Sundstrand serves commercial, military, regional and corporate aviation, as well as space and undersea applications. Its products include power generation management and distribution systems; flight systems, engine control systems, environmental control systems, fire protection and detection systems, auxiliary power units and propeller systems. Otis is one of the world's largest elevator and escalator manufacturing, installation and maintenance companies. Otis designs, manufactures, sells and installs a wide range of passenger and freight elevators for low-, medium- and high-speed applications, as well as a broad line of escalators and moving walkways. Pratt & Whitney produces and services commercial, general aviation and military aircraft engines. It also handles rocket engine production for commercial and government space applications. Sikorsky is a world leader in helicopters manufacturing and design, whose customers include the U.S. military and 40 other countries. UTC Fire & Security operates in the electronic security industry and the fire safety industry. UTC Power develops and markets distributed generation power systems and fuel cell power plants for stationary, transportation, space and defense applications. UTC Power recently acquired Architectural Energy Corp, a private energy engineering firm working to optimize the environmental performance of buildings.

FINANCIALS: **Sales and profits are in thousands of dollars—add 000 to get the full amount. 2008 Note: Financial information for 2008 was not available for all companies at press time.**

2008 Sales: $58,681,000	2008 Profits: $4,689,000	**U.S. Stock Ticker: UTX**
2007 Sales: $54,759,000	2007 Profits: $4,224,000	**Int'l Ticker:** Int'l Exchange:
2006 Sales: $47,829,000	2006 Profits: $3,732,000	Employees: 225,600
2005 Sales: $42,725,000	2005 Profits: $3,069,000	Fiscal Year Ends: 12/31
2004 Sales: $37,445,000	2004 Profits: $2,788,000	Parent Company:

SALARIES/BENEFITS:

Pension Plan:	ESOP Stock Plan:	Profit Sharing:	Top Exec. Salary: $1,883,333	Bonus: $4,000,000
Savings Plan:	Stock Purch. Plan:		Second Exec. Salary: $1,012,500	Bonus: $2,000,000

OTHER THOUGHTS:

Apparent Women Officers or Directors: 2
Hot Spot for Advancement for Women/Minorities:

LOCATIONS: ("Y" = Yes)

West:	Southwest:	Midwest:	Southeast:	Northeast:	International:
Y	Y	Y	Y	Y	Y

Note: Financial information, benefits and other data can change quickly and may vary from those stated here.

URS CORPORATION

www.urscorp.com

Industry Group Code: 541330 **Ranks within this company's industry group:** Sales: 2 Profits: 4

Techology:		Medical/Drugs:		Engineering:		Transportation:		Chemicals/Petrochemicals:		Specialty:	
Computers:		Manufacturer:		Design:	Y	Aerospace:		Oil/Gas Products:		Special Services:	
Software:		Contract Research:		Construction:	Y	Automotive:		Chemicals:		Consulting:	
Communications:		Medical Services:		Eng. Services:	Y	Shipping:		Oil/Chem. Svcs.:		Specialty Mgmt.:	
Electronics:		Labs:		Consulting:				Gases:		Products:	
Alternative Energy:		Bio. Services:						Other:		Other:	

TYPES OF BUSINESS:

Engineering Design Services
Systems Engineering & Technical Assistance
Operations & Maintenance Services

BRANDS/DIVISIONS/AFFILIATES:

EG&G Division
URS Division
Washington Division
LopezGarcia Group, Inc.
Washington Group International

CONTACTS: *Note: Officers with more than one job title may be intentionally listed here more than once.*

Martin M. Koffel, CEO
Martin M. Koffel, Pres.
H. Thomas Hicks, CFO/VP-Finance
Joseph Masters, General Counsel/Sec.
Thomas W. Bishop, VP-Strategy/Sr. VP-Construction Svcs.
Susan B. Kilgannon, VP-Comm.
Reed N. Brimhall, VP/Controller/Chief Acct. Officer
Thomas H. Zarges, Pres., Washington Div.
Gary V. Jandegian, VP/Pres., URS Div.
Randall A. Wotring, VP/Pres., EG&G Div.
Martin M. Koffel, Chmn.

Phone: 415-774-2700 **Fax:** 415-398-1905
Toll-Free:
Address: 600 Montgomery St., Fl. 26, San Francisco, CA 94111 US

GROWTH PLANS/SPECIAL FEATURES:

URS Corp. is an engineering design services worldwide firm and a U.S. federal government contractor for systems engineering and technical assistance and operations and maintenance services. The company focuses primarily on providing fee-based professional and technical services in the engineering and construction services and defense markets, although it performs some limited construction work. The firm operates in two divisions: URS division and the EG&G division. The URS division provides professional planning and design; program management; construction management; and operations and maintenance services to various government agencies and departments in the U.S. and internationally, as well as to private industry clients. The EG&G division provides planning; systems engineering and technical assistance; operations and maintenance; and program management services to various U.S. federal government agencies, primarily the Departments of Defense and Homeland Security. URS focuses its services on eight key markets: transportation; environmental; facilities; industrial infrastructure and process; water/wastewater; homeland security; defense systems; and installations and logistics. The company has a network of offices and job sites across the U.S. and in more than 30 foreign countries in the Americas, Europe, the Middle East and Asia-Pacific. The federal government accounted for 41% of the company's revenues in 2007, while state and local governments, private industry and international clients accounted for 21%, 27% and 11%, respectively. In November 2007, the company acquired rival Washington Group International, Inc. for about $3.1 billion. These assets became the Washington Division of URS, a third operating division. In August 2008, the firm acquired LopezGarcia Group, Inc. as well as most of the assets of Tryck Nyman Hayes, Inc.

The company offers its employees health and dental insurance; a 401(k) plan; an employee stock purchase plan; short- and long-term insurance; life and accident insurance; an employee assistance program; flexible spending accounts; and group legal services.

FINANCIALS: **Sales and profits are in thousands of dollars—add 000 to get the full amount. 2008 Note: Financial information for 2008 was not available for all companies at press time.**

2008 Sales: $10,086,289	2008 Profits: $219,791	**U.S. Stock Ticker: URS**
2007 Sales: $5,383,007	2007 Profits: $132,243	**Int'l Ticker:** Int'l Exchange:
2006 Sales: $4,222,869	2006 Profits: $113,012	Employees: 50,000
2005 Sales: $3,890,282	2005 Profits: $82,475	Fiscal Year Ends: 12/31
2004 Sales: $3,381,963	2004 Profits: $61,704	Parent Company:

SALARIES/BENEFITS:

Pension Plan:	ESOP Stock Plan:	Profit Sharing:	Top Exec. Salary: $988,467	Bonus: $1,997,892
Savings Plan: Y	Stock Purch. Plan: Y		Second Exec. Salary: $544,250	Bonus: $563,299

OTHER THOUGHTS:

Apparent Women Officers or Directors: 1
Hot Spot for Advancement for Women/Minorities: Y

LOCATIONS: ("Y" = Yes)

West:	Southwest:	Midwest:	Southeast:	Northeast:	International:
Y	Y	Y	Y	Y	Y

Note: Financial information, benefits and other data can change quickly and may vary from those stated here.

UTSTARCOM INC

www.utstar.com

Industry Group Code: 334210 **Ranks within this company's industry group:** Sales: 6 Profits: 5

Techology:		Medical/Drugs:		Engineering:		Transportation:		Chemicals/Petrochemicals:		Specialty:	
Computers:		Manufacturer:		Design:		Aerospace:		Oil/Gas Products:		Special Services:	
Software:	Y	Contract Research:		Construction:		Automotive:		Chemicals:		Consulting:	
Communications:	Y	Medical Services:		Eng. Services:		Shipping:		Oil/Chem. Svcs.:		Specialty Mgmt.:	
Electronics:	Y	Labs:		Consulting:				Gases:		Products:	
Alternative Energy:		Bio. Services:						Other:		Other:	

TYPES OF BUSINESS:

Telecommunications Equipment
Voice, Data & Broadband Networking Equipment
Network Access Systems
Wireless Network Equipment
Handsets
Telecommunications Software & Hardware
Optical Products

BRANDS/DIVISIONS/AFFILIATES:

mSwitch
RollingStream

CONTACTS:

Note: Officers with more than one job title may be intentionally listed here more than once.

Peter Blackmore, CEO
Peter Blackmore, Pres.
Viraj Patel, Interim CFO
Luis Dominguez, Sr. VP-Int'l Sales & Mktg.
Mark Green, Sr. VP-Worldwide Human Resources & Real Estate
Ari Bose, CIO/Sr. VP-Bus. Transformation Office
Craig Samuel, CTO
Susan Marsch, General Counsel/Sec./Chief Ethics Officer
Craig Samuel, Sr. VP-Bus. Strategy & Innovation
Viraj Patel, Chief Acct. Officer/Controller
Moon Song, Pres., Terminal Bus. Unit
Yanya Sheng, Sr. VP/Gen. Mgr.-Broadband Bus. Unit
Baijun Zhao, Sr. VP/Gen. Mgr.-Multimedia Bus. Unit
K.P. Lim, Chief Quality Officer/VP
Hong Liang Lu, Chmn.
Robert Wu, CEO/Sr. VP-China
Goh Hin Tiang, Sr. VP-Global Supply Chain Oper.

Phone: 510-864-8800	**Fax:** 510-864-8802
Toll-Free:	
Address: 1275 Harbor Bay Pkwy., Alameda, CA 94502 US	

GROWTH PLANS/SPECIAL FEATURES:

UTStarcom, Inc. designs, manufactures and sells telecommunications infrastructure, handsets and customer premise equipment. It also provides services associated with their installation, operation and maintenance. The company operates in six segments: broadband infrastructure; multimedia communications; personal communications; handsets; services; and other, which includes the mobile solutions and custom solutions business units. The broadband infrastructure segment is responsible for software and hardware products that enable end users to access high-speed wireless data, voice and media communications. Products within each of these categories include multiple hardware and software subsystems that can be offered in various combinations to suit individual carrier needs. The multimedia communications segment develops and manages the IPTV and related technologies (such as surveillance) plus the core NGN software. The RollingStream IPTV solution includes storage and streaming device products for combining different video signals onto a unified distribution system. The mSwitch NGN solution provides voice communications over an IP network. The personal communications division markets, sells and supports handsets. The handsets segment designs, builds and sells consumer handset devices that allow customers to access wireless services. The services division assists customers with activities ranging from network planning, circuit-to-packet network migration planning, systems integration, program management, operations management and knowledge transfer. The other segment's mobile solutions unit is responsible for the development, sales and service of the wireless IPCDMA/IPGSM product line and the packet data services node product line that connects CDMA cellular network infrastructure equipment to IP networks. The customer solutions unit develops, sells and services non-core products such as IP messaging, transaction gateways and remove access server, which enables users to access network data and services from remote locations.

Employees are offered medical, dental and vision insurance; flexible spending accounts; life insurance; an employee assistance plan; a stock purchase plan; a 401(k) program; tuition reimbursement; business travel accident and medical insurance; and credit union membership.

FINANCIALS:

Sales and profits are in thousands of dollars—add 000 to get the full amount. 2008 Note: Financial information for 2008 was not available for all companies at press time.

2008 Sales: $1,640,449	2008 Profits: $-150,316	**U.S. Stock Ticker: UTSI**
2007 Sales: $2,466,970	2007 Profits: $-195,575	**Int'l Ticker:** Int'l Exchange:
2006 Sales: $2,458,861	2006 Profits: $-117,345	Employees: 4,400
2005 Sales: $2,929,343	2005 Profits: $-487,359	Fiscal Year Ends: 12/31
2004 Sales: $2,684,379	2004 Profits: $69,824	Parent Company:

SALARIES/BENEFITS:

Pension Plan:	ESOP Stock Plan:	Profit Sharing:	Top Exec. Salary: $750,000	Bonus: $821,181
Savings Plan: Y	Stock Purch. Plan: Y		Second Exec. Salary: $700,000	Bonus: $500,000

OTHER THOUGHTS:

Apparent Women Officers or Directors: 2
Hot Spot for Advancement for Women/Minorities: Y

LOCATIONS: ("Y" = Yes)

West:	Southwest:	Midwest:	Southeast:	Northeast:	International:
Y		Y	Y	Y	Y

Note: Financial information, benefits and other data can change quickly and may vary from those stated here.

VALEO

www.valeo.com

Industry Group Code: 336300 **Ranks within this company's industry group:** Sales: 11 Profits: 15

Techology:		Medical/Drugs:		Engineering:		Transportation:		Chemicals/Petrochemicals:		Specialty:	
Computers:		Manufacturer:		Design:	Y	Aerospace:		Oil/Gas Products:		Special Services:	
Software:		Contract Research:		Construction:		Automotive:	Y	Chemicals:		Consulting:	
Communications:		Medical Services:		Eng. Services:		Shipping:		Oil/Chem. Svcs.:		Specialty Mgmt.:	
Electronics:	Y	Labs:		Consulting:				Gases:		Products:	
Alternative Energy:		Bio. Services:						Other:		Other:	

TYPES OF BUSINESS:

Automobile Parts Manufacturing
Security Systems
Electrical & Electronic Systems
Lighting Systems
Thermal Systems
Aftermarket Products
Transmission Components

BRANDS/DIVISIONS/AFFILIATES:

SmartWash
e-Harness Smart Connector
Nanjing Valeo Clutch Company
Valeo Pyeong Hwa
Foshan Valeo Ichikoh Auto Lighting Systems Co.

CONTACTS: *Note: Officers with more than one job title may be intentionally listed here more than once.*

Thierry Morin, CEO
Luc Bleriot, COO
Hans-Peter Kunze, Sr. VP-Sales & Bus. Dev.
Michel Boulain, VP-Human Resources
Martin Haub, VP-R&D
Andre Gold, Sr. VP-Tech.
Geric Lebedoff, General Counsel
Vincent Marcel, VP-Strategic Oper.
Kate Philipps, Dir.-Comm.
Vincent Marcel, VP-Finance
Robert de la Serve, Sr. VP-Valeo Service Activity
Robert Charvier, Dir.-Financial Control
Quintin Testa, Dir.-Quality
France Curis, Dir.-Taxation
Thierry Morin, Chmn.
Thierry Dreux, VP-Int'l Dev.

Phone: 33-1-40-55-20-20 **Fax:** 33-1-40-55-21-71
Toll-Free:
Address: 43 rue Bayen, Paris, 75848 France

GROWTH PLANS/SPECIAL FEATURES:

Valeo SA is an independent industrial group focused on the design, production and sale of components, systems and modules for cars and trucks, both in the original equipment market and the aftermarket. Valeo is a supplier to major global automakers including Ford Motor Company, General Motors, Porsche, Toyota, Volkswagen Group and many others. The firm is organized into four divisions that group together 10 product family branches and one branch dedicated to aftermarket products. While marketing and logistics activities are shared to improve efficiency, each branch maintains its own customer interface to provide the best solutions for specific customer requirements. The electrical systems division represents approximately half of Valeo's sales and covers the lighting, wipers, switches and detection, electronics and connective systems, security and engine management branches. The thermal systems division represents approximately a quarter of the firm's sales and covers climate control and engine cooling branches. The transmissions division produces products such as friction materials and clutch systems. Valeo's aftermarket business operates two industrial branches: OES for the sale of original equipment spare parts to automakers and IAM for sales to the independent aftermarket. Additionally, the company operates a joint venture, Foshan Valeo Ichikoh Auto Lighting Systems Co., Ltd., with Ichikoh, a Japanese manufacturer of lighting systems. The firm has a presence in 28 countries and operates approximately 125 production sites, 62 research and development centers and nine distribution centers. Approximately two-thirds of Valeo's revenues are generated within Europe, with other major markets in North America, Asia and, to a lesser extent, South America. In December 2008, in response to declining vehicle demand, Valeo announced plans to cut approximately 10% of its workforce worldwide. In February 2009, the company announced a partnership with Michelin Group to coordinate the development of electric and rechargeable hybrid vehicle systems.

FINANCIALS: Sales and profits are in thousands of dollars—add 000 to get the full amount. 2008 Note: Financial information for 2008 was not available for all companies at press time.

2008 Sales: $11,365,800	2008 Profits: $-273,200	**U.S. Stock Ticker: VLEEY**
2007 Sales: $13,150,000	2007 Profits: $210,000	**Int'l Ticker: FR** Int'l Exchange: Paris-Euronext
2006 Sales: $13,556,200	2006 Profits: $225,710	Employees: 70,400
2005 Sales: $13,238,000	2005 Profits: $201,240	Fiscal Year Ends: 12/31
2004 Sales: $12,261,800	2004 Profits: $337,210	Parent Company:

SALARIES/BENEFITS:

Pension Plan:	ESOP Stock Plan:	Profit Sharing:	Top Exec. Salary: $	Bonus: $
Savings Plan:	Stock Purch. Plan:		Second Exec. Salary: $	Bonus: $

OTHER THOUGHTS:

Apparent Women Officers or Directors: 1
Hot Spot for Advancement for Women/Minorities:

LOCATIONS: ("Y" = Yes)

West:	Southwest:	Midwest:	Southeast:	Northeast:	International:
		Y	Y	Y	Y

VERISIGN INC

www.verisign.com

Industry Group Code: 511211 **Ranks within this company's industry group:** Sales: 3 Profits: 3

Techology:		Medical/Drugs:		Engineering:		Transportation:		Chemicals/Petrochemicals:		Specialty:	
Computers:		Manufacturer:		Design:		Aerospace:		Oil/Gas Products:		Special Services:	Y
Software:	Y	Contract Research:		Construction:		Automotive:		Chemicals:		Consulting:	
Communications:	Y	Medical Services:		Eng. Services:		Shipping:		Oil/Chem. Svcs.:		Specialty Mgmt.:	Y
Electronics:		Labs:		Consulting:				Gases:		Products:	
Alternative Energy:		Bio. Services:						Other:		Other:	

TYPES OF BUSINESS:

Software-Security
Telecommunications Services
Network & e-Mail Security
Managed Security Services
Digital Brand Management
Wireless Content Services
Wireless & Wireline Billing Services
Domain Name Registration

BRANDS/DIVISIONS/AFFILIATES:

SSL

CONTACTS:

Note: Officers with more than one job title may be intentionally listed here more than once.

Jim Bidzos, Interim CEO
Mark D. McLaughlin, COO
Mark D. McLaughlin, Pres.
Brian G. Robins, Acting CFO/Sr. VP
Anne-Marie Law, Sr. VP-Global Human Resources
Kenneth J. Silva, CTO/Sr. VP
Grant L. Clark, Chief Admin. Officer/Sr. VP
Richard H. Goshorn, General Counsel/Sr. VP/Corp. Sec.
Kevin A. Werner, Sr. VP-Corp. Dev. & Strategy
Russell S. Lewis, Sr. VP-Strategic Dev.
D. James Bidzos, Chmn.
Teruhide Hashimoto, Pres./CEO-VeriSign Japan

Phone: 650-961-7500 **Fax:** 650-961-7300
Toll-Free:
Address: 487 E. Middlefield Rd., Mountain View, CA 94043 US

GROWTH PLANS/SPECIAL FEATURES:

VeriSign, Inc. operates infrastructure services that enable and protect billions of interactions every day across worldwide voice, video and data networks. It offers a variety of Internet and communications-related service that are marketed through web site sales, direct field sales, channel sales, telesales and member organizations in its global affiliate network. The company operates in two segments: the Internet services group and the communications services group. The Internet services group consists of the information/security and Naming services business. The information/security services business provides products and services that protect online and network interactions, enabling companies to manage reputational, operational and compliance risks. Offerings include SSL certificate services, which enable enterprises and Internet merchants to implement secure networks and web sites that utilize SSL protocol; identity and authentication services, which include the Managed PKI service, the Unified Authentication services and the VeriSign Identity Protection service; and real-time publisher services, which allow organizations to obtain access to and organize large amounts of constantly updated content and distribute it to enterprises, web-portal developers, application developers and consumers. The Naming services business is the authoritative directory provider of all .com, .net, .cc and .tv domain names. In April 2008, the company sold its Self-Care and Analytics business unit to Globys, Inc., provider of online analytic solutions, for an undisclosed amount. In May 2008, VeriSign released its Broadband Content Services assets, which have been reclaimed by the company's former acquisition, Kontiki, Inc. In June 2008, the firm extended its infrastructure, opening new Internet sites in Belgium, Paris, France and Brussels. In October 2008, VeriSign sold its minority share of a joint venture with News Corporation to that company for approximately $200 million. In March 2009, the company agreed to sell its Communication Services Group to TNS, Inc., a global communications company, for $230 million cash.

FINANCIALS:

Sales and profits are in thousands of dollars—add 000 to get the full amount. 2008 Note: Financial information for 2008 was not available for all companies at press time.

2008 Sales: $961,735	2008 Profits: $-374,692
2007 Sales: $847,457	2007 Profits: $-149,328
2006 Sales: $982,734	2006 Profits: $382,930
2005 Sales: $1,612,574	2005 Profits: $428,978
2004 Sales: $1,120,595	2004 Profits: $152,820

U.S. Stock Ticker: VRSN
Int'l Ticker: Int'l Exchange:
Employees: 3,297
Fiscal Year Ends: 12/31
Parent Company:

SALARIES/BENEFITS:

Pension Plan:	ESOP Stock Plan:	Profit Sharing:	Top Exec. Salary: $750,000	Bonus: $
Savings Plan:	Stock Purch. Plan:		Second Exec. Salary: $450,000	Bonus: $

OTHER THOUGHTS:

Apparent Women Officers or Directors: 2
Hot Spot for Advancement for Women/Minorities: Y

LOCATIONS: ("Y" = Yes)

West:	Southwest:	Midwest:	Southeast:	Northeast:	International:
Y	Y	Y	Y	Y	Y

VESTAS WIND SYSTEMS A/S

www.vestas.dk

Industry Group Code: 333611 **Ranks within this company's industry group:** Sales: 1 Profits: 1

Techology:		Medical/Drugs:		Engineering:		Transportation:		Chemicals/Petrochemicals:		Specialty:	
Computers:		Manufacturer:		Design:		Aerospace:		Oil/Gas Products:		Special Services:	
Software:		Contract Research:		Construction:		Automotive:		Chemicals:		Consulting:	
Communications:		Medical Services:		Eng. Services:		Shipping:		Oil/Chem. Svcs.:		Specialty Mgmt.:	
Electronics:		Labs:		Consulting:				Gases:		Products:	
Alternative Energy:	Y	Bio. Services:						Other:		Other:	

TYPES OF BUSINESS:

Wind Turbine Manufacturing
Turbine Installation, Repair & Maintenance Services
Online Turbine Operating Systems

BRANDS/DIVISIONS/AFFILIATES:

Vestas Blades
Vestas Control Systems
Vestas Nacelles
Vestas Towers
VestasOnline

CONTACTS: *Note: Officers with more than one job title may be intentionally listed here more than once.*

Ditlev Engel, CEO
Ditlev Engel, Pres.
Henrik Norremark, CFO/Exec. VP
Anders Soe-Jensen, Pres., Vestas Offshore
Bjarne Ravn Sorensen, Pres., Vestas Control Systems
Finn Strom Madsen, Pres., Vestas Technology
Hans Jørn Rieks, Pres., Vestas Central Europe, Germany
Bent Erik Carlsen, Chmn.

Phone: 45-9730-0000 **Fax:** 45-9730-0001
Toll-Free:
Address: Alsvej 21, Randers, 8940 Denmark

GROWTH PLANS/SPECIAL FEATURES:

Vestas Wind Systems is a world leading manufacturer of wind turbines, having installed over 33,500 turbines in 63 countries worldwide, generating more than 60 million megawatt-hours of electricity annually. The firm offers site and project studies and develops, manufactures, sells and markets wind turbines ranging from the V52-850 kilowatt turbine to the V90-3 megawatt turbine. Vestas offers land and offshore models, as well as installation, repair and maintenance services. The firm's Supervisory Control and Data Acquisition System (SCADA), called VestasOnline, offers a range of monitoring and control functions which allow plants to be operated in a manner similar to conventional power plants. It allows customers to view performance data, monitor and control turbines remotely and receive alarm messages via e-mail through its SCADA web server. The company has four production business units: Vestas Blades, with centers in the UK, Denmark, Germany, Italy, China and the US; Vestas Control Systems, located in China, Spain and Denmark; Vestas Nacelles, in China, India, Spain, Germany, Denmark, Norway and Sweden; and Vestas Towers, in the UK, Denmark and the US. In 2007, sales to 18 European nations accounted for approximately 54% of company revenues; the Americas, including the US, Canada and Chile, represented 29%; and the Asia/Pacific market represented 17%. The strongest growth was recorded in the American market. Vestas has recently announced the opening of new factories in China, Spain and the State of Colarado, as well as the establishment of new research and development centers in the US, Denmark, Singapore and India. It has closed its Australian production facility.

FINANCIALS: **Sales and profits are in thousands of dollars—add 000 to get the full amount. 2008 Note: Financial information for 2008 was not available for all companies at press time.**

2008 Sales: $8,135,660 | 2008 Profits: $688,870
2007 Sales: $7,090,000 | 2007 Profits: $420,000
2006 Sales: $5,085,000 | 2006 Profits: $146,300
2005 Sales: $4,243,300 | 2005 Profits: $-137,000
2004 Sales: $3,493,500 | 2004 Profits: $-53,500

U.S. Stock Ticker: VWSYF.PK
Int'l Ticker: VWS Int'l Exchange: Copenhagen-CSE
Employees: 20,829
Fiscal Year Ends: 12/31
Parent Company:

SALARIES/BENEFITS:

Pension Plan:	ESOP Stock Plan:	Profit Sharing: Y	Top Exec. Salary: $	Bonus: $
Savings Plan:	Stock Purch. Plan:		Second Exec. Salary: $	Bonus: $

OTHER THOUGHTS:

Apparent Women Officers or Directors: 1
Hot Spot for Advancement for Women/Minorities:

LOCATIONS: ("Y" = Yes)

West:	Southwest:	Midwest:	Southeast:	Northeast:	International:
Y					Y

Note: Financial information, benefits and other data can change quickly and may vary from those stated here.

VINCI

www.vinci.com

Industry Group Code: 234000 **Ranks within this company's industry group:** Sales: 2 Profits: 1

Techology:		Medical/Drugs:		Engineering:		Transportation:		Chemicals/Petrochemicals:		Specialty:	
Computers:		Manufacturer:		Design:	Y	Aerospace:		Oil/Gas Products:		Special Services:	
Software:		Contract Research:		Construction:	Y	Automotive:		Chemicals:		Consulting:	
Communications:		Medical Services:		Eng. Services:	Y	Shipping:		Oil/Chem. Svcs.:		Specialty Mgmt.:	Y
Electronics:		Labs:		Consulting:	Y			Gases:		Products:	
Alternative Energy:		Bio. Services:						Other:		Other:	

TYPES OF BUSINESS:

Heavy Construction
Infrastructure Management
Information & Energy Technologies
Commercial Construction
Engineering Services
Highway Construction
Airport Management & Support Services
Power Transmission Services

BRANDS/DIVISIONS/AFFILIATES:

VINCI Concessions
VINCI Energies
Eurovia
VINCI Construction
Taylor Woodrow Construction Unit
Taylor Wimpey PLC

CONTACTS: *Note: Officers with more than one job title may be intentionally listed here more than once.*

Xavier Huillard, CEO
Christian Laberyrie, CFO/Exec. VP
Jean-Luc Pommier, VP-Bus. Dev.
Jean-Yves le Brouster, CEO-VINCI Energies
Xavier Huillard, CEO-VINCI Concessions
Louis-Roch Burgard, COO-VINCI Concessions
Jacques Tavernier, CEO-Eurovia
Yves-Thibault de Silguy, Chmn.

Phone: 33-1-47-16-35-00 **Fax:** 33-1-47-51-91-02
Toll-Free:
Address: 1 Cours Ferdinand-de-Lesseps, Rueil-Malmaison, 92851 France

GROWTH PLANS/SPECIAL FEATURES:

VINCI, one of the largest companies operating in construction and related services worldwide, consists of four major divisions: VINCI Concessions, VINCI Energies, Eurovia and VINCI Construction. VINCI Concessions is engaged in the design, turnkey construction, financing and operation of facilities, as well as outsourced infrastructure management. Its dual approach is applied to major public facilities such as the Stade de France stadium near Paris. In 2007, VINCI Concessions set up a new organizational structure comprising five divisions: VINCI Autoroutes France; VINCI Park; VINCI Concessions Greece; VINCI Concessions Business Development; and VINCI Concessions Asset Management. The overall Concessions business line accounts for approximately 15% of company revenues. VINCI Energies is a leading European producer of information and energy technologies for infrastructure, industry, the service sector and telecommunications. It operates mainly through six brands in Europe: Actemium, offering energy services to industry; Axians, offering voice-data-image communication services; Citeos, specializing in urban lighting; Graniou, supporting telecommunications infrastructure; Omexom, specializing in high-voltage power; and Opteor, offering industrial and services maintenance. The Energies business line accounts for approximately 14% of company revenues. Eurovia is a leading European company in the road industry and in recycled materials, operating in roadworks, materials production, environment-related activities and services. It accounts for approximately 25% of company revenues. VINCI Construction, representing close to half of overall company revenues, is an industry leader in building, civil engineering, hydraulics and facilities management. The division is composed of three main components: Mainland France; Local Markets outside mainland France; and Worldwide activities, including major structures, specialized civil engineering and dredging. VINCI was recently engaged in a design-build project for a causeway between Qatar and Bahrain, which will be among the world's longest bridges. In September 2008, the company acquired the Taylor Woodrow Construction Unit from U.K. company Taylor Wimpey PLC.

FINANCIALS:

Sales and profits are in thousands of dollars—add 000 to get the full amount. 2008 Note: Financial information for 2008 was not available for all companies at press time.

2008 Sales: $42,717,900
2007 Sales: $33,820,000
2006 Sales: $35,200,919
2005 Sales: $31,785,190
2004 Sales: $26,625,600

2008 Profits: $2,003,070
2007 Profits: $1,680,000
2006 Profits: $
2005 Profits: $1,053,100
2004 Profits: $997,500

U.S. Stock Ticker:
Int'l Ticker: DG Int'l Exchange: Paris-Euronext
Employees: 133,513
Fiscal Year Ends: 12/31
Parent Company:

SALARIES/BENEFITS:

Pension Plan: ESOP Stock Plan: Profit Sharing: Top Exec. Salary: $ Bonus: $
Savings Plan: Stock Purch. Plan: Second Exec. Salary: $ Bonus: $

OTHER THOUGHTS:

Apparent Women Officers or Directors:
Hot Spot for Advancement for Women/Minorities:

LOCATIONS: ("Y" = Yes)

West:	Southwest:	Midwest:	Southeast:	Northeast:	International:
Y	Y	Y	Y	Y	Y

VISTEON CORPORATION

www.visteon.com

Industry Group Code: 336300 **Ranks within this company's industry group:** Sales: 12 Profits: 18

Techology:		Medical/Drugs:		Engineering:		Transportation:		Chemicals/Petrochemicals:		Specialty:	
Computers:		Manufacturer:		Design:		Aerospace:		Oil/Gas Products:		Special Services:	
Software:		Contract Research:		Construction:		Automotive:	Y	Chemicals:		Consulting:	
Communications:	Y	Medical Services:		Eng. Services:		Shipping:		Oil/Chem. Svcs.:		Specialty Mgmt.:	
Electronics:	Y	Labs:		Consulting:				Gases:		Products:	Y
Alternative Energy:		Bio. Services:						Other:		Other:	

TYPES OF BUSINESS:

Automobile Parts
Climate Control Products
Interior & Exterior Components
Chassis & Power Train Components
Multimedia Systems
Fuel Storage & Delivery Products

BRANDS/DIVISIONS/AFFILIATES:

CONTACTS: *Note: Officers with more than one job title may be intentionally listed here more than once.*

Donald J. Stebbins, CEO
Donald J. Stebbins, Pres.
William G. Quigley III, CFO/Exec. VP
Dorthy L. Stephenson, Sr. VP-Human Resources
John Donofrio, General Counsel/Sr. VP
Jim Fisher, Corp. Comm.
Michael J. Widgren, VP/Controller/Chief Acct. Officer
Steve Meszaros, VP-Electronics Products Group
Eric D. Sachs, VP/Treas./Chief Tax Officer
Donald J. Stebbins, Chmn.
Jonathan K. Maples, VP-Global Purchasing

Phone: **Fax:** 734-736-5560
Toll-Free: 800-847-8366
Address: 1 Village Center Dr., Van Buren Township, MI 48111 US

GROWTH PLANS/SPECIAL FEATURES:

Visteon Corp. supplies automotive systems, modules and components to global vehicle manufacturers and the aftermarket for replacement and appearance enhancement parts. The company is in the process of restructuring, and as a result operations have split into five segments: Climate, Electronics, Interiors, Services and Other. Climate operations produce products such as climate air handling modules; engine induction systems; powertrain cooling modules; heat exchangers; compressors; fluid transport; and climate controls. The Electronics sector primarily manufactures infotainment, driver information and audio systems; powertrain, feature and electronic control modules; and lighting. The Interiors division mainly produces door trim, instrument panels, floor consoles and cockpit modules. The Services sector offers transition services for divestiture transactions, primarily those involving ACH Transactions and Chassis Divestiture. The Other division is primarily involved in the production of parts sold and distributed to the automotive aftermarket, as well as fuel and powertrain products. The company operates through regional headquarters in Germany, China and Brazil; it maintains manufacturing sites, sales offices and joint ventures in North and South America, Africa, Europe and the Asia-Pacific region. The firm is a member of the Automotive Open System Architecture partnership, which intends to develop and establish an open industry standard for automotive electrical architecture. Ford makes up 39% of the firm's sales. In February 2008, Visteon sold non-core North American facilities to Centrum Equities, resulting in Centrum's acquisition of three of Visteon's aftermarket underhood and remanufacturing facilities (one in Tennessee, two in Mexico). In July 2008, Visteon sold its plant in Swansea, U.K., to Canada-based Linamar Corporation, an auto parts manufacturer; Visteon also announced plans to discontinue its Bedford, Indiana, operation and close two German fuel tank facilities. In November 2008, the company released a new internal heat exchanger, which improves vehicle cooling power by as much as 14% and increases operating efficiency by up to 12%.

FINANCIALS: **Sales and profits are in thousands of dollars—add 000 to get the full amount. 2008 Note: Financial information for 2008 was not available for all companies at press time.**

2008 Sales: $9,544,000	2008 Profits: $-681,000	**U.S. Stock Ticker: VC**
2007 Sales: $11,275,000	2007 Profits: $-372,000	**Int'l Ticker:** Int'l Exchange:
2006 Sales: $11,256,000	2006 Profits: $-163,000	Employees: 33,500
2005 Sales: $16,976,000	2005 Profits: $-270,000	Fiscal Year Ends: 12/31
2004 Sales: $18,657,000	2004 Profits: $-1,536,000	Parent Company:

SALARIES/BENEFITS:

Pension Plan:	ESOP Stock Plan:	Profit Sharing:	Top Exec. Salary: $1,341,667	Bonus: $4,497,734
Savings Plan:	Stock Purch. Plan:		Second Exec. Salary: $919,167	Bonus: $2,066,975

OTHER THOUGHTS:

Apparent Women Officers or Directors: 4
Hot Spot for Advancement for Women/Minorities: Y

LOCATIONS: ("Y" = Yes)

West:	Southwest:	Midwest:	Southeast:	Northeast:	International:
	Y	Y	Y	Y	Y

VOLKSWAGEN AG

www.volkswagen-ag.de/english

Industry Group Code: 336111 **Ranks within this company's industry group:** Sales: 2 Profits: 3

Techology:		Medical/Drugs:		Engineering:		Transportation:		Chemicals/Petrochemicals:		Specialty:	
Computers:		Manufacturer:		Design:		Aerospace:		Oil/Gas Products:		Special Services:	
Software:		Contract Research:		Construction:		Automotive:	Y	Chemicals:		Consulting:	
Communications:		Medical Services:		Eng. Services:		Shipping:		Oil/Chem. Svcs.:		Specialty Mgmt.:	
Electronics:		Labs:		Consulting:				Gases:		Products:	
Alternative Energy:		Bio. Services:						Other:		Other:	

TYPES OF BUSINESS:

Automobiles, Manufacturing
Truck Manufacturing
Car Rental Services
Consumer Financing

BRANDS/DIVISIONS/AFFILIATES:

SEAT SA
Porsche Automobil Holding SE
Bentley Motors
Skoda Auto AS
Volkswagen Financial Services AG
Volkswagen Bank GmbH
Volkswagen Leasing GmbH
LeasePlan Corporation NV

CONTACTS: *Note: Officers with more than one job title may be intentionally listed here more than once.*

Martin Winterkorn, CEO
Hans D. Potsch, CFO
Horst Neumann, Dir.-Human Resources & Labor
Jochem Heizmann, Dir.-Prod.
Hans D. Potsch, Controller
Ferdinand K. Piech, Chmn.-Supervisory Board
Francisco Javier Garcia Sanz, Dir.-Procurement

Phone: 49-53-61-90	**Fax:** 49-53-61-928282
Toll-Free: 800-822-8987	
Address: Berliner Ring 2, Wolfsburg, 38436 Germany	

GROWTH PLANS/SPECIAL FEATURES:

Volkswagen AG (VW) is one of the world's leading automobile manufacturers and the number-one automobile manufacturer in Europe, with yearly production of more than six million cars, trucks and vans. The company's two primary divisions are Automotive and Financial Services. The automotive group is made up of nine brands from six European countries: Volkswagen, Audi, Bentley, Bugatti, Lamborghini, SEAT, Skoda, Scania and Volkswagen Commercial Vehicles. Each brand operates as an independent entity on the market, with products ranging from low-consumption small cars to luxury class vehicles. Models offered under the Volkswagen brand include the New Beetle, Jetta, Passat, Golf, Fox and Polo, as well as the Jetta wagon, the Passat wagon, the Eos convertible, the Touareg (the company's first-ever sports utility vehicle) and the Phaeton, a 12-cylinder luxury sedan. In the commercial vehicle segment, products include pick-ups, busses and heavy trucks. The company operates 48 production plants in 13 European countries, North and South America, Africa and Asia, which collectively produce over 25,000 vehicles daily. The firm sells its vehicles in more than 150 countries worldwide. The financial services division, operated through wholly-owned subsidiary Volkswagen Financial Services AG, is responsible for coordinating the worldwide financial services of the company, with offerings including vehicle financing; direct bank business, offered through Volkswagen Bank GmbH; insurance products, with offering for both private and corporate customers; leasing; and fleet management, including the activities of subsidiaries Volkswagen Leasing GmbH and LeasePlan Corporation N.V. In January 2009, the company established a vehicle finance arm to serve the Indian market. Also, as of January 2009, Porsche Automobil Holding SE raised its stake in Volkswagen to over 50%. The company has been utilizing planned short-term stoppages at its manufacturing facilities to contend with slowing international demand in late 2008 and early 2009.

FINANCIALS: **Sales and profits are in thousands of dollars—add 000 to get the full amount. 2008 Note: Financial information for 2008 was not available for all companies at press time.**

2008 Sales: $150,559,000	2008 Profits: $6,201,850	**U.S. Stock Ticker: VLKAY**
2007 Sales: $144,062,000	2007 Profits: $5,453,080	**Int'l Ticker: VOW** Int'l Exchange: Frankfurt-Euronext
2006 Sales: $137,750,000	2006 Profits: $3,610,000	Employees: 369,928
2005 Sales: $112,825,900	2005 Profits: $1,326,400	Fiscal Year Ends: 12/31
2004 Sales: $121,345,500	2004 Profits: $923,400	Parent Company:

SALARIES/BENEFITS:

Pension Plan: Y	ESOP Stock Plan:	Profit Sharing:	Top Exec. Salary: $1,095,932	Bonus: $2,624,631
Savings Plan:	Stock Purch. Plan:		Second Exec. Salary: $1,093,231	Bonus: $1,010,596

OTHER THOUGHTS:

Apparent Women Officers or Directors: 2
Hot Spot for Advancement for Women/Minorities:

LOCATIONS: ("Y" = Yes)

West:	Southwest:	Midwest:	Southeast:	Northeast:	International:
				Y	Y

Note: Financial information, benefits and other data can change quickly and may vary from those stated here.

VOLVO CAR CORPORATION

www.volvocars.com

Industry Group Code: 336111 **Ranks within this company's industry group:** Sales: Profits:

Techology:		Medical/Drugs:		Engineering:		Transportation:		Chemicals/Petrochemicals:		Specialty:	
Computers:		Manufacturer:		Design:		Aerospace:		Oil/Gas Products:		Special Services:	
Software:		Contract Research:		Construction:		Automotive:	Y	Chemicals:		Consulting:	
Communications:		Medical Services:		Eng. Services:		Shipping:		Oil/Chem. Svcs.:		Specialty Mgmt.:	Y
Electronics:		Labs:		Consulting:				Gases:		Products:	
Alternative Energy:		Bio. Services:						Other:		Other:	

TYPES OF BUSINESS:

Car Manufacturer

BRANDS/DIVISIONS/AFFILIATES:

Ford Motor Co
S40
V50
XC90
Flexi-Fuel
Bi-Fuel
Partial Zero Emission Vehicle (PZEV)
Volvo Cars Driving Academy

CONTACTS: *Note: Officers with more than one job title may be intentionally listed here more than once.*

Stephen Odell, CEO
Steven Armstrong, COO
Stephen Odell, Pres.
Gerry Keaney, Sr. VP-Mktg. Sales & Customer Service
Bjorn Sallstrom, Sr. VP-Human Resources
Magnus Jonsson, Sr. VP-R&D
Steve Mattin, Sr. VP-Design
Magnus Hellsten, Sr. VP-Mfg.
Elisabet Wenzlaff, General Counsel/Sr. VP
Lex Kerssemakers, Sr. VP-Brand, Bus. & Prod. Strategy
Olle Axelson, Sr. VP-Public Affairs
Stuart Rowley, Sr. VP-Finance
Paul Welander, Sr. VP-Quality & Customer Satisfaction
Lena Olving, Sr. VP-Process & Oper. Excellence
Bernt Ejbyfeldt, Sr. VP-Purchasing

Phone: 46-31-590-000	**Fax:** 46-31-544-064
Toll-Free:	
Address: SE-405 31, Goteborg, Sweden	

GROWTH PLANS/SPECIAL FEATURES:

Volvo Car Corporation (VCC), founded in 1927, is a Swedish designer, developer and manufacturer of cars known for safety and reliability. It is a wholly-owned subsidiary of the Ford Motor Co., which acquired the company in 1999 from AB Volvo. VCC's largest markets are the U.K., the U.S., Germany and Sweden, with additional sales centers located throughout Europe and Japan. During 2007, the firm sold over 458,000 vehicles, manufactured mainly at facilities in Sweden and Belgium, with additional assembly plants in China and Southeast Asia. Its current models include the S40, S60 and S80 sedans; the V50 and V70 versatility models; the XC70 and XC90 SUVs; and the new C70 convertible. VCC's convertibles are manufactured in Sweden at the Uddevalla factory, which is jointly operated with Pininfarina SpA. For the 2008 model year, VCC is counting on new models to boost sales, including a two-door compact, the C30, designed to compete with the Mini. Also, the firm is introducing a sportier S80 sedan, with a V-8 engine. Over the years, the firm's cars have won numerous awards for safety, design, environmental issues and overall value. The firm offers environmentally savvy cars known as FlexiFuel and Bi-Fuel cars (so named because they can run on either ethanol or gasoline), and hopes to expand its production of those models. PremAir is the company's smog-reducing technology, developed in collaboration with the Engelhard Corporation, which converts ground-level ozone passing through the radiator into oxygen. Available in California and certain Northeastern states in the U.S., VCC's PZEV (Partial Zero Emission Vehicle) engines produce exhaust which, in heavy city traffic, may even be cleaner than the ambient air. At the Volvo Cars Driving Academy, located in Stockholm and Gothenburg, 20 world-class Volvo instructors train thousands of people every year in safe driving techniques with a fleet of about 100 vehicles. As of late 2008, Ford has placed its Volvo unit up for sale, part of a continuing downsizing and reorganization at Ford.

FINANCIALS: **Sales and profits are in thousands of dollars—add 000 to get the full amount. 2008 Note: Financial information for 2008 was not available for all companies at press time.**

2008 Sales: $	2008 Profits: $	**U.S. Stock Ticker: Subsidiary**
2007 Sales: $	2007 Profits: $	**Int'l Ticker:** Int'l Exchange:
2006 Sales: $	2006 Profits: $	Employees:
2005 Sales: $	2005 Profits: $	Fiscal Year Ends: 12/31
2004 Sales: $	2004 Profits: $	Parent Company: FORD MOTOR CO

SALARIES/BENEFITS:

Pension Plan:	ESOP Stock Plan:	Profit Sharing:	Top Exec. Salary: $	Bonus: $
Savings Plan:	Stock Purch. Plan:		Second Exec. Salary: $	Bonus: $

OTHER THOUGHTS:

Apparent Women Officers or Directors: 2
Hot Spot for Advancement for Women/Minorities: Y

LOCATIONS: ("Y" = Yes)

West:	Southwest:	Midwest:	Southeast:	Northeast:	International:
					Y

VSE CORP

www.vsecorp.com

Industry Group Code: 541330 **Ranks within this company's industry group:** Sales: 9 Profits: 9

Techology:		Medical/Drugs:		Engineering:		Transportation:		Chemicals/Petrochemicals:		Specialty:	
Computers:		Manufacturer:		Design:		Aerospace:		Oil/Gas Products:		Special Services:	Y
Software:	Y	Contract Research:		Construction:		Automotive:		Chemicals:		Consulting:	Y
Communications:		Medical Services:		Eng. Services:	Y	Shipping:		Oil/Chem. Svcs.:		Specialty Mgmt.:	Y
Electronics:		Labs:		Consulting:	Y			Gases:		Products:	
Alternative Energy:		Bio. Services:						Other:		Other:	

TYPES OF BUSINESS:

Technical Services to Government
Engineering Services
Logistics Services
Technology Research & Development
Equipment Maintenance, Refurbishment & Implementation
Information Technology Support

BRANDS/DIVISIONS/AFFILIATES:

Energetics, Inc.
BAV
Communications and Electronics
Coast Guard
Engineering and Logistics
Fleet Maintenance
G&B Solutions, Inc.
Integrated Concepts and Research Corporation

CONTACTS: *Note: Officers with more than one job title may be intentionally listed here more than once.*

Maurice Gauthier, CEO
Maurice Gauthier, Pres.
Thomas R. Loftus, CFO/Exec. VP
Randy Hollstein, VP-Mktg.
Elizabeth M. Price, Dir.-Human Resources
Carl Williams, Pres., Integrated Concepts & Research Corp.
David Chivers, CIO
Randy Hollstein, Dir.-Prod. Dev. & New Bus.
Thomas M. Kerinan, General Counsel/VP/Asst. Sec.
James W. Lexo, Jr., Exec. VP-Strategic Planning & Bus. Initiatives
Sylvia Gethicker, Dir.-Public Rel., Advertising & Mass Comm.
Craig S. Weber, Investor Rel./Corp. Sec.
Thomas G. Dacus, Exec. VP/Pres., Federal Group
James E. Reed, Pres., Energy & Environment Group
Carl M. Williams, Pres., ICRC
Linda Berdine, Pres., G&B Solutions, Inc.
Donald M. Ervine, Chmn.
James M. Knowlton, Exec. VP/Pres., Int'l Group
A.J. Rose, Dir.-Purchasing

Phone: 703-960-4600	**Fax:** 703-960-2688
Toll-Free:	
Address: 2550 Huntington Ave., Alexandria, VA 22303-1499 US	

GROWTH PLANS/SPECIAL FEATURES:

VSE Corp. is a contract provider of diversified engineering, logistics, management, and technical services mostly to the U.S. government. The firm provides these services through its wholly-owned subsidiaries Energetics, Inc., Integrated Concepts and Research Corporation (ICRC) and G&B Solutions, Inc. and the following divisions: BAV, providing assistance to the U.S. Navy in executing its Foreign Military Sales Program; Communications and Electronics; Coast Guard; Engineering and Logistics; Fleet Support Services; Fleet Maintenance; Management Sciences; and Systems Engineering. The company also divides its business operations into four segments: the Federal Group; the International Group; the IT, Energy and Management Consulting Group (formerly the Energy and Environmental Group); and the Infrastructure Group (formerly the Infrastructure and Information Technology Group). The Federal Group provides engineering, technical, management, integrated logistics support and information technology services to all U.S. military branches and to other government agencies. The International Group provides engineering, industrial, logistics and foreign military sales services to similar groups. The IT, Energy and Management Consulting Group, which includes Energetics, Inc. and G&B Solutions, Inc., provides technical and consulting services primarily to various civilian government agencies. Energetics, Inc. provides technical and management support in the areas of nuclear energy, technology research, development and demonstration, and consulting services in the energy and environmental management fields. The Infrastructure Group encompasses ICRC and is engaged in providing technical and management services to the U.S. government, including transportation infrastructure services, advanced vehicle technology, aerospace services and engineering and information technology. In 2007, VSE acquired Integrated Concepts and Research Corporation, a technical and management services company principally serving the U.S. government. In April 2008, the company acquired G&B Solutions, Inc., an information technology and management consulting provider. In September 2008, the firm opened an operations center in Pennsylvania.

FINANCIALS: **Sales and profits are in thousands of dollars—add 000 to get the full amount. 2008 Note: Financial information for 2008 was not available for all companies at press time.**

2008 Sales: $1,043,735	2008 Profits: $19,040	**U.S. Stock Ticker: VSEC**
2007 Sales: $653,164	2007 Profits: $14,102	**Int'l Ticker:** Int'l Exchange:
2006 Sales: $363,734	2006 Profits: $7,789	Employees: 1,920
2005 Sales: $280,139	2005 Profits: $6,169	Fiscal Year Ends: 12/31
2004 Sales: $216,011	2004 Profits: $3,444	Parent Company:

SALARIES/BENEFITS:

Pension Plan:	ESOP Stock Plan:	Profit Sharing:	Top Exec. Salary: $337,000	Bonus: $337,000
Savings Plan:	Stock Purch. Plan:		Second Exec. Salary: $208,000	Bonus: $208,000

OTHER THOUGHTS:

Apparent Women Officers or Directors: 4
Hot Spot for Advancement for Women/Minorities: Y

LOCATIONS: ("Y" = Yes)

West:	Southwest:	Midwest:	Southeast:	Northeast:	International:
Y	Y	Y	Y	Y	Y

VTECH HOLDINGS LIMITED

www.vtech.com

Industry Group Code: 334210 **Ranks within this company's industry group:** Sales: 7 Profits: 2

Techology:		Medical/Drugs:		Engineering:		Transportation:		Chemicals/Petrochemicals:		Specialty:	
Computers:	Y	Manufacturer:		Design:		Aerospace:		Oil/Gas Products:		Special Services:	
Software:		Contract Research:		Construction:		Automotive:		Chemicals:		Consulting:	
Communications:	Y	Medical Services:		Eng. Services:		Shipping:		Oil/Chem. Svcs.:		Specialty Mgmt.:	
Electronics:	Y	Labs:		Consulting:				Gases:		Products:	Y
Alternative Energy:		Bio. Services:						Other:		Other:	

TYPES OF BUSINESS:

Cordless Telephone Sets
Electronic Learning Products
Contract Manufacturing Services
Data Networking Products

BRANDS/DIVISIONS/AFFILIATES:

VTech Communications
VTech Electronics
Write & Learn
V.Smile Learning System
Genius Notebook
infoPhone
KidiJamz Studio
V.Smile Cyber Pocket

CONTACTS: *Note: Officers with more than one job title may be intentionally listed here more than once.*

Chi Yun (Allan) Wong, CEO
Edwin Ying Lin Kwan, COO/Exec. VP
Pang King Fai, Pres.
Ka Hung Tong, CFO
Wai Keung (Gary) Tam, Sr. VP-Sales
Yuen Fung Poon, Dir.-R&D
Chi Ming (Vincent) Yuen, Dir.-Prod. Dev.
Gary Rogalski, VP-Eng.
Yu Wai Chang, Corp. Sec./Chief Compliance Officer
Ching Pun (Rix) Chan, Mgr.-Opcr.
Chi Kin (Kenneth) Lam, Dir.-Bus. Dev.
Andy Leung Hon Kwong, Div. CEO-Contract Mfg. Svcs.
Wah Shun Wong, Div. CEO-Branded Bus.
Chi Hoi Tong, Pres., Original Design Mfg.
Nicholas P. Delany, Pres., Vtech Communications Inc.
Chi Yun (Allan) Wong, Chmn.
Gilles Sautier, Div. CEO-Europe

Phone: 852-2680-1000 **Fax:** 852-2680-1300
Toll-Free:
Address: 23rd Fl., Tai Ping Ctr., Block 1, 57 Ting Kok Rd., Hong Kong, China

GROWTH PLANS/SPECIAL FEATURES:

VTech Holdings, Ltd. is a leading consumer electronics company focused on the design, manufacture and global marketing of electronic learning and telecommunications products. The company's VTech Communications unit is among the largest suppliers of corded and cordless phones in North America, marketing a variety of consumer phones branded both as VTech and under license as AT&T products. VTech sells a line of data networking products under the AT&T brand in North America, including wireless routers, notebook and PCI adapters and other data networking accessories. The company's VTech Electronics unit produces and markets various electronic learning products targeting children and young adults, with product lines including Write & Learn, V.Smile Learning System and Genius Notebook, with featured trademark characters licensed from Disney, Warner Brothers, Marvel, Nickelodeon and Sesame Street. VTech's contract manufacturing service unit produces home appliances, switching mode power supplies, RF modules and mobile phone products, as well as medical, audio and automotive equipment. The majority of the company's manufacturing occurs in mainland China's Pearl River Delta region, just outside of Hong Kong. In February 2008, the company introduced several new products in the electronic learning category, including the motion-activated V-Motion gaming system; the V.Smile Cyber Pocket, a pocket-sized portable version of the V.Smile Learning System; the KidiJamz Studio, an interactive music station; and KidiDoodle, a touch-sensitive drawing pad.

VTech offers its employees benefits including a medical scheme, staff discounts, paid vacation time, travel insurance and a trainings subsidy.

FINANCIALS: **Sales and profits are in thousands of dollars—add 000 to get the full amount. 2008 Note: Financial information for 2008 was not available for all companies at press time.**

2008 Sales: $1,552,000	2008 Profits: $228,900	**U.S. Stock Ticker: VTKHY**
2007 Sales: $1,463,800	2007 Profits: $194,000	**Int'l Ticker: 0303** Int'l Exchange: Hong Kong-HKEX
2006 Sales: $1,024,600	2006 Profits: $128,800	Employees: 29,000
2005 Sales: $1,022,000	2005 Profits: $56,900	Fiscal Year Ends: 3/31
2004 Sales: $915,200	2004 Profits: $46,300	Parent Company:

SALARIES/BENEFITS:

Pension Plan: Y	ESOP Stock Plan:	Profit Sharing:	Top Exec. Salary: $	Bonus: $
Savings Plan:	Stock Purch. Plan:		Second Exec. Salary: $	Bonus: $

OTHER THOUGHTS:

Apparent Women Officers or Directors:
Hot Spot for Advancement for Women/Minorities:

LOCATIONS: ("Y" = Yes)

West:	Southwest:	Midwest:	Southeast:	Northeast:	International:
Y		Y		Y	Y

WANXIANG GROUP CORPORATION

www.wanxiang.com.cn

Industry Group Code: 336300 **Ranks within this company's industry group:** Sales: Profits:

Techology:		Medical/Drugs:		Engineering:		Transportation:		Chemicals/Petrochemicals:		Specialty:	
Computers:		Manufacturer:		Design:		Aerospace:		Oil/Gas Products:		Special Services:	
Software:		Contract Research:		Construction:		Automotive:	Y	Chemicals:		Consulting:	
Communications:		Medical Services:		Eng. Services:		Shipping:		Oil/Chem. Svcs.:		Specialty Mgmt.:	
Electronics:		Labs:		Consulting:				Gases:		Products:	Y
Alternative Energy:		Bio. Services:						Other:		Other:	

TYPES OF BUSINESS:

Automotive Parts Manufacturer
Agricultural Engineering
Aquaculture
Real Estate Development
Restaurant & Hotel Management
Power Plant Construction
Leasing & Financial Services
Infrastructure Development & Construction

BRANDS/DIVISIONS/AFFILIATES:

QC Bearing Company
QC Driveline Company
Wanxiang Group Corporation
Universal Automotive Industries
Rockford Powertrain

CONTACTS: *Note: Officers with more than one job title may be intentionally listed here more than once.*

Weiding Lu, CEO
Guanqui Lu, Chmn.

Phone: 86-571-8283-2999 **Fax:** 86-571-8283-3999
Toll-Free:
Address: Wang Xiang Road, Xiao Shan District, Hangzhou, China

GROWTH PLANS/SPECIAL FEATURES:

Wanxiang Group Corporation is one of China's largest auto parts manufacturers. The company serves domestic and international clients such as Volkswagen AG; PAS Peugot Citroen S.A.; Toyota Motor Corporation; Iveco SpA; and Isuzu Motors Limited. It also supplies parts to General Motors, Ford Motor Co.; Daimler AG; Caterpillar, Inc.; and Deere & Company. In addition to auto parts, the Wanxiang Group is involved in agricultural engineering; aquaculture, raising eels and snakes; real estate development; restaurant and hotel management; power plant construction; leasing and financial services; and infrastructure development and construction. The company operates through several subsidiaries, including Wanxiang America Corporation (WAC), a supplier of universal joints, bearings, CV joints, drive shafts and other drivetrain parts to customers in over 40 countries around the world. WAC specializes in casting, forging, stamping, heat treatment, machining and grinding industrial processes. In addition to North America, WAC also operates in Canada; Central and South America; and Europe. Another subsidiary, The QC Bearing Company, operates in southern China, producing a line of bearings and components, alongside sister company QC Driveline, which produces CV joints, auto batteries, shock absorbers, leaf springs, brake discs and tools. Wanxiang owns significant stakes in six companies in the U.S., including Universal Automotive Industries and Rockford Powertrain.

FINANCIALS: **Sales and profits are in thousands of dollars—add 000 to get the full amount. 2008 Note: Financial information for 2008 was not available for all companies at press time.**

2008 Sales: $ | 2008 Profits: $
2007 Sales: $ | 2007 Profits: $
2006 Sales: $ | 2006 Profits: $
2005 Sales: $ | 2005 Profits: $
2004 Sales: $ | 2004 Profits: $

U.S. Stock Ticker: Private
Int'l Ticker: Int'l Exchange:
Employees:
Fiscal Year Ends:
Parent Company:

SALARIES/BENEFITS:

Pension Plan: | ESOP Stock Plan: | Profit Sharing: | Top Exec. Salary: $ | Bonus: $
Savings Plan: | Stock Purch. Plan: | Second Exec. Salary: $ | Bonus: $

OTHER THOUGHTS:

Apparent Women Officers or Directors:
Hot Spot for Advancement for Women/Minorities:

LOCATIONS: ("Y" = Yes)

West:	Southwest:	Midwest:	Southeast:	Northeast:	International:
		Y			Y

WESTERN DIGITAL CORP

www.westerndigital.com

Industry Group Code: 334112 **Ranks within this company's industry group:** Sales: 3 Profits: 3

Techology:		Medical/Drugs:		Engineering:		Transportation:		Chemicals/Petrochemicals:		Specialty:	
Computers:	Y	Manufacturer:		Design:		Aerospace:		Oil/Gas Products:		Special Services:	
Software:		Contract Research:		Construction:		Automotive:		Chemicals:		Consulting:	
Communications:		Medical Services:		Eng. Services:		Shipping:		Oil/Chem. Svcs.:		Specialty Mgmt.:	
Electronics:		Labs:		Consulting:				Gases:		Products:	
Alternative Energy:		Bio. Services:						Other:		Other:	

TYPES OF BUSINESS:

Data Storage Hardware
Hard Drives

BRANDS/DIVISIONS/AFFILIATES:

Komag Inc.
Caviar
Raptor
Scorpio
VelociRaptor
My Passport
My Book
GreenPower

CONTACTS:

Note: Officers with more than one job title may be intentionally listed here more than once.

John F. Coyne, CEO
John F. Coyne, Pres.
Timothy M. Leyden, CFO/Exec. VP
Hossein M. Moghadam, CTO/Sr. VP
Raymond M. Bukaty, Sr. VP-Admin.
Raymond M. Bukaty, General Counsel/Corp. Sec.
Thomas E. Pardun, Chmn.

Phone: 949-672-7000 **Fax:** 949-672-5490
Toll-Free:
Address: 20511 Lake Forest Dr., Lake Forest, CA 92630-7741 US

GROWTH PLANS/SPECIAL FEATURES:

Western Digital Corporation is a leader in the data storage industry through hard drive manufacturing for desktop and notebook computers; enterprise applications such as servers, workstations, network attached storage, storage area networks and video surveillance equipment; and consumer electronic devices such as digital video recorders (DVRs) and satellite and cable set-top boxes. In addition, the company's hard disk drives are used in external hard disk drive products that feature high-speed buses such as FireWire, Universal Serial Bus 2.0 (USB), external Serial Advanced Technology Attachment (SATA) and Ethernet. A range of hard drives are available, including desktop hard drive, mobile hard drive and enterprise hard drive products, which the company markets under the WD Caviar, WD Raptor, WD VelociRaptor, WD Scorpio, WD Elements, My Passport, My Book, My DVR Expander and GreenPower brands. The firm also offers a line of hard drives, under the WD AV brand, designed for use in DVRs, STBs, karaoke systems, multi-function printers and gaming systems. The company's hard drives include .5-inch and 2.5-inch form factor drives, having capacities ranging from 40 gigabytes to 1 terabyte; nominal rotation speeds of 5,400, 7,200 and 10,000 revolutions per minute; and offer interfaces including both Enhanced Integrated Drive Electronics (EIDE) and SATA. Recently introduced hard drives include the GreenPower drives, designed to consume substantially less power than standard drives. Late in 2007, the firm announced its hard drive density achievement of 520 Gb/in2, the hard drive industry's highest demonstrated density using continuous media. The company has manufacturing operations in Malaysia, Thailand and California. In September 2007, the firm's wholly-owned subsidiary, State M Corporation, completed the acquisition of Komag, Inc., a manufacturer of data-recording rotating disks.

Western Digital employees receive health care benefits, dependent care and educational reimbursements and an employee assistance program.

FINANCIALS:

Sales and profits are in thousands of dollars—add 000 to get the full amount. 2008 Note: Financial information for 2008 was not available for all companies at press time.

2008 Sales: $8,074,000	2008 Profits: $867,000	**U.S. Stock Ticker: WDC**
2007 Sales: $5,468,000	2007 Profits: $564,000	**Int'l Ticker:** Int'l Exchange:
2006 Sales: $4,341,300	2006 Profits: $395,900	Employees: 50,072
2005 Sales: $3,638,800	2005 Profits: $198,400	Fiscal Year Ends: 6/30
2004 Sales: $2,046,700	2004 Profits: $151,300	Parent Company:

SALARIES/BENEFITS:

Pension Plan:	ESOP Stock Plan:	Profit Sharing: Y	Top Exec. Salary: $800,000	Bonus: $135,000
Savings Plan: Y	Stock Purch. Plan:		Second Exec. Salary: $442,904	Bonus: $84,375

OTHER THOUGHTS:

Apparent Women Officers or Directors: 1
Hot Spot for Advancement for Women/Minorities:

LOCATIONS: ("Y" = Yes)

West:	Southwest:	Midwest:	Southeast:	Northeast:	International:
Y					Y

WESTINGHOUSE ELECTRIC COMPANY LLC

www.westinghousenuclear.com

Industry Group Code: 335000 **Ranks within this company's industry group:** Sales: Profits:

Techology:		Medical/Drugs:		Engineering:		Transportation:		Chemicals/Petrochemicals:		Specialty:	
Computers:		Manufacturer:		Design:	Y	Aerospace:		Oil/Gas Products:		Special Services:	Y
Software:		Contract Research:		Construction:		Automotive:		Chemicals:		Consulting:	
Communications:		Medical Services:		Eng. Services:	Y	Shipping:		Oil/Chem. Svcs.:		Specialty Mgmt.:	
Electronics:		Labs:		Consulting:				Gases:		Products:	
Alternative Energy:	Y	Bio. Services:						Other:		Other:	

TYPES OF BUSINESS:

Nuclear Power Plant Equipment
Nuclear Power Plant Repair Services
Nuclear Fuel
Nuclear Power Plant Design & Engineering
Technology Training

BRANDS/DIVISIONS/AFFILIATES:

Toshiba Corporation
Fauske and Associates, Inc.
PCI Energy Services
PaR Nuclear
WesDyne International, Inc.
Westinghouse Nuclear Fuel
Westron

CONTACTS: *Note: Officers with more than one job title may be intentionally listed here more than once.*

Stephen R. Tritch, CEO
Stephen R. Tritch, Pres.
Kazumasa Uchida, CFO/Sr. VP
James A. Fici, Sr. VP-Sales & Customer Rel.
Anthony D. Greco, Sr. VP-Human Resources & Corp. Rel.
Regis A. Matzie, CTO/Sr. VP
F. Ramsey Coates, General Counsel/Sr. VP-Legal & Contracts
Rick Etling, VP-Strategy
Jack Allen, Sr. VP-Operational Excellence
Aris Candris, Sr. VP-Nuclear Fuels
F. Ramsey Coates, Sr. VP-Environment, Health & Safety
Shigenori Shiga, Chief Coordination Officer/Sr. VP

Phone: 412-374-4111 **Fax:** 412-374-3272
Toll-Free:
Address: 4350 Northern Pike, Monroeville, PA 15146 US

GROWTH PLANS/SPECIAL FEATURES:

Westinghouse Electric Company LLC, a wholly-owned subsidiary of Toshiba Corp., provides fuel, services, technology, plant design and equipment to utility and industrial customers for the worldwide commercial nuclear electric power industry. The company is primarily engaged in fuel manufacture, reactor design, electricity generation, management and recycling of used fuel and decommissioning and environmental services. The firm operates in three segments: nuclear services, nuclear fuel and nuclear power plants. The nuclear services division provides field services such as outage support, component services and training; engineering services that improve plant reliability and regulatory compliance; and repair, replacement and automation services for plant equipment. Nuclear service subsidiaries include Fauske and Associates, Inc.; PCI Energy Services; Westron; PaR Nuclear; and WesDyne International, Inc. The nuclear fuel division, under the name Westinghouse Nuclear Fuel, offers fuel products, materials and components, as well as services and technology for reactor operators. The nuclear power plants division supplies plant design expertise, equipment and component manufacturing for nuclear power plants. Westinghouse also offers nuclear technology training programs. Westinghouse has locations in the U.K., Spain, Germany, France, Belgium, Bulgaria, Ukraine, Sweden, Russia, Korea, China, Japan, Taiwan and the U.S. In July 2008, The Shandong Nuclear Power Company, Westinghouse Electric Company LLC and its consortium partner, The Shaw Group Inc., began construction of the Haiyang Nuclear Power Facility in China. The Westinghouse consortium and State Nuclear Power Technology Corporation Ltd. plan to construct four nuclear power facilities in China.

The company offers employees a tuition reimbursement and a training program in Sweden and has an association for female employees called Westinghouse Women in Nuclear.

FINANCIALS: **Sales and profits are in thousands of dollars—add 000 to get the full amount. 2008 Note: Financial information for 2008 was not available for all companies at press time.**

2008 Sales: $	2008 Profits: $	**U.S. Stock Ticker: Subsidiary**
2007 Sales: $	2007 Profits: $	**Int'l Ticker:** Int'l Exchange:
2006 Sales: $	2006 Profits: $	Employees: 7,716
2005 Sales: $1,814,800	2005 Profits: $	Fiscal Year Ends: 3/31
2004 Sales: $	2004 Profits: $	Parent Company: TOSHIBA CORPORATION

SALARIES/BENEFITS:

Pension Plan:	ESOP Stock Plan:	Profit Sharing:	Top Exec. Salary: $	Bonus: $
Savings Plan:	Stock Purch. Plan:		Second Exec. Salary: $	Bonus: $

OTHER THOUGHTS:

Apparent Women Officers or Directors:
Hot Spot for Advancement for Women/Minorities:

LOCATIONS: ("Y" = Yes)

West:	Southwest:	Midwest:	Southeast:	Northeast:	International:
Y		Y	Y	Y	Y

WHIRLPOOL CORP

www.whirlpoolcorp.com

Industry Group Code: 335000 **Ranks within this company's industry group:** Sales: 7 Profits: 7

Techology:		Medical/Drugs:		Engineering:		Transportation:		Chemicals/Petrochemicals:		Specialty:	
Computers:		Manufacturer:		Design:		Aerospace:		Oil/Gas Products:		Special Services:	
Software:		Contract Research:		Construction:		Automotive:		Chemicals:		Consulting:	
Communications:		Medical Services:		Eng. Services:		Shipping:		Oil/Chem. Svcs.:		Specialty Mgmt.:	
Electronics:	Y	Labs:		Consulting:				Gases:		Products:	Y
Alternative Energy:		Bio. Services:						Other:		Other:	

TYPES OF BUSINESS:

Home Appliance Manufacturer
Laundry Appliances
Refrigerators & Freezers
Air Conditioning Equipment
Kitchen Appliances

BRANDS/DIVISIONS/AFFILIATES:

Whirlpool
KitchenAid
Maytag
Brastemp
Bauknecht
Amana
Jenn-Air
Consul

CONTACTS: *Note: Officers with more than one job title may be intentionally listed here more than once.*

Jeff M. Fettig, CEO
Roy Templin, CFO/Exec. VP
David A. Binkley, Sr. VP-Global Human Resources
David Szczupak, Exec. VP-Global Prod. Organization
Daniel F. Hopp, General Counsel/Sr. VP-Corp. Affairs
Marc Bitzer, Pres., U.S. Oper.
Michael A. Todman, Pres., Whirlpool North America
Bracken Darrell, Pres, Whirlpool Europe/Exec. VP
Jose Drummond, Pres., Whirlpool Latin America/Exec. VP
Jeff M. Fettig, Chmn.
Paulo F.M.O. Periquito, Pres., Whirlpool Int'l

Phone: 269-923-5000 **Fax:** 269-923-3525
Toll-Free:
Address: 2000 N. M-63, Benton Harbor, MI 49022-2692 US

GROWTH PLANS/SPECIAL FEATURES:

Whirlpool Corp. is a worldwide manufacturer and marketer of major home appliances. It manufactures products in 12 countries under 13 principal brand names, including Whirlpool, Maytag, KitchenAid, Jenn-Air, Amana, Bauknecht, Brastemp and Consul; operates 69 manufacturing and technology research centers internationally; and markets products in nearly every country around the world. The company's principal products are laundry appliances, refrigerators, cooking appliances, dishwashers and mixers and other small household appliances. It also produces hermetic compressors for refrigeration systems. In North America, Whirlpool markets and distributes major home appliances and portable appliances under a variety of brand names. In addition to its extensive operations in Western Europe, Whirlpool has sales subsidiaries in Russia, Ukraine, Hungary, Poland, the Czech Republic, Slovakia, Greece, Romania, Bulgaria, Latvia, Estonia, Lithuania, Croatia, Morocco and Turkey, with representative offices in Ukraine, Kazakhstan, Slovenia, Serbia and Montenegro. In Latin America, the company manages appliance sales and distribution in Brazil, Argentina, Chile, and Peru through its Brazilian subsidiary, and in Bolivia, Paraguay, and Uruguay through distributors. In Asia, the firm organizes the marketing and distribution of its major home appliances into five operating groups: China; Hong Kong and Taiwan; India, which includes Bangladesh, Sri Lanka, Nepal, and Pakistan; Oceania, which includes Australia, New Zealand, and Pacific Islands; and Southeast Asia, which includes Thailand, Singapore, Malaysia, Indonesia, Vietnam, the Philippines, Korea and Japan. Whirlpool is a supplier to Sears, which accounts for about 11% of sales, of laundry, refrigerator, dishwasher and trash compactor appliances. Sears markets some of the products under the Kenmore brand name.

Whirlpool offers its employees benefits that include health, dental and vision insurance; life and AD&D insurance; a 401(k) plan; flexible spending accounts; educational reimbursement; fitness and weight loss rebates; adoption assistance; and an employee assistance program.

FINANCIALS: **Sales and profits are in thousands of dollars—add 000 to get the full amount. 2008 Note: Financial information for 2008 was not available for all companies at press time.**

2008 Sales: $18,907,000	2008 Profits: $418,000	**U.S. Stock Ticker: WHR**
2007 Sales: $19,408,000	2007 Profits: $640,000	**Int'l Ticker:** Int'l Exchange:
2006 Sales: $18,080,000	2006 Profits: $433,000	Employees: 69,612
2005 Sales: $14,317,000	2005 Profits: $422,000	Fiscal Year Ends: 12/31
2004 Sales: $13,220,000	2004 Profits: $406,000	Parent Company:

SALARIES/BENEFITS:

Pension Plan:	ESOP Stock Plan:	Profit Sharing:	Top Exec. Salary: $1,262,500	Bonus: $420,000
Savings Plan: Y	Stock Purch. Plan:		Second Exec. Salary: $729,168	Bonus: $100,008

OTHER THOUGHTS:

Apparent Women Officers or Directors: 2
Hot Spot for Advancement for Women/Minorities:

LOCATIONS: ("Y" = Yes)

West:	Southwest:	Midwest:	Southeast:	Northeast:	International:
Y	Y	Y	Y	Y	Y

WIPRO LTD

www.wiprocorporate.com

Industry Group Code: 541512 **Ranks within this company's industry group:** Sales: 12 Profits: 3

Techology:		Medical/Drugs:		Engineering:		Transportation:		Chemicals/Petrochemicals:		Specialty:	
Computers:		Manufacturer:		Design:		Aerospace:		Oil/Gas Products:		Special Services:	
Software:	Y	Contract Research:		Construction:		Automotive:		Chemicals:		Consulting:	
Communications:		Medical Services:		Eng. Services:		Shipping:		Oil/Chem. Svcs.:		Specialty Mgmt.:	
Electronics:		Labs:		Consulting:	Y			Gases:		Products:	Y
Alternative Energy:		Bio. Services:						Other:		Other:	

TYPES OF BUSINESS:

IT Consulting & Outsourcing
Computer Hardware & Software Design
Hydraulic Equipment
Medical Electronics
Lighting Equipment
Soaps & Toiletries

BRANDS/DIVISIONS/AFFILIATES:

Wipro Technologies
Wipro Infotech
Wipro Consumer Care and Lighting
Wipro Infrastructure Engineering
Wipro GE Medical Systems Ltd
Infocrossing
Unza Holdings Limited
Citi Technology Services Ltd

CONTACTS: *Note: Officers with more than one job title may be intentionally listed here more than once.*

Girish Paranjpe, Joint CEO
Suresh Vaswani, Joint CEO
Azim Premji, Chmn.

Phone: 91-80-2844-0011 **Fax:** 91-80-2844-0256
Toll-Free:
Address: Doddakannelli, Sarjapur Rd., Bangalore, 560 035 India

GROWTH PLANS/SPECIAL FEATURES:

Wipro, Ltd. is a leading global provider of comprehensive IT solutions and services, including systems integration; software application development and maintenance; research and development; and business consulting. Wipro operates through multiple subsidiaries, including Wipro Technologies; Wipro Infotech; Wipro Consumer Care and Lighting; Wipro Infrastructure Engineering; and Wipro GE Medical Systems, Ltd. Wipro Technologies is a premier technology company and one of the world's first SEI CMM Level 5 certified IT services firms. The firm provides IT consulting, general IT services (including package implementation, IT infrastructure services, product design and embedded services), application development and management, and outsourcing services to some of the largest companies in the world, competing in automotive, computing, industrial, medical and telecommunications enterprises. Wipro Infotech is responsible for technology operations in the Indian, Asia-Pacific and Middle-East markets. Wipro Consumer Care and Lighting focuses on niche markets and offers a mix of consumer products, including soaps and toiletries, light bulbs and fluorescent tubes, lighting accessories and hydrogenated oil. Its brands include the Santoor and Wipro Active lines of soap and talcum powders, as well as the Wipro Baby Soft line of infant and child care products. Wipro Infrastructure Engineering Limited, formerly Wipro Fluid Power, Ltd., develops and delivers precision hydraulic cylinders and components to original equipment manufacturers (OEMs) worldwide. Wipro GE Medical Systems, a joint venture with General Electric (GE) Medical Systems South Asia, is one of India's largest exporters of medical systems. In 2007, Wipro Technologies acquired Infocrossing, an IT infrastructure management and outsourcing services provider. Wipro Consumer Care and Lighting also acquired Unza Holdings Limited, one of the largest independent manufacturers of personal care products in Southeast Asia. In December 2008, the company agreed to acquire Citi Technology Services Ltd., for approximately $127 million.

FINANCIALS: **Sales and profits are in thousands of dollars—add 000 to get the full amount. 2008 Note: Financial information for 2008 was not available for all companies at press time.**

2008 Sales: $4,933,000 | 2008 Profits: $806,000
2007 Sales: $3,467,000 | 2007 Profits: $677,000
2006 Sales: $2,385,500 | 2006 Profits: $455,710
2005 Sales: $1,863,000 | 2005 Profits: $363,000
2004 Sales: $1,349,800 | 2004 Profits: $230,800

U.S. Stock Ticker: WIT
Int'l Ticker: 507685 Int'l Exchange: Bombay-BSE
Employees: 53,700
Fiscal Year Ends: 3/31
Parent Company:

SALARIES/BENEFITS:

Pension Plan: ESOP Stock Plan: Profit Sharing: Top Exec. Salary: $ Bonus: $
Savings Plan: Stock Purch. Plan: Second Exec. Salary: $ Bonus: $

OTHER THOUGHTS:

Apparent Women Officers or Directors:
Hot Spot for Advancement for Women/Minorities:

LOCATIONS: ("Y" = Yes)

West:	Southwest:	Midwest:	Southeast:	Northeast:	International:
Y	Y	Y	Y	Y	Y

Note: Financial information, benefits and other data can change quickly and may vary from those stated here.

WS ATKINS PLC

www.atkinsglobal.com

Industry Group Code: 541330 **Ranks within this company's industry group:** Sales: 7 Profits: 5

Techology:		Medical/Drugs:		Engineering:		Transportation:		Chemicals/Petrochemicals:		Specialty:	
Computers:		Manufacturer:		Design:	Y	Aerospace:		Oil/Gas Products:		Special Services:	
Software:		Contract Research:		Construction:		Automotive:		Chemicals:		Consulting:	Y
Communications:		Medical Services:		Eng. Services:		Shipping:		Oil/Chem. Svcs.:		Specialty Mgmt.:	Y
Electronics:		Labs:		Consulting:	Y			Gases:		Products:	
Alternative Energy:		Bio. Services:						Other:	Y	Other:	

TYPES OF BUSINESS:

Engineering Services-Building Design
Infrastructure & Transportation Engineering
Consulting
Technology Support Services

BRANDS/DIVISIONS/AFFILIATES:

Atkins Benham
Faithful & Gould
Lambert Smith Hampton

CONTACTS: *Note: Officers with more than one job title may be intentionally listed here more than once.*

Keith Clarke, CEO
Robert MacLeod, Dir.-Finance
Alun Griffiths, Dir.-Human Resources
Ivor Catto, Managing Dir.-Design & Eng. Solutions
Richard Webster, Company Sec.
Sara Lipscombe, Dir.-Comm
Richard Barrett, Managing Dir.-Europe
Richard Hall, Managing Dir.-Faithful & Gould
Neil Thomas, Managing Dir.-Highways & Transportation
Samson Sin, Managing Dir.-Atkins China
Edward Wallis, Chmn.
Tim Askew, Managing Dir.-Middle East & India

Phone: 44-372-726-140	**Fax:** 44-372-740-055
Toll-Free:	
Address: Woodcote Grove, Ashley Rd., Epsom, Surrey KT18 5BW UK	

GROWTH PLANS/SPECIAL FEATURES:

WS Atkins plc, a turnover engineering consultancy company, plans, designs and enables delivery of complex infrastructure and buildings, primarily in the U.K. It has six primary business segments: Design and Engineering Solutions; Highways and Transportation; Rail; Management and Project Services; Middle East and China; Equity Investments; and Asset Management. The Design and Engineering Solutions segment operates in the following areas: nuclear and power; water and environment; oil and gas; infrastructure; and aerospace and defense. The Highways and Transportation segment is involved in designing new roads; developing intelligent transport systems; transport planning; road improvements; integrated road network management; and road maintenance management. The Rail segment offers electrification, civil and signaling engineering services, as well as strategic planning, systems integration, asset management and safety specialist services. The Management and Project Services segment mainly offers IT and management consultancy, as well as cost, project and program management services. The Middle East and China segment offers engineering, design and project management services for infrastructure including transportation and buildings. Project and cost management consultancy subsidiary Faithful & Gould, Inc. operates in both the Middle East and China and Management and Project Services segments. The Equity Investment segment consists of property advisory firm Lambert Smith Hampton and several joint ventures, such as Metronet, which manages 66% of the London Underground. Lastly, the Asset Management segment manages property for private and public sector clients. Atkins has 200 offices in 25 countries and ongoing projects in more than 80. In October 2008, the company acquired MG Bennett & Associates Ltd., an engineering design firm.

Employees of Atkins receive an employee assistance program, an employee car purchase program and extensive development programs.

FINANCIALS: **Sales and profits are in thousands of dollars—add 000 to get the full amount. 2008 Note: Financial information for 2008 was not available for all companies at press time.**

2008 Sales: $2,076,210	2008 Profits: $148,360	**U.S. Stock Ticker:**
2007 Sales: $1,840,040	2007 Profits: $-85,010	**Int'l Ticker: ATK** Int'l Exchange: London-LSE
2006 Sales: $2,150,000	2006 Profits: $113,800	Employees: 17,300
2005 Sales: $1,910,000	2005 Profits: $77,800	Fiscal Year Ends: 3/31
2004 Sales: $1,810,800	2004 Profits: $68,300	Parent Company:

SALARIES/BENEFITS:

Pension Plan:	ESOP Stock Plan:	Profit Sharing:	Top Exec. Salary: $730,895	Bonus: $345,327
Savings Plan:	Stock Purch. Plan:		Second Exec. Salary: $242,451	Bonus: $99,422

OTHER THOUGHTS:

Apparent Women Officers or Directors: 2
Hot Spot for Advancement for Women/Minorities:

LOCATIONS: ("Y" = Yes)

West:	Southwest:	Midwest:	Southeast:	Northeast:	International:
Y	Y	Y	Y	Y	Y

WYETH

www.wyeth.com

Industry Group Code: 325412 **Ranks within this company's industry group:** Sales: 10 Profits: 11

Techology:		Medical/Drugs:		Engineering:		Transportation:		Chemicals/Petrochemicals:		Specialty:	
Computers:		Manufacturer:	Y	Design:		Aerospace:		Oil/Gas Products:		Special Services:	
Software:		Contract Research:		Construction:		Automotive:		Chemicals:		Consulting:	
Communications:		Medical Services:		Eng. Services:		Shipping:		Oil/Chem. Svcs.:		Specialty Mgmt.:	
Electronics:		Labs:	Y	Consulting:				Gases:		Products:	
Alternative Energy:		Bio. Services:						Other:		Other:	

TYPES OF BUSINESS:

Drugs-Diversified
Wholesale Pharmaceuticals
Animal Health Care Products
Biologicals
Vaccines
Over-the-Counter Drugs
Women's Health Care Products
Nutritional Supplements

BRANDS/DIVISIONS/AFFILIATES:

Chap Stick
Premarin
Dimetapp
Advil
Robitussin
Preparation H
Thiakis Limited
Fort Dodge Animal Health

CONTACTS: *Note: Officers with more than one job title may be intentionally listed here more than once.*

Bernard Poussot, CEO
Bernard Poussot, Pres.
Gregory Norden, CFO/Sr. VP
Denise Peppard, Sr. VP-Human Resources
Jeffrey E. Keisling, CIO/VP-Corp. Info. Svcs.
Lawrence V. Stein, General Counsel/Sr. VP
Thomas Hofstaetter, Sr. VP-Corp. Bus. Dev.
Timothy P. Cost, Sr. VP-Corp. Affairs
Justin R. Victoria, VP-Investor Rel.
Mary K. Wold, Sr. VP-Finance
Mikael Dolsten, Sr. VP
Joseph M. Mahady, Sr. VP
Leo C. Jardot, VP-Gov't Rel.
Andrew F. Davidson, VP-Internal Audit
Bernard Poussot, Chmn.

Phone: 973-660-5000 **Fax:** 973-660-7026
Toll-Free:
Address: 5 Giralda Farms, Madison, NJ 07940 US

GROWTH PLANS/SPECIAL FEATURES:

Wyeth is a global leader in pharmaceuticals, consumer health care products and animal health care products. The firm discovers, develops, manufactures, distributes and sells a diversified line of products arising from three divisions: Wyeth Pharmaceuticals, Wyeth Consumer Health care and Fort Dodge Animal Health. The pharmaceuticals segment is itself divided into women's health care, neuroscience, vaccines and infectious disease, musculoskeletal, internal medicine, hemophilia and immunology and oncology. The division sells branded and generic pharmaceuticals, biological and nutraceutical products as well as animal biological products and pharmaceuticals. Its branded products include Advil, Dimetapp, Premarin, Prempro, Premphase, Triphasil, Ativan, Effexor, Altace, Inderal, Zoton, Protonix and Enbrel. The consumer health care segment's products include analgesics, cough/cold/allergy remedies, nutritional supplements, lip balm and hemorrhoidal, antacid, asthma and other relief items sold over-the-counter. The segment's well-known over-the-counter products include Advil, cold medicines Robitussin and Dimetapp and nutritional supplement Centrum, as well as Chap Stick, Caltrate, Preparation H and Solgar. The company's animal health care products include vaccines, pharmaceuticals, endectocides (dewormers that control both internal and external parasites) and growth implants under the brand names LymeVax, Duramune and Fel-O-Vax. In December 2008, Wyeth acquired Thiakis Limited, a U.K.-based private biotechnology company for approximately $30 million. In January 2009, the firm announced its agreement to be acquired by Pfizer for $68 billion.

Employees are offered a pension plan; a 401(k) plan; child care subsidies; and educational assistance.

FINANCIALS: **Sales and profits are in thousands of dollars—add 000 to get the full amount. 2008 Note: Financial information for 2008 was not available for all companies at press time.**

2008 Sales: $22,833,908	2008 Profits: $4,417,833	**U.S. Stock Ticker: WYE**
2007 Sales: $22,399,798	2007 Profits: $4,615,960	**Int'l Ticker:** Int'l Exchange:
2006 Sales: $20,350,655	2006 Profits: $4,196,706	Employees: 50,527
2005 Sales: $18,755,790	2005 Profits: $3,656,298	Fiscal Year Ends: 12/31
2004 Sales: $17,358,028	2004 Profits: $1,233,997	Parent Company:

SALARIES/BENEFITS:

Pension Plan: Y	ESOP Stock Plan:	Profit Sharing:	Top Exec. Salary: $1,728,500	Bonus: $3,200,000
Savings Plan: Y	Stock Purch. Plan:		Second Exec. Salary: $1,050,400	Bonus: $2,000,000

OTHER THOUGHTS:

Apparent Women Officers or Directors: 5
Hot Spot for Advancement for Women/Minorities: Y

LOCATIONS: ("Y" = Yes)

West:	Southwest:	Midwest:	Southeast:	Northeast:	International:
Y	Y	Y	Y	Y	Y

XEROX CORP

www.xerox.com

Industry Group Code: 333313 **Ranks within this company's industry group:** Sales: 2 Profits: 3

Techology:		Medical/Drugs:		Engineering:		Transportation:		Chemicals/Petrochemicals:		Specialty:	
Computers:	Y	Manufacturer:		Design:		Aerospace:		Oil/Gas Products:		Special Services:	Y
Software:	Y	Contract Research:		Construction:		Automotive:		Chemicals:		Consulting:	
Communications:		Medical Services:		Eng. Services:		Shipping:		Oil/Chem. Svcs.:		Specialty Mgmt.:	
Electronics:		Labs:		Consulting:				Gases:		Products:	
Alternative Energy:		Bio. Services:						Other:		Other:	

TYPES OF BUSINESS:

Business Machines-Copiers, Printers & Scanners
Managed Print Services Outsourcing
Software
Multipurpose Office Machines
Consulting Services
Desktop Printers

BRANDS/DIVISIONS/AFFILIATES:

Fuji Xerox
DocuColor
CopyCentre
Xerox Canada Inc
Palo Alto Research Center
Global Imaging Systems Inc
Advectis Inc
Image Quest Inc

CONTACTS: *Note: Officers with more than one job title may be intentionally listed here more than once.*

Anne M. Mulcahy, CEO
Ursula M. Burns, Pres.
Lawrence A. Zimmerman, CFO/Corp. Exec. VP
Michael C. Mac Donald, Sr. VP/Pres., Mktg. Oper.
Patricia M. Nazemetz, Chief Human Resources & Ethics Officer/VP
John McDermott, CIO/VP
Sophie V. Vandebroek, CTO/VP/Pres., Xerox Innovation Group
Anthony M. Federico, Chief Engineer
Don Liu, General Counsel/Sr. VP/Sec.
James A. Firestone, Corp. Exec. VP Corporate Oper.
Eric Armour, Corp. VP-Strategy
James H. Lesko, VP-Investor Rel.
Gary R. Kabureck, Chief Acct. Officer/VP
Erid Armour, Pres., Global Bus. & Strategic Mktg. Group
Jean-Noel Machon, Sr. VP/Pres., Developing Markets Oper.
Jule Limoli, Pres., North American Agent Oper.
Rick Dastin, Pres., Xerox Office Group
Anne M. Mulcahy, Chmn.
Stephen Cronin, Corp. Sr. VP-Xerox Global Svcs.

Phone: 203-968-3000 **Fax:** 203-968-3944
Toll-Free:
Address: 45 Glober Ave., P.O. Box 4505, Norwalk, CT 06856 US

GROWTH PLANS/SPECIAL FEATURES:

Xerox Corp. is a technology and services company operating in the global document market. It operates in four segments: Production, Office, Developing Markets Operations (DMO) and Services/Paper/Other. The Production segment manufactures high-end digital monochrome and color systems designed for customers in the graphic communications industry and for large enterprises. These products enable digital on-demand printing, digital full-color printing and enterprise printing. The division offers a complete family of monochrome production systems from 65-288 pages per minute (ppm) and color production systems from 40-110 ppm. Additionally, it offers a variety of pre-press and post-press options, as well as workflow software. The Office segment's systems and services, which offer monochrome devices at speeds up to 95 ppm and color devices up to 60 ppm, include the family of CopyCentre, WorkCentre and WorkCentre Pro digital multifunction systems; DocuColor printer/copiers; color laser, LED (light emitting diode), solid ink and monochrome laser desktop printers; digital copiers; and light-lens copiers and facsimile products. The DMO segment includes the marketing, sales and servicing of Xerox products, supplies and services around the world. The Services/Paper/Other segment primarily includes revenue from paper sales, value-added services and wide-format systems. This unit includes managed print services, an outsourcing service where Xerox assumes complete ownership and/or operation of a client company's desktop printers, copiers and similar machines, with a goal of saving the client up to 30% in yearly costs. Xerox received about 20% of its 2008 revenues from managed print services. Fuji Xerox, an unconsolidated entity of which Xerox owns 25%, develops, manufactures and distributes document management system, supplies and services. In 2007, Xerox acquired Global Imaging Systems, Inc. for $1.46 billion. In 2008, Global Imaging Systems acquired Precision Copier Service, Inc.; Saxon Business Systems; and Sierra Office Solutions. In 2009, the subsidiary completed its acquisition of ComDoc, a dealer of document management systems.

The company offers its employees medical and dental insurance; an employee assistance program; and tuition reimbursement.

FINANCIALS: **Sales and profits are in thousands of dollars—add 000 to get the full amount. 2008 Note: Financial information for 2008 was not available for all companies at press time.**

2008 Sales: $17,608,000	2008 Profits: $230,000	**U.S. Stock Ticker: XRX**
2007 Sales: $17,228,000	2007 Profits: $1,135,000	**Int'l Ticker:** Int'l Exchange:
2006 Sales: $15,895,000	2006 Profits: $1,210,000	Employees: 57,100
2005 Sales: $15,701,000	2005 Profits: $978,000	Fiscal Year Ends: 12/31
2004 Sales: $15,722,000	2004 Profits: $859,000	Parent Company:

SALARIES/BENEFITS:

Pension Plan:	ESOP Stock Plan:	Profit Sharing:	Top Exec. Salary: $1,320,000	Bonus: $2,178,000
Savings Plan: Y	Stock Purch. Plan:		Second Exec. Salary: $797,500	Bonus: $1,168,750

OTHER THOUGHTS:

Apparent Women Officers or Directors: 6
Hot Spot for Advancement for Women/Minorities: Y

LOCATIONS: ("Y" = Yes)

West:	Southwest:	Midwest:	Southeast:	Northeast:	International:
Y	Y	Y	Y	Y	Y

Note: Financial information, benefits and other data can change quickly and may vary from those stated here.

YAHOO! INC

www.yahoo.com

Industry Group Code: 514199B **Ranks within this company's industry group:** Sales: 2 Profits: 2

Techology:		Medical/Drugs:		Engineering:		Transportation:		Chemicals/Petrochemicals:		Specialty:	
Computers:		Manufacturer:		Design:		Aerospace:		Oil/Gas Products:		Special Services:	Y
Software:	Y	Contract Research:		Construction:		Automotive:		Chemicals:		Consulting:	
Communications:	Y	Medical Services:		Eng. Services:		Shipping:		Oil/Chem. Svcs.:		Specialty Mgmt.:	
Electronics:		Labs:		Consulting:				Gases:		Products:	
Alternative Energy:		Bio. Services:						Other:		Other:	Y

TYPES OF BUSINESS:

Online Portal-Search Engine
Broadcast Media
Job Placement Services
Paid Positioning Services
Advertising Services
Online Business & Consumer Information
Search Technology Licensing
E-Commerce

BRANDS/DIVISIONS/AFFILIATES:

Yahoo.com
Yahoo! Mail
Yahoo! Messenger
Yahoo! Shopping
Gmarket Inc.
HotJobs.com, Ltd.
BlueLithium
Right Media, Inc.

CONTACTS:

Note: Officers with more than one job title may be intentionally listed here more than once.

Carol Bartz, CEO
Susan Decker, Pres.
Elisa Steele, Chief Mktg. Officer
David Windley, Chief Human Resources Officer
Usama Fayyad, Exec. VP-Research & Strategic Data Solutions
Usama Fayyad, Chief Data Officer
Aristotle Balogh, CTO/Exec. VP-Prod.
Qi Lu, Exec. VP-Search & Advertising Tech. Group
Michael Callahan, General Counsel/Sec./Exec. VP
Jill Nash, Chief Comm. Officer
Michael Murray, Chief Acct. Officer
David Filo, Chief Yahoo
Hilary Schneider, Exec. VP-North America
Ash Patel, Exec. VP-Audience Prod. Div.
Carl Icahn, Chmn.

Phone: 408-349-3300	**Fax:** 408-349-3301
Toll-Free:	
Address: 701 First Ave., Sunnyvale, CA 94089 US	

GROWTH PLANS/SPECIAL FEATURES:

Yahoo!, Inc. is a provider of online products and services to consumers and businesses worldwide. For users, the company's offerings fall into five categories: Front Doors; Search; Communications and Communities; Media; and Connected Life. The majority of these offerings are available in more than 20 languages. For advertisers and publishers, the firm provides a range of marketing solutions and tools that enable businesses to reach users who visit Yahoo! Properties and our Affiliate sites. For developers, Yahoo provides an innovative and easily accessible array of Web Services and Application Programming Interfaces (APIs), technical resources, tools, and channels to market. Yahoo! is present in 20 markets in Europe, Latin America, Asia Pacific and Canada. The company has entered into relationships with business partners that offer content, technology and distribution capabilities, which permit the company to bring Yahoo!-branded, targeted media products to the market more quickly. The company also operates HotJobs.com, Ltd., a leading Internet job placement and recruiting company. In February 2008, the company acquired Maven Networks Inc., an online video platform provider. Also in February 2008, the company agreed to enter into a new strategic partnership with T-Mobile. The partnership will bring Yahoo!'s mobile services to millions of consumers and sets the stage for Yahoo! oneSearch to become the exclusive mobile search service for T-Mobile customers beginning in March 2008. In April 2008, Yahoo! entered into an agreement to acquire Index Tools, as well as its subsidiary, Tensa R&D Kft. Index Tools is a provider of web analytics software for online marketing.

Yahoo! offers employees discount movie passes; basic life insurance and accidental death and dismemberment insurance, short and long term disability, commuter subsidies; a game room; health club membership and massages; on-site dental care, car washes and haircuts; and tuition reimbursement.

FINANCIALS:

Sales and profits are in thousands of dollars—add 000 to get the full amount. 2008 Note: Financial information for 2008 was not available for all companies at press time.

2008 Sales: $7,208,502	2008 Profits: $424,298	**U.S. Stock Ticker: YHOO**
2007 Sales: $6,969,274	2007 Profits: $660,000	**Int'l Ticker:** Int'l Exchange:
2006 Sales: $6,425,679	2006 Profits: $751,391	Employees: 13,600
2005 Sales: $5,257,668	2005 Profits: $1,896,230	Fiscal Year Ends: 12/31
2004 Sales: $3,575,000	2004 Profits: $839,553	Parent Company:

SALARIES/BENEFITS:

Pension Plan:	ESOP Stock Plan:	Profit Sharing:	Top Exec. Salary: $657,500	Bonus: $1,100,250
Savings Plan: Y	Stock Purch. Plan: Y		Second Exec. Salary: $351,250	Bonus: $225,000

OTHER THOUGHTS:

Apparent Women Officers or Directors: 3
Hot Spot for Advancement for Women/Minorities: Y

LOCATIONS: ("Y" = Yes)

West:	Southwest:	Midwest:	Southeast:	Northeast:	International:
Y	Y	Y	Y	Y	Y

Note: Financial information, benefits and other data can change quickly and may vary from those stated here.

ZF FRIEDRICHSHAFEN AG

www.zf.com

Industry Group Code: 336350 **Ranks within this company's industry group:** Sales: Profits:

Techology:		Medical/Drugs:		Engineering:		Transportation:		Chemicals/Petrochemicals:		Specialty:	
Computers:		Manufacturer:		Design:	Y	Aerospace:	Y	Oil/Gas Products:		Special Services:	Y
Software:		Contract Research:		Construction:		Automotive:	Y	Chemicals:		Consulting:	
Communications:		Medical Services:		Eng. Services:	Y	Shipping:	Y	Oil/Chem. Svcs.:		Specialty Mgmt.:	
Electronics:		Labs:		Consulting:				Gases:		Products:	
Alternative Energy:		Bio. Services:						Other:		Other:	

TYPES OF BUSINESS:

Automotive Components
Transmissions & Power Trains
Axles
Steering Systems
Chassis Components
Repair Services
Agricultural & Construction Machinery
Boat & Helicopter Transmissions

BRANDS/DIVISIONS/AFFILIATES:

ZF Lenksysteme
ZF Sachs AG
ZF Boge Elastmetall
ZF Trading
ZF-AS Tronic Mid
ZF-AS Tronic Lite
ZF Lemforder
ZF Electronics GmbH

CONTACTS: *Note: Officers with more than one job title may be intentionally listed here more than once.*

Hans-Georg Härter, CEO
Uwe Berner, Exec. VP-Human Resources & Service Companies
Willi Berchtold, Exec. VP-IT
Willi Berchtold, Exec. VP-Finance & Controlling
Michael Paul, Exec. VP-Tech. Div.
Wolfgang Vogel, Exec. VP-Aviation Tech. & Marine Propulsion
Reinhard Buhl, Group Exec.-ZF Lemforder GmbH
Andreas Hartmann, Chief Compliance Officer
Rainer Thieme, Chmn.
Manfred Schwab, Exec. VP Asia Pacific

Phone: 49-7541-77-0 **Fax:** 49-7541-77-90-80-00
Toll-Free:
Address: Graf-von-Soden-Platz 1, Friedrichshafen, 88046 Germany

GROWTH PLANS/SPECIAL FEATURES:

ZF Friedrichshafen AG designs and manufactures automatic and manual transmissions for commercial vehicles, cars, aircraft, and marine vessels. It operates approximately 119 production plants in 25 countries worldwide. The company also makes industrial drives such as servo gearboxes, as well as rail transmissions. Its off-road division makes transmissions for construction equipment and farm machinery. ZF's chassis unit makes automotive rear-axle systems and suspension modules. Through subsidiary ZF Lenksysteme (a joint venture with Robert Bosch GmbH), the company makes steering systems. Subsidiary ZF Sachs AG produces vibration dampers and other components for chassis regulation. ZF Boge Elastmetall, the rubber-metal technology business unit, develops and produces components and modules for vibration damping. The marine propulsion systems division produces transmissions for all types of pleasure boats and commercial marine craft. The aviation technology division develops, produces and maintains helicopter transmissions. ZF Trading is responsible for the worldwide aftermarket business for Sachs, Boge and Lemforder products. The company also has a sales and service organization. Prominent customers of ZF Friedrichshafen AG include AB Volvo; BMW Group; Chrysler LLC; Fiat S.p.A.; Ford Motor Company Inc.; General Motors Corporation; Honda Motor Co. Ltd; Renault-Nissan BV; Tata Group; Toyota Motor Corporation; and Volkswagen AG. In May 2008, the firm opened a new production facility in Germany dedicated to hybrid modules for cars, buses and delivery vehicles. In November 2008, the company acquired Cherry Corporation, an electronic components business, now operating as ZF Electronics GmbH and focused on the production of switching systems, sensor technologies and controls for the automobile industry.

FINANCIALS: **Sales and profits are in thousands of dollars—add 000 to get the full amount. 2008 Note: Financial information for 2008 was not available for all companies at press time.**

2008 Sales: $	2008 Profits: $	**U.S. Stock Ticker: Private**
2007 Sales: $18,618,100	2007 Profits: $	**Int'l Ticker:** Int'l Exchange:
2006 Sales: $18,308,740	2006 Profits: $	Employees: 57,372
2005 Sales: $13,843,500	2005 Profits: $304,650	Fiscal Year Ends: 12/31
2004 Sales: $13,502,600	2004 Profits: $115,700	Parent Company:

SALARIES/BENEFITS:

Pension Plan:	ESOP Stock Plan:	Profit Sharing:	Top Exec. Salary: $	Bonus: $
Savings Plan:	Stock Purch. Plan:		Second Exec. Salary: $	Bonus: $

OTHER THOUGHTS:

Apparent Women Officers or Directors:
Hot Spot for Advancement for Women/Minorities:

LOCATIONS: ("Y" = Yes)

West:	Southwest:	Midwest:	Southeast:	Northeast:	International:
Y	Y	Y	Y	Y	Y

ZTE CORPORATION

www.zte.com.cn

Industry Group Code: 334210 **Ranks within this company's industry group:** Sales: 3 Profits: 1

Techology:		Medical/Drugs:		Engineering:		Transportation:		Chemicals/Petrochemicals:		Specialty:	
Computers:		Manufacturer:		Design:		Aerospace:		Oil/Gas Products:		Special Services:	
Software:		Contract Research:		Construction:		Automotive:		Chemicals:		Consulting:	
Communications:	Y	Medical Services:		Eng. Services:		Shipping:		Oil/Chem. Svcs.:		Specialty Mgmt.:	
Electronics:	Y	Labs:		Consulting:				Gases:		Products:	Y
Alternative Energy:		Bio. Services:						Other:		Other:	

TYPES OF BUSINESS:

Telecommunications Equipment Manufacturing
Optical Networking Equipment
Intelligent & Next-Generation Network Systems
Mobile Phones

BRANDS/DIVISIONS/AFFILIATES:

CONTACTS:

Note: Officers with more than one job title may be intentionally listed here more than once.

Yin Yimin, Pres.
Wei Zaisheng, CFO/Exec. VP
Shi Lirong, Exec. VP
He Shiyou, Exec. VP
Xie Daxiong, Exec. VP
Tian Wenguo, Exec. VP
Hou Weigui, Chmn.

Phone: 86-755-26770000 **Fax:** 86-755-26771999
Toll-Free:
Address: ZTE Plz., Hi-Tech Rd. S., Hi-Tech Industrial Park, Shenzhen, 518057 China

GROWTH PLANS/SPECIAL FEATURES:

ZTE Corporation (Zhongxing Telecom) is one of China's largest listed telecommunications equipment providers, specializing in offering customized network solutions for telecom carriers worldwide. The company develops and manufactures telecommunications equipment for fixed, mobile, data and optical networks, intelligent networks and next generation networks as well as mobile phones. ZTE's business is organized into three primary divisions: wireless, wirelines and terminal (mobile phone) services. In the wireless division, the company provides CDMA2000, GSM, and WiMAX products, including base stations and switching stations. The company's CDMA capacity has exceeded 20 million lines, and its GSM equipment has entered over 20 different countries' markets around the world. ZTE's wirelines products include data, optical transmission, switching, video conferencing, power supply and monitoring. The company provides its products for use in narrowband, broadband, wired and wireless applications. Its optical transmission products are used in several national and provincial backbone transmission networks in China, and they are also used in over 20 countries and regions abroad. ZTE's mobile phones division designs and manufactures devices supporting GSM, CDMA2000, TD-SCDMA and W-CDMA. The company has independent intellectual property rights to the core software, hardware circuits, core chips and overall design of all its mobile devices. ZTE has historically sold to customers in China, elsewhere in Asia, and Africa. However, the firm has been expanding its marketing to telecom companies in Europe and North America. In March 2008, the company entered a contract with Pakistan Telecommunication Co. Ltd. to build part of the country's largest wavelength-division multiplexing (WDM) backbone transmission network. Upon completion, the project will provide network coverage spanning 3,700 miles. In October 2008, ZTE announced plans to build an $877 million research, development and manufacturing facility in Xi'an, in the central Chinese province of Shaanxi.

FINANCIALS:

Sales and profits are in thousands of dollars—add 000 to get the full amount. 2008 Note: Financial information for 2008 was not available for all companies at press time.

2008 Sales: $6,470,650	2008 Profits: $330,520	**U.S. Stock Ticker: ZTCOF**
2007 Sales: $5,013,857	2007 Profits: $181,411	**Int'l Ticker: 000063** Int'l Exchange: Shanghai-SHE
2006 Sales: $3,358,368	2006 Profits: $111,118	Employees:
2005 Sales: $3,125,787	2005 Profits: $173,023	Fiscal Year Ends: 12/31
2004 Sales: $2,563,823	2004 Profits: $153,000	Parent Company:

SALARIES/BENEFITS:

Pension Plan:	ESOP Stock Plan:	Profit Sharing:	Top Exec. Salary: $52,847	Bonus: $87,454
Savings Plan:	Stock Purch. Plan:		Second Exec. Salary: $48,349	Bonus: $52,472

OTHER THOUGHTS:

Apparent Women Officers or Directors:
Hot Spot for Advancement for Women/Minorities:

LOCATIONS: ("Y" = Yes)

West:	Southwest:	Midwest:	Southeast:	Northeast:	International:
	Y			Y	Y

ADDITIONAL INDEXES

Contents:

INDEX OF FIRMS NOTED AS HOT SPOTS FOR ADVANCEMENT FOR WOMEN & MINORITIES

INGERSOLL-RAND COMPANY LIMITED
INTEL CORP
INTERNATIONAL BUSINESS MACHINES CORP (IBM)
INTUIT INC
ITT CORPORATION
JABIL CIRCUIT INC
JACOBS ENGINEERING GROUP INC
JDS UNIPHASE CORPORATION
JOHNSON & JOHNSON
JOHNSON CONTROLS INC
JUNIPER NETWORKS INC
KBR INC
KIMBERLY-CLARK CORP
L-3 COMMUNICATIONS HOLDINGS INC
LEXMARK INTERNATIONAL INC
LOCKHEED MARTIN CORP
LOGICA PLC
LOGITECH INTERNATIONAL SA
LSI CORPORATION
LUXOTTICA GROUP SPA
MARATHON OIL CORP
MEDTRONIC INC
MERCK & CO INC
MICHAEL BAKER CORPORATION
MICRON TECHNOLOGY INC
MICROSOFT CORP
MONSANTO CO
MOTOROLA INC
MWH GLOBAL INC
NAVTEQ CORPORATION
NCR CORPORATION
NETAPP INC
NORTEL NETWORKS CORP
NORTHROP GRUMMAN CORP
NOVARTIS AG
NOVELL INC
NOVO-NORDISK AS
NOVOZYMES
ORACLE CORP
PALM INC
PALO ALTO RESEARCH CENTER
PAREXEL INTERNATIONAL CORP
PARSONS BRINCKERHOFF INC
PFIZER INC
PHARMACEUTICAL PRODUCT DEVELOPMENT INC
PITNEY BOWES INC
PLANTRONICS INC
PSA PEUGEOT CITROEN SA
QUALCOMM INC
RAYTHEON CO
RENAULT SA
ROCHE HOLDING LTD
ROYAL DUTCH SHELL (SHELL GROUP)
SAAB AB
SAIC INC
SANOFI-AVENTIS SA
SAS INSTITUTE INC
SASOL LIMITED
SCHERING-PLOUGH CORP
SEMBCORP INDUSTRIES LTD
SIEMENS AG
SNC-LAVALIN GROUP INC
ST JUDE MEDICAL INC
STATOILHYDRO ASA
STRYKER CORP
STV GROUP INC
SUN MICROSYSTEMS INC
SYBASE INC
SYMANTEC CORP
SYNOPSYS INC
TAIWAN SEMICONDUCTOR MANUFACTURING CO LTD (TSMC)
TELCORDIA TECHNOLOGIES
TELEDYNE TECHNOLOGIES INCORPORATED
TELEFON AB LM ERICSSON (ERICSSON)
TELLABS INC
TEREX CORPORATION
TEXAS INSTRUMENTS INC (TI)
TEXTRON INC
THQ INC
TIETOENATOR
TRW AUTOMOTIVE HOLDINGS CORP
TYCO INTERNATIONAL LTD
UNISYS CORP
URS CORPORATION
UTSTARCOM INC
VERISIGN INC
VISTEON CORPORATION
VOLVO CAR CORPORATION
VSE CORP
WYETH
XEROX CORP
YAHOO! INC

INDEX OF SUBSIDIARIES, BRAND NAMES AND AFFILIATIONS

Brand or subsidiary, followed by the name of the related corporation

INDEX OF SUBSIDIARIES, BRAND NAMES AND AFFILIATIONS, CONT.

INDEX OF SUBSIDIARIES, BRAND NAMES AND AFFILIATIONS, CONT.

INDEX OF SUBSIDIARIES, BRAND NAMES AND AFFILIATIONS, CONT.

INDEX OF SUBSIDIARIES, BRAND NAMES AND AFFILIATIONS, CONT.

INDEX OF SUBSIDIARIES, BRAND NAMES AND AFFILIATIONS, CONT.

INDEX OF SUBSIDIARIES, BRAND NAMES AND AFFILIATIONS, CONT.

INDEX OF SUBSIDIARIES, BRAND NAMES AND AFFILIATIONS, CONT.

INDEX OF SUBSIDIARIES, BRAND NAMES AND AFFILIATIONS, CONT.

INDEX OF SUBSIDIARIES, BRAND NAMES AND AFFILIATIONS, CONT.

INDEX OF SUBSIDIARIES, BRAND NAMES AND AFFILIATIONS, CONT.

INDEX OF SUBSIDIARIES, BRAND NAMES AND AFFILIATIONS, CONT.

INDEX OF SUBSIDIARIES, BRAND NAMES AND AFFILIATIONS, CONT.

INDEX OF SUBSIDIARIES, BRAND NAMES AND AFFILIATIONS, CONT.

INDEX OF SUBSIDIARIES, BRAND NAMES AND AFFILIATIONS, CONT.

INDEX OF SUBSIDIARIES, BRAND NAMES AND AFFILIATIONS, CONT.

INDEX OF SUBSIDIARIES, BRAND NAMES AND AFFILIATIONS, CONT.

INDEX OF SUBSIDIARIES, BRAND NAMES AND AFFILIATIONS, CONT.

INDEX OF SUBSIDIARIES, BRAND NAMES AND AFFILIATIONS, CONT.

INDEX OF SUBSIDIARIES, BRAND NAMES AND AFFILIATIONS, CONT.

INDEX OF SUBSIDIARIES, BRAND NAMES AND AFFILIATIONS, CONT.

INDEX OF SUBSIDIARIES, BRAND NAMES AND AFFILIATIONS, CONT.

INDEX OF SUBSIDIARIES, BRAND NAMES AND AFFILIATIONS, CONT.

INDEX OF SUBSIDIARIES, BRAND NAMES AND AFFILIATIONS, CONT.

INDEX OF SUBSIDIARIES, BRAND NAMES AND AFFILIATIONS, CONT.

INDEX OF SUBSIDIARIES, BRAND NAMES AND AFFILIATIONS, CONT.

INDEX OF SUBSIDIARIES, BRAND NAMES AND AFFILIATIONS, CONT.

INDEX OF SUBSIDIARIES, BRAND NAMES AND AFFILIATIONS, CONT.

INDEX OF SUBSIDIARIES, BRAND NAMES AND AFFILIATIONS, CONT.

INDEX OF SUBSIDIARIES, BRAND NAMES AND AFFILIATIONS, CONT.

INDEX OF SUBSIDIARIES, BRAND NAMES AND AFFILIATIONS, CONT.

INDEX OF SUBSIDIARIES, BRAND NAMES AND AFFILIATIONS, CONT.

INDEX OF SUBSIDIARIES, BRAND NAMES AND AFFILIATIONS, CONT.

INDEX OF SUBSIDIARIES, BRAND NAMES AND AFFILIATIONS, CONT.

INDEX OF SUBSIDIARIES, BRAND NAMES AND AFFILIATIONS, CONT.